SOURCEBOOK ON
THE SPACE SCIENCES

SOURCEBOOK ON
THE SPACE SCIENCES

by

SAMUEL GLASSTONE

WRITTEN UNDER THE SPONSORSHIP OF THE
NATIONAL AERONAUTICS AND
SPACE ADMINISTRATION

D. VAN NOSTRAND COMPANY, INC.

PRINCETON, NEW JERSEY

TORONTO   NEW YORK   LONDON

D. VAN NOSTRAND COMPANY, INC.
120 Alexander St., Princeton, New Jersey (*Principal office*)
24 West 40 Street, New York 18, New York

D. VAN NOSTRAND COMPANY, LTD.
358 Kensington High Street, London, W.14, England

D. VAN NOSTRAND COMPANY (Canada), LTD.
25 Hollinger Road, Toronto 16, Canada

PRINTED IN THE UNITED STATES OF AMERICA

FOREWORD

In the sounding language of the Space Act of 1958, "the aeronautical and space activities of the United States shall be conducted so as to contribute . . . to the expansion of human knowledge in the atmosphere and space." And the National Aeronautics and Space Administration "shall provide for the widest practicable and appropriate dissemination of information concerning its activities and the results thereof."

As to the first of the mandates, the energies and skills of the National Aeronautics and Space Administration have for some years been focussed on attaining these high goals. It has been—as it will continue to be, at a still greater pace—a time of historically unparalleled expansion of human knowledge. Not in the 16th and 17th Centuries, when the foundations of modern science were laid, nor during the Industrial Revolution, nor even during the feverish days of the Manhattan Project, were the boundaries of man's understanding of nature extended as rapidly as they have been during these beginnings of the space age.

In response to the dissemination mandate of the Space Act, NASA has been developing an extensive information system designed to distribute most effectively its scientific and technical findings in the different forms required by the variety of users both within and outside the aerospace community.

While NASA's findings have been and will continue to be reported in the agency's own research and development reports and in journals of the learned and professional societies, there nevertheless remains a clear need to speak to other, broader, equally important audiences. This book is a lucid and scholarly compaction that sets forth a baseline summary of the broad field of space science. It is oriented not only toward the university readership but also to interdisciplinary and informed lay audiences.

Dr. Samuel Glasstone, engaged by NASA to prepare this manuscript, is both a distinguished scientist himself and the dean among scientific writers at work today. It is hoped that a broad spectrum of Americans will find knowledge and perspective in this volume.

MELVIN S. DAY, *Director*
Scientific and Technical Information Division
National Aeronautics and Space Administration

PREFACE

The space sciences may be defined as those areas of science to which new knowledge can be contributed by means of space vehicles, i.e., sounding rockets, satellites, and lunar and planetary probes, either manned or unmanned. Thus, space science does not constitute a new science but represents an important extension of the frontiers of such existing sciences as astronomy, biology, geodesy, and the physics and chemistry of Earth and its environment and of the celestial bodies. In the few years that spacecraft have been available for research purposes, a number of significant discoveries have been made and many more may be expected in the future as the program of space exploration develops.

The main objectives of this book are: first, to provide a broad background of the sciences which can be advanced by studies utilizing space vehicles; second, to describe in the appropriate context some of the progress that has already been made by such studies; and third, to indicate the lines along which further investigations are being considered or planned. In addition, the book contains material that does not strictly fall into the category of space sciences, e.g., propulsion and power supplies for space vehicles, applications of spacecraft in meteorology, communications, etc., and manned space flight. These topics are included in order to present an overall picture of the United States' program for exploring the uses of space.

In view of the wide range of subjects covered, the technical level of the treatment is inevitably somewhat uneven. It is aimed generally, however, at the reader with an elementary knowledge of the conventional sciences, particularly physics and chemistry. Of necessity, some of the more complicated material has been simplified to conform with this requirement, but it is hoped not to the extent of being misleading. Mathematics has been kept to the essential minimum in the body of the text and the derivations of important relationships requiring the use of calculus are given in appendices. Each chapter is more or less independent and the inclusion of frequent cross references should make it possible to read the book in any desired order.

As a consequence of the many areas of science and technology discussed in this book, the problem has arisen of the units to be used to express mass, length, force, etc. In principle, a single uniform system could have been adopted, but this would have led to the employment of unusual units for one discipline or another. The only satisfactory solution to this problem seemed to be to use the units most appropriate to each topic. Wherever possible, however, the meter-kilogram-second (MKS) system, which is finding increasing favor, has been given preference.

In the preparation of this book, help was received from many individuals to whom I wish to express my indebtedness. The names of some of these are listed separately on the following pages. I also wish to thank several members of the Scientific and Technical Information Division of the National Aeronautics and Space Administration; they include Howard G. Allaway, Assistant Director, and Frank Rowsome, Jr., Chief, Technical Publications Branch, for their interest and encouragement, and Dr. Arthur C. Hoffman, to whom special thanks are due for his invaluable help in securing both published and unpublished material, in obtaining extensive reviews of the draft manuscript, and in many other ways. I am also grateful to my friends Robert E. Barry and Paul A. Wilson who reviewed the whole of the manuscript from the standpoint of the potential reader of the book. Finally, I would like to thank Dr. Norris E. Bradbury, Director, Los Alamos Scientific Laboratory, for use of the Laboratory's excellent Technical Library.

March 1965   SAMUEL GLASSTONE

ACKNOWLEDGMENT

I wish to thank those named below for contributing to the review of the draft manuscript; the affiliations given are those at the time the reviews were made. If there are any whose names have been inadvertently omitted, their help is nevertheless appreciated. Since it did not prove possible to incorporate all the suggestions made by the reviewers, I must accept full responsibility for the material presented in this book.

Anderson, C. E., Douglas Aircraft Company
Belleville, R. E., NASA Headquarters
Bos, W. F., NASA Headquarters
Brownstein, H. S., NASA Headquarters
Bruch, C. W., NASA Headquarters
Brunk, W., NASA Headquarters
Bryson, R. P., NASA Headquarters
Buckley, E. C., NASA Headquarters
Chase, J. B. E., NASA Marshall Space Flight Center
Chatham, G. N., NASA Headquarters
Cherry, W. R., NASA Goddard Space Flight Center
Cline, S. T., NASA Marshall Space Flight Center
Cohen, W., NASA Headquarters
de Fries, P. J., NASA Marshall Space Flight Center
Del Duca, M., NASA Headquarters
DeMeritte, F. J., NASA Headquarters
Dunning, R. S., NASA Langley Research Center
Edwards, A., NASA Headquarters
Ehrlich, E., NASA Headquarters
Emme, E. M., NASA Headquarters
Firor, J. W., High Altitude Observatory
Fryklund, V. C., Jr., NASA Headquarters
Geissler, E. D., NASA Marshall Space Flight Center
Gerathewohl, S. J., NASA Headquarters
Gilchrist, L. F., NASA Headquarters
Gill, J. R., NASA Headquarters
Gillespie, W., NASA Manned Spacecraft Center
Goodwin, H. L., NASA Headquarters
Gray, E. Z., NASA Headquarters

Hall, H., NASA Headquarters
Hall, L. B., NASA Headquarters
Hearth, D. P., NASA Headquarters
Hensley, R. V., NASA Headquarters
Huang, S-S., NASA Goddard Space Flight Center
Jaramillo, V., NASA Headquarters
Kee, R. M., NASA Headquarters
Kellogg, W. W., The RAND Corporation
Kessler, G., University of Maryland
Kuettner, J. P., NASA Marshall Space Flight Center
Liddel, U., NASA Headquarters
Lowman, P. D., NASA Headquarters
Mackey, R. J., Jr., NASA Goddard Space Flight Center
Manganiello, E. J., NASA Lewis Research Center
Michaux, C. M., Douglas Aircraft Company
Moody, A. B., NASA Headquarters
Moore, R. C., NASA Headquarters
Morrissey, J. E., AEC-NASA Space Nuclear Propulsion Office
Moseson, M. L., NASA Goddard Space Flight Center
Musen, P. D., NASA Goddard Space Flight Center
Natrella, J. V., NASA Headquarters
Nicks, O. W., NASA Headquarters
O'Keefe, J. A., NASA Goddard Space Flight Center
Pearson, E. O., Jr., NASA Headquarters
Pearson, H. A., NASA Langley Research Center
Pieper, G. F., NASA Goddard Space Flight Center

Quimby, F. H., NASA Headquarters
Rogers, D. P., NASA Headquarters
Rosche, M. G., NASA Headquarters
Ross, S., NASA Headquarters
Schrock, P. D., NASA Headquarters
Schulman, F., NASA Headquarters
Schwartz, I. R., NASA Headquarters
Schwenk, F. C., AEC-NASA Space Nuclear Propulsion Office
Serice, D. S., NASA Headquarters
Sharpe, M. R., NASA Marshall Space Flight Center
Sherman, W. L., NASA Langley Research Center
Silber, R., NASA Marshall Space Flight Center
Simas, V. R., NASA Goddard Space Flight Center

Sloop, J. L., NASA Headquarters
Spinrad, H., Jet Propulsion Laboratory
Stauss, H., NASA Headquarters
Steinle, W. C., NASA Headquarters
Stuhlinger, E., NASA Marshall Space Flight Center
Sullivan, F. J., NASA Headquarters
Swain, R. L., NASA Langley Research Center
Swanson, C. D., NASA Marshall Space Flight Center
Tennyson, G. P., Jr., NASA Headquarters
Tischler, A. O., NASA Headquarters
Tomayko, D. W., NASA Headquarters
Warren, R. E., NASA Headquarters
Wilford, R. R., Jet Propulsion Laboratory
Wilson, R. H., Jr., NASA Headquarters

Several other individuals have been most courteous in responding to my requests for information or for illustrative material; to them also I wish to express my indebtedness.

SAMUEL GLASSTONE

TABLE OF CONTENTS

Chapter 1

INTRODUCTION TO SPACE SCIENCES

APPLICATIONS OF SPACE STUDIES

THE PURPOSE OF SPACE EXPLORATION

1.1. In the exploration of space, it may well be said that the fiction of yesterday is the science of tomorrow. For hundreds of years, astronomers, philosophers, and novelists have dreamt of voyages to the Moon and the planets. Now, in the latter half of the twentieth century, these dreams are coming true. The current period will thus go down in history as the time when man began to develop the capability to meet the long-standing challenge of space. Already cameras and other instruments have been sent from Earth to its celestial neighbors to take photographs and make scientific measurements. And it will not be long before human beings will follow.

1.2. Since 1957, when the first artificial satellites were launched into orbit about Earth, there has been a worldwide interest in the study of space. Both the United States and the U.S.S.R., in particular, have very large and costly programs devoted to various aspects of space science and technology. It is appropriate, therefore, to consider the purpose of these efforts. In the United States, one stated objective is to land men on the Moon and to bring them back safely to Earth. But this should be regarded merely as the focus of the immediate space activities and only a stage, although a highly significant one, in an overall concept of unlimited potential. The basic and ultimate purpose of space exploration must be to increase the store of human knowledge. Even landing on the Moon will be impossible without a vast background of new information in many areas of science and engineering.

1.3. Some of the studies of space have already found practical applications in daily life; for example, in long-distance communications, in weather forecasting, in navigation, in problems related to the shape of Earth, as well as in military science. Furthermore, the advances in technology, which must inevitably result from the space effort, will make possible a more effective exploitation of Earth's natural resources. Not only will existing manufactured products be improved but new ones will be developed.

1

1.4. One of the consequences of the program to place man on the Moon—and later on the planets—will undoubtedly be a better understanding of human physiology and life processes. It is reasonably safe to predict that progress will result in medicine, although the nature of the advances may be quite unforeseen.

1.5. Finally, much knowledge will be gained from space exploration which may never find any practical use; included in this category is an improved comprehension of the nature of the universe and perhaps of the origin of life. But all knowledge, whether it has obvious applications or not, enriches humanity and stimulates mental activity to the ultimate benefit—both spiritual and material—of mankind.

1.6. The information which has already been derived or which is being sought from the investigation of space is described in some detail in later chapters. In order to provide a general orientation, however, brief summaries will be given here of various areas of space study and what may be learned from them.

COMMUNICATION BY SATELLITE

1.7. With the growth of the world's population, the increase in trade, and the improvement in living standards, there has been associated a greatly increased load on the facilities for long-distance communications. In recent years the demand has been met by the extension of radiotelephony and television transmission into the microwave region of the spectrum. Because these radiations of short wavelength, like ordinary light, are effective only over line-of-sight distances, their direct range is limited by the curvature of Earth. Consequently, overland transmission of microwaves is generally achieved by the utilization of relay towers, carrying antennas, located about 25 to 30 miles apart. Although it is drawn very much out of scale for purposes of clarity, Fig. 1.1 illustrates

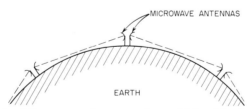

Fig. 1.1.   Microwave relay towers located 25 to 30 miles apart

the general principles of microwave transmission over land. For overseas communication, submarine coaxial cables are used, but these require repeaters at frequent intervals to amplify the signals in order to compensate for the decrease in strength due to line losses. The maintenance of these underwater repeater amplifiers obviously represents a problem.

1.8. If a radio-wave reflector or relay of some kind could be established at a high altitude above Earth's surface, e.g., in a satellite, the problem of long-distance transmission would be simplified in principle, as indicated in Fig. 1.2. Two general types of satellite systems are being studied for possible use

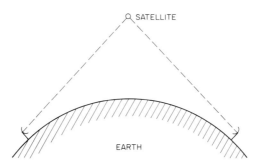

Fig. 1.2.   Use of satellite as radio-wave relay

in this connection; these are called "passive" and "active" satellites, respectively. Each has its advantages and drawbacks, as will be seen in the more detailed discussion of the use of satellites for communication purposes in Chapter 5. A passive system, of which the Echo satellites are examples, merely acts as a reflector of radio waves of high frequency (short wavelength). The great disadvantage of this scheme is that the reflected signal received on the ground is extremely weak. In the alternative approach, used in Telstar, Relay, and Syncom, the active satellite carries a receiver-amplifier system. The radio signal is received from a ground station and is transmitted with increased power although at a somewhat different frequency. Such an active satellite thus behaves in a manner generally similar to a submarine repeater amplifier.

SATELLITES IN METEOROLOGY

1.9. Weather forecasting in the past has been hampered by a lack of adequate information; this has been available only from a small fraction of the atmosphere, the conditions in the remainder being unknown. A satellite orbiting Earth can make observations of large uninhabited areas, such as oceans, deserts, mountains, and polar regions, from which meteorological data are very sparse. Television cameras, carried by satellites, e.g., TIROS and Nimbus,* can transmit to Earth photographs of large-scale cloud distributions. These pictures, obtained at regular intervals in successive orbits of the satellite, provide information on the evolution and movement of severe atmospheric disturbances, such as hurricanes.

1.10. It should be understood that the observations made from a satellite,

---

* The convention adopted in this book is to use capital letters for names, such as TIROS, SNAP, SPUR, etc., which are acronyms or abbreviations of phrases describing the system.

which include measurements of heat radiation as well as cloud photographs, will probably not replace, but will supplement, conventional meteorological forecasting systems. The latter depend on measurements made at definite points within the atmosphere of such properties as pressure, temperature, humidity, and wind direction. A meteorological satellite, however, orbits outside the region of the atmosphere that directly affects the weather, and is more suited to the observation of cloud masses. The satellite can also provide information of a more basic nature relating to the absorption and emission of heat radiation from Earth; this information has not been obtainable in any other way. Ultimately, meteorology and weather prediction may undergo modification and improvement as a consequence of the utilization of satellites.

SATELLITES AS NAVIGATIONAL AIDS

1.11. Ships and aircraft, especially on long journeys over oceans, make use of the methods of celestial navigation, among others, to determine their positions. By measuring the altitudes (or angular elevations) above the horizon of at least two celestial bodies, at a known time, the location of the observation point can be determined using data contained in an ephemeris.* But when the sky is obscured by clouds or fog, conventional celestial navigation, based on visual sighting, becomes impractical.

1.12. A navigational system is possible by making use of a satellite carrying a radio transmitter; the signal can then be received on Earth's surface or in the air under all weather conditions. Several different techniques are available, as will be seen in Chapter 5, but in all cases a basic requirement, as in celestial navigation, is an appropriate satellite ephemeris. Because the orbit of a satellite is subject to perturbations, not all of which can be calculated long in advance, it would not be possible to publish an ephemeris ahead of time, as is done in the Nautical and Air Almanacs. A solution to the problem is for the characteristics (or elements) of the satellite orbit, as determined at frequent intervals from tracking measurements, to be transmitted to the satellite by radio. The data are then rebroadcast and can be received by a ship or aircraft. In other words, the satellite would serve as its own ephemeris and provide data from which its exact location at any time can be calculated. Because Earth satellites appear to move across the sky more rapidly than do the heavenly bodies, satellite navigation requires that time be determined with much greater accuracy than is necessary for navigation by the stars.

1.13. Navigation is related more or less directly to mapping and the science of geodesy (Greek, *ge*, "Earth"; *daiein*, "to divide"). One aspect of the latter is the determination of the positions of points or important geographical fea-

---

* An ephemeris (Greek, *ephemeros,* "daily") is a publication, e.g., *The American Ephemeris and Nautical Almanac,* giving the locations of celestial bodies, e.g., the Sun, Moon, planets, and certain fixed stars, for each day of the year. Similar information is available in the *Air Almanac.*

tures on Earth's surface. The information so obtained is essential for accurate mapping of Earth. The methods in general use are based on the familiar technique of triangulation commonly employed in land surveying. For this purpose, the land areas of Earth are divided into 14 geodetic networks (or datums). Within each network, the locations of points are known within an accuracy of 50 feet or less, but when it comes to locating a point in one network relative to that in another, the accuracy is no better than about 500 feet. In other words, there may be an error of anything up to 1000 feet, even in the very best maps, in determining the distance between points on different geodetic networks.

1.14. The situation can be greatly improved with the aid of geodetic satellites of various types. For example, the satellite may carry a flashing light, as in the ANNA spacecraft, which can be photographed against a background of stars by means of a telescope-camera combination. With the aid of a star chart (or ephemeris), the position of the satellite at a given instant of time will become a reference point, just like a star in celestial navigation. If observations are made simultaneously from several points located in two geodetic networks, the distance between two points on different networks can be calculated. It is expected that relative positions can thus be determined to within an accuracy of 50 feet. An alternative technique, which is somewhat less accurate and more involved, is based on the observation of radio signals transmitted from the satellite. This procedure has the advantage over the flashing-light method in being applicable in any weather and at all times of the day or night.

SCIENCE IN SPACE

1.15. In the realm of what might be called "pure" space science, that is, scientific observations made in space, there is almost unlimited scope for obtaining knowledge about Earth and the Moon, about the Sun and its planets, about the other stars in the Galaxy, the Milky Way, of which the Sun is a member, and finally of the universe which contains several billion galaxies of various kinds. Although many space science studies are made without any thought of possible practical applications, there will inevitably be such applications.

1.16. As far as Earth is concerned, the perturbations of satellite orbits (§ 2.82) provide information on what is commonly referred to as the "shape" of Earth, although a more accurate description would be the distribution of its gravitational force. Furthermore, both sounding rockets and satellites are used to study the structure of the upper atmosphere and the properties of the interesting layer, above an altitude of about 50 miles, called the *ionosphere*. The ionosphere plays an important role in long-distance radio communications at certain wavelengths (or frequencies). It has been established that electrically charged particles are sometimes emitted from the Sun in such large numbers as to produce marked changes in the composition of the ionosphere. At such times, radio communications which depend on the normal ionosphere may be completely disrupted. It is probable that, as a result of a study of the Sun made from space vehicles, it will be possible to predict, at least a day or so ahead, when these radio blackouts may be expected.

1.17. As is well known, Earth has a significant magnetic field; in other words, Earth behaves as if it had an enormous bar magnet imbedded within it. The two ends (or poles) of this magnet are close to Earth's geographical north and south poles, respectively. It is, of course, the magnetism of Earth which causes a compass needle to orient itself so that one end points to the north and the other to the south. The magnetic field of Earth, that is, the sphere of influence of Earth's magnetism, extends for thousands of miles. Theoretically, like the field of gravitation (§ 2.14), the magnetic field has no limit, but it becomes so weak as to be negligible at a distance of several thousand miles from Earth. This distance represents the approximate boundary of the *magnetosphere*, which is defined more precisely in § 8.214. One of the consequences of the existence of Earth's magnetic field is that electrically charged atomic (and subatomic) particles are trapped in the Van Allen *radiation belt* which surrounds Earth. This belt, with its zones of high-energy particles, is studied by means of instruments carried on space vehicles.

1.18. A knowledge of the characteristic properties and intensity variations of the radiation belt is not only of considerable scientific interest but is necessary for protection of man in space. The altitudes of manned satellites are chosen to be well below the closest radiation zone, so that the electrically charged particles do not represent a biological hazard. Journeys to the Moon and beyond, however, must involve passage through or avoidance of the radiation zones and an understanding of their distribution and behavior is therefore essential in the interest of safety. A somewhat related problem is concerned with the harmful effects of the charged particles on certain electronic equipment used on satellites.

1.19. The Moon, Earth's satellite and nearest celestial neighbor, is an obvious target for research, especially as it is the first extraterrestrial body upon which man will set foot. Apart from the obvious challenge represented by manned exploration of the Moon, because of its proximity, direct human observations appear to be essential if there is to be a complete understanding of the Moon's structure. Because the Moon has no appreciable atmosphere or water to change its surface features, these features have remained largely unaltered for many millions of years. It is expected, therefore, that scientific exploration of the Moon will shed light on the origin of the solar system.

1.20. Some close observations of the Moon have already been made by means of cameras and other instruments carried by lunar probes. But much more data concerning the characteristics of the Moon's surface must be available before a manned landing on the Moon can be attempted. These will be obtained by taking close-up photographs, by placing instruments on the Moon, and also by utilizing both manned and unmanned lunar satellites (Moon orbiters).

1.21. Near approach to the Sun, either by man or instruments, will be impossible because of the tremendous amount of heat energy radiated from it. Nevertheless, solar probes will be used to make a detailed study of the Sun at moderately close distances because a knowledge of its behavior is of basic significance in understanding many phenomena on (or near) Earth. Mention may be made of weather, the ionosphere, the radiation belt, and the auroras, all of which respond to changes in the Sun. In addition, charged atomic particles (protons) emitted by the Sun represent a greater hazard to man in space than does Earth's radiation belt.

1.22. As a result of observations made from Earth, it has long been known that there is an 11-year cycle in which the number and size of the "spots" on the Sun pass from a minimum through a maximum and back to a minimum. The sunspots are merely an external and obvious indication of variations in the Sun's internal activity, and these variations are associated with effects on Earth's immediate environment. For reasons to be explained shortly, the presence of Earth's atmosphere restricts the range of observations on the Sun that can be made from Earth. Consequently, an extensive study of the Sun's behavior over a complete 11-year cycle, made from a variety of space vehicles outside the atmosphere, is necessary for understanding the Earth-Sun relationship.

1.23. Exploration of the planets constitutes another important aspect of space science. The information obtained will help to clarify the history of the solar system and may possibly throw some light on the origin of life. A study of the planets will first be made by means of space (planetary) probes, then by depositing instruments on the surface, later by unmanned and manned orbiters, and perhaps eventually by landing men directly onto the surface. The targets for the more immediate planetary explorations are Earth's closest neighbors, Venus and Mars; the former is nearer than Earth to the Sun and the latter is more distant. One of the problems associated with a study of the planets is that, with the available propulsion systems, a favorable relationship in their position with respect to Earth is necessary. As a result, launching of space vehicles capable of reaching Venus is possible during a limited period about once in every 18 months; to reach Mars, the corresponding interval is roughly two years. In due course, probes and other space systems will travel from Earth to Mercury, the planet nearest the Sun, and also to the remarkable planet Jupiter, lying beyond Mars. These expeditions, however, may have to await the development of novel types of space propulsion now in the experimental stage.

1.24. New perspectives in astronomy are opened up by the ability to make observations from space of the Sun and of stars in the Milky Way, as well as of other galaxies. As a general rule, stars emit radiations covering a very wide range of wavelengths. Because of absorption by the atmosphere, including the ionosphere, observations from Earth have been restricted to two limited portions of this range (or *spectrum*) of wavelengths. These are, first, the region of visible light and, second, that part of the spectrum consisting of certain radio waves. Even the use of the visible region, by means of the telescope and camera, has been handicapped by the presence of clouds in and even by the turbulent motion of Earth's atmosphere. It is this turbulence, in fact, that is responsible for the familiar twinkling of stars. When taking photographs of faint stars, requiring long exposures, the loss of detail due to twinkling has been a severe drawback.

1.25. With the aid of satellites above Earth's atmosphere, it is possible, in the first place, to make very much better telescopic studies of distant celestial bodies and even of the Sun than from Earth's surface. In the language of the astronomer, the "seeing" is greatly improved, and it is independent of terrestrial weather conditions. Perhaps more important is the ability, in addition, to make observations over the whole range of wavelengths, instead of in the limited, and not especially significant, visible and radio regions. The results obtained from the vast field of investigation made possible in this manner will contribute to an understanding of the structure and composition of the Sun and other stars, and of the fundamental evolutionary processes occurring within these bodies.

LIFE IN SPACE

1.26. In conclusion, some reference must be made to the biological aspects of space research. The most immediate problems are associated with the physiological and psychological effects on man of the space environment, particularly of charged-particle radiations, gravitational forces, weightlessness and disorientation, and confinement for long periods in a relatively small vehicle at a great distance from Earth. Other subjects of investigation of a more general nature are the effects on living organisms of variations in the gravitational and magnetic fields and of periodic revolution in a satellite. Some answers may be obtained to the question whether the particular values of gravity and the length of the day on Earth have influenced the evolution of plants and animals.

1.27. Perhaps the most intriguing aspect of space science is the search for evidence of life, either at present or in the past, outside Earth. There is a possibility that fossil indications of extinct life may be found on the Moon and that there may even be primitive forms of life still existing beneath the surface. The extraterrestrial body within the solar system which is the most likely to have an environment conducive to the support of some form of life is the planet Mars. If life does exist on Mars, it will be probably of a primitive nature and different in many respects from that on Earth. But, the discovery of anything even resembling a living organism on Mars would be an event of outstanding scientific significance. Efforts are being made to obtain information on the subject by means of instruments dropped onto the Martian surface, although a definite answer may well have to await the landing of man on the planet.

1.28. It will be apparent from the foregoing summary that the extension of science into space, made possible by the use of high-altitude probes, Earth satellites, lunar, solar, and planetary probes, lunar and planetary orbiters, and finally by landing unmanned and manned vehicles on the Moon and the planets, opens up many new and exciting areas of study. Much information can be obtained with recording instruments, but ultimately it will be necessary to use man himself to explore celestial bodies just as he explored Earth. Because of the versatility and adaptability of the human brain and the capacity to respond to unforeseen situations, of which even the most intricate electronic devices are not capable, man has an essential role to play in the study of space.

HISTORICAL BACKGROUND OF SPACE EXPLORATION

SPACE SCIENCE FICTION

1.29. Before proceeding with a discussion of the scientific and technical problems involved in the exploration of space, it is of interest to review the historical background. Long before the first glimmerings of the true basis of space travel began to be apparent toward the end of the nineteenth century, many fanciful stories had been published of journeys from Earth to the Moon and to the nearest planets, Mars and Venus. The earliest known fictional account of man's venture into space was written about 160 A.D. by the Greek satirist Loukianos, generally referred to by the Latinized name Lucian (of Samosata in Syria). This work, entitled *True History*,* was evidently intended as a parody of Homer's Odyssey. A ship is lifted from the ocean and carried to the Moon by a powerful whirlwind and the book describes the fantastic characteristics of the Moon's human and animal inhabitants. Lucian's story came at a time when Greek scholars were beginning to accept the Moon as a solid body, somewhat like Earth. Thus, as might be expected, the concept of space travel and the development of astronomy were closely related.

1.30. Significantly, no space fiction appeared during the long, intellectually barren period preceding the renaissance of the fifteenth and sixteenth centuries. With the laying of the foundations of modern astronomy and the invention of the telescope in 1608, there came a revival of interest in possible other worlds. One of the consequences was that, at the beginning of the seventeenth century,

---

* The general practice adopted here is to give the English translations of the titles of publications in other languages.

Lucian's book was reprinted in the original Greek and translations were made into Latin, English, and other languages. Furthermore, it undoubtedly influenced later writers.*

1.31. In 1634, some four years after the death of its author, the pioneer German astronomer Johannes Kepler, there was published a book in Latin called *Sleep* which, like Lucian's work, recounted experiences during an imaginary visit to the Moon. However, the two stories differed in an important respect. Kepler, who had explained the motion of the planets around the Sun (§ 7.7), knew a great deal more than Lucian about the nature of the Moon. Observations with the telescope, then only recently developed as an astronomical instrument by the Italian, Galileo Galilei, had shown that the Moon always presents the same face toward Earth and that its surface is not smooth but appeared to have many mountains and valleys. These facts played important parts in Kepler's *Sleep*, so that it may perhaps be regarded as the first real work of science fiction.

1.32. Almost simultaneously with the posthumous publication of Kepler's fantasy, there appeared the first original book on space travel in the English language. It was written by Bishop Francis Godwin and was called *The Man in the Moone: a Discourse of a Voyage Thither by Domingo Gonzales, the Speedy Messenger*. There is internal evidence that the author was influenced to some extent by Kepler's *Sleep*, but it is less accurate from the scientific standpoint. In the same general category are two novels by the French satirical writer Savinien Cyrano de Bergerac,† which appeared in 1657 and 1662, respectively, describing visits to the Moon and the Sun. The former of these novels is noteworthy because it contains the first mention of the use of rockets in space travel (§ 1.38).

1.33. Soon after the middle of the seventeenth century, astronomical studies indicated that the Moon had little, if any, atmosphere and probably no water. Hence, it appeared unlikely that life resembling that on Earth could exist on the Moon. Various writers then turned their imaginations to the planets. As a result of the realization of the great size of the solar system, however, there was less emphasis on journeys into space and more on descriptions, some satirical and others meant to be realistic, of life on the planets.

1.34. The year 1865 was marked by the publication of several fictional accounts of space travel by French writers; one, *Journey to the Moon*, was by Alexandre Dumas, another, *From the Earth to the Moon*, by Jules Verne, and a third, *Voyage to Venus*, by a lesser known writer, Achille Eyraud. The last two of these works are of interest in connection with modern developments in space exploration. Jules Verne realized, quite correctly, that for a spaceship to

---

* It has been asserted that Jonathan Swift, in *Gulliver's Travels* (**1727**), and other authors of fanciful and satirical tales were influenced by Lucian's *True History*.

† The hero of Edmond Rostand's poetic drama *Cyrano de Bergerac* is a largely fictional representation of this author.

leave Earth it was necessary for it to have an upward velocity sufficient to overcome the effect of gravity. In his story, Verne proposed to attain this velocity by shooting the vehicle from an enormous cannon, a procedure now known to be completely impractical. Eyraud, on the other hand, did describe a basically correct propulsion principle making use of a reaction motor, essentially a rocket. But Eyraud's motor, with water as the propellant, would not have raised the spacecraft off the ground.

1.35. The theoretical possibility of establishing an artificial satellite of Earth, similar to the Moon, Earth's natural satellite, had been mentioned in 1687 by the famous English mathematician, Isaac Newton, as a direct consequence of his theory of gravitation (§ 2.13). Writers, however, did not find the satellite an appropriate subject for science fiction until the appearance of a story entitled *The Brick Moon* by Edward Everett Hale,* published as a serial in the *Atlantic Monthly* during the latter part of 1869 and the early months of 1870. The idea apparently originated from discussions between Edward Hale and his brother, Nathan, at Harvard University more than 30 years earlier. The Brick Moon is a manned satellite of Earth propelled into orbit, accidentally as it transpires, by rapidly rotating water wheels. The main purpose of the artificial moon was to provide a means of determining longitude as an aid to navigation, an objective similar to that of some modern satellites (cf. § 1.14, § 5.116).

1.36. Toward the end of the nineteenth century, a clearer understanding developed of the importance of counteracting gravity in the initial stages, at least, of space flight. Consequently, writers invented antigravity materials to permit travel from Earth to the Moon and Mars. Among these authors mention may be made of two with good backgrounds of scientific knowledge: one was the German, Kurd Lasswitz, who wrote *On Two Planets,* published in 1897, and the other was the famous English man of letters, H. G. Wells, whose *First Men on the Moon* appeared in 1901.

1.37. These books marked the end of the epoch of purely imaginative writing about space travel. Contemporaneously with their publication more realistic ideas of propulsion were beginning to take shape. Hence, later novelists, while speculating about life and adventures on celestial bodies, could at least utilize scientifically correct means for reaching these bodies.

SPACE PROPULSION BY ROCKETS

1.38. As far as is known, the only practical methods for propulsion in space, that is, beyond Earth's tangible atmosphere, are based on the rocket principle.† There are three main reasons for this assertion. First, rocket propulsion is possible in any medium, such as air or water, and even in space where there is

* The Rev. Edward E. Hale is perhaps best known for his short novel *The Man Without a Country,* published anonymously in 1863.
† The proposed solar sail, which may or may not be practical (§ 3.224), is an exception.

essentially no material medium. In fact, a rocket can be more efficient in the vacuum (or near vacuum) of space than it is in Earth's atmosphere (§ 3.5). Second, a rocket is completely self-contained and its operation does not depend on the presence of air. The reason is that a rocket carries its own source of power and it does not require oxygen from its surroundings. Finally, the rocket engine is the only practical machine capable of attaining the high velocities necessary to counteract the force of gravity. Unless this force is overcome, a space vehicle would be unable to leave Earth's environment and reach the Moon or the planets or even to orbit Earth as a satellite.

1.39. Rockets operate on the principle of direct reaction,* expressed by Isaac Newton in his third law of motion (1687): Every action (or force) is accompanied by an equal and opposite reaction (or force).† Familiar examples of direct reaction are the recoil of a gun or rifle and the operation of a rotary lawn-sprinkler. In the former instance, the expulsion of a shell or a bullet in one direction causes a "kick" or recoil in the opposite direction. In the lawn-sprinkler, the action of the streams (or jets) of water produces a reaction that makes the sprinkler head rotate. The direction of rotation is opposite to that in which the water is ejected. A rocket vehicle, although not a very practical one, could be constructed by attaching a machine gun firmly to a car consisting of a platform on wheels. Every bullet expelled by the gun would exert a reaction force on the car and tend to drive it in the opposite direction.

1.40. In the most common type of rocket system used for propulsion, the continuous ejection of a stream of hot gas (or gases) causes a steady motion of the vehicle due to reaction, as indicated in Fig. 1.3. The reaction does not require

FIG. 1.3.   Principle of rocket action

the presence of an ambient medium for propulsion to occur. The material which generates the hot gas in a rocket is called the *propellant;* it may consist of a single liquid, two liquids, a solid, or a combination of liquid and solid. In these cases the gas is produced by chemical changes involving the propellant (or propellants) and no other substance is required.‡ It is in this respect, in particular, that rocket propulsion differs from conventional jet propulsion, such as is employed for aircraft, although both utilize the reaction principle. In a jet

---

* The qualification "direct" is used because all forms of propulsion depend on reaction of some kind, but in most other cases it is indirect.

† Newton's first and second laws of motion are given in § 2.5 and § 2.17, respectively.

‡ There are some special rocket designs (§ 3.158 *et seq.*) in which the ejected gas (or other material) is not produced in a chemical reaction. The general principle of operation is, however, the same as described here.

engine the high-temperature gas is formed by the combustion (or burning) of the kerosene fuel with oxygen from the ambient air. Hence, a jet engine cannot operate in the absence of air. A rocket carries all the necessary oxygen, or equivalent oxidizing material, and uses none from outside sources. Some propellants, e.g., hydrogen peroxide, produce hot gases by chemical decomposition without utilizing oxidizing reactions. In any event, the system, like other rocket systems, is self-contained and is not dependent on the surroundings.

1.41. An important factor in determining the maximum speed attainable by a rocket vehicle is the velocity with which the hot gas is expelled from the rocket motor. This exhaust gas velocity depends mainly on two properties of the gas, namely, its temperature and its average molecular weight, i.e., the average weight of the molecules (or atomic groupings) present in the gas. High temperature and low molecular weight are known to enhance the exhaust velocity (§ 3.19), and hence they also increase the maximum speed of the vehicle. The choice of the propellant and the design of the rocket motor are influenced by these considerations. Rocket vehicle velocities are now high enough to permit orbiting of Earth by fairly massive satellites or to send spacecraft to the Moon and to the planets Venus and Mars. There is no known way, except by use of the rocket principle, for realizing such high velocities—about 5 miles per second (18,000 miles per hour) for a near-Earth orbit or at least 7 miles per second (25,200 miles per hour) to escape from Earth's environment.*

Rockets in Space Exploration

1.42. The word "space" has been defined in many different ways. Among the definitions to be found in publications of the U.S. National Aeronautics and Space Administration are the following: "that part of the universe between celestial bodies" and "specifically, the part of the universe lying outside the limits of Earth's atmosphere; more generally, the volume in which all spatial bodies, including Earth, move." Unfortunately, a precise definition of space is impossible. It would be convenient to regard space as the region above Earth's atmosphere, but the atmosphere extends outward an indefinite distance with steadily decreasing density and pressure and changing composition. There would thus be no distinct line of demarcation between the atmosphere and space.

1.43. In order to prescribe some limitations for the scope of this book, space will be treated as that part of the universe beyond Earth which is most conveniently studied by means of rockets. This admittedly does not represent a very exact definition of space, but at least it provides a convenient frame of reference for the topics to be treated here.

1.44. It was suggested at one time that the so-called *von Kármán line,*† the

---

* These velocities apply to the situation in which the vehicle goes into orbit or into an escape trajectory near Earth's surface (cf. § 2.24).

† Named for Theodore von Kármán (§ 1.84).

region above which winged aircraft cannot operate, be taken as the lower limit of space. Such aircraft require the presence of an appreciable density of air to enable the wings to provide lift. But there is no exact value for this density, since it depends on the design of the aircraft and other conditions; hence, it is not possible to state specifically the maximum altitude attainable by winged vehicles. It is usually accepted that this is between 40 and 60 miles, but the actual value will vary with the type of aircraft and may not be the same on two successive days because of changes in the atmosphere. However, apart from special experimental systems, such as the X-15,* there are few winged craft that can fly above altitudes of 30 miles or so.

1.45. The record altitude for a balloon is 146,000 feet (27.7 miles) attained by an unmanned U.S. Army weather balloon in February 1959, and it is doubtful whether appreciably greater heights can be expected for lighter-than-air vehicles. The lift is dependent on the mass of the air displaced being greater than that of the balloon, including its gas and attachments. To realize this condition when the air density is very low requires balloons of extremely large size. At an altitude of 30 miles, for example, the density of the air is about one thousandth part of that at sea level; the mass of the displaced air will thus be small unless the volume is extremely large. Generally speaking, therefore, this book will be mainly concerned with the investigation, particularly by means of rocket-propelled devices, of that part of the universe extending beyond an altitude of about 30 miles above Earth's surface.

History of Rocketry

1.46. Although recent years have seen great advances in the science of rocketry, rockets have been in use for several centuries, principally as a means for propelling weapons and for fireworks. There is evidence, for example, that the Chinese utilized rockets in warfare in the year 1232 A.D. One such weapon, described as an "arrow of flying fire," is believed to have consisted of an arrow attached to a rocket propelled by gunpowder; it was thus somewhat similar, and presumably related, to the familiar fireworks rocket. The arrow, like the guiding stick of the fireworks rocket, served to stabilize the weapon in flight (§ 4.93).† In the course of time, rockets spread from China to Europe, where they were used only sporadically as weapons, at least until the beginning of the nineteenth century. Their main interest during the intervening period appears to have been for fireworks displays. Rockets for warfare or amusement were made by packing a slow-burning gunpowder into a tube of cardboard, wood, or metal.

---

*The X-15 is actually a winged rocket; it carries its own oxidizer (liquid oxygen) as well as the fuel (liquid ammonia).

†The term rocket is said to have the same origin as the German *rocken* or the Italian *rocca*, meaning "distaff," i.e., the rod (or staff) used for holding the bunch of fibers from which thread is drawn in hand spinning. The fireworks rocket, with its guiding stick, resembles a distaff in general appearance.

Ignition of the powder charge produced the hot gases which were expelled through a nozzle and thus propelled the rocket in the opposite direction.

1.47. The early 1800's were marked by a strong resurgence of rocket weapons. This was largely the result of their effective use against the British, toward the end of the preceding century, by Haidar Ali, Maharajah of Mysore, India, and particularly by his son and successor, Tippoo Sahib. Around 1801, William Congreve, a colonel in the British army, heard about these weapons and from that time until his death in 1826 he devoted himself to the design, testing, and production of a variety of rockets for military purposes.* Congreve's war rockets aroused considerable interest throughout Europe and also in the United States. The later American rockets incorporated the discovery by the British inventor William Hale (1846) that stabilization could be achieved by rotating (or spinning) the rocket during flight, thus making the guiding stick unnecessary.

1.48. With improvements in the fabrication of artillery and the use of rifled gun barrels, to improve firing range and accuracy, rockets became less significant as weapons. They were employed to some extent in World War I, mostly against airships, but it was not until World War II that interest in various types of rocket weapons was revived. Of these devices, the German V-1 and V-2 missiles led more or less directly to present-day rockets for intercontinental ballistic missiles† and for space exploration. The history of this development will be described later.

1.49. Apart from the military applications of rockets, the nineteenth century marked their use to throw lines from shore to nearby wrecked vessels. They were thus responsible for saving the lives of many stranded sailors. The rocket principle was also considered as a means for propelling vehicles on land, on the sea, and in the air. Although many schemes were proposed, even before 1800, there is no evidence that any were successful, except perhaps on a laboratory scale, until relatively recent times.

EARLY PIONEERS OF SPACE TRAVEL

1.50. As already seen, Cyrano de Bergerac and, later, Achille Eyraud had mentioned the possibility of using the reaction (or rocket) principle to achieve flight in space. Their proposals were, however, more in the realm of fancy than of reality. The first semi-scientific design of a rocket-propelled vehicle was made by a German named Hermann Ganswindt about the year 1891. Ganswindt,

---

* Congreve's rockets were used by the British toward the end of the War of 1812; hence, the reference to "the rocket's red glare" in Francis Scott Key's *The Star-Spangled Banner*, written in 1814.

† A true ballistic missile, as distinct from a guided missile, has no guidance system and is also wingless. Once the propellant supply is consumed (or cut off), the path (or trajectory) of the ballistic missile is affected only by inertia and by the action of gravity and air resistance. A long-range artillery shell, which is shot at an angle to the horizontal and lands a considerable distance away, is a form of ballistic missile.

who had started out to study law, was an inventor of the Edisonian (or empirical) school. Among the many inventions he made were an automobile, an airship and a helicopter, but only a few of them actually worked.

1.51. The spacecraft proposed by Ganswindt was designed to operate in a manner somewhat similar to the hypothetical car driven by a machine gun, as described earlier. Since he thought that ejection of a gas would not produce enough reaction, Ganswindt proposed to expel heavy steel cartridges containing dynamite charges. As each charge was exploded, part of the cartridge would be expelled and the reaction would drive the spaceship in the opposite direction. The remaining part of the cartridge would strike the wall of the explosion chamber and, before dropping out, would transfer its kinetic energy to the vehicle in the direction of its motion.

1.52. Ganswindt conjectured, quite correctly, that when the rocket attained a sufficiently high velocity, expulsion of the cartridges could be stopped and the vehicle would continue to coast through space. During the period of non-powered (ballistic) flight, the passengers of the spacecraft would experience the peculiar phenomenon of *weightlessness* that Jules Verne had described some 25 years earlier (Fig. 1.4).* Ganswindt suggested that it could be counteracted by rotation of the cabin, thereby producing an effect similar to gravity. The problem of weightlessness will be treated in greater detail in Chapter 13.

1.53. Contemporaneously with Ganswindt, but quite independently, a self-taught Russian schoolmaster, Konstantin Eduardovitch Tsiolkovsky,† also became interested in airships and in space travel by means of rockets. Unlike Ganswindt, however, Tsiolkovsky made an effort to understand the scientific basis of rocket propulsion and was the first to derive some of the fundamental equations of rocketry (§ 3.109). He realized the importance of expelling the exhaust gas at a high velocity and suggested that this could be more readily attained by using liquid propellants instead of the solids, e.g., gunpowder, which had always been previously employed. Many of Tsiolkovsky's ideas, now accepted as basic in rocket design and space travel, were described in a report on the *Investigation of Interplanetary Space by Means of Rocket Devices*, completed in 1898 and published five years later. A series of technical articles by Tsiolkovsky on space travel, issued during the period from 1911 to 1913, attracted the interest of a Russian scientific writer, Jakov I. Perelman. His book, *Interplanetary Communications*, which appeared in 1915, presented Tsiolkovsky's ideas in a simple form and made them accessible to the nontechnical reader.

1.54. Although Tsiolkovsky's work was scientifically sound, its influence on the development of rocket technology and space exploration, either in Russia or

---

* Jules Verne was under the erroneous impression that weightlessness would be experienced only where the gravitational effects of Earth and the Moon (or other body) are equal.

† The name is sometimes transliterated as Ziolkovsky, and in other ways.

FIG. 1.4.   Passengers in Jules Verne's imaginary spaceship (1865) experiencing weightlessness on the way to the Moon

elsewhere, was delayed. In the early decades of the present century, there were very few scientists who regarded space travel as anything but a fantastic dream. Consequently, at the time they were put forward and for some years thereafter, Tsiolkovsky's ideas received little serious attention.

1.55. A special niche in the history of rocketry and space exploration must be assigned to the American physicist Robert Hutchins Goddard.* As a youth, Goddard was an avid reader of Jules Verne and of H. G. Wells and became fascinated by the idea of space travel. Already in 1901, at the age of 19, he had written a brief (unpublished) article entitled *The Navigation of Space.* About 1908, Goddard became actively interested in rockets as a means of propulsion in space, and in 1913 and 1914 he applied for and was granted (in 1914) United States patents for inventions "relating to a rocket apparatus . . . adapted to transport . . . recording instruments to extreme heights." The first of these patents is for a two-stage, solid-fuel rocket, in which an enhanced efficiency is obtained by exhausting the combustion gases through an expanding nozzle shaped like a long truncated cone. Nozzles of this type are invariably employed in rockets of the present day (§ 3.58). The second of the aforementioned patents contained, somewhat in the nature of an addendum, a description of a liquid fuel rocket for which possible propellants are given as gasoline and liquid nitrous oxide.

1.56. In 1916, in an effort to obtain financial support for his experiments with rockets, Goddard presented to the Smithsonian Institution of the United States a report on *A Method of Reaching Extreme Altitudes.* This report, with some minor addenda, was published at the end of 1919. It consisted mainly of a theoretical treatment of various aspects of rocket propulsion, but the author had mentioned, in passing, the possibility of utilizing a rocket to reach the Moon. He suggested that its arrival there could be signaled to Earth by the explosion of a load of flash powder. It was only this trivial, but spectacular, aspect of Goddard's ideas that attracted any significant public attention at the time.

1.57. Goddard's first experiments were performed with the familiar powder rockets and in 1915 he proved his contention, about which some authorities had expressed doubt, that rockets can operate in a vacuum such as would be experienced in space. In fact, as expected from theory, the force (or thrust) produced in a low-pressure, space-like environment was found to be greater than at normal atmospheric pressure.

1.58. Because powder rockets were somewhat unreliable and inefficient, Goddard began in 1920 to investigate the feasibility of using liquid propellants, such as had been mentioned in his second patent.† Although it requires extreme

* For whom the U.S. National Aeronautics and Space Administration's Goddard Space Flight Center, Greenbelt, Maryland, was named.
† It has been reported that a Peruvian engineer, Pedro E. Paulet, claimed to have experimented with a liquid-propellant rocket in 1895.

refrigeration, liquid oxygen was chosen as being ideally the best oxidizing agent, and gasoline was selected as the fuel because of its low cost and ready availability. With these materials, Goddard achieved the world's first successful flight of a liquid-propellant rocket, on March 16, 1926, on a farm near Auburn, Massachusetts (Fig. 1.5). A little more than three years later, in 1929, he

Fig. 1.5. Robert H. Goddard and his liquid-propellant rocket at Auburn, Mass., on March 16, 1926, just prior to the historic first flight of such a rocket. (*Esther C. Goddard photo. Courtesy of Mrs. Robert H. Goddard*)

launched the first instrumented rocket carrying a barometer and a thermometer together with a camera to record the readings at maximum altitude.

1.59. For most of the time from 1930 to 1941, Goddard, aided by three or four machinists and technicians, and with the financial assistance of the Guggenheim Foundation, devoted his efforts to improvements in rocketry (Fig.

1.6). During this period, he obtained patents on various ideas which are now widely used in rocket design; included were centrifugal pumps for the propellants, methods for cooling the rocket (combustion) chamber, gyroscopic stabilization, and the introduction of vanes in the rocket exhaust for guidance. Several gasoline-oxygen rockets were constructed by Goddard and tested on an

Fig. 1.6. R. H. Goddard, at left, with his assistants, N. T. Ljungquist, A. Kisk, and C. W. Mansur, and a rocket assembly without casing, at Roswell, New Mexico, in 1940. (*Photograph by B. Anthony Stewart, copyright National Geographic Society. Courtesy of Mrs. Robert H. Goddard*)

isolated ranch near Roswell, New Mexico. But as far as altitude, an important objective of rocket propulsion, was concerned, he was not able to improve on the height of 7500 feet attained in May 1935.

1.60. In spite of the pioneering contributions made by Goddard to the theory and early practice of rocketry, his work did not make the impression that it merited. The reason for this, as given by Goddard himself in 1944, a few months before his death, was that the optimum application of liquid-propellant systems was in rockets of large size and long range. And, he went on to say, "The U.S. had no need for long-range rockets at the time." In the opinion of the present writer, however, there may have been another reason. Goddard was his own inventor, designer, engineer, and mechanic, and, remarkable man as he was, his aims were beyond the capacity of himself and his small group of assistants. On several occasions, he declined help from competent organizations because it would have meant disclosure of the results of his work, and this he refused to do (cf. § 1.89).

1.61. Apart from patent applications and the original Smithsonian Institution report of 1919, only one description of his extensive work on rocketry was published during Goddard's lifetime. This was a short paper consisting of ten pages of text and some illustrations, entitled *Liquid-Propellant Rocket Development*, issued by the Smithsonian Institution in March 1936. One possible explanation for this reticence, which is unusual among scientists, will be given shortly.

1.62. A significant event in the history of space exploration was the publication in Germany in 1923 of a small book entitled *The Rocket into Interplanetary Space*. It was written by a mathematics teacher, Hermann Oberth, who was born in Transylvania, at the time a province of the Austro-Hungarian empire. In this pamphlet, the author discussed many theoretical and speculative aspects of rocket flight and space travel, to a certain extent duplicating and in some respects surpassing the work of his predecessors, Tsiolkovsky and Goddard. Among other things, Oberth argued in favor of liquid propellants for rockets on the grounds that they would provide higher exhaust gas velocities, and hence higher vehicle velocities, than solid propellants. Although he never succeeded in building an operating rocket, Oberth's monograph was destined by circumstances to have highly important consequences in the development of rocketry.

1.63. A short account of the relationship between Oberth and Goddard is worthy of a digression at this point. In May 1922, Oberth had written to Goddard stating that, just as he was on the point of publishing the results of several years of study on the problem of space propulsion by rockets, he had learned that Goddard had already done much important work on this subject. Oberth then went on to say that, in spite of his efforts, he had been unable to secure Goddard's publications, and so he was now asking for them. To this request, Goddard responded by sending a copy of the Smithsonian Institution report of 1919.

1.64. In due course, after its publication, Goddard received a copy of Oberth's pamphlet. In an appendix, Oberth had acknowledged Goddard's contribution to rocketry and space travel, but asserted that his own studies had been carried out quite independently. Although there was no reason to doubt this claim, Goddard was apparently convinced that it was not true. As a result he became highly secretive about his experiments on rocket propulsion. In answer to a statement in the May 1931 issue of the *Bulletin of the American Interplanetary Society* (§ 1.70) to the effect that "Goddard . . . has carefully prevented the results of his work from becoming public," he wrote ". . . so many of my ideas and suggestions have been copied abroad without acknowledgment . . . that I have been forced to take this attitude." As mentioned earlier, "this attitude" was to cause Goddard in later years to refuse collaboration with others who could have contributed greatly to his work.

1.65. Although Goddard's Smithsonian paper had aroused only passing notice, the appearance of Oberth's monograph attracted continued attention. In Germany, two popular expositions of his work were published, namely, *The Thrust into Space* by Max Valier (1924) and *Travel in the Universe* by Willy Ley (1926). Furthermore, Walter Hohmann, a German engineer and architect, wrote *The Attainability of Celestial Bodies* (1925), consisting largely of a mathematical discussion of the conditions for leaving and returning to Earth, for flight in space, and the circumnavigation of and landing upon celestial bodies. The so-called Hohmann transfer ellipses (§ 2.72) provide the most economical, although not the shortest, paths for interplanetary travel.

1.66. At about the same time, someone in the U.S.S.R. recalled that Oberth— and even Goddard—had been anticipated by Tsiolkovsky; the latter's report of 1903 was then re-issued in 1923 to establish Russian priority in the field of space travel. In addition, many other articles and books on the subject were produced in Russia. Especially noteworthy is the nine-volume work entitled *Interplanetary Communications* by Nikolai A. Rynin, a veritable encyclopedia of rocketry and space travel, published between the years 1928 and 1932. Two other significant Russian technical publications during this period were *The Conquest of Space* by Y. V. Kondratyuk in 1929, and *The Problem of Flight by Means of Reaction Devices* by F. A. Tsander (or Zander) in 1932.

1.67. In spite of Goddard's work, general interest in space developed relatively slowly in the United States. A three-part article entitled *Problems of Space Flying*, based mainly on Oberth's second book, with approximately this title (§ 1.71), published in 1929, appeared in the same year in a popular science magazine. This was followed in 1931 by the first American book devoted exclusively to space travel, *The Conquest of Space* by David Lasser. In 1930, a journal concerned with rocket propulsion and related topics commenced publication in the United States (§ 1.70).

SOCIETIES FOR THE STUDY OF SPACE TRAVEL

1.68. One of the consequences of the growing enthusiasm for space travel was the formation of societies of those interested in the subject. Perhaps the first of these was the Russian Society for the Study of Interplanetary Travel founded in Moscow in 1924. It was disbanded in the early 1930's because some of its members were regarded as "enemies of the régime." But in 1931, a new organization, called the Group for the Study of Reactive Propulsion, generally abbreviated to GIRD, was created in Leningrad with branches in the major Russian cities. This organization ultimately formed the basis for the State Rocket Scientific Research Institute in the U.S.S.R.

1.69. In Germany, the Verein für Raumschiffahrt (Society for Space Travel) was founded in June 1927; within a year it had nearly five hundred members including many non-Germans. The monthly journal of this society, the world's first magazine of space technology, called *The Rocket*, commenced publication soon after the society was formed although it did not last beyond December 1929. The activity of the Society for Space Travel was brought to the attention of the German public in 1928 in a book edited by Willy Ley, *The Possibility of Space Travel*, in which some of the leading members collaborated. The latter included Oberth and Hohmann, and the Austrians Franz von Hoefft and Count Guido von Pirquet who helped to found Societies for High-Altitude Exploration and for Rocket Technology, respectively, in their country.

1.70. The success of the German and Austrian societies for the study of space travel stimulated the formation of others in Europe and in the United States. The American Interplanetary Society, soon renamed the American Rocket Society, was organized in 1930 by G. Edward Pendray, David Lasser, and others.* In June of that year, the *Bulletin of the American Interplanetary Society* commenced publication in mimeographed form. This journal acquired different names in the course of time, including Astronautics, Jet Propulsion, and Journal of the American Rocket Society, and in 1963 it was absorbed into the new American Institute of Aeronautics and Astronautics (A.I.A.A.) Journal. It holds the record of longer continuous publication than any other journal devoted to space interests. A second United States rocket society was founded in Cleveland, Ohio, in 1933, but it succumbed in 1937. The British Interplanetary Society, which still exists, was also started in 1933.

1.71. In France, a pioneer in the study of space travel was Robert Esnault-Pelterie, whose article on *Principles of Rocket Flight and Planetary Exploration* appeared in a technical journal in 1913. But, as with much of the work preceding that of Oberth, his publication had little impact. Later, space activities became an important part of the program of the Astronomical Society of France and in 1928 this society published a lecture by Esnault-Pelterie entitled *Exploration of the Very High Atmosphere and the Possibility of Interplanetary Travel*. A greatly enlarged and improved version of this lecture was issued in 1930 as a book called *Astronautics*.† To stimulate and encourage efforts in connection with space exploration, Esnault-Pelterie and the French banker

---

* In 1962, the American Rocket Society was merged with the Institute of Aerospace Sciences to form the American Institute of Aeronautics and Astronautics.

† According to Frank J. Malina, one of the founders of the California Institute of Technology Rocket Research Project (§ 1.84), the French word "astronautique" (or astronautics) was coined by J. H. Rosny, a writer and member of the space travel committee of the Astronomical Society of France.

André Hirsch offered an annual prize of 5000 francs. The first award, made in 1929, went to Oberth for his second book, *Ways of Space Travel,* published in that year. Although Goddard's contribution to the subject was undoubtedly greater than that of Oberth, the secrecy in which Goddard conducted his work was probably responsible for his being overlooked.

1.72. In 1934, the REP-Hirsch prize was given to a Russian, Ari (or Ary) J. Shternfeld, then living in Paris, for an unpublished French manuscript entitled *Introduction to Cosmonautics.* The work was translated into the Russian language and published in 1937. It is of interest in this connection that in Russia the terms "cosmonautics" and "cosmonaut" are now in general use, whereas "astronautics" and "astronaut" are preferred in the United States.

Early Liquid-Fuel Rocket Developments

1.73. Simultaneously with the growth of interest in space, another event was occurring in Germany which was to have somewhat surprising consequences. In 1928, the well-known motion-picture producer Fritz Lang had started work on a film to be titled *The Girl in the Moon* (also called *By Rocket to the Moon*), and Oberth had agreed to serve as technical adviser. In order to provide publicity, Oberth was encouraged to build a rocket to be fired about the time of the first showing of the motion picture. Two different types of rocket were designed but neither was completed before the film's première in October 1929. The film itself utilized a full-scale mockup of a spaceship bearing a decided resemblance to a large modern rocket, but there was, of course, no actual scene of firing and liftoff. In order to enhance the dramatic effect, however, Lang invented the now familiar countdown. The picture was one of the last of the silent era and so the numbers indicating seconds before the supposed firing were flashed successively on the screen.

1.74. After completion of the film, the producers agreed to transfer the experimental rocket parts and other equipment to a small group of members of the German Society for Space Travel. In July 1930, a successful static test of a rocket, using liquid oxygen and gasoline as propellants, was performed by an engineer named Klaus Riedel assisted by an 18-year-old student, Wernher von Braun. The first significant flight of a liquid-propellant rocket in Europe was demonstrated in March 1931 by Johannes Winkler, the founding president of the Society for Space Travel. His rocket used liquid methane as the fuel and liquid oxygen as the oxidizer.

1.75. By the latter part of 1933, the Germans, civilian and military, had made considerable progress in rocketry. Among other things, they developed the use of a mixture of ordinary (ethyl) alcohol and water (fuel) and liquid oxygen (oxidizer) as the propellants. Alcohol has an apparent advantage over gasoline as fuel because it requires less liquid oxygen per unit mass for combustion, and the presence of a certain amount of water improves the operation of the rocket by increasing the exhaust gas velocity. The water lowers the gas temperature but it also decreases the molecular weight to a greater extent, so that there is an overall advantage (§ 1.41). Furthermore, it has been stated that water in the fuel improves its capacity for cooling the combustion chamber.

1.76. Soon after the formation of the American Interplanetary Society in 1930, some of its members became interested in the possibility of building liquid-propellant rockets. As they were unable to obtain any information from Goddard, they turned to the German Society for Space Travel. Following a visit by Pendray to Berlin in the spring of 1931, he and H. F. Pierce designed a rocket "generally following the ideas of the Germans." Between 1932 and 1941, members of what was by then the American Rocket Society made static tests of a number of liquid-propellant rockets and several achieved successful flights. In September 1941 the experiments were terminated, presumably as a consequence of the wartime situation.

1.77. In the U.S.S.R., the GIRD organization was dedicated to research in and construction of rockets, and an operative liquid-fuel rocket engine was designed and built by Tsander (§ 1.66) in 1932. By 1935, it is claimed that an altitude of over 30,000 feet (6 miles) had been attained, thus surpassing, as the Russians are at pains to point out, the maximum height of 7500 feet reached by any of Goddard's rockets. A number of papers were published in the U.S.S.R. in 1935 in connection with a conference on the use of rockets for the study of the stratosphere, and these revealed considerable competence in various aspects of rocket technology and high-altitude atmospheric research. Subsequently, the Russian government took complete control of this work and publication of original papers on rocketry was suspended.

THE V-2 ROCKET

1.78. About the time when the situation from the standpoint of the technical development of rocket engines in Germany appeared to be promising, the Society for Space Travel was plagued by numerous problems of a nonscientific nature. Shortage of funds, the political and economic problems in Germany, and the development of military interest in rocketry, as described below, as well as various other factors, led to a complete termination of private rocket experiments in the winter of 1933-34. At the same time, the Society, which had been steadily losing its membership, ceased to exist. However, while this marked the end of one phase in the investigation of space propulsion, another had already begun.

1.79. The treaty of Versailles, after World War I, prohibited Germany from developing heavy artillery, but it said nothing about missiles propelled by rockets. Consequently, in 1929 the Ballistic and Missiles Branch of the German Army's Department of Weapons Development was assigned the task of undertaking the development of rockets, in particular liquid-propellant rockets, for military purposes. An experimental station was established at Kummersdorf, near Berlin, in 1931; the military commandant was Walter Dornberger and the first civilian employee was Wernher von Braun. Others who had gained experience in rocket technology from the Society for Space Travel soon joined the organization, and as a result of the facilities and financing which became available progress was fairly rapid.

1.80. Before the end of 1934, a rocket weighing 660 pounds, employing alcohol-water and liquid oxygen as propellants, had reached an altitude of about 6500 feet, so that, at this time, achievements in rocketry were about the same in Germany and the United States (§ 1.59). In the United States, little further progress was made for several years, whereas in Germany the growth of the rocket project was such as to require a larger and preferably more remote test site, partly for reasons of secrecy and partly because of the hazardous nature of rocket experiments. This site was established in 1937 at Peenemünde on an island off Germany's Baltic Sea coast.

1.81. At Peenemünde several rocket designs were developed, the best known being the A-4, an abbreviation for Aggregate (meaning Assembly or Proto-type) Number 4, later called the V-2, for Vergeltung (or Vengeance) Number 2.* The V-2 was, for its time, a highly sophisticated and complex system, 47 feet in length and having a total weight of over 28,000 pounds at liftoff. The propellants were liquid oxygen (11,000 pounds) and a mixture of 75 percent ordinary alcohol and 25 percent water (8450 pounds). With a warhead weigh-ing 2200 pounds, the peak altitude of the V-2 rocket was roughly 60 miles and its range about 200 miles. Among the novel components were centrifugal pumps for the propellants driven by a steam turbine; the steam (mixed with oxygen) was supplied by the chemical reaction between concentrated hydrogen peroxide and an aqueous solution of potassium permanganate.

1.82. A satisfactory test of the V-2 rocket was made in October 1942, but there still remained many problems to be solved. Consequently, it was not until September 6, 1944 that the first operational use of V-2 bombs was made against Paris, and two days later they were directed toward London. It is reported that, of the more than a thousand V-2's fired on Britain between September 1944 and the end of March 1945, nearly 8 percent failed close to the firing site and about half of the remainder did not reach their intended targets.

1.83. Many of the features incorporated in the V-2 system were based on the same principles as the ideas patented and partly tested by Goddard be-tween 1932 and 1940. Nevertheless, there is every reason to believe, as stated by Wernher von Braun, that the German inventions were made quite inde-

* The V-1 weapon, developed by the German Air Force, was essentially an unmanned jet aircraft; it required oxygen from the air for combustion of the fuel and the presence of atmosphere for its winged flight. The V-2, on the other hand, was independent of the atmosphere.

pendently. Faced with the same problems as Goddard, the Germans found essentially the same solutions.

Rocket Development in the United States

1.84. In 1936, the Hungarian-born Theodore von Kármán, a world-renowned authority on aerodynamics, and a group of scientists and engineers at the Guggenheim Aeronautical Laboratory of the California Institute of Technology (GALCIT) formed the Rocket Research Project, for the primary purpose of developing rockets for high-altitude atmospheric research.* The work of this group led to the production of a new type of solid propellant that was superior in many respects to those previously used.

1.85. The new propellant consisted of asphalt, with a small quantity of asphalt oil, to serve as the fuel, intimately mixed with a solid perchlorate as oxidizer. More recently other composite propellants have been formulated in which the same (or similar) oxidizer is combined with a fuel consisting of a synthetic organic polymer (or plastic) resembling synthetic rubber, and finely divided particles of a metal, e.g., aluminum. Since such propellants can be stored in the rocket vehicle and are ready for instant use, they have an advantage from the military standpoint. The JATO (jet-assisted take-off) devices for aircraft, and several solid-propellant missiles, e.g., Nike, Pershing, Sergeant, Polaris, and Minuteman, as well as other rocket systems, e.g., Scout, were developed from the work of the GALCIT Rocket Research Project.

1.86. Although the liquid propellants mentioned earlier have an advantage over solid propellants in being capable of yielding somewhat higher exhaust gas velocities, their great drawback is that oxygen has to be cooled to very low temperatures (about $-182°C$, $-295°F$) to maintain it in the liquid state at normal pressures. Storage of liquid oxygen in the rocket vehicle for any significant time is quite impractical, and so it is loaded into the oxidizer tank just prior to launching.† A rocket weapon utilizing liquid oxygen as one of the propellants is thus not always "combat ready" and this could be a serious disadvantage in many circumstances.

1.87. Concurrently with their work on the development of solid propellants described above, the GALCIT scientists were therefore seeking an oxidizer which, unlike liquid oxygen, could be stored for a considerable period in the rocket vehicle. A satisfactory substitute was found in red fuming nitric acid (or RFNA), i.e., concentrated nitric acid containing a few percent of dissolved

---

* In 1943, the title was changed to the Jet Propulsion Laboratory (of the California Institute of Technology) because the word "rocket" was said to be in disrepute at the time. The Laboratory, which is now very active in the space program, is generally called JPL. In 1944, at the request of the U.S. Army Ordnance Corps, it started Project ORDCIT for the development of missiles of moderate range.

† Liquid oxygen is commonly referred to as "lox" and the process of loading it into the rocket vehicle before launching is called "loxing."

nitrogen tetroxide (N_2O_4).* in 1941, an engine was operated with gasoline and RFNA as propellants, and the following year it was found that the "throbbing" from which this motor suffered could be eliminated by utilizing aniline as the fuel. Moreover, the aniline-RFNA propellant combination differed from other liquid systems, such as kerosene-liquid oxygen, in an important respect: it was self igniting. In other words, aniline and RFNA do not require a spark or flame to start combustion because ignition occurs spontaneously upon mixing the two liquids. Such propellants are said to be *hypergolic*.†

1.88. In addition to being storable and able to yield fairly high exhaust gas velocities in a rocket engine, the liquid hypergolic propellants have the great merit of what is called "restart capability." In other words, while in flight, the engine can be readily stopped and started again at will, simply by turning the propellant pumps off or on, respectively. Ignition occurs automatically as soon as the fuel and oxidizer liquids come into contact. Several hypergolic propellant combinations are now available, as will be seen in Chapter 3. They are (or have been) employed in a variety of missiles and rockets, including Corporal, WAC-Corporal, Aerobee, Agena, and the large Titan II and Titan III.

1.89. Before leaving the work of the group at the California Institute of Technology, an interesting historical fact should be mentioned. Both GALCIT and Goddard were receiving financial support from the Guggenheim Foundation. Realizing the benefits that would accrue from a collaboration, Harry F. Guggenheim brought von Kármán, director of GALCIT, and Goddard together in New York in September 1938 to see if suitable arrangements for such collaboration could be made. The meeting was, however, fruitless because Goddard would not accept von Kármán's justifiable condition of full disclosure of information on all aspects of a problem that was to be studied cooperatively. The progress in rocketry in the United States that might have resulted from the combination of GALCIT's competence and Goddard's experience with liquid propellants is a matter for speculation.

POST-WAR DEVELOPMENTS IN RUSSIA

1.90. With the capitulation of Germany in May 1945, the scientists and engineers who had been working on the V-2 rocket surrendered to the advancing allied armies. Most of those responsible for design and planning, including

---

* It is reported that the Peenemünde group independently developed the use of concentrated nitric acid as an oxidizer for rocket applications, based upon earlier work of F. W. Sander in Germany in 1930. It is also claimed that, in Russia, V. P. Glushko made static firings of rockets with nitric acid and liquid nitrogen tetroxide as the oxidizers during the years 1931 to 1933.

† The term hypergolic is derived from Greek words meaning "excess energy." By contrast, propellants which do not ignite spontaneously when mixed, e.g., liquid oxygen and kerosene or alcohol, are sometimes called *anergolic*.

Dornberger and von Braun (§ 1.79), were taken by the Americans, whereas the production personnel were captured by the Russians. With the help of these and other German technicians, the Russians restored some of the laboratories and shops, which were transported to the U.S.S.R., together with several hundred workers, in 1946. In Russia, V-2 production was resumed, with some modifications, and beginning in the autumn of 1947 the rockets were used for high-altitude atmospheric research. The launch site at Kapustin Yar, near Volgograd, is said to have been equipped with material from Peenemünde.

1.91. After gaining experience in this manner, Russian engineers, with little or no help from the captured Germans, designed and built an improved version of the V-2 rocket, called the Pobeda. In addition to having a greater range than the V-2, the Pobeda had a more reliable self-contained guidance system. The latter, which was used to stabilize the flight and to turn the vehicle in the desired direction prior to the commencement of the ballistic trajectory, had been one of the weaker aspects of the V-2 design (cf. § 1.82). By September 1949, production of Pobedas was in full swing and V-2's were no longer used for atmospheric research. The German workers had by now served their purpose, and by 1952 most of them had returned home; electronics experts, however, were not repatriated until 1958.

1.92. Of rocket development in the U.S.S.R. subsequent to 1949, little is known. It is certain, however, that considerable effort was devoted to the production of powerful rockets, primarily because of their military value. Such rockets were used from 1957 on to place relatively massive satellites into Earth orbit and to send spacecraft into trajectories toward the Moon, Venus, and Mars.

Post-War Developments in the United States

1.93. During 1945, nearly 130 German rocket scientists and engineers voluntarily accepted contracts to come to America, and by the end of the year many of them, including von Braun, had been assigned to the U.S. Army's Fort Bliss, Texas, and the nearby White Sands Proving Ground (now the White Sands Missile Range), New Mexico. At the latter location, 67 complete V-2 rockets were ultimately assembled from a conglomeration of parts that had been hastily and haphazardly packed and sent to the United States from the captured underground factory in the Harz Mountains in central Germany. With the advice of the German experts, the assembly work was performed by American engineers and technicians, who thereby obtained experience in handling— what were at the time—large liquid-propellant rockets. More than 60 V-2's were launched at White Sands Proving Ground between April 1946 and the termination of the project in June 1951. An important objective of these rocket flights was to make observations of the upper atmosphere. The problems associated with the operation will be apparent from the fact that about half of the launchings were recorded officially as being unsuccessful for one reason or another. The failures were due about equally to propulsion and guidance difficulties.

1.94. After 15 months at White Sands, von Braun's entire group was transferred to Fort Bliss and then, in April 1950, to the U.S. Army's Redstone Arsenal (now also the location of the George C. Marshall Space Flight Center of the National Aeronautics and Space Administration), Huntsville, Alabama. Here the first large, liquid-propellant military missile to become operational, the 200-mile range Redstone, was designed and built. It was, in principle, a scaled-up version of the V-2 rocket with a launch weight of approximately 62,000 pounds. Subsequently, Redstone Arsenal produced the United States' first operational Intermediate Range Ballistic Missile (IRBM), Jupiter, with a range of 1600 miles. The Thor IRBM, however, was developed independently by the U.S. Air Force. Instead of alcohol, the fuel in these rockets was a high-grade kerosene, with liquid oxygen as the oxidizer. Similar fuels have since been widely employed in large rockets, such as the Air Force's Inter-Continental Ballistic Missiles (ICBM) Atlas and Titan I (first stage), and the first stage of the Saturn vehicles which are expected to play an important role in the exploration of space (Chapter 3).

1.95. It is of interest to mention, for historical and other reasons (cf. § 1.111), that in 1946 the U.S. Naval Research Laboratory initiated plans for the construction by industry of a rocket especially designed for high-altitude studies of the atmosphere. This rocket, first called Neptune and later Viking, used the same fuel (alcohol-water mixture) and oxidizer (liquid oxygen) as the V-2 and Redstone missiles. But it was developed quite independently and was intended for a different purpose. The first successful launch of a Viking rocket occurred at White Sands Proving Ground in May 1949; the Redstone, however, was not flown until August 1953.

DEVELOPMENT OF SOUNDING ROCKETS

1.96. It will be recalled that in his earliest patents and in his Smithsonian report of 1919, Goddard specifically referred to the use of rockets for making scientific measurements at high altitudes. And in 1929 he launched the world's first instrumented rocket for studying the upper atmosphere, although it attained a height of only 90 feet. Oberth, in his publication of 1923, also referred to the possibility of using rockets to provide information about the regions above Earth's atmosphere. Moreover, as mentioned in § 1.77, Russian scientists in the early 1930's were making measurements above the stratosphere by means of rockets. In the United States, WAC-Corporal,* first used in September 1945, was developed by the Jet Propulsion Laboratory for upper-

---

* The WAC-Corporal utilized hypergolic liquid propellants, namely, red fuming nitric acid as the oxidizer and a mixture of aniline and furfuryl alcohol as the fuel.

atmosphere research. When the V-2 rockets became available in April 1946, they were employed for the same purpose.

1.97. Before the supply of V-2's became exhausted, plans were made for the production of rockets, such as Aerobee, Deacon, Viking,* and others, designed specifically as *sounding rockets*, i.e., rockets which ascend in a vertical (or nearly vertical) direction and descend to Earth at a location not far from the launch site. In general, the term sounding rocket is used to describe a probe that rises no higher than one Earth radius, i.e., about 4000 miles, and then returns; many sounding rockets, however, do not reach altitudes above 200 miles. Such rockets have been employed extensively for atmospheric and meteorological studies and their approximately vertical trajectories make possible a series of measurements above a selected location. Sounding rockets are especially useful when the payload of instruments must be recovered for examination. In these circumstances the instrumented capsule is released at a predetermined altitude and its descent is slowed down by means of a parachute.

1.98. It will be seen in Chapter 3 that there are advantages to the operation of a rocket vehicle in stages. In a multistage rocket, the first (or lowest) stage burns and then drops away when its propellant is consumed; at this point, or later, the second stage ignites and then drops off in due course, and so on. Multistage sounding rockets are now in common use but the first built in the United States in 1947 for high-altitude research was the Aerobee, which reached heights of about 70 miles. A significant advance was achieved with a modified V-2 carrying a WAC-Corporal as the second stage in Project Bumper.† The maximum altitude reached by a V-2 rocket was about 114 miles and that of the WAC-Corporal was some 25 miles, yet the combination attained a height of 244 miles in a test flight in New Mexico in February 1949.

1.99. If the rocket motor of the WAC-Corporal had been ignited when the V-2 reached its maximum altitude, the ultimate height would probably not have exceeded 140 miles, because the initial velocity of the WAC-Corporal would have been essentially zero. The altitude attained would then be not much greater than the sum of the altitudes that could be reached by the two stages individually. However, the WAC-Corporal was actually ignited when the V-2 reached its maximum velocity, i.e., when the propellants were just about consumed. By adding its own velocity acquired during burning to that of the V-2, namely, 5500 feet per second, the WAC-Corporal was able to reach an altitude of over 240 miles before beginning to fall back to Earth.

---

* Aerobee-150 (or Aerobee-Hi) has two stages, a solid-propellant first stage followed by a second stage related to WAC-Corporal; Deacon is a single-stage, solid-propellant rocket; Viking is described in § 1.95.

† Although the multistage principle had long been used in fireworks rockets, the first modern multistage vehicle was the German four-stage Rheinbote, a relatively small (overall length 37.5 ft, weight 3775 pounds) solid-propellant combat rocket, successfully flown in 1944.

Rockoons for High-Altitude Research

1.100. A relatively simple and inexpensive technique for attaining high altitudes evolved in March 1949 from a discussion among M. L. Lewis, G. Halvorsen, S. F. Singer, and J. Van Allen during an Aerobee firing cruise on the rocket-launching ship U.S.S. Norton Sound. Essentially the same method had been suggested earlier by Oberth, but no attempt was made to put it into practice. A moving rocket loses much of its energy overcoming the frictional resistance of the atmosphere, commonly referred to as *aerodynamic drag.* The magnitude of the drag force, for a body of given cross-sectional area in the direction of motion, depends, among other factors, on the density of the atmosphere through which it moves and on the square of its velocity. Consequently, much of the energy loss caused by aerodynamic drag occurs at low altitudes, i.e., soon after launch, because that is where the air density is highest. Furthermore, a small, light rocket accelerates rapidly and attains a high velocity while still at a fairly low altitude. Hence, for a rocket of this type, the drag losses are relatively high if it is launched from the ground.

1.101. It was proposed, therefore, to launch a small rocket from a balloon at an altitude of about 80,000 feet where the density of the air is about a factor of 30 less than at Earth's surface. At this height, therefore, the aerodynamic drag on the rocket would be reduced to a few percent of that experienced in a launching from the ground. Between July and September 1952, a number of rocket-balloon combinations, called *rockoons,* were launched successfully. These and many others were used for high-altitude research on cosmic rays and solar flares, particularly in 1957, as part of the United States' contribution to the International Geophysical Year (§ 1.110).

Earth Satellites

1.102. The sounding rocket is a valuable device for making detailed studies of the upper atmosphere and space at several different altitudes above a given point (or limited area) on Earth. When it is required to make repeated observations of space over a large part of the globe, it is more convenient to make use of an artificial satellite, i.e., a body which revolves about Earth in a fairly definite orbit. Unless it is at a very high altitude, aerodynamic drag of the atmosphere will cause a gradual slowing down in the motion of a satellite. As a result, for reasons which will be apparent later (§ 2.92), it will lose altitude and may possibly be destroyed by frictional heating when it enters the region of fairly high air density.

1.103. The lifetime of a satellite depends on its size (and shape), its mass, and the altitude of its orbit. For a high orbit, both the atmospheric density and the orbital velocity (cf. § 2.30) are less than for a lower orbit, and the aerodynamic drag force is correspondingly smaller. Furthermore, the drag on a small satellite is less than on a larger one. The rate of slowing down (or deceleration) of a body in orbit depends on its mass; the larger the mass, the smaller the deceleration for a given drag force.* Consequently, a small, heavy satellite orbiting at high altitude may be expected to have a long life. Increase in size, decrease in mass, and decrease in altitude will all contribute to a shortening of the lifetime. It is doubtful if satellites to be used in making scientific measurements are economically practical for altitudes less than about 200 miles. Above 200 miles or so, however, a small, fairly massive satellite may remain in orbit for many years. For a larger or less massive satellite, a higher altitude would be necessary to achieve a useful life in orbit.

1.104. As noted in § 1.35, Newton had indicated, in theory, how an artificial satellite could be placed in orbit, and both Tsiolkovsky and Oberth considered the possibility of space stations consisting of man-carrying satellites orbiting Earth. Such a satellite could be launched by utilizing a powerful rocket carrier vehicle to raise it to the desired altitude, and to inject it into space with the required velocity. Among the early technical writers on space, however, there was no mention of unmanned satellites, presumably because at the time radio telemetry (§ 4.149) had not been invented and no use could be envisaged for such vehicles.† In the United States, the concept of an unmanned satellite developed gradually in the years between 1945 and 1954.

1.105. In October 1945, the U.S. Navy's Bureau of Aeronautics Committee for Evaluating the Feasibility of Space Rocketry submitted a proposal for an experimental program directed toward the launching of an Earth satellite to carry instruments for scientific purposes. When it appeared that the Navy would not provide financial support, members of the Committee approached the Army Air Force in the hope of establishing a joint project. A meeting of representatives of the Air Force and the Navy was held in March 1946, and it was agreed that the advantages to be derived from the development of an Earth satellite were sufficient to justify a major program. After reviewing the situation, however, the senior officers of the Army Air Force decided that they would not support the Navy's satellite project, but left the matter open for further discussion.

1.106. At this point the Air Force turned to Project RAND ‡ to make a study of the subject of Earth satellites, and in May 1946 a report entitled *Preliminary Design of an Experimental World-Circling Spaceship* was issued. In this report, the Project RAND personnel argued strongly in favor of developing an Earth satellite, both as a scientific tool and for its psychological impact on

---

* This is a consequence of Newton's second law of motion (§ 2.17).

† A possible exception, mentioned by W. Dornberger, was the suggestion that the bodies of pioneers in space travel should be enclosed in glass capsules which would be put into permanent orbit around Earth.

‡ Project RAND was established by the Army Air Force in 1945 to review long-range research projects. It was originally operated by the Douglas Aircraft Corporation, but it became a completely autonomous research institution when the RAND Corporation was formed in November 1948.

"the imagination of mankind." It was estimated that a 400-pound satellite could be constructed and placed into an orbit 300 miles above Earth within five years, that is by 1951, if work on the project was started immediately. Unfortunately, the financial support required to proceed with the plans was not forthcoming.

1.107. During the next few years, the armed services continued with their separate studies of Earth satellites. But by 1949 only the U.S. Air Force, which had been separated from the Army in 1947, retained an active interest in the project, mainly in the form of feasibility and applications studies by the RAND Corporation. The U.S. Navy terminated its efforts, temporarily at least, and the Army was assigned the task of developing missiles. There the matter remained for a time.

1.108. Prior to November 1954, the only public reference to the official United States interest in Earth satellites was a brief mention by the Secretary of Defense, James Forrestal, near the end of 1948.* Civilian scientists discussed the matter freely and several articles on the subject were published. In particular, an important contribution came from the American physicist, born in Austria, S. Fred Singer; at the International Astronautical Congress meeting in Switzerland in August 1953, he described in detail the possible scientific uses, instrumentation, and orbital path of a small satellite weighing about 100 pounds.†

1.109. In June 1954, a group of scientists and engineers interested in space exploration met unofficially at the U.S. Office of Naval Research and outlined a proposal for launching a small satellite by means of a rocket into an orbit about 200 miles above Earth. Some two months later, another meeting was held at Redstone Arsenal, and as a result a joint Army-Navy program called Project Orbiter was initiated. In the spring of the following year, von Braun and his associates submitted to the Department of Defense a proposal entitled *A Minimum Satellite Vehicle Based upon Components Available from Missile Development of the Army Ordnance Corps*. It was asserted that an Earth satellite could be launched within a short time by utilizing the Redstone rocket (§ 1.94) as the first stage with clusters of existing (Loki) solid-propellant motors in the upper stages.

1.110. In the meantime, plans were being made for the participation of the United States in the International Geophysical Year (IGY), which was to last from July 1, 1957 to December 31, 1958. Consequently, in May 1955 a detailed Earth-satellite program, prepared by the U.S. National Committee for IGY, was submitted to the National Science Foundation for governmental considera-

---

* This provoked the Russian Journal *New Times* to refer to the "madman Forrestal's idea of an Earth satellite" and to call it an "instrument of (international) blackmail."

† The name MOUSE, an acronym for Minimum Orbital Unmanned Satellite of Earth, was coined by S. F. Singer together with A. C. Clarke and A. V. Cleaver of the British Interplanetary Society.

tion. The program was approved, and a statement issued from the White House on July 29, 1955 represented the first official public announcement of the decision to launch "small, unmanned, earth-circling satellites as part of the U.S. contribution in the IGY." An advisory committee was then appointed by the Department of Defense to determine the best way to implement this decision.

1.111. Three proposals for launch vehicles were presented to the committee for consideration: (*a*) the rocket engine of the Atlas missile, (*b*) the Redstone rocket with upper stages of clustered solid-propellant rockets, as suggested for Project Orbiter, and (*c*) the Naval Research Laboratory's Viking, with some improvements, as the first stage, the hypergolic-propellant Aerobee (or similar) as the second stage, and a solid-fuel motor, still to be designed, as the third stage. By a majority vote, the committee chose the last of these modes for placing the satellite in orbit. The main reasons for the choice were that Atlas was still under development and was not a ready vehicle, and Redstone, as then designed, would be able to launch only a small mass into orbit. The Viking-based system, on the other hand, was believed to be capable of orbiting a larger mass. Moreover, it could be developed without interfering with urgent military work on ballistic missiles. Hence, Project Orbiter was terminated and the new Project Vanguard, a tri-service program under Navy management, was initiated on September 9, 1955.

1.112. Many difficulties were encountered in the project, so that even before the first test had been made of the complete three-stage Vanguard rocket, there came news of the successful launch in the U.S.S.R., on October 4, 1957, of Sputnik I, the first artificial satellite of Earth, with a payload of 184 pounds.* This was soon followed by a second Russian satellite on November 3, 1957, when Sputnik II (1957 Beta), with a payload of over 1000 pounds, was put into orbit. In addition to various scientific instruments for the study of solar radiation and cosmic rays, Sputnik II carried a live dog for biomedical experiments on the effects of space on animals. This was the first time a living creature had been placed in Earth orbit by man.

1.113. The Russian achievement came as a great surprise, to many scientists as well as to laymen, the world over; but it certainly should not have done so. On January 10, 1955, Radio Moscow asserted that, according to U.S.S.R. scientists, the launching of an Earth satellite was possible "in the near future." This was followed on April 15, 1955, by a statement in the Soviet press that there

---

* The Russian word *sputnik* means "attendant," "companion," or "satellite" in the astronomical sense, e.g., the Moon; it was used by Tsiolkovsky to describe the artificial, manned satellite he proposed.

Following the suggestion of the astronomers F. L. Whipple and J. A. Hynek, a system was adopted in the United States for designating artificial satellites similar to that employed for newly discovered comets, i.e., the year of launching followed by a Greek letter indicating its ordinal number; thus Sputnik I became 1957 Alpha. As of January 1, 1963 the system was changed and the actual ordinal number is now used instead of a Greek letter

had been created during the preceding autumn an Interdepartmental Commission on Interplanetary Communication of the U.S.S.R. Academy of Sciences to develop an artificial satellite to improve weather prediction. Then, on August 2, 1955, at the International Congress on Astronautics, held in Denmark, L. I. Sedov, Chairman of this Commission, announced Russia's intention to launch Earth satellites during the IGY, and on June 10, 1957, an official report was sent to IGY headquarters stating that the satellite project was ready. Evidently these announcements were not taken seriously, for it had not been realized that, under a cloak of secrecy, the U.S.S.R. had been developing powerful military rockets presumably to serve as carriers for heavy nuclear warheads.

1.114. Because of the low priority of the United States' Vanguard program, the Russian successes prompted the decision by the Department of Defense on November 8, 1957 to launch, as soon as possible, a scientific satellite using a modified Jupiter C (Juno I) rocket. This represented essentially a return to the discarded Project Orbiter. Within less than three months, on January 31, 1958, the first U.S. Satellite, called Explorer I (1958 Alpha), was placed in Earth orbit. The payload weighed about 31 pounds, of which some 11 pounds consisted of scientific instruments mainly for the study of cosmic rays (Fig. 1.7). The launch vehicle had as its first stage a somewhat elongated Redstone rocket in which the alcohol-water fuel was replaced by a more powerful one, called Hydyne, which had the same density.* The oxidizer was liquid oxygen, as in Redstone. The second stage was a cluster of eleven scaled-down Sergeant (solid-fuel) motors, followed by a cluster of three rockets of this type as the third stage, and a single one in the fourth stage.† The overall length of the vehicle was 68.6 feet and the weight at liftoff was 64,000 pounds. The initial altitude of the orbit ranged from 217 miles (minimum) to 1155 miles (maximum). The spacecraft Explorer I was significant, not only in the respect that it was the first Earth satellite to be launched from the United States, but also because the information transmitted by the instruments it carried made possible the identification by James Van Allen of the belt of electrically charged particles surrounding Earth (§ 8.267).

1.115. On March 17, 1958, after some test failures, a Vanguard carrier launched into orbit the second U.S. satellite, Vanguard I (1958 Beta). The first stage of the vehicle was a modified Viking using a kerosene-base fuel and liquid oxygen as propellants; the second stage employed a hypergolic liquid system, consisting of unsymmetrical dimethylhydrazine and fuming nitric acid; the third stage was a solid-fuel rocket.‡ The overall length was 72 feet and the

---

* Hydyne consists of 60 percent unsymmetrical dimethylhydrazine (§ 3.30) and 40 percent diethylenetriamine.

† Substitution of the scaled Sergeant motors for the Lokis originally contemplated in Project Orbiter was made as the result of a study by the Jet Propulsion Laboratory, which supplied the three upper stages of the Jupiter C launch vehicle.

‡ It is of interest that the second and third stages of the Vanguard launch vehicle became the upper stages of the highly successful Delta rocket (§ 3.142).

FIG. 1.7. Payload (with shrouds) of Explorer I satellite. The experimental instrumentation is in the upper central section; a low-power telemetry transmitter is above and a high-power transmitter below

launch weight was 22,600 pounds; the orbital altitude was initially 409 miles at the closest approach and 2453 miles at the farthest. The payload was an aluminum sphere, 6.4 inches in diameter and weighing 3.25 pounds, containing two radio transmitters for tracking purposes. A detailed study of the orbit of Vanguard I revealed a previously unknown distortion in the shape of Earth (§ 8.10).

1.116. Since 1958, numerous instrumented satellites have been launched into orbit both from the United States and the U.S.S.R. Some of these were designed to obtain scientific information about space, others to study the weather, and still others have been utilized to investigate the possibility of intercontinental communications by means of satellites. In addition, a number of probes have been sent out to the Moon and to the planets Venus and Mars. These and other applications of instrumented, unmanned spacecraft will be described in the later chapters.

MANNED SPACE FLIGHT

1.117. The early pioneers of space travel thought mainly, if not exclusively, in terms of manned vehicles. A possible explanation is that, to them, there seemed to be no way to obtain information from space without the presence of man. The significant developments in radio and related techniques that occurred around the middle of the twentieth century changed the situation, so that the inclusion of man is no longer essential. Nevertheless, there are several purposes that can be served by man in space. To the scientist, man, if properly trained, is to be regarded as an invaluable observer for whom instruments are no adequate substitute. Thus, manned vehicles have a definite role in space science.

1.118. The first man to travel in space was the Russian, Yuri Gagarin, who made a single orbit of Earth on April 12, 1961 in the spacecraft Vostok I* (1961 Mu). The maximum altitude of the elliptical orbit was about 188 miles and the minimum was 109 miles; the period was 89 minutes. A manned sub-orbital flight was made from the United States in May 1961, and this and other American manned space flights will be described below. On August 2, 1961, a second Russian cosmonaut, Gherman Titov, orbited Earth over 17 times in Vostok II (1961 Tau), remaining in space almost 25 hours. The orbit was almost circular, ranging from 110 to 115 miles in altitude. On August 11, 1962, Andrian Nikolayev was launched into orbit in Vostok III and on the following day Vostok IV, carrying Pavel Popovich, attained an Earth orbit very close to that of Vostok III. During the course of Vostok III's more than 64 orbits (94 hours) and Vostok IV's over 48 orbits (71 hours) the spacecraft were often in visual contact. Another dual flight was achieved about a year later when Valery Bykovsky, after launching on June 14, 1963, made almost 80 orbits (119 hours) in Vostok V and was followed by Miss Valentina Tere-

* The Russian word *vostok* means "east."

shkova, the first woman in space, on June 16, 1963, with 48 orbits (71 hours) in Vostok VI. The orbital planes of Vostok V and Vostok VI were inclined at an angle of 30 deg and the spaceships approached one another for a short interval, when their paths crossed, twice during each of the early orbits. A flight of 16 orbits, lasting approximately 24 hours, with three men (V. M. Komarov, K. P. Feoktistov, and B. B. Yegorov) in one spaceship named Voshkod (Sunrise) was achieved on October 12, 1964; this was the first time that more than one individual had been orbited in a single vehicle. Voshkod II, which made a flight of 26-hours duration on March 18, 1965, carried two cosmonauts, P. Belyayev and A. Leonov; the latter left the spaceship for a period of 10 minutes while in orbit.

1.119. In the United States, a manned orbital flight was not achieved until February 1962, although two suborbital flights had been made during the preceding year. As far back as February 1956, the Air Research and Development Command of the U.S. Air Force had put forward a proposal to place a man in orbit by 1960, by using the rocket engine from an Inter-Continental Ballistic Missile, such as Titan. Two years later, a study program was started for Project MISS (Man in Space Soonest), which it was hoped would lead to a manned space flight by October 1960. However, before this and other similar military projects were put into practice, Project Mercury for manned space flight was initiated in October 1958. This project then became a responsibility of the newly formed civilian National Aeronautics and Space Administration (NASA). Preliminary specifications for a proposed space capsule were immediately distributed to a number of industrial firms, and on April 2, 1959 announcement was made of the selection of seven individuals to be trained as astronauts.

1.120. On May 5, 1961, a Redstone rocket carried Alan B. Shepherd, Jr., in a Mercury capsule (Mercury-Redstone 3 or MR-3), on a ballistic (suborbital) flight path, reaching a peak altitude of 116 miles and traveling a downrange distance of 302 miles. The total duration of the flight was 15 minutes and 22 seconds. A second suborbital flight, peak altitude 118 miles and downrange distance 301 miles, was made by Virgil J. Grissom in MR-4 on July 21, 1961. These United States flights were carried out to obtain experience prior to undertaking orbital flights, but there is no information as to whether or not such preliminary measures were taken in the U.S.S.R.

1.121. The first U.S. manned orbital flight was successfully completed on February 20, 1962. An Atlas rocket launched a Mercury capsule (Mercury-Atlas 6 or MA-6), carrying astronaut John H. Glenn, Jr., into an elliptical orbit of altitude ranging from 99 to 162 miles. Three orbits were completed in a period of a little under 5 hours. A second flight (MA-7) of three orbits was made by M. Scott Carpenter on May 24, 1962, and an almost six-orbit mission of about 9-hours duration was achieved by Walter M. Schirra, Jr., in MA-8 on October 3, 1962. Project Mercury was terminated after the fourth orbital flight (MA-9), on May 15 and 16, 1963, when L. Gordon Cooper made 22 orbits of Earth in some 34 hours. It was felt that, at this stage, sufficient had been learned to make it possible to proceed with the next phases of manned space flight, Projects Gemini and Apollo (Chapter 13). The first manned Gemini flight of three orbits was carried out successfully with two astronauts, Virgil I. Grissom and John W. Young, on March 23, 1965. During the flight, changes were made in the dimensions and direction of the orbit by firing rockets on the spacecraft as a test of the ability to perform rendezvous operations in space (§13.25). Although unmanned satellites have had their orbits changed by command from the ground, this had not been done previously with a manned spacecraft by one of its occupants.

1.122. The events described above mark the opening of a new era in science and exploration. There will be many difficulties to overcome and many problems to solve, but the rewards, as indicated at the beginning of this chapter, will be great.

Chapter 2

SPACE ORBITS AND TRAJECTORIES

CIRCULAR ORBITS

INTRODUCTION

2.1. The purpose of the present chapter is to describe the factors which determine the characteristics of the path of a body in space. The term *orbit* is used when the path is closed and is repetitive; the traveling body is then a *satellite*. Thus, the Moon, the natural satellite of Earth, and artificial satellites are said to travel in orbits. Similarly, Earth and the other planets move in orbits about and are satellites of the Sun.

2.2. On the other hand, if the path has more or less specific initial and end points, it is referred to as a *trajectory*. While in a trajectory, the moving body is described as a *probe*. A spacecraft that is directed from Earth to the close vicinity of the Moon or other celestial body is said to be a space probe that follows a trajectory to the Moon, etc. If the spacecraft approaches the Moon, but does not impact upon the surface, it will generally go into orbit about Earth. Similarly, a space probe following a trajectory toward a planet may actually be in an orbit about the Sun. After approaching the planet, the space vehicle will then continue to travel in repetitive orbits around the Sun.

2.3. As an aspect of the subject of orbits and trajectories, it is appropriate to consider first the circumstances that make it possible for a satellite to be placed into and remain in orbit without falling back to Earth. The general conditions that allow the Moon to be a satellite of Earth were derived by the famous English mathematician Isaac Newton in his development of the theory of gravity. It is precisely the same conditions that permit the existence of artificial satellites.

WHY SATELLITES REMAIN IN ORBIT

2.4. Suppose a body (or object) is projected with a certain velocity in an exactly horizontal direction, i.e., precisely parallel to Earth's surface at the point where the body has the prescribed velocity. In order to simplify the following discussion and to consider conditions representing those in which a satellite actually orbits Earth, it will be assumed for the present that the body is located at an altitude of about 100 miles or more. The atmospheric density is then so low that the resistance of the air, i.e., the aerodynamic drag force, can be neglected.

2.5. According to Newton's first law of motion (cf. § 1.39), sometimes called Galileo's law of inertia, a body either remains at rest or moves with constant speed in a straight line provided it is not acted upon by any external force. Consequently, if the body referred to above were not subjected to any outside force, it would continue to move with the same speed along the path AB in Fig. 2.1, where A is the point of injection. But the force of gravity acting on

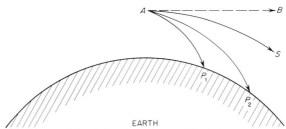

Fig.   2.1.   Injection of a satellite into orbit

the body tends to pull it back to Earth, so that the actual path will be something like AP_1. The object will thus strike Earth at the point P_1, the position of which depends on the velocity and altitude at the time of injection. By increasing the injection velocity, the body travels farther and farther, e.g., along the path AP_2, before reaching Earth.

2.6. Taking into account the curvature of Earth's surface, it is apparent that, for a certain speed of injection, the body will fall back to Earth under the influence of gravity just as fast as Earth's surface is receding because of its curvature. This situation is indicated by the path AS in Fig. 2.1. The object will then never reach Earth's surface but will continue to revolve (or orbit) about Earth; it is, therefore, an Earth satellite with a circular orbit. The minimum velocity with which a body must be projected in a horizontal direction in order to realize the condition described is called the *circular orbital velocity*, or in brief, the *orbital velocity*. The value of the velocity varies with the altitude above Earth at which injection takes place; the higher the altitude the smaller the orbital velocity (§ 2.30).

2.7. If the injection velocity should exceed the circular orbital velocity for the given altitude, the orbit will change from a circle to an ellipse. This and other aspects of the properties of satellite orbits will be treated later in this chapter. The present section, however, will be devoted to an elementary discussion of circular orbits, and the opportunity will be taken to develop some basic concepts concerning gravity which are applicable to all types of orbital and related motions.

2.8. An indication of the magnitude of the orbital velocity of an Earth satellite can be obtained in the following manner. It will be shown in § 2.21 that an object dropped from a height of **4.9** meters (**16** feet) takes approximately 1 second to reach the ground because of the action of Earth's gravity. Furthermore, it is known that, as a result of its curvature, Earth's surface drops **4.9** meters (**16** feet) in a distance of 8 kilometers (5 miles); this is represented schematically, *but not to scale*, in Fig. **2.2.** Consequently, if an object moves

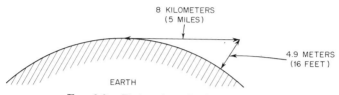

Fɪɢ. 2.2.   Estimation of orbital velocity

around Earth with a speed of **8** kilometers per second, the distance it falls back to Earth in 1 second, i.e., **4.9** meters, is exactly equal to the amount Earth's surface recedes because of its curvature. The orbital velocity of a satellite near Earth's surface is thus roughly **8** kilometers (5 miles) per second, i.e., **18,000** miles per hour. In other words, in order to make a body go into circular orbit about (and near to) Earth, it must be given a speed of **8** kilometers (5 miles) per second or **18,000** miles per hour in a horizontal direction. It is only by means of powerful rockets that such very high speeds can be attained.

2.9. When one body revolves about another, the orbital velocity, in general, depends on the masses of both bodies. But in the case of a satellite of relatively small mass orbiting about a much more massive central body, e.g., Earth, the orbital velocity is essentially independent of the satellite's mass. The central body is called the *primary body*, generally abbreviated to *primary*. Thus, Earth is the primary for the Moon or for an artificial satellite, whereas the Sun is the primary for Earth and the other planets. The orbiting of a planet about the Sun is accounted for, in the manner described above, by the gravitational attraction between the Sun and the planet.

2.10. Strictly speaking, the motion of a satellite is determined by the net gravitational effect of all other bodies, especially those in its general vicinity. Thus, the orbit of the Moon about Earth is affected by the Sun and that of an artificial satellite by both the Sun and the Moon. The attraction of the primary is, however, dominant under most conditions of interest and, as a first approximation, the influence of other bodies will be neglected. But when it is required to make accurate calculations of orbital characteristics, proper allowance must be made for secondary gravitational attractions.

2.11. The ability of a satellite to remain in orbit about its primary is the result of the combined effects of the inertia of the moving body and gravity. Consider a body traveling in a circular orbit and suppose that the gravitational force were suddenly cut off, e.g., when the satellite is at the point P (or P') in Fig. 2.3. As a consequence of its inertia, the body would then tend to move off in a direction that is a tangent to the orbit at P (or P'), i.e., along PQ (or $P'Q'$). This would be true for any point of the orbit. The fact that the satellite remains in orbit, and does not fly off at a tangent, is due to the action of gravity which continuously attracts the moving body toward the center of the primary. The orbital motion is thus the result of the action of gravity and inertia, and of nothing else.

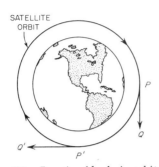

FIG. 2.3.   Inertia of body in orbit

2.12. It is sometimes stated that a satellite remains in orbit and does not fall back to Earth (or other primary) because the inwardly directed (or centripetal) force of gravity is exactly balanced by an equal outward centrifugal force arising from the circular motion.* This explanation can be misleading because the so-called centrifugal force is purely hypothetical; apart from minor disturbing effects due to radiation pressure, air resistance, etc., there is only one force acting on an orbiting satellite and that is gravity. What is known as the centrifugal force is really the effect of the inertia of the moving body. As seen in Fig. 2.3, if the centripetal force (gravity) were to cease suddenly, the inertia would cause the orbiting body to move outward, away from its normal orbital path. Thus, it would appear *as if* there were an outwardly directed (or centrifugal) force acting on the satellite; actually, there is no such force, since inertia is not a force. If the centrifugal concept is to be retained, it should be referred to as the *centrifugal effect* (not force) arising from the inertia of a body traveling in a circular path.

THE LAW OF UNIVERSAL GRAVITATION

2.13. To permit the development of a general expression for the orbital velocity, it is necessary to digress somewhat to consider the force of gravity and some of its consequences. In 1666, Isaac Newton formulated the law of universal gravitation which states that every particle of matter in the universe attracts every other particle with a force that is directly proportional to the product of the masses of the two particles and inversely proportional to the square of the distance between their centers. It is this force of attraction

* The words centripetal and centrifugal arise from the Latin, *centerus,* "center"; *petere,* "to move toward"; and *fugere,* "to flee" or "to fly away from."

between matter that is called the force of gravity or the gravitational attraction.

2.14. Because the force of gravity is related in an inverse manner to the square of the distance, it weakens fairly rapidly with increasing distance between the attracting masses; for example, doubling the distance between the centers of two masses decreases the gravitational force by a factor of four. Nevertheless, the force of gravity extends to infinite distances and never ceases to exist entirely, no matter how far two masses are apart. For very great distances, the gravitational attraction is often so small as to be negligible; thus, although Earth is attracted by the nearest group of stars, Alpha and Proxima Centauri, the distance is so great that the force between them can be neglected for all practical purposes. The gravitational force between Earth and the Sun, 93 million miles away, is of course quite considerable and is responsible for Earth remaining in orbit about the Sun.

2.15. Consider any two bodies, having masses M and m, respectively, as shown in Fig. 2.4; the distance between their centers is R. If the bodies are fairly large, as is certainly the case for celestial bodies and artificial satellites, they will consist of many individual particles. Every particle making up the body of mass M then exerts a force of attraction on every particle in the other body of mass m, and vice versa. The total force of gravitational

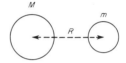

FIG. 2.4.   Gravitational attraction of two masses

attraction between the two bodies is then the sum of all the attractions between the individual particles.

2.16. The process of summation (or integration) can be avoided in the case of a *central force field*. Such a field exists when the bodies have spherically symmetric mass distribution, i.e., when the distribution of the mass is the same in all radial directions outward from the center. A sphere of uniform density is spherically symmetrical and so also is a body consisting of a series of concentric spherical shells of uniform thickness but with different densities. In these cases the gravitational attraction is the same as if the whole of the mass of each body were concentrated at its center. According to the law of gravitation, the force F, acting between the two bodies whose centers are a distance R apart, is then

$$F = G\frac{Mm}{R^2},\tag{2.1}$$

where G is a universal constant of nature, called the *gravitational constant*. The magnitude of the gravitational constant was first measured in experiments made in 1797 by the British scientist Henry Cavendish. In the MKS system of units, which is the main one employed in this chapter, i.e., with mass in kilograms, length (or distance) in meters, and time in seconds, the value of G is 6.673×10^{-11}; the force F is then given in newtons.*

2.17. Newton's second law of motion states that a force acting on a body causes it to accelerate in the direction of the force, the acceleration being directly proportional to the force and inversely proportional to the mass of the body. Suppose a force F acting on a body of mass m produces an acceleration a; then F, m, and a are related by

$$a = k \frac{F}{m}, \tag{2.2}$$

where k is a proportionality constant. The value of this constant depends on the manner in which the unit of force is defined in terms of the specified units of mass, length, and time. In the MKS system, with the force in newtons, it can be readily seen that k is unity, and so equation (2.2) can be written as

$$a = \frac{F}{m} \quad \text{or} \quad F = ma. \tag{2.3}$$

It should be mentioned that in the common engineering system of **units**, i.e., with mass in pounds mass, distance in feet, time in seconds, and force in pounds force, which is used in Chapter 3, the value of k is not unity (§ 3.7)

EARTH'S GRAVITY

2.18. The Newton second-law equation (2.3) is applicable to the force of gravity. Suppose the body of mass M is restrained but the one of mass m is free to move; the latter body will then be accelerated toward the former. The value of the acceleration caused by gravity can be calculated by comparing equations (2.1) and (2.3); thus,

$$F = G \frac{Mm}{R^2} = ma.$$

The gravitational acceleration is commonly represented by the letter g, so that

$$a = g = \frac{GM}{R^2}, \tag{2.4}$$

where R is now the distance of the body of mass m from Earth's center. The acceleration is thus seen to be independent of the mass of the body that is free to move; this fact was established by Galileo when he showed that different masses fall at essentially the same rate under the influence of Earth's gravity. Small variations actually observed were due to the drag (or resistance) of the atmosphere.

2.19. Any body (or object) falling toward Earth will be continuously ac-

---

* A newton is the force which will produce an acceleration of 1 meter per second per second in a mass of 1 kilogram; it is equivalent to 10^5 dynes.

celerated due to the action of gravity; an approximate value of this acceleration may be calculated from equation (2.4). The mass of Earth is 5.98×10^{24} kilograms and the average radius is 6.37×10^{6} meters; in the MKS system, G is 6.67×10^{-11} and so the acceleration due to gravity is

$$g = \frac{6.67 \times 10^{-11} \times 5.98 \times 10^{24}}{(6.37 \times 10^{6})^{2}}$$

$$= 9.83 \text{ meters per second per second}$$
$$= 983 \text{ centimeters per second per second.}$$

Since 1 meter is 3.28 feet, the equivalent value of g in common engineering units is $(9.83)(3.28) = 32.25$ feet per second per second.

2.20. In practice, the acceleration due to gravity at (or near) Earth's surface is not a constant quantity. In the first place, Earth is not exactly spherical; the radius is smallest at the poles and increases steadily toward the equator (§ 8.3). The gravitational force and the acceleration due to gravity thus decrease in going along the surface from the poles to the equator, because of the increasing distance from Earth's center. Another possible cause of variation is that the distribution of mass in the interior of Earth is probably not spherically symmetrical, i.e., it is not the same in all directions outward from the center. The gravitational acceleration at points on the surface will differ accordingly. Finally, the inertia of a body at the surface due to Earth's rotation about its axis produces an outward centrifugal effect which reduces the gravitational acceleration. This effect is zero at the poles and increases toward the equator where it is a maximum. For a rotating Earth, g is 9.832 meters (32.26 feet) per second per second at the poles and 9.780 meters (32.09 feet) per second per second at the equator, the average value used for many calculations is 9.8067 meters (32.174 feet) per second per second at sea level.

2.21. Suppose a body, initially at rest, is dropped from a height h feet above Earth's surface. As it falls, its speed will increase at a uniform rate of g meters per second every second; hence, if it requires t seconds to reach the ground, the body will have then gained gt meters per second in speed. The original downward speed was zero, because the body was at rest relative to Earth, and so the speed at the end of the time t seconds will be gt meters per second. Since acceleration occurs uniformly in time, the average speed while falling is $\frac{1}{2}gt$ meters per second. The distance fallen, h meters, in t seconds must thus be equal to $\frac{1}{2}gt \times t$, i.e.,

$$h = \tfrac{1}{2}gt^{2}. \qquad (2.5)$$

If t is 1 second and g is taken as 9.8 meters per second per second, the distance h is 4.9 meters, i.e., close to 16 feet. Thus, a body 4.9 meters (or 16 feet) above the ground will fall to Earth in approximately 1 second under the influence of gravity.

ORBITAL VELOCITY AND PERIOD OF A SATELLITE

2.22. By utilizing the result derived above, in conjunction with the known curvature of Earth's surface, it was possible to derive an approximate value for the circular orbital velocity of a satellite close to Earth. A more general method

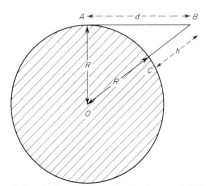

for determining the orbital velocity of a satellite moving in a circular orbit of any given radius about any primary is based on Fig. 2.5; the circle, of radius R, with its center at O represents the orbit of the satellite. As before, A is the point of horizontal injection into orbit and AB is the path the injected body would follow if it were not for gravity. However, as a result of the gravitational attraction toward the center of the primary, the actual path is along the circular arc AC. The satellite has thus 'fallen" a distance BC toward Earth's center in the time it would have reached B in the absence

FIG. 2.5. Calculation of circular orbital velocity

of gravity. If v_c is the horizontal injection velocity at A, i.e., the circular orbital velocity in the present case, and t is the elapsed time between A and B, the distance AB, represented by d, is given by

$$d = v_c \times t$$

or

$$v_c = \frac{d}{t}. \tag{2.6}$$

In this time t, a body would have fallen a distance BC, represented by h, under the influence of gravity; hence, according to equation (2.5),

$$h = \tfrac{1}{2}gt^2,$$

where g is the acceleration due to the gravity of the primary at a distance R from its center.

2.23. Since the satellite was projected horizontally into orbit at the point A, the angle OAB in Fig. 2.5 is a right angle. Hence, by the Pythagorean theorem,

$$(OB)^2 = (OA)^2 + (AB)^2$$

or

$$(R + h)^2 = R^2 + d^2,$$

since $OB = OC + CB = R + h$. Upon multiplying out and canceling terms that appear on both sides, it is found that

$$d^2 = 2Rh + h^2. \tag{2.7}$$

For purposes of clarity, the distance AB and BC in Fig. 2.5 have been exaggerated. To make the calculations more precise, AB should be a short distance, so that BC, i.e., h, is also small. The reason is that the force of gravity, which is toward O, should act at right angles to the direction of motion of the satellite, otherwise its speed will change. If h is small, h^2 on the right side of equation (2.7) may be neglected in comparison with $2Rh$ because R is invariably large, e.g., Earth's radius at least; hence,

$$d^2 = 2Rh.$$

Upon introducing the expression for h given above, it follows that

$$d^2 = (2R)(\tfrac{1}{2}gt^2) = Rgt^2$$

and

$$d = t\sqrt{Rg}. \tag{2.8}$$

The horizontal injection velocity, v_c, for a circular orbit, which is also the constant speed of the satellite in that orbit, is given by equation (2.6) as $v_c = d/t$; combination with equation (2.8) then yields the result

$$v_c = \sqrt{Rg} \tag{2.9}$$

for the speed of a satellite in a circular orbit of radius R, where g is the acceleration due to gravity at that radius.*

2.24. Suppose it is required to calculate the horizontal velocity of injection (or orbital velocity) for a satellite in a circular orbit near Earth, neglecting the drag of the atmosphere. If the orbit is near Earth's surface, the radius is essentially the same as Earth's mean radius, namely, 6.37×10^6 meters. Since the rotation of Earth does not affect a satellite's motion, the value of g to be used is that derived in § 2.19, i.e., 9.83 meters per second per second. If these values are inserted into equation (2.9), the circular velocity is

$$v_c = \sqrt{6.37 \times 10^6 \times 9.83}$$
$$= 7.91 \times 10^3 \text{ meters (7.91 kilometers) per second.}$$

The circular orbital velocity for a near-Earth orbit is thus **7.91 kilometers**, i.e., **4.92 miles or 25,950 feet**, per second, in agreement with the rough value of 8 kilometers (5 miles) per second derived in § 2.8.

2.25. A circle of radius R has a circumference of $2\pi R$, where the constant π is 3.1416; consequently, the total length of a single circular orbit of a satellite

---

* It follows from equations (2.3) and (2.4) that the gravitational force acting on a body of mass m is mg; by equation (2.9), g is equal to v_c^2/R, and so the gravitational (centripetal) force on a satellite in orbit is mv_c^2/R. In general, for a mass m moving with a velocity v in a circular path of radius R, the centripetal force is mv^2/R. The angular velocity, ω, of the mass is v/R radians per unit time (second); hence, the centripetal force is $m\omega R$. The value of the centrifugal effect of the inertia of the body traveling in a circular path is thus commonly expressed as mv^2/R or $m\omega R$.

is $2\pi R$. Since the speed in orbit is v_c, the *orbital period* or *period of revolution*, i.e., the time taken to complete a single circular orbit, represented by P_c, is

$$P_c = \frac{2\pi R}{v_c}.$$

Upon introducing equation (2.9) for v_c, it is found that

$$P_c = \frac{2\pi R}{\sqrt{Rg}} = 2\pi \sqrt{\frac{R}{g}}. \tag{2.10}$$

For a near-Earth orbit, R is 6.37×10^6 meters, as seen above, so that

$$P_c = 2 \times 3.14 \sqrt{\frac{6.37 \times 10^6}{9.83}}$$

$$= 5060 \text{ seconds}$$

$$= 84.3 \text{ minutes},$$

neglecting the atmospheric drag effect.

2.26. If equations (2.9) and (2.10) are to be used to calculate the orbital velocity and period at a distance from Earth, the appropriate value of g at that distance must be known. This can be readily derived from the fact that the force of gravity, and hence the acceleration, is inversely proportional to the square of the distance between the centers of the attracting bodies. Thus, if g is the gravitational acceleration at a distance R from Earth's center and g_0 is the value at the surface at a distance R_0, the average radius of Earth, then

$$\frac{g}{g_0} = \left(\frac{R_0}{R}\right)^2$$

or

$$g = g_0 \left(\frac{R_0}{R}\right)^2. \tag{2.11}$$

Since g_0 and R_0 are known, the acceleration g can be calculated at any distance R from Earth's center.

2.27. The result just obtained is strictly correct only if the mass distribution in Earth's interior is spherically symmetric, i.e., it is the same in all radial directions from the center. This requirement is implicit in equation (2.1) upon which equation (2.11) is really based. As already seen, Earth is not truly spherical, and its radial mass distribution is probably not uniform with direction; hence, equation (2.11) cannot apply exactly. Nevertheless, bearing in mind the limitations, equation (2.11) is commonly used, as a first approximation, to determine the variation of the acceleration due to gravity with the distance from the center of Earth.

2.28. Another way of expressing equation (2.9), which takes into account the variation of the gravitational acceleration with altitude, is based on equation (2.4). Since G is a universal constant and M, the mass of the primary body, i.e., Earth, is also a constant, the quantity GM which appears in the numerator of equation (2.4) may be replaced by a constant K; thus,

$$K = GM. \tag{2.12}$$

With this substitution, equation (2.4) for a spherically symmetric mass becomes

$$g = \frac{K}{R^2}, \tag{2.13}$$

where R is the distance from Earth's center. At Earth's surface, g is g_0 and R is R_0, and so equation (2.13) may be written

$$g_0 = \frac{K}{R_0^2} \tag{2.14}$$

or

$$K = g_0 R_0^2. \tag{2.15}$$

The mean value of g_0 is **9.83** meters per second per second and R_0 is 6.37×10^6 meters; hence, if distance is expressed in meters and time in seconds,

$$\begin{aligned} K &= 9.83 \times (6.371 \times 10^6)^2 \\ &= 3.99 \times 10^{14} \text{ (meters)}^3/\text{(seconds)}^2. \end{aligned}$$

Orbital distances are frequently expressed in statute miles, and then

$$K = 9.55 \times 10^4 \text{ (miles)}^3/\text{(seconds)}^2.$$

2.29. The value of g given by equation (2.13), i.e., K/R^2, may now be substituted in equation (2.9); the result is

$$v_c = \sqrt{\frac{K}{R}}. \tag{2.16}$$

Since K is known, the circular orbital velocity of a satellite can be calculated for an Earth orbit of any given radius. An alternative form of this equation may be obtained by replacing R by $R_0 + h$, where h is the altitude of the orbit above Earth (Fig. 2.6); then,

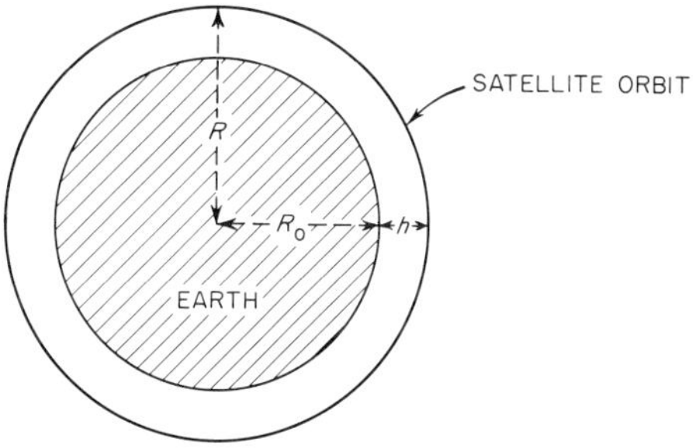

$$v_c = \sqrt{\frac{K}{R_0 + h}}, \tag{2.17}$$

FIG. 2.6.   Altitude and distance of orbit from Earth's center

where R_0 and h must, of course, be expressed in the same units. Similar substitution for g in equation (2.10) gives

$$P_c = 2\pi \sqrt{\frac{R^3}{K}} = 2\pi \sqrt{\frac{(R_0 + h)^3}{K}}. \tag{2.18}$$

2.30.   The results of calculations of the circular orbital velocity and the orbital period for Earth satellites at various altitudes above Earth's surface, using equations (2.17) and (2.18) and the values of K derived above, are summarized in Table 2.1. It is apparent that, with increasing altitude, the velocity required to maintain a satellite in orbit decreases whereas the period increases. This is also seen to be the case in Fig. 2.7, in which the curves show how the velocity and period vary with the altitude of the orbit.

TABLE 2.1   CIRCULAR ORBITAL VELOCITIES AND ORBITAL PERIODS
FOR EARTH SATELLITES AT VARIOUS ALTITUDES

Altitude		Velocity		Period
Kilometers	Miles	Kilometers per second	Miles per second	
0	0	7.91	4.92	1 h 24.3 min
161	100	7.80	4.85	1 h 27.7 min
322	200	7.70	4.79	1 h 30.8 min
644	400	7.53	4.68	1 h 37.5 min
1609	1000	7.06	4.39	1 h 57.7 min
8045	5000	5.26	3.27	4 h 46.6 min
35,880	22,300	3.07	1.91	24 h

2.31. The orbital velocity decreases with increasing distances from Earth because the gravitational force is less. The satellite thus "falls" more slowly toward Earth, in the sense described in § 2.6; as a result, it can travel at a lower speed and still remain in its circular orbit. With increasing altitude, the circumference of the orbit increases and since the velocity of the satellite decreases, the orbital period must increase, as is seen in Table 2.1 and Fig. 2.7.

2.32. A special case of interest in Table 2.1 is the last entry for which the satellite altitude is 35,880 kilometers (22,300 miles) and the circular orbital period is 24 hours, i.e., 1 day. For such a satellite the orbital period is exactly equal to the period of rotation of Earth about its axis. If the direction in which this satellite is traveling is the same as that of Earth's rotation, i.e., from west to east, and the plane of the satellite's orbit coincides with Earth's equatorial plane, the satellite will appear to be stationary. In other words, from any given point on Earth the satellite will always be seen in the same direction in the sky.

2.33. A satellite moving from west to east with a 24-hour circular orbital period is said to have a *synchronous orbit* (or to be a *synchronous satellite*). In the special case considered above in which the orbital plane of the synchronous satellite is the same as Earth's equatorial plane, the satellite is referred to as *geostationary*, i.e., stationary with respect to Earth. If the synchronous orbit is inclined to the equator, the satellite will appear to move back and forth following a figure-eight path in a north-south direction. The range of the apparent motion increases with the angle of inclination. Synchronous (and particularly geostationary) satellites have important applications in intercontinental communications and possibly also in meteorology (Chapter 5).

2.34. It was seen earlier that the velocity that a satellite must attain in order to remain in orbit decreases with increasing radius (or altitude) of the orbit. But the significance of this fact must not be misunderstood. Although the

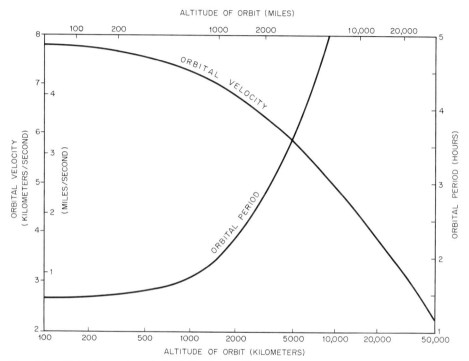

Fig. 2.7.   Velocity and period of Earth satellite in circular orbit at various altitudes

velocity (and kinetic energy) in orbit is less at high altitudes, the energy required to put the satellite into orbit is greater than at lower altitudes. The reason is that more (potential) energy must be expended, i.e., more work must be done against the force of gravity, in raising the satellite from Earth into its high-altitude orbit.

THE CHARACTERISTIC VELOCITY

2.35. The energy required to overcome the force of gravity and place a satellite in a specified circular orbit can be expressed in terms of the square of the *characteristic velocity* for that orbit.* The magnitude of the character-

* The term characteristic velocity is also used in other senses in space technology.

istic velocity for a circular orbit of radius R (or altitude h) is represented by

$$v_{\text{char}} = \sqrt{2K\left(\frac{1}{R_0} - \frac{1}{2R}\right)} = \sqrt{2K\left[\frac{1}{R_0} - \frac{1}{2(R_0 + h)}\right]}, \qquad (2.19)$$

where, as before, R_0 is Earth's radius.* The characteristic velocities correspond-ing to the various orbital altitudes in Table 2.1 are given in Table 2.2. Since the energy expenditure is proportional to the square of the characteristic velocity, it is evident that it increases markedly with increasing altitude of the satellite orbit.

TABLE 2.2   CHARACTERISTIC VELOCITIES FOR EARTH
SATELLITES AT VARIOUS ALTITUDES

Altitude		Characteristic Velocity	
Kilometers	*Miles*	*Kilometers per second*	*Miles per second*
0	0	7.91	4.92
161	100	8.00	4.97
322	200	8.10	5.03
644	400	8.26	5.13
1609	1000	8.66	5.38
8045	5000	9.85	6.13
35,880	22,300	10.8	6.68
∞	∞	11.2	6.95

2.36. The two extreme values of the characteristic velocity for Earth orbits are obtained by setting $R = R_0$, i.e., a theoretical orbit at Earth's surface, and R equal to infinity, i.e., an infinitely large orbit, respectively. For the orbit at Earth's surface

$$v_{\text{char}(0)} = \sqrt{\frac{K}{R_0}},$$

whereas for the infinitely large orbit,

$$v_{\text{char}(\infty)} = \sqrt{\frac{2K}{R_0}}.$$

Comparison of the former with equation (2.16) shows that at Earth's surface the characteristic velocity is identical with the circular orbital velocity; this is to be expected since no energy is expended against gravity in raising the satellite. Furthermore, it is apparent that $v_{\text{char}(\infty)}$ is equal to $\sqrt{2}$ times $v_{\text{char}(0)}$, i.e., $\sqrt{2}$ times the circular orbital velocity at zero elevation. As will be seen

* A derivation of the expression for the characteristic velocity is given in the Appendix to this chapter (§ 2.103).

shortly (§ 2.69), the characteristic velocity for an infinite orbit is equal to the velocity a satellite injected at Earth's surface must acquire if it is to escape entirely from orbiting Earth. This result is also not unexpected.

Effect of Earth's Rotation

2.37. The characteristic velocities given above do not take into account the effect of Earth's rotation. When it is in orbit, the motion of a satellite is not affected by this rotation (§ 2.95), but the speed of rotation of Earth at the launch point will influence the energy required to put the satellite into orbit. There are two important factors involved, namely, the direction of launching and the latitude of the launch site. If the satellite is launched from west to east, i.e., in the same direction as Earth's rotation, the orbit is said to be a *direct orbit* or a *progressive* (or *prograde*) *orbit* (Fig. **2.8**, I). In this event,

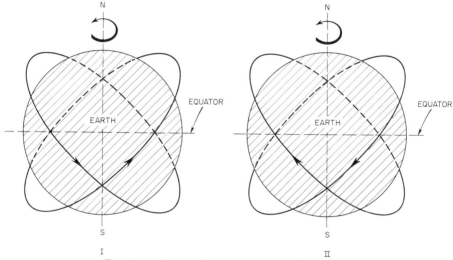

Fig. 2.8.   Direct (I) and retrograde (II) orbits

Earth's rotational energy can contribute to the energy of the space vehicle, and less energy is required from the rocket engine than would be the case for a nonrotating Earth. The characteristic velocity is then smaller than given by equation (2.19). For an east-to-west (or *retrograde orbit*) launch (Fig. **2.8**, II), the rotational energy of Earth must be overcome; more energy must thus be supplied to inject a satellite into an orbit of specified altitude. The actual characteristic velocity is then greater than the calculated value.

2.38. Every point on the equator rotates through about 4.00×10^7 meters (4.00×10^4 kilometers), i.e., Earth's equatorial circumference, in **24** hours. The rotational velocity is therefore 1670 kilometers (1040 miles) per hour or only 0.47 kilometer (0.29 mile) per second, but it is still of significance. The actual characteristic velocity for an orbit around the equator is then **7.44** kilometers (**4.63** miles) per second. For launch points at other latitudes, the rotational velocity is less than at the equator; it is roughly equal to the equatorial velocity multipled by the cosine of the latitude angle. At Cape Kennedy, Florida, for example, which is at a latitude of about 28.5°N, the cosine is approximately **0.89**; the velocity of rotation is then $0.89 \times 0.47 = 0.42$ kilometer (**0.26** mile) per second.

2.39. In order to take full advantage of Earth's rotation in decreasing the energy required to launch a satellite, it would be necessary for the spacecraft to be injected in an easterly direction in an orbit parallel to the equator. This is possible only if the launch site is on the equator. For launching at other latitudes, the speed of rotation of Earth is less, as just seen, and so the effect on the energy requirement is decreased. In any event, the benefit derived from Earth's rotation depends on the angle of inclination of the orbit, i.e., the angle between the orbital plane and the plane of the equator (Fig. **2.9**). The larger

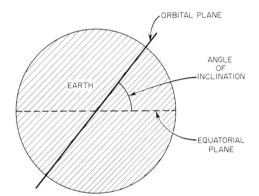

FIG. 2.9.   Angle of inclination of a satellite orbit

the angle, the smaller the effect. For a polar orbit, i.e., one passing over the poles, the plane is perpendicular to the equatorial plane and Earth's rotation contributes nothing to the launch energy (or characteristic velocity) regardless of the latitude of the launch site. For retrograde orbits, the contribution of the rotational velocity of Earth at the launch site must be added to the characteristic velocity from equation (**2.19**) to obtain the actual value.

KEPLER'S LAWS AND THEIR APPLICATIONS

ORBITS AND TRAJECTORIES AS CONIC SECTIONS

2.40. The preceding discussion has referred to the simple case of a circular orbit, but such an ideal situation is rarely realized. The present section will be concerned with a more general treatment in which the circular orbit is a special case. In a circular orbit the satellite has a particular velocity for a given altitude, and no other value is possible at that altitude. For example, it is seen in Table 2.1 that for an altitude of 322 kilometers (200 miles) above Earth, the circular velocity is 7.70 kilometers (4.79 miles) per second. If a satellite were injected horizontally at a lower velocity, it could not go into a circular orbit, and it would fall to the ground, following a path such as AP_1 or AP_2 in Fig. 2.1.* Suppose, on the other hand, the velocity of the satellite is greater than the circular velocity for the particular altitude. The force of gravity is now not large enough to pull the satellite back into a circular orbit. In other words, the inertia of the satellite is greater than it would be for a circular orbit at the same distance from Earth. The actual path of the satellite then diverges from a circle.

2.41. Calculations show that, if the horizontal injection velocity is somewhere between the circular velocity at the injection altitude and $\sqrt{2}$ (or 1.414) times that velocity, the orbit of the satellite must be an *ellipse*. For an elliptical orbit, therefore, the injection velocity is generally greater than v_c but less than $\sqrt{2}v_c$, where v_c is the circular velocity for the particular injection altitude. If the injection velocity is exactly equal to $\sqrt{2}v_c$, then the path (or trajectory) of the body will be a *parabola*, and if it exceeds $\sqrt{2}v_c$, the trajectory will be a *hyperbola*. In these two cases, the moving body will not travel in a closed orbit about Earth; that is to say, it will not be a satellite of Earth but will become a space probe (§ 2.1).

2.42. The ellipse, parabola, and hyperbola, as well as the circle, are geometrical figures called *conic sections*. They can be obtained by cutting sections of increasing slope, from horizontal to vertical, through a cone, as indicated in Fig. 2.10. Strictly speaking, a hyperbola consists of two identical curves (or branches) which are mirror images of one another; for the present discussion, however, only one branch has any significance. From Fig. 2.10, it is seen that, whereas the circle and ellipse are closed curves, the parabola and hyperbola are open curves; their arms are continuously diverging and never come together. It is for this reason that, if a body is to become a satellite of a given primary, its injection velocity must be such as to permit it to travel in either a circular or an elliptical orbit.

2.43. That the path of a body of relatively small mass moving about a primary is always a conic section is a direct consequence of the law of gravitation, namely, that the gravitational force between two masses is inversely proportional to the square of the distance between their centers. If the force varied with some other power of the distance, then the path of the moving body would usually not be a conic section. The circle is, however, a special case and does not depend on the precise form of the gravitational law. It is of interest to

---

* An exception can arise if the injection point is sufficiently high above Earth's surface (cf. § 2.80).

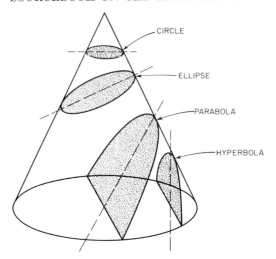

FIG. 2.10.   Conic sections

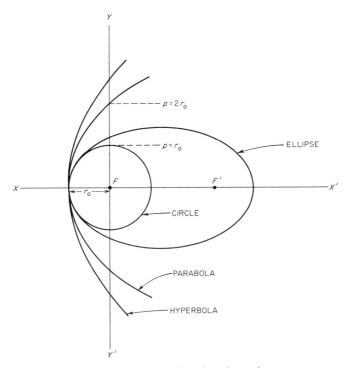

FIG. 2.11.   Properties of conic sections

mention that curves such as AP_1 and AP_2 in Fig. 2.1 are actually parts of an ellipse, the lower portions being cut off by Earth's surface.

2.44. There are several ways of expressing the relationship between the different conic sections; the following approach has been chosen because of its simplicity. All conic sections have at least one *focus* or *focal point;* the ellipse

TABLE 2.3   CHARACTERISTICS OF CONIC SECTIONS

Curve	*Parameter*	*Eccentricity*
Circle	Equal to r_0	0
Ellipse	Between r_0 and $2r_0$	Between 0 and 1
Parabola	Equal to $2r_0$	1
Hyperbola	Greater than $2r_0$	Greater than 1

has two focal points, symmetrically located, and so also has the hyperbola one for each branch. Through the focal point F (or points F and F' for an ellipse) can be drawn on axis XX', as depicted in Fig. 2.11. The line YY' is drawn through F perpendicular to XX'. It is seen that each curve is depicted so that it cuts (or intersects) the XX' axis at the same distance, r_0, from the focal point. The intercept of the YY' axis, often called the *parameter* of the conic section, is, however, different in each case.* If this parameter is represented by p, then the various conic sections are characterized either by the relation of p to r_0, or by the *eccentricity* defined by

$$\text{Eccentricity} = \frac{p}{r_0} - 1. \qquad (2.20)$$

The conditions which must be met by the parameter, p, and by the eccentricity for each conic section are summarized in Table 2.3.

2.45. The circle and the parabola may be regarded as being limiting cases of the ellipse and the hyperbola, respectively; alternatively, the parabola may be thought of as representing the transition between an ellipse and a hyperbola It is evident that, whereas ellipses and hyperbolas can have a range of values for the eccentricity, e, as shown in Fig. 2.12, circles and parabolas have only single values, i.e., exactly 0 and 1, respectively.

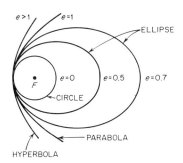

FIG. 2.12.   Eccentricities of conic sections

2.46. Returning to the question of the motion of a body with respect to a primary, another way of stating the conditions in § 2.41 is that, as the hori-

* The *latus rectum* of a conic section is equal to twice the parameter as defined here.

zontal injection velocity of the body increases at a given altitude, the eccentricity of its path increases steadily from zero for a circle to greater than unity for a hyperbola. For each value of the eccentricity there is a corresponding velocity, and vice versa. Because the injection velocity and direction of a satellite or of a space probe are difficult to control precisely, it is clear that perfectly circular and parabolic paths, which require the eccentricity to be exactly zero and unity, respectively, are rarely, if ever, attained. Most satellite orbits and probe trajectories are thus either ellipses or hyperbolas. The focal point of the path of the satellite or probe is always located at the center or, more exactly, at the center of mass of the primary body.*

2.47. There is one, perhaps obvious, point concerning orbits and trajectories that is worthy of mention. No matter where or in what direction a satellite or probe is launched, the plane of the orbit or trajectory, while it is under the influence of Earth's gravitational field, must pass through the center of Earth. This is a somewhat idealized situation which ignores the nonuniformity of Earth's gravity and the attraction of the satellite or probe by the Moon, Sun, etc. However, these effects are relatively small so that, for many purposes, the generalization stated above may be accepted as being substantially correct.

KEPLER'S LAWS OF SATELLITE MOTION

2.48. It was Johannes Kepler, one of the founders of modern astronomy as well as of space fiction (§ 1.31), who first realized in 1609 that the planets revolve in elliptical orbits about the Sun as focal point. His three laws of planetary motion, which Isaac Newton later showed to be direct consequences of the universal law of gravitation, referred in particular to the movement of the planets. Kepler's laws apply equally, however, to the motion of satellites about any primary body, and so they will be given here in a more general form.† They can then be utilized to determine the orbital motion of Earth satellites, including the Moon, as well as of the planets. Kepler's laws of planetary (or satellite) motion, the first two being enunciated in 1609 and the third in 1618, may be stated as follows:

1. The orbit of a satellite is an ellipse with the center (or center of mass) of the primary located at one of its focal points.

2. As a satellite moves in its orbit, the line, called the *radius vector*, joining the satellite's center to the focal point sweeps out equal areas in equal periods of time.

3. The square of the period of revolution (or orbital period) of a satellite is

---

* In simple terms, the *center of mass* of a body (or system of bodies) may be regarded as the point through which the force of gravity acts no matter how the body is oriented.

† The English word satellite owes its origin to the Latin *satelles*, meaning "attendant" or "companion," which Kepler used to describe any body moving in an orbit about a primary.

proportional to the cube of the semi-major axis of the elliptical orbit (see § 2.61).

These laws will be discussed in turn.

2.49. The first of Kepler's laws summarizes the conclusions reached earlier and does not require further consideration. The second law, however, introduces new concepts, and before examining them some appropriate terms will be defined. Suppose the ellipse in Fig. **2.13** represents the orbit of a satellite about a primary body located at the focus, F, of the ellipse. The point P on the orbit nearest to the primary is called the *pericenter* or *perifocus;* correspondingly, the point A, which is farthest from the focus, is referred to as the *apocenter* or *apofocus*.* If the central (or primary) body is Earth, the nearest and farthest points in the satellite's

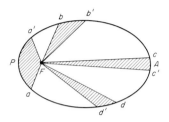

FIG. 2.13. Illustration of Kepler's second law

orbit are known as the *perigee* and *apogee* (Greek, *ge*, "Earth"); the equivalent locations in the orbit of a planet around the Sun are the *perihelion* and *aphelion†* (Greek, *helios*, "Sun").

2.50. The shaded portions in Fig. 2.13, enclosed by radius vectors in four different parts of the elliptical orbit, have equal areas. Consequently, according to Kepler's second law, the satellite will traverse the distances aa', bb', cc', and dd' in equal times. But since the distance aa' is greater than bb' (or dd'), which is, in turn, greater than cc', it is evident that the satellite travels fastest near the pericenter (or perigee), slowest near the apocenter (or apogee), and at intermediate speeds in between. Thus, in an elliptical orbit, the speed of a satellite changes continuously. It will be recalled that in a given circular orbit, however, the orbital velocity has only a single value; that is to say, the speed is constant.

2.51. Kepler's second law is another way of saying that the *angular momentum* of a satellite is constant throughout its orbit although its velocity may be continually changing. In general, if a body travels in an elliptical (or circular) path, the angular momentum is equal to $mv_{\perp}r$, where m is the mass of

---

* The Greek prefix *peri* means "around," implying "near by," so that the pericenter is the point on an orbit nearest to the primary (central) body or focus. The prefix *apo*, on the other hand, means "away from"; hence, the apocenter is the point on the orbit most distant from the primary. Either of the extreme points P or A, is called an *apsis* (Greek, "bow" or "arch"), the plural being *apsides*. The pericenter of an orbit is thus also called the *periapsis* and the apocenter the *apoapsis;* the line joining these points is known as the *line of the apsides.*

† These latter terms were introduced by Johannes Kepler in connection with his enunciation of the laws of planetary motion about the Sun. Corresponding terms for orbits about stars and galaxies are *periastron* and *apoastron* and *perigalacticon* and *apogalacticon,* respectively.

the body, $v_\perp$ is the component of its velocity at right angles to the radius vector at any point, and r is the length of the radius vector at that point (Fig. **2.14**); v

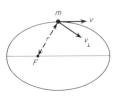

FIG. 2.14. Angular momentum parameters

is the actual velocity of the body in its orbit at the given point. The areas of the shaded sections in Fig. **2.13** are equal to the mean values of $\frac{1}{2}v_\perp r$ for each section. Since these are equal, by Kepler's second law, it follows that the angular momentum, $mv_\perp r$, must be constant. For a circular orbit, $v_\perp$ is equal to the actual orbital velocity v_c, and then the angular momentum is

$mv_c r$. An alternative expression for the angular momentum of a body traveling in a circular path is $mr^2\omega$, where ω, the angular velocity, is equal to v_c/r, in accordance with the definition in § **2.23**, footnote.

ORBITAL VELOCITIES OF SATELLITES

2.52. In the case of an artificial satellite of Earth, the perigee is the point at which the orbital velocity is a maximum. As the satellite travels in the elliptical path, as represented in Fig. **2.15**, its velocity decreases steadily until it reaches the apogee of its orbit, where the velocity is a minimum. Subsequently, the velocity increases until the maximum is again attained at the perigee. Assuming that there is no atmospheric drag and no extraneous (or perturbing) forces on the satellite (cf. § **2.82**), the orbit will be stable. In other words, the satellite will continue to revolve indefinitely about the primary body in the same orbit undergoing the same velocity changes in each revolution. This is essentially the situation in the motion of the planets about the Sun and of the Moon about Earth.

2.53. The reason for the varying velocity of a satellite in elliptical orbit can be readily understood from Fig. **2.15**. At a point, such as M, on the path between perigee and apogee, the general direction of motion of the satellite is indicated by the arrow, i.e., from left to right. The force of gravity, however, is pulling the satellite toward the focal point F, representing the center of the

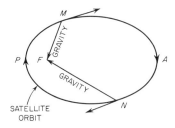

FIG. 2.15. Variation of velocity in an elliptical orbit

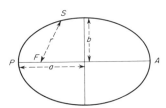

FIG. 2.16. Semi-axis of ellipse and radius vector

primary body. It is seen that this force acts in a direction inclined from right to left; consequently, the gravitational force has a component directed toward the left and this will tend to slow down the satellite. At a location such as N, between apogee and perigee, the force of gravity also has a component from right to left. But since this is now in the same direction as the motion of the satellite, the velocity will increase.

2.54. The derivation of an expression giving the velocity of a satellite (or probe) at any point in its orbit (or trajectory) is based on the law of gravitation. The mathematical treatment is fairly complicated but the result is relatively simple. If M represents the mass of a primary and m is that of a satellite, then the velocity of the satellite at any point S is an elliptical orbit, as indicated in Fig. 2.16, is given by the expression, called the *vis viva* integral (§ 2.102),

$$v^2 = G(M + m)\left(\frac{2}{r} - \frac{1}{a}\right), \tag{2.21}$$

where G is the gravitational constant defined earlier, and the distances r and a are shown in Fig. 2.16; a is the semi-major axis of the ellipse and r is the length of the radius vector, i.e., the distance from the point S to the focus, F, of the ellipse. If the mass (m) of the satellite is very small in comparison with that (M) of the primary, as is commonly the case, $M + m$ may be replaced by M, and then equation (2.21) becomes

$$v^2 = GM\left(\frac{2}{r} - \frac{1}{a}\right) = K\left(\frac{2}{r} - \frac{1}{a}\right)$$

or

$$v = \sqrt{K\left(\frac{2}{r} - \frac{1}{a}\right)}, \tag{2.22}$$

since GM is equal to the constant K, as defined by equation (2.12).

2.55. As the satellite S travels from the perigee P to the apogee A, the value of r increases steadily; hence, according to equation (2.22), the velocity, v, must decrease correspondingly. On the other hand, when returning from A to P, the distance r decreases continuously and the velocity then increases. By inserting the appropriate value for r into equation (2.22), the velocity of the satellite can be determined at any point in the elliptical orbit.

2.56. The maximum (or perigee) velocity of a satellite in an elliptical orbit is

$$v_{\text{peri}} = \sqrt{K\left(\frac{2}{r_0} - \frac{1}{a}\right)} = \sqrt{\frac{K(2a - r_0)}{ar_0}}, \tag{2.23}$$

where r_0 represents the distance PF, from the perigee to the focal point of the ellipse, i.e., to the center of the primary body. Similarly, the minimum (or apogee) velocity is

$$v_{\text{apo}} = \sqrt{K\left[\frac{2}{(2a - r_0)} - \frac{1}{a}\right]} = \sqrt{\frac{Kr_0}{a(2a - r_0)}} \tag{2.24}$$

since the distance AF from the apogee to the focus is $2a - r_0$. Upon comparing the expressions for v_{peri} and v_{apo} in equations (2.23) and (2.24), it is readily found that

$$\frac{v_{\text{peri}}}{v_{\text{apo}}} = \frac{2a - r_0}{r_0}. \tag{2.25}$$

The maximum (perigee) and minimum (apogee) velocities are thus inversely related to their respective radius vectors, i.e., the distances r_0 and $2a - r_0$ from the center of the primary body or focal point. This result follows directly from the constancy of the angular momentum, $mv_\perp r$ (§ 2.51); at the perigee and apogee $v_\perp$ is equal to the actual velocity, so that vr is constant. The velocity is consequently inversely proportional to the length of the radius vector.

2.57. The satellite spacecraft Explorer XI was launched into an elliptical orbit of Earth with an initial perigee altitude of 490 kilometers (304 miles) and an apogee altitude of 1790 kilometers (1113 miles); what were the velocities at these points? The value of r_0 is equal to the perigee altitude plus the mean radius of Earth, i.e., $490 + 6370 = 6860$ kilometers $= 6.86 \times 10^6$ meters. The length of the major axis of the ellipse, $2a$, is the sum of the perigee and apogee altitudes and Earth's diameter, i.e., $490 + 1790 + 12,740 = 15,020$ kilometers; hence, a is 7510 kilometers or 7.51×10^6 meters. Since K is 3.99×10^{14} with distances in meters and time in seconds, it is found from equation (2.23) that

$$v_{\text{peri}} = 7.95 \text{ kilometers (4.94 miles) per second}$$
$$= 17,800 \text{ miles per hour.}$$

The apogee velocity is $6860/8160$ times this value; hence,

$$v_{\text{apo}} = 6.68 \text{ kilometers (4.15 miles) per second}$$
$$= 14,900 \text{ miles per hour.}$$

There is thus a difference of almost 3000 miles per hour between the maximum and minimum orbital velocities.

2.58. By means of equation (2.22) it is possible to determine the velocity of a satellite in a circular orbit or of a probe in a parabolic trajectory. A circle may be regarded as an ellipse with the focus at the center. In this case, r, which is the same for all points on the orbit, is equal to a; both are now identical with R, the radius of a circular orbit. Hence, equation (2.22) reduces to

$$v_c = \sqrt{\frac{K}{R}}$$

as derived in § 2.29. At the other extreme, a parabola may be treated as an ellipse with an infinitely long major (or semi-major) axis, so that $1/a$ is zero;

if R, the distance from Earth's center, is substituted for r in equation (2.22), the parabolic velocity, v_p, is found to be

$$v_p = \sqrt{\frac{2K}{R}}.$$

It follows, therefore, that at a given distance from Earth's center, i.e., at a specified altitude, the parabolic velocity is $\sqrt{2}$ times the circular velocity for the same altitude, as stated in § 2.41.

2.59. As the perigee velocity, i.e., v_{peri}, at a given altitude increases, the dimensions and eccentricity of the elliptical orbit also increase. This result, which is to be expected from general considerations, is implicit in equation (2.23). Since the focus of the ellipse is always at the center of the primary body, e.g., Earth, injection at a specified altitude means that r_0 has a constant value. Consequently, an increase in v_{peri} must be accompanied by an increase in a, the length of the semi-major axis of the ellipse. Because the position of the focal point remains unchanged, it is a geometrical necessity that both the length of the minor axis, i.e., $2b$ in Fig. 2.16, and the eccentricity of the ellipse must increase.* In other words, the elliptical orbit becomes both broader and longer with increase in the perigee velocity of a satellite at a given height above Earth. If the perigee velocity decreases, the ellipse becomes narrower and shorter.

ORBITAL PERIODS

2.60. Calculations based on the law of gravitation and the geometry of the ellipse show that, if a satellite of mass m orbits about a primary of mass M, the orbital period is given by

$$P^2 = \frac{4\pi^2 a^3}{G(M + m)}. \qquad (2.26)$$

where, as before, a is the semi-major axis of the ellipse and G is the gravitational constant. For the common situation in which the mass of the satellite is negligible in comparison with that of the primary, $M + m$ may be replaced by M and GM by K; hence,

$$P^2 = \frac{4\pi^2 a^3}{K} \qquad (2.27)$$

or

$$P = 2\pi \sqrt{\frac{a^3}{K}}. \qquad (2.28)$$

---

* The eccentricity, e, of an ellipse is given by $e = 1 - (r_0/a)$; since r_0 is constant in the cases under consideration and a increases with increasing injection velocity, r_0/a decreases. Consequently, the eccentricity of the elliptical orbit must increase. The eccentricity was defined by equation (2.20) as $(p/r_0) - 1$, and since r_0 is constant, the parameter, p, must increase with the perigee velocity. It will be apparent from Fig. 2.11 that, if r_0 is constant and p increases, the breadth of the ellipse becomes greater and, hence, so also must the minor axis.

Since π and K are constants, equation (**2.27**) may also be written in the form

$$P^2 = \text{constant} \times a^3.$$

The square of the orbital period (or period of revolution) of a satellite is thus proportional to the cube of the semi-major axis, in agreement with Kepler's third law. For a circle, the semi-major axis, a, is equivalent to the radius, R; equation (**2.28**) then becomes identical with equation (**2.18**) for a circular orbit.

2.61. In Kepler's original formulation of his third law, he stated that the orbital period of a planet (satellite) is proportional to the cube of its mean distance from the Sun (primary). If the eccentricity of the orbit is small, i.e., it does not deviate greatly from a circle, as is the case for all the planets except Pluto, the mean distance of the satellite from the primary is very close to the average of the distances of the perigee and apogee from the primary. These distances are r_0 and $2a - r_0$, respectively, as seen in § 2.56, and so the average is equal to a, the semi-major axis of the orbit. Thus, for a planet (and the Moon), the mean distance from the primary is essentially identical with the semi-major axis.

GENERAL CHARACTERISTICS OF ORBITS

SIDEREAL AND SYNODIC PERIODS

2.62. In considering the period of a satellite orbit, a distinction must be made between the *sidereal period* and the *synodic period*.* The same distinction is applicable to the period of revolution of the Moon about Earth, i.e., the month, and, in a somewhat different but related sense, to the rotational period of Earth, i.e., the day. The differentiation between sidereal and synodic periods is necessary because time on Earth is commonly reckoned by the Sun and Earth revolves in its orbit about the Sun. The sidereal period is the time of revolution of a satellite (or rotation of Earth) with reference to a fixed, i.e., distant, star, whereas the synodic period is the time with reference to the Sun.

2.63. The distinction between sidereal and synodic periods may be understood by means of the exaggerated representation in Fig. 2.17, I and II; in each case A represents the position of Earth in its orbit about the Sun at the beginning of the satellite's revolution and B is that at the end of one period. Fig. 2.17, I shows the sidereal period with reference to a distant star; it is the time between successive conjunctions (or alignments) of the satellite and the reference star, as seen by an observer on Earth. The sidereal period is the value determined by calculation, e.g., from equation (**2.18**) or (**2.28**), and is

---

* Sidereal is derived from the Latin *sidus* (or *sideris*), meaning "constellation" or "star group," and synodic from the Latin *synodus* (or Greek *synodos*), a "meeting" or "conjunction."

the time required for the satellite to travel from a given point in space back to that same point. The corresponding orbit is sometimes called a *Keplerian orbit* or an *inertial orbit*.

2.64. The synodic period, on the other hand, depicted in Fig. 2.17, II, is the time between successive conjunctions of the satellite and the Sun. In other

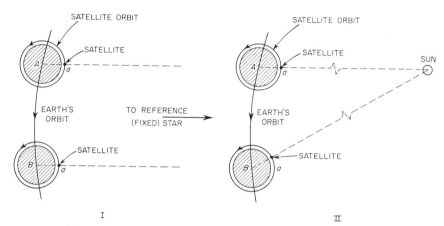

FIG. 2.17.   Sidereal (I) and synodic (II) periods of a satellite

words, the synodic period is the period of revolution of a satellite about Earth as determined by conventional (or Sun) time. The orbit is then referred to as an *Earth orbit*. In practice, the synodic period would be obtained by observing the times of successive passages of the satellite across a particular meridian, i.e., an imaginary circle in the sky extending between the north and south geographic poles and passing directly overhead. If the orbital motion of the satellite is progressive, i.e., in the same sense as the rotation of Earth, as is that of the Moon and most artificial satellites, the synodic period is longer than the sidereal period, as is the case in Fig. 2.17. But if the satellite has a retrograde orbit, the reverse will be true. In connection with U.S. manned space flights, the recorded orbits, e.g., as given in § 1.121, are the numbers of Earth orbits and are less than the corresponding numbers of true (or Keplerian) orbits.

2.65. In determining the conventional (or Sun) time at which a satellite will be observed at a given location on Earth, allowance must be made for the difference between the calculated sidereal period and the synodic period. Close to Earth's surface the synodic period for a progressive (circular) orbit at the equator is about 5 minutes longer than the sidereal period of 84 minutes (§ 2.25). With increasing altitude of the equatorial orbit, both periods increase (cf. Table 2.1), but the synodic period increases much more rapidly. In fact, at an altitude of 22,300 miles above Earth's surface the sidereal period is exactly 24 hours but the synodic period is infinite. That is to say, to an observer on Earth, the satellite appears to be stationary with respect to the Sun. This is the condition for the geostationary (or synchronous equatorial) orbit described in § 2.33. At still higher altitudes, the synodic period starts to decrease and can, at great distances, become smaller than the sidereal period; however, it is never less than 24 hours.* For retrograde orbits, the synodic period at the equator is less than the sidereal period, its maximum value being 24 hours.

2.66. The greatest differences between sidereal and synodic periods are observed when the Earth satellite is in an equatorial orbit. For inclined orbits, the differences become smaller the greater the angle of inclination and the latitude, both north and south. To an observer at either of the poles, there would be no distinction between the sidereal and synodic periods of a satellite in polar orbit.

ESCAPE VELOCITY

2.67. With increasing perigee velocity, the eccentricity of the elliptical orbit of a satellite increases toward 1, and finally a velocity is reached at which the ellipse opens up into a parabola, having an eccentricity of exactly unity. Since a parabola is not a closed curve, a body traveling in a parabolic trajectory will move away continuously from its primary, e.g., Earth, and will not return. Thus, the body ceases to be an Earth satellite and becomes a space probe. The velocity in a parabolic trajectory at any altitude is called the *escape velocity* for that altitude.

2.68. An object injected at (or more than) the appropriate escape velocity will not return to the vicinity of Earth. It should be understood, however, that the body does not escape from Earth's gravitational field but only from Earth's environment. As seen in § 2.14, gravity, in principle, extends to an infinite distance, although the magnitude of the gravitational attraction decreases rapidly as the distance increases. As the body moves farther and farther away, the influence of Earth's gravity decreases, but that of the Sun's gravitational field increases relatively. At a certain distance, the Sun's gravity becomes the dominant factor in determining the motion of a body in space. Earth still exerts some effect, and so does the Moon, especially if the body comes sufficiently close, but Earth's gravity becomes less and less significant. Ultimately the object with an injection velocity greater than the Earth escape velocity will become a satellite of the Sun, like a planet, and will travel in an elliptical orbit with the Sun at one focal point.

2.69. Since the escape velocity is equal to the velocity in a parabolic trajectory, it follows from the expression derived in § 2.58 that the escape velocity at a point that is a distance R from Earth's center is given by

$$v_{esc} = \sqrt{\frac{2K}{R}} = \sqrt{\frac{2K}{R_0 + h}},\qquad(2.29)$$

* The average sidereal period of revolution of the Moon about Earth is approximately 27⅓ days and the average synodic period (or lunar month) is about 29½ days.

where h is the corresponding altitude and R_0 is the radius of Earth. Comparison with equation (2.16) or (2.17) shows that the escape velocity is $\sqrt{2}$ (or 1.414) times the circular velocity for the same injection altitude. For hypothetical injection at Earth's surface, the circular velocity is 7.91 kilometers (4.92 miles) per second (§ 2.30); hence, the corresponding escape velocity, which is identical with the characteristic velocity for an infinite orbit (§ 2.36), is 11.2 kilometers (6.95 miles) per second. For injection at higher altitudes the escape velocity decreases, just as does the circular velocity (Table 2.1).

2.70. A parabolic trajectory can be attained only if the injection velocity is precisely that given by equation (2.29). In practice, the velocity of a probe intended to escape from Earth will be greater than the minimum escape velocity for the given altitude. The trajectory will then be a hyperbola, with an eccentricity exceeding unity. As in the case of a parabolic path, the motion of the body is increasingly affected by the Sun, as it travels farther away from Earth, and eventually it becomes a satellite (or planet) of the Sun. As long as a body is a satellite of Earth, the fact that it is traveling, with Earth, at a velocity of 29.77 kilometers (18.50 miles) per second around the Sun is of no significance. But when the Sun's gravitational attraction becomes dominant, this velocity is important in determining the body's orbit about the Sun. Some reference to this subject will be made in Chapter 10 in connection with the launching of space probes to the planets Venus and Mars. The trajectory and velocity variations of the probe as it leaves Earth can be determined by the classical methods of celestial mechanics. The procedures, although well established from astronomical studies over many years, are highly mathematical and too complicated to describe in this book.

2.71. Before leaving the subject of escape velocity, there are two points of clarification that should be mentioned. First, at a given altitude, the value of the escape velocity, i.e., the velocity at which the path of a spacecraft becomes a parabola (or hyperbola), is independent of the means whereby the particular altitude was attained. It might be in a single step, by rapid acceleration from Earth's surface, in two or more steps involving intermediate orbits, or by gradual and continuous acceleration over a long period. The second point is that the escape velocity given by equation (2.29) is based on the simplifying assumption made in § 2.10, i.e., the effects of the Sun and Moon are ignored. At such distances from Earth at which the gravitational attraction of other bodies becomes significant, the velocity required for escape from Earth's environment is decreased and might even be zero.

HOHMANN TRANSFER ELLIPSE

2.72. A path of special interest for a spacecraft that can escape from Earth is the minimum energy trajectory from Earth to another planet or, in general, from one satellite to another of a given primary. This problem was first examined by W. Hohmann (§ 1.65). Consider a somewhat idealized case in which the orbits of the planets are circular and all lie in the same plane; Hohmann showed that the trajectory requiring the least expenditure of energy was one in which the spacecraft left one planet in a direction tangential to its orbit and reached the other planet in a direction tangential to the orbit of the latter.[*] The situation is represented in Fig. 2.18, I for the trajectory from Earth to a planet closer to the Sun, e.g., Venus, and in Fig. 2.18, II for the trajectory to a planet more distant from the Sun, e.g., Mars. These trajectories of minimum energy are generally known as *Hohmann transfer ellipses* or *Hohmann orbits*.

2.73. The appropriate heliocentric injection velocity, i.e., relative to the Sun, can be calculated from equation (2.24) when the injection point is at the apocenter of the transfer semi-ellipse (Fig. 2.18, I) or from equation (2.23) when

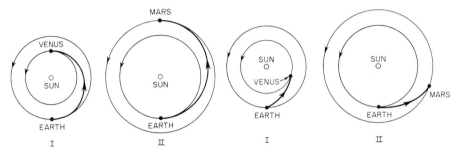

FIG. 2.18.   Hohmann orbits from Earth to interior (I) and exterior (II) planets

FIG. 2.19.   Shorter, high-energy trajectories

the injection point is at the pericenter (Fig. 2.18, II). The transit time is half the period for the complete elliptical orbit and hence is derived from equation (2.28) as

$$\text{Transit time} = \pi \sqrt{\frac{a^3}{K_s}},$$

where K_s is equal to GM_s; in MKS units, G is 6.67×10^{-11} and M_s, the mass of the Sun, is 1.99×10^{30} kilograms. The semi-major axis, a, is equal to $\frac{1}{2}(R_1 + R_2)$, where R_1 and R_2 are the radii of the orbits of the two planets involved in the trajectory. For example, in the case of a Hohmann transfer from Earth to Venus, the average value of a, allowing for the fact that the orbits are not quite circular, is 1.29×10^{11} meters. The transit time, after conversion from seconds into days, is found to be 145 days. For Mars, the corresponding Hohmann transit time is about 260 days.

2.74. Interplanetary trajectories that are shorter and require less time than the Hohmann ellipse are possible, as indicated in Fig. 2.19. The energy requirement, however, increases as the length of the trajectory and the transit

---

[*] Basic assumptions are that the spacecraft receives no significant impulse after injection and that the trajectory is not influenced by a third planet.

time decrease. In practice, the actual trajectory adopted for a space probe from Earth to another planet represents a compromise based on a number of considerations. For example, if the power (or thrust) of the rocket vehicle is available, it might better be used in increasing the useful payload of the spacecraft rather than in shortening the transit time. On the other hand, the longer the trajectory, the more serious will be the effect of errors in injection velocity and direction; that is to say, the guidance problem becomes more difficult and the chances of missing the target planet are increased.

2.75. Another factor that must not be overlooked is the launch time. For a Hohmann orbit to be feasible, the target planet must arrive at the distant apsis of the transfer ellipse at the same time as the spacecraft. This is possible only during very limited periods which occur at considerable intervals, e.g., 19 months for Venus and 26 months for Mars (Chapter 7). If the launch cannot be achieved at the optimum time, some of the available energy must be sacrificed and a shorter trajectory, with a shorter transit time, is selected. In the case of the Mariner II probe to Venus, which is described in Chapter 10, the transit time from Earth was almost 110 days, compared with the 145 days for a minimum-energy trajectory. The transit time for Mariner IV to Mars (§ 10.200) is 228 days, whereas the Hohmann-orbit time is 260 days.

2.76. Although the Hohmann orbits are of primary interest for ideal interplanetary trajectories, they can also be applied to the transfer of a satellite from one Earth orbit to another. For example, in a rendezvous operation, in which a chaser vehicle is launched from the ground to join up with a target vehicle already in orbit, a Hohmann transfer ellipse could be employed in the following manner. The chaser vehicle is first placed in a temporary (or parking) orbit at a lower altitude; when it is in a suitable position with regard to the target vehicle, the chaser would then go into a Hohmann transfer orbit to bring it close to the target, in a manner similar to that shown in Fig. 2.18, II.

ECCENTRIC ELLIPTICAL ORBITS

2.77. Comparison of equation (2.23) with the corresponding expression for the escape velocity, i.e., with a equal to infinity, shows that

$$\frac{v_{\text{peri}}}{v_{\text{esc}}} = \sqrt{1 - \frac{r_0}{2a}}. \qquad (2.30)$$

If the elliptical orbit is fairly eccentric, i.e., r_0 is small in comparison with $2a$, the quantity $2a$ may be replaced by $2a - r_0$, which is the distance of the apogee from Earth's center. Hence, equation (2.30) then takes the form

$$\frac{v_{\text{peri}}}{v_{\text{esc}}} \approx \sqrt{1 - \frac{R_{\text{peri}}}{R_{\text{apo}}}},$$

where R_{peri} and R_{apo} are the respective distances of perigee and apogee of the orbit from Earth's center. Moreover, since R_{peri}/R_{apo} is small, e.g., less than 0.1, it is a good approximation to write

$$\frac{v_{peri}}{v_{esc}} \approx 1 - \frac{R_{peri}}{2R_{apo}}.$$

If a spacecraft is launched near to, i.e., within a few hundred miles of, Earth's surface into an elliptical orbit that extends out to 10 Earth radii, $R_{peri}/2R_{apo} = 1/20$; the required injection velocity (v_{peri}) is then as much as 95 percent of the escape velocity. For a launch to the Moon, some 60 Earth radii distant, $R_{peri}/2R_{apo}$ is about 1/120 and the injection velocity is over 99 percent of the escape value.

Effects of Injection Conditions

2.78. Apart from perturbing effects, the path of a spacecraft launched from Earth depends only on the altitude, velocity, and direction of injection. If the injection velocity is less than the escape velocity, it follows from equation (2.22) that, for specified values of the altitude, i.e., r, and of the velocity, v, the semi-major axis a (or the major axis $2a$) must always be the same regardless of the direction of injection. Consequently, according to equation (2.28), the orbital period will have the same value in every case. The direction of injection, however, does influence the shape, i.e., the eccentricity, of the orbit and the orientation of the line of the apsides.* The situation is illustrated in Fig. 2.20 which shows the orbits for injection at a

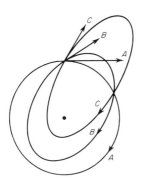

FIG. 2.20. Injection with same velocity in three different directions

particular altitude and prescribed velocity but in three different directions. In the particular case shown, the velocity is equal to the circular velocity at the given altitude. For horizontal injection, indicated by A, the orbit is therefore a circle. If the direction of injection departs from the horizontal, the orbit is an ellipse (B or C) with a semi-major axis equal to the radius of the circle. The perigee of the ellipse is not, however, at the injection point.

2.79. The general situation depicted in Fig. 2.20 is applicable for any injection velocity, even if it differs from the circular velocity for the particular altitude. When injection is in a horizontal direction, the point of injection becomes the perigee of the elliptical orbit, except for a special case to be considered below when it is the apogee. If the direction of injection is not horizon-

---

* See first footnote in § 2.49.

tal, the point of injection cannot coincide with the perigee (or apogee) of the ellipse.

2.80. If horizontal injection occurs at a sufficiently high altitude with a velocity somewhat less than the circular velocity for this altitude, the orbit is an ellipse with its apogee, rather than the perigee, at the injection point (Fig. 2.21). This is the special case referred to above and in the footnote to § 2.40. The injection altitude and velocity must, of course, satisfy the requirement that the minor axis of the ellipse is greater than Earth's diameter. If this is not the case, the trajectory will intersect Earth's surface and the injected body will fall to the ground, as in AP_1 and AP_2 of Fig. 2.1, following a ballistic path that is part of an ellipse. The same general conclusions are applicable even if the direction of injection deviates somewhat from the horizontal.

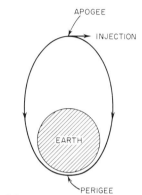

Fig. 2.21.   Orbit with apogee at the injection point

2.81. As a general rule, satellites are injected in a direction that is as close as possible to the horizontal, because this makes it simpler to attain an orbit with the desired characteristics, e.g., perigee and apogee altitudes. If the direction of injection is not quite horizontal, an elliptical orbit with the same major axis and period may still be achieved. The altitudes of the perigee and apogee will be different from the case of horizontal injection and so also will the (initial) direction of the line of the apsides. If the direction of injection is at a moderately large angle to the horizontal and the altitude is not too high, it may prove impossible to put a satellite into orbit, although the launching of a space probe could be achieved, as represented in Fig. 2.22. At low and moderate injection velocities the trajectory is elliptical, but it intersects Earth. If the injection velocity is equal to or greater than the parabolic (or escape) velocity, however, the injected object will escape from Earth and become a space probe.

Perturbation of Orbits

2.82. The derivations of the equations given earlier for the characteristics of satellite orbits have been based on the simplifying assumption of a central force field (§ 2.16). In other words, it has been assumed that both Earth and the satellite have spherical symmetry. The force of gravity would then be directed toward Earth's geometrical center. It is supposed, further, that no forces other than this symmetrical gravitational attraction act on the satellite once it is in orbit. Such orbits are said to be *undisturbed* or *unperturbed*. Deviations from spherical symmetry due to nonuniformity in mass distribution and departure from spherical shape of the primary, and the presence of forces other than those of Earth's gravity, however, cause *perturbations* of the orbit.

2.83. An important source of perturbation of a satellite orbit is the non-spherical shape of Earth. Since the radius (or diameter) is greater at the equator than at the poles, Earth is said to have an "equatorial bulge." This

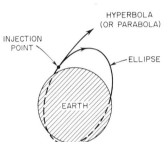

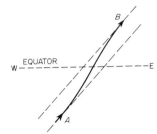

Fɪɢ. 2.22. High-angle injection at fairly low altitude

Fɪɢ. 2.23. Displacement of orbit (regression of nodes) by Earth's equatorial bulge

expression, although widely employed, is somewhat misleading since the bulge, representing the departure from sphericity, extends all the way from the poles to the equator (see Fig. 9.10). The term equatorial bulge is used presumably because the effect becomes more significant as the equator is approached.

2.84. As a consequence of the so-called bulge, the force of gravity on a body (satellite) at a given distance from Earth's center is greater when near the equator than elsewhere.* Therefore, when a satellite approaches the equator, it experiences an additional force due to the increased gravitational attraction. As a result, the plane of the orbit is gradually displaced. The behavior may be understood by reference to Fig. 2.23. Suppose an Earth satellite is traveling from west to east on an orbit whose plane is represented by the line marked *A*. As the satellite approaches the equator, the gravitational force increases so that the plane of the orbit is diverted slightly in a westward direction. As the distance from the equator increases, however, the gravitational force decreases again and the orbit gradually moves into plane *B*, approximately parallel to the original direction. The net effect is seen to be that the orbital plane of the eastward moving satellite is shifted somewhat to the west each time it passes the equator. If the satellite is traveling from east to west, the situation is exactly reversed; the orbital plane direction then changes from *B* to *A*, so that it is shifted to the east at each equatorial passage.

2.85. It may appear surprising, at first sight, that the so-called equatorial bulge causes a shift of the orbital plane to the west or to the east. What might perhaps have been expected is that the satellite would be pulled down-

---

* It will be recalled from § 2.20 that the gravitational force *on the surface* is least at the equator, because of the greater distance from the center of Earth.

ward, toward Earth, by the increased gravitational force as it passes by the equator. The actual behavior arises from the fact that the orbiting satellite has properties similar to those of a gyroscope, which are described in Chapter 4. The change in the direction of motion is then perpendicular to both the original direction and that of the perturbing force.

2.86. The points at which the orbit of any satellite crosses the plane of the equator are called the *nodes* of the orbit (Fig. 2.24). The movement of these crossing points caused by perturbations is referred to as *regression of the nodes*. Consequently, a satellite orbiting Earth from west to east exhibits a westerly regression of the nodes. On the other hand, if the orbit is from east to west, the regression of the nodes is toward the east. The time required for the nodes to regress completely around Earth's circumference, i.e., through 360 deg, depends on the angle of inclination the satellite's orbit makes with the equator and also on the altitude of the orbit. For small angles of inclination, e.g., less than about 20 deg, it requires about 45 days (or roughly 650 orbits) for complete rotation of the nodes at satellite altitudes of a few hundred miles. The time increases to some 60 days (roughly 900 orbits) when the angle of inclination of the orbit is 45 deg. This means that the rate of regression of the nodes becomes less with increasing angle of inclination, and for a polar orbit, which has a 90-deg angle of inclination, there is no regression due to the equatorial bulge.* As is to be expected, the rate of regression also decreases to some extent with increasing altitude because of the decrease in the gravitational force.

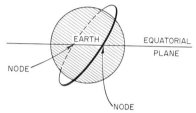

FIG. 2.24.   Nodes in the orbit of an Earth satellite

2.87. A situation of special interest arises in connection with certain satellites used for meteorological studies. For an orbital inclination of 80 deg to the equator and an altitude of about 700 miles, the time required for the nodes to regress completely around Earth's circumference is 365 days, i.e., just 1 year.

2.88. Another type of orbital perturbation due to Earth's equatorial bulge is the effect on the position of the line joining the perigee and apogee, i.e., the line of the apsides (§ 2.49, footnote). The attraction of the bulge causes the satellite to accelerate or decelerate somewhat, depending on the angle of inclination of the orbit, as it passes the equator. If the angle is small, for example, the path, which would otherwise have been along the broken lines in Fig. 2.25, I, actually follows the continuous one. The net result is that, although the orbit remains in the same plane, except in so far as it is affected by regression of the nodes, the position of the apogee, in particular, changes

---

* At 90-deg inclination there is a slight regression, as at other angles, caused by the perturbing effect of the Moon.

continuously, e.g., counterclockwise in the situation shown in Fig. 2.25, II. This effect is referred to as *rotation of the line of the apsides.*

2.89. The time required for the line of the apsides to make a complete rotation, i.e., through an angle of 360 deg in the orbital plane, depends on the angle of inclination of the orbit to the equator, the ellipticity of the orbit,

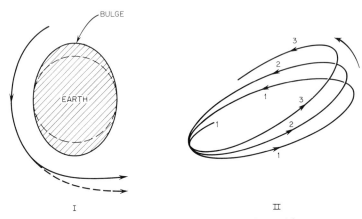

Fɪɢ. 2.25.   Rotation of the line of the apsides

and the altitude of the perigee. At an angle of 63 deg 26 min, the rotation rate is essentially zero;* for smaller inclinations, the orbit advances in the same direction as the satellite revolves, such as is the case in Fig. 2.25. If the angle of inclination exceeds 63 deg 26 min, the motion is in the opposite direction. For an equatorial orbit (inclination angle 0 deg) of relatively small eccentricity and a perigee of 300 miles altitude, it would take some 25 to 30 days (400 to 500 orbits) for the line of the apsides to make a complete rotation. For a polar orbit (inclination angle 90 deg), the corresponding time is about 100 days (1600 orbits) for the same perigee.

2.90. The regression of the nodes and the rotation of the line of the apsides are not the only gravitational perturbations experienced by a satellite in orbit about Earth. It is the existence of these additional effects that has led to important information about the so-called shape of Earth to which brief reference was made in § 1.16; the subject will be treated more fully in Chapter 8.

2.91. The gravitational attraction of the Sun and the Moon also cause perturbations of an Earth satellite's orbit. The effect of the Moon is somewhat the larger, but even this is small, although it increases with the altitude of the orbit above Earth. For altitudes below about 500 miles the orbital perturbations due to the Moon and the Sun are not very significant. Where the characteristics

---

* The theoretical expression for the extent of rotation of the line of the apsides contains the term $4 - 5 \sin^2 i$, where i is the angle of inclination to the equator; this term is zero when $\sin^2 i = 0.8$ or $\sin i = 0.8945$, and then i is 63 deg 26 min.

of an orbit must be known with great accuracy, however, e.g., for navigational or geodetic purposes (Chapter 5), the effect of the Sun and Moon may not be negligible.

2.92. An entirely different, i.e., nongravitational, perturbation can arise from air resistance or aerodynamic drag. As stated in § 1.103, the magnitude of this effect depends on the size and shape of the satellite or, more correctly, the cross-sectional area in the direction of motion, the mass of the satellite, and the altitude of the orbit. Because of the complex dependence on these quantities, it is not a simple matter to derive the value of the orbital perturbations in precise terms. There are some general results, however, in connection with the phenomenon called *orbital decay*, which apply in all cases.

2.93. Suppose the conditions are such that the satellite experiences an appreciable aerodynamic drag in the region of the perigee, i.e., where it is closest to Earth. Each time it approaches its orbital perigee, therefore, the velocity of the satellite will be decreased; as a result, the lengths of both the major and minor axes of the elliptical orbit are diminished (cf. § 2.59). The altitude of the apogee decreases relatively rapidly and that of the perigee more slowly. The path of the satellite decays into the form of a somewhat distorted spiral which comes closer and closer to Earth upon each revolution. The decay becomes more rapid as Earth is approached because of the increasing atmospheric density.

2.94. Another force that can cause disturbance of a satellite's orbit is that due to the pressure of the radiation from the Sun. At Earth's distance, the magnitude of the pressure is 2×10^{-7} pound per square foot of highly reflecting surface exposed to the Sun. Consequently, it is only for a satellite of large area and relatively small mass that the perturbing effect is appreciable. Such is the case for the Echo balloon-like satellites used for tests of long-distance communications. Echo I, for example, when inflated was a sphere with a total exposed area of about 31,000 square feet and weighed only 135 pounds. Its initial orbit was approximately circular with an altitude of about 1000 miles, but the pressure of solar radiation brought the perigee down to 600 miles at times.

Earth Coverage by Satellite Orbits

2.95. Were it not for the effects of various perturbing forces, the orbit of a satellite would remain fixed in both direction and dimensions with respect to Earth's center. Although the satellite moves with Earth around the Sun, it does not participate in Earth's west to east rotation about the poles. Consequently, to an observer on Earth, the orbital plane of the satellite appears to move in a westward direction, except in the special case of the 24-hour synchronous orbit. That is to say, the satellite will pass over different parts of Earth in successive orbits. This will be apparent from Fig. 2.26 which shows the orbital plane in the same location at two different times. In the interval the rotation of Earth has changed the position in space of the point A; hence, although the satellite appears over A at the earlier time, it will be over B at the later time.

2.96. If P is the true orbital period in minutes, the number of Keplerian orbits the satellite will make per day is $1440/P$, since there are 1440 minutes in a day. During this time, Earth will have rotated through 360 deg; consequently, in each orbital period Earth rotates through $360 \times P/1440 = \frac{1}{4}P$ deg. For an

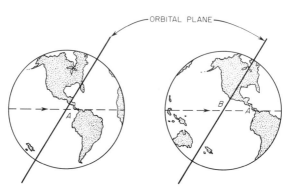

Fig. 2.26.   Earth coverage by satellite orbits

orbit of roughly 150 to 200 miles altitude, P is about 90 minutes, and so the rotation of Earth is about 22.5 deg per orbit. The plane of the orbit appears to shift westward through 22.5 deg in longitude for each revolution of the satellite. In other words, for a 90-minute orbit successive crossings of a given parallel of latitude occur at 22.5-deg intervals of longitude.

2.97. The apparent path of the orbits with reference to a fixed Earth, in a particular case, are shown on a Mercator projection in Fig. 2.27. The maximum north and south latitudes covered by the orbits, about 30° in the figure, are

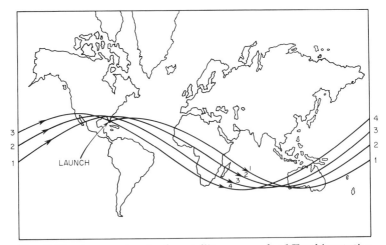

Fig. 2.27.   Apparent path of a satellite as a result of Earth's rotation

approximately equal to the angle of inclination of the orbital plane with respect to Earth's equatorial plane. The larger the angle of inclination, the greater will be the area of Earth's surface over which the satellite will pass in the course of a day.

The Elements of an Orbit

2.98. The orbital characteristics, either of a natural (the Moon) or artificial satellite about Earth or of a planet about the Sun, are defined by a number of quantities called the *elements* (or *parameters*) of the orbit. Theoretically, six independent parameters should describe the position of a satellite of a given primary, but seven are sometimes used. The elements can be chosen in several different ways according to convenience for the particular problem being considered. Those given below, which are commonly employed, are relatively easy to comprehend.

2.99. The semi-major axis and the eccentricity of the ellipse describe the dimensions and shape of the elliptical orbit, apart from minor perturbations. The time (or epoch) of last passage through the perigee (or perihelion for a planet) then permits the location of the satellite in its orbit to be determined at any instant. The other three elements are angles which define the orientation of the orbit in space; they are (*a*) the inclination of the orbital plane to Earth's equatorial plane (or the ecliptic plane for a planet), (*b*) the angle between the radius vector of the perigee (or perihelion) and the line joining the nodes, and (*c*) the angle between the line of the nodes from the ascending end, i.e., where the satellite goes from south to north, and a fixed reference direction in space, usually the "first point of Aries," i.e., the direction of the Sun when it crosses the equator at the vernal equinox (cf. § 9.36). In astronomical work, the orbital period is often regarded as an additional element, but it is not really an independent parameter because in principle it can be calculated from the semi-major axis by equation (2.26) if the masses of the satellite and the primary are known. The elements usually refer to a particular orbit at a given epoch since they may change from one orbit to the next as a result of perturbations. These changes are sometimes expressed in analytical form as a function of time.

APPENDIX

The Circular Velocity

2.100. An alternative method to that given in § 2.22 *et seq.* for calculating the velocity of a satellite in a circular orbit is to consider a body moving in a circular path with a constant velocity, v, as indicated in Fig. 2.28, I. At any point, such as A, the direction of motion is perpendicular to the radius vector OA, where O is the center of the circular orbit; similarly, at B the velocity, which is the same as at A, is in the direction perpendicular to OB. In Fig. 2.28, II are indicated the vectors oa and ob representing the instantaneous velocities at

A and B, respectively; the lengths oa and ob are each equal to v, but their directions are different. The vector ab, equal in magnitude to Δv, consequently represents the change in velocity of the satellite as it travels from A to B in the time interval Δt. Since oa is perpendicular to OA and ob to OB, the triangles

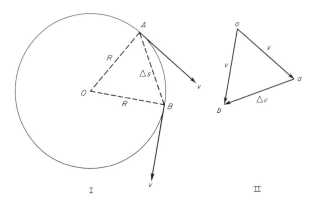

I   II

FIG. 2.28.   Calculation of circular velocity

OAB and oab are similar, and hence ab is perpendicular to the line joining A and B. In other words, the velocity change ab is directed toward O, the center of the circular orbit. The time rate of this change in velocity is the acceleration of the satellite toward the center of the primary and is equal to the acceleration produced by the gravitational attraction.

2.101. Because of the similarity of the triangles OAB and oab,

$$\frac{\Delta v}{v} = \frac{\Delta s}{R} \quad \text{or} \quad \Delta v = \frac{v}{R} \Delta s,$$

where Δs is the length of the chord AB. Upon dividing both sides of this equation by the time Δt, the result is

$$\frac{\Delta v}{\Delta t} = \frac{v}{R} \cdot \frac{\Delta s}{\Delta t}.$$

In the limit, as Δt goes to zero, $\Delta v/\Delta t$ represents the instantaneous acceleration, a, of the satellite, and $\Delta s/\Delta t$ is the circular velocity, v; hence,

$$a = \frac{v^2}{R},$$

where R is the radius of the satellite's orbit. If the primary body is Earth, this acceleration must be equal to g at the distance R from Earth's center; it follows, therefore, that

$$g = \frac{v^2}{R} \quad \text{or} \quad v = \sqrt{Rg},$$

as in equation (2.13).

2.102. The derivation of the general expression from which the velocity of a body in any conic-section orbit or trajectory may be derived, known as the *vis viva* integral (from the Latin, meaning "living force" or what is now called "kinetic energy"), is too complicated to be given here. Reference may however be made to the following texts: K. A. Ehricke, "Space Flight, I: Environmental and Celestial Mechanics," D. Van Nostrand Co., 1960, p. 265; M. Vertregt, "Principles of Astronautics," Elsevier Publishing Co., 1960, p. 56; A. I. Berman, "Physical Principles of Astronautics," John Wiley & Sons, Inc., 1961, p. 127.

THE CHARACTERISTIC VELOCITY

2.103. The equation (2.19) for the characteristic velocity for a circular orbit is obtained in the following manner. In general, the work done in moving the point of application of a force F through a distance dr is $F\,dr$. If the work is done against the attraction of gravity, the force, F, acting on unit mass, i.e., $m = 1$, is equal to GM/R^2 (see § 2.18) or K/R^2, by equation (2.12); hence, $F\,dr$ is equal to $(K/R^2)\,dR$. Suppose a body of unit mass is raised from Earth's surface, radius R_0, to an orbit of radius R, the work done is given by

$$\text{Work done} = \int_{R_0}^{R} \frac{K}{R^2}\,dR = K\left(\frac{1}{R_0} - \frac{1}{R}\right). \tag{2.31}$$

This is equal to the increase in the potential energy from $-K/R_0$ per unit mass at Earth's surface to $-K/R$ at a distance R from the center.

2.104. The velocity in a circular orbit is $\sqrt{Rg}$, and so the kinetic energy per unit mass is $Rg/2$. Since g is equal to K/R^2 by equation (2.13), the kinetic energy is $K/2R$. If this is added to the work (or potential energy) term in equation (2.31), the result is the total energy required to raise unit mass from Earth's surface and place it in an orbit of radius R; thus,

$$\text{Total energy} = K\left(\frac{1}{R_0} - \frac{1}{R}\right) + \frac{K}{2R}$$

$$= K\left(\frac{1}{R_0} - \frac{1}{2R}\right).$$

To obtain the characteristic velocity, as defined in § 2.35, this energy is regarded as the kinetic energy and hence v_{char} is the square root of twice the total energy, i.e.,

$$v_{\text{char}} = \sqrt{2K\left(\frac{1}{R_0} - \frac{1}{2R}\right)}, \tag{2.32}$$

as in equation (2.19).

THE ESCAPE VELOCITY

2.105. The escape velocity from Earth's surface may be calculated by setting R equal to infinity directly in equation (2.32) or by starting with equation

(2.31). In the latter case, if R is set equal to infinity, the result will be the energy required to move unit mass from Earth's surface to infinity; this is found to be K/R_0. The corresponding velocity, which is the escape velocity from the surface, is then $\sqrt{2K/R_0}$. By integration of equation (2.31) from R to infinity, instead of from R_0 to infinity, the escape velocity at a distance R from Earth's center is readily shown to be $\sqrt{2K/R}$.

2.106. The kinetic energy (per unit mass) corresponding to the escape velocity is $\frac{1}{2}\sqrt{(2K/R)^2}$, i.e., K/R, which is numerically equal to the potential energy at the distance R. The escape velocity at a particular altitude is thus the velocity at which the kinetic energy of a body becomes equal to the potential energy due to gravity at the given altitude.

Chapter 3

PROPULSION AND POWER FOR SPACE

ROCKET PROPULSION

CLASSIFICATION OF ROCKET SYSTEMS

3.1. Propulsion has been described as the key to space exploration and, in space, the only known practical method of propulsion is based on the use of the rocket (or reaction) principle (§ 1.38). Hence, rocket propulsion is fundamental to the study of space both by manned flight and by vehicles carrying instruments. A rocket propulsion system is entirely self-contained and carries all the material required for its operation. In a sense, this also represents a drawback because at the time it is launched the rocket vehicle must carry all the propellant required for the attainment of the desired objective. The useful load (or payload) of a rocket thus represents a relatively small fraction of the total weight at liftoff. On the other hand, a rocket has the great advantage of being able to function in any environment, including the virtual vacuum of space. In fact, the operating efficiency of a rocket motor is somewhat better in a vacuum than it is at normal atmospheric pressure.

3.2. In essence, a rocket produces a stream of gas molecules (or other particles) which are ejected in a given direction with a very high exhaust velocity. The reaction to this action, in accordance with Newton's third law of motion, then propels the vehicle in the opposite direction. Rocket engines can be classified in various ways; one classification in common use is based on the nature of the energy source. A rocket, like any other kind of motor, is a device for converting one form of energy into another, and so it must be provided with a source of energy. This energy may be either chemical, nuclear, or electrical, and rocket engines are often distinguished accordingly.

3.3. A more fundamental classification, however, can be made in terms of the manner in which the high exhaust velocity is attained. There are then three main categories of rocket engines depending upon whether the gas molecules (or other particles) of high velocity are produced by (1) chemical reactions, (2) direct heating (or heat transfer), or (3) acceleration of electrically charged particles. Apart from experimental devices, all rockets presently in use for space exploration are of the first type, i.e., chemical rockets. The long-range future of space travel, however, may be largely determined by progress made in the development of rocket engines in the other categories. In addition to the three classes mentioned above, there are a few rocket concepts of special types which are still in the somewhat speculative stage. These will be referred to later.

ROCKET THRUST AND ACCELERATION

3.4. The reaction force produced on a rocket vehicle as a result of the expulsion of the high-velocity exhaust gas is called the *thrust* and is generally stated in pounds of force. The value of the thrust is dependent mainly on the product of the rate at which the exhaust gases are expelled, expressed as the mass per unit time, and the expulsion (or exhaust) velocity. This product determines a quantity called the *momentum thrust.** Thus, if the gas is exhausted at the rate of $\dot{m}$ pounds mass per second † at a velocity of v_e feet per second, the momentum thrust is $\dot{m}v_e/g_c$ pounds force, where g_c, equal to 32.174, is the constant required when force and mass are expressed in pounds (§ 3.7).

3.5. Another contribution to the overall thrust can be made by the *pressure thrust*, which may be positive, negative, or zero. The pressure thrust, in pounds force, is equal to $A_e(p_e - p_a)$, where A_e is the area in square feet of the nozzle where the gas is exhausted, p_e is the pressure of the exhaust gas, and p_a is that of the surrounding atmosphere; both pressures must be expressed in pounds force per square foot.‡ Thus, the thrust of the rocket, represented by F, is

$$F = \frac{\dot{m}v_e}{g_c} + A_e(p_e - p_a). \tag{3.1}$$

For reasons which will be explained in § 3.62, it is desirable in rocket operation for p_e to be equal to p_a, but this is generally not possible at all altitudes, since p_a decreases with altitude but p_e usually remains constant. The rocket system is therefore designed so that p_e is less than p_a at sea level but is slightly greater than p_a at high altitudes. Hence, at sea level $p_e - p_a$ is negative, and so also is the pressure thrust, whereas at high altitudes $p_e - p_a$ and the pressure thrust are positive but small. This change in the pressure thrust, from a negative to a small positive value, is responsible for the increase in the total thrust of a rocket as it ascends from sea level to high altitudes.

3.6. If the exhaust gas pressure is assumed to be constant, the increase in thrust can be readily calculated, since it then depends only on the decrease in the atmospheric pressure with altitude. At sea level, the ambient pressure is

---

* In general, the *momentum* of a body is defined as the product of its mass and its velocity; force is equal to the rate of change of momentum with time. The momentum thrust, as defined above, is thus a force, since it represents the time rate of change of momentum of the exhaust gas.

† According to the common convention, a dot placed over a symbol represents the rate of change with time of the quantity indicated by the symbol, in this case the mass, m, of the exhaust gas.

‡ Pressure is defined as force per unit area.

14.7 pounds per square inch, whereas at high altitudes it is virtually zero; hence, the change in p_a is 14.7 pounds per square inch or 2116 pounds per square foot. If the exhaust area, A_e, of the rocket is taken to be 10 square feet, for example, the increase in total thrust due to the change in the pressure thrust will then be over 21,000 pounds of force.

3.7. As it rises from the ground, the thrust of a rocket is opposed by the downward force of gravity. According to Newton's second law equation (2.2), the gravitational force is equal to Mg/k, where M is the mass of the rocket vehicle, g is the acceleration due to gravity, and k is a proportionality constant which depends on the units of mass, force, length, and time. In rocket engineering, force is usually expressed as pounds force, mass as pounds mass, length in feet, and time in seconds; the constant k is then represented by the symbol g_c and has the value 32.174 (pounds mass) (feet per second per second)/(pounds force).* The gravitational force on the rocket vehicle is thus Mg/g_c.

3.8. When launched from the ground, a rocket vehicle, especially if large, is usually in a vertical position and if it is to rise from the ground, the upward thrust, F pounds of force, must exceed the downward gravitational pull, Mg/g_c. In other words, the net upward thrust, $F - Mg/g_c$ must be positive. To be more exact, allowance should be made for the aerodynamic drag force, D, so that the required condition is that $F - (Mg/g_c + D)$ should be positive. Since D is generally small in comparison with the other terms, it will be ignored for the present.

3.9. In general, the acceleration a feet per second per second achieved by a body of mass M pounds which is acted upon by a force of F pounds is given by equation (2.2) as

$$a = g_c \frac{F}{M}.$$

The net upward thrust $F - Mg/g_c$ of the rocket will thus produce an acceleration given by

$$a = g_c \frac{F - Mg/g_c}{M} = g_c \frac{F}{M} - g. \tag{3.2}$$

At sea level, the average value of g in feet per second per second is numerically equal to g_c, and M in pounds mass is then equal numerically to the sea-level weight W_0 of the rocket in pounds force; hence, equation (3.2) can be written as

$$a = g_c \left(\frac{F}{W_0} - 1 \right), \tag{3.3}$$

where F and W_0 are both expressed in pounds force. The quantity F/W_0 is called the *thrust-to-weight ratio* of the rocket; it must obviously be greater than unity if the rocket is to leave the ground.

---

* This follows from equation (2.2), since, by definition, 1 pound force will accelerate a body of 1 pound mass by 32.174 feet per second per second.

3.10. For the smaller rockets, the thrust-to-weight ratio may be as much as 2 or more, but for larger and heavier rockets, it is generally about 1.5. In the latter case, the net upward acceleration at liftoff is no more than about 0.5 g, according to equation (3.3). This explains why large rockets rise fairly slowly at first. As the propellant material is consumed in flight, however, the total sea-level weight, W_0, of the rocket vehicle decreases. There is thus an increase in F/W_0, especially as F also increases to some extent with increasing altitude, as seen above. Consequently, the value of a increases and the vehicle accelerates more and more rapidly until the propellant is consumed. In some large rockets, the maximum acceleration attained may exceed 320 feet per second per second, i.e., about ten times the normal gravitational acceleration.

3.11. In deriving equations (3.2) and (3.3), it was assumed that the rocket vehicle is traveling vertically upward. As the trajectory turns toward the horizontal, however, as required for the injection of the spacecraft, the gravitational force in the direction of motion is not Mg/g_c but $(Mg \cos \theta)/g_c$, where θ is the angle of the trajectory with the vertical. Hence, the gravitational component in the direction of motion decreases as the trajectory bends over and it becomes zero for a horizontal path, since θ is then 90 deg and $\cos \theta$ is zero. In these circumstances, equation (3.2) becomes $a = g_c F/M$, where a is the acceleration in the direction of motion. The rocket motor can thus cause acceleration even though the thrust is quite small relative to the mass (or weight as determined at sea level). The same situation applies to a vehicle in space at a distance from Earth or any celestial body when the force of gravity is very small. Acceleration, i.e., a continuous increase in velocity, is possible even when the ratio of thrust to mass is quite small. This point is significant in connection with some advanced propulsion techniques intended for use in interplanetary travel (§ 3.184).

SPECIFIC IMPULSE

3.12. An important criterion of rocket performance, called the *specific impulse,* is related to the thrust produced. It is defined as the pounds (force) of thrust obtained from each pound mass of propellant, i.e., total of fuel and oxidizer, consumed in 1 second. The rate at which the propellant is used up is exactly the same as the rate at which exhaust gas is expelled because the propellant material is converted into exhaust gas in the operating rocket (§ 1.40). Since F pounds force is the rocket thrust and $\dot{m}$ is the rate in pounds mass per second at which exhaust gas is expelled (or propellant consumed), it follows that the specific impulse, I_{sp}, can be represented by

$$I_{sp} = \frac{F \text{ (pounds force)}}{\dot{m} \text{ (pounds mass per second)}}$$

$$= \frac{F}{\dot{m}} \frac{\text{(pounds force) (seconds)}}{\text{pounds mass}}. \qquad (3.4)$$

Although the specific impulse should be given in units of (pounds force)/(pounds mass per second) or (pounds force) (seconds)/(pounds mass), it is the general practice to express the value in seconds. The specific impulse is then the period in seconds for which 1 pound mass of propellant will produce a thrust of 1 pound force.

3.13. Some writers define specific impulse as the pounds force of thrust produced for a propellant consumption of 1 pound weight (force) per second. The specific impulse is then expressed appropriately in seconds. The definition gives the correct numerical values of the specific impulse only if the weight of propellant is referred to a location where the acceleration due to gravity is 32.174 feet per second per second. Unfortunately, the qualification is generally omitted and this leads to difficulties in certain applications of the specific impulse concept. The approach adopted in this book avoids such problems.

3.14. The origin of the term specific impulse will be understood if numerator and denominator of equation (3.4) are multiplied by t, the operating time of the rocket. If the mass rate of propellant consumption and the thrust are assumed to be constant,* the numerator, Ft, is equal to the total impulse, and the denominator, $\dot{m}t$, is the total mass of propellant used up during the time t; hence, equation (3.4) becomes

$$I_{sp} = \frac{\text{Total impulse}}{\text{Mass of propellant consumed}}.$$

The specific impulse is thus the rocket impulse per unit mass of propellant consumed.

3.15. The specific impulse is a characteristic property of the propellant system, although its exact value varies to some extent with the operating conditions and design of the rocket engine. It is for this reason that different numbers are often quoted for a given propellant or combination of propellants. If the engine conditions and external pressure are known, the specific impulse can be evaluated for any given propellant system, and it is this theoretical (or ideal) value which is generally recorded. The actual specific impulse in an operating rocket is invariably somewhat smaller. Nevertheless, the theoretical specific impulse is a useful quantity for comparing the performances of rocket propellants of different types. More detailed data will be given later, but for the present it may be mentioned that, for the liquid propellants in common use in chemical rockets, I_{sp} is about 300 seconds at sea level and roughly 350 seconds at altitudes above 20 miles. That is to say, the consumption of 1 pound mass of propellant per second produces ideally a thrust of 300 (or 350) pounds force. For most solid propellants, the specific impulse is somewhat less.

3.16. Propellant consumption at the rate of 1 pound mass per second produces I_{sp} pounds force of thrust; hence, the thrust, F pounds force, resulting from the

---

* If these quantities are not constant, the same result is obtained by integration over the operating time.

use of propellant at the rate of $\dot{m}$ pounds mass per second, is given by

$$F = \dot{m}I_{\mathrm{sp}}, \qquad (3.5)$$

a result which can, of course, be derived directly from equation (3.4). It follows, therefore, that the higher the specific impulse the greater is the thrust which can be produced for a given mass rate, $\dot{m}$, of propellant consumption. Alternatively, it is seen that a particular thrust value can be obtained at a lower rate of propellant consumption if the specific impulse is large. To perform a particular mission, as represented by the total impulse, i.e., the product (or integral) of the thrust and the operating time of the rocket, the total weight of propellant which must be carried will be less the greater the specific impulse. A reduction in the mass of the propellant will mean a decrease in the total weight of the rocket vehicle, for a given payload, and an increase in the thrust-to-weight ratio and acceleration. Alternatively, a rocket vehicle employing a propellant system of high I_{sp} will be able to achieve the required mission with a larger payload than is possible with the same mass of a propellant of lower specific impulse.

3.17. It is of interest to consider the rate of propellant consumption in a typical rocket engine such as the Atlas which was used in the earliest U.S. manned orbital space flights. The sea-level thrust is 367,000 pounds, but this increases with altitude, and the mean operational thrust is probably about 400,000 pounds. The average specific impulse of the propellant combination (liquid oxygen and kerosene jet fuel) during flight is about 275 seconds. The propellant is therefore consumed at the average rate of 400,000/275, i.e., about 1450 pounds per second. The first stage of the Saturn I produces a sea-level thrust of 1,300,000 pounds in its cluster of eight engines, and the total rate of propellant consumption during flight is over 5000 pounds per second. In the Saturn V (or Advanced Saturn) the total sea-level thrust of the first stage will be about 7,500,000 pounds and the propellants will be used up at the enormous rate of some 30,000 pounds per second, i.e., roughly 6000 pounds per second in each of its five engines. If this engine cluster operates for 1 minute, it will consume 1,800,000 pounds (or 900 short tons) of propellant.

3.18. Another aspect of the specific impulse will be apparent from a comparison of equations (3.1) and (3.5), both of which give the total thrust of a rocket engine; thus, upon equating the right sides of these two expressions, it is seen that

$$\dot{m}I_{\mathrm{sp}} = \frac{\dot{m}v_e}{g_c} + A_e(p_e - p_a). \qquad (3.6)$$

In the ideal situation, the pressure of the exhaust gas is equal to the ambient pressure, i.e., $p_a = p_e$, and then the second term on the right of this equation is zero. In any event, for a large rocket, the pressure thrust is relatively small in comparison with the momentum thrust, especially at moderate and high altitudes; that is to say, the second term on the right of equation (3.6) may be neglected in comparison with the first. The equation can then be written as

$$\dot{m} I_{sp} = \frac{\dot{m} v_e}{g_c}$$

or

$$v_e = g_c I_{sp}. \tag{3.7}$$

Since g_c is a constant, regardless of altitude, the velocity of the exhaust gas is proportional to the specific impulse of the propellant system; thus, a high specific impulse means a high exhaust velocity. It will be seen later that, under comparable conditions, the higher the exhaust velocity, the greater the velocity a given rocket vehicle can attain. Propellants of large specific impulse are therefore desirable for space missions for which high velocities are required.

3.19. Provided the pressure conditions in different rockets are the same, as is generally true to a fair degree of approximation, a theoretical treatment based on the well-known behavior of gases shows that the velocity of the exhaust gas is proportional to the square root of the temperature of the gas before ejection divided by its molecular weight (cf. § 3.60); that is,

$$v_e = \text{constant} \times \sqrt{\frac{T}{\text{M.W.}}}, \tag{3.8}$$

where T is the temperature of the gas on the absolute scale* and M.W. is its molecular weight. A high exhaust velocity and, consequently, a high specific impulse are favored by a high temperature and low molecular weight of the gas which is expelled from the rocket motor. In nearly all rockets, the exhaust gas is a mixture of different substances and the molecular weight is then an average value, based on the relative amounts of the various molecules present. The desirability of high gas temperature and low average molecular weight is taken into consideration in the choice of rocket propellant systems.

CHEMICAL ROCKETS: LIQUID PROPELLANTS

PROPELLANT CHARACTERISTICS

3.20. In the great majority of chemical rockets, the propulsion energy is produced by combustion (or burning) reactions similar to those taking place in automobile, aircraft, and Diesel engines. In each case a chemical reaction takes place between two components, one being the *fuel* and the other the *oxidizer*. As a result of the reaction, gases are formed and at the same time a considerable amount of heat energy is released; this is the *heat of combustion* or *calorific value*, which is a characteristic quantity for each fuel and oxidizer combination. The propellants are the substances taking part in the combustion

* On the Kelvin scale, based on centigrade (or Celsius) degrees, the absolute temperature is 273° plus the centigrade temperature; on the Rankine (Fahrenheit) scale it is 460°F plus the Fahrenheit temperature.

or other chemical reaction that produces the hot gas exhausted from the rocket. Most rockets utilize either liquid or solid propellants, although hybrid systems, employing both a liquid and a solid, are being investigated.

3.21. In order to achieve high exhaust gas velocities, one requirement of a propellant is that it should contain only elements of low atomic weight. If an element of high atomic weight is present, the molecular weight of the exhaust gas will inevitably be large. Another requirement is that the calorific value per unit mass should be high; this will make possible the attainment of a high gas temperature. Furthermore, a high density of the propellant materials is advantageous, for then the volume (and mass) of the tanks or other containers will not be too large. Other desirable characteristics of propellants are that they should be storable, safe to handle, noncorrosive, and nonpoisonous in nature. It will be seen in due course that few, if any, rocket propellants satisfy all the requirements, and so in practice it is necessary to compromise. The propellants chosen are such that their desirable characteristics outweigh the undesirable ones.

MONOPROPELLANT SYSTEMS

3.22. Liquid-propellant chemical rockets can be either of the *monopropellant* or the *bipropellant* type, depending upon whether one or two separate liquids, respectively, are employed. In a monopropellant rocket, a single liquid produces the propulsive energy as the result of a chemical reaction. A monopropellant could consist of a material which combines within one compound (or mixture) the characteristics of both fuel and oxidizer, to some extent at least. An example is the organic compound nitromethane (CH_3NO_2), but this propellant has found limited application.

3.23. Only two monopropellants are in common use, namely, hydrogen peroxide (H_2O_2) and hydrazine (N_2H_4), and the ability of these liquids to produce hot gases does not depend upon combustion but upon chemical decomposition. In the presence of a suitable catalyst, such as metallic silver or platinum or a permanganate salt in solution, hydrogen peroxide forms water (steam) and oxygen gas at high temperature by the chemical reaction

$$2\ H_2O_2 \rightarrow 2\ H_2O + O_2.$$

In some rocket engines, the hot gases so produced have been used to drive the turbopumps (§ 1.81) which pump the propellants, but they can also serve as the hot exhaust gas for small rocket motors (or jets). Hydrogen peroxide rockets are used in a few special cases of propulsion, but their main application has been to changing the orbit or trajectory of a spacecraft or to altering the orientation of a manned space capsule.*

* In the Mercury orbital flights the hydrogen peroxide was commonly referred to as the "fuel," although it should, more correctly, be called the propellant. However, the latter term was not used presumably because the hydrogen peroxide does not actually propel the capsule, but is merely used to orient it in space.

3.24. Hydrazine is employed as the monopropellant in the rocket motors that provide the velocity adjustment required for midcourse guidance of Ranger (§ 9.227) and Mariner (§ 10.83) spacecraft. The decomposition of the hydrazine into a mixture of hot nitrogen and hydrogen gases takes place on the surface of a catalyst. With the older catalysts, e.g., aluminum oxide, the reaction had to be initiated by means of a small quantity of nitrogen tetroxide, but new catalysts have been developed for which this is not necessary.

BIPROPELLANT SYSTEMS

3.25. Nearly all liquid propellant rockets are of the bipropellant type; that is to say, there are two liquids, the fuel and the oxidizer, which are stored separately, but are brought together in the rocket motor where the combustion reaction takes place. The description of liquid-propellant chemical rocket engines given in this chapter refers particularly to bipropellant systems since they are of the type used to launch space vehicles from Earth.

3.26. Although ethyl alcohol was the fuel employed in some of the earliest rocket missiles, e.g., V-2 and Redstone, it is now mainly of historical interest. The liquid fuels extensively used for the propulsion of large rockets, e.g., Atlas, Thor, Titan I, and Saturn, are mixtures of hydrocarbons, i.e., compounds of hydrogen and carbon, somewhat related to kerosene, such as are used for jet engines. These fuels have such designations as JP-4, JP-5, RP-1, etc., where JP and RP are abbreviations for jet propellant and rocket propellant, respectively. The corresponding oxidizer is then liquid oxygen. With the same oxidizer, improved performance, i.e., higher specific impulse, can be obtained with liquid hydrogen as the fuel. This combination of propellants is employed in the upper stage (or stages) of the Saturn vehicles. In the Centaur, a liquid hydrogen-oxygen stage is used in conjunction with an Atlas rocket.

CRYOGENIC PROPELLANTS

3.27. At ordinary temperatures hydrogen and oxygen, and some other potential propellants, e.g., fluorine, are gases and it is, in fact, as gases that they undergo chemical reaction in the rocket engine. But in the gaseous form they have such low densities that it would require extremely large tanks to store them in the rocket vehicle. The storage of propellants in the gaseous form is thus completely impractical. It is for this reason that the substances mentioned above are stored as liquids at very low temperatures; they are consequently referred to as *cryogenic propellants* (from *kryos*, Greek, "ice cold"). In the liquid form, the densities are much greater than in the gaseous state, and consequently the propellant tanks can be much smaller and less massive. This advantage is offset, however, by the low temperatures required, so that liquid hydrogen, liquid fluorine, and liquid oxygen or lox (§ 1.86, footnote) cannot be stored in the rocket tanks for long periods of time. Such nonstorable, cryogenic propellants must be loaded into the tanks shortly before the rocket is launched.

3.28. The cryogenic liquids are made by simultaneously compressing and cooling the gases to the required low temperatures. They are then stored and transported, with moderate loss, in special vacuum-jacketed tanks called dewar vessels.* These containers are designed on the same principle as the familiar vacuum bottles, such as the Thermos flask, used to store hot or cold liquids in the home.

3.29. In Table 3.1 are listed the temperatures at which a number of cryogenic liquids, of possible use as propellants, liquefy at ordinary atmospheric pressure. These temperatures represent the conventional boiling points of the various

TABLE 3.1   BOILING POINTS OF CRYOGENIC PROPELLANTS

Substance	Density (grams/cu cm)	Boiling Point	
		°C	°F
Hydrogen	0.07	−253	−423
Oxygen	1.1	−183	−298
Fluorine	1.5	−188	−307
Oxygen difluoride	1.5	−145	−229

liquids. By increasing the pressure in the containing vessels the boiling points can be raised to a certain extent, so that the liquid form can exist at somewhat higher temperatures. It can be seen, however, that the temperatures required to produce and store cryogenic propellants are extremely low by normal standards.

STORABLE PROPELLANTS

3.30. In order to avoid the problems associated with cryogenic propellants and to make rockets ready for launching at all times, storable liquid propellants have been developed. Although kerosene fuels, e.g., RP-1, JP-4, etc., are storable, they are generally used with a cryogenic oxidizer and so are not included in this category. Most storable rocket fuels now in use are based on hydrazine; for example, the derivatives, monomethylhydrazine, $CH_3NH \cdot NH_2$, abbreviated to MMH, and unsymmetrical dimethylhydrazine, $(CH_3)_2N \cdot NH_2$ (or UDMH), have been used alone or in mixtures with each other and with hydrazine. A mixture of 60 percent by weight of UDMH and 40 percent of diethylenetriamine, known as Hydyne, has also been used as a rocket fuel (§ 1.114). These liquids can be stored readily because they do not boil except

---

* The vessels are named after the inventor of the vacuum-jacket principle, the British scientist James Dewar.

at moderately high temperatures; their densities are about the same as those of kerosene and ethyl alcohol and they have high calorific values. Hydrazine and its methyl derivatives are toxic materials, however, and must be handled with care.

3.31. The storable liquid oxidizer employed with hydrazine fuels is usually either nitrogen tetroxide (NTO), i.e., N_2O_4, or some form of nitric acid. Because NTO has a relatively low boiling point, 21°C or 70°F, it tends to vaporize easily; it is therefore kept in closed tanks under moderate pressure. Fairly pure nitric acid (HNO_3) containing no more than about 2 percent of water is called white fuming nitric acid (WFNA). In order to suppress the liberation of gases, as a result of decomposition, about 13 to 15 percent of nitrogen tetroxide is dissolved in WFNA to produce red fuming nitric acid (RFNA). These strong acid oxidizers are highly corrosive, so that they attack the steel containers. This attack can be inhibited by the presence of a small proportion (about 0.6 percent) of hydrogen fluoride. The latter forms a coating of iron fluoride on the interior of the vessel thereby protecting the metal from attack by the nitric acid. The propellants treated in this manner are called inhibited white and inhibited red fuming nitric acids, i.e., IWFNA and IRFNA, respectively. The latter is used extensively with UDMH as fuel in several reliable rocket motors, e.g., the Agena, which has served as the upper stage in such combinations as Thor-Agena and Atlas-Agena that have been used to launch several Earth satellites and space probes.

3.32. In addition to being storable, the propellant systems based on hydrazine (or its derivatives) and nitrogen tetroxide or nitric acid have the further advantage of being hypergolic (§ 1.87). The fuel and oxidizer consequently ignite spontaneously upon mixing. Other propellant systems, e.g., kerosene and liquid oxygen, must be ignited in some way before chemical reaction can occur.

POTENTIAL PROPELLANT SYSTEMS

3.33. The propellants already considered involve four elements of low atomic weight, namely, hydrogen (atomic weight 1.0), carbon (12.0), nitrogen (14.0), and oxygen (16.0). Other elements having low atomic weights and the capability of yielding large amounts of energy upon combustion are lithium (6.9), beryllium (9.0), boron (10.8), and fluorine (19.0). Among the compounds of these elements, those of boron are of potential interest for use either alone as liquid fuels or as additives to other fuels. The substances proposed for this purpose are the boranes, compounds of boron and hydrogen, since they are capable of producing large amounts of energy upon interaction with a suitable oxidizer.

3.34. The simplest and most common borane is diborane, B_2H_6, but it is a cryogenic liquid and is inclined to be somewhat unstable in certain circumstances. Nevertheless, it is being given serious consideration as a possible fuel in rockets of advanced design having high specific impulses, as will be indicated below. The more complex boranes, such as B_4H_{10}, B_5H_9, and B_5H_{11}, are, to a certain extent, storable liquids, although like diborane, they tend to decompose in storage. The utilization of boron in the form of borohydrides, e.g., with lithium, $LiBH_4$, or aluminum, $Al(BH_4)_3$, may prove advantageous. Since boron compounds appear to be potentially useful as rocket fuels, they are being studied with this objective in mind.

3.35. In principle, a bipropellant system consisting of liquid hydrogen as fuel and liquid fluorine as the oxidizer should be capable of performing better than liquid hydrogen and oxygen. It should be noted that, although fluorine contains no oxygen, it is described as an oxidizer since it is an oxidizing agent in the broad sense in which this term is used by chemists. Another promising system of high specific impulse, involving only a single cryogenic propellant, consists of fluorine as oxidizer with a fuel based on hydrazine or its derivatives. However, in addition to being a nonstorable cryogenic liquid (see Table 2.1), fluorine is an extremely corrosive and poisonous material as also is the product of its chemical interaction with hydrogen, namely, hydrogen fluoride. The employment of liquid fluorine as a rocket propellant thus presents many problems, but they are not regarded as being insoluble. In fact, at least one hydrogen-fluorine motor, of moderate thrust, has been fired successfully in a static test.

3.36. As a preliminary step in the utilization of fluorine as an oxidizer, studies are being made with a mixture of 30 percent liquid fluorine and 70 percent liquid oxygen, known as "flox." It is to be tried in the so-called floxed Atlas, with the usual kerosene type fuel. The specific impulse is expected to be 12 to 18 seconds larger than the normal value with liquid oxygen. If this test is successful, the liquid oxygen-fluorine mixture may well replace liquid oxygen as oxidizer in other rocket motors in which kerosene or hydrogen is the fuel.*

3.37. Some simplification of the problems may perhaps be possible by utilizing a compound of fluorine, instead of elemental fluorine itself, as the oxidizing propellant. Among such compounds are the cryogenic liquids oxygen difluoride (OF_2), tetrafluorohydrazine (N_2F_4), chlorine trifluoride (ClF_3), and perchloryl fluoride (ClO_3F). Of special interest is the combination of oxygen difluoride with diborane. This system is expected to have a specific impulse approximately the same as that of liquid hydrogen-oxygen, but it has the following advantages over the latter. Oxygen difluoride and diborane have similar boiling points, so that they can be readily stored in adjacent tanks in a rocket vehicle. The boiling points of hydrogen and oxygen are substantially different (about 65°C or 120°F), and precautions must be taken to prevent the liquid oxygen from vaporizing the colder liquid hydrogen and the hydrogen from freezing the liquid oxygen. Furthermore, the densities of oxygen difluoride and of diborane are greater than those of hydrogen and oxygen, so that smaller, less massive tanks would be adequate for the same mission.

* The floxed Atlas program was terminated in 1965.

Specific Impulse Values

3.38. Before proceeding to the discussion of other aspects of rocket propulsion, some specific impulse values for various bipropellant systems will be presented. The data in Table 3.2 are theoretical values calculated for a combustion chamber pressure of 1000 pounds per square inch and for an external pressure equal to the atmospheric pressure at sea level. The calculation of the theoretical specific impulse involves the assumption that chemical equilibrium is always attained in the combustion chamber and the nozzle, as the temperature of the gas changes. In an operating rocket, the specific impulse of the propellants depends on the conditions in the combustion chamber and on the external pressure, which becomes negligibly small at high altitudes. Nevertheless, the values given in Table 3.2 are useful as a basis for comparison of the specific impulses of a number of common bipropellant systems.

TABLE 3.2   CALCULATED SPECIFIC IMPULSES AT SEA LEVEL
OF LIQUID BIPROPELLANT SYSTEMS

Oxidizer	Fuel	I_{sp} (seconds)
Oxygen	Hydrogen	390
	RP-1	300
	UDMH	310
	Ethyl alcohol (75%)	280
	Hydyne	305
Fluorine	Hydrogen	410
	RP-1	320
	UDMH	340
IRFNA	RP-1	270
	JP-X*	270
	UDMH	275
	Hydyne	270
Nitrogen tetroxide	UDMH	285
	Hydrazine	290

* JP-X is a mixture of a kerosene fuel with UDMH; it is hypergolic with IRFNA.

3.39. It is seen that the storable, hypergolic systems, such as IRFNA-UDMH, have appreciably lower specific impulses than does the common combination of liquid oxygen with a kerosene-type hydrocarbon, e.g., RP-1, used in several rockets, such as Atlas, first stage of Saturn, etc. Nevertheless, the storable propellants have advantages that make their use preferable in certain circumstances; the restart capability in space, for example, is an important consideration (§ 1.88), as also is their instant readiness.

3.40. The specific impulses of the only two monopropellants of present interest are considerably lower than those of the usual bipropellant systems. The value for hydrogen peroxide (95 percent) is 160 seconds and that for hydrazine is 185 seconds. Hence, monopropellants are employed only in motors of low thrust where simplicity and reliability are the prime considerations.

3.41. According to equation (3.7), the velocity of the gas expelled from a rocket engine is essentially equal to the specific impulse multiplied by the constant g_c, the latter being equal to 32.174 in the pound(force and mass)-foot-second system of units. An average specific impulse of a little over 300 seconds thus corresponds to an exhaust gas velocity of some 10,000 feet (about 2 miles) per second. How this exhaust velocity can be made to propel a rocket to a velocity several times greater will be apparent later (§ 3.109).

The Rocket Engine*

3.42. For liquid propellants, the rocket engine consists of the pumps, feed system, combustion chamber, nozzle, etc. An important part of the engine is the *thrust chamber assembly,* commonly abbreviated to *thrust chamber,* which consists basically of four components: a propellant injector, an ignition system, a combustion chamber, and a nozzle (Fig. 3.1). In brief, the propellants are

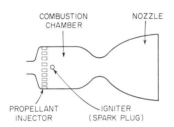

introduced through the injector into the combustion chamber; here the fuel and oxidizer are ignited and thus interact chemically to produce the hot gases which are then exhausted through the nozzle. Compared with the overall dimensions of the rocket vehicle the thrust chamber is quite small, since most of the volume is occupied by the propellant tanks, with some space being taken up by the pumps and other

Fig. 3.1. Simple representation of thrust chamber of a liquid-propellant rocket

components required to transfer the propellants from the tanks to the thrust chamber. The H-1 engine, eight of which are used to provide 1.5 million pounds of thrust in the first stage of the Saturn I rocket vehicle, has a height

---

* There is no generally accepted rocket nomenclature, but the following probably represents the common usage. The term *rocket engine* is used for a liquid-propellant system. For solid propellants, the term *rocket motor* is preferred, although motor is also frequently used for liquid propellants. Some writers use engine to describe solid-propellant rockets, but it is the consensus that this should be avoided, since engine suggests moving parts and there are none in a solid-propellant rocket. Small, low-thrust rockets for attitude control (§ 4.80) are often referred to as *thrustors* (or *thrusters*), and the same term is used to describe the system of low thrust and low thrust-to-mass ratio that make use of electricity as the source of energy (§ 3.178). The word *jet* is often employed in connection with devices operating on the rocket principle in which a compressed gas, e.g., nitrogen, streams through a nozzle.

of a little over 12 feet, but more than half of this is taken up by the nozzle (cf. Fig. 3.17). The propellant tanks, however, are some 60 feet high.

The Injector

3.43. The purpose of the *injector* is to introduce the propellants into the head of the combustion chamber in a form that will insure efficient combustion. The mechanism of the combustion process has been, and still is, the subject of much research but it is not yet completely understood.* Nevertheless, it is generally accepted that the propellants should enter the chamber in the form of a mist of fine droplets in order to favor rapid combustion. Furthermore, in a bipropellant system, the two components must be well mixed in predetermined proportions.

Fig. 3.2.   Injector for 15,000-pound thrust bipropellant rocket

3.44. Many different types of injectors have been designed to achieve these objectives. In essence, an injector consists of a number of small jet orifices through which the propellants are forced under pressure (Fig. 3.2). The liquids leave the orifices as fine sprays which then become intimately mixed. In some cases it is possible to mix the propellants before they are injected into the

* Much more needs to be known, for example, about the causes of various types of combustion instability which are accompanied by vibrations of a more-or-less serious nature. Instability has been a significant problem in some liquid-propellant rocket engines, especially large ones.

combustion chamber, but this may involve a certain element of risk because the mixture could explode.

THE IGNITION SYSTEM

3.45. When starting a rocket engine, the propellant must first be ignited; once ignition has taken place, the heat produced in the combustion reaction will serve to maintain the burning process. The situation is exactly equivalent to igniting a gas flame with a spark, as in the familiar cigarette lighter, or by means of a match flame or pilot light. Hypergolic propellants will, of course, ignite spontaneously upon mixing, so that no special means of ignition is required. But other liquid propellants need an *igniter* to initiate combustion, and several forms have been developed. In certain instances, an electric spark, similar to that produced by an automobile spark plug, is sufficient to ignite the propellant mixture. Another method of ignition is to introduce at startup either an auxiliary liquid which is hypergolic with one of the propellants or a catalyst to facilitate interaction between the two propellants. Some rockets utilize a small charge of pyrotechnic powder that is ignited by an electrically heated wire. The powder burns with a hot flame which then starts the combustion of the propellant mixture.

3.46. If a rocket is intended for variable operation, e.g., if it is to be capable of being stopped and restarted, it may be advantageous to use a *precombustion chamber* to insure ignition when required. Small amounts of fuel and oxidizer are injected into this subsidiary chamber where they are ignited by a spark or other suitable means. The burning gases then enter the combustion chamber and ignite the main propellant mixture. In order to stop the rocket motor, the main propellant supply is cut off, but the burning in the precombustion chamber continues in the same manner as a pilot light. When the main propellant flow is resumed to restart the engine, the mixture is thus ignited immediately.

3.47. When launching large rockets which have clusters of two or more engines in the first stage, e.g., Atlas and Saturn, the vehicle is often held down by powerful clamps until there are definite indications that a condition of stable combustion has been achieved in each of the engines. A possible indicator of this type is the pressure in the combustion chamber. If burning is satisfactory in all the engines, the clamps are released. This will explain why flames are observed to emerge from some rocket engines for a few seconds before actual liftoff occurs.

OXIDIZER-FUEL RATIO

3.48. In order to realize complete combustion of the fuel, the two propellants should be used in definite proportions, called the *stoichiometric ratio;* this ratio can be calculated from the equation expressing the chemical process. Consider, for example, a liquid hydrocarbon (kerosene) fuel having the reasonable average formula C_7H_{16}; complete combustion with oxygen would then be represented by

$$C_7H_{16} + 11\ O_2 = 7\ CO_2 + 8\ H_2O,$$

the products being carbon dioxide (CO_2) and water (H_2O) vapor. From the known atomic weights, it is readily found that 100 parts by mass, e.g., pounds, of the fuel would require 352 pounds of oxygen for complete combustion. The theoretical (stoichiometric) mass ratio of oxidizer to fuel is thus about 3.5 to 1. But in a rocket, the theoretical ratio of the propellants is rarely, if ever, employed. One reason is that the complete combustion implied by the theoretical mass ratio is not attainable in practice.

3.49. It was stated in § 3.19 that the specific impulse is proportional to the square root of $T/\text{M.W.}$, where T, in this case, is the combustion temperature and M.W. is the average molecular weight of the exhaust gases. By varying the proportion of oxidizer to fuel, both the temperature and the average molecular weight will be changed so that the specific impulse will usually increase or decrease.

3.50. It has been found by experiments that, as a general rule, the optimum specific impulse is obtained when the amount of oxidizer is less than the quantity required theoretically to produce complete combustion of the fuel. In the case considered above, for example, the theoretical mass ratio of oxidizer to fuel is 3.5 to 1, but the maximum specific impulse is realized when the ratio is 2.5 to 1. The exhaust gas then contains some unburnt fuel. However, at the very high existing temperature, namely, about 3200°C (5800°F), the hydrocarbon will have split up (or dissociated) into simpler molecules, such as methane (CH_4), ethylene (C_2H_6) and acetylene (C_2H_2), etc., which tend to decrease the average molecular weight of the gas.

3.51. The use of a deficiency of oxidizer or, what is the same thing, an excess of fuel is particularly advantageous when the latter is hydrogen. The presence of unburnt hydrogen molecules (H_2), with a molecular weight of 2.0, in the exhaust gas helps to decrease the average molecular weight. The normal combustion product is water (H_2O), with a molecular weight of 18. Although the combustion temperature is lower when excess hydrogen is used, this is more than compensated by the decrease in average molecular weight of the exhaust gas. The consequent increase in the ratio $T/\text{M.W.}$ means that there is an increase in the specific impulse.

3.52. The combustion temperatures in a rocket are generally so high that the reaction products and other molecules, such as carbon dioxide, water, hydrogen, oxygen, etc., which are normally regarded as being very stable, break down to some extent into simpler molecules, e.g., carbon monoxide (CO), into free radicals, e.g., hydroxyl (OH), and even into atoms, e.g., H and O. As a result of this dissociation, the extent of which depends upon the temperature and pressure of the gases, the average molecular weight of the exhaust gas is often lower than expected from the ordinary chemical formulas, such as CO_2, H_2O, H_2, O_2, etc. But the dissociation process is accompanied by the consumption of heat energy, so that the temperature of the gases is less than would be attained in the absence of dissociation. The advantage of the decrease in molecular weight, as far as specific impulse is concerned, may then be more than offset by the decrease in temperature. As indicated above, experimental procedures are used to determine the conditions required to achieve the optimum specific impulse in a particular rocket engine.

THE COMBUSTION CHAMBER

3.53. Once the propellant mixture is ignited, the heat generated will raise the temperature of the incoming fuel and oxidizer to the point at which they interact. The heat produced by combustion then increases the temperature of more propellant which burns to liberate heat, and so on. As a result, combustion proceeds in a continuous manner. The combustion process is not an instantaneous one; it takes place at a finite rate that increases with increasing temperature. There is a short time delay, therefore, before the propellants heat up to the point at which combustion occurs with the desired rapidity. The *combustion chamber*, shown in Fig. 3.1, provides a volume in which the propellants can vaporize, mix completely, then heat up to the temperature required for rapid combustion.

3.54. The size of the combustion chamber is generally a compromise necessitated by a variety of opposing factors. A long chamber has the advantage of permitting adequate time for the propellants to interact as completely as possible. Furthermore, when the combustion chamber has a large cross section, the gases formed leave the chamber at a low mass velocity; nearly all the combustion energy is then in the form of random kinetic energy of the molecules and this means a higher gas temperature, and a higher specific impulse, than if the gas velocity were high. On the other hand, a large combustion chamber adds considerably to the overall mass (or sea-level weight) of the rocket vehicle, thus decreasing the thrust-to-weight ratio. At the other extreme, if the chamber is too short, the combustion (or burning) process will be incomplete and the temperature attained will be lower than desired.

3.55. Efficient mixing and vaporization of the propellants, by suitable injector design, the use of reactive fuel and oxidizer, and high operating pressures make possible the design of combustion chambers which are large enough to permit effective burning but are not so large as to add excessive mass to the vehicle. As a general rule, chamber pressures are in the range from about 300 to 1000 pounds per square inch, i.e., 20 to 70 atmospheres. The gas temperatures may vary from roughly 2800° to 3300°C, i.e., approximately 5000° to 6000°F. The steps that must be taken to prevent the chamber walls from becoming too hot, and thus losing their physical integrity, also have a bearing on the size; this matter will be considered shortly.

3.56. The shape of the combustion chamber is not critical; it is generally cylindrical, sometimes with a slight taper toward the nozzle end, or spherical (or approximately spherical). An advantage of spherical chambers is that they have a minimum mass for a given volume. They also have a minimum surface area, so that less cooling is required. In addition, for a given wall thickness a spherical (or pseudo-spherical) chamber is stronger than a cylindrical one. On the other hand, spherical chambers require more complicated fabrication procedures and the design of an efficient injector for the propellants is more difficult. Rocket motors manufactured in the United States generally have cylindrical (or slightly tapered) combustion chambers, but the German V-2 rocket had a pseudo-spherical chamber.

3.57. Because they must withstand the high temperatures and pressures of the gaseous reaction products, combustion chambers must be made from materials having substantial strength at elevated temperatures. Almost all materials become less strong as their temperature is raised. Thin walls of high thermal conductivity are desirable to facilitate cooling and also to decrease the overall mass. Obvious considerations in the choice of structural material are ease of fabrication and cost. The foregoing requirements are commonly met by constructing the combustion chamber from a stainless or low-carbon steel or from a suitable aluminum alloy. Many other problems of a strictly engineering nature are also involved in the design of a vessel which operates under such extreme conditions of temperature and pressure. For example, a cryogenic propellant enters the combustion chamber at one end, at a temperature hundreds of degrees below zero, whereas the combustion gases leave at the other end at a temperature of several thousand degrees. Although these aspects of combustion chamber design are of great importance, they lie outside the scope of this book.

THE NOZZLE

3.58. Ideally, the gaseous products should leave the combustion chamber at a low velocity, but they must be exhausted from the rocket motor at high velocity. As a general rule, this increase is achieved by means of a *convergent-divergent nozzle* (cf. Fig. 3.1) ; a picture of such a nozzle for a large rocket motor is shown in Fig. 3.3. It is frequently referred to as a *de Laval nozzle* because it is similar in design to the nozzle invented in 1889 by the Swedish engineer Carl de Laval for use in gas turbines. The purpose of the nozzle is to convert the random heat (or thermal) energy released by the combustion of the propellants into directed energy of motion (or mass kinetic energy) of the exhaust gas. The kinetic energy of any moving body or mass is half the product of the mass and the square of its velocity.* Consequently, a high directed kinetic energy of the exhaust gas means a high exhaust velocity, as required for rocket propulsion.

---

* In mathematical symbols, the kinetic energy of a mass m moving with a velocity v is $\frac{1}{2}mv^2$.

3.59. In the combustion chamber, the gas molecules have a high temperature and consequently a high individual kinetic energy, since the average kinetic

energy of the molecules is proportional to the absolute temperature. But the motion of the gas molecules is completely random; that is to say, the molecules are moving in all directions and these directions are continually changing due to frequent collisions among the molecules. As a result, there is little net (or overall) mass motion in any particular direction. The directed (or mass) kinetic energy of the gas in the combustion chamber is thus, ideally, quite small, although the internal kinetic or thermal energy of the individual molecules is large. In the convergent-divergent nozzle, much of this internal random molecular kinetic energy is converted into directed mass kinetic energy, and hence into directed velocity, of the exhaust gas. Because of this energy conversion, the temperature of the gas leaving the nozzle is less than that entering it from the combustion chamber.

Fig. 3.3.   Rocket engine with bell-shaped de Laval nozzle

3.60. It is now possible to see, in a general qualitative manner, why the exhaust velocity and specific impulse are favored by a high combustion chamber temperature and low average molecular weight of the gases formed. The thermal (or heat) energy content per unit mass of any substance is equal to the product of its absolute temperature and specific heat.* For gases, the specific heat, particularly at high temperatures, is inversely related to the molecular weight, i.e., a gas of low molecular weight has a high specific heat. It is apparent, therefore, that the thermal energy per unit mass of gas in the combustion chamber varies directly as the temperature and inversely as the molecular weight of the gas; thus,

$$\text{Thermal energy per unit mass} = \text{constant} \times \frac{T}{\text{M.W.}}$$

If it is assumed that a definite fraction of the thermal energy is converted into directed (or mass) kinetic energy of the exhaust gas in the convergent-divergent nozzle, it follows that the directed kinetic energy per unit mass is proportional to $T/\text{M.W.}$ In view of the definition in § 3.58, footnote, the kinetic energy per unit mass of exhaust gas is equal to the half of the velocity squared; hence, the exhaust velocity, v_e, is given by

---

* The specific heat of any material is the quantity of heat, usually expressed in calories or British thermal units (Btu), required to raise the temperature of unit mass by one degree.

$$v_e = \text{constant} \times \sqrt{\frac{T}{\text{M.W.}}},$$

in agreement with equation (3.8).*

3.61. For a properly designed convergent-divergent nozzle, it is predicted by theory and confirmed by experiment that there is a steady decrease in pressure and temperature, from the values in the combustion chamber to those in the exhausted gas. At the same time the directed velocity of the gas passing through the nozzle increases continuously. At the throat of the nozzle, where the cross-sectional area has a minimum value, the velocity of the gas is equal to the velocity of sound in the gas at the existing temperature and pressure. In other words, the *Mach number*, i.e., the ratio of the gas velocity to the velocity of sound, is exactly unity. It should be noted that the velocity of sound in a gas is proportional to the square root of the absolute temperature of the gas, and at the throat of the nozzle the velocity of sound may be three (or more) times as high as at normal temperatures. In the divergent portion of the nozzle, the gas velocity exceeds that of sound; that is to say, the velocity is supersonic and the Mach number is greater than unity. The actual value of the exhaust velocity, under ideal conditions, is determined by the specific impulse, i.e., by the nature of the propellants and the operating conditions of the rocket engine.

3.62. To obtain maximum efficiency, the nozzle should be designed so that the pressure of the exhaust gas at the discharge end is equal to the pressure of the surrounding atmosphere. Of course, for a rocket that is launched into space from Earth's surface, it is possible to realize this condition at only a single altitude when the exhaust gas pressure remains almost constant but that of the atmosphere is continually decreasing. The choice of the design

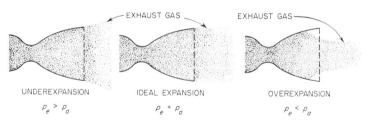

EXHAUST GAS   EXHAUST GAS

UNDEREXPANSION   IDEAL EXPANSION   OVEREXPANSION

$p_e > p_a$ $p_e = p_a$ $p_e < p_a$

FIG. 3.4.   Expansion of exhaust gas in rocket nozzle

pressure will be explained presently, but first it is necessary to consider what happens when the exhaust gas pressure differs from the outside pressure.

3.63. If the divergent part of the nozzle is not long enough for the particular operating conditions, the exhaust gas is said to be *underexpanded* (Fig. 3.4). The exhaust pressure, p_e, is then greater than that of the ambient atmosphere, p_a, and the exhaust gas velocity is less than the theoretical maximum value. There

* For a more precise method of derivation, see § 3.267.

is some compensation in the total thrust of the rocket, as indicated by equation (3.1), since $p_e - p_a$ is positive. On the other hand, if the divergent region is too long and the pressure in the nozzle falls below the ambient value, the exhaust gas is said to be *overexpanded*. If the exhaust pressure is considerably lower than the ambient pressure, a sharp pressure front, i.e., a shock wave, can develop; this generally occurs when p_e/p_a is less than about 0.25 to 0.4, depending on the circumstances. The exhaust gas then separates from the walls of the nozzle and energy is wasted in useless processes, e.g., the formation of gas vortices and turbulent motion. The result is a decrease in efficiency and the exhaust velocity is lower than for ideal expansion, i.e., when p_e is equal to p_a.

3.64. Both underexpansion and overexpansion are undesirable situations, but the latter is to be preferred to the former. Consequently, a rocket system which is to operate over a range of altitudes is usually designed so that the exhaust gas is overexpanded, i.e., p_e is less than p_a, at sea level, but is slightly underexpanded, i.e., p_e is a little larger than p_a, at high altitudes. When the rocket ascends, the ambient pressure, p_a, decreases, but the exhaust pressure, p_e, remains essentially unchanged.* Hence, the exhaust gas can be overexpanded at sea level but underexpanded at high altitudes. Many rockets consist of several stages which ignite successively at increasingly higher altitudes (§ 3.116 *et seq.*). The nozzle for each stage is then designed to give the best efficiency at the appropriate altitude.

3.65. In designing a nozzle for a particular rocket engine, the cross-sectional area of the combustion chamber is first selected on the basis of the considerations in § 3.54. This area may be taken as equal to the entrance area of the convergent part of the nozzle, since it is attached directly to the combustion chamber (cf. Fig. 3.1). The next step is to calculate the throat area and this is commonly determined by the chamber pressure and the desired thrust level of the rocket engine. Finally, the exit area of the divergent portion of the nozzle is calculated by prescribing the exhaust gas design pressure, as indicated above. The ratio of the exit area to that at the throat, i.e., the *expansion ratio,* is largely dependent on the ratio of the exhaust pressure, p_e, to the pressure, p_0, in the combustion chamber. A low value of p_e/p_0, resulting from low exhaust pressures, e.g., for high-altitude applications, or high chamber pressure, requires the exit area to be large relative to the throat area. Typically, the cross-sectional area at the exit of a convergent-divergent nozzle might be about 5 to 10 times the cross section at the throat for low levels up to around 50 or so for high altitudes.

3.66. With the three basic cross-sectional areas, i.e., at entrance, throat, and exit, of the nozzle known, the next step is to decide on the lengths and contours (or shapes) of the convergent and divergent portions. The design of the con-

---

* This condition is true for the conventional convergent-divergent (de Laval) nozzle, but in some experimental nozzles of unusual design, the exhaust pressure adjusts itself to the ambient pressure (§ 3.69).

vergent section is not critical, and it is usually relatively short. The divergent portion of the nozzle, however, requires more careful attention. When the divergence angle at the throat is large, the length is short; the weight of the nozzle is then relatively small and, in addition, energy losses from the gas due to friction at the walls are minimized. But if the angle is too large, significant energy losses can occur. For example, the gas may acquire an appreciable component of motion in the radial (or sideways) direction; the associated radial kinetic energy is useless for rocket propulsion since it is at right angles to the main direction of gas motion. Moreover, the flowing gas may separate from the nozzle wall, as it does when considerably overexpanded, and this is also a source of loss of efficiency.

3.67. To simplify fabrication, nozzles have frequently been made with straight-sided walls, so that they have a conical form. Tests made with such nozzles indicate that the divergence angle at the throat should be roughly between 30 and 40 deg for maximum efficiency. However, simple conical nozzles are inclined to be long, especially when the chamber and exhaust pressures are such as to require a large value of the exit-to-throat area ratio. To decrease the length while maintaining a high efficiency, nozzles having a bell-like shape are now commonly employed (Fig. 3.3).

3.68. As noted earlier, the conventional convergent-divergent nozzle suffers from the drawback that the exhaust gas pressure is unaffected by the ambient pressure, so that overexpansion or underexpansion may occur with changing altitude. In nozzles of a different type under development this difficulty is overcome, so that high efficiency is possible at all altitudes. The basic difference in principle between the conventional nozzles and the newer ones is that, in the former, the combustion gases always travel in the axial direction, i.e., in the direction of propulsion. In the novel designs, however, the gas has initially a component in the radial direction, but the nozzle gradually changes the flow direction so that it becomes parallel to the axis.

3.69. In the *plug-type nozzle*, shown in section in Fig. 3.5, the combustion chamber has an annular (or toroidal) form and the gases flow out through an annular throat surrounding a conical "plug." As they emerge from the throat the gases have a radial component inward, as shown by the arrows in the figure. The design of the plug is such as to change the direction of gas flow during expansion so that, at the exit, it is entirely in the axial direction. The expansion of the exhaust gas is determined by the ambient pressure, and there is consequently no overexpansion or underexpansion. For the same performance, a plug-type nozzle is considerably shorter than a conventional conical (straight-sided) nozzle. A further decrease in length can be achieved if the plug has a bell-shaped contour; this is known as a *spike-type nozzle*.

3.70. A similar principle is involved in the *expansion-deflection type nozzle* depicted in Fig. 3.6, which is, in a sense, a cross between conventional and spike-type nozzles. The combustion chamber is annular, but it has a smaller radius than for the plug or spike-type nozzles. Here also, the annular throat is designed to give the combustion gases a radial motion which is deflected into the axial direction by the bell-shaped nozzle. As in the cases considered above, the expansion is dependent only on the ambient pressure. The length of the ex-

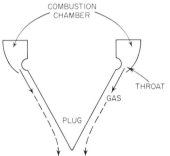

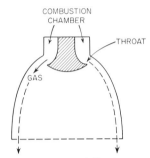

FIG. 3.5.   Plug-type nozzle   FIG. 3.6.   Expansion-deflection type nozzle

pansion-deflection type nozzle is about the same as for a spike-type nozzle of equal performance.

3.71. The annular (or toroidal) combustion chambers depicted in Figs. 3.5 and 3.6 are completely novel in rocket propulsion and will require considerable development work. In the meantime, it is proposed to test the modified nozzle concepts by arranging a number, e.g., ten or more, of smaller chambers of the common cylindrical form in a symmetrical manner around a toroidal duct. The combined gases are then exhausted from this duct through one of the nozzles described above (Fig. 3.7).

Thrust Chamber Cooling

3.72. Because of the very high temperatures generated in the combustion chamber, it is inevitable that a significant amount of heat is transferred to the walls. Unless special precautions are taken, there is a danger that, at the high pressures of several hundred pounds per square inch developed in the combustion chamber, the latter may burst after a short period of operation. In relatively small rockets that do not operate at very high temperatures, the interior walls of the combustion chamber and nozzle are lined with a heat-resistant (refractory) ceramic material. The ceramic gets hot but, being a poor conductor of heat, it prevents the metal walls of the motor from becoming overheated during the short operating period. For the large rockets used in many aspects of space exploration, however, this procedure is not adequate and steps are taken to provide some means of removing heat from the walls of the thrust chamber.

3.73. The most common technique employed in cooling thrust chambers, especially of large rockets, is the method of *regenerative cooling*. By providing appropriate cooling jackets, one of the propellants is circulated around the combustion chamber and nozzle before it enters the injector. The propellant removes heat from the walls, so that the temperatures do not become excessively high. At the same time, the temperature of the propellant is raised, with the result that it vaporizes more readily upon injection into the combustion chamber.

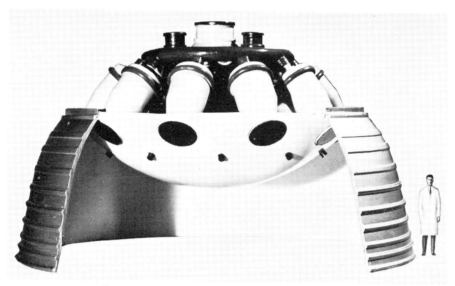

FIG. 3.7.　Model of multichamber rocket system

A cryogenic liquid, e.g., hydrogen, is sometimes used for regenerative cooling, in which case there is some conversion of the liquid into gas.

3.74. In the method of *film cooling,* some of the liquid propellant is forced through small holes, commonly at the periphery of the injector, so as to form a film of liquid on the interior surface of the combustion chamber. The film has a low thermal (or heat) conductivity and protects the wall material from the hot combustion gases. Moreover, a certain amount of cooling results from vaporization of the liquid film. Film cooling is particularly useful in regions where the walls tend to become exceptionally hot, e.g., in the vicinity of the nozzle throat.

3.75. Another technique, which bears a resemblance to film cooling, is called *transpiration cooling;* it is also sometimes referred to as evaporative cooling or, more commonly, as sweat cooling. The combustion chamber has a double-walled construction, the inside wall being made of a porous material. Propellant is circulated through the space between the walls and some of the liquid seeps continuously through the pores into the chamber. Here it forms a film which is rapidly vaporized. The film provides some protection but most of the cooling is due to the heat absorbed in converting the liquid into vapor, i.e., to the latent heat of vaporization of the liquid. The difficulty of fabricating chamber walls having the proper uniform degree of porosity and of maintaining a steady flow of liquid through the pores are drawbacks to the method of cooling by transpiration. A special form of transpiration cooling has been developed especially for use in the nozzle throat region of solid-propellant rockets, but there is no reason why it cannot be utilized in liquid-propellant systems (§ 3.94).

3.76. Because they have a tendency to decompose as the temperature is raised, hypergolic propellants are not particularly suited for use in the common cooling procedures. Alternative methods that have been proposed are cooling by ablation, by charring, and by radiation. In *ablation cooling*,* the interior of the thrust chamber is lined with the ablative material, consisting typically of a siliceous, e.g., glass fiber, or graphitic substance imbedded in a matrix of a synthetic organic polymer resin. When the surface of the material is heated, it chars, melts, and vaporizes (cf. § 13.9). The heat absorbed in these processes prevents the temperature from becoming excessively high. Furthermore, the charred material serves as an insulator and protects the rocket case from becoming too hot. In some instances, charring of an organic material alone can apparently prevent overheating of the case.

3.77. In *radiation cooling*, the interior of the rocket chamber is covered with a refractory material, such as graphite, particularly in the form of pyrographite, or a high-melting-point metal, e.g., tungsten, tantalum, molybdenum, or one of their alloys. Cooling then occurs by heat loss as radiation; the rate of loss varies as the fourth power of the absolute temperature (§ 6.35) and so it becomes increasingly significant as the temperature rises. Radiation cooling can thus set an upper limit to the temperature attained by the walls of the thrust chamber.

THE FEED SYSTEM

3.78. An important component of a rocket engine is the *feed system* for transferring propellants from the storage tanks to the thrust chamber at the required rate. It was seen in § 3.16 that the total thrust of a rocket is the product of the specific impulse of the propellant system and the rate of propellant consumption. Hence, in a given rocket, the magnitude of the propellant flow determines the thrust generated. Regulation of the flow rate thus provides a means of varying the thrust. The foregoing arguments are based on the tacit assumption that the rate at which the propellants burn is virtually the same as that at which they enter the combustion chamber. This is essentially true, in general, within the limitation of the considerations in § 3.48, *et seq.*

3.79. Perhaps the simplest form of feed system is the *pressure-fed type*. A gas maintained at a moderate pressure, above the liquid surface in the propellant tank, forces the liquid from the tank, through the cooling system, and on to the injector of the thrust chamber (Fig. 3.8). A pressure regulator in the gas line is used to maintain the propellant flow rate corresponding to the design

* The dictionary meaning of "to ablate" is to remove or carry away.

value of the thrust. The gas employed is generally helium or nitrogen which does not interact chemically with the propellant.

3.80. For the high-thrust rockets required for launching heavy satellites and space probes, *pump-fed systems* are employed. In order to sustain the very high propellant flow rates, e.g., up to several thousand pounds per second (§ 3.17), relatively high gas pressures would have to be used in a pressure-fed system. The propellant tanks would thus have to be thick-walled and, consequently, have a large mass to withstand the pressure. It is then more economical from the mass standpoint to use pumps to transfer the propellants to the thrust chamber. The pumps are driven by a turbine which obtains its power from a hot gas and the combination is known as a *turbo-pump system*. The turbine is similar in principle to the conventional gas turbine, such as is used in aircraft, in industry, and for various marine pur-

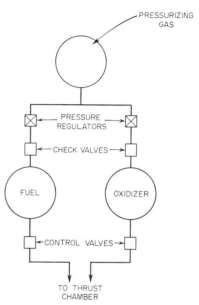

FIG. 3.8. Schematic representation of pressure-fed system

poses. The hot gas required to operate the turbine can be generated in various ways. In the rocket engine used in the V-2 weapon, for example, the turbine gas was obtained by the chemical decomposition of concentrated hydrogen peroxide (§ 1.81).

3.81. The most general procedure for producing the turbine gas, especially for large rockets, is to employ a small subsidiary chamber in which hot gas is generated by combustion of the rocket propellants (Fig. 3.9). Small quantities of the fuel and oxidizer, in proportions different from those employed in the rocket motor, are fed into the gas generator. Here combustion occurs with the formation of hot gas, at a temperature of about 650° to 1000°C (1200° to 1800°F), suitable for driving a turbine. To start the gas generator, in the first place, a pressure-fed system, at fairly low pressure, can be used to introduce the propellants.

3.82. Once the rocket is operating, other schemes can be utilized to provide the gas for driving the turbines. For example, in the "bleed" system, hot gas, which may be cooled to some extent, is bled off from the combustion chamber. In rockets that are regeneratively-cooled with liquid hydrogen, the "topping" system may be used. Some of the high-pressure gas produced when the hydrogen is heated is drawn off to operate the turbines; it then passes, at a lower pressure, to the combustion chamber.

3.83. The propellant pumps are usually of the centrifugal type because they are relatively light in weight and occupy little space. An impeller rotating at high speed discharges the liquid from the pump at the required pressure. Since it is invariably necessary for the fuel and oxidizer to be supplied to the thrust

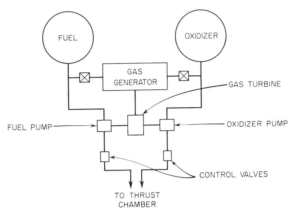

FIG. 3.9. Schematic representation of pump-fed system with separate gas generator for turbine

chamber in different amounts, separate pumps and turbines are often used for the two propellants. In some cases, however, it is possible to operate pumps of different capacities by means of a single turbine.

CHEMICAL ROCKETS: SOLID PROPELLANTS

INTRODUCTION

3.84. Rockets employing solid propellants are inherently simple, since they require no turbopumps or complex feed system. The propellant is contained within the combustion chamber and the only other components of the rocket motor are the igniter and the convergent-divergent nozzle. Although solid-propellant rockets of small and moderate sizes are extensively employed for various purposes in both civilian and military space programs, most of the large rockets of high thrust have utilized liquid propellants. This situation is the result of historical circumstances, and not because there is any fundamental drawback to solid-propellant rockets of large size. The interest in liquid propellants arose during the 1920's and 1930's because the solid propellants available at the time had such low specific impulses. Thus, the black powder (or gunpowder) in common use as a rocket propellant before 1940 had a specific impulse of about 140 seconds, at best. Consequently, the V-2, the first large rocket, was designed for liquid propellants and the latter were also employed in the earliest U.S. rocket vehicles for ballistic missiles, e.g., Redstone, Jupiter, Thor, and Atlas.

3.85. For military purposes, solid-propellant rockets have the great advantage of transportability and of being ready for immediate use, and with the discovery of improved solid propellants, effort was devoted to the successful production of such long-range missiles as Polaris and Minuteman. The experience thus gained in the fabrication and handling of solid-propellant motors of large dimensions has led to the construction of rockets with diameters up to 156 inches (13 feet). Motors of this size have been fired for periods up to 150 seconds, producing an average thrust of over a million pounds. An indication of future possibilities is provided by existing plans for investigating the feasibility of fabricating a motor 260 inches (21 feet 8 inches) in diameter and 120 feet long, capable of yielding 6 million pounds of thrust.

SOLID PROPELLANT TYPES

3.86. Before 1940, black powder was almost the only solid propellant employed in rockets. Some experiments with smokeless powders based on cellulose nitrate (nitrocellulose, nitro-cotton, or gun cotton) and glyceryl trinitrate (nitroglycerine) had been made by R. H. Goddard (§ 1.58) in the United States in 1918 and by F. W. Sander (§ 1.87, footnote) in Germany around 1935, but the results did not appear to be very promising. It was not until World War II that successful solid propellants of the smokeless powder type were produced. Since that time, considerable progress has been made in the development of new types of solid propellants, such as those described in § 1.85. The most important solid propellants now in general use fall into three classes: the first is the so-called double-base type related to the smokeless powders; the second is the composite type consisting of an inorganic salt as oxidizer suspended in a matrix of organic fuel, generally mixed with a finely divided metal; and the third is the composite double-base type which is essentially a combination of the other two.

3.87. *Double-base propellants* consist mainly of nitrocellulose and a gelatinizer, such as nitroglycerine or a similar chemical compound, e.g., ethylene glycol dinitrate.* Small proportions of various additives are included to provide stability during storage, to improve the burning characteristics, to facilitate fabrication, and so on. Each of the two main constituents of a double-base propellant may be regarded as possessing within itself the properties of both fuel and oxidizer. In principle, therefore, either could be used alone as a propellant, although the gelatinizer is a liquid. But the combination actually

---

* The term "double base" originated from the application of these mixtures as gun propellants; it was used to distinguish them from the "single base" smokeless powders which utilized either nitrocellulose (gun cotton) or nitroglycerine singly as the active constituent.

employed exhibits more desirable physical and burning behavior than does either component alone.

3.88. For use as a rocket propellant, the gelatinized mixture of the proper composition is either cast or extruded through a die to produce the desired size and shape. This mass of propellant is referred to as the *grain*. Upon ignition, the nitrates of cellulose and glycerol (or ethylene glycol) burn rapidly, even in the absence of air, liberating large quantities of high-temperature gases. These gases are a complex mixture of nitrogen, water vapor, and oxides of nitrogen and carbon, all consisting of elements of low atomic weight. Passage of the hot gas through a convergent-divergent nozzle produces the thrust for rocket propulsion.

3.89. Propellants of the *composite type*, containing separate fuel and oxidizer intimately mixed, are now replacing the simple double-base propellants to a considerable extent. The organic fuel material is initially in liquid (or semi-liquid) form that can set to a solid; among the earliest substances used were asphalt and various synthetic rubbers. Synthetic plastics (or resins) of several different types are now employed as the fuel; these include polyurethanes and polybutadienes and copolymers of these substances with acrylic nitrile or acrylic acid. The combination known as PBAA (polybutadiene-acrylic acid) appears to be a very promising material. The most common oxidizers are ammonium and potassium nitrates (NH_4NO_3 and KNO_3) and ammonium and potassium perchlorates (NH_4ClO_4 and $KClO_4$). These are all solid salts which are ground to a fine powder and mixed, together with appropriate additives, with the fuel in liquid form; after suitable treatment, the whole sets to a plastic (or semi-plastic) solid mass. As with double-base propellants, this is called the grain. In the formulation of most composite propellants, a light element, especially aluminum, as a finely divided powder, is added to provide a higher combustion temperature and thus increase the specific impulse. Other possible additives of the same type are lithium, boron, beryllium, magnesium, and some of their compounds.

3.90. The *composite double-base propellants* represent a combination of the double-base and composite types. They consist of a perchlorate and aluminum powder suspended in a matrix of nitrocellulose and nitroglycerine.

3.91. Currently, solid propellants with specific impulses of 245 seconds are being manufactured, and higher values may be expected in the future. The specific impulses of even the better solid propellants are, however, still below the values for the common bipropellant liquid systems. The higher density of the solids and the greater simplicity of the rocket motor may nevertheless offset the drawback of lower specific impulse.

MOTOR DESIGN

3.92. In a solid-propellant rocket, the propellant container is also the combustion chamber and the addition of an igniter and a nozzle completes the rocket motor. Because there is no simple way of cooling the motor, such as is possible with a liquid propellant, provision is made for protecting the nozzle. It is in the region of the throat, where the conditions are most severe owing to the high temperature and high gas velocity, that protection is particularly necessary. The convergent-divergent form of the nozzle is generally achieved by means of a shaped insert of a suitable material. By proper choice of this material, it is possible to keep the throat sufficiently cool to prevent significant damage during the operating time of the rocket motor.

3.93. A common approach is to make the insert from a refractory substance, such as pyrographite, tungsten (or a tungsten alloy), or a ceramic, which can withstand high temperatures. Cooling then occurs as a result of heat loss by radiation. Another procedure is to utilize an ablative material for the insert. Tests have shown that the small change in cross section of the throat of a solid-propellant rocket nozzle due to ablation does not have any important effect on the operating characteristics of the motor.

3.94. A form of transpiration cooling has been achieved by means of a porous tungsten structure containing a metal of moderately low melting (and boiling) point, e.g., copper, lead, or silver, infiltrated into the pores. The throat of the Polaris missile motor nozzle is constructed in this manner, using silver. When the temperature gets sufficiently high, the infiltrated metal, which constitutes about 20 percent of the volume of the tungsten, melts and vaporizes; the absorption of the latent heats of fusion and vaporization serves to prevent overheating.

3.95. Two simple designs of solid-propellant rocket motors are depicted in Fig. 3.10, I and II; in the first, the grain is in the form of a solid cylinder, whereas in the second there is a channel down the whole length of the central axis. The inner wall of the motor case is coated with a *liner* which serves a dual purpose. It provides a good bond between the grain and the case, to prevent combustion from spreading along the walls, and it also acts as a thermal insulator. The *igniter*, not shown in the figures, usually consists of a small quantity of a sensitive pyrotechnic powder, the primer, in which is imbedded a wire that can be heated electrically. The primer is surrounded by the main igniter charge. Upon passing

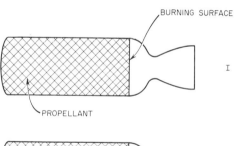

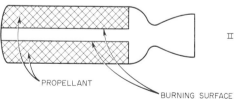

Fig. 3.10. Solid-propellant rockets with end-burning (I) and internally-burning (II) grains

an electric current through the wire, the primer burns rapidly and ignites the main powder charge; this in turn ignites the propellant. The location of the igniter depends on the particular design of the grain.

BURNING CHARACTERISTICS

3.96. The solid propellant burns only where it has an exposed surface. In Fig. 3.10, I the only such surface is at the end near the nozzle; the grain is therefore described as being *end-burning*. As burning progresses, the exposed surface recedes down the combustion chamber, but its area remains essentially constant. In the *internal-burning* grain, shown in Fig. 3.10, II, the end is protected by means of an *inhibitor;* burning now occurs outward from the central channel extending along the whole length of the propellant. Ignition in this system is initiated at the far end of the grain, i.e., at the end opposite to the nozzle. If the central channel has a circular cross section, the burning process will be accompanied by a continuous enlargement of the exposed area. By special shaping of the interior channel of the internal-burning grain, however, this increase in area can be avoided (§ 3.99).

3.97. As is the case with rockets in general, the thrust produced by a solid-propellant motor is proportional to the rate of consumption (or burning) of the propellant. For a given grain, the burning rate is directly related to the exposed burning area. The thrust of the rocket motor will thus vary if this area changes during operation. A rocket in which the exposed area and, hence, the thrust increase with the burning time is said to exhibit *progressive burning;* if, on the other hand, the area and the thrust decrease, the characteristics are those of *regressive burning.* When the burning area and thrust remain virtually unchanged over the operating time of the rocket motor, *neutral burning* is said to occur. The nearest approach to neutral burning is realized in an end-burning rocket.

3.98. In most situations, it is desirable to maintain the rocket thrust almost constant; the simplest way to achieve this would appear to be to utilize an end-burning design. But such a motor has the great drawback of exposing the walls of the combustion chamber to the hot gases as the end of the grain recedes. Furthermore, the burning area is relatively small, so that the rate of burning and the thrust will be low. With internal-burning grains, however, the still unburned solid propellant acts as a heat insulator and protects the walls of the combustion chamber. In addition, it is possible for the grain to have a fairly large burning area, thereby increasing the thrust.

3.99. The general practice, therefore, in large solid-propellant rockets is to employ an internal-burning system with the central channel specially shaped to minimize the change in area during burning. One of the most common is the star-shaped channel shown in Fig. 3.11, which has approximately neutral burning characteristics. The large burning surface of such a grain is an added advantage.

3.100. The overall rate of propellant burning, which multiplied by the specific impulse gives the rocket thrust, is dependent upon the density of the grain and the pressure in the combustion chamber as well as on the exposed burning area. High grain density and high gas pressure, up to a point, both enhance the total thrust. If the combustion chamber pressure is too high, controlled burning is difficult to sustain and an explosion may result; on the other hand, if the pressure is too low the burning is unsteady. The actual operating pressure is determined by the nature of the propellant material and by the design of the grain. As a general rule, the chamber pressures are in the range of about 500 to 700 pounds per square inch, although lower and higher pressures are not uncommon.

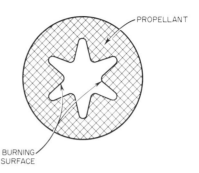

FIG. 3.11.   Star-shaped channel of solid-propellant rocket motor

3.101. If properly designed to prevent access of hot gases, the walls of the combustion chamber of a solid-propellant rocket do not become excessively hot. The motor case must be able, nevertheless, to withstand the high pressures existing in the interior. High-strength steel of moderate wall thickness has been used to fabricate cases of relatively low mass. Advantage is being taken in this connection of the development of the new maraging (or mar-aging) steels containing 18 percent of nickel and smaller proportions of cobalt (about 8 percent) and molybdenum (about 5 percent) but very little carbon. These steels have an iron-nickel martensite structure and are hardened by aging for a few hours at a moderate temperature, in the vicinity of 900°F (480°C).

3.102. Other developments in case design are based on the use of alloys of the strong, lightweight metal tantalum or of epoxy (or similar) synthetic resins strengthened by glass fibers (or filaments). The latter are drawn through a bath of liquid resin and then wound on a mandrel of the required dimensions. When the desired case thickness is attained, the mandrel is removed from the interior. The resulting rocket cases are both strong and light in weight. They require no special thermal insulation since the glass fiber is itself a poor conductor of heat.

3.103. Grains of double-base propellants were originally produced by extrusion into the desired shape but they are now commonly cast directly into the case. Composite propellant grains are also fabricated by casting, thus making possible the *case-bonded* design. The propellant mixture is poured into the case in a semi-liquid form and is allowed to cure, i.e., solidify, in place. When it is set, the grain adheres to the case and there is no gap into which the hot gases can penetrate. The interior of the case is usually lined with an inert material which facilitates adhesion (bonding) of the grain and also serves as a thermal insulator. To provide a central channel of the desired shape, an internal mandrel is inserted prior to casting and is withdrawn when the grain has set. The casting technique lends itself readily to the fabrication of large grains. When very large solid-propellant grains are required, the material may be made in segments of convenient length which are then assembled one on top of another.

3.104. The properties of the grain are sensitive to storage and to temperature. At low ambient temperature, for example, combustion starts slowly and the maximum thrust is lower than it is at normal temperature, although the burning time is increased. To insure reproducible behavior, solid-propellant rockets must be kept within a prescribed temperature range before firing. Some grains deteriorate in storage and their characteristics change as a result of slow chemical reaction or the absorption of moisture.

Thrust Variation and Termination

3.105. The thrust of a liquid-propellant rocket can be varied, to some extent, by adjusting the rates of flow of the liquids. But this is not feasible with solid-propellant motors. In some designs, a predetermined thrust variation is achieved by building the grain in layers having different burning characteristics. A change in the prescribed burning program is difficult, however; one possibility is to permit controlled venting of the combustion gases through suitable openings. To extinguish the burning solid propellant with the possibility of restarting, it has been proposed to use a burst of inert gas or vapor at high pressure, e.g., by injecting an inert liquid (water) into the combustion chamber. At a later time, burning can be reinitiated by means of an igniter or, better, a hypergolic liquid.

3.106. Several methods have been proposed for terminating the thrust of a solid-propellant rocket; these include venting of the hot gas through openings in such a manner as to produce no thrust or perhaps a thrust in the reverse direction, ejection of the nozzle, and even complete destruction of the combustion chamber. Another possibility, mentioned above, is the injection of an inert liquid which is rapidly converted into a pulse of high-pressure vapor that terminates the burning process.

Hybrid Propellants

3.107. Some effort is being devoted to the development of *hybrid-propellant rockets* which, it is hoped, might combine some of the favorable aspects of both liquid- and solid-propellant systems. In the hybrid rocket, a solid fuel is used in conjunction with a liquid oxidizer to form a hypergolic propellant combination. The reverse arrangement, i.e., liquid fuel and solid oxidizer, is possible, but the specific impulses are lower for the more convenient systems. The solid fuel may be of the same type as in composite solid propellants, e.g., a polymer containing aluminum powder, or it may be a more exotic material, such as a hydride of a light element. Among the liquid oxidizers under consideration are hydrogen peroxide, oxygen, fluorine, oxygen difluoride, nitrogen tetrafluoride, and chlorine trifluoride. These possible propellant systems have high specific impulses, some in the range of 350 to 400 seconds.

3.108. Hybrid propellant rockets appear to have several advantages. For example, it is necessary to store and pump only a single liquid. Burning can be stopped instantaneously by cutting off the flow of the oxidizer, and since the propellant system is hypergolic, restarting is achieved by resuming the flow. Furthermore, the thrust can be varied by changing the flow rate. As seen above, the specific impulses that might be attained with solid fuels and liquid oxidizers would approach the values for the better liquid bipropellant systems.

GENERAL ROCKET CHARACTERISTICS

THE ROCKET EQUATION

3.109. Since very high velocities are an essential requirement for space flight, it is of interest to consider the maximum velocity that can be realized by means of a particular rocket vehicle. Because of the continuous thrust of the motor, the speed of the vehicle increases steadily and reaches a maximum when the propellant is consumed; this velocity is, therefore, known as the *burnout velocity*, represented by v_b. It is related to the gas exhaust velocity, v_e, by a theoretical expression, called the *rocket equation*, first derived by K. E. Tsiolkovsky (§ 1.53),[*] namely,

$$v_b = v_e \ln \frac{M}{M_b} \tag{3.9}$$

$$= 2.30 v_e \log \frac{M}{M_b}, \tag{3.10}$$

where M is the total mass of the rocket vehicle when it is launched, i.e., at liftoff, and M_b is the mass remaining when burnout occurs; the symbol "ln" refers to the natural logarithm, i.e., the logarithm to the base e, whereas "log" is the common logarithm to the base 10. The relationships are sometimes written in the following alternative forms:

$$\frac{M}{M_b} = e^{v_b/v_e} \tag{3.11}$$

$$= 10^{v_b/2.30 v_e} = \text{antilog} \frac{v_b}{2.30 v_e}, \tag{3.12}$$

[*] For a method of derivation, see § 3.266.

where "antilog" implies the common antilogarithm found in the familiar tables and slide rules. In the foregoing equations, the effects of gravity and of aerodynamic drag in decreasing the burnout velocity have been ignored. These matters will be considered later, but for the present purpose they are not important.

3.110. The mission for which a rocket vehicle is to be used determines the magnitude of the desired burnout velocity and the exhaust velocity depends essentially on the nature of the propellants. If these quantities are prescribed, the *vehicle mass ratio, M/M_b*, can be calculated from the equations given above. Whether this mass ratio is a practical one or not for the specified mission depends on various circumstances.

3.111. Consider, for example, a liquid oxygen-kerosene engine of the type in common use in the U.S. space program, but consisting of a single stage only; that is to say, during the launch period there is no loss of mass other than that of the propellants consumed and exhausted through the nozzle. The average specific impulse of such a system under practical conditions may be taken as approximately 280 seconds; hence, by equation (3.7), the exhaust gas velocity, v_e, is roughly 280 × 32, i.e., approximately 9000 feet per second. Suppose the rocket is to be used to launch a satellite into Earth orbit at an altitude of 200 miles; the required injection velocity is about 25,000 feet per second (17,250 miles per hour), which may be set equal to v_b, the burnout velocity of the rocket motor. For this particular mission, therefore, v_b/v_e is 25,000/9000, i.e., approximately 2.79; this value is close enough for the subsequent calculation. The vehicle mass ratio can now be obtained from any of the expressions in § 3.109; for example, by equation (3.12),

$$\frac{M}{M_b} = \text{antilog} \frac{2.79}{2.30}$$

$$= \text{antilog } 1.21 = 13.2.$$

The mass ratio in this particular instance would thus be about 13.2.

3.112. The decrease in mass between liftoff and burnout is simply due to the consumption of propellant during flight; consequently, the mass of propellant is $M - M_b$. The fraction which the propellant constitutes of the total liftoff (or launch) mass, i.e., *the propellant mass ratio*, is then $(M - M_b)/M$; hence, if the propellant mass is represented by M_p,

$$\frac{M_p}{M} = \frac{M - M_b}{M} = 1 - \frac{M_b}{M}.$$

Thus, a high vehicle mass ratio implies a high propellant mass ratio. In the case under consideration, M_b/M is 1/13.2, i.e., 0.076; hence,

$$\frac{M_p}{M} = 1 - 0.076 = 0.924 \text{ (or 92.4 percent)},$$

which means that the propellant mass would have to represent **92.4** percent of the total mass of the vehicle when it is launched. Thus, only **7.6** percent of the mass would be available for the rocket motor and associated equipment, e.g., turbopumps, propellant tanks, etc., and all structural components, in addition to the payload, i.e., the useful load that the vehicle can carry into orbit.

3.113. It is doubtful if a liquid-bipropellant rocket could be constructed in which the mass of the structure and equipment is less than about **10** percent of that of the propellants. Since only **7.6** percent is available in the present case, it is evident that the launch vehicle would not be suitable for the given mission. In the best solid-propellant motors, the structure has been reduced to **5** percent of the propellant mass, but the lower specific impulse would make the propellant ratio larger than **0.924**. Hence, in this case also, the mission would not be possible.

3.114. One way out of the difficulty is to make use of propellants of higher specific impulse. The exhaust velocity is thereby increased and a smaller propellant mass ratio would be required for a particular mission. This represents one of the important benefits to be gained from the employment of a propellant system having a high specific impulse. Because a lower rate of propellant consumption is needed to produce a particular thrust, a given burnout velocity can be obtained with a smaller mass of propellant than would be the case for a system with a lower specific impulse. The mission can then be realized with a lower propellant (and vehicle) mass ratio, thus making available a larger portion of the total mass for structure, components, and, in particular, payload.

3.115. For purposes of illustration, consider the liquid hydrogen-oxygen system with an average specific impulse under operational conditions of roughly 370 seconds. The corresponding exhaust velocity would be $370 \times 32 = 11,800$ feet per second and the vehicle mass ratio for an orbital mission requiring an injection velocity of 25,000 feet per second is given by

$$\frac{M}{M_b} = \text{antilog} \frac{25,000}{11,800 \times 2.30}.$$

$$= 8.34.$$

The corresponding propellant mass ratio is then

$$\frac{M_p}{M} = 1 - \frac{M_b}{M}$$

$$= 0.880 \text{ (or 88 percent)},$$

and so **12** percent of the total weight is now available for components, structure, and payload for the prescribed mission. This is a significant improvement over the situation with the kerosene-oxygen propellant combination for the same mission.

Multistage Rocket Vehicles

3.116. In the foregoing discussion it has been assumed that the decrease in mass, $M - M_b$, is due entirely to propellant consumption. Suppose, however, that mass unnecessary to the mission could be jettisoned in flight as it became superfluous; the situation would then be quite different. In these circumstances, the propellant would represent a smaller fraction of the total mass for a given burnout velocity, because M_p would be less than $M - M_b$. This is the essential idea underlying the *step rocket* or *multiple stage (multistage) rocket*, the principle of which has been used empirically by fireworks manufacturers for hundreds of years. It was proposed independently by K. E. Tsiolkovsky (1903), by R. H. Goddard (1919), and by H. Oberth (1923) and was applied in a combat device in Germany in 1944 (see § 1.98, footnote). In a single-stage rocket, sufficient propellant must be carried to accelerate the whole rocket vehicle, including the propellant itself, to the required burnout velocity. By discarding unnecessary mass under appropriate conditions, obviously less propellant would be needed to attain the specified velocity.

3.117. A multistage rocket consists of two or more independent rockets arranged in tandem, one on top of the other; each stage has its own motor and its own propellant supply.* The lowest (or first stage) has the highest thrust because it has to lift the largest mass, and the thrust decreases in subsequent stages. To launch the vehicle, the first-stage motor is ignited, and when the propellant supply for this stage is exhausted, the exhausted stage is dropped off.† At this point, or sometimes a short time later, the second-stage rocket is ignited. Since the overall mass is now much less than the initial mass at liftoff, an engine of lower thrust and a lower rate of propellant consumption is adequate to accelerate the remainder of the rocket vehicle. The second stage is jettisoned, in turn, when its propellant is exhausted and a third stage, if present, is ignited, and so on. The final stage, whichever it is, carries the payload, e.g., an instrumented satellite, a manned capsule, a space probe, etc. When this final stage attains the requisite velocity for the particular mission, the payload is usually detached, e.g., by means of an explosive charge. Whereas the earlier rocket stages will have fallen back, the last stage, if it has been given a sufficiently high velocity, will remain in space.

3.118. If each stage of a step rocket is ignited immediately after the preceding stage has burnt out and drops away, the final velocity will be the sum of the burnout values for the individual stages. When each stage is ignited, it already has a velocity equal to the burnout velocity attained by the pre-

---

* A multistage (or step) rocket must, of course, be distinguished from a cluster of rockets which form a single stage. Clusters are frequently used to increase the thrust of a given stage by combining two or more engines of lower thrust.

† The separation of stages in flight is referred to colloquially as *staging,* and the rocket vehicle is said to *stage* as the burnt-out stage separates from the remainder.

ceding stage, and so the burnout velocities are additive. The final burnout velocity is consequently given by

$$v_b = \left[(v_e)_1 \ln \left(\frac{M}{M_b} \right)_1 \right] + \left[(v_e)_2 \ln \left(\frac{M}{M_b} \right)_2 \right] + \dots, \qquad (3.13)$$

where the subscripts 1, 2, etc., refer to successive stages. For each stage, M represents the total mass of the vehicle remaining when the indicated stage is ignited, i.e., after the preceding stage (if any) is detached, and M_b is the mass remaining when the indicated stage has consumed its propellant but has not yet been discarded. It should be noted that, because the engine, propellant tanks, structure, etc., of each stage are discarded before the next stage is ignited, M for any stage is less than M_b for the immediately preceding stage.

3.119. In order to derive some semi-quantitative conclusions from equation (3.13), it will be assumed, for simplicity, that the exhaust velocity, i.e., specific impulse, and mass ratio are the same for each stage. Then, for a three-stage rocket vehicle, for example, equation (3.13) can be written as

$$v_b = 3 \left(v_e \ln \frac{M}{M_b} \right)$$

$$= 3 \left(2.30 v_e \log \frac{M}{M_b} \right),$$

where M/M_b is the vehicle mass ratio for each stage. If, as in § 3.111, v_e is taken as 9000 feet per second and v_b as 25,000 feet per second, the mass ratio is

$$\frac{M}{M_b} = \text{antilog} \frac{2.79}{3 \times 2.30}$$

$$= \text{antilog } 0.405 = 2.54.$$

The ratio of propellant mass consumed in any stage to the mass at ignition of that stage is

$$\frac{M_p}{M} = 1 - \frac{M_b}{M} = 1 - \frac{1}{2.54}$$

$$= 0.606 \text{ (or 60.6 percent)}.$$

3.120. To see what this result means, suppose that the initial mass of a three-stage rocket vehicle when it is launched is 100,000 pounds. It will carry 60.6 percent of this mass, i.e., 60,600 pounds, of propellant, so that the mass of the first-stage components, i.e., engine, tanks, structure, etc., plus that of the upper two stages and payload is 39,400 pounds. Suppose the mass of each stage, apart from the propellant, is set at a very conservative value of 20 percent of the propellant mass (cf. § 3.113). The mass of the components will thus be 12,100 pounds for the first stage, leaving 39,400 − 12,100 = 27,300 pounds for the vehicle weight after the first stage has been jettisoned. This is the initial weight when the second stage ignites. The mass of the second-stage propellant is 60.6 percent of 27,300, i.e., 16,600 pounds, and the mass of the components is 20 percent of this, namely, 3300 pounds. Hence, the initial weight of the third stage is 27,300 − (16,600 + 3300) = 7400 pounds. Again, 60.6 percent of 7400 pounds, i.e., 4500 pounds, is the mass of propellant and 20 percent of the latter, i.e., 900 pounds, is the mass of the components. This would leave 7400 − (4500 + 900) = 2000 pounds for the payload and its structure. The situation is summarized in Table 3.3.

TABLE 3.3   COMPONENT MASSES OF HYPOTHETICAL THREE-STAGE ROCKET VEHICLE

Initial weight at liftoff		100,000 pounds
First Stage		
Propellant	60,600 pounds	
Components	12,100	
	72,700	
Weight at second-stage ignition		27,300 pounds
Second Stage		
Propellant	16,600 pounds	
Components	3,300	
	19,900 pounds	
Weight at third-stage ignition		7,400 pounds
Third Stage		
Propellant	4,500 pounds	
Components	900	
	5,400 pounds	
Weight of payload and its structure		2,000 pounds.

3.121. Assuming a thrust-to-weight ratio of 1.5 for each stage, the thrust would have to be 150,000 pounds for the first stage, nearly 41,000 pounds for the second stage, and 11,100 pounds for the third stage. Because the final stage is usually traveling in an almost horizontal direction, it does not have to overcome the whole force of gravity; considerable acceleration is thus possible even if the thrust-to-weight ratio is appreciably less than 1.5. In general, it is the thrust available in the first stage, frequently referred to as the *booster* (or *booster rocket*),* that determines the overall weight of the vehicle at liftoff, based on an acceptable thrust-to-weight ratio. Each of the upper stages is considerably lighter than the preceding stage, since it carries less propellant

---

* The term booster is also used to describe the rocket stage or combination of stages which raises a satellite or space probe to a particular altitude where it subsequently receives the increase in velocity, from the final stage, required for the prescribed mission.

and has less massive components, and also has less thrust. As a result, a mission which would be impossible for a single-stage rocket utilizing a given propellant system becomes readily feasible with a multistage vehicle.

3.122. In the particular situation described above, i.e., v_e and M/M_b the same for all stages and no delay between burnout of one stage and ignition of the next, each stage contributes the same fraction, namely, one third, to the final burnout velocity. The vehicle velocity at first-stage burnout is thus about 8330, at the second-stage burnout 16,600, and at final burnout 25,000 feet per second.

3.123. Although the actual numbers derived in the preceding paragraphs are specific to the postulated system, the general conclusions are applicable to any multistage rocket vehicle; that is to say, for a given initial vehicle weight, a multistage system can put a larger payload into Earth orbit or send it into space and use less propellant than can a single-stage rocket based on the same propellant. In fact, the single-stage rocket of the same total thrust may not be able to put any payload at all into the required orbit or trajectory. Of course, it is assumed that the specific impulse and mass ratio characteristics of the multistage system are, at least, not greatly inferior to those of the single-stage rocket. The inferiority would have to be considerable to outweigh the advantages that result from the decreasing mass during flight. In practice, in many multistage vehicles, the upper stages use propellants with higher specific impulse than the first stage. This is done for two reasons: first, the payload mass fraction is maximized by such an arrangement,* and second, engines of very large thrust using propellants of high specific impulse, e.g., hydrogen and oxygen, have not yet been built and so they cannot be employed at present in the first stages of massive launch vehicles.

3.124. The larger the number of stages, the greater the benefits to be gained in decreased total propellant consumption and increased payload fraction. But the advantage realized from each subsequent stage decreases with increasing number of stages. Furthermore, an increase in the number of stages adds to the overall complexity of the rocket vehicle. Although a special seven-stage rocket has been fired in the United States, viz., a modified six-stage Trailblazer launched from Wallops Station, Virginia, on April 22, 1961, only three rocket systems used in the U.S. space program have as many as four stages. They are the sounding rockets Javelin and Journeyman, and the more powerful Scout, which can be used either as a sounding rocket or to place a relatively small payload in orbit. These four-stage rockets use solid propellants in all the stages.

---

* An increase in specific impulse means that a smaller mass of propellant is required for a certain increase in vehicle velocity. This saving in propellant mass makes possible an increase in mass of the payload. The effect of a given saving in mass of propellant (or structure) in increasing the payload mass is greater the higher the stage at which the saving occurs.

EFFECTS OF GRAVITY AND AERODYNAMIC DRAG

3.125. So far, the effects of gravity and of the aerodynamic drag of the atmosphere have been ignored, and so the numerical values derived may be regarded as being ideal. Since the gravitational and drag forces both oppose the acceleration of the rocket vehicle, they will cause a decrease in the burn-out velocity for a given exhaust velocity and mass ratio. Hence, in order to achieve a particular mission, i.e., a specified burnout velocity, it would be necessary to increase the vehicle (and propellant) mass ratio. Thus, a larger proportion of the overall mass would have to consist of propellant. The actual increase is determined by the nature of the initial flight path of the rocket vehicle.

3.126. The problem to be considered is how to choose a path which minimizes the consequences of gravity and aerodynamic drag. An extreme, somewhat impractical, case would be to launch the vehicle in a vertical direction and to permit it to move vertically upward until the desired altitude is reached. At this point, the motion would be turned into a horizontal direction, and the vehicle, i.e., what still remains, would then become a satellite or space probe, according to its velocity (Fig. 3.12, *A*). Although it is not a practical possibility,

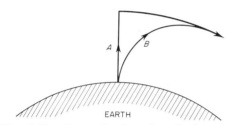

FIG. 3.12.   Alternative launch paths for a satellite

a change in direction of motion through a right angle, from vertical to horizontal, is of interest because it is simple to treat theoretically. If *t* is the time of vertical travel, the decrease in velocity resulting from the force of gravity is then *gt*, where *g* is the average value of the acceleration due to gravity during the ascent period. Provided the injection altitude is not more than a few hundred miles, the average accelera-

tion may be taken as 32 feet per second per second. If the time *t* is expressed in seconds, the decrease in burnout velocity caused by gravity is 32*t* feet per second. For example, for a reasonable ascent time of 100 seconds, the loss in velocity due to gravity would be 3200 feet per second.

3.127. An alternative, and more practical, method of launching a space vehicle would be to make it follow a curved path, similar to that shown in Fig. 3.12, *B*. A typical path of this kind is the gravity (or zero-lift) turn, described in § 4.99. The decrease in velocity caused by the downward force of gravity is now only the component in the direction of motion and is less than *gt*. But the time, *t*, required for the vehicle to attain the injection altitude is greater than for a vertical ascent, because of the longer path. Nevertheless, the curved trajectory, *B*, in Fig. 3.12, requires the expenditure of less total energy, since there is no sharp change in the direction of motion.

3.128. The aerodynamic force, which retards a moving object regardless of the direction in which it is moving, is proportional to the density of the ambient atmosphere, to the square of the velocity of the body, and to its cross-sectional area perpendicular to the direction of motion.* To minimize the effect of drag, therefore, the vehicle velocity should be small in the lower regions of the atmosphere where the air density is highest. Fortunately, this situation exists normally in the launching of a rocket vehicle from Earth's surface. The vehicle initially rises slowly, as seen in § 3.10, and speeds up as it ascends.

3.129. The decrease in velocity resulting from aerodynamic drag, like that due to gravity, is proportional to the time the force is operative. From this standpoint, a vertical ascent with a right-angle turn at altitude, as in Fig. 3.12, *A*, would provide the smallest velocity loss. The reason for not adopting this type of launch trajectory has already been given. In general, the most effective launch program is similar to that in Fig. 3.12, *B*. The vehicle is launched vertically, so that a minimum time is spent in the dense, lower part of the atmosphere; at a suitable height the path is gradually curved until the vehicle is moving in the desired direction at the injection altitude, e.g., horizontally for an Earth satellite. The optimum launch program, which is calculated beforehand, will depend on the characteristics of the rocket vehicle, e.g., specific impulse, mass ratio, etc., but it is usually of the type just described. The problem of stability during ascent and the nature of the trajectory is discussed in § 4.90, *et seq.*

3.130. For multistage vehicles, a short *coasting period* is frequently allowed between the ignition of the last stage and the burnout of the preceding one. When the objective is merely the attainment of a high altitude, as is the purpose of the boosting stages, it is generally advantageous to ignite the second (or later) stage soon after burnout of the preceding stage, for the reason given in § 1.99. For launching a satellite into Earth orbit or a probe into a desired trajectory, however, it may be preferable to permit the vehicle to coast after the booster stages have burnt out in order that the approximate required altitude be attained before the final stage is ignited (Fig. 3.13). The main purpose of the coasting phase is to provide a more efficient trajectory and thus decrease propellant consumption. In addition, the retarding effect of aerodynamic drag is diminished by not increasing the velocity to the required injection value until the air density is low. Furthermore, coasting reduces the tendency of the vehicle to become unstable as a result of the action of aerodynamic forces (§ 4.97). During the coasting period the vehicle follows

---

* The aerodynamic drag force is equal to $(\frac{1}{2}\rho v^2)AC_d$, where ρ is the density of the ambient atmosphere, v is the velocity of the body, A is a characteristic area (usually the cross-sectional or frontal area) of the body, and C_d, called the *drag coefficient*, depends upon a variety of factors, including the shape and size of the body, its velocity, the viscosity of the air, etc. For most rocket vehicles, C_d has an average value of about 0.4. The quantity $\frac{1}{2}\rho v^2$ is the *dynamic pressure* exerted by the air on the moving body; it is represented by the symbol q, and is commonly referred to by this letter.

a ballistic path (§ 1.48, footnote), in which the only force acting is gravity, apart from aerodynamic drag. The velocity decreases to some extent, but the altitude increases toward that prescribed for injection.

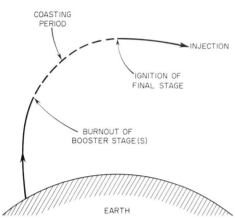

COASTING
PERIOD

INJECTION

IGNITION OF
FINAL STAGE

BURNOUT OF
BOOSTER STAGE(S)

EARTH

FIG. 3.13. Launch trajectory with coasting period

3.131. The decrease in velocity due to drag forces varies directly as the cross-sectional area of the rocket vehicle and inversely as its mass. These effects are not difficult to understand from a purely physical standpoint. A body of large cross-sectional area clearly offers a greater resistance to motion than does one of smaller area (§ 3.128, footnote). On the other hand, a given drag force acting on a mass, so as to oppose its motion, will produce a smaller deceleration the larger the mass. This result is in accordance with Newton's second law of motion (§ 2.17), since the deceleration is inversely proportional to the mass of the body.* Acting over a specified time, the larger mass will suffer a smaller decrease in velocity, provided other conditions are the same.

3.132. If the cross-sectional area and mass of a body were changed in proportion to each other with increasing size of rocket vehicles, the velocity loss would be unaffected. As a general rule, however, the mass of a rocket vehicle increases more rapidly than does the cross section. Consequently, the decrease in velocity due to drag becomes relatively less significant with the larger and heavier vehicles. When the first stage is jettisoned, there is a substantial decrease in mass, although the cross-sectional area is not changed greatly. By this time the ambient air density is relatively small and the drag deceleration is not very significant for a heavy vehicle.

3.133. As a general rule, for large rockets of the type used to launch Earth satellites and space probes of appreciable mass, the total decrease in velocity caused by aerodynamic drag forces will not be more than about 1000 feet per second. The loss due to gravitational forces is approximately 3000 feet per second, so that the total diminution in the velocity of the vehicle is roughly 4000 feet per second. For a normal three-stage vehicle, about two thirds of this total loss is experienced before the first stage is discarded and the remain-

---

* Although the law is generally stated in terms of a force producing acceleration, it is equally applicable to the deceleration of a moving body when the force acts in the direction opposite to its motion. If F is the magnitude of the drag force, the deceleration of a body of mass m is proportional to F/m; if the force is constant, and acts over a time t, the decrease in velocity is determined by Ft/m. In practice, however, F is rarely constant and Ft must be replaced by the integral of $F\,dt$, where dt is a small time interval.

ing one third occurs during the next stage. While the third-stage rocket is operating, the space vehicle is generally moving in a horizontal direction in a medium of very low density. Both gravitational and aerodynamic forces are then negligible.

STRUCTURAL DESIGN OF ROCKET VEHICLES

3.134. The structural design of a rocket vehicle is a complex engineering problem which must take into consideration a variety of forces acting on the vehicle during flight; these forces include the effects of air drag and wind, of bending moments, and of the bulk motion ("sloshing") of liquid propellants in the tanks. The only aspects of structural design to be considered here, however, are those related to the topics already discussed.

3.135. Since high mass ratio is a desirable feature of rocket-vehicle design, it is required to keep the mass of structural (and other) components as small as possible, thereby reducing the burnout mass, M_b. The container, representing the main vehicle structure, must therefore be made of materials that are light in weight yet strong enough to withstand the forces acting on it during flight. Steel and aluminum (or an alloy) have been commonly used for this purpose, but other, less common and more expensive, materials, e.g., titanium (or an alloy) and beryllium, may find some application in the future.

3.136. From the point of view of optimizing the ratio of strength to weight, propellant tanks should be spherical. Altough spherical vessels are being considered for special situations, this shape is not compatible with other aspects of the design of a launch vehicle, e.g., the high ratio of length to diameter. Furthermore, the location of two spherical tanks, for fuel and oxidizer, one above the other, would result in wasted space and additional external structure. Consequently, propellant tanks are generally constructed in cylindrical form. Other interesting concepts have been proposed to save space, e.g., a sphere fitted into one end of a cylinder or two cylinders, one of which has a concave and the other a convex end-cap. Special constructional features, such as the use of a waffle-like pattern, have been developed for building propellant tanks of light weight with adequate strength. In addition, the tank walls are generally made part of the vehicle wall, thereby achieving a saving in the overall weight.

3.137. Another problem of rocket vehicle design is the reduction in aerodynamic drag during launching. One way to achieve this is to have the cross-sectional area as small as possible. But if the ratio of length to diameter is too large, the bending forces acting on the vehicle during flight may cause it to break apart. Consequently, although rocket vehicles intended for flight through the atmosphere are designed to be long relative to their width, the ratio must be such as to provide the strength required to withstand the bending movements.

3.138. The aspect, or form, of a body in motion will also affect the aerodynamic drag force. A streamlined form, e.g., a smooth, rounded conical shape, will offer less resistance than a blunt or rough shape.* This accounts for the use of what is referred to as the *nose cone* at the tip of a rocket vehicle (Fig. 3.14). Frequently, the payload of a spacecraft consists of a number of instruments of odd shapes which would not only cause considerable aerodynamic drag but might be destroyed by the accompanying increase in temperature due to friction. It is the practice, therefore, to employ a cover, called a *shroud* or a *fairing*,† having a conical shape, which is discarded when the space vehicle reaches a sufficiently high altitude.

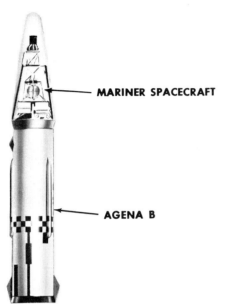

MARINER SPACECRAFT

AGENA B

Fig. 3.14. Mariner spacecraft protected by nose cone (shroud) for launching

U.S. LAUNCH VEHICLES

INTRODUCTION

3.139. With the exception of the Aerobee, sounding rockets commonly used in the United States, e.g., Astrobee, Argo, Deacon, Nike-Cajun, etc., employ one or two stages of solid propellants. All forms of the Aerobee have a solid-propellant first stage and a liquid-propellant second stage. In the Aerobee 100 the liquid propellants are a kerosene-base fuel (JP-4) with inhibited red fuming nitric acid (IRFNA) as the oxidizer; in the Aerobee 150 (and 150A), the oxidizer is the same but the fuel is a mixture of aniline and alcohol. The Aerobee 300 consists of the Aerobee 150 with a solid-propellant third stage.

3.140. For the launching of manned and unmanned satellites, space probes, and orbiters, for which large thrusts are required, a number of basic rocket vehicles have been used or are under development. These are Scout, Delta, Thor-Agena, Thor-Able-Star (or Thor-Epsilon), Atlas D, Atlas-Agena, Titan II, Titan III, Centaur, Saturn I, Saturn I B, and Saturn V (or Advanced Saturn). Each vehicle has its particular sphere of usefulness, as described below.

SCOUT

3.141. Scout, the smallest of the group of U.S. launch vehicles, is a four-stage rocket employing solid propellant in each stage. It is, in fact, the only

---

* When a manned space capsule re-enters the atmosphere, aerodynamic drag is utilized to decelerate the vehicle. In this case, the blunt end faces the direction of motion (§ 13.7).

† In an aircraft, a fairing is any structure having the primary purpose of producing a smooth outline to decrease aerodynamic drag.

one that uses solid propellants exclusively. Scout was designed to provide a reliable, relatively inexpensive launch vehicle for many of the smaller pay-loads needed for some aspects of space research. The vehicle is 65 feet long, without the spacecraft; it has a maximum diameter of 3.3 feet, exclusive of the terminal fins, and is capable of placing a 220-pound satellite in an orbit about 350 miles above Earth. It is expected that the payload capability will be increased to 300 pounds for the same orbit. Alternatively, when used as a sounding rocket, Scout can raise a 400-pound payload to high altitudes for atmospheric research. The characteristics of the four solid-propellant rocket stages are as follows:

Stage	Name	Thrust (pounds)
1	Algol II-A	86,000 (sea level)
2	Castor	64,000
3	Antares	23,000
4	Altair	3,000
	(or X-258)	5,700

The fourth stage (Altair) rocket is mounted on a spin table to which are attached four small hydrogen peroxide jets. Just before ignition, these jets set the fourth stage and its attached payload spinning in order to stabilize the spacecraft in its orbit (cf. § 4.100).

Delta

3.142. The three-stage Delta vehicle was originally intended for interim use in launching satellites of medium payload, pending the development of Scout and Thor-Agena B. However, Delta has proved to be an extremely reliable system and it is planned to continue its use. It has placed in orbit such important satellites as Telstar, Relay, the Orbiting Solar Observatory (OSO), and nearly all the TIROS spacecraft. Delta is 88 feet long and 8 feet in maximum diameter; it can place a payload of 800 pounds in a satellite orbit of approximately 350 miles altitude or provide escape velocity to a 100-pound space probe (Fig. 3.15, I). Its characteristics are as follows:

Stage	Propellants	Thrust (pounds)
1	LOX-RP (Thor)	170,000 (sea level)
2	UDMH-IRFNA	7,700
3	Solid (Altair)	3,000
	(or X-258)	5,700

The first stage of Delta is a modified and improved version of the Thor inter-mediate range ballistic missile and so Delta is sometimes called Thor-Delta. As in Scout, the last (Altair) stage of Delta is spun before firing to provide flight stability for the payload.

3.143. In the Thrust-Augmented Delta (TAD), three solid-propellant (XM-33-52) motors, about 31 inches in diameter and nearly 20 feet long, are strapped to the Thor booster and are ignited almost immediately after lift-off. The sea-level thrust of the first stage is thereby increased to some 333,500 pounds. In addition, the third stage can be relaced by an X-258 motor with a thrust of 5700 pounds. The TAD can place a payload of nearly 1000 pounds in a 350-mile-altitude orbit or permit the escape of 150 pounds. Plans are also being made to increase the volume of the propellant tanks of the second stage, so that even larger payloads will be possible.

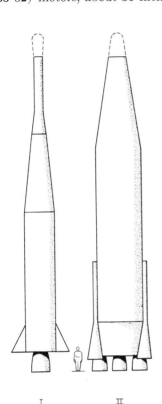

I   II

FIG. 3.15. Delta (I) and Atlas (II) launch vehicles

THOR-AGENA

3.144. The Thor-Agena B employs the same first stage (Thor) as in Delta, but the second stage, while utilizing the same propellants as Delta, namely unsymmetrical dimethylhydrazine and inhibited red fuming nitric acid, has a thrust of about 16,000 pounds. Furthermore, the second-stage (Agena B) rocket is designed to be restartable in space, thereby making possible great precision in adjusting the velocity, and hence the orbit, of a satellite. The length of the Thor-Agena B vehicle is 76 feet and its maximum diameter is 8 feet; it is capable of placing a 1600-pound payload in a 350-mile orbit. The payload for the same orbit is increased to nearly 2200 pounds in the thrust-augmented modification of Thor-Agena (TAT). Like the TAD, the TAT has three XM-33-52 rockets strapped to the booster.

3.145. The standardized form of the Agena B is called Agena D. The latter is designed so that it can be readily adapted for the attachment of different kinds of spacecraft, as required for various missions. The Agena B, on the other hand, must be modified for each type of mission. An improved version of Agena D, known as the Additional Basic Capability (or ABC) Agena, is 80 pounds lighter than the original form. Since the Agena is the last stage of the rocket vehicle, this means that the mass of the payload into orbit can be increased by 80 pounds.

Thor-Able-Star (Thor-Epsilon)

3.146. The Thor-Able-Star launch vehicle has been utilized mainly to place in orbit satellites of military interest, e.g., Courier for long-distance communications, and Transit for global navigation. It has two stages, the first being a modified Thor rocket, such as is used in Delta, and the second is like Agena B, having restart capability and using the same hypergolic propellants, but the thrust is about half that of Agena B.

Atlas D

3.147. Atlas D is of unusual design, since it is a compromise between one and two stages, called a "one and one-half stage" vehicle. The purpose is to provide some of the advantage of staging without the possible drawback of having to ignite an upper stage in space. Because of its adequate thrust and availability, this vehicle was used in the Mercury manned orbital spaceflight program. Altas D has three rocket motors, two being called booster engines and the third is the sustainer engine (Fig. 3.15, II). All three are supplied from the same liquid oxygen-kerosene (RP-1) propellant tanks and are ignited simultaneously for launching. The two booster engines together supply 287,000 pounds of thrust and the sustainer engine 80,000 pounds, so that the (sea-level) thrust at liftoff is 367,000 pounds. After burning for nearly $2\frac{1}{2}$ minutes, the two booster engines are jettisoned and the sustainer engine continues to operate until the required orbital velocity is attained, in about $4\frac{1}{2}$ minutes from liftoff. By igniting the sustainer engine before the vehicle is launched, this motor is able to utilize liquid oxygen-kerosene propellants which have a higher specific impulse than the hypergolic systems generally employed in the upper stages of other rockets with large thrusts.

3.148. As used in the manned satellite program, the length of the Atlas vehicle is just over 67 feet without the Mercury capsule, and more than 95 feet when launched, i.e., with the capsule and emergency escape tower. It is 16 feet wide at the base, where the two booster engines are attached, and 10 feet in diameter in the main body of the vehicle. Atlas D has the capability of orbiting a spacecraft weighing some 3000 pounds at an altitude of over 100 miles. Instead of the floxed Atlas (§3.36), it is proposed to retain the standard propellants and to increase the payload by engine design changes to give a somewhat larger thrust and by increasing the volume of the propellant tanks.

Atlas-Agena

3.149. The Atlas-Agena B launch vehicle consists of an Atlas D with the 16,000-pound thrust Agena B as the upper stage. It is 91 feet long, without its spacecraft, and at the base it has the same diametrical measurements as the Atlas D. The Atlas-Agena B combination can place a payload of 6000 pounds in a 350-mile Earth orbit or can launch a 425-pound spaceprobe to Mars or Venus. This vehicle was utilized for the successful Ranger (lunar) and Mariner (planetary) missions. In operation, a coasting period is generally allowed after burnout of the Atlas D before Agena B is ignited. After injecting the carrier vehicle into a parking orbit, the Agena B is extinguished and is subsequently restarted when the location is favorable for the required space mission. In due course, Agena B will be replaced by the standardized Agena D and by the advanced ABC Agena.

Titan II and III

3.150. Like Atlas D, Titan II is primarily a rocket vehicle for launching intercontinental ballistic missiles, but it has been selected to place the two-man Gemini spacecraft into orbit (Fig. 3.16, I). It is a two-stage vehicle using the same hypergolic propellants in each stage, namely, a mixture of equal parts of hydrazine and UDMH, called Aerozine 50, as the fuel and nitrogen tetroxide as the oxidizer. The first stage is a cluster of two engines with a total thrust of 430,000 pounds (at sea level), and the thrust of the second stage is 100,000 pounds. The total length of the vehicle, apart from the spacecraft, is 90 feet and its maximum diameter is 10 feet. The Titan II has the capability of inserting a payload of nearly 7000 pounds in a low-altitude Earth orbit.

3.151. The Titan III system, which is expected to be operational in 1965, has five basic parts: the two stages of Titan II, a new storable-propellant third stage, called the Transtage, producing 16,000 pounds of thrust, and two solid-propellant motors, each 70 feet long and 120-inches in diameter, which are strapped onto the lower part of the Titan II section. With the two strap-on motors contributing to the first stage, a thrust of 2,000,000 pounds should be attainable at liftoff. This should be sufficient to place a payload of 25,000 pounds into orbit around Earth.

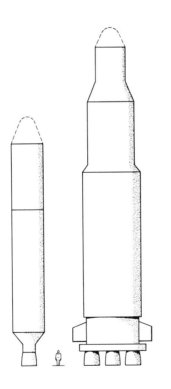

I   II

Fig. 3.16.   Titan II (I) and Saturn IB (II) launch vehicles

CENTAUR

3.152. Centaur is the first rocket vehicle to use liquid hydrogen (LH_2) as fuel, with liquid oxygen (LOX) as oxidizer. A cluster of two hydrogen-oxygen engines (RL-10 Model A-3), each producing a thrust of 15,000 pounds, is used in the upper stage with an Atlas D booster. The overall length is about 100 feet, the maximum diameter being that of the Atlas D. The Centaur should be capable of orbiting a payload of 8500 pounds or of sending over 2000 pounds on a flight to the Moon. One of the objectives of this vehicle is to launch the Surveyor spacecraft, designed to land on the Moon and perform unmanned exploration of its surface.

SATURN I AND SATURN I B

3.153. The main purpose of the Saturn launch vehicle program is to make possible a manned landing on the Moon. Both Saturn I (originally known as Saturn C-1) and Saturn I B (or Saturn C-1B) have the same first stage, designated S-I, consisting of a cluster of eight H-1 engines (LOX-RP) producing a total thrust of 1,500,000 pounds at sea level. The upper stage of Saturn, called S-IV, is a cluster of six RL-10 Model A-3 (LOX-LH_2) engines, such as are used in the second stage of Centaur; the total thrust is thus 90,000 pounds. In Saturn I B, the second stage, S-IVB, is a single LOX-LH_2 engine, the J-2, capable of developing 200,000 pounds of thrust. The characteristics of Saturn I and Saturn I B are summarized below:

Saturn I

Stage	Engines	Thrust (pounds)
1	S-I: Eight H-1 (LOX-RP)	1,500,000 (sea level)
2	S-IV: Six RL-10 (LOX-LH_2)	90,000

Saturn I B

Stage	Engines	Thrust (pounds)
1	S-I: Eight H-1 (LOX-RP)	1,500,000 (sea level)
2	S-IVB: J-2 (LOX-LH_2)	200,000

3.154. The Saturn I vehicle, 125 feet long and $21\frac{1}{2}$ feet in maximum diameter, is able to place a payload of about 10 tons into an Earth orbit at an altitude of 350 miles. It is to be used to launch development models of the Apollo lunar spacecraft for testing purposes. The Saturn I B has a length of about 150 feet and is also intended for various tests on vehicles to be utilized for the manned lunar landing. It should be capable of inserting 16 tons into Earth orbit (Fig. 3.16,II).

SATURN V

3.155. The actual manned Apollo mission to the Moon will be achieved by means of Saturn V (or Advanced Saturn, formerly called Saturn C-5). The height of this very large vehicle, apart from the spacecraft, will be about 280 feet and its width, exclusive of fins, will be 33 feet. Its thrust at sea level will be 7,500,000 pounds and its capability includes the launching of a 120-ton payload into a 350 mile Earth orbit, of 45 tons to escape velocity, i.e., to reach the Moon, and of 30 tons on planetary missions. The initial weight of the Apollo spacecraft at liftoff will be about 45 tons.

3.156. The Saturn V is to be a three-stage vehicle, with the following characteristics:

Stage	Engines	Thrust (pounds)
1	S-IC: Five F-1 (LOX-RP)	7,500,000 (sea level)
2	S-II: Five J-2 (LOX-LH$_2$)	1,000,000
3	S-IVB: J-2 (LOX-LH$_2$)	200,000

The second and third stages utilize the same LOX-LH$_2$ engine (J-2) planned for Saturn I B, but the first stage is based on the development of the F-1 engine with a sea-level thrust of 1,500,000 pounds for a single engine (Fig. 3.17).

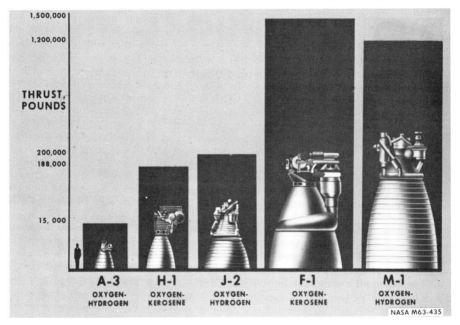

F$_{IG.}$ 3.17.   Rocket engines of advanced types for the United States space program

3.157. A more powerful liquid hydrogen-liquid oxygen engine, the M-1, with a thrust of at least 1.2 million pounds, has been under consideration. The use of such engines in the upper stages would add very greatly to the launch capability of the Advanced Saturn vehicles.

HEAT-TRANSFER ROCKET ENGINES

Attainment of High Specific Impulse

3.158. For advanced space missions, such as the manned exploration of the planets, the launch vehicles should be capable of providing a large burnout (or payload) mass at the required velocity for the given mission. The design of launch vehicles can be improved in two ways: one is to decrease the effective vehicle mass ratio, e.g., by increasing the number of stages in the launch vehicle; and the other is to increase the exhaust gas velocity by using propellants of high specific impulse. There are, however, practical limitations to both procedures. In the first place, there is little to be gained in effectiveness, and much to be lost because of complexity, in adding stages beyond the third or fourth (§ 3.124). Furthermore, as far as can be seen at present, it does not seem possible for the specific impulse of chemical propellants to exceed about 420 seconds at sea level. The maximum exhaust velocity of a chemical rocket would thus be roughly 13,500 feet per second. Since increasing the number of stages is not a promising approach to improvement in the capability of launch vehicles, consideration is being given to the possibility of realizing higher specific impulses.

3.159. A number of techniques for increasing the specific impulse of a rocket engine are being studied; the one which appears to be closest to reality is based on the utilization of nuclear energy to heat a propellant (or working fluid) of low molecular weight. In this manner, it is expected that specific impulses of 700 to 900 seconds may be possible, depending on the temperature that can be tolerated. For various reasons, cost, shielding requirements, safety considerations, availability of large chemical boosters, etc., it is improbable that nuclear rockets will be used in the first stage of a launch vehicle. Because of their high potential specific impulse, however, nuclear rockets are well suited to the upper stage (or stages) of a rocket having a lower stage (or stages) employing chemical propellants.

3.160. Chemical and nuclear rockets are similar in the respect that they both operate by the expulsion of a hot gas through a convergent-divergent nozzle. There are, however, some significant differences. In a chemical rocket engine, the attainable temperature, and hence the specific impulse, is dependent on the heat of combustion (or calorific value) per unit mass of propellant; the molecular weight of the exhaust gas is automatically determined by the products of the chemical reactions in the combustion chamber.

3.161. In a nuclear rocket, on the other hand, the temperature is limited only by the strength of the available structural materials. As materials with improved high-temperature strength are developed, the specific impulse can be increased correspondingly. In addition, any liquid or gas, in principle, can be chosen as the propellant to be heated and exhausted as gas through the nozzle of a nuclear rocket. This is possible because heat is produced by a nuclear—as distinct from a chemical—reaction which is completely independent of the propellant. The heat generated is then transferred to the chosen propellant, commonly referred to in these circumstances as the *working fluid*. The nuclear rocket is thus an example of what is called a *heat-transfer rocket*. The propellant selected is hydrogen because it has the lowest molecular weight, namely 2.00, among the stable gases. The combination of high temperature and low molecular weight of the exhaust gas makes possible the attainment of high specific impulses, i.e., high exhaust gas velocities, by means of a nuclear rocket engine.

3.162. In order to understand the operation of the nuclear rocket, it is necessary to consider some aspects of atomic structure and the phenomena of nuclear fission. Every atom consists of a central region, referred to as the *nucleus*, which carries essentially the whole of the mass, surrounded by a number of much lighter particles known as *electrons*. The atomic nucleus is itself made up of definite numbers of two types of particles, called *protons* and *neutrons*. These two particles have almost the same mass, approximately unity on the conventional atomic weight scale, but they differ in the respect that the proton has a unit positive charge of electricity, whereas the neutron, as its name implies, is uncharged electrically, i.e., it is neutral. Because of the protons present in the nucleus, the latter has a positive electrical charge, but in the normal (neutral) atom this is balanced by the negative charge carried by the electrons surrounding the nucleus.

3.163. The essential difference between atoms of different elements lies in the number of protons (or positive charges) in the nucleus. The number increases regularly from one in the nucleus of the hydrogen atom, the lightest known atom, to 92 in the nucleus of the uranium atom, the heaviest existing in nature.* All the nuclei of a given element contain the same number of protons, but they may have different numbers of neutrons and, consequently, different masses. The resulting different atomic species are called *isotopes* of the particular element.

3.164. For example, the element uranium exists in nature in the form of two main isotopes; the nuclei of all the atoms contain 92 protons but most, about 99.3 percent, have 146 neutrons, so that the total mass is 92 + 146 = 238 units. The remainder, approximately 0.7 percent, of the atoms contain 143 neutrons, giving a mass of 92 + 143 = 235 units. These two isotopes of uranium are thus designated uranium-238 and uranium-235, respectively. It is the latter which is employed for the release of energy in a nuclear rocket.

3.165. When a free (or unattached) neutron enters the nucleus of a uranium-235 atom, it can cause the nucleus to split into two smaller parts con-

* There are very minute traces of naturally occurring elements with 93 and 94 positive charges in the nucleus. These and other elements with higher nuclear charges have been produced artificially by means of various nuclear reactions starting with uranium.

sisting of lighter nuclei. This is the nuclear *fission process* that is associated with the release of a large amount of energy. The lighter nuclei formed by splitting the uranium nucleus are called *fission products*. The significance of the nuclear fission of uranium-235 is that, in addition to the liberation of energy, the process is accompanied by the emission of two or three neutrons; thus,

Uranium-235 + neutron → Fission products + 2 or 3 neutrons + energy.

The neutrons generated in this manner are able to induce fission of additional uranium-235 nuclei, each such process resulting in the emission of more neutrons capable of causing fission, and so on. Thus, in principle, a single neutron could initiate a self-sustaining chain of nuclear fission with the continuous release of energy. The rate of energy production in this manner is proportional to the number of nuclei undergoing fission per unit time, and to this there is essentially no theoretical upper limit.

3.166. About 90 percent of the nuclear fission energy appears in the form of heat, and the complete fission of 1 pound of uranium-235 could produce 2.5×10^{13} foot pounds or 3.2×10^{10} British thermal units of heat energy. This may be compared with approximately 2×10^4 British thermal units obtained by the combustion of 1 pound of kerosene rocket fuel. Thus, nuclear fuel, which requires no oxidizer, represents a highly concentrated source of energy; weight for weight, the complete fission of uranium-235 would produce about two million times as much heat energy as the combustion of chemical rocket propellants. Although this is often mentioned as one of the advantages of nuclear rockets, it is not of major significance. The reason is that, for a self-sustaining fission chain carried by neutrons to be possible, the total amount of uranium-235 must exceed a certain quantity called the *critical mass*. The actual value of the critical mass depends upon a variety of circumstances, but in a nuclear rocket it would probably be a few hundred pounds. It is only the excess, over and above the minimum critical mass, that is available for the release of energy.

The Nuclear Rocket

3.167. The device or arrangement which includes the fissile material, i.e., uranium-235, with appropriate structure and other components, is called a *nuclear reactor*. The central portion, containing the critical mass of uranium-235, where the heat energy is produced is known as the *core* of the reactor. This is surrounded by a *reflector*, which serves the purpose of returning (or reflecting) to the core some of the neutrons that would otherwise escape. As a result, the mass of fissile material required to make the core critical is less than in the absence of a reflector.

3.168. In a nuclear rocket, the reactor is enclosed in a pressure shell that is the equivalent of the combustion chamber of a chemical rocket. A nozzle of conventional design is then attached to the reactor vessel in the usual manner to form a rocket motor (Fig. 3.18). The propellant (or working fluid), hydrogen, is stored in the liquid state in a tank (or tanks) from which it is pumped through tubes around the nozzle to cool it. The partially heated fluid, possibly a mixture of liquid and gas, then enters the reactor pressure vessel at the end

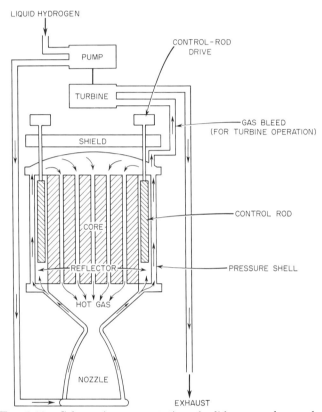

FIG. 3.18.   Schematic representation of solid-core nuclear rocket

opposite to the nozzle and flows through channels in the core where its temperature is raised by transfer of heat from the fissile material. The hot gas then passes into the nozzle where its velocity (or mass kinetic energy) is increased at the expense of the heat energy taken up in the reactor core (§ 3.59).

3.169. The maximum gas temperature attainable in a chemical rocket motor is determined by the heat of combustion (or reaction) of the propellants and the heat capacity (or specific heat) of the gaseous products. In a nuclear rocket, on the other hand, it is the necessity for maintaining physical integrity of the structure that limits the upper temperature. Were it not for this restriction, extremely high temperatures could be attained by nuclear fission. Among the structural materials which might be expected to have sufficient high-temperature strength are graphite, tungsten (and certain of its alloys), and some refractory carbides, oxides, and sulfides; of these, graphite was used in the experimental Kiwi reactors for rocket propulsion.*

3.170. In the Kiwi reactors, the graphite served another purpose, in addition to providing structural support, by acting as the medium in which the uranium-235 (as oxide or carbide) is dispersed. Graphite, a form of the element carbon, has the ability, as do other elements of low atomic weight, to slow down neutrons as a result of collisions with the atomic nuclei. In this capacity, the graphite (carbon) is called a *moderator*. The slowed-down (or moderated) neutrons are absorbed by, and cause fission of, the uranium-235 nuclei more readily than do the faster neutrons, thereby decreasing the critical mass.

3.171. Because heat must be transferred from the fission-heated graphite to the hydrogen gas, the temperature of the latter is always lower than that of the graphite in the reactor core. At the present time, the maximum gas temperature which appears to be attainable in a system of the type under consideration is about 2500°C (4500°F) owing to the materials limitation. This is probably less than is possible with kerosene and liquid hydrogen chemical fuels using oxygen as the oxidizer. In chemical rockets, the high temperature is produced in the gas phase and the combustion chamber walls are very much cooler; consequently, the problem of materials is less acute. Thus, the gas temperatures in a chemical rocket may be appreciably higher than in a nuclear rocket where the temperature of the structural material must exceed that of the gas.

3.172. If the hydrogen gas leaving a nuclear reactor has the maximum temperature indicated above, the specific impulse would be about 865 seconds. The development of new materials, permitting higher core operating temperatures, would permit an increase in the specific impulse. But it is doubtful if this could exceed 1000 seconds for high-thrust rockets operating at high gas flow rates. For purposes in which a low thrust-to-weight ratio would be adequate, e.g., where gravitational forces are small, lower rates of gas flow could be employed and specific impulses up to 1200 seconds might be possible.

3.173. The outstanding potential advantage of the nuclear rocket is, of course, the high specific impulses, i.e., exhaust velocities, that appear possible. Except for space missions requiring high burnout velocities and relatively large payloads, this advantage over chemical rockets may be offset, as far as total vehicle weight is concerned, by the greater weight of the nuclear rocket engine. Furthermore, since the density of liquid hydrogen is so low, the tankage mass for a given amount of propellant would be greater than for a liquid-bipropellant chemical system. This would be compensated to some extent by the lower rate of propellant consumption, for a particular thrust, because of the higher specific impulse. One advantage of nuclear over chemical rockets is that the former use

---

* These reactors were not intended for actual rockets and so they were named after the kiwi, the flightless bird from New Zealand. They are being followed by Phoebus reactors of larger thrust as part of the overall U.S. Project Rover.

a single propellant and so require only one turbopump. After initial startup, the turbine could be driven by hydrogen gas obtained from either bleed or topping cycles, as described in § 3.82.

3.174. The thrust of a nuclear rocket motor can be varied in either (or both) of two ways. First, if the rate of flow of propellant through the reactor core is maintained constant, the gas temperature, and hence the specific impulse, can be changed by altering the fission rate by means of neutron-absorbing control elements. Since the flow rate of propellant has not been changed, the thrust will vary in proportion to the specific impulse. Second, the temperature of the gas in the reactor core can be kept constant, by proper adjustment of the fission rate, and the thrust changed by varying the flow rate of the propellant. The latter procedure is the one that appears to be preferable; one reason is that a constant temperature minimizes thermal stresses in the reactor core.

3.175. Although a nuclear rocket engine can be stopped and restarted at will, the nature of the fission reaction is such that rapid startup must be carried out with care to avoid possible damage to the core material as a result of overheating. In any event, although no ignition is required, startup and control of a nuclear reactor are more complicated than for a chemical rocket motor. Automatic control mechanisms have been designed but further development is required to achieve complete reliability. One problem with such mechanisms is that any difficulty is likely to lead to instant shutdown of the reactor.

3.176. Finally, mention must be made of the radiation problems associated with a nuclear reactor. During its operation, a reactor emits large amounts of neutrons—about half of the neutrons produced in a reactor in the fission process escape—and gamma rays. The latter are highly penetrating electromagnetic radiations like X-rays (§ 6.51). Even after operation has ceased, neutrons continue to be expelled from the core for a few minutes and gamma rays for many days, although with gradually decreasing intensity. Not only are these radiations a hazard to human beings, but they might be a problem even in unmanned spacecraft because they can damage various semiconducting materials, which are used in transistors and other electronic components, thereby perhaps rendering ineffective communication and guidance equipment and interfering with scientific measurements. Adequate protection for astronauts could be provided by the liquid hydrogen propellant, since the tanks would be located between the nuclear reactor and the crew compartment. Semiconductor devices may have to be located some distance from the reactor, but if this is not feasible vacuum tubes, which are not so sensitive to radiation, can be used. Some shielding will probably be required for the propellant tanks to minimize heating of the liquid hydrogen and formation of gas by the absorption of gamma rays. To prevent the possible spread of radioactive fission products in the vicinity of the launch site in case of an accident, nuclear rockets would be used only in the upper stages of a launch vehicle, so that they would operate only in space.

Heating by Radioactivity

3.177. It will be seen in § 3.241 *et seq.* that there is another way in which nuclear energy can be made available, namely, by the spontaneous process of radioactivity. Radioactive substances emit various radiations of high energy and upon absorption in a suitable material, e.g., a solid of medium or high density, the energy is converted into heat. It has been suggested that hydrogen could thus be heated by means of a radioactive material to a temperature in the range of 1500° to 2000°C (2700° to 3600°F), and the hot gas exhausted through a conventional rocket nozzle to produce thrust. The specific impulse is estimated to be about 600 to 700 seconds. There is a possibility that this technique might be adapted to rockets of low or medium thrust, and preliminary experiments are under way with the relatively inexpensive radioactive species cobalt-60 or polonium-210 as the heat source.*

Electrothermal Thrustors

3.178. Besides the nuclear rockets, other types of heat-transfer rockets are under consideration for propulsion in space, in particular for missions in which small ratios of thrust to weight might be useful provided the specific impulse is high. In *electrothermal thrustors*, the heat to be transferred to the propellant is produced by electrical means (see § 3.42, footnote).

3.179. A type of electrothermal thrustor that is the subject of experiment is the *resistance jet* (or *resistojet*) which utilizes resistance (or ohmic) heating to obtain a high temperature. In one form of the resistance jet, an electric current is passed through a tungsten tube which is thereby heated. The propellant, e.g., hydrogen, flows along the exterior of the tube and then back through the interior, so that the temperature is raised by the transfer of heat from the hot tungsten. In other modifications, the hydrogen flows past resistance coils or screens of tungsten heated electrically. Expansion in a convergent-divergent nozzle then produces the required high exhaust velocity. The gas temperature is limited by the physical integrity of the tungsten to about 3000°C (5400°F), and the maximum specific impulse attainable is probably in the vicinity of 1000 seconds. The resistance-heated thrustor is expected to be efficient, simple, and reliable, and specific impulses of about 800 seconds have already been achieved in laboratory devices. The great drawback, however, as with other rocket motors requiring the use of electricity, is the production of electrical power in space. This subject will be treated later in the present chapter.

3.180. Another possible type of electrothermal, heat-transfer thrustor, with some advantages over that described above, makes use of an electric arc to raise the temperature of the propellant gas. In the *electric-arc* (or *arc-jet*)

---

* Because this may be regarded as a minor Project Rover (§ 3.169, footnote), it has been named Project Poodle.

thrustor, the working fluid, e.g., hydrogen or ammonia, is heated by means of an electric arc. The high-temperature gas is then exhausted through a nozzle in the usual manner. In one experimental device, known as the *constricted arc-jet thrustor,* shown in Fig. 3.19, the arc chamber, which serves as one of the electrodes, is shaped to form the convergent-divergent nozzle. So far, the arc-jet thrustor is similar to both the nuclear and resistance-heated rocket systems. But the situation is different with respect to the strength of the materials involved. As in a chemical rocket motor, the heat in an electric arc thrustor is generated within the gas and not in a solid material; provided the chamber walls are kept reasonably cool, e.g., by circulation of the cold propellant, very high gas temperatures, up to about 22,000°C (40,000°F), can be realized.

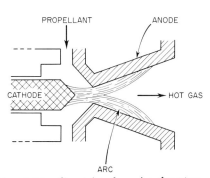

FIG. 3.19.   Constricted arc-jet thrustor

3.181. One of the factors that limits the attainable temperature in an electric-arc thrustor is the disintegration of the material of the electrodes between which the arc is passed. Furthermore, at sufficiently high temperatures, the propellant gas becomes a good electrical conductor and this leads to energy losses. In principle, therefore, specific impulses up to about 2500 seconds are believed to be possible with hydrogen as propellant. Experimental arc-jet rocket motors have already been constructed with specific impulses of about 2000 seconds.

3.182. With some sacrifice in specific impulse, much more convenient propellants of higher density, e.g., liquid ammonia or even water, could be utilized in the electric-arc, heat-transfer rocket instead of hydrogen. Because of the very high temperatures, ammonia would be largely dissociated into nitrogen and hydrogen atoms and water into oxygen (or hydroxyl radicals) and hydrogen atoms. The average molecular weight of the exhaust gas would thus be only about 5 or 6, instead of the 17 for ammonia and 18 for water at lower temperatures. The dissociation would result in the removal of heat energy, thus lowering the gas temperature to some extent. But this decrease would be more than offset, as far as its effect on specific impulse is concerned, by the decrease in molecular weight by a factor of three or more.

3.183. An electric-arc rocket could be easily stopped by switching off the current; restarting would not be very difficult, although it would be necessary to take steps to restrike the arc. The specific impulse could be decreased by increasing the rate of propellant flow past the arc, since a more rapid flow would cause the gas temperature to drop. However, since the thrust developed is the product of the specific impulse and the propellant flow rate, there might well be an increase in the thrust produced by the arc-jet rocket. Conversely, a decrease in flow rate would cause an increase in temperature and probably a decrease in thrust. Control of the electric-arc rocket by adjustment of the propellant flow rate thus appears to be feasible.

3.184. It is expected that the equipment required to generate electricity for an electrothermal thrustor will be heavy. Such devices will thus undoubtedly have a low ratio of thrust to sea-level weight; values in the range of 10^{-4} to 10^{-2} have been quoted, although they are somewhat speculative. For space propulsion in regions where the gravitational force is small, e.g., on interplanetary flights, however, low thrust-to-weight motors with high specific impulses may have an important role, provided they are capable of operating for long periods of time. Possible disintegration or erosion of the arc electrodes would then be a problem requiring special attention.

3.185. The success or failure of the electrothermal rocket, as well as of other rocket systems described below requiring the use of electricity, depends ultimately on the ability to develop a practical source of electric power that can be carried by a space vehicle. The consensus at present is that this can be achieved by the use of nuclear energy. It is in this connection that the concentrated nature of nuclear fuel, referred to in § 3.166, becomes highly significant. For the generation of electric power over extended periods, the nuclear reactor has a decided weight advantage over generators using conventional fuels. Because power production in space is a problem common to several aspects of space exploration, the subject will be treated in a separate section later in this chapter.

CHARGED-PARTICLE ROCKET MOTORS

ACCELERATION OF CHARGED PARTICLES

3.186. Devices which employ electrically charged particles to produce rocket action differ from those already described in the respect that they do not utilize either a hot gas or expansion in a convergent-divergent nozzle to produce a high exhaust velocity. The charged particles are accelerated directly and ejected at high velocity by making use of electric and magnetic fields. In these circumstances, the specific impulse is not related to the temperature and molecular weight of the exhaust gas. But the basic relationship between specific impulse and exhaust velocity, as given in § 3.60, is still applicable.

3.187. The exhaust velocities which should be possible by the acceleration of charged particles are so high that specific impulses of several thousand seconds are believed to be feasible. Two general principles are being investigated for rockets using electrically charged particles as the working material: these are (a) electrostatic (or ion) acceleration; and (b) electromagnetic (or plasma) acceleration. Both procedures are in the early experimental stages, but progress is being made. As is the case with electrothermal rockets, the charged-particle acceleration systems will require generation of electric power in space. The thrust-to-weight ratios are expected to be in the range from 10^{-5} to 10^{-3}.

THE ION ROCKET

3.188. As stated earlier, the atoms of all elements consist of a central nucleus, carrying a positive electrical charge, surrounded by a number of negatively charged electrons; the atom as a whole is, therefore, electrically neutral. By various means, e.g., high temperature, electrical discharge, radiation, etc., it is possible to remove one or more electrons from an atom. The residual portion of the atom must then be positively charged, and it is called a positive *ion*. The process of converting neutral atoms into free electrons and positive ions is known as *ionization*. By passage across an electrical field of moderately high voltage, the positive ions can be accelerated to high velocities. This is the basic principle of the *ion rocket* or *ion thrustor*. It is sometimes referred to as the *electrostatic thrustor* because the electrical field is of the static type; that is to say, it is applied between two electrodes separated by an essentially nonconducting gap, so that the flow of electric current is insignificant. Specific impulses of 5000 to 50,000 seconds should be attainable with ion rockets.

3.189. Operation of an ion rocket involves three principal processes: generation of the ions, their acceleration by an electrostatic field, and electrical neutralization of the resulting ion beam. Since the beam of ions is positively charged, there must be an equivalent negative electrical charge somewhere on the system. It is generally accepted that neutralization of the ion beam by the addition of electrons is necessary to prevent energy loss. This may result from deceleration of the positive ions as a consequence of attraction by the oppositely charged parts of the engine.

3.190. Contact ionization and electron-beam ionization are being investigated, among other possibilities, for the production of positive ions. The *contact ionization* method is particularly useful for the element cesium; upon heating the solid, it melts and vaporizes, and the cesium vapor is passed through a heated tungsten grid or porous slab where ionization occurs upon contact.* The cesium ions are formed in the vapor (or gas) phase but, under suitable conditions, most of the electrons remain on the tungsten. In the alternative procedure of *electron-beam ionization*, a beam of fast electrons emitted from an electrically heated cathode, i.e., negative electrode, passes through the vapor of the material to be ionized. The method can be used for a variety of elements but mercury vapor has been found to be convenient for experimental purposes.

3.191. It will be noted that both cesium and mercury have high atomic (or molecular) weights, viz., 133 and 200, respectively. They were chosen because

---

* Cesium has a low *ionization potential* (3.89 volts), which is a measure of the energy necessary to remove an electron from an atom, as it exists in the vapor, and form a cesium ion. Tungsten has a high *thermionic* (or *electronic*) *work function* (4.54 volts), so that a relatively large amount of energy is required to remove an electron from the surface of the solid. Consequently, when cesium vapor is in contact with heated tungsten, there will be a tendency for electrons to pass from the cesium atoms to the tungsten surface, leaving cesium ions in the vapor.

they can be ionized relatively easily and their mass is not a significant disadvantage in the ion-acceleration system. Although the voltage required to produce a particular specific impulse increases with the ratio of mass to charge of the ion,* this voltage is not particularly high even when the mass-to-charge ratio is large. For example, an electrostatic field of 2000 volts should be capable of producing a specific impulse of 4500 seconds with singly-charged mercury ions as the propellant. Furthermore, the use of ions of high mass makes possible an increase in the thrust per unit area and, consequently, in the thrust-to-weight ratio of the ion engine.

3.192. The positive ions formed in one of the ways described above are now accelerated by an electrostatic field of a few thousand volts applied from a grid electrode maintained at a negative potential (or voltage) with respect to the ion source (Fig. 3.20). The ions pass through the accelerating grid at a

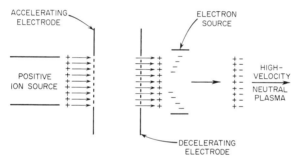

FIG. 3.20.   Principles of operation of ion rocket (thrustor)

high velocity, but before being exhausted they are decelerated to some extent by means of an electrode at a somewhat less negative potential than the accelerating grid. This combination of electrodes is designated an *acceleration-deceleration* (or *accel-decel*) *system*. A high negative potential of the accelerating electrode permits operation at high ion-current densities, i.e., high ion current per unit area, thus increasing the rocket thrust. The negative potential, however, tends to force high-speed electrons back into the ion source where they can cause physical damage. The decelerating electrode, being slightly positive with respect to the accelerating grid, decreases this tendency. Thus, the accel-decel system makes possible the production of intense ion beams at the cost of a small decrease in exhaust velocity.

3.193. Before being exhausted from the ion rocket, the positive-ion beam must be neutralized by the addition of negative electrons, as explained earlier. A suitable electron source (or sources), e.g., an electrically heated filament or grid, is located in such a manner that it can inject the appropriate number of

* The specific impulse (or exhaust velocity) is proportional to $\sqrt{Vi/m}$, where V is the accelerating voltage, m is the mass of the ion, and i the number of unit charges it carries; m/i is the mass-to-charge ratio.

electrons into the ion beam, at approximately the same speed as the ions. The exhaust is then an electrically neutral beam, although it may consist largely of separate ions and electrons.

3.194. In order to determine if ion thrustors would operate in the near-vacuum of space, in particular if neutralization of the ion and electron beams would take place, two ion rockets, one using mercury (Fig. 3.21) and the other cesium, were tested in the Space Electric Rocket Test (SERT I) on July 20, 1964. The spacecraft carrying the two engines was flown in a ballistic path to an altitude of about 2500 miles over a range of 2000 miles for a period of 50 minutes. The mercury-ion (electron-beam ionization) thrustor, weighing 11.6 pounds, operated satisfactorily for a period of 20 minutes and produced a thrust of 0.00637 pound force, slightly more than the design value. The engine was then turned off, restarted and allowed to operate for another 10 minutes. The estimated specific impulse was close to 5000 seconds. No problems were experienced during the test. The engine utilizing cesium ions failed to start, apparently because

Fig. 3.21.   Mercury-ion thrustor flight-test model

of a high-voltage short circuit. However, the U.S. Air Force achieved the successful operation of a cesium-ion (tungsten contact) device for 17 minutes during a suborbital flight.

The Colloid Rocket

3.195. In a modification of the ion rocket, called the *colloid rocket,* the electrically charged particles to be accelerated are colloidal in nature. Such particles, perhaps a few millionths of an inch across, are small by normal standards, but are large and heavy compared with atomic ions. Solid particles of colloidal dimensions can be obtained by condensation from the vapor and even by fine grinding of solid masses. These particles readily acquire an electrical charge, often during their formation. For liquids, a simple method of producing small charged droplets utilizes an electrical discharge from a pointed or sharp-edged electrode.

3.196. Like ions, the charged colloidal particles can be accelerated by means of an electrostatic field and exhausted to produce rocket action. Because of their high ratio of mass to charge, higher accelerating voltages are required for colloidal than for ionic particles. Nevertheless, it appears that, in the specific impulse range of about 1000 to 3000 seconds, the colloid rocket should be more

efficient than the ion rocket. One reason is that, in the former, a smaller proportion of the energy is utilized in the production of the electrically charged particles to be accelerated. Furthermore, with the heavier particles, it is possible to
have an engine with a higher thrust-to-weight ratio, as indicated in § 3.191.

THE ELECTROMAGNETIC (PLASMA) ROCKET

3.197. The *electromagnetic* (or *plasma*) *rocket* operates on the same principle
as the familiar electric motor. If an electric current flows in the presence of a
magnetic field, then an electromagnetic force, called the *Lorentz force*, acts on
the conductor carrying the current in a direction at right angles to both the
current and the magnetic field (Fig. 3.22). In the electromagnetic rocket, the
electrical conductor is not a solid, as it
is in a motor, but an ionized gas, called
a *plasma*. Under suitable conditions,
e.g., sufficiently high temperature, ions
and electrons can exist alongside each
other in a gas without combining to
reform neutral atoms. The gas (or
plasma) as a whole is electrically neutral, since it contains equivalent quantities of positive (ions) and negative
(electron) particles. But, owing to the
presence of the charged particles, the
plasma is able to conduct an electric
current. For immediate practical pur-

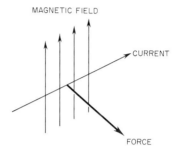

FIG. 3.22. Electromagnetic (Lorentz)
force of magnetic field on an electric current

poses, therefore, the plasma may be regarded as a mixture of ions and electrons
in equivalent amounts.

3.198. The simultaneous application of an electric current and a magnetic
field at right angles to one another causes a force to act on the charged particles
in the plasma and accelerates them all in the same direction, regardless of the
sign of their charge.* The expulsion of these accelerated particles at high
velocity produces the rocket thrust. Since the plasma is electrically neutral, the
problem of charge separation, present in the ion rocket, does not arise. The basic
principle of rocket propulsion by plasma acceleration is sometimes referred to
as *magneto-fluid dynamic propulsion* or *magnetohydrodynamic* (or *MHD*) *propulsion*, because it involves the motion in a magnetic field of a plasma which behaves like a fluid. It has been estimated that, with this propulsion technique,
specific impulses up to 25,000 seconds should be attainable; the thrust-to-weight
ratio would probably be in the range of 10^{-5} to 10^{-3}.

3.199. Electromagnetic rocket thrustors are still in the first stages of develop-

---

* It should be noted that an electric field alone would accelerate the oppositely charged
ions and electrons in opposite directions, as is the case in the ion rocket. In most cases, a
magnetic field alone would not accelerate the charged particles at all; the motion of
charged particles in a magnetic field is discussed in § 8.278.

ment. Although several different methods have been proposed for applying the basic principles of plasma acceleration, it is not known which, if any, will prove to be practical for space propulsion. A relatively simple device is the pulsed accelerator or *plasma gun,* in which the plasma and the accelerating electromagnetic field are produced simultaneously. The coaxial plasma gun consists of two metal electrodes, an outer tube and an inner concentric (coaxial) rod, as shown in Fig. 3.23. A small quantity of a gas is admitted at the left into the

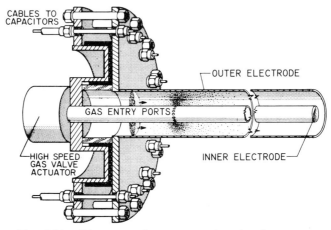

Fɪɢ. 3.23.   Diagrammatic representation of a plasma gun

annular space between the electrodes and then a high-voltage discharge is passed across the gas. The discharge ionizes the gas to form a conducting plasma and a radial sheet current, as indicated by the shaded disc in Fig. 3.23. At the same time, the current in the electrodes generates an azimuthal magnetic field encircling the inner electrode, that is, in a direction perpendicular to the plasma current. The combined action of the magnetic field and the electric current flow produces a force which drives the plasma to the right.

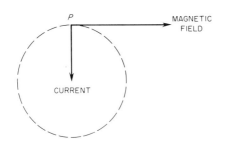

Fɪɢ. 3.24.   Electric current and magnetic field in a plasma gun

3.200. The situation may be understood more clearly by considering a section through the gun, as in Fig. 3.24. At any point in the plasma, such as P, the electric current is flowing toward the center (or tube axis), whereas the magnetic field, represented by the dotted circle, acts in a perpendicular direction, i.e., at a tangent to the circle. Comparison with Fig. 3.22 shows that there will be a Lorentz force acting on P in the direction out of the plane of the paper. This is the force driving the plasma out of the gun; the resulting reaction could be utilized, in principle, to produce rocket propulsion. Specific impulses of about 5000 seconds have been reported in the operation of plasma guns.

3.201. A device of the type described above would operate in pulses in rapid succession, but other electromagnetic systems have been proposed for continuous operation. Some are designed to avoid the necessity of having electrodes within the plasma, so that there are no erosion problems. Such problems may be significant in plasma guns. Two particular matters are receiving attention: first, the development of methods of generating strong magnetic fields economically in a small volume by utilizing the phenomenon of superconductivity, which is observed in certain metals and alloys at very low temperatures. Second, procedures are being investigated for producing plasmas without considerable expenditure of energy. Success in these directions will help greatly to advance the techniques of electromagnetic propulsion.

ADVANCED PROPULSION TECHNIQUES

INTRODUCTION

3.202. Mention should be made of certain possible advanced, but somewhat speculative, procedures for rocket propulsion that are still in the conceptual stage. The rocket types already described in preceding sections are known to be feasible in principle, but will require development before they become practical. In contrast, the propulsion techniques reviewed below may not even be feasible, although they have sound theoretical bases. It is not yet known whether, in these instances, theory can be translated into reasonable practice, even in experimental devices. The problems involved are still a long way from being solved.

CAVITY REACTOR ROCKETS

3.203. Because of the limitation set by materials on the permissible temperature (§ 3.169), it does not appear likely that the specific impulse of a nuclear fission rocket with a solid core can exceed about 1200 seconds. But if the fission chain could be sustained in a gas space, in what is called a *cavity reactor*, very much higher gas temperatures, in the vicinity of 30,000°C (45,000°F), might be attainable. With hydrogen as the propellant, the specific impulse would then be approximately 3500 seconds. The fissile material, e.g., uranium-235 or plutonium-239, would presumably be used in elemental form since at the proposed temperatures compounds would be decomposed. Furthermore, because of the high temperature, the uranium or plutonium would be in the form of a gas (or vapor) which is, at least partly, ionized; in other words, it would be in the form of a plasma. The cavity in which heat is produced by fission would be the equivalent of the combustion chamber in a chemical rocket, and hydrogen propellant entering the cavity would be heated by direct contact, i.e., as a result of interatomic collisions, with the fission products. The hot gas would be expelled through a conventional nozzle, thus producing the required thrust.

3.204. As just described, the gas-phase fission reactor has a serious drawback: the fissile material would be expelled continuously with the propellant. The increase in average molecular weight would, of course, decrease the specific impulse, but this is a relatively minor matter. Much more serious is the cost of the uranium-235 * that would be required for developing and operating such cavity reactors. Another factor is the mass of fissile material that would have to be carried in order to run the rocket engine for an appreciable time. This would greatly offset the advantage of the high specific impulse. Some means must therefore be found for preventing or minimizing the escape of uranium from the reactor cavity. Several proposals have been made in this connection, but there is no certainty that any of them will prove successful.

3.205. One proposal is the *vortex reactor* in which advantage would be taken of the large ratio of the masses of the uranium and hydrogen atoms, i.e., **235 to 1**. The mixture of uranium and hydrogen gases (or vapors) would be introduced into the cavity in a tangential direction (Fig. 3.25, I). As a result of gas-

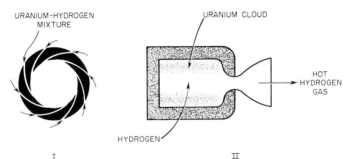

URANIUM-HYDROGEN MIXTURE

URANIUM CLOUD

HOT HYDROGEN GAS

HYDROGEN

I   II

Fig. 3.25.   Schematic representation of vortex (gas-core) nuclear reactor

dynamic action and the centrifugal (inertial) effect, the heavy uranium atoms would tend to form a hollow cylindrical cloud (Fig. 3.25, II) in which heat is generated by fission. The much lighter hydrogen atoms and molecules would diffuse through the cloud toward the center of the vortex, and the hot gas would be expelled through the nozzle. Laboratory experiments with a mixture of bromine vapor (heavy molecules) and air (light molecules) have shown that some degree of separation can be achieved by the vortex, but the mechanism is much more complex than had been anticipated.

3.206. A drawback to the foregoing scheme is that the highest temperatures are attained at the outside of the vortex, i.e., closest to the walls of the chamber.

---

* The current price of uranium-235 in relatively pure form is about $5000 per pound of contained uranium-235.

The cooler entering gas may provide some protection, but it would be preferable if the hydrogen propellant were on the outside and the much hotter fissile material were on the inside, away from the walls. This situation might be realized in the *coaxial flow* concept for a cavity reactor. The uranium and hydrogen would be introduced in separate coaxial streams at different flow rates, the uranium forming the central stream with the hydrogen surrounding it (Fig. 3.26). By maintaining a much lower rate of flow of uranium than of hydrogen,

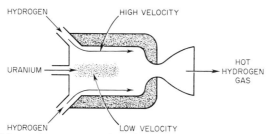

Fig. 3.26.   Schematic representation of coaxial flow (gas-core) nuclear reactor

a stable system might be realized in which relatively little of the uranium would be expelled through the nozzle. In the coaxial flow reactor, the hydrogen would be heated by radiation from the central fissile core. But below about 5500°C (10,000°F) hydrogen does not absorb thermal (heat) radiation, and consequently an opaque, absorbing material, e.g., graphite dust, would have to be added. The particles (or atoms) of the latter would then transfer part of their kinetic energy to the hydrogen by collisions and thereby raise its temperature. Preliminary tests with mixtures of bromine vapor and air indicate that coaxial flow separation has possibilities for development.

3.207. Another proposal for a gaseous core reactor for rocket propulsion is the *plasma core* concept. As stated earlier, at sufficiently high temperatures the fissile material would be in the form of an ionized plasma. Confinement by a magnetic field might then be possible, in principle (§ 3.219). The hydrogen propellant would then flow around the central plasma core confined in this manner; heat generated by fission in the core would then be transferred to the propellant by radiation, provided a suitable absorber were present. Apart from other problems, there would be difficulties in providing the equipment for generating the strong magnetic fields required to confine the plasma core.

3.208. In the "glo-plug" or "light bulb" system, a material wall would be used for keeping the gaseous nuclear fuel and the propellant apart. The uranium-235 constituting the reactor core would be contained in a vessel of a material that can withstand high temperatures but is transparent to and is not damaged by the various radiations emitted by the nuclei undergoing fission. The propellant flowing outside the containing vessel would then be heated by the radiations from the core. The presence of a substance that is opaque to these radiations and can thus absorb them would, of course, be required. The walls of the vessel separating the fissile material from the propellant could be prevented from becoming excessively hot by utilizing the cold, transparent propellant as a regenerative coolant (§ 3.73).

3.209. It has been assumed in all the gaseous core concepts described above that the propellant is hydrogen. In view of the very high temperatures expected, it might be possible to make use of liquid ammonia, which is easier to store, or even of water as the propellant material. The molecules of these compounds would be completely dissociated into their constituent atoms, i.e., nitrogen and hydrogen or oxygen and hydrogen, respectively. The average molecular (or atomic) weight would then be 3.5 in the former case and 6.0 in the latter. The advantage of a cheap, storable propellant might well outweigh the drawback of the accompanying decrease in specific impulse.

Propulsion by Nuclear Explosions

3.210. An entirely different approach to the employment of nuclear energy for rocket propulsion, designated Project Orion, is to utilize the explosion of nuclear bombs to impart kinetic (or motion) energy to a space vehicle. Because of the health hazard arising from the radioactivity of the fission products, such a mode of propulsion could be used only at some distance from Earth. In these circumstances, the air density would be very low and the blast (or shock) wave, normally responsible for much of the destructive action of a nuclear explosion, would be of minor consequence. When the bomb explodes, the first result would be the emission of a large amount of energy as electromagnetic radiation (§ 6.47), including X-rays, ultraviolet and visible light, infrared radiation, etc. All such radiation travels in a vacuum with the velocity of light. Within a millionth of a second or so, the bomb residues would begin to expand very rapidly and the particles would move outward at high speed but less than the velocity of light.

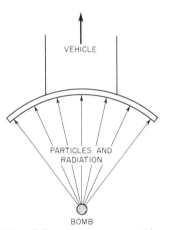

FIG. 3.27. Schematic representation of Project Orion

3.211. One way in which the effects of nuclear explosions in space might be realized for propulsion purposes is represented in Fig. 3.27. Attached to the space vehicle is a pusher plate of relatively large area, and bombs are exploded at intervals a moderate distance behind the plate. The rapid expansion of the bomb residues would cause material (fission product) particles to strike the pusher plate at high velocity. As a result of the impact, momentum would be imparted to the vehicle and its velocity would increase. In this manner, very high velocities might be attained by the successive explosion of a number of atomic bombs. Specific impulses attainable in this manner are estimated to be from 2000 to 3000 seconds.

3.212. In order to protect the pusher plate from the high temperature accompanying the nuclear explosions, the plate would be coated with an ablative material. Absorption of the electromagnetic (and other) radiations would heat the material and cause ablation to occur (§ 3.76). The reaction (or rocket action) resulting from the vaporization of the ablated material would add some thrust to the vehicle.

3.213. Many difficult problems are associated with the concept of propulsion by utilizing nuclear explosions. A large number of bombs of small energy yield must be stored on the vehicle, released at regular intervals, and exploded at an appropriate distance from the vehicle. The efficiency would be very low since most of the energy would be wasted because it would be spread over a large, mostly ineffective, area. The succession of sharp impulses imparted to the vehicle could lead to structural damage. Consequently, a method must be devised, e.g., by the use of powerful springs, to smooth out (or damp) the impulses into a more-or-less continuous steady thrust. Finally, in order to experience appreciable thrust the pusher plate must have a large area, and unless the impulse from the exploding bombs is applied uniformly the attached space vehicle will tend to tip over in one direction or the other.

THERMONUCLEAR (FUSION) PROPULSION

3.214. In addition to fission, there is another way in which nuclear energy can be released; this is by *fusion* (or combination) of the lightest nuclei, as distinct from fission (or splitting) of the heaviest nuclei. Of the possible fusion reactions, four are of present interest; they are the only ones that may be utilized for the production of energy. These reactions involve the nuclei of the two heavier isotopes of hydrogen, namely, deuterium (D^2), having a mass of 2 units, and tritium (T^3), with a mass of 3 units, and of the lighter isotopes of helium (He^3); they may be written as

$$D^2 + D^2 \rightarrow T^3 + H^1$$
$$D^2 + D^2 \rightarrow He^3 + n^1$$
$$D^2 + T^3 \rightarrow He^4 + n^1$$
$$D^2 + He^3 \rightarrow He^4 + H^1,$$

where n^1 represents a neutron. The total energy of these fusion reactions is so high that, if the very small amount of deuterium present in one gallon of ordinary water* could be utilized completely, the energy released would be

---

* Ordinary water, e.g., oceans, rivers, lakes, rain, etc., contains one atom (or nucleus) of deuterium for every 6800 atoms of common hydrogen (H^1). Tritium is radioactive and does not exist in nature except in very small traces; it has to be made artificially by the interaction of neutrons with nuclei of lithium-6, the less common, but naturally occurring, isotope of the element lithium.

equivalent to that obtained by the combustion of over 300 gallons of kerosene.

3.215. It is known that there are two general ways whereby nuclear fusion reactions can be brought about. The essential problem is to provide sufficient energy for one or both of the reacting nuclei to overcome the electrical (electrostatic) repulsion of the positive charges they carry. When brought close together, there is a good probability that the nuclei will combine and bring about the appropriate fusion reaction. One method of supplying the necessary energy to the nuclei is to accelerate the reacting nuclei of one type to a high velocity (and kinetic energy) in a charged-particle accelerator, e.g., a cyclotron-like machine or similar device, and to cause them to impinge on a target consisting of the other reactant. But this procedure, although of great experimental importance, has no practical value because the energy expended in accelerating the nuclei is much greater than is released by the fusion reactions.

3.216. The other way in which nuclei could acquire a large amount of energy is to raise their temperature. For example, it is possible to utilize the extremely high temperatures—tens of millions of degrees—attained in a nuclear fission explosion. At these temperatures, many of the nuclei of hydrogen and helium isotopes have sufficient energy to permit them to fuse and release energy; this is the principle of the so-called hydrogen bomb. The reactions are now described as *thermonuclear* because the nuclei acquire a high energy by virtue of their temperature.* Strictly speaking, the term thermonuclear implies that the nuclei have a range (or distribution) of energies characteristic of their temperature (cf. § 9.165). It is this distribution of energies that plays an important role in the rate of the fusion reactions at any given temperature.

3.217. Of course, there is a remote possibility that thermonuclear (hydrogen) bombs could be employed for propulsion of a space vehicle by the procedure described in § 3.211. But it would be much more useful if thermonuclear reactions could be made to take place at a controlled rate, rather than in the very rapid, uncontrolled manner of an explosion. This matter has been the subject of much experimental study since 1951 as a means for producing nuclear energy for power purposes. If successful, a method could probably be developed for the utilization of fusion energy for rocket propulsion.

3.218. In order to establish a self-sustaining thermonuclear reaction, it would be necessary first to heat the gas, i.e., deuterium alone or a mixture with tritium or helium-3, to a very high temperature, in the vicinity of 100 million degrees centigrade or more.† The fusion reactions could then take place fast enough to provide somewhat more energy than is required to heat fresh gas to the appropriate reaction temperature and to allow for inevitable losses. Once started,

---

* The average kinetic energy of the molecules of a gas is directly proportional to the absolute temperature (§ 3.59).

† The temperature in the interior of the Sun is about 15 million degrees centigrade. Thermonuclear (fusion) reactions occur in the Sun, as well as in the stars, but they are too slow to be utilized on Earth. It is because of the enormous mass of the Sun that there is such a large amount of energy released from these relatively slow nuclear reactions.

the nuclear fusion process would then sustain itself, generating energy continuously, as long as the deuterium or other gas was being supplied. The excess energy could, in principle, be transferred to a rocket propellant material.

3.219. Since the initiation and maintenance of a fusion reaction requires the production of extremely high temperatures, much hotter than the interior of the Sun, there is the difficulty of containing the reacting gases at such temperatures. The problem is not so much the heating of the vessel, but the loss of energy and rapid cooling of the gas particles when they strike the walls. A possible solution arises from the fact that, at high temperatures, the atoms of deuterium, tritium, etc., are completely ionized; the so-called gas is thus really a plasma of electrically charged particles. In this event, theory indicates that the plasma can be confined, i.e., kept away from the walls of the containing vessel, by means of a magnetic field. Furthermore, electric and magnetic fields can probably be used to produce the high temperatures necessary for the operation of a fusion reactor. In general, these expectations have been confirmed by laboratory experiments, but study of the behavior of plasmas in magnetic fields has revealed so many instabilities at densities of interest that confinement beyond a fraction of a second has not been achieved. Longer stable confinement periods will be necessary before a thermonuclear fusion reactor even approaches feasibility. It is felt that if the problems of instability can be overcome with plasmas of sufficiently high density, the attainment of the necessary high thermonuclear temperatures will not prove to be a serious obstacle.

PHOTON PROPULSION

3.220. A mode of rocket propulsion different from any of those already considered, and possibly even more in the realm of speculation, is the *photon rocket*. It is of unusual interest because it offers the prospect of space travel at a speed approaching that of light. If man is ever to leave the solar system and explore the stars beyond, such speeds will be required. The nearest star group to Earth, namely, Alpha and Proxima Centauri, is 4.3 light-years distant;* that is to say, even traveling with the velocity of light, i.e., 186,000 miles (or 3×10^8 meters) per second, the journey would take 4.3 years. No other means of propulsion could provide velocities approaching that of light, and the journey would require more than a normal lifetime (see, however, § 13.134). It is for this reason that the somewhat speculative concept of the photon rocket is being given serious consideration.

3.221. According to modern theory, all electromagnetic radiations are emitted, and travel from one place to another, as particles, known as *photons* (cf. § 6.76). In a vacuum, all photons move with the velocity of light; in fact, the expressions "velocity of a photon" and "velocity of light" have exactly the

* A light-year is the distance traveled by light in a vacuum, e.g., through space, in one year. It is equal to 5.88×10^{12} miles or 9.46×10^{15} meters (§ 12.4, footnote), i.e., more than 60,000 times the distance from Earth to the Sun.

same significance. Each photon carries a specified amount of energy, called a *quantum,* the magnitude of which depends on the frequency (or wavelength) of the radiation (§ 6.74). It has been long known, even before the development of the theory of photons, that light rays and electromagnetic radiations in general can produce a pressure when they impinge on a surface. This pressure is ascribed to the impact of the photons (§ 3.224).

3.222. A purely schematic design for a photon rocket is shown in Fig. 3.28. The engine consists essentially of a strong source of photons, e.g., a solid body at high temperature, with a means of focusing the photons into a roughly parallel beam. Emission of the photons in the direction indicated would produce a reaction in the opposite direction, in the usual manner. The system would be equivalent to a rocket with an exhaust gas velocity equal to the velocity of light. The ideal specific impulse is equal to the exhaust velocity divided by the acceleration due to gravity at Earth's surface, i.e.,

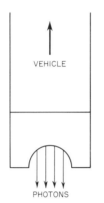

FIG. 3.28.   Simplified representation of a photon rocket

32.2 feet (or 9.83 meters) per second per second. Since the velocity of light is 9.82×10^8 feet (or 3.00×10^8 meters) per second, it is seen that the theoretical value for the specific impulse of a photon rocket is more than 3×10^7, i.e., 30 million, seconds.*

3.223. The highly attractive prospect of such an exceptionally large specific impulse is offset, however, by the enormous amount of power required to operate the photon rocket. For example, a thrust of 1 pound force would necessitate the expenditure of 4.8×10^9 British thermal units per hour, assuming all the energy could be converted into usable photons. In a chemical rocket, employing kerosene and liquid oxygen as propellants, for example, the same thrust would require a power of about 66 British thermal units per hour. Because a photon rocket would have to operate for a long period of time, if it is to perform the particular missions for which it is especially suitable, the mass of fuel, even of nuclear fuel material, would reach overwhelming proportions.

SOLAR SAILING

3.224. An entirely different form of photon propulsion can perhaps be used within the solar system, but probably not beyond. This is the concept called *solar sailing,* which would utilize the pressure exerted on a surface by photons

---

*Since masses are infinite at the velocity of light, it is doubtful if this value has any physical significance.

from the Sun. That the Sun's radiation does produce an appreciable thrust in the vicinity of Earth is known, for example, from the observed perturbations of the orbit of the Echo I balloon satellite (§ 2.94). If I is the intensity of the solar radiation, i.e., the energy of the radiation (in ergs) falling per second on an area of 1 square centimeter perpendicular to the direction of the radiation, and c is the velocity of light, i.e., 3.00×10^{10} centimeters per second, the pressure (in dynes per square centimeter) exerted on a completely absorbing surface is given by (see § 3.270)

$$p = \frac{I}{c}.$$

If the surface is a perfect reflector, the pressure is doubled and is consequently

$$p = \frac{2I}{c}. \tag{3.14}$$

3.225. Solar sailing could be achieved by attaching to a vehicle a "sail" consisting of a large area of a strong, lightweight material, e.g., Mylar plastic film, coated on one side with a thin layer of a good reflector of light, e.g., aluminum. The thrust that might be obtained can be calculated in the following manner. The quantity called the solar constant (§ 6.25) is the energy received from the Sun per square centimeter per second at Earth's distance; its value in the centimeter-gram-second system of units is 1.39×10^6 ergs per square centimeter per second. If this is substituted for I in equation (3.14), the corresponding radiation pressure on a good reflecting surface is found to be 9.3×10^{-5} dyne per square centimeter, which is equivalent to 2.0×10^{-7} pound (force) per square foot. A solar sail with a reasonable area of 1000 square feet would thus develop a thrust of 2×10^{-4} pound. Although this is small, it would be produced continuously in space where gravitational forces are small, so that considerable velocities could be built up in the course of time. One of the features of the solar sail is that it does not have to carry any propellant, since the photons are supplied by the Sun. Consequently, the ideal specific impulse is effectively infinitely large.

3.226. The solar-sail vehicle could be steered to some extent by changing the direction of the sail with reference to the Sun; this would, of course, require the expenditure of energy. Because of the large area of the solar sail, it could be employed only where aerodynamic drag is negligible, e.g., to explore the regions between the planets. Thus, solar sailing may be of interest for the propulsion of instrumented, unmanned interplanetary probes. It should be noted that the thrust per unit area due to solar radiation pressure varies inversely as the square of the distance from the Sun. Consequently, the thrust will increase steadily in a journey from Earth to Venus but will decrease in going to Mars.

POWER SUPPLIES IN SPACE

INTRODUCTION

3.227. Several of the proposed novel, but feasible, propulsion methods, such as resistance-heating and arc-jet systems and those based on ion or plasma acceleration, require the availability of fairly large amounts of electric power in space. Apart from propulsion, electricity is utilized in both manned and unmanned space vehicles for a variety of purposes, e.g., operation of radio receivers and transmitters and many other instruments. Electric power will also be needed in the lunar and space laboratories that will undoubtedly be constructed in due course. Although there are many different applications, it is convenient to consider them together since the basic sources of power are often the same.

NUCLEAR POWER SOURCES

3.228. The most promising means of obtaining significant quantities of power in space, at least within the foreseeable future, appears to be through the utilization of nuclear fission energy. The purpose of the SNAP * program is to study various systems of this kind. Where the electrical power demand is more than about 1 kilowatt, nuclear fission reactors are expected to have advantages over other power sources, particularly with respect to size and weight. Such reactors operate on the same general principles as the nuclear rocket reactor described in § 3.167, although they differ in design details.

3.229. The SNAP-2 and SNAP-8 reactors† are similar except for power output; the former was intended to produce 3 kilowatts of electricity and the latter roughly 35 kilowatts.‡ In each case, the reactor core, which has a cylindrical form, some 18 inches in length and 15 inches in diameter, is made up of a number of fuel rods (or elements) consisting of uranium-235 intimately mixed with zirconium hydride. The hydrogen atoms in this hydride serve as the moderator (§ 3.170) to slow down the neutrons which maintain the fission chain. The heat produced by fission is removed from the fuel elements by circulating the coolant, a liquid alloy of sodium and potassium, through the core (Fig. 3.29). In the SNAP-2 reactor, the coolant enters the core at a temperature of about 550°C (1000°F) and leaves at roughly 660°C (1200°F); in SNAP-8, both temperatures are some 55°C (100°F) higher. The choice of zirconium hydride as moderator and of sodium-potassium alloy as coolant was

---

* SNAP is an acronym for Systems for Nuclear Auxiliary Power; SNAP projects identified by even numbers are based on nuclear fission, whereas the odd-numbered projects involve the use of radioactive isotopes.

† SNAP-4 is a compact, ground-based reactor which utilizes some of the technology developed in connection with SNAP-2, but heat is removed by boiling water in the core; the SNAP-6 project has been abandoned.

‡ The SNAP-2 reactor project has been terminated and the technology incorporated into SNAP-10A (§ 3.237).

determined largely by the need for compactness and the ability to function at high temperatures for extended periods. For various reasons, the reactor core must operate at high temperatures if there is to be efficient conversion of heat into electricity.

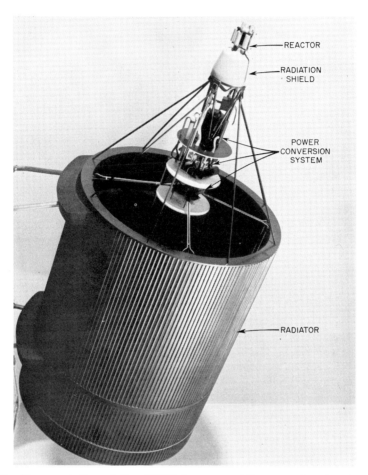

REACTOR

RADIATION
SHIELD

POWER
CONVERSION
SYSTEM

RADIATOR

Fig. 3.29.   Representation of the SNAP-8 reactor. (*Courtesy Atomics International Division, North American Aviation, Inc.*)

3.230. To convert the heat gained from the reactor into electric power, the high-temperature sodium-potassium alloy coolant is passed through a heat exchanger (or boiler). Here, liquid mercury—the working fluid—is boiled, and the emerging coolant is circulated back to the reactor core for further heat removal. The mercury vapor is used to drive a turbine connected to an electrical generator, so that electricity is produced. In order to complete the

(Rankine) cycle, the mercury vapor leaving the turbine must be condensed to liquid by cooling before it is returned to the boiler. In space, the only method available for cooling is by discarding the heat as radiation. This is one reason why the operating temperature of the reactor must be high, since the loss of heat by radiation becomes significant only at such temperatures.

3.231. The design of a suitable radiator presents a formidable problem. It must be light in weight yet strong, large in area, completely free from leaks, not subject to corrosion by the working fluid, able to withstand the impact of micrometeoroids (§ 7.155), and capable of being carried into space. For maximum efficiency of conversion of the reactor heat into electrical power, it is necessary that the mercury vapor (or other working fluid) enter the turbine at a high temperature and that liquid return to the boiler at a lower temperature, the lower the better. The latter requirement makes the function of the radiator highly important.

3.232. An advanced reactor system, with a design power of 300 to 1000 kilowatts of electricity, is SNAP-50.* The coolant will be an alkali metal, possibly lithium, at temperatures up to about 1100°C (2000°F), and boiling potassium will be the working fluid for the turbogenerator in a Rankine cycle. Both lithium and potassium are very corrosive at high temperatures, and there are only a few metals, e.g., columbium (niobium), tantalum, and tungsten or their alloys, able to contain lithium under these conditions. Since there has been essentially no prior experience in the use of lithium and boiling potassium for the particular purposes indicated, much research and development are required before SNAP-50 becomes an operational system for power production. But if it is successful, it will represent an important step toward the realization of electrical methods of spacecraft propulsion.

3.233. In addition to the design of an effective radiator, a major problem in the SNAP reactors is corrosion of various components, e.g., containing vessels, pipes, pumps, etc., by the molten alkali metals, lithium, sodium, and potassium, at the high operating temperatures. If this problem cannot be solved satisfactorily, it may be necessary to utilize a gas, e.g., helium or argon, to serve as the reactor coolant and the working fluid to drive the turbine. Furthermore, from what is known of the peculiar behavior of liquid surfaces in the so-called "weightless" condition experienced in space (§ 13.83), there is a possibility that difficulties may arise in the heat exchanger (or boiler), where the working liquid is vaporized, and in the condenser, where it is converted back to liquid. But if the working fluid is a gas, weightlessness would present no problem.

3.234. With a gas as the working fluid, it would be necessary to operate the turbine on a Brayton cycle, instead of the Rankine cycle in which condensation of the vapor, e.g., of mercury or potassium, is an essential stage. But for

---

* This is also designated SPUR or SPUR/SNAP-50; SPUR is an acronym used by the U.S. Air Force for Space Power Unit Reactor.

the same operating temperature limits, the Brayton cycle is less efficient and requires a larger radiating surface than does the Rankine cycle. The overall weight of the Brayton cycle equipment is believed to be greater, for a given power output, but this may not be a serious drawback for nonpropulsive applications of electricity.

3.235. Nuclear reactors intended for power production, like those designed for propulsion, emit neutrons and gamma rays in substantial amounts (§ 3.176). Even in unmanned vehicles, it would be necessary to protect semiconductor and other devices from these radiations with appropriate shielding. This will involve a substantial increase in weight of the overall system.

THERMOELECTRIC CONVERSION

3.236. Because a conventional turbogenerating system involves moving parts, consideration is being given to other techniques for converting heat into electricity which are simpler mechanically. One of these makes use of the principle of *thermoelectric conversion*. It is well known that if one junction between two different metals is at a higher temperature than another similar junction, an electromotive force (or potential difference) is produced. This electromotive force can drive an electric current through an external load between the hot and cold junctions. By utilizing the heat liberated in a fission reactor to maintain one junction at a high temperature and a radiator to keep the other junction cold, a device would be available for generating electricity without any moving components. A disadvantage of the thermoelectric system is the low efficiency for the conversion of heat into electricity.

3.237. The purpose of the SNAP-10A reactor is to test the thermoelectric conversion concept utilizing fission heat. The general design of the core is similar to that of the other SNAP reactors and the coolant is sodium-potassium alloy. A number of thermoelectric elements, made from a germanium-silicon alloy, are connected in series and arranged in the form of an annular shroud. The junctions on the inner surface are heated by the hot sodium-potassium alloy coming from the reactor whereas the junctions on the outer surface are cooled by radiation to space. The design power of the SNAP-10A system is 0.5 kilowatt, but it is believed that this value can be exceeded. Whether it will be possible to extend the thermoelectric design to higher powers is not known.

THERMIONIC CONVERSION

3.238. The direct generation of electricity from heat, without a turbogenerator, can also be achieved by *thermionic conversion*. In principle the converter consists of two electrodes of different metals; one of these, preferably the one with the larger thermionic (or thermoelectric) work function (§ 3.190, footnote), is maintained at a higher temperature than the other (Fig. 3.30). Both electrodes tend to emit electrons but the hotter one will do so more copiously. Since the electrons carry a negative charge, a positive charge will build up on the hotter electrode, referred to as the *emitter* or *cathode;** a charge of opposite sign will tend to form on the colder electrode, called the *collector* or *anode*. There will thus be a difference of potential (or electromotive force) between the two electrodes and an electric current will flow in

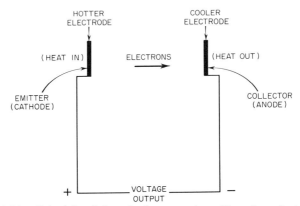

Fig. 3.30. Principle of thermionic conversion of heat into electricity

an external circuit (or load) connecting them. If heat is continuously supplied to the emitter and removed from the collector, there will be a steady flow of current. The situation is then somewhat analogous to that described above for a thermoelectric converter.

3.239. The electric current generated by a thermionic converter is limited by the accumulation of electrons in the space between the electrodes; this results in the development of a *space charge potential* that retards electron emission from the cathode. Two possible solutions of this undesirable situation are being studied. One is to reduce the spacing between the electrodes to a few thousandths of an inch; such thermionic cells are satisfactory, but fabrication is difficult except in small sizes yielding only small currents. This approach has therefore been abandoned. A preferable alternative is to introduce cesium vapor in the space between the electrodes. The cesium atom ionizes readily (§ 3.190) and the positive ions help to neutralize the negative space charge. Furthermore, some of the cesium atoms condense and are deposited on the relatively cold collector, thereby decreasing the work function of the surface; the result is an increase in the voltage developed by the thermionic cell.

3.240. A number of different methods are being investigated for utilizing fission heat to operate a thermionic converter. For example, the cathodes (emitters) of a number of cells containing cesium, connected in series, may be maintained in contact with the fuel elements in the reactor core. A coolant,

---

* The electron emission occurring is similar to that from the cathode of a conventional vacuum tube.

e.g., sodium-potassium alloy, flows past the anodes (collectors) to remove heat which is then dissipated by radiation to space. If the emitter consists of uranium or a suitable compound of this element, it will be heated by nuclear reactions, e.g., fission and capture, resulting from the absorption of neutrons. It appears, therefore, that in one way or another a fission reactor might become a direct source of electricity. It is believed that power generators of this type, with an output of 1000 kilowatts or more, are possible for use in space propulsion.

POWER FROM RADIOISOTOPES

3.241. An entirely different concept for utilizing nuclear energy for space power supplies is based on the phenomenon of *radioactivity*. All elements can exist in unstable, radioactive forms called *radioisotopes;* over 40 radioisotopes are found in nature in certain minerals, but the great majority have been produced by various nuclear reactions, in particular by fission. A characteristic manifestation of the instability (or decay) of radioisotopes is that the nuclei emit electrically charged particles, either a positive *alpha particle,* which is the same as a nucleus of the normal helium atom, or a negative *beta particle,* identical with an electron.* As a consequence of particle emission, the original nucleus is converted into the nucleus of a different element. This product (or daughter) nucleus may be stable or it, in turn, may be radioactive and emit either an alpha or a beta particle, and so on. Many, but not all, radioactive changes are accompanied by gamma rays, which are electromagnetic radiations of high energy (§ 3.176). Like X-rays, which they resemble, they are able to penetrate appreciable thicknesses of matter.

3.242. The rate of the radioactive decay process, i.e., the rate of emission of alpha or beta particles, is usually expressed by means of the *half-life* of the individual radioisotope. This may be defined as the time required for the radioactivity of a given quantity of a particular radioisotope to decrease (or decay) to half of its original value. Each radioactive species has a definite half-life that is independent of its state or its amount. Measured half-lives range from a very small fraction of a second to many billions of years.

3.243. Alpha and beta particles are absorbed quite readily in solid material and when such absorption takes place the considerable amount of energy carried by the particles is converted into heat.† The energy of the particles arises from or is a manifestation of the instability of the radioactive nucleus and so it is a form of nuclear energy. By virtue of its continuous emission of alpha or beta particles, a radioisotope is thus a source of heat, and this heat can, in principle, be converted into electrical energy by any of the procedures

---

* Although a beta particle and an electron are identical, the use of the former description indicates that the particle was produced in a radioactive decay process.

† A similar conversion into heat occurs when gamma rays are absorbed, but these radiations are very penetrating and difficult to absorb.

already described, e.g., by means of a turbogenerator or by utilizing thermo-electric or thermionic effects.

3.244. To provide a useful heat source for the generation of electricity, however, a radioisotope should satisfy certain requirements. In the first place, the alpha or beta particles should have reasonably high energies; this is generally the case for alpha particles but not always for beta particles. Second, the radioisotope should not have a short half-life, otherwise its activity, i.e., the rate of particle emission, and the rate of heat generation will fall off rapidly. On the other hand, if the half-life is too long, the rate of particle emission, for a given mass, will be too slow to produce heat at a useful rate. The selection of the radioisotope will depend upon circumstances; for example, where a generator of short lifetime is adequate, it would be satisfactory to use a species with a moderately short, but not too short, half-life to take advantage of the high activity per unit mass. A final requirement is that the radioisotope used should either produce no gamma rays or only gamma rays of low energy, otherwise heavy shielding might be necessary.

3.245. The characteristics of a number of radioisotopes which have been considered for supplying electrical power in space are given in Table 3.4. Of

TABLE 3.4 RADIOISOTOPES FOR SPACE POWER

Radioisotope	Particle Emitted	Half-life	Form Used
Strontium-90	Beta (no gamma)	28 years	Strontium titanate (or oxide)
Cesium-137	Beta (no gamma)	30 years	Cesium chloride
Cerium-144	Beta (weak gamma)	285 days	Cerium dioxide
Promethium-147	Beta (weak gamma)	2.6 years	Promethium sesquioxide
Polonium-210	Alpha (weak gamma)	138 days	Polonium (element)
Plutonium-238	Alpha (weak gamma)	86.4 years	Plutonium carbide
Curium-242	Alpha (weak gamma)	162 days	Curium sesquioxide
Curium-244	Alpha (weak gamma)	18.4 years	Curium sesquioxide

these, strontium-90, cesium-137, cerium-144, and promethium-147 are extracted from the products of fission; polonium-210 is found in nature, but it is commonly made from bismuth by nuclear reactions. The radioisotopes plutonium-238, curium-242, and curium-244 are relatively rare and expensive products of a series of nuclear reactions.

3.246. SNAP-1A was designed to employ cerium-144 and it was planned to utilize the heat to vaporize mercury which was to drive a turbogenerator. Difficulties were encountered in this somewhat ambitious project and it was discontinued. The first proof of the practicality of the radioisotope power generation concept was provided by SNAP-3 in January 1959; the radioactive material was polonium-210 and electricity was generated by thermoelectric conversion. The thermoelectric elements were made from a semiconductor, lead telluride (PbTe); each junction was formed between a rod of material treated with bismuth (negative or n-type) and one treated with sodium (positive or p-type).* The polonium-210 was placed in a central capsule, surrounded by a close array of 54 (hot) junctions; the same number of cold junctions were on the outside where they could be kept cool by radiation (Fig. 3.31). The maximum temperature of the hot junction was about 550°C

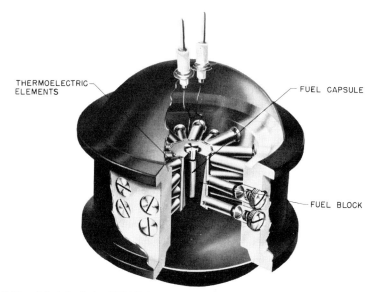

THERMOELECTRIC ELEMENTS

FUEL CAPSULE

FUEL BLOCK

Fig. 3.31.   Model of the SNAP-3 generator. (*Courtesy The Martin Company*)

(1050°F) and the cold junction was 150°C (300°F); these temperatures are fairly typical of thermoelectric junctions for radioisotope generators. The complete SNAP-3 device was a cylinder 5.5 inches high and 4.75 inches in diameter and weighed 5 pounds; it had an initial electrical power output of 5.3 watts.

3.247. The SNAP-3 generator was not intended for actual flight, and the first application of nuclear energy in space was demonstrated on a similar device with plutonium-238, instead of polonium-210, as the heat source. It was used to provide electric power for the instruments carried on the navigational satellite Transit IVA launched on June 29, 1961; it has performed very satisfactorily and is expected to do so for several years. A similar radioisotope generator was utilized in Transit IVB in November 1961. A somewhat larger version, with an initial power of 25 watts, using the same radioisotope, is the

* The elements in lead telluride have a valence of 2; the addition of bismuth, valence 3, results in the presence of extra electrons that are not required for the bond structure of the crystal. A semiconductor of this nature is called n (for negative)-type, because of the negative charge of the electron. The presence of sodium, valence 1, on the other hand, means that there is an electronic deficit in the bond structure. Each atom of sodium thus produces a "hole" in the lead telluride structure. The hole is equivalent to the absence of a negative electron or the presence of an excess positive character; hence the designation p (for positive)-type is used for such a semiconductor material.

SNAP-9A. Generators of this type, also carried by Transit satellites, were orbited in September and December 1963. To supply power for the Surveyor spacecraft that is to achieve a soft landing of instruments on the Moon, it has been proposed to use SNAP-11, a thermoelectric system with curium-242 to supply the heat energy. Consideration is being given to a possible alternative, SNAP-13, which will employ thermionic conversion of heat into electric power. Other thermoelectric generators under study are SNAP-17 with strontium-90 and SNAP-19 with plutonium-238 as the heat source.*

Nuclear Cells

3.248. A completely different means of utilizing radioisotopes for space power under study is based on the principle of the *nuclear cell*, in particular of the *beta-current cell*. Such a cell would consist of two parallel conducting electrodes, an emitter coated with a radioactive material, e.g., a source of beta particles, and a collector. Many of the beta particles, i.e., negative electrons, traveling at high speed reach the collector and build up a negative charge on it, whereas the emitter acquires a positive charge. In this way, a potential difference of several thousand volts can be built up between the two electrodes.

3.249. The amount of electricity which can be drawn from such a beta-current cell is small, and so it does not lend itself to conventional power uses. However, the high voltages that are possible make this type of cell of special interest as a means of providing the electric fields required for electrostatic propulsion devices (§ 3.188). Although the early forms of the nuclear cell have used isotopes emitting beta particles, it can be adapted to employ alpha-particle emitters. In this case the emitter electrode would become negative and the collector positive, because the alpha particle carries a positive charge.

Solar Energy Power Sources

3.250. The most common source of power for unmanned spacecraft has been the *solar cell*, and it is likely to remain so for some time to come. Cells of this type, which are connected in large numbers to form a *solar battery*, use *photovoltaic conversion* to produce electricity from sunlight. The early cells were made of thin (about 0.5-millimeter) wafers of an *n*-type silicon (valence 4) semiconductor crystal with a small amount of boron (valence 3) impurity diffused into it to form a *p*-type surface; this is known as a *p*-on-*n* type cell. For reasons given below, *n*-on-*p* cells are now in general use.

3.251. If the surface of the solar cell is exposed to light, free electrons and holes are produced in equal numbers, as a consequence of the well-known photoelectric effect. Electrons reaching the region near the *p-n* junction with sufficient energy tend to pass into the *n*-type layer whereas the holes move into the *p*-type material. This produces a difference of potential of about 0.5

---

* A series of SNAP-7 generators, with strontium-90 as the energy source, has been designed for several Earth-based applications, including a weather station in Antarctica.

volt between the two layers which can cause a current to flow in an external circuit. The current represents a passage of electrons from the n-layer to the p-layer, so that there is a restoration of the initial conditions. In principle, therefore, current can be produced, without any change in the materials, as long as the surface of the cell is exposed to light.

3.252. Solar cells usually have an exposed area of 1 or 2 square centimeters and the required number of cells are connected in series to supply the desired voltage. Several of these subunits are then arranged in parallel to form a complete unit. This parallel arrangement serves two purposes; first, it increases the current which can be drawn from the battery of cells, and second, the system will still operate, although with a decrease in current output, if a cell (or cells) in any subunit should fail.

3.253. The main advantage of the solar cell is that it does not have to carry any fuel to serve as a source of energy, since the energy is provided by the Sun. This is partially offset, however, by the large area required to produce an appreciable amount of electric power. The quantity of electricity generated is proportional to the area exposed to the Sun. In some satellites, such as Telstar and Relay, the solar cells are disposed over essentially the whole of the outside of the spacecraft; in others, such as Mariner and Nimbus, the array of solar cells is laid out on panels. Because of their large area, the panels are folded up for launching. When the craft is in space and aerodynamic drag is negligible, the panels are spread out to permit exposure to the Sun. At the distance of Earth's orbit, the solar power available is about 130 watts per square foot of surface perpendicular to the Sun's rays,* but only about 10 percent of the energy is converted into electricity in solar cells of present design. The power varies inversely as the square of the distance from the Sun, so that it is greater at closer distances and smaller when farther from the Sun. The maximum electrical power at any location is generated only when the cells face directly toward the Sun; if they are exposed at an angle, the power output is reduced. Thus, if i is the angle of incidence of the solar rays, i.e., the angle between the direction of the rays and the perpendicular to the surface of the cells, the solar power available is $130 \cos i$ watts per square foot.

3.254. In the absence of sunlight there is no production of electricity, and for use in satellites, which pass into Earth's shadow at regular intervals, the solar cell unit is supplemented with chemical storage batteries. The batteries are charged when the spacecraft is in sunlight and hence power is available for the dark periods. Even for missions into space, where the sunshine is continuous, storage batteries are included in the electrical supply system. They provide for increases in power demand for special instrumental observations when the space probe approaches its objective, e.g., the Moon or a planet.

---

* This number is derived from the value of the solar constant given in § 3.225 by noting that 1 watt is equivalent to a power of 10^7 ergs per second and 1 square foot is equal to 930 square centimeters.

3.255. The great weakness of the solar cell has been the loss in effectiveness it suffers from the action of various nuclear and similar radiations in space; these include natural radiations, such as protons (hydrogen nuclei) and electrons, as well as the radiations, mainly beta particles and gamma rays, produced as a result of nuclear explosions at high altitudes.[*] In order to decrease the damage, solar cells have been covered with a layer of quartz or sapphire, for absorbing some of the harmful radiations. Under normal conditions, this protection permits an operating life that is sufficient for the required purpose. Exceptional conditions often arise, however, apart from those due to nuclear explosions, e.g., an increase in the Sun's activity, and solar cells with a greater radiation resistance are highly desirable.

3.256. In the course of efforts to develop better solar cells, it has been found that the resistance to space radiation can be increased significantly by using an *n*-on-*p* cell instead of the *p*-on-*n* cell in general use before 1963. The *n*-on-*p* cell is produced by diffusing a thin layer of phosphorus (valence 5) into a *p*-type silicon wafer. Other promising materials being studied for photovoltaic cells are extremely pure silicon, gallium arsenide, and cadmium sulfide.

Solar Heat as a Power Source

3.257. Another possible way to utilize solar energy, to which some consideration is being given, is to absorb the Sun's radiation and to use the heat to produce electricity by means of a conventional turbogenerator. This is the principle employed in the solar heat engine developed in several Earth-based forms. Whether it can be adapted to space applications or not is somewhat uncertain.

3.258. In the Sunflower system, which is under study, it is proposed to use a parabolic mirror, about 1000 square feet in area, consisting of a highly polished aluminum skin bonded to a honeycomb plastic material. The energy collected as heat at the focus of the mirror would be stored in lithium hydride, partly as sensible heat, i.e., by increasing the temperature, and partly as latent heat of fusion. A reserve supply of heat would thus be available when the spacecraft is in Earth's shadow. The vapor from boiling mercury contained in a vessel within the lithium hydride would drive the turbogenerator and produce electricity in a Rankine cycle, as described in § 3.230. The design power of the Sunflower generating system would be 3 kilowatts of electricity.

3.259. Among the problems connected with the implementation of the Sunflower concept into a practical system for operation in space are the following. The possible effect of micrometeoroids in space on the reflectivity of the aluminum mirror is unknown and might be deleterious. The reflector must

---

[*] A case in point is the radiation belt around Earth produced by the U.S. high-altitude detonation (Starfish) over the Pacific Ocean on July 9, 1962; this is expected to last for several years, although with diminishing intensity (§ 8.327). The radiation caused severe damage, and loss of efficiency, to the solar cells of some satellites.

always be kept oriented toward the Sun, otherwise the power output will vary to some extent. Finally, the construction of a vessel to contain the highly corrosive lithium hydride at high temperatures may not be a simple matter.

CHEMICAL POWER SOURCES

3.260. Secondary (or storage) batteries, which can be recharged, are used in conjunction with solar cells. Except for the initial charge, required during the launch phase and for the orientation of solar-cell arrays, chemical sources do not supply the energy. The chemical reactions in the battery merely provide a means for storing the electricity produced by the Sun's energy. Before satisfactory solar cells were developed, several of the earlier experimental satellites used primary-cell batteries, which were not recharged, as the source of electrical power. Manned spacecraft have also utilized batteries of this type. The energy is then derived from chemical reactions of materials in the battery electrodes (or plates) and in the electrolyte solution.

3.261. Primary cells consisting of zinc and silver-silver oxide electrodes, immersed in a potassium hydroxide electrolyte, were used to supply the current for operating instruments, radio, etc., in the Mercury capsules in 1962 and 1963. In these batteries energy is derived from the chemical reaction between zinc and silver oxide. Such batteries have a limited life, determined by the quantity of active material they contain. Since the periods the manned capsules spent in orbit were not very long, primary batteries that are not recharged were adequate.

3.262. When a supply of electricity is required in a manned spacecraft for a somewhat longer time, there is a definite weight advantage in employing chemical *fuel cells;* these are being developed for the Gemini and Apollo capsules. The energy is supplied by the chemical reaction between hydrogen and oxygen which are stored as liquids, to save space, and fed to the cell as gases. Normally, interaction between hydrogen and oxygen requires a high temperature, as in the combustion chamber of a rocket motor. But the fuel cell is designed so that the reaction does not take place between molecules or atoms, as in combustion, but between electrically charged positive (H^+) and negative (OH^-) ions or between ions (OH^-) and atoms (H) attached to the electrode surface. In either case, the chemical reactions, leading to the formation of water (H_2O), can occur readily at ordinary temperatures with the simultaneous production of electricity. Some of the energy of the reactions is liberated as heat in the fuel cell and steps must be taken to remove it in order to maintain the desired operating temperature.

3.263. The fuel cell for the later Gemini spacecraft will be made of two woven metal wire screens, acting as electrodes, separated by a solid cation-exchange (polystyrene) resin* membrane that serves as the electrolyte (Fig.

* The material is similar to the ion-exchange resins extensively employed for the softening of hard water both in the home and in industry.

3.32). Hydrogen gas is supplied to one electrode (anode) and oxygen to the other (cathode). Ionic reactions occur leading to the transfer of electrons, i.e., negative charges, through the electrolyte from the cathode, which thus becomes the positive electrode, to the anode, the negative electrode. As a result, an

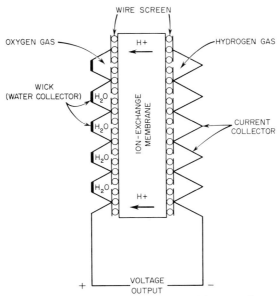

Fig. 3.32.   Schematic representation of fuel cell with ion-exchange membrane

electromotive force of about 1 volt per cell is produced; this can cause an electric current of appreciable strength (in amperes) to flow through an external circuit. The water formed in the chemical reactions is pure enough to be potable.

3.264. Another type of hydrogen-oxygen fuel cell, operating at a higher temperature, has been proposed for the Apollo mission. The electrodes are of sintered porous nickel and the electrolyte is a concentrated solution of potassium hydroxide in water. Although the operating details are different, the results are the same as described above. Each cell has an electromotive force of about 1 volt and potable water is obtained as a by-product.

3.265. The familiar combustion reaction between hydrogen and oxygen is being considered as the energy source in a chemically fueled engine combined with a turbogenerator. The hydrogen and oxygen would be stored as liquids and converted into gaseous form in a heat exchanger by exhaust heat from the turbine. The gases would then pass into a combustion chamber where direct chemical reaction occurs by the burning of hydrogen in oxygen. The resulting hot gases would drive the turbine which operates the electrical generator. Of course, other fuels, e.g., kerosene, could be used instead of hydrogen, but the latter provides the maximum energy for a given weight, although not for a given volume. The chemical engine has weight advantages over other electrical generators where fairly large amounts of power are required for moderate periods. It may perhaps be used as the main power system on the Apollo lunar excursion module (§ 13.39) in some later missions, or as a portable electric power supply for operations on the Moon.

APPENDIX

The Rocket Equation

3.266. The general form of Newton's second law of motion is that, in the appropriate units, force is equal to the rate of change of momentum, i.e.,

$$F = \frac{d(Mv)}{dt} = M\frac{dv}{dt} + v\frac{dM}{dt},$$

where F is the force produced by a body of mass M moving with a velocity v. Consider a rocket vehicle of mass M traveling through space with a velocity v and expelling mass dM of propellant as exhaust gas in the time interval dt. The mass of the vehicle remains essentially constant during this time interval, and so the force F_1 acting on the rocket is given by

$$F_1 = M\frac{dv}{dt},$$

since dM/dt is negligible. The force F_2 on the exhaust gas, which acts in the opposite direction, is

$$F_2 = v_e\frac{dM}{dt},$$

since in this case the exhaust gas velocity, v_e, is constant and the dv/dt term is zero. Neglecting the effect of gravity, it follows by Newton's third law of motion that the two forces derived above must be equal in magnitude but opposite in direction, i.e., $F_1 = -F_2$; hence,

$$M\frac{dv}{dt} = -v_e\frac{dM}{dt}$$

or

$$dv = -v_e\frac{dM}{M}.$$

This expression may be integrated, noting that M is equal to M, the initial mass of the rocket vehicle, when its velocity $v = 0$, and that M is equal to M_b, the burnout mass, when $v = v_b$, the burnout velocity; thus,

$$\int_0^{v_b} dv = -v_e \int_M^{M_b} \frac{dM}{M}$$

or

$$v_b = v_e \ln \frac{M}{M_b}$$

as in equation (3.9).

The Exhaust Gas Velocity

3.267. The relationship between the rocket exhaust gas velocity (or the specific impulse) and the gas temperature and molecular weight may be derived in the following manner for an ideal situation. Consider a perfect gas flowing in one direction from a region where its temperature is T_1 to another region where its temperature has the lower value T_2; the decrease in enthalpy (or heat content) will then be equal to the increase in mass kinetic energy of the gas. The decrease in enthalpy of unit mass is $c_p(T_1 - T_2)$, where c_p is the specific heat of the gas at constant pressure; this is assumed to be constant in the given temperature range. The increase in kinetic energy per unit mass is $\frac{1}{2}(v_2{}^2 - v_1{}^2)$, where v_1 and v_2 are the flow velocities of the gas in the regions where the temperatures are T_1 and T_2, respectively. It follows, therefore, that, in appropriate units,

$$2c_p(T_1 - T_2) = v_2{}^2 - v_1{}^2. \tag{3.15}$$

For a perfect (or ideal) gas

$$c_p - c_v = r, \tag{3.16}$$

where c_v is the specific heat at constant volume and r is the gas constant per unit mass, i.e., the molar gas constant divided by the (average) molecular weight of the gas. By definition, the ratio of the specific heats is represented by the symbol γ, although some engineering writers use k; thus,

$$\frac{c_p}{c_v} = \gamma. \tag{3.17}$$

Combination of equations (3.16) and (3.17) to eliminate c_v then yields

$$c_p = r \frac{\gamma}{\gamma - 1} = \frac{R}{\text{M.W.}} \cdot \frac{\gamma}{\gamma - 1}, \tag{3.18}$$

where R is the molar gas constant and M.W. is the molecular weight of the gas.

3.268. If the gas flow under consideration is isentropic (or adiabatic), the pressures p_1 and p_2 corresponding to the *absolute temperatures* T_1 and T_2 for a perfect gas are related by

$$\frac{T_2}{T_1} = \left(\frac{p_2}{p_1}\right)^{\frac{\gamma-1}{\gamma}}$$

and upon subtracting each side from unity and multiplying by T_1, the result is

$$T_1 - T_2 = T_1\left[1 - \left(\frac{p_2}{p_1}\right)^{\frac{\gamma-1}{\gamma}}\right]. \tag{3.20}$$

If equation (3.20) for $T_1 - T_2$ and equation (3.18) for c_p are inserted into equation (3.15), it is readily found that

$$v_2 = \left\{\frac{T_1}{M.W.} \cdot \frac{2R\gamma}{\gamma-1}\left[1 - \left(\frac{p_2}{p_1}\right)^{\frac{\gamma-1}{\gamma}}\right] + v_1^2\right\}^{0.5}. \tag{3.21}$$

3.269. Equation (3.21) may be regarded as applicable to a rocket operating under ideal conditions; then, T_1 is the temperature and v_1 the gas flow velocity in the combustion chamber and v_2 is the velocity of the exhaust gas, i.e., v_e; p_1 and p_2 are the gas pressures in the combustion chamber and of the exhaust gas, p_e, respectively. As a general rule, v_1 is small and may be neglected (cf. § 3.54). Since R is a universal constant and γ is constant for a perfect gas, it follows from equation (3.21) that, since p_2/p_1 is generally small,

$$v_e = \text{constant} \times \sqrt{\frac{T_1}{M.W.}},$$

where v_e has been written for v_2, and v_1 has been neglected; this result is in agreement with equation (3.8). It is evident from the derivation given above that the relationship between exhaust velocity (or specific impulse) and temperature and molecular weight of the gas can be regarded as only approximate when applied to actual conditions in a rocket.

RADIATION PRESSURE

3.270. According to Einstein's relationship concerning the equivalence of mass and energy (§ 6.187), a mass M is equivalent to energy Mc^2, where c is the velocity of light. If M is the mass of the radiation photons falling on unit area in unit time then, by definition (§ 3.224), the energy equivalent is equal to the radiation intensity, I; thus,

$$I = Mc^2.$$

Since the photons travel with the speed of light, their momentum is equal to Mc, and hence to I/c. If the photons of total mass M are absorbed by unit area in unit time, the rate of change of momentum, i.e., the force, per unit area, which is equal to the pressure, is thus I/c. For a perfect reflector of the radiation, the rate of change of momentum is $2I/c$, since the photons strike the surface with momentum I/c and are reflected with equal momentum in the opposite direction. The radiation pressure is then $2I/c$, as given in equation (3.14).

Chapter 4

GUIDANCE, TRACKING, AND INFORMATION SYSTEMS

ROCKET VEHICLE AND SPACECRAFT GUIDANCE

INTRODUCTION

4.1. The present chapter will be concerned with a number of related topics, including guidance of a spacecraft into the desired orbit or trajectory, tracking the flight path, maintenance of the attitude of the vehicle in space or with respect to a particular body, e.g., Earth or the Sun, and transfer of various kinds of information to and from the spacecraft. These aspects of space flight are very complex and their implementation involves the use of advanced and highly sophisticated concepts in several branches of engineering science and technology. Consequently, all that can be attempted here is a general description of the basic principles involved. It should be borne in mind, however, that the application of these principles is by no means a simple matter. Furthermore, the stringent requirements of accuracy, reliability, and compact design, which are essential for spacecraft systems, add greatly to the complexity of the overall problems.

4.2. The first subject to be considered is that of *guidance*. In the technology of rocket and space vehicles, the term guidance refers to the information required by a vehicle in order to make it follow a prescribed path or fulfill a particular objective. Guidance is thus distinguished from *control*, which is defined as the actual, mechanical procedure used to steer the vehicle along that path or to maintain its attitude in a specified orientation in space. Guidance and control together constitute navigation, in its broadest sense.

4.3. Because the problems involved in the different phases of guidance are generally different, it is the common practice to distinguish three such phases, namely, initial, midcourse, and terminal. *Initial guidance*, sometimes called preinjection guidance, is applied during the powered phase of the space flight when the vehicle is being brought to the predetermined injection conditions, i.e., speed, altitude, and direction required for its intended mission. At this point the motor is cut off and the rocket vehicle is generally detached from the spacecraft (or space vehicle). The latter then coasts along its intended orbit or trajectory in space, following a ballistic course (§ 3.130), with gravitational attraction, e.g., of Earth, the Moon, the Sun, etc., as the only force acting on the spacecraft.

4.4. In some situations, the initial guidance is divided into two phases because of the constraints arising from such matters as the geographic location of the launch site, the direction (or orbital inclination) in which launching is permissible because of safety considerations, and the limited launch windows or optimum periods for launching the satellite or space probe. If the circumstances were ideal, a guidance program could be developed that would achieve the objective in a single step. But since this is rarely the case, a two-phase launching procedure is adopted. For example, suppose it is required to send a spacecraft to the Moon or to another planet. The vehicle is first injected into a temporary parking orbit at a moderate altitude. The rocket engine is then shut off and the vehicle coasts in this orbit until it reaches a suitable location. Here the second phase of the guidance program is initiated. The rocket, which is still attached to the spacecraft, is restarted and the velocity of the vehicle is increased to the value required for the particular mission. A two-phase launch procedure of a somewhat different type is used to place a synchronous (24-hour period) satellite into orbit (§ 5.104).

4.5. In theory, it should be possible to calculate the injection conditions so precisely that no further guidance is necessary before the spacecraft reaches the final stages of its flight. In practice, however, it is virtually impossible to attain such a degree of accuracy either in the calculations or in the actual injection conditions. The purpose of *midcourse guidance* is to make the needed corrections at a convenient point in the trajectory to compensate for the inevitable errors and so bring the vehicle closer to its intended target.

4.6. Finally, *terminal guidance* is used in the final stage of the mission, which may be a return to Earth, the landing of instruments or a manned spacecraft on the Moon, etc., orbiting the Moon or a planet, and so on. If the requirements are not too stringent, the situation might be met by a second or possibly a third midcourse correction. But when a spacecraft or instruments must be landed in a selected area or if the landing velocity must lie within certain limits, terminal guidance would be mandatory. In general, an increase in guidance accuracy will mean an increase in complexity and weight of the guidance equipment; hence, in practice it may sometimes be necessary to compromise between accuracy, on the one hand, and complexity, on the other hand.

4.7. It should be noted that not all of these guidance phases are necessarily applicable to a particular mission. A satellite intended for making instrumental observations in space may require only initial guidance to inject it into the desired orbit. A manned satellite, on the other hand, must also have terminal guidance to return it to Earth, but, in general, there is no midcourse guidance. However, if two manned vehicles are to meet or *rendezvous*, as it is called, in space, a combination of several kinds of guidance is necessary for satisfactory completion of the operation. A space probe, making a lengthy journey to a distant planet, and even to the Moon, will generally need some midcourse guidance. If all or part of a spacecraft is to be landed at a given location or with a prescribed velocity on a celestial body, terminal guidance will, of course, be required.

GUIDANCE MODES

4.8. The guidance mode, i.e., the concept upon which the guidance system of a launch vehicle bases its steering decisions during flight, can be divided into two areas. These are sometimes called the "performance problem" and the "guidance problem." The first is concerned with the selection of a path (or trajectory) for the vehicle to follow in order to perform the required mission in the most efficient manner, e.g., with a maximum payload. The guidance problem, on the other hand, involves the development of a steering program based on a comparison of the actual state of the vehicle at any instant with that required by the performance problem. The guidance problem also includes the requirement that the thrust of the rocket be terminated when the objective of the mission, i.e., injection of a spacecraft at a prescribed altitude, velocity, and direction, has been attained.

4.9. A number of different guidance modes, based on the foregoing general principles, have been used. Perhaps the simplest is to derive from theoretical calculations a nominal trajectory, starting from the launch point, which will permit the vehicle to achieve the desired mission with the maximum payload, for example. This represents the solution to the performance problem. The nominal trajectory defines the altitude, speed, and direction of motion (or equivalent parameters) of the launch vehicle at every instant in the initial guidance phase. During the flight, the actual values of these parameters are determined and compared with the nominal values and the differences, if any, are immediately corrected by the control (steering) system. Thus, the actual trajectory is made to coincide as closely as possible with the nominal one. This guidance mode is satisfactory only when the deviations from the nominal trajectory are always small.

4.10. A better procedure is to implement the performance problem by the development of guidance equations, based on the initial and final points of the mission, which again optimize some variable, such as the payload. A number of solutions of these equations are possible, depending on the velocity vector* (or related parameters) of the vehicle at any altitude; these solutions can be obtained by means of a computer. The parameters are measured during the flight and are fed continuously to the computer which determines the changes in direction necessary to fulfill the mission requirements. The control system is then instructed to make these changes. A modification of the foregoing technique under development is called adaptive guidance. In this mode, the guidance

_____
* *Vector* is a mathematical term implying both magnitude and direction.

equations are effectively changed during flight so that, at every point, the best trajectory is computed for the fulfillment of the remainder of the mission from that point on to the injection point.

Types of Initial Guidance

4.11. For the initial guidance operation, two general procedures have been used: (a) command guidance and (b) inertial guidance. Celestial guidance can be employed for midcourse adjustment, and this will be considered later. In *command guidance* the characteristics of the vehicle's motion are determined by tracking from Earth. Instructions are then transmitted to the launch vehicle to make the necessary steering corrections as indicated by the particular guidance mode that is being used. Because the exchange of information between the space vehicle and the tracking and computing stations on Earth is invariably made by radio (or radar) waves, the system is referred to as command radio guidance or, in brief, as *radio guidance*.

4.12. *Inertial guidance* differs from command guidance in the respect that the whole system is contained within the space vehicle. In a completely inertial system there is no information link with Earth once the vehicle is in flight. In some inertial guidance systems a periodic compensating adjustment, to correct for extraneous errors which have accumulated during operation, is made from Earth by means of radio. These are called *radio-inertial guidance systems*.

Radio Guidance

4.13. In a command radio guidance system, the position and velocity vector of the launch vehicle are obtained by means of radio techniques. Although the methods used are given here in connection with the initial guidance operation, i.e., the guidance of the launch vehicle, it should be pointed out that they can also be applied to the spacecraft after it has been detached from the launch vehicle. Because conventional radio waves of fairly long wavelength tend to be turned back to Earth by the layer of the atmosphere known as the ionosphere (§ 8.104), it is the practice to employ radar waves for space guidance purposes. These radiations have relatively short wavelengths and are able to penetrate the ionosphere more readily than those of longer wavelength. But since radar waves are basically identical with radio waves, except possibly for differences in wavelengths, the general term radio guidance is employed.

4.14. The common (or echo) method of using radar to determine the distance of an object in space is to beam a radar pulse toward the object from a station on Earth; the pulse is reflected back from the object and the time is observed when the return pulse is received at the station. Radar waves, like other electromagnetic radiations (§ 6.47 *et seq.*), travel with the speed of light, 3.00×10^8 meters (or 186,000 miles) per second. In the interval between transmission and receipt of the radar pulse, the waves will have covered twice the distance between the station and the object in space. If this distance is repre-

sented by d, and c is the velocity of light, the time interval, t, is represented
by

$$t = \frac{2d}{c}$$

or

$$d = \tfrac{1}{2}ct. \tag{4.1}$$

Hence, if the time t is measured, the distance d can be determined since the
velocity of light is known. In practice, a series of closely spaced pulses are sent
out, rather than a single pulse, and the time interval is averaged by a computer
over several pulses in order to improve the accuracy of the measurement.

4.15. Because the reflected radar signal from a launch vehicle or a spacecraft may be very weak, the general practice is to utilize the pulse to trigger
a repeater radar set on the vehicle to transmit a return pulse. The transmitting
device is called a *radio transponder*.* The radar pulse it sends out is considerably stronger than the initiating pulse and usually has a different wavelength
(or frequency) to facilitate detection. Since the time between receipt of the
trigger pulse by the radio transponder and the transmission of the return
pulse is negligibly small, the distance between the moving vehicle and the
ground station is still given by equation (4.1).

4.16. The velocity of a launch (or space) vehicle can be obtained by an application of the *Doppler effect*. In 1842, the Austrian physicist C. J. Doppler
enunciated the principle that if a source of vibrations, e.g., light or sound, is
moving steadily away from an observer, the frequency of the vibrations appears
to decrease continuously, or in other words, the wavelength appears to increase.
Conversely, if the vibration source is traveling toward the observer, the frequency appears to increase and the wavelength to decrease. A familiar example
of the Doppler effect is the change in pitch of an automobile horn or train
whistle as the moving vehicle approaches or recedes from a listener. Similar
phenomena are evident when the source of the vibrations is stationary and the
observer is moving either toward or away from it. In general, if the distance
between the source and the observer is decreasing, the apparent frequency will
increase, and vice versa.

4.17. Radar (or radio) waves are vibrations similar to light and they exhibit
the Doppler frequency change if the radar source (or transmitter) is in motion
toward or away from a fixed receiving station. If v_r is the radial velocity of
the moving transmitter, that is, the component in the direction of a straight
line between it and the receiver (Fig. 4.1), the *Doppler shift*, f_d, i.e., the difference between the true frequency at the transmitter and that observed at the
receiver, is given by

---

* The name *transponder* originates from the Latin *trans*, "across" and *pondus*, "weight,"
implying a device which changes weight; in this case it is the strength (or energy) of the
trigger pulse which is changed.

$$f_d = f_0 \frac{v_r}{c}$$

or

$$v_r = \frac{f_d}{f_0} c, \qquad (4.2)$$

where f_0 is the true frequency of the transmitted radar waves and c is the velocity of light. The same units, e.g., meters, kilometers, or miles per second, must of course be used in expressing the velocities v_r and c. Equation (4.2) is strictly applicable to a vacuum transmission path; it is therefore more accurate when applied to a vehicle in space at a considerable distance from Earth than for a close-in satellite or a launch vehicle.

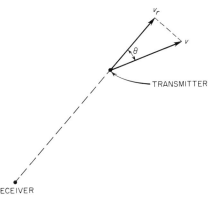

FIG. 4.1.   Determination of radial velocity from the Doppler shift

4.18. It is important to understand the exact significance of the radial velocity v_r, as derived from equation (4.2). As stated above, it is the component of the velocity of the transmitter in the radial direction i.e., along a line joining the receiver and transmitter at the instant of measurement. For this reason, the quantity v_r is generally called the *range rate*, since it represents the rate at which the range of the receiver is changing with time; the subscript r is used to distinguish it from the true velocity. If the receiver is not moving in the radial direction, as will generally be the case, the actual velocity will be greater than the radial velocity. Let θ be the angle between the direction of motion and the radial direction (Fig. 4.1) ; the true velocity, v, is then

$$v = \frac{v_r}{\cos \theta} = \frac{f_d}{f_0} \cdot \frac{c}{\cos \theta}. \qquad (4.3)$$

In order to determine the velocity v by the Doppler technique it is necessary, therefore, to measure both the Doppler frequency shift and the angle θ. The procedure is not applicable when the transmitter is moving at right angles to the radial direction; in this case, $\cos \theta$ is zero as also is f_d, and equation (4.3) provides no useful information.

4.19. There are various ways in which the Doppler effect can be utilized to obtain the range rate of a rocket (or space) vehicle. Perhaps one of the simplest is for the moving vehicle to carry a continuous-wave (or CW) radar transmitter operating at a constant, known frequency. A continuous-wave transmitter is one that broadcasts an uninterrupted succession of waves rather than a series of pulses at intervals. The frequency of the signal received at a ground station is measured and the amount it differs from the known frequency, f_0, of the transmitter is equal to the Doppler shift, f_d. The range rate can then be calculated from equation (4.2).

4.20. The accuracy of the foregoing procedure is dependent on the constancy of the transmitting frequency. Since this may be uncertain, a more reliable, but less simple, approach has been developed (Fig. 4.2). A continuous-wave

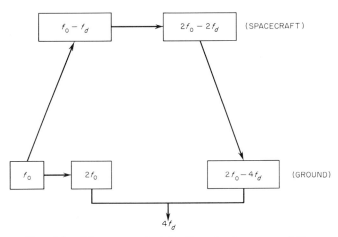

FIG. 4.2. Measurement of the Doppler frequency shift

signal, of frequency f_0, is sent out from a ground station and is received on the moving space vehicle at a frequency $f_0 - f_d$, assuming the vehicle to be moving away from the transmitter. (If the vehicle were moving toward the transmitting station, the received signal would have a frequency $f_0 + f_d$.) A transponder on the spacecraft doubles the received frequency and retransmits it, with increased power, at a frequency of $2f_0 - 2f_d$. By making this substantial change in the frequency, it is possible to transmit and receive the respective radar signals by means of a single antenna on the ground. Because of the further Doppler shift of $2f_d$ in the return signal to the ground, it is received at a frequency of $2f_0 - 4f_d$. The value of $4f_d$ is then obtained by comparing the received signal with twice the frequency of the signal originally sent out from the transmitter, i.e., $2f_0$. The difference (or beat*) frequency is equal to $4f_d$. In this manner, any changes occurring in the transmitted signal are canceled

---

* The term "beat" arises from the fact that when two notes of slightly different pitch are sounded together, a series of distinct throbs (or beats) is heard, their frequency being equal to the difference in frequency of the two sounds. The same principle is employed in the so-called heterodyne systems in radio reception.

out; furthermore, the increase in the measured shift from f_d to $4f_d$ increases the accuracy of the observations.

4.21. The radar signals are received on Earth from a moving vehicle in space by means of a dish-like (paraboloidal) antenna (see Fig. 4.36) which focuses into a small region the radar energy collected over a large area, thereby producing a measurable signal. The same antenna can be used to concentrate the continuous-wave radar into a narrow beam for transmission to the spacecraft. The signal of maximum strength is received when the axis of the dish antenna points directly to the spacecraft. Automatic tracking is achieved by means of four subsidiary dipole antennas located around the circumference of the dish; only when the main antenna is correctly oriented do the four dipoles receive signals of the same strength. Any difference in the signals actuates a mechanism which moves the dish in the required direction.

4.22. From the way in which the pointing direction of the antenna changes, the direction of motion of the vehicle can be determined; the angle θ can thus be derived for converting the radial velocity into the actual velocity, by equation (4.3). Another method for observing the actual direction of motion is utilized in connection with the system for tracking satellites; this is described in § 4.125.

4.23. It has been seen that the determination of the distance (or range) of a spacecraft requires the use of radar pulses whereas for the application of the Doppler shift for range-rate measurement it is best to employ continuous-wave radar. It is possible, however, to obtain both range and range rate with a single system. To do this, the continuous-wave radar is modulated by superimposing upon it an identifiable signal, equivalent to a pulse. The time interval between transmission and return of this particular signal can be used to calculate the range. The range-rate is derived from the Doppler frequency shift in the normal manner.

4.24. Radar measurements of range, range-rate, and angle can be made only provided the launch (or space) vehicle is within the line of sight of the observation (or tracking) station on the ground. Radar guidance for launch vehicles can thus be used for the initial phase, or at least part of it, especially if the injection altitude is high. It is particularly adapted, however, to the midcourse guidance phase of space probes, for which tracking stations are available in different parts of the world (§ 4.136).

4.25. Although radar waves of high frequency are less influenced by passage through the ionosphere than are conventional radio waves, their transmission is affected to some extent. In passing through the ionosphere, the path of the signal may be bent (or refracted) and it may travel with a speed slightly less than that of light in a vacuum. These and other effects will introduce errors in range and range-rate measurements. Such errors can be minimized by utilizing suitable radar waves of short wavelength and by avoiding observations of the launch vehicle or spacecraft when it is near the horizon. Some corrections can be made for the changes caused by the ionosphere, but these are not too reliable because of the variable nature of this region of the atmosphere (Chapter 8).

TRAJECTORY ADJUSTMENT

4.26. The measurements made as described above are compared by means of a computer on the ground with the values required by a nominal trajectory or which satisfy the guidance equations, as described in § 4.8 *et seq.* The necessary corrections are then coded into an appropriate signal that is transmitted by radio to the space vehicle. This represents the guidance command. From a receiver on the vehicle the coded signal passes through an amplifier, to increase its strength, and then to a decoder. The output of the latter then initiates the action to produce the required change in the vehicle trajectory.

4.27. In the initial guidance phase, the adjustments are made by altering the *attitude* of the rocket vehicle, i.e., its orientation in space. This property is expressed in terms of displacements about three axes, at right angles to each other, passing through the center of mass of the vehicle. These axes are the roll axis, the pitch axis, and yaw axis, shown in Fig. 4.3. The *roll axis* is the same as

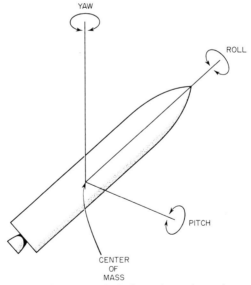

FIG. 4.3.   Roll, yaw, and pitch motions of a rocket vehicle

the main axis, along the length of the rocket vehicle, and rolling refers to a rotary motion about this axis. The *yaw axis* lies in the plane of the trajectory of the vehicle, and rotation about this axis causes yawing, a side-to-side movement with reference to the flight direction. Finally, the pitching motion, i.e., rotation about the *pitch axis*, which is at right angles to the other two axes, is represented by an up-and-down movement of the nose of the vehicle.*

4.28. If rotation of the vehicle about the roll axis is prevented or, in other words, if the attitude of the vehicle about the roll axis is stabilized, the trajectory can be changed by displacements about the yaw and pitch axes. For example, the rate of ascent, i.e., increase in altitude, of the space vehicle can be altered by rotation about the pitch axis, whereas motion about the yaw axis will change the plane of the flight trajectory. Displacements about the pitch and yaw axes are thus used to provide the necessary guidance. These displacements are achieved by changing the direction of thrust of the rocket motor in the manner described in § 4.79, *et seq.*

GYROSCOPES

4.29. Stabilization of a rocket vehicle about a particular axis and changes in attitude about the other axes are achieved by the use of *gyroscopes*, often referred to as *gyros*. Because gyroscopes play such an important role in both command and inertial guidance, the general principles of their operation will be reviewed. A gyroscope consists basically of a heavy disc (or wheel) rotating rapidly about a central axis; this axis is supported by a framework, known as a *gimbal*, that permits a certain amount of free movement. In gyroscopes for space guidance, the high-speed rotation of the disc, at a rate of several thousand revolutions per minute, is achieved by making it the rotor of an electric (synchronous) motor driven by alternating current. In Fig. 4.4 is shown a gyroscope with *a single degree of freedom*. The disc rotates rapidly about the *spin axis*, AA', whereas the gimbal is free to rotate about the axis BB', called the *output axis*, perpendicular to the spin axis. It is the output axis about which the gyroscope has its single degree of freedom.

4.30. The characteristic behavior of the gyroscope is in accordance with the principle of the conservation of angular momentum, which follows from Newton's second and third laws of motion.† It can be shown that a rotating (or spinning) body tends to resist any attempt to change the direction of the axis about which it spins. As a consequence of this resistance, if the gyroscope frame (or case) is rotated about the axis CC', the *input axis*, perpendicular to both the axes AA' and BB', the gimbal supporting the spinning disc will rotate about the output axis, BB'. This forced rotation is called *gyroscopic precession*.

4.31. The effect of precession is thus to cause the gyroscope to produce a *torque*, or twisting force, about the axis BB'. In other words, an external force

---

* It should be noted that the roll, yaw, and pitch *motions* are in planes at right angles to the directions of the respective *axes*.

† The angular momentum of a particle of mass m rotating with an angular velocity ω is $mr^2\omega$, where r is the distance of the particle from the axis of rotation (cf. § 2.51). For a rigid body of appreciable size, the angular momentum is the integral of all the $mr^2\omega$ terms for the particles of which the body may be regarded as made up. It is commonly expressed as $I\omega$, where I is the moment of inertia of the body about the axis of rotation

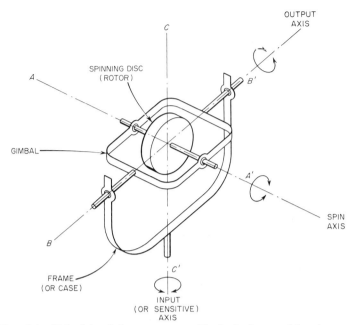

Fɪɢ. 4.4.   Principle of the gyroscope with single degree of freedom

or torque applied about the input axis of the gyroscope produces a torque about the output axis, perpendicular to both the input and spin axes. If the output (or gyroscopic) torque is resisted by a spring (Fig. 4.5), the angle through which the output axis precesses is proportional to the rate of the ex-

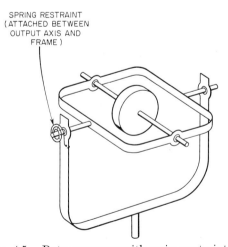

Fɪɢ. 4.5.   Rate gyroscope with spring restraint

ternal rotation about the input axis that is responsible for the precession. A single-degree-of-freedom gyroscope with a spring restraint on the output axis is thus designated a *rate gryroscope* (or *rate gyro*). When the input rotation ceases, the output (or gimbal) axis returns to its original position.

4.32. If, instead of a spring restraint, the precession of the gyroscope is opposed by a viscous restraint, the result is a *rate-integrating gyroscope*, also called an *integrating, position,* or *displacement gyroscope*. The manner in which this can be achieved is indicated in Fig. 4.6, a diagrammatic representa-

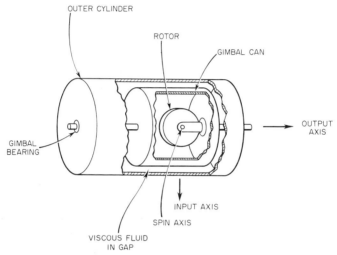

FIG. 4.6.   Hermetic integrating gyroscope (HIG)

tion of the hermetic integrating gyroscope (or HIG). The spinning disc is supported inside a sealed, cylindrical gimbal can and this is suspended within an outer cylindrical case. The narrow annular space between the gimbal can and the case contains a viscous fluid of such density that the can floats in it. In the integrating gyroscope, the angle of rotation of the output axis is proportional to the product of the rate of the input rotation and the time over the whole period during which rotation occurs. In mathematical terms, the angle is proportional to the integral over the rotation period of the rate of input rotation. The total angle of precession of the output (or gimbal) axis is then proportional to the angle through which the input axis is rotated, i.e., to the angular change in position. The names position or displacement gyroscope, mentioned above, arise from this property of the viscously restrained gyroscope with one degree of freedom.

FREE GYROSCOPES

4.33. The addition of a second gimbal to a gyroscope produces a system with two degrees of freedom, as shown in Fig. 4.7; the inner gimbal is free to rotate about the axis BB', as before, and the outer gimbal can rotate about the axis CC'. A gyroscope with two degrees of freedom is also referred to as a *free gyroscope* because it can rotate, without restraint, about three axes at right angles to each other. The resistance of the spinning disc to a change in the direction of the spin axis AA' is shown by the fact that this axis remains unchanged in direction regardless of the direction or extent of rotation of the frame (or case) upon which the gimbals are mounted.

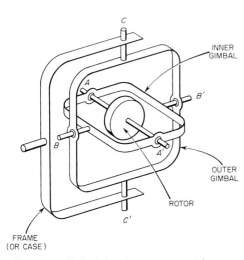

Fig. 4.7. Principle of gyroscope with two degrees of freedom

4.34. A gyroscope with two degrees of freedom can be used to determine the angle of rotation of the frame about the *sensitive axes*, BB' and CC'. For example, if the frame is rotated about BB', the plane of the outer gimbal will rotate through the same angle, but the position of the inner gimbal, as well as of the spin axis AA', will remain unchanged. Thus, the change in angle between the inner gimbal and the case is equal to the angle of rotation about the BB' axis. A rotation about the CC' axis will leave the planes of both inner and outer gimbals unaffected. The angle of rotation about CC' is thus equal to the change in angle between the outer (or inner) gimbal and the gyroscopic case. But rotation of the case about the spin axis, AA', will produce no apparent change with respect to the case. Consequently, if it is required to determine rotation about all three axes, it is necessary to use either two free (two-degree-of-freedom), or one free and one integrating (one-degree-of-freedom), or three integrating gyroscopes.

4.35. In the use of a gyroscope with two degrees of freedom, there is a limitation upon determining rotation about the BB' axis. It is seen from Fig. 4.7 that a rotation of 90 deg about this axis would cause the inner and outer gimbals to lie in the same plane. The resulting situation is called *gimbal lock*. Not only does gimbal lock mean a loss of one degree of freedom, but in this condition the gyroscope behaves erratically and frequently both gimbals then rotate rapidly about the gyroscopic spin axis, AA'. The problem of gimbal lock does not often arise in space applications, but if the rotation about BB' is likely to exceed about 85 deg, the difficulty can be overcome by means of an additional gimbal.

4.36. It should be noted that the spin axis of a free gyroscope will always maintain a fixed direction in what is called *inertial space*, i.e., with reference to the distant (or fixed) stars rather than to Earth. The spin axis is also said to remain unchanged in direction in a space-fixed reference frame. Suppose, for instance, that the frame of a two-degree-of-freedom gyroscope is attached to a satellite orbiting Earth in a polar orbit, as represented in Fig. 4.8. In order to make the situation clear, one end of the vertical axis, equivalent to CC' in Fig. 4.7, is marked with an arrow and the other with a cross. To an observer on Earth at the north pole, the arrow end will appear to be up whereas the cross end will be down. On the other hand, at the south pole an observer would see the cross end up and the arrow end down. Furthermore, at the equator, the axis would appear to be horizontal, although it is vertical to observers at the poles. In inertial space, however, the direction remains unchanged during the course of the satellite orbit.*

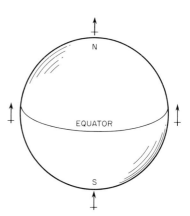

FIG. 4.8.   Direction of gyroscope fixed in inertial space

4.37. Even when external rotation (or torque) appears to be absent, a gyroscope may exhibit some precession (or rotation) of the gimbal due to extraneous factors. Such motion is said to be due to *gyroscopic drift*. Many factors contribute to the drift: they include (*a*) friction in the gimbal and spin bearings, (*b*) small asymmetries or unbalance in the rotating disc or in the gimbals, which produce a torque, and (*c*) changes in temperature and magnetic fields that may affect the unbalance. The drift caused by friction is independent of the acceleration of the system but that due to unbalance will arise only if the gyroscope is in a gravitational field or is being accelerated in other ways. One approach to decreasing gyroscopic drift is to minimize friction in the bearings; among the ideas being studied with this end in view are the use of gas films and of electric and magnetic fields to provide the required support.

ATTITUDE CONTROL BY GYROSCOPE

4.38. First, consideration will be given to the method of stabilization of the attitude of a space vehicle about its roll axis. The frame (or case) of a single-degree-of-freedom position (or displacement) gyroscope is attached to the

---

* The gyroscope owes its name, which is derived from the Greek *gyros*, "circle" or "rotation," and *skopein*, "to observe," to the characteristic of having a fixed direction in inertial space. In 1852, the French physicist J.B.L. Foucault showed that a free gyroscope appeared to rotate relative to a fixed direction on Earth. Actually, however, it is Earth which rotates. Consequently, the gyroscope made it possible to observe the rotation of Earth, and hence its name.

vehicle in such a manner that the input axis coincides with the roll axis. Suppose that, as a result of some extraneous factor, the vehicle is set rotating about this axis; the gyroscope will then start to precess about its output axis. The precessional motion is detected by the movement of an electrical contact, or in an analogous manner, in a device called a *pickoff;* as a result, an electrical signal is sent to the appropriate vehicle control actuator. The main rocket engine or a subsidiary control motor, known as a *vernier rocket,* then produces a thrust in such a direction as to counteract the vehicle roll. When the prescribed, stabilized attitude about the roll axis is restored, the gyroscope is returned to its original orientation; consequently, the correcting thrust action is terminated. By the use of the feedback principle, described below, stabilization occurs in a smooth manner.

4.39. Two one-degree-of-freedom gyroscopes or one gyroscope with two degrees of freedom can be used to cause rotation about the pitch and yaw axes at the command of the guidance system. The general principle is the same as that employed in the *autopilot* of an aircraft; the equipment responsible for attitude changes in a space vehicle is, in fact, often referred to by this name. The operation of the space autopilot will be described with reference to motion about the pitch axis, but exactly the same considerations apply to the yaw axis. It will be assumed, for simplicity, that the pitch gyroscope has a single degree of freedom and is restrained in such a manner that the precession angle is a measure of the total displacement about the input axis, in this case the pitch axis.

4.40. A command (or error) signal, indicating that an attitude change about the pitch axis is required, activates a small electric motor, called a *torque motor* or *torquer;* this produces an appropriate torque (or rotation) about the input axis of the pitch displacement gyroscope. The gyroscope then precesses through an angle which is proportional to the applied torque and, hence, to the pitch error signal. A pickoff, similar to that described above, attached to the output axis of the gyroscope, detects the precession and sends a signal to the pitch control actuators. The actuators then move to the extent corresponding to the commanded change in attitude about the pitch axis. As this change is made, the gyroscope is restored to its initial condition in preparation for any subsequent alterations in pitch that may be needed. Control of the yaw attitude would be realized in an exactly analogous manner.

4.41. In order to achieve smooth action of any control system, it is a common practice to utilize the principle of *negative feedback* in a *closed-loop* arrangement. The term negative feedback is used to describe the behavior of a control (or stabilization) system when the system responds to a change (or error) signal in such a manner as to reduce the error. In other words, in a negative feedback control system, the error is steadily decreased as the system responds to the error signal. Thus, the control actuator moves on receipt of the original command, but it gradually returns to its original position as the command is obeyed.*

4.42. In a control system, negative feedback is achieved by feeding back a signal from an attitude sensor (§ 4.111) into a closed loop circuit, such as that depicted schematically in Fig. 4.9. The *servomechanism* is a combination of

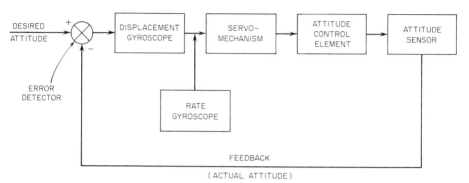

Fɪɢ. 4.9.   Block diagram of closed-loop control system

devices used in a closed loop system to provide the mechanical (or hydraulic) power to operate the control actuators at the response of a relatively weak signal. In the pitch control situation under consideration, the attitude sensor feeds back information of the actual attitude for comparison with the desired (or command) attitude. As the two become closer, the error signal to the displacement gyroscope decreases. The resultant effect is that the attitude is attained in a smooth manner, with a minimum of "overshooting" and consequent pitch oscillations. When the maneuver is completed, the displacement gyroscope and the attitude control actuators will have returned to their initial (or steady) states ready for any further commands that may be received.

4.43. It will be observed that in Fig. 4.9 a box designated "rate gyroscope" has been included. The purpose of the rate gyroscope (§ 4.31) is to prevent the development of significant vibrations in the rocket vehicle that might result from too rapid changes in pitch (or yaw) attitude. Vibrations of this nature could be particularly harmful in a long, flexible vehicle. The rate gyroscope is attached at a location where it would respond to significant bending motion of the vehicle structure. The gyroscope precession angle, which is proportional to the rate of rotation about the input axis, is measured by an electrical pickoff on this axis. A signal is thereby supplied to the servomechanism to provide such damping as may be necessary.

* A familiar instance of negative feedback occurs in steering an automobile round a corner. The steering wheel is first turned fairly rapidly and then, as a result of a negative feedback signal from the brain, the driver gradually brings the wheel back to its original position for traveling in a straight line.

4.44. When the rocket vehicle has attained the prescribed velocity and is moving in the requisite direction, e.g., parallel to Earth's surface at the injection point in the case of a satellite, a signal from the ground commands the rocket engine to shut down. The spacecraft then continues its coasting (or ballistic) motion with gravity as the only force acting upon it; aerodynamic drag may be regarded as essentially absent at high altitude. During this phase of the fight, attitude stabilization control may be necessary about all three axes, but this can be achieved in the manner already described.

INERTIAL GUIDANCE

4.45. Inertial guidance differs from command guidance in being completely self-contained within the vehicle, requiring no contact with the ground once the vehicle has left Earth's surface. The speed and direction of motion at any instant are measured by instruments carried by the vehicle. Furthermore, comparison with the parameters of a predetermined nominal trajectory or with the solutions of the guidance equations, according to the guidance mode employed, is also made by a computer on the vehicle. The trajectory correction signals then actuate an autopilot which controls pitch and yaw motions in a manner similar to that for a command radio guidance system. An important component of the inertial guidance equipment is a precise means of timing to insure exact correlation between the observed and programmed trajectory parameters.

4.46. It will be apparent that the main problem of inertial guidance is to measure the speed and direction of the vehicle by means of self-contained instrumentation. The two basic devices employed for the purpose are the stabilized platform and the accelerometer. The *stabilized* (or *stable*) *platform* is an arrangement which uses three one-degree-of-freedom or two two-degree-of-freedom gyroscopes to provide an attitude reference system that remains fixed in inertial space. The gyroscopes are arranged on the platform which is supported by gimbals, so that it is free to move about roll, pitch, and yaw axes. Suppose that three one-degree-of-freedom, displacement gyroscopes are employed. They are attached to the platform in such a manner that each has its spin axis parallel to a different attitude axis, and the platform is attached to the vehicle. A simplified representation of a stabilized platform of this kind is shown in Fig. 4.10. This is what is called an "external" or "outside-in" gimbal arrangement with the gimbal rings outside the platform. In the alternative "internal" or "inside-out" form, which has a much more compact design, small gimbals are located in the interior of the device.

4.47. The mode of operation of the stabilized platform is essentially the same as that described earlier for the maintenance of the roll attitude of a space vehicle. The orientation of the platform is established before the vehicle leaves the ground and this orientation is maintained during the flight. If, due to any cause, there is a change in orientation, there will be a rotation about one or more of the attitude axes; the corresponding displacement gyroscope (or gyroscopes) will then precess accordingly. A pickoff on the output axis of each gyroscope detects the precession and transmits an error signal to a servomechanism with negative feedback. As a result, a motor produces the required motion of the platform to restore it to its original orientation.

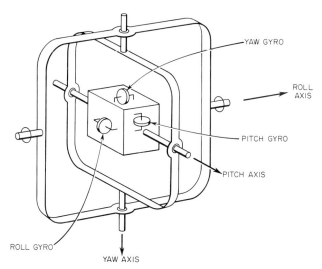

FIG. 4.10.   Principle of the stabilized platform

ACCELEROMETERS

4.48. An *accelerometer,* as its name implies, is an instrument for measuring acceleration. A simple accelerometer consists of a mass suspended between two springs, as represented in Fig. 4.11. The sensitive axis is in the direction of the springs, and any acceleration applied along (or parallel to) this axis, or with a component along this axis, will produce a force on the mass. As a result, the mass will move until the force exerted by the spring in resisting its motion will just balance the force due to the acceleration. By Newton's second law, if the mass is m and a is

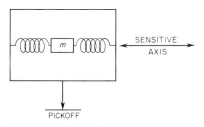

FIG. 4.11.   Suspended-mass accelerometer

the acceleration in the direction of the sensitive axis, the force, F, in appropriate units, exerted on the mass is given by

$$F = ma,$$

in accordance with equation (2.3). The motion of the mass through a distance

x causes one spring to be extended and the other to be compressed by this amount. In the simplest, ideal case the resisting force exerted by the springs is then equal to kx, where k is a constant. When the two forces acting on the mass—one due to the acceleration and the other to the extension and compression of the springs—balance one another, kx is equal to ma, so that

$$a = \frac{k}{m}\,x.$$

Since k/m is a constant quantity for the given accelerometer, the displacement of the mass is proportional to the acceleration. A pickoff attached to the suspended mass provides an electrical voltage signal which is related directly to the acceleration along the sensitive axis.

4.49. The *vibrating-string accelerometer* is a kind of suspended-mass device, depicted in Fig. 4.12. The mass is held in tension between two "strings," that are actually wires or metal ribbons. Provided there is no acceleration in the direction of the sensitive axis, the tension force is the same in both strings. Under acceleration, however, the mass tends to move, thereby causing the tensions to differ. The difference, which is a measure of the acceleration, is determined by causing the strings to vibrate and observing the difference in the two vibration frequencies. The

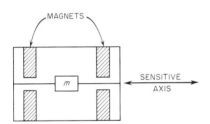

Fig. 4.12.   Vibrating-string accelerometer

strings lie in a magnetic field and they are set into vibration by passing an alternating current through them.

4.50. Instead of employing a mass supported along the sensitive axis, the *pendulum accelerometer* principle, now being widely used, is based on suspension at right angles to this axis (Fig. 4.13). Acceleration causes the bob, *m,* of the pendulum to move to the right or the left. The displacement, which is proportional to the acceleration, as in § 4.48, can be sensed by a pickoff attached to the bob. In practice, the bob (or pendulous mass) is located between two "forcers," e.g., electromagnets, which can oppose the motion of the mass. The forcers are actuated by an electric current controlled by the pickoff. As a result of an acceleration, the pickoff is displaced and a current flows through one or other of the forcers of such strength as to bring the pendulous mass back to its null position. The magnitude of the current is then proportional to the acceleration along the sensitive (or input) axis.

4.51. A modification of the foregoing is the *constrained pendulum accelerometer,* shown in Fig. 4.14. It consists of a pendulous (or unbalanced) mass attached to the axis of a cylinder supported within a surrounding cylinder by an annular film of viscous liquid, similar to the integrating gyroscope. An

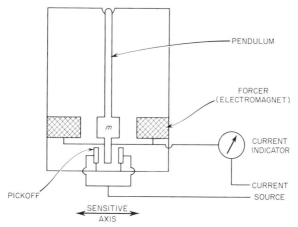

Fig. 4.13. Principle of pendulum accelerometer

acceleration along the input axis, which is vertical in the figure, causes the pendulous mass to produce a torque about the axis of the cylinder. As a result, the cylinder rotates, the angle of rotation being proportional to the acceleration. To measure the latter, an electrical pickoff is attached to one end of the cylinder. By means of a torque generator, the voltage from the pickoff produces a torque which opposes the rotation of the cylinder. The magnitude of the voltage (or the electric current) is proportional to the acceleration.

4.52. For inertial guidance purposes, it is required to know the velocity rather than the acceleration. If the acceleration were constant, the velocity would be simply the product of the acceleration and the time. During the ascent of a rocket vehicle, however, the acceleration changes continuously and in order to

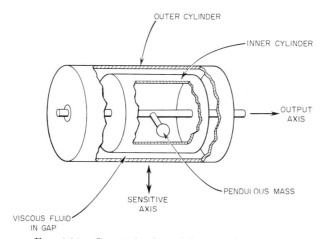

Fig. 4.14. Constrained pendulum accelerometer

obtain the velocity, the acceleration must be integrated with respect to time. In other words, the products of acceleration and time interval, for a number of extremely short intervals, must be added over a period of time The integration can be performed by means of a simple electronic circuit; the input is a variable voltage proportional to the acceleration at any instant and the output voltage continuously indicates the corresponding velocity in the direction of the sensitive axis.*

4.53. The conversion of acceleration to velocity by an integrating circuit can be avoided by means of a pendulous (or unbalanced) *gyro-accelerometer*. The instrument is a combination of the constrained pendulum accelerometer and the integrating gyroscope described in § 4.32. A gyroscope with a viscous constraint has a pendulous mass attached to the axis of the gimbal can, as seen in Fig. 4.15. An acceleration in the direction of the sensitive (precession) axis of

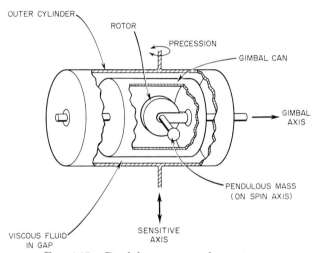

FIG. 4.15.   Pendulous gyro-accelerometer

the gyroscope will cause the unbalanced pendulous weight to produce a torque about the gimbal axis. Consequently, the gyroscope will precess and the angle of precession is proportional to the time integral of the acceleration, i.e., to the vehicle velocity component in the direction of the sensitive axis of the accelerometer.

4.54. In addition to the velocity of the rocket vehicle, it is necessary to know its position or distance from the launch point. Just as velocity is the integral of acceleration over time, so the total distance traversed at any instant is the

---

* If the velocity is constant, so that there is no acceleration or deceleration, the system described above does not give the actual velocity but only indicates that it has not changed.

integral of the velocity over the whole of the flight time at that instant. This integration is performed electronically, as described above.

APPLICATION OF INERTIAL GUIDANCE

4.55. Three accelerometers are attached to a stabilized platform, and oriented so that their sensitive axes are each parallel to one of the three fixed axes of the platform. It is then possible to obtain the simultaneous components, along each axis in three directions at right angles, of the velocity and distance traveled by the rocket vehicle. With these data it is a relatively simple matter for a computer to evaluate the actual distance of the vehicle from the launch point and its velocity at any instant. A comparison of the results with the solutions of the appropriate performance problem or guidance equations (§ 4.8) provides the correction signal, if any, for the autopilot. The remainder of the guidance system is then similar to that described in connection with command guidance (§ 4.26 *et seq.*)

4.56. There are a number of corrections which have to be made in an inertial guidance system. The effect of gyroscope drift, for example, can be corrected for by the use of an external reference (§ 4.65). Another type of correction, which can be made internally, arises from the influence of gravity. An accelerometer on a launch vehicle measures only velocity changes due to nongravitational forces, e.g., propulsion and aerodynamic forces. The total acceleration, however, must include the gravitational acceleration which varies with the distance from Earth. A device called a *gravity computer* is therefore used on the vehicle to determine the gravitational acceleration; this is combined with the output of the accelerometer before integration to give the actual velocity of the vehicle with reference to Earth.

4.57. Inertial guidance utilizes more equipment on the launch vehicle than does a radio command system, but it has the advantage of not needing any ground installations. Furthermore, inertial guidance does not require the vehicle to be within the line of sight of any particular location on Earth. Perhaps the main drawback of inertial guidance is that errors, such as those caused by the effect of gyroscopic drift on the orientation of the stabilized platform, are cumulative. This is especially important in the determination of distance where the summation (or integration) is carried over the whole flight time. Inertial guidance is thus generally restricted to trajectories of short duration, so that the errors do not become too large.

RADIO-INERTIAL GUIDANCE

4.58. A combination of radio command and inertial guidance, known as *radio-inertial guidance,* has the merit of improving the accuracy of purely inertial guidance by utilizing a relatively simple radar system. In radio command guidance it is the practice, as seen earlier, to make separate measurements of distance and velocity. In principle, the velocity could be determined by the rate of change of distance with time; in mathematical terms, the velocity can be obtained by differentiation of the distance with respect to time. However, this procedure involves a certain amount of averaging (or smoothing) of the data and the results are not considered to be sufficiently accurate for guidance purposes. Consequently, in radio command guidance the velocity (or range rate) is measured independently from the ground by means of continuous-wave radar, as described earlier.

4.59. It will be recalled that, in an inertial guidance system, the velocity is derived by integration of the acceleration over a time period. Since integration is mathematically the reverse of differentiation, it can be understood that the resulting errors will tend to be in the opposite direction to those associated with the differentiation of distance with respect to time. In the radio-inertial guidance systems the velocities are determined independently by integration of accelerometer data, on the vehicle, and by differentiation of radar distance (or range) data, at a ground station. The results are then averaged to yield very accurate values of the vehicle velocity at any instant.

4.60. The ground equipment for radio-inertial guidance consists of a pulsed radar transmitter with an antenna capable of following the trajectory of the launch vehicle. The vehicle may (or may not) carry a transponder to increase the strength of the return signal. But it must have radio equipment capable of receiving ground signals giving continuous readings of the range, as determined by the time-delay technique. On the space vehicle, these range signals are fed to a simple electronic differentiating circuit and the output goes to a computer where the resulting velocity signals are combined with those from the accelerometer-integration system (Fig. 4.16). The velocity obtained in this manner can be integrated over time to yield the distance traversed. The data thus

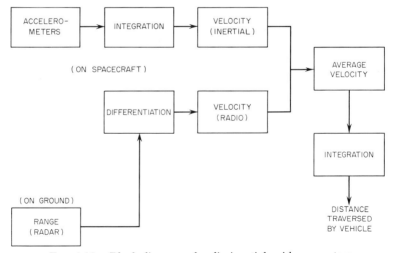

Fig. 4.16. Block diagram of radio-inertial guidance system

derived can be used in the normal manner to yield guidance correction information.

MIDCOURSE GUIDANCE

4.61. Midcourse guidance is used only in connection with long-distance trajectories in space, such as are involved in flights to the Moon, to the planets, and to the vicinity of the Sun. Its purpose, as indicated previously, is to correct for possible errors in velocity and direction at the point of injection, and also for uncertainties in the calculation of the flight trajectory and for perturbations in motion of the vehicle that inevitably arise on a long journey in space.

4.62. There are several respects in which midcourse guidance differs from the guidance employed in the initial pre-injection phase. In the first place, during the course of initial guidance the position and velocity of the vehicle are measured and the needed adjustments are made continuously over the whole flight period. For midcourse guidance, on the other hand, the number of corrections made is small, frequently only one. Instantaneous reliable observations of position and velocity, such as are necessary for guidance, become increasingly difficult to obtain as the vehicle moves farther from Earth. Consequently, several determinations are made from a ground station at intervals, and from these the actual flight path can be predicted with a fair degree of accuracy for some time ahead. Comparison with the desired trajectory then makes possible the calculation, in advance, of the correction which should be applied at a particular instant. At this time, a signal from the ground to the space vehicle causes the correction to be made.

4.63. Suppose that AB in Fig. 4.17 represents the direction and magnitude, i.e., the vector, of the actual velocity of the spacecraft at a given instant of time, and that AC is the calculated velocity vector required to bring it to the desired target. For purposes of clarity, the vectors in Fig. 4.17 are drawn in such a manner that the difference between them is greatly exaggerated. The midcourse velocity correction is then represented by the vector BC; in other words, the velocity correction has a specific magnitude and direction at the given time. This correction is supplied by the thrust from a rocket that provides the necessary midcourse propulsion. The rocket is fixed on the spacecraft, and hence the orientation (or attitude) of the latter must be adjusted so that the thrust correction

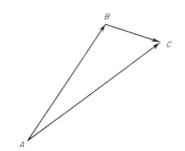

FIG. 4.17. Velocity vector correction for midcourse guidance maneuver

is applied in the proper direction. In unmanned space vehicles, the attitude is determined by automatic observations of the directions of two celestial bodies using suitable trackers or sensors (see § 4.111 *et seq.*). In Mariner II (Venus probe) and Ranger (Moon probe), the reference bodies were Earth and the Sun, and in Mariner IV (Mars probe) and Surveyor (landing instruments on the Moon) the bodies tracked are the Sun and the star Canopus (Alpha Carinae), the second brightest in the sky.* With the attitude defined by the two trackers, a signal from the ground actuates gyroscopes which set and maintain the required direction for the midcourse thrust correction to be made at the appropriate time.

4.64. Doppler shift measurements on continuous-wave radar transmission from a beacon† on the spacecraft have been utilized to some extent for velocity determinations, but the results are not too accurate because of variations in the transmitting frequency. Consequently, the two-way technique is to be preferred, although it involves more complicated equipment both on the vehicle and on the ground. A stable continuous wave radar signal is transmitted to the spacecraft; a transponder on the vehicle changes the frequency to some extent, amplifies the signal, and retransmits it to the ground where the Doppler shift is determined. In this manner, the velocity of the vehicle is evaluated. By suitable modulation of the continuous-wave carrier, the time required for the signal to travel to the spacecraft and back to Earth can be measured. From this time delay, the distance of the vehicle can be calculated in the usual manner. Thus, both the distance and velocity required for midcourse correction calculations are available. Two-way Doppler measurements from the United States have been made with L-band radar in the frequency region in the vicinity of 900 megacycles per second, but in the future there will be an increasing use of frequencies near 2200 megacycles per second in the S-band.

CELESTIAL NAVIGATION

4.65. A number of concepts have been proposed for using celestial bodies, such as planets, the Sun, or fixed stars, in space guidance systems. Since the presence of a human observer can both simplify the equipment on the vehicle and make its operation more reliable, celestial navigation is especially applicable to self-contained guidance systems on manned spacecraft. Some of the possible uses of celestial observations for midcourse guidance will be reviewed briefly.

4.66. By means of a telescope carried on the spacecraft, a measurement can be made of the angle subtended between the center of Earth and a known planet or star. In conjunction with a table of ephemerides (§ 1.11), it is possible to determine a conical surface, with its apex at the center of Earth, upon which the position of the spacecraft must lie at the time of the measurement. To define the location precisely, it is necessary, in principle, to make simultaneous

---

* Excluding the Sun, the brightest star is Sirius.

† A radio beacon is an independent transmitter that is not triggered by an external signal.

sightings on three celestial bodies, and the required point is that at which the three conical surfaces intersect. Identification of this point and the determination of its distance from Earth, using the measured angles and the ephemerides, involves a complicated application of celestial mechanics. The calculation would have to be made by a computer carried on the spacecraft. If considered desirable, the data could be transmitted to Earth by radio and the computations made (or confirmed) there.

4.67. In practice, only two simultaneous observations of stars may be sufficient if the position of the vehicle is known approximately. As a general rule, the telescopes will be mounted on a gyroscopically stabilized platform, in order to simplify tracking of Earth and the stars. If the precise orientation of the platform in space is known, two angular measurements are sufficient to determine the location of the spacecraft. However, because of unavoidable gyroscopic drifts, the orientation of the platform must be checked from time to time by sighting on fixed stars.

4.68. The general procedure described above provides a possible technique for utilizing self-contained instrumentation for determining the distance of a space vehicle from Earth. The velocity can be obtained by calculating the change in position over a known time period. Ideally, several determinations should be made at short successive intervals and from these a fairly accurate average velocity can be computed. Provided the distance from any celestial body or Earth is large, as will presumably be the case in a midcourse situation, the velocity of the vehicle will be almost constant; the individual determinations to be averaged will thus not differ greatly. In this manner, the required midcourse velocity vector correction can be calculated.

4.69. The way in which these data are utilized will vary according to the circumstances. If it is required to be completely independent of equipment on Earth, the observations could be compared with reference values determined beforehand and stored on magnetic tape. The adjustment of the trajectory can then be made in a manner similar to that employed in inertial guidance during the pre-injection phase. Because of unforeseen perturbations, the reference trajectory may not be correct. A competent human navigator on the space vehicle might recalculate the trajectory as new information became available or a computer could be designed to perform this function. A possible alternative (or confirmatory) approach would be to transmit the data to a station on Earth; after several position and velocity values have become available, the subsequent procedure would then be the same as in radio-command guidance.

TERMINAL GUIDANCE

4.70. Terminal (or approach) guidance includes final trajectory correction in preparation for orbiting the Moon or a planet or landing instruments or a manned spacecraft. Descent to Earth of a satellite or a vehicle returning from a space mission also requires terminal guidance; these situations are referred to as re-entry because entry into Earth's atmosphere is the basic problem to be solved. In approaching the Moon or a planet, the direction could be corrected by means of a suitable tracker (or sensor), and the distance determined by measuring the apparent diameter of the target body (cf. § 6.21). In some cases, the distance might be obtained from the time delay interval of pulsed radar signals transmitted from the spacecraft and received again after reflection from the Moon or planet. The velocity can then be derived from the rate of change of distance with time. These data can be used in conjunction with, or in place of, information available at tracking stations on Earth to make a final trajectory correction or to time the dropping of a capsule. If it is desired to orbit the Moon or planet, it will be necessary to decrease the velocity of the space vehicle to that required for the specific primary body at a particular altitude. This can be done by the aid of retrograde (or retro-) rockets which produce a thrust in the opposite direction to the motion of the vehicle. The magnitude of the velocity vector required is calculated from the spacecraft data described above.

4.71. If the vehicle or part of it is to descend from orbit to the surface of the Moon or planet, the procedure will depend upon the presence or absence of an atmosphere. In descending to the surface of the Moon, for example, only gravitational forces need be considered in determining a trajectory. Since the Moon has no significant atmosphere, aerodynamic drag forces, which play a significant role in a return to Earth's surface, are essentially absent. In these circumstances, calculation of the velocities and vehicle altitudes during the landing trajectory would not be very difficult. Retro-rockets would be required to decrease the speed, but because there is no atmosphere parachutes would be useless for exerting a braking effect.

4.72. Re-entry into Earth's atmosphere (or landing on a planet with an atmosphere) must take into account, and take advantage of, the aerodynamic resistance as the space vehicle approaches the surface. Because the properties of Earth's atmosphere are reasonably well known up to high altitudes, the re-entry trajectory for a spacecraft can be calculated before the flight. Many trajectories are theoretically possible and the one generally chosen is short enough to permit good accuracy but not so short as to be accompanied by excessive heating by the resistance (or drag) of the atmosphere. The basic guidance parameters for re-entry and landing within a given area on Earth are the point in space at which the retro-rockets are to be fired, the value to which the velocity is to be decreased, and the re-entry angle (or attitude) with respect to the local horizontal. Once the correct firing time is determined from trajectory observations, made on Earth, the remaining actions are carried out, either automatically or manually, in accordance with a prescribed program. As in the initial guidance phase, gyroscopes or suitable sensors and small (vernier) rockets are used to obtain the desired re-entry attitude. When near Earth, the landing of the vehicle is facilitated by means of parachutes which decrease the rate of descent by virtue of their aerodynamic characteristics. A further description of the re-entry and landing of manned space capsules is given in Chapter 13.

4.73. It is probable that ultimately spacecraft designed for return to Earth will be equipped with wings or their equivalent, like an aircraft or glider. Upon entering the atmosphere, such a vehicle will have aerodynamic lift and drag forces acting upon it (§ 4.91). More precise guidance will then be possible by adjustment of velocity and attitude just as in a conventional aircraft. In these circumstances, the landing pattern might well be determined by radio signals from the ground.

Orbital Rendezvous

4.74. The term *orbital rendezvous* is used to describe the operation of bringing a maneuverable space vehicle, sometimes called a *space ferry* or *chaser vehicle,* into gentle contact with another vehicle, referred to as the *target satellite,* in orbit about Earth, the Moon, or a planet. This operation involves special problems in guidance which have been the subject of many studies because of the great importance of orbital rendezvous for future space exploration. The mass of useful material (or payload) that can be launched into a particular orbit depends on the available rocket thrust. Although it is true, as seen in Chapter 3, that rocket engines of larger and larger thrust are being continually developed, their increasing size and complexity are somewhat of a drawback. There is, consequently, a practical limitation to the orbiting of large payloads such as are required for manned missions to the Moon and the planets or for the establishment of large space stations orbiting Earth.

4.75. The situation could be greatly alleviated by utilizing the concept of orbital rendezvous. Instead of launching all the components required for a given mission as a single payload, they could be launched in parts and assembled by rendezvous in orbit. For example, a more-or-less permanent orbital space station could be established and maintained in this manner. Subsequent escape from an assembled vehicle in orbit, for a journey to the Moon or a planet, is possible by the development of a relatively moderate amount of thrust. Another proposed application of rendezvous is in the return of a space ferry, e.g., the Apollo lunar excursion module, from a landing on the Moon. The ferry would be launched from the surface of the Moon and would rendezvous with its parent vehicle which is in orbit around the Moon (§ 13.47).

4.76. Assuming that the target satellite is in orbit, the launching time of the ferry and the altitude of injection must be selected to bring it within reasonable distance of its target. Furthermore, it is desirable that the orbit planes of the ferry and target be as close as possible, in order to minimize the thrust and fuel expenditure required to bring the two vehicles together. In some circumstances it will be preferable to launch the ferry into a parking orbit in which it will coast until the time is opportune for undertaking the rendezvous maneuver.

4.77. In general, the space ferry is expected to approach within four or five hundred miles of the target satellite as a result of an initial guidance operation. At this point, *terminal* (or *homing*) *guidance* is initiated by appropriate changes in velocity and attitude of the ferry vehicle. For this purpose a rocket, whose thrust can be varied both in magnitude and direction, would be required. The basic guidance data are range and range rate, and these would be determined by on-board radar or an equivalent sensor. Since both ferry and target vehicles are moving, the Doppler shift does not measure the actual range rate of the ferry, but rather the value with respect to the target satellite. Fortunately, it is this quantity which is the important parameter for homing guidance. The range and range-rate data are fed continuously to a computer and the output will adjust the control actuators so as to decrease both parameters simultaneously, bringing them to zero at the same time. In this manner, the ferry would approach the target vehicle gradually and the relative velocity would ideally be zero when contact is achieved.

4.78. Time-delay and Doppler shift measurements can be performed at separation distances down to a few yards by employing radar waves of very high frequency. For the final stage of homing guidance, known as the docking phase, use can be made of an infrared (heat) or visible light emitter on the target and a suitable detector on the ferry vehicle. Such homing devices are familiar in weapons technology. The actual coupling (or mating) of the ferry with the target may demand a change in the attitude orientation of the vehicles with respect to one another. The presence of a man on either (or both) the target and ferry vehicles will greatly simplify this final operation.

ROCKET AND SPACE VEHICLE CONTROL

VELOCITY AND ATTITUDE CONTROL

4.79. The quantities to be controlled in the trajectory of a space or rocket vehicle are velocity and attitude. As seen from the preceding discussion, velocity is controlled in special situations only, e.g., midcourse, rendezvous, and terminal guidance. In most cases, subsidiary rockets are fired for a certain interval of time to produce a required increase or decrease in velocity. Solid-propellant rockets are often employed for this purpose. Where continuous changes or restart capability are necessary, liquid-propellant or gas jet systems are preferable; the thrust is controlled by changing the flow rate of the liquid (or liquids) or the gas.

4.80. Changes in the attitude of a vehicle, i.e., rotation about pitch, roll, and yaw axes, are used in the launch phase, i.e., for initial guidance, and also when the craft is in space. In all cases, some form of thrust control is employed. Since attitude control in space is simpler to describe, this will be disposed of first. The most common method for controlling the attitude of a spacecraft during the unpowered (or ballistic) phase of its flight is by means of gas jets, and nitrogen gas under pressure has been extensively used for this purpose. In the manned Mercury space capsules, however, hydrogen peroxide mono-propellant rockets were utilized for attitude control. The attitude of a vehicle in space can be readily changed by applying a small thrust in one or other of six possible directions.

ROCKET VEHICLE CONTROL

4.81. During the launch phase the attitude of a rocket vehicle is changed by varying the direction of the applied thrust; this is called *thrust vector control*. The effect is illustrated in Fig. 4.18; although the rocket vehicles are

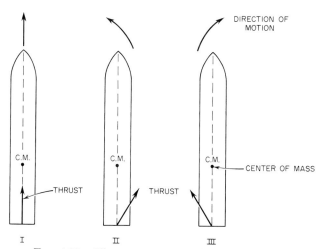

FIG. 4.18.   Thrust vector control of rocket vehicle

drawn upright in the figure, the situations described apply to any direction in space. As is generally the case, the motor is located at the rear end of the vehicle, and this is where the thrust originates. If the rocket thrust is in the direction of the main (or long) axis of the vehicle, passing through its center of mass (C.M.), the vehicle will move in the direction of the axis, as indicated in Fig. 4.18, I. But, if the engine thrust is not along the axis, as represented in Fig. 4.18, II and III, the thrust produces a turning movement about the center of the mass. The direction of motion will thus be changed, as shown in the figures. By suitable choice of the thrust direction, the vehicle may be made to turn about any (or all) of its three attitude axes.

4.82. The means used to vary the thrust vector are called *control members*, and several different types have been used. In one of the simplest procedures, originally employed in the V-2 (§ 1.78) and utilized in the Scout (first stage) and other rocket vehicles, the control members are *jet vanes.* Four hinged vanes of a heat-resistant material, such as graphite, are placed at right angles in the nozzle exit, so that the exhaust gas has to flow past them, as shown both in elevation (I) and plan (II) in Fig. **4.19**. By rotating the vanes about the hinges, the direction in which the exhaust gas is expelled can be varied and the thrust vector is changed accordingly. Pitch, yaw, or roll can be con-

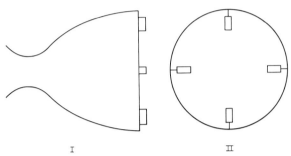

I   II

FIG. 4.19. Control of rocket vehicle by jet vanes

trolled in this manner. Jet vane control of thrust direction is feasible for rockets with either solid or liquid propellants.

4.83. In some cases, the vanes are connected to fins extending beyond the rocket motor diameter. The prime purpose of such fins is to stabilize the vehicle, as will be explained shortly, but their aerodynamic behavior can also be utilized in the control of the vehicle. It should be noted, however, that fin control is not effective at high altitudes where the density of the atmosphere is low. Control by jet vanes is, of course, independent of the ambient atmosphere.

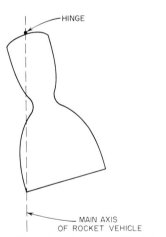

FIG. 4.20. Thrust vector control by hinged rocket motor

4.84. For liquid-propellant rockets that are not too large, a common practice is to mount the motor on a gimbal or hinge, so that its direction can be changed with respect to the remainder of the vehicle (Fig. **4.20**). The thrust vector can thus be altered with reference to the main axis. In solid-propellant rockets, the propellant is included in the motor which constitutes a major proportion of the vehicle. Control of thrust directly by hinging the motor, especially if it is large, may then not be practical. An alternative but equivalent procedure is to have a movable nozzle attached to the thrust chamber by means of a flexible joint. Attitude control can then be achieved by swiveling the nozzle. The technique of changing the direction of the rocket motor or nozzle, as described in this paragraph, can be employed for control of pitch and yaw motions but not of roll.

4.85. Pitch and yaw control of solid-propellant rockets is frequently accomplished by means of a *jetevator* as the control member. A jetevator is a pivoted ring or collar located at the exhaust end of the nozzle (Fig. 4.21) and capable of being rotated in the manner indicated. As the jetevator rotates, it deflects the exhaust gases and hence changes the direction of the rocket thrust. Separate jetevators are required for pitch and yaw control.

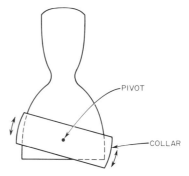

4.86. Another proposal for rocket control, which would be particularly useful in solid-propellant motors, is the local injection of a neutral liquid into the nozzle. Rapid vaporization of the liquid produces a deflection in the exhaust gas stream and thereby affects the thrust vector.

Fig. 4.21.   Thrust vector control of rocket by jetevator

4.87. For large rocket vehicles, with either liquid or solid propellants, a convenient means for changing the thrust vector is by using small auxiliary (or vernier) rocket motors. Six such thrustors, suitably arranged and capable of swiveling, can provide flexible control about all three attitude axes. Because these rockets must be capable of rapid changes in thrust, it may be desirable to use either a liquid monopropellant or a compressed gas. Switching the motor on and off and changing the magnitude of the thrust can then be achieved by control of the propellant flow rate. Thrust direction is adjusted by actuation and, if necessary, swiveling of the appropriate rocket motors. Auxiliary rockets may be used for roll adjustment in cases, such as those described above, in which the normal control is restricted to rotations about the pitch and yaw axes.

CONTROL ACTUATORS

4.88. The guidance system provides the control information that determines the actions of the control members, e.g., jet vanes, swiveling engines or nozzles, jetevators, or vernier rockets. In between these two elements is the control actuator; this may be an electric motor, a hydraulic system, etc., which drives the control member upon instructions received from the guidance system. Although electric motors have been utilized as control actuators, they are suitable only for small rocket vehicles. In order that the controls may respond very rapidly, the motor should be run continuously at a high speed of rotation and means provided for varying the direction and extent of motion of the control member actuated by the motor.

4.89. For large and moderately large rockets, hydraulic actuators are generally employed. They provide a compact system having rapid response and capable of handling high power levels. A schematic arrangement of a hydraulic control actuator system is given in Fig. 4.22. The hydraulic fluid is usually

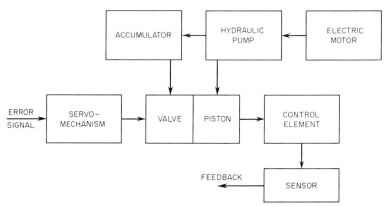

Fɪɢ. 4.22.   Hydraulic control actuator system

a suitable petroleum (hydrocarbon) oil maintained in an accumulator at a constant pressure of about 3000 pounds per square inch by means of a pump driven by an electric motor. Signals from the guidance system actuate an electrically-operated valve which determines the power applied by the hydraulic piston to the control member. A suitable pickoff or other device, that indicates the extent the required change has occurred, provides a feedback signal for a servomechanism, as described in § 4.42.

ROCKET AND SPACE VEHICLE STABILIZATION

Aᴇʀᴏᴅʏɴᴀᴍɪᴄ Fᴏʀᴄᴇꜱ

4.90. An important consideration in steering a rocket vehicle is its aerodynamic stability while passing through the tangible atmosphere. A stable body is one that tends to return to its original position after being disturbed by an external force; an unstable body, on the other hand, departs farther from its initial position if it is disturbed temporarily. The stability or instability of a rocket vehicle is largely dependent upon the relative locations of the center of mass (§ 2.46, footnote) and the *center of pressure*. In order to understand the situation, it is necessary to explain the significance of the center of pressure.

4.91. Consider a rocket vehicle, as represented in Fig. 4.23, and suppose that, due to some disturbance, e.g., a change in the thrust vector, the vehicle is moving at a given instant in the direction *V*, which does not coincide with the main (long) axis. The angle, α, between this axis and the direction in which the vehicle is moving is called the *angle of attack*. As a result of the motion through the sensible atmosphere, aerodynamic forces* act on the vehicle; these are conveniently treated in terms of two components at right angles, namely, the *drag force, D*, acting in the direction opposite to V, the direction of motion, and the *lift force, L*, in a perpendicular direction. Both lift and drag forces depend on the vehicle velocity, the air density, the frontal (or cross-sectional) area of the vehicle in the direction of motion, as well as on the shape of the vehicle (cf. § **3.128**, footnote). The aerodynamic forces acting on all parts of the moving vehicle may be replaced by a single

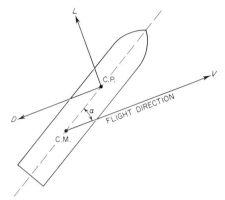

FIG. 4.23.   Angle of attack and aerodynamic forces

resultant force, and the center of pressure (C.P.) is the point on the axis through which this net force passes.

4.92. In the circumstances shown in Fig. 4.24, I the center of pressure lies above, i.e., forward of, the center of mass (C.M.). The effect of the aerodynamic force (A.F.) in this case is to produce a torque (or rotation) of the

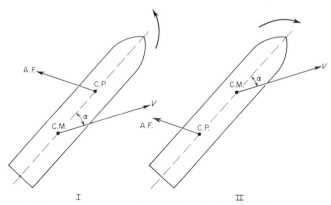

FIG. 4.24.   Center of pressure above (I) and below (II) the center of mass

vehicle about the center of mass in such a manner as to increase the angle of attack. This rotation will cause the frontal area in the direction of motion to

* Aerodynamic forces are the forces which result whenever there is relative motion between a (solid) body and a gas.

increase and as a result, the aerodynamic forces will be enhanced. The angle of attack will consequently become still larger, and so on. The situation is thus an unstable one, in accordance with the definition given earlier. If, however, the center of pressure were to lie below, i.e., to the rear of, the center of mass, the aerodynamic force would tend to decrease the angle of attack and the situation is stable (Fig. 4.24, II). When the angle of attack is zero, i.e., the velocity (or motion) is in the direction of the rocket axis, the lift force is absent and the aerodynamic drag acts along the axis but in the direction opposite to the motion. The rotational or overturning effect of the aerodynamic forces is then absent.

STABILIZATION DURING ASCENT

4.93. In order to minimize aerodynamic drag, a rocket vehicle as launched is a long cylinder. Such a structure without fins has its center of pressure ahead of the center of mass; it is therefore aerodynamically unstable. By the addition of tail fins the aerodynamic forces on the tail end of the vehicle are so greatly increased that the center of pressure is moved to the rear of the center of mass. The purpose of tail fins in a rocket is thus to provide aerodynamic stability. It can be seen, in a qualitative manner, that any disturbance of the vehicle's attitude will tend to be resisted by the aerodynamic forces acting on the large surfaces of the fins. It is of interest to mention that the so-called "guiding stick," which has long been used in fireworks and other rockets (§ 1.46), brings the center of pressure nearer to the end; it thus increases the stability and maintains the flight direction of the rocket.

4.94. Obviously, tail fins provide stability only as long as the atmosphere has an appreciable density. At high altitudes, where the air density is very low, fins are not very effective. Consequently, when fins are used on a multistage rockets, they are generally restricted to the lower stages, usually to the first stage only.

4.95. For large rockets, the tail fins are heavy and represent a significant weight penalty at liftoff. Consequently, they are not used in such vehicles as Polaris, Minuteman, Atlas, and Titan. Stabilization in these cases is achieved by automatic attitude adjustment, controlled by a closed loop, gyroscope system similar to that described in § 4.42. Any disturbance in the attitude of the vehicle is immediately counteracted by the required change in the thrust vector. For this purpose, the use of auxiliary (vernier) rockets is convenient. The Saturn rockets have tail fins, in addition to the automatic stabilization, in spite of their large mass. The fins are included as a precautionary measure in the event of a failure in the automatic attitude control system or its inability to cope with an abnormal situation during the launching of a manned space capsule.

4.96. For the upper stage (or stages) of multistage launch vehicles, spin stabilization is frequently employed. The stage is set spinning about its long axis by utilizing small rockets or gas jets. Stabilization then results from the gyroscopic action which resists any tendency for an external force to displace the spin axis.*

GRAVITY (ZERO-LIFT) TURN

4.97. During the ascent of a rocket vehicle, aerodynamic forces are the main cause of attitude disturbance. Consequently, the flight trajectory should be chosen so as to minimize the effect of these forces. As already seen, when the angle of attack is zero, that is to say, the flight direction V coincides with the vehicle's long axis, the only aerodynamic force is drag and it also acts in the direction of the axis. Hence, apart from gravity, there are no lateral (or sideways) forces acting on the vehicle (Fig. 4.25). The great advantage of this situation is that the bending moments and accompanying loads on the structure are minimized. If appreciable loads of this type were expected, it would be necessary to strengthen the vehicle and thus increase the dead weight to be lifted by the rocket motor.

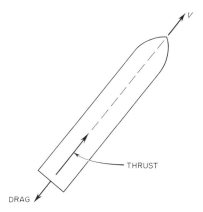

FIG. 4.25.   Zero-lift (or gravity turn) condition of rocket vehicle

4.98. Ideally, therefore, the rocket vehicle trajectory should be such as to maintain a very small or zero angle of attack throughout the ascent. In practice, this is not altogether possible because satellite vehicles, for example, are launched vertically, or almost vertically, and injected horizontally; there is consequently a large change in direction of the vehicle's axis. To minimize the aerodynamic effects, the change in direction of motion or *pitch-over*, which is accompanied by an appreciable angle of attack, as in Fig. 4.23, should be initiated as soon as the situation is compatible with other considerations. Both drag and lift forces are proportional to the square of the vehicle velocity, and so the aerodynamic forces will generally be smaller in the early stages of the trajectory when the velocity is still relatively low.

4.99. As the velocity and the aerodynamic forces increase, the vehicle attitude should be adjusted so that the angle of attack is steadily decreased to zero. The angle should then be held at zero for the remainder of the ascent trajectory. In these circumstances, the lift force is essentially absent and so

---

* It is well known that spinning serves to stabilize and thus improve the flight accuracy of rifle bullets and artillery shells.

also is the bending load on the vehicle structure. Such a path is called a *zero-lift trajectory*. It is also called a *gravity turn* because the trajectory is then determined by the action of the gravitational forces. If it were not for gravity, the vehicle would move in a straight line (Fig. 4.26); since the angle of attack is zero, both thrust and aerodynamic drag act in the direction of the vehicle's long axis. The gravitational force, however, causes the vehicle to pitch over and gradually approach a horizontal direction of motion. The change in attitude required to achieve the desired trajectory is included in the initial guidance program.

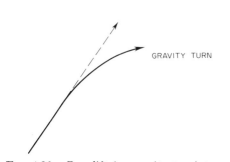

FIG. 4.26.   Zero-lift (or gravity-turn) trajectory

SPIN STABILIZATION IN ORBIT

4.100. A satellite in orbit is in a balanced condition, and quite minor disturbing forces, such as small aerodynamic effects, variations in Earth's gravitational and magnetic fields, and radiation pressure from the Sun can cause changes in attitude. In a manned vehicle, movements of the astronauts might produce a similar effect. In many situations of interest, it is desirable or necessary to stabilize the attitude of the vehicle with respect to Earth, the Sun, or inertial space. Appropriate means must therefore be used to attain this stabilization.

4.101. The simplest method of stabilizing the attitude of a satellite is to cause it to spin about one of its axes (§ 4.96), and this procedure has been used for a number of unmanned Earth satellites, including Vanguard, Telstar, TIROS, etc. The gyroscope effect is enhanced if the spacecraft has a drum-like or pillbox shape, i.e., with the diameter greater than the axial length, as in TIROS (cf. Fig. 5.1), or, at least, has its major contents in this form, as in Telstar. By firing small rocket motors, called *spin* (or *spin-up*) *motors*, attached to a *spin table*, the satellite is set spinning before it is released from the final stage of the carrier vehicle. Of course, if this stage is already spinning (§ 4.96), no further steps would be necessary to stabilize the spacecraft.

4.102. The rate of spin of a satellite is largely dependent upon the intended application of the system. In the meteorological TIROS satellites, for example, the spin rate is about 10 revolutions per minute, but in the communications satellites, e.g., Relay, Telstar, and Syncom, the rate is 150 to 180 revolutions per minute. The action of Earth's gravitational and magnetic fields tends to decrease the rate of spin; consequently, small spin-up rockets, which expel jets of cold, compressed gas, e.g., nitrogen or air, are often used to restore the spin rate. In the TIROS satellites, the spin-up jets are operated by radio command from the ground.

4.103. Provided there are no disturbing forces, a spin stabilized vehicle will retain a constant orientation in inertial space; the spin axis will then always be directed toward a fixed point in space. Earth's gravitational and magnetic fields, however, generally produce changes in the pointing direction; that is to say, the spin axis will precess as a result of the disturbances. If the satellite is not a spherical mass, for example, the force of gravity has a non-uniform distribution, and consequently the direction of the spin axis will change. Precession can also arise from the interaction of Earth's magnetic field with the residual magnetism of the satellite and its contents. The motion of the spin axis of TIROS I was so large that in the later TIROS satellites (cf. § 5.14) an attempt was made to control the precession by winding an electromagnetic coil around the base. Activation of the coil, by a signal from the ground, produced a local magnetic field intended to compensate for the residual magnetism of the satellite. Similar devices for adjusting the orientation of the spin axis were used in the Telstar and Relay satellites.

4.104. Spin stabilization is suitable when all that is needed is for the satellite axis to have a more-or-less fixed direction in space. In many satellites orientation is required with respect to a particular body, such as Earth or the Sun. Appropriate sensing devices, to be described shortly, are then employed to acquire the desired orientation and this is maintained by means of a suitable attitude stabilization system.

OTHER METHODS OF STABILIZATION

4.105. Various methods have been proposed for stabilizing a body-oriented satellite. For example, deviation from the desired orientation (or attitude) can cause the sensor to activate a small rocket; the thrust will then make the vehicle turn in such a manner as to correct the orientation error. Six thrustors, two for each axis, are required to control rotation about pitch, yaw, and roll axes. As mentioned in § 4.80, compressed gas jets and hydrogen peroxide rockets have been used for this purpose. The operation of a rocket or gas jet for attitude control is limited by the quantity of propellant that can be carried, but *inertial methods* of stabilization are not restricted in this respect. Of the many possible procedures, four are of special interest; these involve the use of either a gyrostabilizer, a reaction (or torque) wheel, a free (or reaction) sphere, or gravity gradient.

4.106. It was stated in § 4.30 that if a torque is applied in a direction perpendicular to the spin axis of gyroscope wheel, the gyroscope will tend to rotate, i.e., precess, about an axis perpendicular to both the spin and torque (input) axes. Conversely, if the spinning gyroscope wheel is forced to precess, a torque will be produced about the axes perpendicular to the spin and precession axes, i.e., about the original input axis. In a *gyrostabilizer*, the normal precession axis of the gyroscope is made the sensitive one, so that any rotation of the vehicle about this axis will produce a torque sufficient to restore the attitude. For complete stabilization, three one-degree-of-freedom position (or displacement) gyroscopes are required.

4.107. *Reaction* (or *inertial*) *wheels* are being used in several satellites, such as the Nimbus meteorological satellite and the Orbiting Astronomical and Geophysical Observatories, for attitude stabilization in orbit. Their operation depends on the principle of conservation of angular momentum just as does that of the gyroscope. If a rotary flywheel attached to a satellite is accelerated, a torque will be produced on the vehicle which will cause it to rotate in the opposite direction about the axis of the rotating wheel. If the flywheel is decelerated, on the other hand, the vehicle will rotate in the same direction, in order to maintain constancy of the total angular momentum. Three flywheels with their axes at right angles to each other can serve to stabilize the attitude of a satellite about pitch, roll, and yaw axes. Any deviation from the required orientation causes a change in the rate of rotation of one or more of the flywheels. The resulting reaction on the vehicle then corrects for the deviation.

4.108. A single sphere that is free to rotate in all directions, called a *free* (or *reaction*) *sphere*, can be equivalent to the three flywheels described above for control about all three attitude axes. Proposals have been made for the utilization of a large rotating, metal sphere supported in a spacecraft by means of an electromagnetic field. Since the sphere is "weightless" when in orbit (§ 13.83), relatively little support would be needed. Three magnetic coils, one associated with each attitude axis, are located around the sphere. Departure from the required orientation of the vehicle causes the direction sensor to energize the appropriate coil (or coils). The resulting magnetic field, interacting with the main support field, changes the rate of rotation of the sphere. As is the case with a flywheel, the reaction causes a rotation of the satellite in such a direction as to conserve the total angular momentum. This rotation adjusts the orientation of the vehicle.

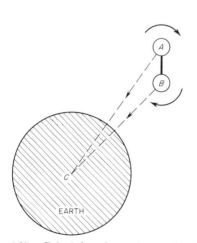

Fig. 4.27.   Principle of gravity-gradient stabilization of spacecraft

4.109. Orientation with reference to Earth (or other primary body) may be stabilized by utilizing the principle of the *gravity gradient*, sometimes referred to as *passive stabilization* because it does not require any special equipment.

If two equal masses are connected to form a vehicle similar in form to a dumb-bell, then in space the system will orient itself so that the long axis is always directed toward Earth's center. To show that this will be the case, suppose the axis does not satisfy this condition, as indicated in exaggerated form in Fig. 4.27. The masses A and B are equal, but since B is closer to the center of Earth than A, it will be attracted more strongly by gravity. Thus, the force in the direction BC, where C is Earth's center, exceeds that in the direction AC. The result is that a torque is developed, as shown by the curved arrows, which tends to turn the axis AB so as to point toward C, the center of Earth.

4.110. To take advantage of this method of Earth orientation, the spacecraft does not necessarily have to be dumbbell-shaped; the essential requirement is that the vehicle should have one axis which is much longer than the others. The name gravity gradient arises from the fact that the stabilization depends on the significant difference in gravitational attraction at the two ends of this long axis. The main difficulty in implementing the gravity gradient (or passive) stabilization principle is the tendency of the spacecraft to oscillate, like a pendulum, about the desired orientation direction, i.e., toward Earth's center. Work is being done on the development of a suitable method for damping these oscillations, e.g., by the use of long rods (or booms) extending from the satellite.

ATTITUDE SENSORS

HORIZON SENSORS

4.111. The direction from a satellite to the center of Earth or other body can be determined by means of a *horizon sensor*. This is a device for sensing the periphery of a body as it would be seen from a satellite and then finding its geometric center. The demarcation between space and the exterior of Earth, for example, is characterized by a change in the intensity of radiation, especially infrared radiation, received as the scanner changes direction. The infrared radiation received from space is negligible, whereas that from Earth is considerable, because of the higher temperature.

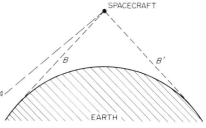

FIG. 4.28.   Horizon-scanning Earth sensor

4.112. Suppose the angle of an infrared detector is changed so that it receives a narrow beam of radiation from different directions. Starting from the west and moving toward the east, for example, it will first receive radiation from space, as indicated by A in Fig. 4.28; then, as at B, when the radiation comes from Earth's horizon, there will be a sharp increase which can be observed by an infrared detector. Similarly, in moving beyond B' there will be a marked drop in the infrared radiation. The direction to Earth's center is in a plane midway between the horizon lines B and B'. If observations of the same kind are made simultaneously at right angles, another midway plane can be located. The direction of Earth's center is the line where the two planes intersect. The two sets of measurements can be combined into one by rotating the scanner so that radiation is received from various directions over a series of conical surfaces.

4.113. There are at least two ways in which the horizon scanning principle may be applied to orient a satellite. Consider a reference axis on the satellite and suppose it is pointing in the required direction, i.e., toward Earth's center. Assuming that, from the satellite, the periphery of Earth, i.e., the horizon, is seen as a circle, it will take the moving scanner the same time to travel from the reference line to the horizon in all directions. If the satellite reference axis is not pointing to the center of Earth, the times will vary. The variation can serve to energize an attitude stabilizer which causes the satellite to rotate in such a manner as to eliminate the variation. The reference axis will then point in the prescribed direction. Another possibility is to make a continuous determination of the angle between the reference axis and the direction of the horizon. Here again, if the reference axis is in the required direction, the angle will remain unchanged as the scanner rotates. If there are variations, the satellite orientation is corrected until the angle is the same in all directions.

4.114. An entirely different approach to horizon scanning utilizes a device with no moving parts. It consists essentially of two pairs of infrared detectors, XX' and YY', located at right angles to the reference axis, as depicted in Fig. 4.29. If this axis is in the requisite direction, all four detectors will receive the same amount of infrared radiation. But a deviation from the correct orientation will produce a detectable difference when X is compared with X' or Y with

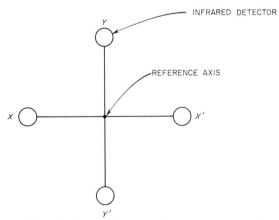

FIG. 4.29.   Earth sensor with no moving parts

Y'. The attitude stabilizer will then respond so as to point the satellite in the prescribed direction.

SUN TRACKER

4.115. The direction of the Sun is important for interplanetary flight guidance and also for the proper orientation of the panels of solar cells that provide electrical power for satellites and space probes (§ 3.250). A simple form of the *Sun tracker* consists of two matched detectors with a shadow shield above them, as shown in the sectional drawing in Fig. 4.30. When the shield is pointed directly at the Sun, both detectors are equally shaded, and both receive the same, small amount of radiation. But if the shield is not oriented toward the Sun, one of the detectors will be shaded while the other is exposed to sunlight. There will then be a marked difference in the radiation re-

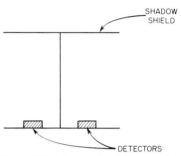

FIG. 4.30.   Principle of Sun tracker

ceived by the two detectors. A useful detector material is cadmium selenide which has an electrical resistance (or conductance) that varies with the amount of light falling upon it.* When the shadow shield is not pointing at the Sun, the difference in resistance can be utilized to cause a current to flow and operate an attitude stabilizer. When the current drops to zero, the vehicle is oriented in the desired direction toward the Sun.

PLANET SENSOR

4.116. A planet sensor, somewhat similar in principle to the Sun tracker, is the *planet tracker*, represented in Fig. 4.31. The radiation from a planet (including Earth) is largely reflected radiation from the Sun and so is very weak. Consequently, detection requires the use of sensitive photomultiplier tubes;† the electrical voltage (or current) output of such a tube is roughly proportional to the intensity of the light falling upon it. Three photomultiplier tubes are arranged as shown in the figure, with a three-holed mask in front. When pointing directly at the planet, the output of all three tubes will be the same.

---

* Cadmium selenide is called a *photoconductive material,* because its electrical conductance (or resistance) varies in proportion to the amount of radiation, e.g., light, in the appropriate wavelength range falling upon it.

† A *photoelectric cell,* also called a *photo-cell* or *prototube,* is a device for converting radiation, such as visible, ultraviolet, or infrared light, into an equivalent electric current; it is thus a type of transducer (§ 4.149). In a *photomultiplier* tube there is considerable internal amplification of the electron current. It responds rapidly, and with a high degree of sensitivity, to changes in radiation intensity.

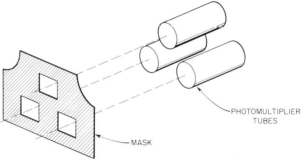

PHOTOMULTIPLIER
TUBES

MASK

Fig. 4.31.   Principle of planet tracker

If the orientation is not as required, the electrical outputs will differ, and the differences can be used to change the orientation of a spacecraft.

Star Sensors

4.117. Certain stars are being used to provide reference points for the attitude control of spacecraft at great distances from Earth (cf. § 4.63). A star is particularly useful in this respect because, being far away, it acts as a point source of light; hence its direction can be indicated with great accuracy. Generally, the Sun and a bright star are used as the attitude reference points in space. The particular star, e.g., Canopus, is selected both for its location with respect to the Sun, approximately at right angles to facilitate the determination of its position, and its characteristic brightness, which must be distinguishable from that of other stars.

4.118. In the application of a star sensor, Sun sensors first cause the spacecraft to point its roll axis toward the Sun, and then the vehicle is rolled by means of jets until the star sensor locates the required star. This is done by using photoelectric cells to measure the brightness of the star relative to that of the Sun and comparing the result with the known brightness ratio at the existing distance from the Sun. If the values agree, the sensor has found the desired star and remains locked onto it; if not, the spacecraft is rolled until another star is in the field of view and its brightness is determined. The procedure is repeated until the correct star has been located.

4.119. In order to simplify the search process, the star sensor is designed so that it does not respond to extended light sources, such as Earth and the Moon at moderate distances, and it will not pick up Mercury or Venus because they are in the wrong direction relative to the Sun. A discriminator built into the star sensor makes it responsive only to light intensities within fairly narrow limits. Hence, the planets Mars and Jupiter are too bright and the other planets are too faint to interfere with the operation. For the same reason, there are very few stars, other than the one being sought, to which the sensor will respond.

TRACKING

INTRODUCTION

4.120. Tracking is the process of determining the location and motion of a rocket vehicle, satellite, or space probe during and after launching. Radio guidance, described earlier in the chapter, involves tracking, particularly in the pre-injection and midcourse phases of the trajectory. Tracking observations are also often made of rocket vehicles employing inertial guidance to make sure that they are following the prescribed path. A manned satellite capsule is tracked continuously to verify the suitability of the orbit and to provide precise timing for various operations, especially those concerned with re-entry into Earth's atmosphere.

4.121. Tracking is performed on satellites used for meteorological, communication, or navigational purposes, so that their exact locations are known at specific times. Similar information is often needed for orbiting vehicles transmitting scientific data to Earth. Furthermore, precise determination of satellite orbits is required both for predicting subsequent orbits and for the analysis of perturbations (cf. § 8.6). Prediction of orbits is also necessary to permit the pointing of antennas to receive telemetry information from satellites.

4.122. Broadly speaking, the major tracking operations carried out in connection with spacecraft launched from the United States fall into four general, although not independent, categories. First, there are observations made at the launch site to study the initial trajectory of the rocket vehicle. Then there is the tracking of unmanned satellites already in orbit, utilizing both radio and optical procedures. Next, mention may be made of the facilities for tracking space probes out to great distances from Earth. Finally, there is the tracking network used for manned orbital flights. These various systems will be considered in the order given.

LAUNCH SITE TRACKING

4.123. After liftoff, the rocket vehicle may be tracked both photographically and by various radio and radar techniques. Because it is essential that reliable information be obtained, in the interest of safety, measurements of the same parameters, e.g., position and velocity, are made in several different ways. The timing of pulsed or modulated radar signals provides information on distance, and the location can be obtained from observations on the phase shift (§ 4.125) of continuous-wave radar beams. The principle used in the Azusa phase-shift system at the Kennedy Space Center, from which many spacecraft are launched, is similar to that of the satellite network, described below. The DOVAP (Doppler Velocity and Position) method, on the other hand, utilizes the Doppler shift of continuous-wave radar to determine the range rate of the vehicle. From simultaneous measurements made at three or more stations, the actual velocity of the vehicle and its direction of motion can be computed.

SPACE TRACKING AND DATA ACQUISITION NETWORK

4.124. The Space Tracking and Data Acquisition Network (STADAN) includes what was formerly known as the Minitrack Network;* the latter consists of 12 ground stations, mostly in North and South America, forming a "fence" in a general north-south direction. The locations of the stations, shown in Fig. 4.32, are as follows: College, Alaska; St. John's, Newfoundland; Gold-

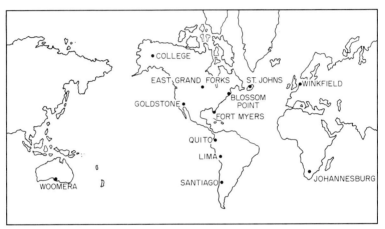

FIG. 4.32.   Locations of Minitrack Network stations for satellite tracking

stone, California; East Grand Forks, Minnesota; Blossom Point, Maryland; Fort Myers, Florida; Quito, Ecuador; Lima, Peru; Santiago, Chile, in the Americas; and Winkfield, England; Johannesburg, Republic of South Africa; and Woomera, Australia. The receiving antennas used at the STADAN Minitrack stations differ from those employed in other tracking systems; they are fixed, linear arrays and are not capable of following the motion of a satellite (Fig. 4.33). At each station, observations are made during passage of the satellite in an orbit within range of the station. Combination of the information from several stations on successive transits makes it possible to determine precise orbital data.

4.125. The operation of the Minitrack system is based on the principle of *radio interferometry*. A radio beacon on a space vehicle emits a signal, at a definite frequency, which is received at two points on Earth separated by a known distance that is not too large. The two receivers are both located at one of the stations mentioned above. In general, the path lengths from the transmitting beacon to the two receiving antennas are different, and so they will not observe the same radio wave signals simultaneously. Let A and B in Fig. 4.34 represent

---

* The name "Minitrack" arose from the minimum size and weight of the radio tracking beacon carried by the satellite.

FIG. 4.33.   Linear antennas (with reflectors below) of a Minitrack Network station

the two receivers, a distance l apart. Provided the distance between A and B is relatively small, the space vehicle is so far away that the lines from A to B to the transmitter may be taken to be parallel, making an angle θ with the horizontal. The difference in the path lengths of the signal from the satellite transmitter to the two receiving antennas is then equal to AC, where BC is perpendicular to AC. If the distance AC is represented by x, then

$$x = l \cos \theta. \tag{4.4}$$

4.126. In the radio interferometer, the magnitude of x is determined by comparing the phases of the radio waves as received at the points A and B. Assuming, for simplicity, a simple sine-wave form (cf. § 4.150), the wave received at B, at any instant, may be represented by the upper curve in Fig. 4.35.

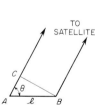 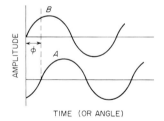 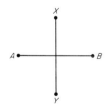

FIG. 4.34.   Principle of radio interferometer for satellite tracking

FIG. 4.35.   Phase angle difference in radio waves.

FIG. 4.36.   Arrangement of antennas in Minitrack system

Since the path from the satellite transmitter to A is somewhat longer than that to B, the wave form at receiver A, at the same instant, is somewhat delayed, as shown in the lower curve. The delay is expressed in terms of the *phase angle, ϕ,* in radians; it can be measured by means of a radio interferometer into which the two signals are fed. A difference in path length equal to one wavelength of the radar is equivalent to a phase angle of 2π radians (360 deg) ; consequently, the actual path length difference is $\phi/2\pi$ wavelengths. If the wavelength of the radar is λ, the path length difference x is equal to $\lambda(\phi/2\pi)$; hence, from equation (4.4)

$$\cos \theta = \frac{x}{l} = \frac{\phi\lambda}{2\pi l}. \tag{4.5}$$

The distance l between the two receiving antennas and the wavelength of the radar may be regarded as known; since the phase angle ϕ is measured by the radio interferometer, the angle θ can be calculated.

4.127. There is an uncertainty in the procedure just described because the radio interferometer cannot distinguish between a phase-shift angle of ϕ radians and one of $\phi + 2\pi$, $\phi + 4\pi$, etc., radians. The situation is resolved in the Minitrack System by having another pair of receiving antennas, called the ambiguity antennas, at a shorter distance apart. Since θ must be the same, regardless of the distance between the antennas, it is not difficult to determine whether the phase angle in the first case is ϕ or $\phi + 2\pi$, etc. The measurement from the two antennas that are farther apart is the more accurate because the phase angle is correspondingly larger and so can be determined with greater precision.

4.128. The angle θ is merely the direction with respect to the horizontal made by the radio path from the space vehicle to the receiving antennas, and it does not define the direction of motion of the satellite. To obtain this direction, it is necessary to employ two additional receivers at the same station. The line joining these two receiving antennas, e.g., X and Y in Fig. 4.36, should be at an angle, preferably a right angle, to the line between the antennas A and B. Since the angle with the horizontal is known for each pair of antennas, the actual direction of the space vehicle can be determined. The situation is depicted in perspective in Fig. 4.37, where one pair of antennas is assumed to be on a north-south line and the other on an east-west line. The two indicated angles with the horizontal fix the radial direction of the satellite. From the manner in which the direction changes, the actual direction of motion of the spacecraft can be derived, if required.

4.129. Each set of four antennas oriented in a particular manner can detect signals from a satellite entering a fan-shaped volume in space with dimensions of about 10.8 deg in one direction and 76 deg in a direction at right angles. A Minitrack Network station has two such sets of antennas, so that there are two fan-shaped volumes, at an angle of 90 deg with one another, in which a satellite can be detected. The layout of such a station is shown in Fig. 4.38. One set of four antennas has the narrow dimensions of the fan beam arranged in the east-west direction; these are called the equatorial set and are indicated by the letter E. The other set, called the polar array, is designated by the letter P; the narrow dimensions of the fan are then in the north-south direction. The distance between each pair of antennas in the equatorial set is 46 wavelengths at the

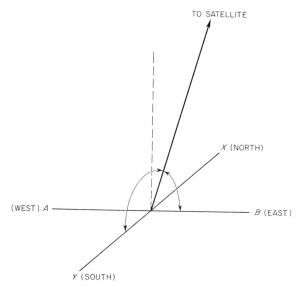

FIG. 4.37.   Determination of satellite direction by Minitrack system

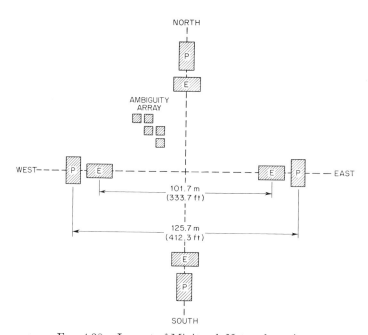

FIG. 4.38.   Layout of Minitrack Network station

operating frequency of 136 to 137 megacycles per second, i.e., 101.7 meters (333.7 feet), and that between the polar set is 57 wavelengths, i.e., 125.7 meters (412.3 feet). In the ambiguity array the antennas are much closer, the distances in a north-south or east-west direction being either 3.5 or 4 wavelengths from center to center, i.e., 7.71 or 8.82 meters (25.31 or 28.93 feet).

4.130. The information from the Minitrack Network stations all over the world, like that from other STADAN stations, is transmitted to the Communications Center at the Goddard Space Flight Center, Greenbelt, Maryland. Although the data from any one Minitrack station give only the direction of the satellite at a particular time, the actual location can be derived from a combination of the data from several stations in the network. After applying corrections for the bending of the radio waves by the ionosphere, the mathematical description of the orbit is produced with the aid of computers.

4.131. The great merit of the Minitrack system lies in its simplicity. The antennas on the ground are fixed and they do not have to be changed as the satellite moves past the station, as is the case with other tracking systems. The data are then recorded automatically as the satellite passes through the fan-shaped volume within which each set of antennas is sensitive. Furthermore, all that is required on the satellite is a simple radio beacon of light weight. To offset these advantages there are, however, a number of limitations.

4.132. In order to compute reasonably accurate orbital parameters, it is necessary to obtain data from several passages of the satellite at different stations, and consequently some hours may elapse before the orbit is defined. Furthermore, although the Minitrack system is suitable for satellites of medium and low altitude, it is not satisfactory for spacecraft in highly eccentric orbits. When such satellites are distant from Earth, they move so slowly through the sensitive volume of the Minitrack antennas that the angular position cannot be correlated precisely with the time. In addition, the system cannot provide the tracking information needed to place a synchronous satellite in orbit and to keep it in a particular location with respect to Earth (cf. § 5.96). The STADAN is therefore being extended by the addition of paraboloidal (dish-shaped) antennas to obtain range and range-rate data, utilizing radar echo techniques and the Doppler effect. There are to be 85-foot diameter antennas at Fairbanks, Alaska; Rosman, North Carolina; and Canberra, Australia; and 40-foot antennas at Johannesburg, Republic of South Africa; Quito, Ecuador; and Santiago, Chile. Smaller antennas are being located near Tananarive, Madagascar. For range and range-rate tracking, a special transponder will be required on the spacecraft, and because of the additional weight this system will be used only when it is essential.

OPTICAL TRACKING NETWORK

4.133. The spatial position of Earth satellites is also determined photographically in the Smithsonian Astrophysical Observatory Tracking Network.

There are 12 stations in the network, each equipped with a Baker-Nunn camera,* especially designed for satellite tracking. The stations are located at Jupiter, Florida; Organ Pass, New Mexico; Arequipa, Peru; San Fernando, Spain; Curaçao, Netherlands West Indies; Maui, Hawaii; Olifantsfontein, Republic of South Africa; Villa Dolores, Argentina; Mitaka, Japan; Naini Tal, India; Shiraz, Iran; and Woomera, Australia.

4.134. The Baker-Nunn camera (Fig. 4.39) has a field of view of 30 deg along the track of the satellite and 5 deg in the direction at right angles. The telescope

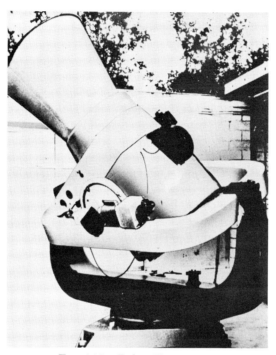

FIG. 4.39.   Baker-Nunn camera

is of the Schmidt type, as commonly used in astronomical photography, with a spherical mirror 30 inches in diameter. It has a gimbal mount that permits the camera to point in any desired direction. The approximate position of the satellite must be known before the camera is actually sighted on it. There are several ways in which the Baker-Nunn camera can be used for tracking satellites. In the most common mode of operation, photographs are taken which show the path of the satellite against a background of fixed stars. The track is divided into segments by the action of an accurately timed rotating shutter which cuts off the light from the satellite at regular brief intervals. In effect, therefore,

* Named for its designers, James G. Baker and Joseph Nunn.

there are a series of exposures of the moving spacecraft on the same plate.*
From photographs obtained at several stations, the position of the satellite can
then be calculated from the computed angles subtended between known stars
and the satellite.

4.135. The optical tracking system is used only at dawn and dusk, when the
sky is fairly dark but the satellite is rendered visible by reflection of the Sun's
rays from just below the horizon. The atmosphere must, of course, be clear
enough for the satellite and stars to be seen. As a compensation for these
limitations, the optical method provides the most accurate data of the position
of a satellite in orbit; in fact, the results up to about 1000 miles or more are
often used to check the values obtained by radar measurements. Another advantage is that optical tracking can be applied to any satellite, regardless of
whether it carries a radio beacon or not.

DEEP SPACE NETWORK

4.136. Tracking of lunar and planetary probes is performed by stations of
the Deep Space Network (DSN); this system was designed especially to detect
intelligible radio signals coming from many million kilometers away.† The
DSN includes the Deep Space Instrumentation Facility (DSIF), which is integrated with a Space Flight Operation Facility (SFOF) at the Jet Propulsion
Laboratory, Pasadena, California, and an interstation communications system. The present DSN consists of three stations equipped with steerable,
paraboloidal antennas 85 feet in diameter (Fig. 4.40); there are three such
antennas at Goldstone, California,‡ and one each at Johannesburg, Republic of
South Africa, and Woomera, Australia. Two additional stations, at Canberra,
Western Australia, and Madrid, Spain, are to become operative in 1965. A
210-foot steerable dish antenna is under construction at Goldstone, and it is
hoped that other similar antennas will be built in due course as the space program develops.

4.137. The sites of the DSN stations have been chosen so that they are
separated by no more than 120° longitude and lie between the latitudes of 30°N
and 30°S. It is consequently possible to keep track of a spacecraft during the
whole of its journey to the Moon or to a distant planet. In spite of the rotation
of Earth, at least one of the DSN stations can always be in radio contact with
the space vehicle.

4.138. For a spacecraft that is a fairly large distance, e.g., several thousand
miles, from Earth, range and range rate are mainly used for tracking purposes.
For lunar and planetary probes, the observations made at the DSN stations

* A stationary camera which records a succession of images of a moving space object on
a single plate is called a *ballistic camera*.

† Signals were received from the Venus probe, Mariner II, at a distance of 86.7 million
kilometers (53.9 million miles).

‡ Of the three antennas at Goldstone, one is generally used only for experimental and
research purposes.

Fig. 4.40.   Dish (paraboloid) antenna, 85 feet in diameter, of Deep Space Network at Goldstone, California

thus consist chiefly of Doppler shift measurements to determine the range rate, and of elapsed time for a coded radio signal to travel from Earth to the spacecraft and back to obtain the range. The angular direction of the space probe is also recorded, from the orientation of a steerable antenna on the ground, but angular data are not used in trajectory analysis because of their relatively low accuracy.

4.139. Data obtained at the DSN stations are used for midcourse guidance, and the tracking antennas can serve to transmit command signals to the spacecraft. Another function of these antennas is to receive radio telemetry data from instruments carried by the distant probes (§ 4.148). Since they must be capable of detecting very weak signals against a background of noise, antennas of large diameter are used in conjunction with special receivers of high sensitivity and high signal-to-noise ratio. Local interference from radio stations, electrical machinery, transmission lines, etc., is minimized by installing the antennas in natural depressions or valleys, at a distance from populated areas; the surrounding higher ground provides a certain amount of shielding.

MANNED SPACE FLIGHT NETWORK

4.140. The communications network (MSFN) for tracking the capsule during the Project Mercury manned orbital flights and for maintaining voice contact with the astronaut consisted of a total of 16 stations encircling the globe. Of these stations, 11 were equipped with radar devices for determining range and angular position. Transponders on the Mercury satellites provided adequate signal strength for tracking purposes. The locations of these stations are as follows: Cape Kennedy, Florida; Bermuda, West Indies; Grand Canary Island; Muchea, Australia; Woomera, Australia; Kauai Island, Hawaii, Point Arguello, California; Guaymas, Mexico; White Sands, New Mexico; Corpus Christi, Texas; and Eglin Field, Florida. All these stations, except those at White Sands and Corpus Christi, had facilities for voice communication with the astronaut and for the receipt of information by radio telemetry, as also did the installations at Kano, Nigeria; Zanzibar; Canton Island in the mid-Pacific; and ships in the Atlantic and Indian Oceans.

4.141. For the Gemini manned space program (§ 13.19) tracking stations are being added at Carnarvon, Australia, and on Madagascar, but those at Muchea and Woomera, Australia, and in Zanzibar are being deactivated. Another six stations, at Antigua, West Indies; Ascension Island, South Atlantic; Goldstone, California; Madrid, Spain; Canberra, Australia; and Guam, Northwest Pacific, will be added for Project Apollo for taking men to the Moon. It is also planned to use five ships, two in the Indian Ocean and three in the western Pacific Ocean, as well as instrumented aircraft, to assist in tracking the Apollo manned capsules (Fig. 4.41).

4.142. The layout of the Mercury network was determined by several important considerations. In the first place, it was necessary to obtain instantaneous and unequivocal information that the capsule, launched from Florida, was in an acceptable orbit before reaching Bermuda. If the initial orbit, calculated on the basis of a single determination of the velocity vector after injection, was unsatisfactory in apogee or perigee, the capsule could then be brought down in the Atlantic Ocean, near the Canary Islands. Another requirement was that the orbit had to be known with considerable accuracy, thus making it possible to calculate exactly when the retro-rockets were to be fired for re-entry. STADAN and Baker-Nunn camera stations are not satisfactory for manned spaceflight tracking because they cannot provide data with the required speed and accuracy.

4.143. In order that all the needed information should be available at the Control Center at the Kennedy Space Center, Florida, the tracking stations of

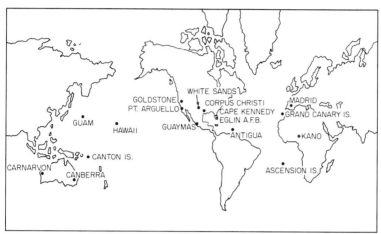

FIG. 4.41.   Locations of tracking stations for Apollo program. In addition, there are several mobile stations on ships in the Pacific and Indian Oceans

the MSFN are connected by land line, underwater cable, or radio to the Goddard Space Flight Center. There, the tracking data are processed immediately to some extent and then transmitted to the Control Center in Florida where they are displayed on large charts. It is here that the decisions concerning the duration of the manned flight are made.

LASER TRACKING

4.144. The laser* technique combines certain features of both optical and radar methods of tracking satellites. A laser is capable of emitting a very narrow beam of high-intensity, coherent light, i.e., the light waves reinforce each other (cf. § 8.172, footnote). The beam is highly directional and spreads out but little as it proceeds from Earth into space. Consequently, the decrease in intensity with increasing distance is very small. By contrast, light rays (and radio waves) from normal sources spread out in all directions and the intensity falls off as the inverse square of the distance.

* The word laser is an acronym for "light amplification by stimulated emission of radiation." Lasers are sometimes called optical masers, since they utilize the same principle as the maser, originally developed for microwave amplification by stimulated emission of radiation. Masers are frequently used for the amplification of very weak radio signals received from spacecraft for tracking and telemetry, because they provide a low signal-to-noise ratio.

4.145. For tracking purposes, laser light is flashed from a station on Earth toward the satellite with the aid of a telescope, at the rate of about one flash a second. On the spacecraft are a number of "corner" reflectors, so called because they are analogous to the corner reflector antennas used in radar to increase the directional effect of the reflected beam. In these devices, reflection occurs at a corner formed by two reflecting planes which make an angle with one another. When the laser light flash strikes the reflectors on the satellite, some of the light is returned in the direction from which it came. The elapsed time between the emission of a laser pulse and its return to Earth after reflection then gives the distance of the satellite from the ground station. The laser method had two advantages over the analogous radar echo technique for determining range. In the first place, the decrease in intensity of the reflected laser light could be much less than a radar beam, and so a transponder on the satellite would be unnecessary. Second, the light rays are hardly affected by their passage through the ionosphere, whereas a radar beam is refracted, as mentioned in § 4.25.

4.146. Tests of the laser method for range determination are being made in connection with the Beacon Explorer and Geodetic Explorer (GEOS) Satellite programs. On Explorer XXII (§ 8.202) there are 360 cube-corner reflectors of one-inch prisms of highly polished fused silica mounted on an eight-sided, flat-topped pyramid. The facets of the prisms are cut accurately to permit reflection of the laser light in the general direction from which it originates. Certain of the facets are coated with aluminum to provide the mirror surfaces of the cube-corner reflectors. Silica is used for the prisms, rather than glass, because the latter tends to darken under the action of the radiations in space whereas silica does not.

RADIO TELEMETRY

Introduction

4.147. Nearly all satellites and space probes carry instruments which acquire a wide variety of information, ranging from the blood pressure of an astronaut to the intensity of microwave radiation from a distant planet. The process whereby the results of measurements made in a spacecraft are conveyed to Earth is called *radio telemetry* or, in brief, *telemetry.** The *raw data*, as received at a ground station, are in symbolic (or coded) form and this is converted into intelligible information by the process of *data reduction*. Each spacecraft generally carries many instruments and the transmission of all the data without confusion represents a formidable problem. Furthermore, "real time" telemetry, i.e., transmission at the same time as the instrument readings are taken, is often not feasible because a satellite may not be within line of sight, as required for radio contact with a telemetry receiver, more than once per orbit. The data are then recorded on magnetic tape as they are observed by the

* From the Greek words *tele*, "far" or "distant," and *metron*, "measure."

instruments and are read out at a rapid rate upon receipt of a command from a ground station.

4.148. In telemetry from a space vehicle, radio waves are used as the carrier of information in a manner similar to that employed in conventional radio communication and in the broadcasting of both visual and sound signals. The instruments on board a particular vehicle are usually designed to measure a variety of different quantities, e.g., attitude, temperature, pressure, magnetic field strength, ultraviolet and other radiations, charged particle densities, etc. In some cases, the output of the instrument is in the form of an electrical voltage signal which varies directly with the magnitude of the quantity being measured.

4.149. If the instrument response is not electrical, it must be converted into this form by means of a suitable device called a *transducer*.* The output may be either in analog or digital form. With an *analog transducer*, the output varies continuously in a way that closely approximates the variations in the input to the transducer. In a *digital system*, on the other hand, the output signals from the transducer vary in a step-like manner, each step corresponding to a particular whole-number, i.e., a digit, in magnitude. The electrical signals from the transducer are imposed on a radio *carrier wave*, and the resulting wave is said to be *modulated*. The process of changing the carrier wave so that it includes the *modulating signal* to be transmitted is called *modulation*.

TYPES OF MODULATION

4.150. It is well known that two methods of modulation are used in radio broadcasting; these are amplitude modulation (or AM) and frequency modulation (or FM). Any simple wave motion can be characterized by the two quantities, amplitude and frequency. In Fig. 4.42 is shown the variation of magnitude (or strength) with time of what is called a *pure sine wave*, because it has the same shape as a curve showing how the sine of an angle changes as the angle increases. The *amplitude* of the wave is the maximum departure of its strength from the average value, as indicated in Fig. 4.42. The *frequency* is the number of cycles (or unit waves) that occur in unit time. In the figure, for example, five cycles are shown, and if the elapsed time were one one-thousandth (0.001) of a second, the frequency of the particular wave would be 5×1000, i.e., 5000 cycles per second or 5000 cps. The term *kilocycle* is used to represent 1000 cycles, and so in the case under consideration the frequency is 5 kilocycles per second.† In

---

* In general, a transducer is a device capable of converting a signal in one form of energy into an equivalent signal in another energy form. For measurement purposes, the converted signal is commonly electrical in nature, since this lends itself particularly to amplification and transmission. A simple transducer of this type is the microphone or telephone mouthpiece which converts sound into electrical signals. The loud-speaker and telephone earpiece are transducers of the reverse type.

† In radio engineering it is a common practice to omit the "per second" and to describe the frequency in kilocycles, often abbreviated to kc; thus a frequency of 5 kc is one of 5 kilocycles (or 5000 cycles) per second.

the United States, the carrier waves used in standard radio (AM) broadcasting each have a definite frequency lying within the range from 535 to 1605 kilocycles per second.

4.151. In modulating the carrier wave by a superimposed signal, it is generally either its amplitude or its frequency which is changed in accordance with the magnitude (or strength) of the modulating signal. An important require-

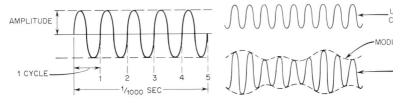

Fig. 4.42.   Characteristics of sine wave curve   Fig. 4.43.   Principle of amplitude modulation of radio carrier wave

ment is that the maximum signal frequency or, in general, the maximum rate of variation of the signal strength with time, should be considerably less than the frequency of the carrier wave. If this is not the case, it will not be possible for the carrier to convey the modulating information in a reliable manner. In *amplitude modulation*, the amplitude of the carrier wave is multiplied by an amount proportional to the modulating signal at each instant. Thus, as the value of the signal changes, the amplitude of the modulated carrier wave changes accordingly, as depicted in Fig. 4.43. This is the situation in ordinary (AM) radio broadcasting; the modulating signal consists of the complex electrical voltage variations produced by a microphone in the studio in response to sound waves. At the receiver, when tuned to the correct carrier-wave frequency, the modulated wave is demodulated; that is to say, the original carrier wave is removed, leaving only the modulating signal. The signal is electrical in nature and, after amplification, it is reconverted into sound by the loudspeaker.

4.152. It would appear that the frequency of the radio carrier wave remains unchanged as a result of amplitude modulation; but this is not strictly true because the modulated wave no longer consists of simple, sine-wave cycles. It can be shown mathematically, by the use of Fourier series, that the modulated wave can be represented as the sum of a number of sine waves having different frequencies. Consider, for purposes of illustration, the simple case in which the modulating signal is a single sine wave, e.g., a pure tone, of frequency f_m. Then if f_c is the frequency of the carrier (sine) wave, the amplitude-modulated wave will be equivalent to the sum of three sine waves having frequencies $f_c - f_m$, f_c, and $f_c + f_m$. There are thus two additional sine waves present with frequencies less and greater, respectively, than that of the carrier wave.

4.153. Actual modulating signals, e.g., those produced by music, consist of a very complex combination of sine waves covering a wide range of frequencies. As a result, the modulated wave is equivalent to the sum of many sine waves, including the carrier. These additional frequencies, both below and above the carrier frequency, are called *sidebands,* as indicated schematically in Fig. 4.44. The total frequency range covered by the lower (LSB) and upper (USB) sidebands is called the *bandwidth.* Because the sidebands extend the frequency range of the carrier wave, there is a danger of interference between waves of adjacent frequencies. In the United States, a bandwidth of 10 kilocycles per second is allowed to

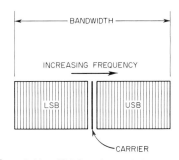

Fig. 4.44. Sidebands and bandwidth of modulated carrier wave

each channel in the standard (AM) broadcast range.* Consequently, the maximum permissible width of a sideband is 5 kilocycles per second, and this represents the maximum (sound) frequency that can be present in the modulating signal.

4.154. Because the two sidebands are symmetrical about the carrier frequency, and each contains all the signal information, it is not really necessary for the transmitter to send out both; neither, in fact, is the carrier frequency necessary to preserve the signal. In order to conserve power and to decrease the total bandwidth, some radio communication systems suppress the carrier and one of the sidebands, so that only a single sideband is transmitted; this is called *single sideband transmission.* In *vestigial sideband transmission,* a major part of the lower sideband is suppressed in the frequency region farthest from the carrier wave. The quality of reception is better than for single sideband transmission, while still permitting some decrease in bandwidth and energy expenditure. Vestigial sideband amplitude modulation is used in the United States to transmit the pictures in television broadcasting.†

4.155. In *frequency modulation,* it is the frequency of the modulated wave at any instant that is proportional to the strength of the modulating signal at that instant. In these circumstances, the modulated wave will represent a combination of many different frequencies. There are upper and lower sidebands, as in amplitude modulation, but the total bandwidth is not limited to twice the maximum modulating frequency. The total bandwidth can, in principle, be very large, but as the departure from the carrier-wave frequency increases, the amplitude decreases. As a result, the frequency-modulated wave has a limited

* This makes possible 108 carrier channels in the AM band from 535 through 1605 kilocycles per second.

† The permitted bandwidth per channel is 6000 kilocycles per second; the upper sideband occupies 4500 kc, the lower (vestigial) sideband 1250 kc, and the remaining 250 kc is utilized for the frequency-modulated carrier of the sound signal.

effective bandwidth which is essentially equal to twice the sum of the highest modulating frequency and the maximum departure (or deviation) of the frequency from that of the unmodulated carrier wave. This is clearly larger than the bandwidth in amplitude modulation; in fact, in frequency-modulated (FM) broadcasting, a bandwidth of 200 kilocycles per second is allowed for each channel. In order to accommodate such large bandwidths in the radio-frequency spectrum, it is necessary for the carrier waves to have much higher frequencies than in standard AM broadcasting. In the United States, the frequency-modulated broadcast band covers the range from 88,000 to 108,000 kilocycles (or 88 to 108 megacycles) per second.*

4.156. An important advantage of frequency modulation in radio telemetry is that it is possible to design receivers which have a low ratio of background noise to the desired signal. Furthermore, for a given receiving antenna, the gain for radio waves of high frequency (short wavelength) is greater than for lower frequencies (long wavelengths). Both of these matters have great significance in connection with the transmission of telemetry from a distant spacecraft, because the power of the signal received on Earth is generally extremely weak.

Multiplexing

4.157. In telemetry from instruments on a spacecraft, the same problem is encountered as in modern telephone and telegraph communication systems on Earth. It is to utilize a single channel, i.e., a single carrier radio wave, to transmit simultaneously and unambiguously a number of independent information signals. The means of achieving this objective is called *multiplexing*. Two general methods of multiplexing are in common use: they are known as frequency division and time division, respectively.

4.158. *Frequency division multiplexing* is actually a multiple-modulation technique; each signal modulates a separate *subcarrier wave* of different frequency, but all the subcarrier radio frequencies are lower than that of the main carrier wave. The resulting modulated subcarrier waves are then added and superimposed on the carrier. The possibility of the simultaneous transmission of several independent signals within a band of frequencies about a single carrier frequency arises from the fact that a number of subcarriers having different frequencies can each be modulated by one set of signals. The radio-wave carrier, modulated by all the subcarriers, is transmitted from the spacecraft, and when received a properly tuned subcarrier discriminator separates the individual modulated subcarriers. The latter are then demodulated in the usual manner (Fig. 4.45).

4.159. Either amplitude or frequency modulation could, in principle, be used for both subcarrier and carrier waves. In telemetry practice, however, only fre-

---

* A megacycle, sometimes abbreviated to mc or Mc, is 1000 kilocycles or 1,000,000 cycles.

quency modulation is used for frequency division multiplexing. The advantages are the high frequency of the carrier and the high signal-to-noise ratio possible in the receiver. In accordance with the statement in § 4.151, it is necessary, in order to permit satisfactory transfer of information, that the frequency of the subcarrier be considerably smaller than that of the main carrier wave. Hence,

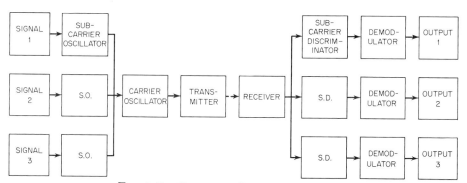

FIG. 4.45.   Frequency division multiplexing

a carrier wave of high frequency is capable of being modulated by several subcarriers of lower frequency. Furthermore, a high-frequency carrier permits the use of a large bandwith. A telemetry system in which both subcarrier and carrier waves are frequency modulated is designated a FM/FM system.

4.160. The frequencies of the main carriers used for radio telemetry from U.S. scientific satellites have been in several narrow bands in the range from about 135 to 2300 megacycles per second. For every carrier wave, 18 subcarriers, with unmodulated (or center) frequencies ranging from 400 to 70,000 cycles per second, have been standardized. The maximum permissible sideband width is 7.5 percent of the unmodulated frequency.

4.161. Because the subcarrier frequencies range from relatively low (400 cycles per second) to fairly high (70,000 cycles per second), the individual bandwidths are different. With increasing frequency, the subcarriers have increasingly greater signal carrying capacity. The subcarriers of lower frequency are suitable only for modulation by signals that vary relatively slowly with time, i.e., low-frequency signals; if the variation is rapid, i.e., high-frequency signals, then subcarriers of higher frequency must be employed. The accepted rule is that the maximum rate of variation of the signal strength, expressed in cycles per second, should not exceed 1.5 percent of the center frequency of the subcarrier, i.e., 20 percent of the corresponding acceptable sideband width. These restrictions make possible accurate reception of individual signals with a high signal-to-noise ratio.

4.162. The majority of telemetry signals do not change very rapidly with time, and a sufficiently accurate indication of the variation can be obtained by sampling the data periodically instead of continuously. That such is the case may be seen from Fig. 4.46; the left-hand (full) curve indicates the variation with time of a measured quantity that does not change very rapidly. The instantaneous values at a number of intervals are shown by the vertical lines in

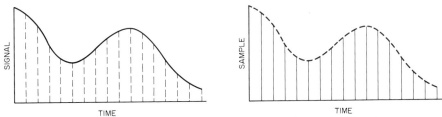

FIG. 4.46.   Periodic sampling of continuously varying signal

the right-hand part of the figure. The dotted curve joining these lines is seen to be a good representation of the actual (full) curve.

4.163. In *time-division multiplexing*, the intervals between the sampling of any given signal are filled, in a definite sequence, by samplings from other signals. The sequential sampling is achieved by means of a switching device called a *multiplexer* or *commutator;* for this reason, the sampling procedure in time-division multiplexing is referred to as *commutation*. Both mechanical and electronic (transistor)* commutators have been employed in telemetry; the latter are preferred for space applications because they permit high sampling rates and have no moving components.

4.164. The general principle of commutation will be understood from the diagrammatic representation in Fig. 4.47. A rotating arm makes contact in turn with a succession of signal channels. In an electronic commutator, the switching from one channel to another is performed by means of vacuum tubes or, preferably, transistors. The sampled signals then modulate a carrier (or subcarrier) wave in an appropriate manner, as described below. An identifying or synchronizing (*sync*) signal is inserted after each sampling cycle in order to permit the sorting out of the information (or data) signals in the receiver. The commutation rate depends on the available sideband width of the carrier (or subcarrier) wave and on the rate of change of the data signals with time (§ 4.172).

PULSE AMPLITUDE MODULATION

4.165. In the application of time-division multiplexing, an electronic pulse generator produces a continuous train of electrical pulses. These pulses are then modulated by the commutator output in one of several different possible ways. Of the modulation procedures which have been developed, only two,

---

* Transistors are also known as solid-state or semiconductor devices.

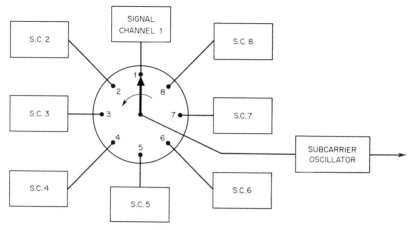

FIG. 4.47.   Principle of commutation (or multiplexing)

namely pulse amplitude modulation and pulse code modulation, commonly used in space telemetry, will be described here.

4.166. As the name implies, in *pulse amplitude modulation* (PAM), each pulse is modulated in such a manner that its amplitude is proportional to the strength of the signal from the commutator at that instant. A simple example of pulse modulation in a PAM multiplexing system with three signal channels is illustrated in Fig. 4.48. The modu-

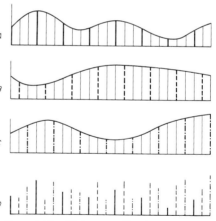

lated pulses (and a sync pulse) serve to modulate a radio carrier wave; as a general rule, frequency modulation is used because of the advantages already mentioned. The resulting double-modulated system is referred to as PAM/FM. If the commutation rate, i.e., number of samples per second, is not extremely high, e.g., less than a few thousand per second, the amplitude-modulated pulses can modulate a subcarrier, as in a FM/FM system Several pulse-modulated subcarriers can then be employed to frequency-modulate a main carrier wave, lead-ing to a triple-modulated system called PAM/FM/FM. It is not neces-sary that all the subcarriers be mod-

FIG. 4.48.   Pulse amplitude modulation; the sampled outputs of three signal chan-nels (*A,B,C*) are superimposed in *D*, which modulates the carrier wave

ulated by pulses; PAM subcarriers may be combined with others which are modulated in other ways, if desired. At the receiver, the subcarriers are separated and each data channel is treated individually to extract the tele-metered information.

4.167. By utilizing the sampling principle, pulse modulation permits a considerable increase in the amount of data that can be transmitted by a single carrier wave, having a given bandwidth. The number of pulsed signals that can be associated with a particular carrier wave depends on the frequency of the latter and on the rate at which the signals vary with time, i.e., the signal frequency. For signals of a given frequency, a high-frequency carrier has a greater capacity than one of lower frequency. If the measured quantity varies slowly with time, i.e., a low-frequency signal, a low sampling rate is adequate and many signal channels can be combined to pulse-modulate a given carrier. The opposite is true, of course, for rapidly varying, i.e., high-frequency, signals. If some of the measured quantities change slowly and others rapidly, they can be multiplexed together simply by adapting the commutator to sample the latter more frequently. The basic requirement for modulation, in any event, is that, as noted earlier, the modulating signals should vary much more slowly, i.e., have a much lower frequency, than the carrier (or subcarrier) wave being modulated.

PULSE CODE MODULATION

4.168. Pulse amplitude modulation is an *analog system*, since the output is always analogous (or proportional) to the input. One characteristic of an analog system is that the magnitude of the signals can vary in a continuous manner. By contrast, a *digital system* is one in which the signals are always expressed in a step-like, rather than continuous, form (cf. § 4.149). In a sense, digital representation cannot be quite as precise as analog representation, but since signal sampling is inevitably an approximation, the difference in accuracy is of little significance. For pulse code modulation, the amplitude-modulated pulses are converted into digital (or code) form before being applied to modulate the carrier (or subcarrier) radio wave. The reasons for making this conversion will be given below.

4.169. In *pulse code modulation* (PCM) telemetry, as in many electronic computers, the *binary number system* is used. In contrast to the familiar decimal system which employs ten digits, i.e., 0, 1, 2, 3, . . . 9, to express any number the binary system utilizes only two, namely, 0 and 1. In the decimal system, a number, such as 56,348, for example, has the following significance:

$$56,348 = 50,000 + 6,000 + 300 + 40 + 8$$
$$= 5(10^4) + 6(10^3) + 3(10^2) + 4(10^1) + 8(10^0),$$

recalling that $10^0 = 1$. Similarly, in the binary system, which makes use of the digits 0 and 1 only,

$$10{,}111 = 1(2^4) + 0(2^3) + 1(2^2) + 1(2^1) + 1(2^0)$$
$$= 1(16) + 0(8) + 1(4) + 2 + 1 = 23.$$

In this manner, any whole number can be expressed in binary form.

4.170. One of the advantages of the binary system is that information can be transmitted in the simple form of "on" and "off" pulses, one representing 0 and the other 1. Furthermore, since the receiver is required to distinguish only between on and off signals, the effect of the unavoidable background "noise" is very much less likely to cause an error than when continuously-varying (analog) signals are being transmitted. As a result, for a specified bandwidth, pulse code modulation makes it possible to increase the amount of information that can be transmitted in a given time.

4.171. The first stage in the use of pulse code modulation is to modulate the amplitude of the pulses by the time-division multiplexed output from a commutator. By the process known as *quantization*, the magnitude of each modulated pulse is then matched as closely as possible by one of a finite set of voltages; each member of the set is equivalent to a whole number, i.e., an integer. The quantized (or integral) signal is then converted into the appropriate binary digital code as a sequence of on and off pulses; this procedure is referred to as *coding*. Each set of pulses represents one *data point* or quantity sampled from an instrument or sensor. Finally, a carrier (or subcarrier) wave is frequency-modulated by the coded signal and transmitted in the usual manner. Both PCM/FM and PCM/FM/FM systems, similar to those referred to in § 4.166, are possible. At the receiver, the coding operation is reversed in a decoder and each output data channel is a sequence of signals whose magnitudes are the integers closest to the values of the sampled data point signals.

4.172. The rate at which binary code information can be transmitted is expressed in terms of the *bit rate*, or number of bits per second, the word *bit* being an abbreviation for binary digit. The relationship between the maximum bit rate capacity, C, and the bandwidth, B cycles per second, as derived from probability theory, is

$$C = B \log_2 \left(\frac{S}{N} + 1 \right), \tag{4.6}$$

where $\log_2$ is the logarithm to the base 2, and S/N is the average signal-to-noise power ratio. It is evident that a high bit rate capacity, i.e., the ability to transmit information at a high rate, requires that both the bandwidth and signal-to-noise ratio be large.* If the bandwidth is large, it is possible to tolerate a relatively low ratio of signal to noise and yet carry a considerable amount of information. On the other hand, if the bandwidth is small, the signal-to-noise ratio must be large if any appreciable amount of information is to be conveyed.

---

* This result is of general applicability and is not restricted to information transmitted in digital form.

4.173. A rough indication of the capacity of a single telemetry channel can be obtained by inserting some reasonable numbers into equation (4.6). For example, suppose the average signal-to-noise ratio of the receiver is taken at 10 * and the carrier bandwidth is 10 kilocycles per second, the capacity is

$$C = 10,000 \log_2 (10 + 1)$$
$$= 35,000 \text{ bits per second.}$$

Thus, in general, several thousand bits can be transmitted per second per carrier (or subcarrier) channel.

4.174. With the increase in the number of spacecraft, both satellites and probes, and the greater scope of the studies being made with the instruments they carry, the demands upon telemetry stations are growing rapidly. In order to handle the increasing amount of data, more and larger antennas are being constructed for the receipt of information from spacecraft. A large dish antenna, capable of concentrating radio waves received over a large area, makes possible an increase in the signal-to-noise ratio and, hence, in the rate at which information can be received. Telemetry antennas are presently located at some STADAN stations as well as at DSN installations, and others will undoubtedly be constructed as the space exploration program develops.

Command and Telemetry

4.175. Although the foregoing discussion has referred in particular to the return of information from a spacecraft to Earth, the binary digital code system is also used to transmit commands from Earth to a space vehicle. Such commands may be required for guidance, for switching radio transmitters on and off, and for the readout at an opportune time of information stored on magnetic tape. Receipt of the appropriate signal, in binary code form, will initiate the corresponding operation which is programmed into the spacecraft information system. It should be mentioned, too, that the unmodulated carrier wave used for telemetry also provides the radio signal for tracking the vehicle. It is for this reason that the radio beacon frequencies for the STADAN and DSN tracking networks are the same as those given in § 4.160.

APPENDIX

The Doppler Effect

4.176. Suppose that a source of waves is moving directly (radially) away from a fixed observer at a velocity v_r, and let t be the time between the emission of two successive wave crests. During this time, the source moves farther away by a distance tv_r. If c is the velocity with which the wave travels, e.g.,

---

* Signal-to-noise ratio is frequently expressed in terms of decibels; thus if S/N is the actual power ratio, the ratio in decibels is $10 \log (S/N)$, the logarithm being to the base 10. If the S/N power ratio is 10, it is also 10 in decibels.

the velocity of light, the second wave takes a time tv_r/c longer than the first wave to reach the observer. Hence, the time between successive waves reaching the observer is increased by a factor of v_r/c. The time between successive wave crests is inversely related to the frequency of the waves; hence, the frequency of the waves reaching the fixed observer from a receding source will be decreased by a factor of v_r/c of the emitted frequency. In the case of a source moving toward the observer, the frequency will be increased by the same factor. If f_0 is the frequency of the waves as they leave the source, the frequency change noted by the observer, f_d, i.e., the Doppler frequency shift, is equal to $f_0 v_r/c$; hence,

$$v_r = \frac{f_d}{f_0} c,$$

as in equation (4.2).

Chapter 5

APPLICATIONS IN METEOROLOGY, COMMUNICATIONS, AND NAVIGATION

METEOROLOGY

PROBLEMS OF WEATHER PREDICTION

5.1. Meteorology is defined as the science that is concerned with the study of the atmosphere and its phenomena. The most important atmospheric phenomenon, at least from the practical standpoint, is the weather; hence, analysis and forecasting of weather is a highly significant aspect of meteorology. A major advance in this science could be of great consequence economically and in the saving of human lives. There are divergent opinions concerning the possibility of changing the weather on a large scale, because of the enormous amounts of energy that would appear to be required. Nevertheless, if weather modification is ever to be realized and weather prediction is to be more reliable, it will be as a result of a greatly improved understanding of meteorological phenomena. It is in this respect that space studies can make contributions that are novel and unique in character. It should be pointed out, however, that meteorology by satellite will supplement, but probably never replace, the conventional measurements of temperature, pressure, humidity, and wind upon which weather forecasts have been based in the past.

5.2. Earth's atmosphere is in a continual state of energy unbalance and as a result it is always in motion, in a vain effort to attain a condition of balanced equilibrium. It is this unceasing motion of the atmosphere that produces the familiar and sometimes devastating effects of weather. Earth and its atmosphere are heated by energy received as radiations from the Sun, especially in daylight, but they are also cooled by a loss of radiation into space, especially at night. Apart from such daily variations, both the absolute and relative values of energy gains and losses depend on the latitude, e.g., more heat is absorbed at the equator than at the poles, and on the nature of the terrain, e.g., mountain, ocean, desert, etc. The unequal heating and cooling of the atmosphere, both in time and in spatial distribution over Earth's surface, are the cause of the energy (and temperature) unbalance that is responsible for the phenomena of weather.

5.3. Weather often appears to be relatively local in nature, sometimes changing markedly within a span of ten or a hundred miles. But the atmosphere is
continuous around the globe and extends upward for a considerable distance.
A particular weather effect at a given location may thus be due to a condition
of unbalance that developed several days previously in a region many miles
away. A complete understanding of weather at any point on Earth's surface
thus requires the accumulation of data from essentially the whole atmosphere.
It is commonly stated that practically all the weather of interest to man is
produced in the lower 10 to 15 miles of the atmosphere, and it is true that
clouds rarely form above an altitude of about 10 miles. However, the atmosphere of appreciable density extends to much greater heights (see Chapter 8)
and winds of high velocity, changing in direction according to the season, have
been observed at heights of nearly 100 miles. It is probable that such winds
have no direct influence on the weather at Earth's surface, but it cannot be
said that phenomena occurring in the atmosphere at high altitudes have no
effect at all.

5.4. Even if atmospheric studies for meteorological purposes are restricted
to the lower levels, the problem of obtaining worldwide information is still
formidable, especially as the data must be available on a continuous basis.
Since much of Earth's surface is covered by mountains, deserts, oceans, and
other uninhabited regions, only a small proportion of the atmosphere receives
adequate study from surface stations. The number of observation points could
perhaps be increased, but it would still be necessary to find some means for
the rapid collection and analysis of the data. Earth-orbiting satellites may
help to fill the meteorological information gap in at least two respects. A single
satellite can view a large part of Earth's surface at least once daily, and hence
observations can be made of areas that are otherwise inaccessible. The data
obtained in this manner are different from those collected at surface stations,
but they are nevertheless valuable, as will be apparent in due course. Another
possible use of an orbiting satellite is to collect information from remote observation points and to relay it to a central station on the ground for analysis.

DEVELOPMENT OF SPACE METEOROLOGY

5.5. As far as is known, the first successful use of a sounding rocket to obtain
photographs of Earth was achieved on March 7, 1947, by means of a V-2 rocket
launched from White Sands Proving Ground, New Mexico. The photographs,
taken from an altitude of about 100 miles, revealed many clearly recognizable
terrestrial and geographical features. Of special interest, however, for the topic
under consideration, is that they showed a great number and variety of cloud
formations over a large area of Earth. The meteorological significance of the
results was described by Delmar L. Crowson of the U.S. Air Force in 1949 in
what is believed to be the earliest discussion of the meteorological use of cloud
pictures secured from space. High-quality cloud photographs were obtained

from two Aerobee rockets launched from White Sands on July 26, 1948, and in 1951, Jacob A. B. Bjerknes of the University of California published the first detailed analysis of synoptic weather* as derived from these photographs. Interest in high-altitude cloud photography was further stimulated and its significance for meteorology was realized more fully after October 5, 1954, when pictures, obtained from rocket-borne, motion-picture cameras, showed the cloud system of an unsuspected tropical storm near Del Rio, Texas.

5.6. In all the cases referred to above, the cloud photographs were taken from sounding rockets, i.e., atmospheric probes (§ 1.97); consequently, they represented the conditions over a relatively limited portion of the atmosphere near the launch site at a particular time. In 1951, Stanley M. Greenfield and William W. Kellogg, in a report prepared for the U.S. Air Force, described the benefits that could accrue from the use of an Earth-orbiting satellite for weather reconnaissance. It was pointed out, in particular, that such a system would provide repeated spatial coverage of large areas, including many which are normally inaccessible. At the Hayden Planetarium Symposium on Space Travel held in New York in May 1954, the basic requirements and uses of a meteorological satellite were outlined by Harry Wexler of the U.S. Weather Bureau. It is of interest that, at the same symposium, S. F. Singer described in some detail his concept of the instrument-carrying satellite MOUSE (§ 1.108).

5.7. By the time plans were being formalized for the participation of the United States in the International Geophysical Year (§ 1.110), interest in the meteorological use of Earth satellites had developed to such an extent that it was decided to include appropriate instrumentation in such a satellite at the first opportunity. In September 1958, an attempt was made to launch a satellite carrying photoelectric cells (cf. § 4.116, footnote) sensitive in the near infrared region of the spectrum.† These instruments were designed to scan the cloud cover of Earth and to transmit the data to a ground station by radio telemetry (see Chapter 4), but the spacecraft failed to orbit. On February 17, 1959, the satellite Vanguard II carried into orbit photo-cells for measuring cloud distribution; unfortunately, the orbital conditions differed from those planned and the spacecraft developed a wobble which made the results difficult to interpret.

5.8. The first crude television pictures of Earth were taken from Explorer VI, launched on August 7, 1959. Although of little meteorological value, they showed that cloud photography of large areas was possible from cameras mounted on a satellite. On August 24, 1959, cloud pictures of the Caribbean

---

* The term *synoptic,* from the Greek, *syn,* "together," "at the same time," and *opsis,* "sight," "view," is used by meteorologists to describe data or information acquired simultaneously over a large area.

† Near infrared radiation is the region of the spectrum with wavelengths slightly greater than that of visible red light. A discussion of the electromagnetic radiation spectrum which includes visible, infrared, ultraviolet, and other radiations is given in § 6.47 *et seq.*

Sea area taken from the nose cone of an Atlas rocket, at altitudes of about 400 to 600 miles, revealed the early stages of the formation of a cyclonic system. An attempt to secure meteorological data related to Earth's heat balance was made from Explorer VII, launched on October 13, 1959; preliminary measurements were obtained of solar radiation and of radiation reflected by and reradiated from Earth.

THE TIROS SATELLITES

5.9. Up to this point, the meteorological information from satellites had not been very significant, but the situation underwent a striking change with the launching of the first TIROS—an acronym for Television and Infra-Red Observation Satellite—on April 1, 1960. TIROS I was intended as a scientific experiment and was very simple, as scientific satellites go. Its observation instruments consisted only of two television-type cameras, together with tape recorders for storing pictures for later readout, and radio equipment for the receipt of instructions for the transmission of data to a ground station. One of the cameras had a wide-angle lens capable of covering a large area; the other, with a narrow-angle lens, had a smaller coverage and was capable of providing greater detail. Pictures were taken and transmitted to Earth upon command, as will be seen later.

5.10. Within a short time of its going into orbit, TIROS I began transmitting pictures that showed clearly a variety of cloud formations and patterns which could be correlated with known meteorological conditions. Subsequently, TIROS I and other satellites of the TIROS series, to be described below, were used to identify and track storm systems and for many other valuable meteorological purposes. The outstanding success of the early TIROS spacecraft has led to the development of more advanced systems which should make important contributions to meteorological science.

5.11. The first eight TIROS satellites, launched between April 1, 1960 and December 21, 1963, are similar in general design. They have a drum-like (or pillbox) shape, 42 inches in diameter and 19 to 22 inches high, and weigh about 270 pounds (Fig. 5.1). The top and sides are covered with solar cells to generate electricity for the cameras and radio transmitters. The orbits of TIROS are nominally circular at an altitude of about 400 to 470 miles. But the attainment of an exactly circular orbit is almost impossible and would probably not remain so very long, as a result of perturbations (§ 2.82), even if it could be realized. Consequently, the TIROS orbits are slightly elliptical. The orbital period in all cases is close to 100 minutes (cf. Table 2.1), and so during each day, i.e., 1440 minutes, the satellite makes roughly 14 orbits. Apart from perturbations, the track of the subsatellite point on the ground is shifted westward by 360/14.4 degrees of longitude, for each orbit, because of Earth's rotation (§ 2.95). The orbits of the first four TIROS spacecraft were inclined at about 48 deg to the equator, so that a perpendicular view of earth was possible only between 48°N and 48°S latitude. An oblique view could sometimes be obtained to about 55° latitude. In order to extend the range of visibility, the inclination of TIROS V, VI, VII, and VIII was increased to 58 deg.

5.12. The TIROS satellites are stabilized in attitude by spinning them at a rate of 9 to 12 revolutions per minute. This rate was chosen as being adequate

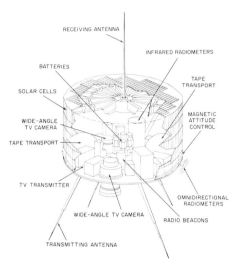

FIG. 5.1.   The TIROS spacecraft

for providing stability while permitting the cameras to take overlapping pictures. Aerodynamic and magnetic drag causes the spin rate to decrease, but it can be restored to the required value by small (spin) rockets actuated by command from the ground.

5.13. As a consequence of the gyroscopic behavior associated with spin stabilization, the satellites should always be oriented with reference to inertial space, rather than to Earth. The cameras are thus directed toward Earth during roughly half of each orbit (cf. Fig. 4.8). Furthermore, since pictures can be taken only during daylight, the cameras can be operated, at best, for roughly 25 percent of the time in orbit; sometimes the useful period is as low as 10 percent of the total time. For this reason, directions are transmitted from the ground for the cameras to take pictures when it is known that the conditions are suitable.

5.14. The TIROS I spacecraft was launched in such a manner that the cameras and radiation detectors pointed toward Earth in the Northern Hemisphere. If the direction of the spin axis had remained essentially unchanged, as it should have done, it would not have been possible to take pictures in the Southern Hemisphere. After a few days, however, it became apparent that the spin axis orientation was changing; as a result, the field of vision of the cameras shifted from the Northern to the Southern Hemisphere of Earth and back again. This perturbation (or precession) of the spin axis was attributed to two factors; the first and most important was interaction of Earth's magnetic field with residual magnetism in the spacecraft and the second was the effect of Earth's gravitational field on the nonuniform mass distribution. In the later TIROS spacecraft, this precession has been partially controlled by producing a subsidiary magnetic field upon command, in the manner described in § 4.103. It has thus been possible to steer the spin axis to some extent and to provide a more satisfactory attitude for obtaining photographs of particular areas of Earth.

5.15. All the TIROS satellites have carried two small vidicon-type cameras,* one at least having a wide field of view 450 to 750 miles across when the camera was pointing directly downward and somewhat more when the satellite was tipped and the camera had an oblique view of Earth. Both TIROS I and II also had a camera with a narrow field of view of roughly 70 miles in each direction. In the later TIROS spacecraft, however, both cameras have been of the wide-angle type, although the field of view has been decreased somewhat in order to reduce image distortion. A successful test of the Automatic Picture Transmission system was made in connection with TIROS VIII, launched on December 21, 1963. This system will be described shortly in the section dealing with data acquisition (§ 5.21).

5.16. The next TIROS spacecraft will have the "cart wheel" configuration which makes much more efficient use of the time the satellite is in orbit. The spacecraft is launched initially in the same manner as the earlier TIROS. But when in orbit, the satellite is gradually rotated in space so that its spin axis is perpendicular to the orbital plane (Fig. 5.2). The side of the spinning satellite is facing toward Earth at all times; hence, the general effect is something like a wheel rolling around Earth. Two television cameras are mounted so that they point in opposite directions through the side of the spacecraft, rather than through the

Fig. 5.2.   TIROS cart-wheel configuration

bottom. Each camera thus looks straight down at Earth once during every rotation; hence, at the contemplated spin rate of 8 to 12 revolutions per minute,

---

* A vidicon camera has a target faceplate coated with a photoconductive material (§ 4.115, footnote) which retains the effects of an exposure for a sufficient time to permit slow scanning by an electron beam, thereby providing improved definition of the transmitted image.

the two cameras can take up to 24 pictures per minute during daylight. A current-carrying coil will permit the satellite to act as the rotor of an electric motor for which Earth supplies the magnetic field. It is hoped in this manner to maintain a constant spin rate of the spacecraft. If successful, the wheel TIROS will probably be adopted in the proposed TIROS Operational Satellite (TOS) System. The objective of this system is to obtain information which will be utilized by the U.S. Weather Bureau, in conjunction with conventional meteorological data, to provide daily weather coverage of the entire globe.

5.17. TIROS IX, the first of the wheel type, was injected into a near-polar, Sun-synchronous orbit (§ 5.34), similar to that of the Nimbus satellites, on January 22, 1965. The event also marked the first time a satellite had been placed in such a highly-inclined orbit from Florida. In order to avoid passage over land areas in the early stages of flight, the initial launch direction was, as usual, southeasterly, i.e., over the Atlantic Ocean. But, as the result of three "dog-leg" maneuvers, the inclination of the orbital plane to the equator was increased to about 81 deg and the satellite entered orbit over the Pacific Ocean, some 300 miles west of Quito, Ecuador. The intended orbit for TIROS IX was approximately circular, at an altitude of 460 miles, but the second stage of the Delta launch vehicle burned longer than intended and so the actual orbit had a perigee of 436 miles and an apogee of 1602 miles. Nevertheless, the spacecraft was successfully reoriented in orbit to provide the desired cart-wheel configuration. The cameras operated in the expected manner, although the resolution of some photographs was not as good as anticipated because of the high altitude of the spacecraft at apogee.

TIROS RADIATION MEASUREMENTS

5.18. In addition to the cameras, several of the later TIROS spacecraft were equipped with *radiometers* or *radiation sensors* for the measurement of various radiation characteristics of Earth and its atmosphere. By means of filters, which permit the passage of radiations within certain specified ranges of wavelength only, it is possible to determine the amounts of radiation energy in these ranges. The following measurements are made by a five-channel radiometer:

(*a*) Radiation energy within the wavelength range of 0.2 to 6 microns,* which includes part of the ultraviolet, through the visible into a portion of the infrared spectrum (cf. Fig. 6.12). The radiation received by the radiometer in this range is a measure of the Sun's energy that is reflected by Earth's surface and atmosphere. About 99 percent of the solar energy reaching the atmosphere is between 0.2 and 6 microns in wavelength. A quantity called the *albedo* (Latin, *albus*, "white,") is commonly used by meteorologists; it is defined as the ratio of the amount of radiation (sunlight) reflected by Earth, or a particular feature of Earth, e.g., ground, ocean, or clouds, to the total

_____

* One micron is 10^{-6} meter or 10^{-4} centimeter (§ 6.53).

incident radiation. The latter is well known (§ 6.28 *et seq.*), and so the albedo can be calculated from the reflection data in the 0.2- to 6-micron range.

(*b*) Radiation energy in the wavelength range of 8 to 30 microns, all in the infrared region. This channel indicates the amount of energy reradiated, after absorption, by Earth and its atmosphere. The sum of (*a*) and (*b*) gives the total energy that leaves Earth in one way or another; comparison with the known amount of energy reaching Earth from the Sun permits a determination of the heat balance in various parts of the globe at the time the satellite is passing over them.

(*c*) Radiation energy in the infrared with wavelengths of 8 to 12 microns, in the so-called *atmospheric window*.* The radiation in this range is emitted from the visible surface, whether it be the exposed Earth or the tops of clouds. If the surface is opaque, its temperature can be calculated from the magnitude of the 8- to 12-micron radiation, on the assumption that the surface behaves like a black body, i.e., an ideal emitter of radiation (§ 6.61).

(*d*) Radiation energy in the range of 6.0 to 6.5 microns. In this region water molecules are strong absorbers of radiation. Consequently, the data provide information on the distribution of water (liquid and vapor) in the atmosphere and on the temperature above the clouds.

(*e*) Radiation energy in the visible range from 0.55 to 0.75 microns. This is the spectral region in which the television cameras are most sensitive; the measurements thus serve to test the response of the cameras. They are also of interest because the 0.55- to 0.75-micron channel is that in which the solar energy distribution exhibits its maximum value.

5.19. In addition to the radiometers described above, which have a moderately high resolution, that is to say, they view a fairly small region of Earth (about 30 miles across when viewed vertically), some of the TIROS spacecraft carried low-resolution (or large-area) radiometers. These consist of black and white conical detectors, which view an area of about 400 miles in each direction, or hemispherical detectors, which can cover the entire area from horizon to horizon, but are most sensitive to radiations coming from a circle about 1000 miles in diameter with its center vertically below the satellite. The black detector is sensitive to both reflected sunlight and long-wave (infrared) radiation, whereas the white detector responds only to the infrared. From the data obtained with such a pair of detectors it is possible to estimate the amount of the Sun's energy that is reflected from Earth and the quantity of infrared radiation emitted. From the former, the albedo can be determined and from the latter the apparent temperature of Earth's surface can be estimated.

TIROS COMMAND AND DATA ACQUISITION

5.20. Operation of the cameras on the TIROS spacecraft is controlled from three Command and Data Acquisition (CDA) Stations, located at Wallops

* The absorption of radiation in this range by the atmosphere is very small.

Island, Virginia, at Point Mugu, California, and near Fairbanks, Alaska. TIROS passes within communication range of one or another of the CDA stations during half, on the average, of its approximately 14 daily orbits of Earth. During each pass, instructions can be transmitted to a clock mechanism for the cameras to take a sequence, at 30-second intervals, of up to 32 photographs of a remote location at a specified time. The pictures are stored on magnetic tape and are read out at a fast rate upon command the next time the satellite is within about 1500 miles or less of a CDA station. The transmission period for 32 pictures is about 3 minutes. If the conditions of satellite attitude and of solar illumination at the station at the time of the pass are suitable, the cameras can be commanded to take photographs and transmit them directly to Earth without intermediate storage on tape. Stored data from the radiometer measurements, if any, are also read out during the pass.

5.21. In the Automatic Picture Transmission (APT) system, mentioned in § 5.15, one of the wide-angle cameras has a timing device that causes it to function in a series of cycles of 208 seconds duration for approximately 30 minutes in each orbit. The first 8 seconds of each cycle are occupied with the necessary preparations for taking a single picture which is recorded on the photosensitive surface of a vidicon tube. The picture is then read out during the subsequent 200 seconds at the relatively low scan rate of 4 lines per second. A 5-watt transmitter on the spacecraft broadcasts the signal at a frequency of

FIG. 5.3.   Antenna for use in Automatic Picture Transmission system

135 megacycles per second. Such a transmission can be received at a station on the ground, within 1500 miles, with a simple hand-tracked spiral antenna (Fig. 5.3), in conjunction with a commercial radio receiver and a standard photo-facsimile machine. Consequently, meteorologists in many parts of the world, who have the relatively inexpensive equipment, can obtain immediate cloud-cover photographs of their own vicinity.

APPLICATIONS OF TIROS PICTURES

5.22. One way in which the TIROS photographs are used is to combine the slightly overlapping pictures of adjacent regions to yield a continuous mosaic strip covering an area several thousand miles in length and about 800 miles wide. The location of the area is known from the satellite's orbit at the time the pictures were taken, and this can often be confirmed by the identification of characteristic geographical features. The photograph in Fig. 5.4, for example,

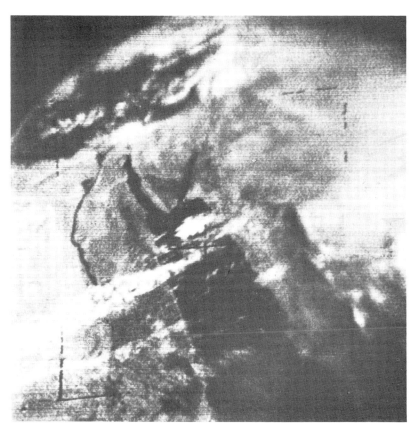

FIG. 5.4.   TIROS picture of cloud cover in eastern Mediterranean Sea, Red Sea, River Nile area

clearly shows the Mediterranean Sea, the Red Sea, and the River Nile. On the TIROS picture, clouds are generally the lightest, because they have the greatest reflectivity (or albedo) for sunlight, and exposed water surfaces, with the smallest albedo, appear darkest.

5.23. One of the most general applications of TIROS photographs for operational use in meteorology, e.g., in weather prediction, is in the procedure called *nephanalysis* or cloud analysis (Greek, *nephele*, "cloud"). The information from the pictures is transferred manually to a latitude-longitude grid in a form suitable for meteorological interpretation. An illustration of a mosaic of cloud photographs, taken from TIROS III on September 11, 1961, and the corresponding nephanalysis chart are given in Fig. 5.5. There is a difference in

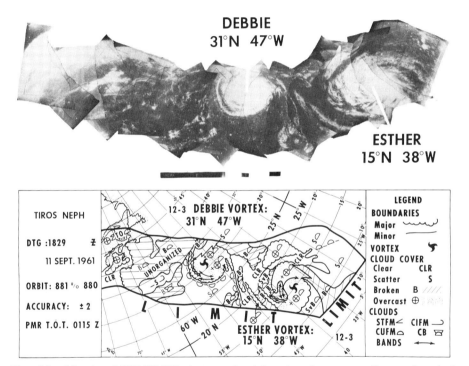

Fig. 5.5.   Mosaic of TIROS III photographs (above) and corresponding nephanalysis chart (below)

shape because some of the photographs were taken with the camera pointing downward and others at an angle. The photographs show clearly the characteristic patterns of hurricanes Debbie and Esther of 1961. It is of special interest to mention that 24 hours earlier TIROS III observed a vortex near 11°N 30°W, that developed into hurricane Esther, before it could have been detected by conventional techniques. It was the first hurricane to be discovered by observations made from a satellite. Since that time, many severe weather disturbances, including various tropical storms and, possibly, tornadoes and severe thunderstorms, have been identified and tracked by means of TIROS pictures.

5.24. Another use of the TIROS photographs is to supplement and sometimes to correct standard weather maps which show isobars, i.e., lines of equal atmospheric pressure, the locations of centers of high and low pressures, and general meteorological phenomena. The upper portion of Fig. 5.6 is a mosaic of pictures obtained from TIROS I on May 20, 1960; in the lower portion the cloud pattern, rectified according to geography, has been superimposed onto the weather map of the same day. The broken lines show the limits of the TIROS photographs which extend for almost 5000 miles from the mid-Pacific to the

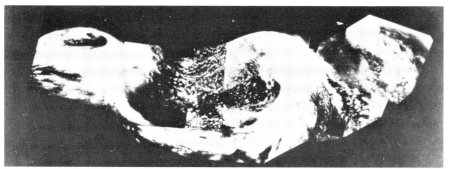

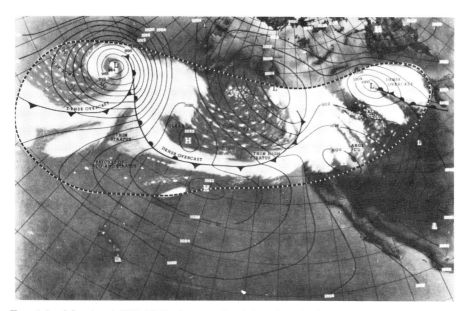

Fig. 5.6.   Mosaic of TIROS I photographs (above) and cloud pattern superimposed on weather map (below)

central United States. The correspondence between the weather map and the cloud system is very striking and confirms the somewhat oversimplified aphorism that "nature draws its own weather map by means of clouds."

5.25. In the situation presented in Fig. 5.6, the weather map had been determined in fair detail from measurements made at surface stations. Even where extensive surface observations are available, it is possible for an organized severe weather situation to be missed. Such was the case on September 6, 1961, when a TIROS photograph revealed an unsuspected squall line, i.e., a long line of thunderstorms, extending from Lake Huron to western Texas. Frequently, weather maps may be incomplete or inaccurate because the data are not available from inaccessible regions. It is evident that, in such circumstances, cloud photographs from a satellite can be utilized to supplement and perhaps complete the surface information. For example, TIROS II pictures showing an approaching cold front were used by the Australian Weather Service on December 28, 1960 to forecast accurately a break in an extended heat wave. Although the photographs from space do not provide all the details usually found on a weather map, they can show general features which might otherwise be completely missed.

5.26. A somewhat novel experimental application of TIROS photographs was made in 1963 in connection with locust control. Locusts need rain and the desert vegetation brought on by rain before they can breed in large numbers. After consuming the vegetation in one area, they migrate to a new area in the direction of the moisture-bearing winds. Weather information is thus essential for predicting the path the locusts are expected to follow. Much of the area of interest, however, is uninhabited desert and meteorological data are not available. By utilizing TIROS cloud pictures in conjunction with other information, it has been possible to forecast the direction in which the locusts will probably migrate and thus to take appropriate countermeasures.

5.27. Apart from the operational use of cloud photographs in the study of weather, such as have been described above, the pictures can contribute to research in meteorology. Detailed observations on the development of hurricanes, for instance, may throw light on the origin of these destructive manifestations of the unbalance in the energy distribution in the atmosphere. The TIROS III satellite was in fact launched on July 12, 1961 in time to provide maximum coverage of the hurricane season in the North Atlantic and in the Gulf of Mexico, as well as of the major typhoon period in the Pacific Ocean.

5.28. In general, it is believed that, on the large scale, clouds are produced by the upward motion of air in the proper humidity field. If this is the case, it should be possible to correlate cloud patterns with vertical movements of the atmosphere and the humidity distribution. The interpretation of the cloud pictures is still largely undeveloped, but it is probable that, in due course, information will be obtained which will not only add to their immediate usefulness but will contribute to the solution of many long-range meteorological problems of a scientific nature.

5.29. An obvious limitation to the operational use of cloud photographs in meteorology is that the cameras can function only during daylight. The radiometer data can, however, provide information concerning night-time weather phenomena. An example of the distribution of cloud top and Earth surface temperatures, derived from TIROS III infrared measurements in the range of 8 to 12 microns, is given in Fig. 5.7. The region of minimum temperature,

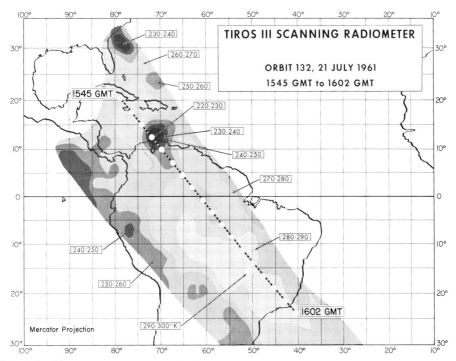

Fig. 5.7.   Temperature contours derived from TIROS III radiometer measurements. (The broken line represents the path of the spacecraft and the circles show the points at which observations were made)

over the north coast of South America, was found to represent a hurricane which was identified by cloud photographs and aircraft reconnaissance. In general, regions where the temperatures are low correspond to cloud-covered areas, whereas the high temperatures occur over clear areas. The coldest regions are those where the clouds are known, from ground observations, to have the greatest altitudes. Since the variation in temperature of the atmosphere with increasing distance from Earth is fairly well understood, it should be possible to estimate cloud heights from the temperatures derived from radiometric measurements.

5.30. The chief importance of radiation data at present lies in their application to purely scientific meteorological studies, e.g., heat balance of Earth, vertical structure of the atmosphere, and global distribution of water vapor. Such studies are essential for a better understanding of atmospheric phenomena, a basic necessity for the improvement of weather prediction.

5.31. Returning to the subject of the TIROS photographs, mention may be made of several features of interest other than cloud formation. The breakup of ice in the Gulf of St. Lawrence and in the Great Lakes areas of North America, for example, has been clearly observed. It has been suggested that photographs taken from satellites could be used for oceanic ice reconnaissance; such a procedure would be more efficient than the conventional surface methods. Provided the area is free from clouds, TIROS pictures show the location and extent of snowfields, and the information may be useful in predicting the availability of water for hydroelectric power and irrigation purposes.

The Nimbus Satellites

5.32. Because the TIROS satellites were spin stabilized, so that they were oriented with reference to inertial space, and orbital inclination was 58 deg at most, the coverage of Earth was limited. Furthermore, the precession of the spin axis as a result of magnetic and gravitational effects caused the observed area to shift between the Northern and Southern Hemispheres of the globe.

5.33. Meteorological satellites of the next generation, called Nimbus (Latin, *nimbus*, "cloud," in particular "rain cloud"), are designed and their orbits chosen to overcome these and other limitations. In the first place, Nimbus is Earth-oriented, so that its television cameras and radiometers always point directly to Earth. Second, the orbits are nominally circular at an altitude of about 500 to 700 miles and are almost polar, the angle of inclination to the equator being approximately 80 deg. To achieve the large angle of inclination, the Nimbus satellites will be launched from Point Arguello, California.* The planned orbital period is about 105 minutes and there are slightly over 14 orbits per day. Because of the rotation of Earth, the orbit appears to move about 26° of longitude westward upon successive crossings at each latitude.

5.34. As a result of the large angle of inclination of the Nimbus orbits, the expected Earth coverage should be from 80°N to 80°S latitude, at least; consequently, except for small areas near the poles, the whole of the globe should be under observation. If launched at the proper time at 80 deg inclination in a circular orbit of about 700 miles altitude, the satellite should remain oriented along the line between Earth and the Sun.† The reason is that the regression of

---

* Because of safety considerations, i.e., the avoidance of land areas, launchings from the United States of satellites into orbits of large inclination, in either prograde or retrograde directions, are usually carried out from the Pacific Coast (cf. § 5.17).

† An orbit of this type is said to be Sun-synchronous.

the nodes of this particular orbit, due to Earth's so-called equatorial bulge (§ 2.86), is nearly 1 deg per day. Since Earth revolves about the Sun once a year, in turns through 360 deg in 365 days, i.e., just less than 1 deg per day, with reference to the Sun. The combined effect of the equal angular rates of regression of the satellite orbit and of the motion of Earth about the Sun is that the satellite should always be seen over a given parallel of latitude at approximately the same local time, no matter what the longitude. For the equator, this time will be close to noon on the sunlit side of Earth and near to midnight on the dark side. Since the period of the prescribed orbit is roughly 105 minutes, Nimbus would pass over any point on Earth not more than an hour or two before or after local noon, once every day.* It is believed that the visibility conditions at these times will be such as to provide satisfactory photography.

5.35. The nearly polar orbit of Nimbus will also simplify considerably the problem of data acquisition. A single station close to either the North or the South Pole should be sufficient to maintain radio contact with the satellite at least once in every orbit. Because of the difficulties associated with these locations, the TIROS CDA station near Fairbanks, Alaska, and another at Rosman, North Carolina, will serve to interrogate the Nimbus satellite. In addition, it is proposed to utilize the APT system to provide local information to meteorologists all over the world.

5.36. The Nimbus instrumentation and associated equipment, e.g., television cameras, radiometers, radio receiver and transmitter, tape recorders, storage batteries, etc., are carried in an annular ring, sometimes known as the *sensory ring,* at the lower end of the spacecraft (Fig. 5.8). This ring, about 57 inches across, is always directed toward Earth. Above the sensory ring, and connected to it by a truss, is the hexagonal housing containing the attitude stabilization and control system. This particular structural arrangement was chosen because the dumbbell-like form should favor gravity-gradient stabilization (§ 4.109), with orientation of the long axis in the direction of Earth's center. The total height of the Nimbus satellite is about 10 feet and its weight is 830 pounds.

5.37. The two panels (or paddles), 8 feet by 2.75 feet in size, one on each side of the control housing, are covered with 10,500 solar cells. The solar panels fold up when the satellite is being launched, and later when in orbit they are unfolded by means of a motor. The panels can rotate about a shaft, as seen in Fig. 5.8, and a Sun sensor (§ 4.115) located on this shaft keeps them always facing the Sun. Because the plane of the Nimbus orbit should be in the Earth-Sun line, rotation about a single axis is sufficient to point the panels in the required direction.

5.38. The proper attitude of the spacecraft is attained partly by its shape, as mentioned above; in addition, there are Sun sensors and horizon scanners

---

* Because of the overlap of fields of view, a single Nimbus in the prescribed orbit will cover the polar regions several times daily.

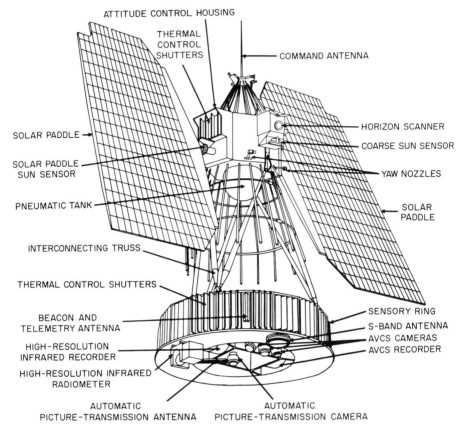

ATTITUDE CONTROL HOUSING

THERMAL
CONTROL
SHUTTERS

COMMAND ANTENNA

HORIZON SCANNER

COARSE SUN SENSOR

SOLAR PADDLE

SOLAR PADDLE
SUN SENSOR

YAW NOZZLES

PNEUMATIC TANK

SOLAR
PADDLE

INTERCONNECTING TRUSS

THERMAL CONTROL SHUTTERS

SENSORY RING

BEACON AND
TELEMETRY ANTENNA

S-BAND ANTENNA

AVCS CAMERAS

HIGH-RESOLUTION
INFRARED RECORDER

AVCS RECORDER

HIGH-RESOLUTION INFRARED
RADIOMETER

AUTOMATIC
PICTURE-TRANSMISSION ANTENNA

AUTOMATIC
PICTURE-TRANSMISSION CAMERA

Fig. 5.8.   The Nimbus spacecraft

to fix the orientation. Stabilization is achieved partly by the gravity-gradient effect and partly by means of three integrating gyroscopes and motor-driven rotating inertia wheels, as described in § 4.107. When the flywheel energy has to be "dumped," i.e., when the wheel attains its maximum speed and has to be slowed down, Freon gas jets provide pitch and roll control; these jets also help to attain the correct orientation when the satellite first goes into orbit.

5.39. The main photographic system on the Nimbus spacecraft consists of three advanced-type television (vidicon) cameras capable of producing pictures with finer detail than those from TIROS. The central camera faces straight down and the others are at an angle of about 35 deg; together they take a three-array picture covering an area of approximately 1500 miles (east-west) by 500 miles (north-south). Simultaneous exposures are made of the three cameras at intervals of 91 seconds, with a total of 96 pictures per orbit or 1440 per day, assuming that the required orbit is attained. The pictures are stored on tape, which is capable of recording **192** pictures taken in two orbits, and these are played back in **4** minutes upon command from one of the ground stations. As stated in § 5.33, the region observed is about **26** deg farther west from each orbit to the next (Fig. 5.9). The pictures border on those from the

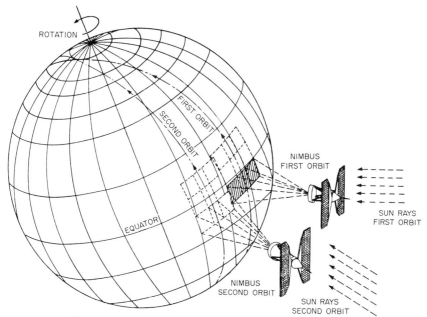

FIG. 5.9.   Areas observed in successive orbits of Nimbus

preceding orbit at the equator, but they overlap increasingly toward the poles. When the satellite approaches the night side of Earth in each orbit, the cameras are automatically shut off and the infrared radiometer described below is switched on. The reverse operation takes place as the spacecraft comes into sunlight again.

5.40. In addition to the three cameras already mentioned, Nimbus will have a camera for use in the APT system (§ 5.21). This camera does not store pictures for later transmission, but functions in a series of **208**-second cycles in the manner explained earlier. The system operates continuously during the daylight hours.

5.41. Nimbus satellites will carry either a five-channel, medium-resolution infrared radiometer (MRIR) or a high-resolution, infrared radiometer (HRIR), sensitive to radiations in the wavelength region of **3.4** to **4.2** microns. At an altitude of **600** miles, the HRIR scans an area about **5** miles across directly below the spacecraft. The purpose of the high-resolution radiometer is to provide a representation of the cloud pattern at night by measuring the infrared emission from

Earth's surface and cloud tops. In TIROS, this was determined in the spectral region of 8 to 12 microns (and 10 to 11 microns in the Nimbus five-channel MRIR), but for high resolution, in the HRIR, it was decided to use the 3.4- to 4.2-micron channel in which there is relatively little atmospheric absorption; the sensitive material, lead selenide,* is particularly suitable as a radiation detector in the 4-micron region.

5.42. Unlike a television camera, a radiometer forms no image, but its electrical output is a measure of the infrared radiation energy, in the indicated wavelength range, received from an exposed area of the ground or from the tops of clouds. The latter are generally, but not always, colder than Earth's surface, and then they emit smaller amounts of infrared radiation; hence, in these circumstances, the radiometer can distinguish between cloud-covered and cloud-free regions. By scanning the area in a manner similar to that employed in a conventional television camera, it is possible to obtain a representation from infrared measurements that indicates the cloud pattern at night. Like a television picture, this can be stored on magnetic tape and read out upon command.

5.43. The Nimbus satellite has been designed as a flexible system. Modification of its instrumentation can be made, if desired, without the necessity for structural changes. The electronic equipment is contained in "modules" inserted in the sensory ring, so that they can be readily removed and replaced if necessary. As improved models of the vidicon cameras become available, they can be substituted for the old ones, and a choice can be made of different types of radiation measuring instruments or other sensors. Among those being considered are a special type of infrared spectrometer for the determination of temperature variations in a vertical direction, a radar system for detecting snow and rain, and an optical sensor for determining cloud heights.

5.44. The first satellite in the Nimbus series, Nimbus I, was launched from California on August 28, 1964 by means of a Thor-Agena rocket. The Agena engine did not operate for its scheduled time and as a result the desired circular orbit at an altitude of 575 miles was not attained; the actual orbit was elliptical, with an initial perigee of 263 miles and an apogee of 579 miles. With this orbit, about 70 percent of Earth's surface could be observed. Nimbus I was equipped with three of the advanced type cameras, one camera for APT, and the HRIR equipment, as described earlier. All the photographs received were of excellent quality and the HRIR operated successfully. The pictures taken when the spacecraft was near the perigee of its orbit had better resolution than expected, because of the lower altitude. An interesting observation from the radiometer data was the existence of four small areas in Antarctica which were interpreted as mountains, with a strong possibility of volcanic activity. On September 23,

---

* Lead selenide is a photoconductive material (§ 4.115, footnote) that is especially sensitive to infrared radiation; it is most effective if maintained at a low temperature, e.g., about −80°C (−112°F).

1964, after having made 380 orbits of Earth and transmitting more than 27,000 pictures, the solar panels became locked so that they could not be oriented toward the Sun. With the loss of power, transmission from Nimbus I ceased.

OTHER METEOROLOGICAL SATELLITES

5.45. In spite of the great meteorological value of the cloud photographs and infrared measurements obtained from satellites, the fact remains that they do not provide the parameters, namely, pressure, vertical temperature distribution, and wind speed and direction, that are most commonly used in weather forecasting. The suggested Interrogation, Recording, and Location Subsystem (IRLS) may provide a means for obtaining such information on a worldwide scale. A satellite, perhaps of the Nimbus type, might be utilized to make regular collections of environmental data from instruments on a great variety of stationary and mobile observation platforms, e.g., manned and unmanned weather stations, on land or sea, moored and drifting buoys on water, and constant-level balloons at different altitudes. The measurements made at these stations would be stored on tape and read out upon interrogation by the satellite when in the vicinity of each station. The spacecraft could also determine and record the location of a station, if necessary. The data would then be transmitted to a central control station on the ground for analysis.

5.46. The Advanced (or Applications) Technological Satellite (ATS) system is not directed specifically toward meteorological observations, but it has potential application in this respect which will be investigated. Since it is also intended to utilize the ATS system for studying long-distance communication and other problems, it will be described later (§ 5.112).

METEOROLOGICAL SOUNDING ROCKETS

5.47. The objective of the sounding rocket studies of the atmosphere is to provide conventional meteorological data at altitudes of from about 20 to 60 miles, i.e., beyond those that can be reached by common methods, such as weather balloons. This information cannot be obtained from ordinary weather stations or even from the special type that would be interrogated by a satellite.

5.48. Three main techniques are used for making measurements of the upper atmosphere by means of sounding rockets. A successful method for obtaining data on temperature and wind structure at various altitudes, for example, is by means of *rocket grenades*. The grenades are ejected and exploded at successively higher altitudes in the course of the upward flight of a sounding rocket. The time of arrival of the sound wave from each explosion is recorded by microphones on the ground. The locations of the grenades at the time of firing are determined either by means of optical instruments or by radar, utilizing the DOVAP system (§ 4.123). By combining the time and distance data, it is possible to calculate the velocity of sound and hence to derive the average atmospheric temperature and wind characteristics between the various heights where the grenade explosions occurred. The results of some wind measurements, made in winter and summer, respectively, at Fort Churchill, Canada, latitude 59°N, are shown in Fig. 5.10. The change in the summer wind direction, in the region between about 32 and 80 kilometers (20 and 50 miles) altitude, is of special interest since it could not have been observed from balloons.

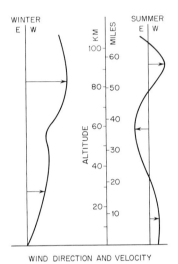

WIND DIRECTION AND VELOCITY

FIG. 5.10. Summer and winter winds at different altitudes near Fort Churchill, Canada

5.49. Another application of sounding rockets, of special value for studying winds at altitudes above about 40 kilometers (25 miles), involves the release of a quantity of a tracer, such as sodium, into the air. The sodium vaporizes at the high altitude and forms a cloud emitting an orange-yellow glow visible at night for several minutes. As an alternative, trimethylaluminum has been used to produce a luminous cloud. Optical observations of the cloud provide information about the direction and velocity of the winds. Powerful wind shear effects, i.e., several adjacent layers of strong winds moving with different velocities and in different directions, have been observed in this manner at altitudes of from 115 to 160 kilometers, i.e., **70 to 100** miles (Fig. 5.11).

5.50. A third type of experiment makes use of a *Pitot-static tube,* which is a modification of the familiar Pitot tube employed for measuring pressures in moving fluids. The Pitot-static tube, carried at the tip of the sounding rocket, has an orifice at its forward (or front) end and one at the side some distance from this end. A pressure sensor exposed at the front orifice measures the stagnation pressure, also called the ram impact, Pitot, or total pressure, whereas one at the side indicates the static (or normal) pressure of the surroundings. From the difference in these two pressures, the density of the ambient atmosphere can be calculated. Pressure determinations are made by observing the ionization current that flows between two electrodes in a chamber exposed to radiations from a radioactive source. The magnitude of this current is related to the air pressure in the ionization chamber. The readings from the two chambers are telemetered to the ground where the data are used to calculate both the atmospheric pressure and density at various altitudes in the course of the flight of the sounding rocket.

5.51. The conventional method for making pressure (or density) and temperature measurements at altitudes up to about 20 miles is to employ balloons to carry the instruments up into the atmosphere. The data are then telemetered to Earth by radio. The devices used for this purpose are called *radiosondes*. An analogous system for higher altitudes is to have instruments, attached to a parachute, carried aloft by means of a sounding rocket. Wind velocities and directions are obtained by tracking the balloon or parachute from the ground.

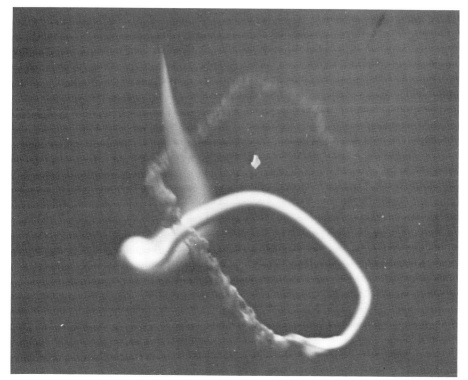

Fig. 5.11.   Luminescent sodium vapor trail showing wind shear at high altitudes

5.52. In a simpler technique, for which small rockets are adequate, a balloon is released and inflated at a high altitude. The balloon is equipped with a metallized reflector and its trajectory is followed by means of radar. The direction and rate of motion in space determine the wind characteristics and the density of the air at various altitudes. In modifications of this general procedure, wind velocities are obtained by tracking a radar-reflecting parachute or a quantity of metallic "chaff," i.e., short pieces of fine wire, which acts as a radar reflector, is ejected from the rocket and tracked. In all these cases, the object (or objects) released merely serves as a passive tracking target.

COMMUNICATIONS BY SATELLITE

INTRODUCTION

5.53. The demand for communications channels, i.e., telephone, telegraph, and radio and television broadcasting, has increased rapidly in recent years and will undoubtedly continue to do so in the future. In the past, the demand has been met by the development of two types, in particular, of broad-band systems, namely, coaxial cables and radio waves (and microwaves) of very high frequency. It was seen in Chapter 4 that, in general, the rate at which intelligible information, detectable above the background noise, can be transmitted over a given channel increases with the bandwidth of the channel. Consequently, broad-band communication systems are the only ones obviously capable of meeting the projected requirements of the future.

5.54. A coaxial cable consists of a conducting wire, e.g., of copper, which carries the information being transmitted, supported by insulators within a tube also made of a conducting material. Such cables can each carry several hundred telephone conversations over land and they are widely used for this purpose. To compensate for the unavoidable losses that occur during transmission, the signals are amplified by repeaters at frequent intervals. Coaxial submarine cables are also employed for transoceanic communications; but the difficulties associated with the reliability, location, and supply of power to underwater repeater amplifiers greatly decrease the effective bandwidth. As a result, the number of voice or other channels that can be carried by a coaxial submarine cable is only about one fifth of the capacity of a similar cable on land.

5.55. A partial solution to the problem of intercontinental communications has been found in the use of the so-called high frequency (HF) radio waves, with frequencies in the range of 3 to 30 megacycles per second and corresponding wave lengths of 100 to 10 meters. Their ability to traverse distances up to several thousand miles depends on the repeated reflections of the waves that occur alternately from the ionospheric layer of the upper atmosphere (§ 8.104) and from the ground. The great drawback to HF radio communication is that changes in the ionosphere, such as occur from day to night and especially during magnetic storms (§ 8.119), can disturb or even disrupt the transmission of signals. Furthermore, channels in the HF range cannot have a particularly large bandwidth without interference occurring; consequently, they have a limited information capacity.

5.56. For overland communications, very-high-frequency (VHF) and ultra-high-frequency (UHF) radio and microwaves, with wavelengths in the meter, decimeter, and centimeter ranges, respectively, have come into common use, as carriers for telephone, television, and FM radio signals. A standard broadcast television signal requires a bandwidth up to 6 megacycles, and this is possible only by means of a broad-band channel. Coaxial cables have been utilized in this connection, but increasing use is being made of atmospheric transmission with carriers in the microwave region. Such waves normally have only a line-of-sight range; that is to say, their range is limited by the horizon. Consequently, relay stations, located on towers, are used every 25 to 30 miles or so, when the signals are to be transmitted over long distances (§ 1.7).

5.57. From the foregoing review, it will be apparent that coaxial cables and radio waves of very high frequency (or short wavelength) can probably meet the requirements of communications on land for some time to come. But for transoceanic and intercontinental communications, the situation is less satisfactory. Ordinary HF radio is erratic and submarine cables are expensive; moreover, both have such limited bandwidths that they are inadequate for the transmission of television signals. One way of increasing the overseas communications channels lies, in principle, in the use of Earth satellites as relay stations for radio waves of very high frequency. A satellite of this kind would be equivalent to a relay tower hundreds or thousands of miles high. Even if the transmission distance were restricted to the horizon, it would still be sufficient to provide wideband communication from one continent to another. Long-distance communications over land could, of course, also benefit from the use of satellite relay stations.

HISTORICAL DEVELOPMENT

5.58. The original suggestion that an Earth satellite might be used for radio broadcasting was made in 1945 by Arthur C. Clarke, a pioneer of the British Interplanetary Society. He proposed placing three manned space stations, carrying the required equipment, in synchronous equatorial, i.e., geostationary, orbits, so that the broadcasts could cover all of Earth, except for small regions near the poles. Some ten years later, John R. Pierce, of the Bell Telephone Laboratories in the United States, revived the concept of communication by satellite; he indicated that they might act merely as reflectors of radio waves or they could carry radio receivers and transmitters capable of being controlled from the ground. Such satellites would not require the presence of man in space. Pierce also pointed out that the communications satellites would not necessarily have to be in synchronous orbits, although a larger number would be required to provide worldwide coverage if the orbits were of lower altitude.

5.59. The first successful use of an Earth satellite for communications purposes was made in connection with Project SCORE (Signal Communication by Orbiting Relay Equipment), a simple, unsophisticated, research project designed as a test of technique. A spacecraft containing radio instruments was launched into an elliptical orbit on December 18, 1958, and on the following day, upon command, it broadcast a message from President Dwight D. Eisenhower which had been recorded on magnetic tape and placed on board the satellite before launching. On subsequent days, the radio equipment received, stored, and re-broadcast upon command both voice and teletype messages.

5.60. A more advanced test of the feasibility of global communication by radio repeater satellite was made in connection with the Courier spacecraft launched on October 4, 1960. Information was received and transmitted later at a very much greater rate than had been achieved in Project SCORE. In between these two experiments, on August 12, 1960, the passive Echo satellite was placed in orbit. It carried no radio equipment, except for tracking purposes, but served merely to reflect radio signals from one location to another, thus providing a long-distance communication link. Although SCORE, Courier, and Echo were experimental projects, they did show that satellites could play a role in a worldwide communications network.

PASSIVE (REFLECTOR) SATELLITES

5.61. As mentioned in Chapter 1, communications satellites fall into two general categories, described as passive and active, respectively; in each category, the orbits could be synchronous (high altitude) or nonsynchronous (low or medium altitude). It will be seen in due course that each of these systems has its advantages and disadvantages, and it is not immediately apparent which will prove to be best, from both economic and practical standpoints, for an operational worldwide communications system. Consequently, a program of tests is under way in the United States to study the possibilities of various passive and active repeater satellites. There is no doubt of the magnitude of the problems involved, but if they can be solved successfully and economically, the benefits would be very great.

5.62. A *passive satellite* operates solely as a reflector of radio waves transmitted from Earth. The great merits of the passive reflector are its basic simplicity and the possibility of using a single reflector for several different radio frequencies. A passive reflector has no solar cells or transistors, which can be damaged by radiation in space. Damage to the satellite itself by micrometeoroids is, however, a potential hazard. The main weakness of a passive reflector satellite is the matter of available power. In order to permit useful communications over long distances on Earth, the reflector must be at a high altitude, e.g., above about 1000 miles. The radio power received on Earth after reflection from the satellite is thus an extremely small fraction of the original transmitted power.

5.63. The situation may be visualized by noting that a reflector with a diameter of 100 feet at an altitude of 1000 miles—roughly the conditions for the Echo I satellite described below—is equivalent to a disc about the size of half a dollar (1.2 inches) at a distance of 1 mile! A passive system thus requires the use of a high-power transmitter, a high-gain antenna, and special receivers of great sensitivity and very low background noise. It is the resulting signal-to-noise ratio that determines the equivalent bandwidth or amount of information than can be transmitted by means of a passive repeater satellite. Some improvement in the situation is possible, in principle, by an increase in the area of the reflector, but a surface of large area is affected by solar radiation pressure, in particular, and even to some extent by aerodynamic drag. The orbit is thus highly perturbed and variable, although its characteristics can be predicted with fair accuracy for a short time ahead.

5.64. An experimental passive reflector satellite, called Echo I, for obvious reasons, was launched on August 12, 1960. It soon established that long-distance communication by means of a passive satellite was possible. Actually, the reflection of radio waves from space had been achieved by the U.S. Army Signal Corps as far back as 1946 by utilizing a natural satellite, the Moon, and in May 1959 a radio transmission from the 250-foot dish antenna at Jodrell Bank, England, was received at Bedford, Massachusetts after reflection from the Moon. But these were crude tests and did not involve the transmission of significant amounts of intelligible information. Echo I, on the other hand, served as a reflector for useful communications of several different kinds.

5.65. Echo I was an inflatable sphere, 100 feet in diameter, i.e., about the height of a ten-story building, weighing 124 pounds; it was made of Mylar plastic film 500 millionths (5×10^{-4}) of an inch in thickness. The reflectivity of the surface for radio waves was achieved by depositing on it a very thin layer of aluminum; for radar frequencies up to about 20,000 megacycles per second, about 98 percent of the energy falling on the fresh aluminum surface was reflected. Before launching, the deflated sphere was folded so that it could be packed into a spherical magnesium container, 26.5 inches in diameter. A subliming powder, consisting of a mixture of benzoic acid and anthraquinone, vaporized and the expansion of the vapors inflated the sphere in space. The solid benzoic acid vaporizes rapidly and provides the immediate pressure, whereas the anthraquinone, having a lower vapor pressure and subliming more slowly, was intended to sustain the inflation by compensating for the gradual loss of gas.

5.66. About 2 minutes after the payload was in orbit, the magnesium container was blown open by an explosive charge; the folded sphere was ejected and it inflated immediately. The initial orbit was slightly elliptical, apogee 1049 miles and perigee 945 miles, and its period was 118.3 minutes. As a result of aerodynamic drag and solar radiation pressure, however, the orbit became much more eccentric with time (§ 2.59). Echo I carried two lightweight radio beacons, operated directly by solar cells and storage batteries, but these were used only to facilitate tracking of the satellite for orbit determination.

5.67. An interesting feature of the Echo system was the special receiving antenna at Holmdel, New Jersey, designed to minimize extraneous noise from the atmosphere and the ground. Instead of the familiar, paraboloid (dish) antenna, which receives a certain amount of noise around the edges even when pointing upward, the Holmdel antenna is horn shaped (Fig. 5.12). The reflected signals from the Echo satellite enter the opening, seen at the right of the horn. Here they strike an aluminum reflecting surface having a paraboloidal curvature and are focused onto a low-noise receiver in the enclosure at the left. This antenna is insensitive to radio noise from the back of the horn and, provided it is pointed at an angle to the horizon greater than about 5 deg, ground noise is low, especially in the frequency range of 1000 to 10,000 mega-cycles per second.

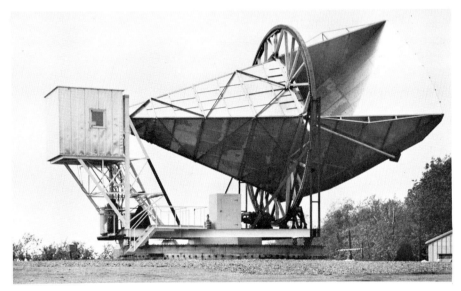

Fig. 5.12.   Antenna at Holmdel, New Jersey, for Echo communications satellite. (*Bell Telephone Laboratories*)

5.68. Upon its first orbit, Echo I reflected, from Goldstone, California, to Holmdel, New Jersey, a message previously recorded on magnetic tape by President Dwight D. Eisenhower. This achievement was of particular signifi-cance because, at the time of transmission, conventional high-frequency radio communication had been "blacked out," i.e., disrupted, by a magnetic storm. Subsequently, two-way telephone conversations were conducted across the United States and signals were sent from the United States to Europe. Trans-missions over long distances of music, facsimile pictures, teletype signals, and other information were also achieved successfully.

5.69. Within about 3 weeks after being launched, there were indications that the Echo I sphere was shrinking to some extent. This may have been partly due to escape of the inflating vapors through holes produced by micrometeoroid impact in space. At first, the reflectivity of the sphere was not greatly affected, but in the course of time the efficiency of the surface for reflecting radio signals deteriorated.

5.70. To reduce the amount of shrinkage, the second passive reflector satellite, Echo II, has a more rigid construction. The sphere is made of a laminated material consisting of a layer of Mylar film 350 millionths (3.5×10^{-4}) of an inch in thickness with a layer of aluminum 180 millionths (1.8×10^{-4}) of an inch on each side. The total thickness is thus 710 millionths (7.1×10^{-4}) of an inch, i.e., less than a one-thousandth part of an inch. The Echo II sphere is considerably more resistant to buckling than was Echo I, and when it has been inflated at somewhat of an overpressure, it tends to retain a smooth, un-wrinkled surface even after the pressure has dropped. The diameter of the Echo II sphere is 135 feet, so that it has nearly twice the reflecting area of Echo I; its weight is about 550 pounds, apart from about 200 pounds of miscellaneous equipment.

5.71. Echo II was launched on January 25, 1964 from Point Arguello, California, into a near-polar orbit, with an inclination of 81.5 deg. The perigee of the orbit is 642 miles and the apogee 816 miles; the orbital period is 109 minutes. Initial partial inflation was caused by expansion of air trapped in the folded balloon and the process was completed in orbit by the vapor produced when the solid compound pyrazole sublimed as a result of exposure to the Sun's heat. The procedure, a test of controlled inflation which has other possible applications in space systems, lasted about 90 minutes. The Echo II reflector satellite has been used for communications similar to those of Echo I.

MODIFICATIONS IN PASSIVE SYSTEMS

5.72. In seeking to improve the operation of passive satellites, several different reflector configurations are being considered as alternatives to the simple sphere. One is a sphere having many small holes etched over its surface in order to decrease its weight substantially. A given rocket launch vehicle can then place in a particular orbit a larger sphere, thus making possible the reflection of a larger proportion of the transmitted radio power. The mass of the sphere can also be decreased by fabricating it from a wire-mesh material.

5.73. An interesting possibility is based on the fact that only part of the sphere, namely the segment facing Earth, is actually involved in the reflection of radio waves. The reason for using a sphere is, of course, that no matter how its attitude changes there is always a reflecting surface directed toward Earth. But the same result could be realized, in principle, if the passive satellite consisted of a spherical segment, shaped somewhat like an

FIG. 5.13.   Passive communications satellite in spherical segment form

umbrella (Fig. 5.13), stabilized by gravity so that the reflecting surface is always facing Earth. Whether such gravity-gradient stabilization (§ 4.109) can be achieved in a suitable manner, without sacrificing the basic simplicity of the passive repeater concept, remains to be determined.

5.74. Of course, a single reflector at an altitude of a few hundred, or even a few thousand, miles has a limited coverage, because the satellite, with an orbital period of 2 or 3 hours (altitude 1000 to 2500 miles), for example, is within line of sight of any two ground stations for a short time only. To insure continuity of operation, it would be necessary to have a number of repeater satellites in orbit simultaneously; they would be distributed in space so that at least one is always available to be used as a communications link between any two stations.*

5.75. In theory, some means could be provided to maintain each satellite in a specified orbit or sequence of orbits, but this would require relatively complicated equipment and is probably impractical at present. It is expected, therefore, that after a short time the orbits will become distributed in space in an essentially random manner. Assuming this to be the case, it is possible to calculate the number of satellites required to provide substantially continuous global service. For ground stations up to about 3000 miles apart, 25 satellites at an altitude of about 3000 miles would provide a 90 percent continuity of service; for a 99 percent continuity, the number of satellites would have to be doubled.

5.76. Since launch vehicles are very expensive, the cost of launching singly a large number of satellites for a commercial communications system would be prohibitive. A scheme of multiple launching of passive satellites has therefore been considered as a possible means of overcoming this problem. A single rocket vehicle would carry several satellites to be released one at a time upon successive orbits of Earth. An illustration of the multilaunch concept is represented in Fig. 5.14, based on the supposition that three satellites are to be launched from a single vehicle. The satellites are carried on a spacecraft which is injected into an elliptical (parking) Earth orbit in the usual manner. When the vehicle reaches the apogee of its orbit (Fig. 5.14, A) the first satellite is released, and simultaneously an attached rocket gives it the additional thrust (and velocity) required to put it into a circular (or nearly circular) orbit. In the meantime, the spacecraft, now carrying two satellites, continues to travel in its elliptical orbit; when it returns to the apogee, the second satellite is released and accelerated into a circular orbit. The period of the satellite in circular orbit is greater than that of the spacecraft in elliptical orbit, and so the two satellites occupy different positions in the same circular orbit (Fig. 5.14, B). Finally, the third satellite is released in the same manner as the other two. This is clearly a complex operation and would require careful control.

---

* The problem considered here is applicable to active, as well as to passive, satellites. But for active satellites the geostationary (24-hour) equatorial orbit may provide a possible solution (§ 5.95). The required altitude of 22,300 miles, however, appears to be much too high for a passive satellite to serve as an adequate reflector.

5.77. Mention may be made of an entirely different and very simple technique for reflecting radio signals from space, proposed by William E. Morrow of the Lincoln Laboratory, Massachusetts. He suggested the use of a belt of fine, hairlike wires, half of a particular wavelength long, called *dipoles*, en-

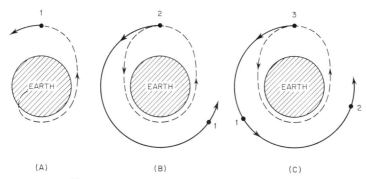

Fig. 5.14. Satellite multiple launch concept

circling Earth. A belt of this kind would serve as a reflector for the given wavelength. Two such complete belts, one around the poles and the other around the equator (Fig. 5.15), at an altitude of 3000 to 4000 miles, would be sufficient to provide worldwide communications at all times with no more than two reflections. Although the belts would appear to be essentially stationary, the wires constituting the belt would actually be continuously orbiting Earth. The distribution density of the wires could be quite small, perhaps only one in several thousand cubic feet of space.

5.78. In order to test the possibility outlined above, *Project West Ford*, named for the location of the Lincoln Laboratory, has been inaugurated by the U.S. Air Force. A preliminary attempt to place the dipoles in orbit, made in October 1961, failed because of a malfunction in the mechanism for dispensing the needles. Success was achieved, however, on May 10, 1963,

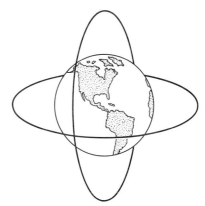

Fig. 5.15. Passive worldwide communication by means of two belts of dipoles

when some 400 million copper needles, 0.70 inch long and 7×10^{-4} inch in diameter,* were launched into an approximately polar orbit at an altitude of

---

* The average thickness of a human hair is about 2×10^{-3} inch, i.e., roughly three times that of the dipole needles.

about 2000 miles. The dipoles should serve as reflectors of microwave radiation of 1.4 inches (3.6 centimeters) wavelength, i.e., a frequency of approximately 8000 megacycles per second.

5.79. The needles, in batches of 22 million, were imbedded in naphthalene which vaporized gradually in space and thus released the dipoles to orbit around Earth. In the course of a few weeks, the needles dispersed into a continuous belt, initially about 5 miles wide and 25 miles in depth, at an altitude of over 2000 miles. This distribution represents about 50 needles per cubic mile or an average separation of more than a quarter of a mile between needles. The pressure of solar radiation is expected ultimately to drive the needles into the tangible atmosphere where they will become heated as a result of aerodynamic drag and burn up. On this basis, a lifetime of less than five years is anticipated for the dipole belt.*

5.80. Three types of two-way communications experiments have been performed successfully between ground stations in California and Massachusetts, using frequencies of 8350 and 7750 megacycles per second, respectively. The tests involved voice transmission, teletype communication, and digital data transmission. Before the belt had formed completely, the peak rate of transmission of voice information was 20,000 bits per second (§ 4.172), but this dropped off to 1000 bits per second when the belt was complete.

ACTIVE REPEATER SATELLITES: LOW ALTITUDE

5.81. An active repeater satellite carries a radio transponder (§ 4.15) which receives a signal from a ground station, amplifies it, and retransmits it on another frequency to another station on the ground. The main argument in favor of active over passive satellites is that for the transmission of the same amount of information, the former requires less ground transmitter power, smaller antennas, and less sensitive receivers on the ground. Although the equipment on the ground is simpler and less expensive, the active satellite itself is, however, considerably more complex and more costly than a passive reflector.

5.82. Several thousand solar cells are required to provide the electric power for operating the transponder of an active repeater satellite, and these contribute greatly to the overall cost. Moreover, the solar cells and other semiconductor (solid-state) devices, such as transistors, are susceptible to damage by the radiations in space, particularly by protons of high energy (§ 3.255). Because of the possibilities of failure in the solar cells, storage batteries, electronic and radio equipment, etc., an active repeater system is inevitably less reliable than a passive repeater. It is for the purpose of studying the effectiveness and reliability of active satellites for communications purposes that the experimental program described below is being carried out.

* Objections to the orbiting of the needles was voiced on the grounds that they may interfere with observations in both optical and radio astronomy, but no such interference has been reported to date.

5.83. It was mentioned in § 5.61 that active repeater satellite systems may involve either synchronous or nonsynchronous orbits; the latter are referred to as *low-(or medium-)altitude* orbits because they are lower than the 22,300-mile orbit of a synchronous satellite. The first low-altitude active repeater systems were SCORE and Courier (§ 5.59), but these were very preliminary in nature. Two more advanced communications systems utilizing low-altitude repeater satellites are now under investigation in the United States in the Telstar and Relay programs. Both have the capability of being used as direct, simultaneous communications links between distant stations.

5.84. The first Telstar spacecraft, weighing 170 pounds, was lofted into an elliptical orbit (apogee 3500 miles, perigee 590 miles, period 157 minutes) on July 10, 1962. As seen in Fig. 5.16, the satellite is approximately spherical in

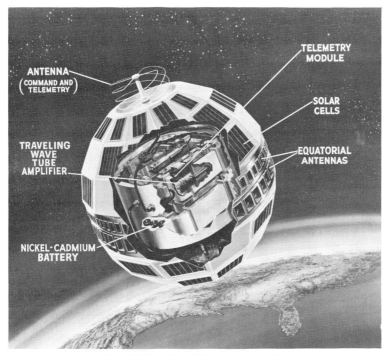

Fig. 5.16.   The Telstar spacecraft

shape (34.5 inches diameter); the radio command receiver, transponder, telemetry equipment, tracking beacon, and batteries are contained in the interior. They are arranged in the equatorial region to provide gyroscopic stabilization when the satellite is set spinning. The large square dark patches on the top and bottom hemispheres are the arrays of 3600 solar cells. The two bands of openings around the middle of the spacecraft are the receiving (smaller openings) and transmitting (larger openings) antennas; they are thus effective in all directions about the spin axis. The spiral antenna at the top is for command and telemetry signals. Telstar I was spin stabilized; the original rate of spin was 178 revolutions per minute, but it has been gradually decreased by the action of Earth's magnetic field. This field also caused a change in the orientation of the spin axis, and some attitude control was achieved by means of a magnetic coil similar to that in the later TIROS satellites (§ 5.14).

5.85. Telstar I carried a single transponder which received signals at a frequency of 6390 megacycles per second and retransmitted them, by means of a traveling-wave tube transmitter, at a frequency of about 4170 megacycles per second, with an output of $2\frac{1}{4}$ watts.* The useful bandwidth is 3 to 4 megacycles per second, which is sufficient for a single television channel. The first direct television transmissions between the United States and Europe were, in fact, achieved by means of Telstar I on July 10, 1962. To facilitate the transmission and receipt of signals, a large horn antenna, of the type shown in Fig. 5.12 but larger, has been built near Andover, Maine, and another in Brittany, France. These antennas are also used for other studies in space communications, such as Relay, mentioned below. A number of smaller, dish-type antennas have been erected for the same purpose at various locations in the United States and in other parts of the world.

5.86. Operation of Telstar I for trans-Atlantic communications was satisfactory until November 24, 1962 when the satellite's command decoders failed. As a result, it was not possible to activate the Telstar I transmitters by command from the ground. The failure was attributed to surface effects on silicon transistors due to ionization of the gases in the transistor case. The ionization was caused by the unexpectedly large number of electrons, mainly at altitudes of 1000 to 2000 miles, produced by the high-altitude nuclear explosion of July 9, 1962 (§ 8.327). By sending a series of ingeniously modified command signals from the ground, recovery of the command system was achieved and on January 3, 1963 normal operation of Telstar I was resumed and continued for another 49 days.

5.87. On May 7, 1963, Telstar II was placed in a highly elliptical orbit with an apogee of about 6710 miles and a perigee of 604 miles; the orbital period was 225 minutes. Structurally, the satellite is similar to Telstar I except that it has components with improved radiation-resistant characteristics. In addition, the transistors in one of the two command decoders are in an evacuated case, so that their behavior may be compared with that of the others which, like those in Telstar I, still contain some gas. The higher apogee of Telstar II has some advantages. First, exposure to the artificial (electron) radiation belt that caused the malfunction of Telstar I will be greatly decreased. Furthermore,

---

* The low value of this transmitter power may be appreciated by comparison with regional radio and television broadcasting stations which generally operate at powers of several thousand watts.

longer continuous periods of transmission between the United States and Europe are possible, although the number of passes per day is decreased somewhat. Upon its tenth orbit, Telstar II recorded the first (taped) trans-Atlantic transmission of color television.

5.88. The Telstar spacecraft were intended primarily as experimental active repeater systems, but much of their complexity arises from their use in related tests. For example, they carry instruments for measuring the intensity of electron and proton radiation in space and associated telemetry for transmitting the information back to Earth. In addition, there are a number of special solar cells and transistors which are part of a series of investigations of the effects of space radiation on semiconductor devices utilized in space communications equipment.

5.89. Although Relay, shown in Fig. 5.17, is similar in principle to Telstar it differs in shape and in several structural and operational details. The overall length of the Relay satellite, including the protruding antennas, is 51 inches

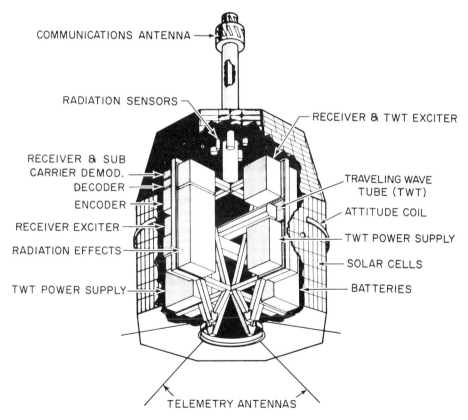

COMMUNICATIONS ANTENNA

RADIATION SENSORS

RECEIVER & TWT EXCITER

RECEIVER & SUB CARRIER DEMOD.

DECODER

ENCODER

RECEIVER EXCITER

RADIATION EFFECTS

TWT POWER SUPPLY

TRAVELING WAVE TUBE (TWT)

ATTITUDE COIL

TWT POWER SUPPLY

SOLAR CELLS

BATTERIES

TELEMETRY ANTENNAS

FIG. 5.17.   The Relay spacecraft

and its diameter is 29 inches; its weight is about 170 pounds. The particular shape was chosen in order to take maximum advantage of the volume permitted inside the launch vehicle's protective (low-drag) shroud. The exterior of the Relay spacecraft is almost completely covered with over 8200 solar cells; these provide sufficient power for the operation of an 11-watt transmitter, compared with $2\frac{1}{4}$ watts for Telstar I. There are two identical transponder systems to provide redundancy, i.e., a complete duplicate for use if one system should fail. Radio signals are received at a frequency of about 1725 megacycles per second but are retransmitted at the same frequency and maximum bandwidth as Telstar. The electrical circuits in the Relay and Telstar transponders are, however, different. Relay has the capability of supporting one television channel or 300 one-way telephone conversations;* alternatively, it can be switched to a narrow-band mode which provides 12 simultaneous two-way telephone channels.

5.90. Relay is spin stabilized, the initial spin rate being 167 revolutions per minute; it also has a magnetic coil to provide some degree of attitude adjustment upon receipt of a command signal from the ground. The receiving and transmitting antennas are on the extended post seen at the top of the illustration in Fig. 5.17; the telemetry, beacon, and radio command antennas are the short wires extending from the bottom of the spacecraft. Like Telstar, the Relay satellite carries a variety of instruments to record and telemeter space radiation measurements and to determine the effects of such radiations on semiconductor devices.

5.91. Relay I was launched on December 13, 1962; the orbit had an initial apogee of 4611 miles and a perigee of 818 miles, with a period of 185 minutes. A malfunction caused an excessive drain of power from the batteries, necessitating periodic shutdown of transmission to permit recovery, but this difficulty was partly overcome early in January 1963. Since that time, Relay I has been used for trans-Atlantic and trans-Pacific television transmissions and for voice communications and facsimile and teletype experiments between the United States and South America and between South America and Europe. On several occasions, during successful test transmissions via Relay I between Nutley, New Jersey,† and Rio de Janeiro, Brazil, normal radio communication between the ground stations was completely disrupted by disturbances in the ionosphere.

5.92. In addition to providing much information on the many problems arising in long-distance communications by satellite, useful data were obtained from Relay I in connection with the radiation experiments and tests already mentioned. In view of the success of Relay I, no radical changes were made in the design of the Relay II spacecraft launched on January 21, 1964,

---

* A single voice (telephone) channel requires a bandwidth of about 3 kilocycles per second.

† The command and control station for Relay satellites was transferred to the Space Tracking and Data Acquisition Network (STADAN) Station at Blossom Point, Maryland, in April 1964.

although advantage has been taken of improvements in components, e.g., solar cells, batteries, traveling-wave tubes, transistors, etc. The unexpectedly high power drain in Relay I was apparently caused by overheating of transistors in the voltage regulator-switch circuitry. Steps have been taken to eliminate this defect in Relay II and, in addition, a positive electromechanical switch has been placed in series with the regulator.

5.93. The problem of limited coverage, referred to in § 5.74, arises in relation to the use of low-altitude active repeater satellites, exactly as it does for passive systems. To provide continuous communication between all parts of the globe, the required number of randomly located satellites would be the same in both cases. Consequently, multiple launching would probably be carried out in the manner described in § 5.76.

5.94. It is of interest to mention in this connection that the U.S. Department of Defense has been considering a scheme for placing a number of active communications satellites at random in near-equatorial orbits. It has been estimated that 16 satellites at an altitude of about 18,000 miles or 24 at an altitude of 6000 miles would provide more than 90 percent continuity of service between Washington, D.C. and Hawaii. The satellites would be orbited eight at a time by means of a Titan III launch vehicle (§ 3.151).

ACTIVE REPEATER SATELLITES: SYNCHRONOUS ORBIT

5.95. Three satellites in synchronous (geostationary) circular orbits around the equator, one over the Atlantic Ocean, one over the Pacific Ocean, and a third over the Indian Ocean, would permit continuous communication between nearly the whole inhabited area of Earth (Fig. 5.18). Apart from the small

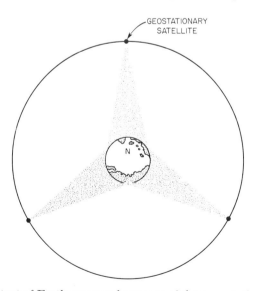

FIG. 5.18.   Extent of Earth coverage by means of three geostationary satellites

number of spacecraft which could provide essentially complete global coverage, a system of synchronous repeater satellites would have other advantages. Since the direction of each satellite with respect to any ground station is fixed, the transmission and receiving antennas on the ground can be greatly simplified in comparison with the steerable antennas required for low-altitude repeater satellites. It is possible, too, that damage caused by radiation to solar cells and transistors may be less at an altitude of 22,300 miles than it is at lower levels in Earth's radiation belt (§ 8.267).

5.96. Among the disadvantages of geostationary satellites is the necessity for periodic correction in order to maintain the proper location; this is referred to as *station keeping*. The shape of the orbit, for example, is continuously perturbed, especially by the noncircular distribution of Earth's gravitational field around the equator (§ 8.18). Moreover, to obtain the full benefit of the synchronous-orbit repeater satellite, the antennas should be Earth-oriented and attitude control is essential. Both of these operations require expenditure of power; if reaction jets are used, then a sufficient supply of gas (or other propellant) must be carried for the expected life of the spacecraft.

5.97. Station keeping and attitude stabilization are problems which can undoubtedly be solved. There are, in addition, some difficulties that are inherent in the system and for which no solutions are apparent; it remains to be seen how significant they will prove to be. One such difficulty arises because radio waves, like electromagnetic radiations in general, travel with a finite velocity, namely, the speed of light. Consequently, it requires about one fourth of a second for a signal to travel the 22,300 miles from Earth to the repeater satellite and back to Earth. In a telephone conversation between two individuals, there would be an unavoidable delay of about half a second between the termination of the remarks made by one party and the receipt of a reply from the other. If two repeater satellites were involved, e.g., in a conversation between the eastern United States, South America, or Western Europe and Australia, the delay would be one second. A gap of half a second would perhaps be tolerable, but one of a second might not be acceptable.

5.98. Another permanent problem is that of *solar noise*. Whenever the Sun appears in the same direction as the repeater satellite, as seen from a particular ground station, the radiations from the Sun will interfere with radio reception at that station. However, the times at which this solar noise will interrupt communications would be known in advance for every day of the year, and the duration would be no more than a few minutes once a day. It may be noted, incidentally, that the solar noise problem applies also for low-altitude satellites, but the latter have a more rapid motion relative to the Sun and so the interference is of negligible duration.

5.99. In order to insure continuity of service, it would be necessary to maintain at least one, and possibly two or three, standby geostationary satellites in orbit. If the equipment in any one repeater failed, one of the previously inactive satellites could be commanded to transfer to the required location and commence operation. It is possible, of course, that station keeping might not be adequate to retain the proper positions of the repeater satellites in equatorial orbit. If the positions and orbits should become completely random, it would require as many as 19 satellites at an altitude of 22,300 miles to provide essentially continuous worldwide communication between stations 3000 miles apart.

5.100. In the experimental synchronous satellites, the orientation of the transmitting antenna is such that half of the power radiated is wasted (cf. Fig. 5.20). In a commercial communications system, however, steps would have to be taken to make better use of the available power. One way of achieving this objective, first suggested in connection with the military communications Project Advent, is to control the satellite attitude so that the transmitting antenna is always directed toward Earth's center. An alternative approach is to retain the spin about the axis parallel to that of Earth, and to use an antenna that produces a conical beam. The beam can be kept oriented toward Earth by mechanical means or it can be achieved automatically by means of what is called a *phased array*. By continuously changing the phase (§ 4.126) of the radio wave that feeds the antenna, it is possible to spin the beam at the same rate as the satellite is spinning, but in the opposite direction. As a result, the radio beam is always pointed to Earth.

5.101. An interesting, long-range aspect of the geostationary satellite is the possibility of direct broadcasting over a large area. Because of the low transmitter power on board the satellite at present, high-gain antennas and sensitive, low-noise receivers are now required on the ground. Consequently, the number of receiving stations is very limited. At these stations, the signals must be amplified, and then sent out to local stations for broadcasting. It has been estimated, however, that if the transmitter power could be increased to 10 kilowatts (for television) or about 1 kilowatt (for AM radio) and with high-gain antennas suitably stabilized on the satellite, reception would be possible directly from a geostationary satellite with ordinary home antennas of moderate dimensions and normal receivers. Incidentally, this cannot be done with nonsynchronous satellites because they do not remain within line-of-sight. But, the intriguing prospect of direct broadcasting from satellites must await several developments. These include sufficiently large power sources for use in space, and precise stabilization, orientation, and station-keeping systems that will permit the use of highly directional, high-gain antennas on the satellite.

SYNCOM SATELLITES

5.102. The earlier Syncom (an abbreviation of the words "synchronous" and "communication") satellites have been designed as research tools with limited communications capability. Their purpose is, first, to test the principles of injection into a synchronous orbit and of control in such an orbit, and, second, to provide some information on the operation of communications and command systems at high altitudes. The Syncom satellite has a drum-like, flat cylindrical shape, as seen in Fig. 5.19, and is covered with 3840 solar cells. The cylinder has a diameter of 28 inches and a depth of 15 inches; the overall length, includ-

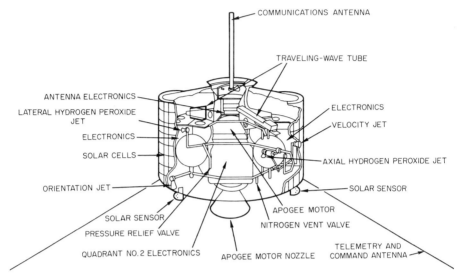

Fig. 5.19. The Syncom spacecraft

ing the communications antenna, is 46 inches. The four whip antennas for telemetry and command are shown around the lower portion of the spacecraft. The weight of the satellite in its final orbit is about 80 pounds.

5.103. The Syncom I and II satellites have two (receiver-transmitter) transponders; one is wide band, with a bandwidth of 5 megacycles per second, and the other is narrow band, with two 500 kilocycles per second bandwidth channels. The former can be used for several simultaneous one-way telephone, teletype, and facsimile transmissions, and the latter for two-way telephone conversations. Signals from Earth are received at a frequency of about 7360 megacycles per second and, after amplification, are retransmitted at 1815 megacycles per second; the power of the transmitter is 2 watts. The Syncom transmitting and receiving stations are located at Lakehurst, New Jersey, with a back-up at Fort Dix, New Jersey, and on the U.S. Naval Ship Kingsport, which is mobile.

5.104. A significant problem of the Syncom system is to inject the satellite into a synchronous, circular orbit at the required altitude. The general procedure is somewhat as follows. The satellite is launched into a highly elliptical (transfer) orbit with its apogee at the desired altitude of 22,300 miles. Before separating from the second stage of the launch (rocket) vehicle, the third stage and the satellite are spun at a rate of about 160 revolutions per minute, in order to stabilize the attitude during the remainder of the flight. Then the final stage of the rocket is fired and when the required injection velocity is attained the spacecraft, still spinning, is separated. When the apogee of the transfer orbit is reached, some 5 hours after liftoff, an on-board rocket is fired to provide the increase in velocity (4800 feet per second) needed to change to a circular orbit at the same altitude. This process, commonly described as an *apogee kick,* is achieved by means of a solid-fuel rocket motor indicated in Fig. 5.19. When the correct orbital position is attained, an off-center, nitrogen gas jet, commanded from the ground, turns the satellite so that its spin axis is parallel to Earth's polar axis. The communications antenna of the Syncom satellite then remains properly oriented, so that Earth lies within its disc-like, "pancake" radiation pattern shown in Fig. 5.20.

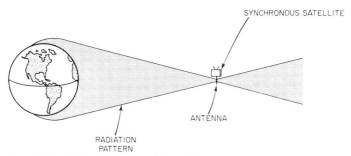

FIG. 5.20.   Radiation pattern from Syncom transmitting antenna

5.105. In order to establish and retain its synchronous orbit, the velocity of the satellite must be accurately achieved at injection and maintained during its lifetime. For this purpose, the spacecraft carries a thrustor utilizing hydrogen peroxide or nitrogen gas as propellant. The same device is used to change the location of the satellite if required. For example, a satellite launched from Florida will generally attain an orbital apogee of 22,300 miles when it is over the east coast of Africa, near Madagascar. For direct communications tests from stations in the United States, however, it should be located over the Atlantic Ocean between Africa and South America. The change in longitude is achieved by means of the hydrogen peroxide (or other) rockets over a period of several days.

5.106. The orbits of the earliest Syncoms were synchronous, but it was not intended that they should be equatorial. They were in fact inclined at an angle of about 33 deg to the equator, and hence were not geostationary. In such a synchronous orbit, the satellite appears to move back and forth, once daily, in a figure-eight pattern. The apparent path with reference to Earth ranges from 33°N to 33°S latitude, which is the angular inclination of the orbit (Fig. 5.21).

5.107. The first Syncom satellite was launched on February 14, 1963 into a highly elliptical orbit inclined to the equator. It attained an apogee of 22,800 miles some 5 hours after launching, as required. But communications radio contact with the satellite was lost about 20 seconds after the command was

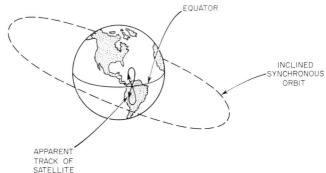

FIG. 5.21.   Apparent path of synchronous satellite with orbit inclined to the equator

given to fire the apogee motor which was to change the orbit from elliptical to circular. It was estimated from optical observations (§ 4.133) that the final orbit was almost circular with a perigee of about 21,400 miles and an apogee of 22,800 miles; the orbital period was 23 hours 45 minutes. Because of the failure of radio communications, apparently as the result of the rupture of a nitrogen propellant tank, no tests could be made with Syncom I.

5.108. The launch of Syncom II on July 26, 1963 was completely successful and the satellite was maneuvered into a synchronous orbit at an altitude of close to 22,230 miles and a period of 23.9 hours. By August 18, 1963, the satellite, as seen from Earth, appeared to follow a north-south, figure-eight path at 55°W longitude. The drift rate was then very small. Subsequently, as a result of natural perturbations of the orbit and of experiments with the control system, the spacecraft moved slowly westward. Successful direct communications tests, including two-way telephone conversations, and teletype and facsimile transmissions, between the United States and Africa were made with Syncom II.

5.109. Syncom III, the first satellite to be placed into a geostationary orbit, was launched from Cape Kennedy, Florida, on August 19, 1964. The launch vehicle was a Thrust-Augmented Delta (TAD) rocket, which included the more powerful third stage mentioned in § 3.143; this represented the initial use of the TAD. As far as the first apogee at an altitude of about 23,000 miles, attained roughly 5.5 hours after liftoff, the launch operation was similar to that described for a synchronous, but not geostationary, orbit in § 5.104. Instead of firing the apogee-kick motor on the spacecraft at this time, the satellite was allowed to complete an orbit, and on its second apogee, some 11 hours later, when over the west coast of South America, the attitude of the orbit was changed by means of hydrogen peroxide thrusters so as to bring the orbit more nearly parallel with the equator. After completing another orbit, i.e., about 28 hours after liftoff, and the spacecraft was near its third apogee, the on-board (apogee-kick) motor was fired at a precisely calculated time to bring Syncom III into a circular, equatorial orbit. The spacecraft appeared to be almost stationary over a point in the western part of the Indian Ocean. It was then allowed to drift slowly westward and its position was adjusted by means of the hydrogen peroxide thrusters so that it seemed to hover over the equator near the International Date Line.

5.110. One of the objectives of Syncom III was to transmit television pictures of the Olympic Games held in Japan from October 10 to 24, 1964. It is for this reason that the spacecraft was located close to the International Date Line. Transmissions could then be made from a station near Tokyo to a receiver at Point Mugu, California, and thence by land line and microwave to all parts of the United States. Since television transmission was an important objective, the equipment on Syncom III was somewhat different from that on the earlier Syncoms. One receiver had a bandwidth of 5 megacycles per second, as before, but the second had an intermediate frequency (I.F.) bandwidth of 13 megacycles to provide improved television transmission.

5.111. Excellent television pictures of the opening ceremonies of the Olympic Games were received in the United States via Syncom III on October 10, 1964, and several successful transmissions of short duration were made on subsequent days. On one occasion, television signals from Japan received in California in this manner were transmitted by microwave to the Atlantic coast and then to Europe by means of Relay I.

APPLICATIONS (OR ADVANCED) TECHNOLOGICAL SATELLITES

5.112. Future development in the use of satellites for communications and also for meteorological purposes requires additional experience in a number of technological areas. It is the general objective of the Applications (or Advanced) Technological Satellite (ATS) program to provide this experience. Passive, gravity-gradient stabilization, for example, appears to have advantages for communication and meteorological satellites as a simple means for maintaining continuous orientation of antennas and cameras, respectively, toward Earth. Very little is known about the effectiveness of this mode of attitude stabilization and of the methods that may be used to damp out the expected oscillations. This is one of the problems that will be studied in the ATS program.

5.113. It has been seen that satellites in synchronous (geostationary) orbits may contribute to a worldwide communications system; furthermore, they may have a considerable potential in meteorology. A geostationary meteorological satellite could follow continuously the development of a weather system in a given region of Earth's surface and it could detect severe storms of short duration, such as tornadoes and thunderstorms, that might be missed by observations made at intervals. In order to make possible the design of advanced geostationary satellites, more experience is needed in stabilization, orientation, and station keeping in synchronous orbits. Further information is also required on the effects of radiation and of micrometeoroid particles at the altitude of 22,300 miles on various structural materials, solar cells, electronic equipment, meteorological sensors, etc.

5.114. The basic spacecraft of the Applications Technological Satellite program is cylindrical in shape, about 5 feet in diameter and 50 inches in height. Its mass in orbit is about 700 pounds, of which instruments will constitute from 100 to 300 pounds, depending on the mission. Three types of mission are under consideration. The first is to place a satellite in an orbit of medium altitude, about 6000 miles, and to utilize it for experiments on gravity-gradient stabilization. A feature of this satellite is the four 100-foot long booms with masses at their ends. The direction of the booms can be changed to some extent upon command from the ground, to study the effect on the damping of oscillations. This satellite will probably carry equipment, e.g., cameras and infrared radiometers, for making meteorological observations and transponders for long-range communications.

5.115. The second ATS mission involves the orbiting of a spin-stabilized, geostationary satellite intended partly to determine if useful cloud-cover photographs of Earth can be obtained from the 22,300-mile altitude of such a spacecraft. Experiments to test the effect of the radiation and micrometeoroid environment will also be carried. The third and final mission will include some of the features of the other two: the satellite, utilizing gravity-gradient stabilization, will be placed into a geostationary orbit. The purpose of this mission is to make a variety of meteorological, engineering, and technological studies at high altitude. The information derived from the ATS program will form the basis for future developments in satellites for meteorological, communication, and other purposes, e.g., navigation.

NAVIGATIONAL SATELLITES

INTRODUCTION

5.116. The basic operation in the navigation of ships, aircraft, or other vehicles is the determination of position, either in terms of Earth coordinates or with reference to a point of known location. Four types of navigational techniques have been used in the past; these are dead reckoning, piloting, celestial navigation, and electromagnetic (or radio) navigation systems.

5.117. In *dead reckoning** the position at a given time is estimated from the

---

* The expression dead reckoning has been described as a corruption or abbreviation of "deduced reckoning," but other ideas concerning its origin have been put forward.

distances and directions traveled since a previously known position. The draw-back to this procedure is that uncertainties in determining the distances and directions tend to accumulate, and so after a time the estimated position may be seriously in error. It is necessary, therefore, to check the position whenever possible by obtaining what is called a *fix*, using either piloting or celestial navigation.

5.118. *Piloting* (or *pilotage*) is the name used for the determination of position relative to external reference points, e.g., identifiable geographical features, optical and radio beacons, etc. Where piloting relies upon visibility, it will, of course, depend on the weather conditions. The use of radio beacons may not be affected by the weather, but it is limited by the availability of such beacons, by distortion due to intervening land configurations and atmospheric conditions, and so on.

5.119. *Celestial navigation* requires observation of at least two (or possibly three) stars that are not too near the horizon. It can be performed, therefore, only when visibility of the sky is good.

5.120. Finally, there are the *electromagnetic (radio) navigation systems* using fixed, ground-based radio transmitters, of which LORAN (Long Range Navigation) is an example. Measurement of the difference in the arrival times of radio-frequency signals transmitted simultaneously from two widely-spaced, fixed shore stations gives a hyperbolic line of position of the receiving vehicle, e.g., an aircraft or a ship. The intersection of two lines of position determines the location of the vehicle. The use of LORAN is limited to ranges within about 1000 to 1500 miles from the shore stations.

5.121. The use of Earth satellites for navigational purposes would avoid the difficulties and limitations associated with the conventional procedures described above. One system for navigation by satellite, which has been tested in the United States, involves determination of the rate of change with time of the slant range of a satellite; this will be described first. Reference will then be made to other proposals that are being considered.

NAVIGATION BY RANGE RATE MEASUREMENTS

5.122. It will be recalled that the range rate of a satellite can be derived from measurements of the Doppler frequency shift of a radio signal received from a beacon carried by the satellite. When the satellite passes in the vicinity of a given ground station, the range rate changes with time, and so also does the frequency shift, in the manner depicted in Fig. 5.22. As the satellite approaches the observation point, the Doppler frequency shift is positive but decreases, at first slowly and then more rapidly; at the distance of closest approach the shift is zero and subsequently it becomes more and more negative as the satellite moves farther away.* It has been shown theoretically that,

* An exactly equivalent situation is the change in pitch of a locomotive whistle as perceived by a stationary listener (§ 4.16).

except for certain special cases, such as equatorial orbits, the shape of the curve in Fig. 5.22, representing the change in Doppler shift with time, is characteristic of the position of the observation point on the ground in relation to the satellite orbit. In other words, for a given orbit, there is only one point

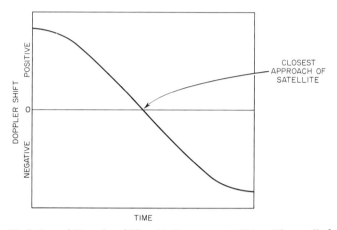

Fig. 5.22.   Variation of Doppler shift with time as a satellite with a radio beacon passes the observation station on the ground

on Earth at which the Doppler frequency shift will vary with time in the particular manner observed. Consequently, measurements of the Doppler shift and a knowledge of the path of the satellite are sufficient to identify the location of the observation point. If Earth did not rotate, there would be two positions, one on each side of the orbital plane, at which the Doppler shift curve would be the same. This uncertainty is eliminated, however, by Earth's rotation which causes a small, but detectable, difference at the two locations.

5.123. The time variation of the Doppler frequency shift is the basis of a satellite navigational system, known as the *Transit project*. The data required at an observation station, e.g., a ship, to permit its location to be determined are the characteristic parameters (or elements) of the satellite orbit (§ 2.98) and the precise universal (Greenwich) time. This information is stored in the satellite and is broadcast at short intervals.

5.124. Because of various perturbing forces, the path of a satellite does not repeat itself every day, as it otherwise would. Consequently, the satellite is tracked continuously by means of a fixed network of ground stations where computers predict the orbital elements for some time ahead. The results are transmitted to the satellite where they are recorded on magnetic tape, after erasing the previous elements, and then rebroadcast at short intervals, as indicated above. At the observation point, the latest orbital data, the time of closest approach of the satellite, and the Doppler frequency shift measurements are fed into a computer; the output then gives the latitude and longitude of the station.

5.125. A complicating factor in the accurate calculation of position arises from the refraction (or bending) of the radio waves as they traverse the ionosphere in their passage from the satellite to Earth (§ 4.25). The effect on the Doppler shift, to a good approximation, is inversely proportional to the square of the frequency of the radio waves; consequently, it would be advantageous to employ extremely high frequency radio for transmission purposes. However, this would necessitate the use of either a transmitter of very high power on the satellite or a directional antenna of high gain at the receiving station. Since neither of these alternatives is practical in the circumstances, a different approach has been adopted. The beacon on the Transit satellite transmits on two harmonically related frequencies in the range of 50 to 400 megacycles per second, so that two Doppler shift curves are obtained. By assuming the refraction effect to be inversely proportional to the square of the frequency, the correction is readily computed. Although this procedure is satisfactory under normal conditions, it may not be reliable when magnetic storms cause disturbances in the ionosphere.

5.126. The altitude of the Transit orbit, which is nominally circular, has been chosen as approximately 500 to 600 miles, for the following reasons. If the altitude is too high, the rate of change of Doppler frequency shift with time is not large enough to permit accurate determinations to be made. On the other hand, if the altitude is too low, the orbital elements change more rapidly than they do at higher altitudes. Furthermore, the effect of ionospheric refraction is also more marked when the altitude is low. The selected orbital altitude is believed to be a suitable compromise.

5.127. An operational system might consist of four satellites simultaneously in circular polar orbits at an altitude of 600 to 700 miles. The orbital planes would be 45° latitude apart, so that they are distributed uniformly around the globe. With these orbits, a navigational fix should be possible at any point about every 110 minutes at low latitudes, i.e., near the equator, and more frequently at higher latitudes, i.e., nearer the poles. Since an overhead pass does not yield accurate results, it may sometimes be necessary to wait 220 minutes, but not more, between successive determinations of position.

5.128. The first Transit test satellite (Transit 1B) was launched from Florida on April 13, 1960; the initial apogee was 470 miles and the perigee 235 miles, with an orbital inclination of 51.3 deg to the equator. Other Transit spacecraft have attained orbits inclined at about 67, 32, and 28 deg, the orbital periods being about 100 minutes in each case. From the observations made, it is estimated that positions on Earth can be determined within half a mile or better under favorable conditions. The main sources of error appear to be variations in the frequency of the radio beacon on the satellite, inaccuracies in the measurement of the Doppler shift, and incomplete knowledge of Earth's gravitational field.*

NAVIGATION BY RANGE MEASUREMENTS

5.129. The objective of a proposed system of determination of position by range measurements only is to concentrate the complex and costly equipment at a number of ground stations, whereas the equipment on the satellites and on the ships and aircraft using the system is relatively simple. To utilize the system the ship or aircraft, i.e., the user, would require that two satellites should be passing in orbit within range and that a ground station be nearby.

5.130. The user would send out a ranging pulse which is received by one of the satellites; the satellite then returns the transmission to the user causing it to repeat the pulse. The two pulses are retransmitted by the satellite and received by the ground station (Fig. 5.23); from the elapsed time between the

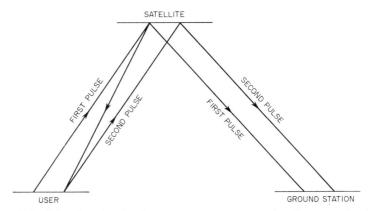

FIG. 5.23.   Principle of navigation by range measurement; signals are sent out to two satellites at an interval of 1 millisecond

receipt of the pulses, the ground station computes the distance (or range) from the user to the satellite. One millisecond after sending out the first set of pulses, the user sends out another pulse to a second satellite. The ground station then determines the range from the user to the second satellite.

5.131. From a knowledge of the distance of each satellite, the ground station would obtain a circle of position of the user from each of the two ranges. The

* The gravitational field of Earth affects the elements of the orbit. Observations on Transit 4A confirmed that the gravitational field distribution of Earth is not circular, but elliptical, around the equator (§ 8.18).

circles intersect at two points, and one of these is the position of the user. As a general rule, the points are so widely separated that there is no doubt which is the correct one. When the latitude and longitude have been determined, the ground station transmits the information to the user via a satellite. The results are displayed automatically on the user vehicle. To obtain the altitude as well as the latitude and longitude of an aircraft, ranges from three satellites would be required.

5.132. Since a given pair of satellites can respond to only one user at a time, definite periods are allocated to each user. The whole operation described above, however, would require only 0.5 second. By broadcasting the position of one user while obtaining data from another, it has been estimated that about 14,000 fixes could be provided every hour. For a worldwide navigation network of this type, 24 satellites would be required, in circular orbits of 6400-mile altitude, and six ground stations.

NAVIGATION BY RANGE AND DIRECTION

5.133. A scheme has also been proposed for a navigational system based on measurement from a satellite of the user's range and direction. The satellite would interrogate the user and determine its distance by recording the time interval between the transmission of a radar pulse and its return by a transponder on the user vehicle. The direction is obtained by utilizing the interferometer principle employed in the Minitrack system (§ 4.125 *et seq.*); the measurements are made with four antennas located at the ends of 50-foot long booms in a cruciform arrangement mounted on the spacecraft. In addition to the phase angle, the altitude of the satellite must be known.

5.134. In order to convert the information giving range and direction from the satellite into the position of the user, the position and attitude (or orientation in space) of the satellite must be available. For this purpose, it is proposed that three fixed reference stations on the ground, whose locations are known accurately, should be utilized. Simultaneous measurements made from the satellite of the distance and direction of the three stations can give the required position and attitude. The procedure and equipment would be exactly the same as that used in obtaining the distance and direction of a user.

5.135. To simplify the equipment on the satellite, on the user vehicle, and at the reference stations, the transit time and phase angle data, both from the user and the three fixed stations, are transmitted to a control center. Here, all the necessary computations would be made and the user's position transmitted to the satellite and relayed to the user. By employing three geostationary satellites, this navigational system would be operative over most of Earth's surface. A maximum of nine, and probably fewer, reference stations would be required on the ground, and three control centers where the computers are located.

GEODETIC SATELLITES

APPLICATIONS OF GEODESY

5.136. Geodesy is a mathematical science concerned chiefly with the determination of (*a*) the shape and size of an idealized Earth, (*b*) the distribution of Earth's gravitational field, and (*c*) the exact position of points on Earth's surface. The results of geodetic studies are largely of scientific interest, but they do have an application in mapping by making possible the precise evaluation of the distances between reference points or datums on different geodetic networks, as described in § 1.13. It is mainly with the use of satellites in the latter connection that the present section will be concerned; other, purely scientific, applications of geodesy will be considered in Chapter 8.

INTERVISIBLE METHOD

5.137. The simplest technique in which use is made of a satellite for measuring distances between geodetic datums is called the *intervisible* (or *simultaneous*) *method*. It requires that the satellite be visible at the same time from points in two geodetic networks on opposite sides of the orbital plane of the satellite. Photographs are taken simultaneously from two locations in each network of the satellite against a background of stars. By means of an ephemeris (§ 1.11, footnote) the celestial coordinates of the satellite at the given instant can be determined from the relationship of its position to that of known stars. If the distances between the two stations in each network are known, the distance between a station on one network and the stations on the other can be calculated by conventional triangulation procedures.

5.138. In order to obtain results of high accuracy, the four photographs of the sky should be taken within less than a one-thousandth of a second. Since it is virtually impossible to achieve such simultaneity from stations at a distance, it would be necessary to take several photographs from each station within a prescribed period. From these, the required simultaneous data could be derived by interpolation. A check on the results can be obtained by comparing the distances between the stations as calculated from two or more sets of simultaneous data. This modified procedure makes it possible to obtain the required information from a single observation station in each geodetic network. An advantage of the intervisible photographic technique is the simplicity of the ground equipment, namely, a ballistic camera, e.g., of the Baker-Nunn or similar type (§ 4.133). Furthermore, exact information concerning the satellite orbit is not required; all that is necessary is to know where the cameras should be pointed at a given time.

5.139. Normally, a satellite can be seen and photographed only at dawn and at dusk (§ 4.135) and this restricts the distance over which the simultaneous (or nearly simultaneous) observations can be made. If the satellite carries a light, however, it could be observed against a background of stars throughout the night, provided the sky is clear. The distance over which the intervisible method could be applied would thus be greatly extended. In practice, the quantity of electricity consumed by a light which would be continuously visible for several hundred miles would be beyond the capacity of space power supplies based on solar cells. Consequently, a flashing light is used; each flash is of short duration, so that the power consumption is tolerable.

FLASHING-LIGHT SATELLITES

5.140. The orbiting of a satellite with a flashing light was proposed as part of the International Geophysical Year program in the United States (§ 1.110), but some time elapsed before the initiation of the project called ANNA, an acronym for Army, Navy, National Aeronautics and Space Administration, and Air Force who cooperated in its implementation. The ANNA 1-B, flashing-light satellite was launched from Florida on October 31, 1962, but the principle of determining distances on Earth by the simultaneity technique had been tested earlier. Satellite photographs, obtained at the Baker-Nunn optical tracking stations at dawn and dusk, have been utilized to determine the location of these stations with an uncertainty of about 100 feet. Furthermore, on the night of December 8, 1961, a sounding rocket fired from Point Arguello, California, released three sets of flares at a distance of about 900 miles from the Pacific Coast at an altitude of 1300 miles. The flares were photographed simultaneously from Alaska, California, and Hawaii, and from the results a more precise location was determined for Hawaii with respect to the mainland of North America.

5.141. The ANNA satellite has a diameter of about 36 inches and a weight of 355 pounds. Its initial orbit was approximately circular, with an apogee of roughly 740 miles and a perigee of 680 miles; the angle of inclination was about 50 deg. High intensity (1 million watt) optical beacons, consisting of xenon lamps, emit a sequence of light flashes, each lasting slightly more than a millisecond, spaced 5.6 seconds apart. In order to conserve the electrical power, there are not more than four such sequences each day at prescribed times. The satellite also carries the usual radio equipment required for range and range-rate measurements. The particular orbit and inclination selected for the ANNA 1-B satellite were a compromise based on such considerations as the rocket thrust available for launching, location of observation stations, and maximum coverage. A complete geodetic system would require five or six satellites in orbits at different angles of inclination and with various apogees. The higher the apogee, the greater the distance between stations from which simultaneous observations can be made of a particular satellite.

RADIO TECHNIQUES

5.142. Since observations on a satellite with a flashing light are limited to the hours of darkness and when the sky is clear, it has been recommended that the optical method be supplemented by radio techniques. Although such techniques are more complex and often less accurate, they are not dependent on the satellite being visible. Two radio methods are possible: one is based on the simultaneous determination of the satellite range from different stations at successive times; the other is similar in principle to that employed for navigational purposes and requires the measurement of the time variation of the range rate. A radio wave of constant frequency is transmitted from a station of unknown location to a satellite. The Doppler shift-time curve obtained on the satellite is then telemetered to the ground.

Orbital Method

5.143. An extension of the intervisible procedure has been called the *orbital* (or *dynamic*) *method;* it is used where simultaneous observations are not possible because of the distance between the two geodetic networks. If the orbit of the satellite is known precisely, by utilizing established tracking techniques, it is possible to relate the positions of the satellite at two different times at the distant networks. From photographs taken from stations on the two networks at these respective, precisely known times, the distance between the datums of the networks can be calculated. The accuracy in these circumstances is limited by that with which the elements of the satellite orbit are known. Because of the uncertainties in these parameters, it would be advisable to base the determinations on photographs of two or more satellites in different orbits. In addition to the flashing light, the satellite would carry a radio beacon to facilitate continuous tracking.

Geodetic Satellite Program

5.144. The purpose of the geodetic satellite program is to make possible a more detailed mapping of Earth's surface, as an aid to navigation, and to provide more precise information about Earth's gravitational field, to permit accurate calculation of spacecraft orbits and trajectories (cf. § 8.22). Although intended primarily for studying the ionosphere, the Beacon Explorer Satellites, described in § 8.202, each carry radio beacons which transmit on two harmonic frequencies. They can then be utilized by ground stations in a manner similar to that employed in the Transit system (§ 5.123). In addition, two types of satellites have been especially designed for geodetic studies. The satellites of the first type, called Geodetic Explorer Satellites (or GEOS), which are to be placed in orbits having inclinations of 59 and 80 deg, weigh about 350 pounds. The altitudes of these satellites are expected to be between 500 and 700 miles. The equipment consists of a flashing light, various radio beacons, optical (laser) reflectors, and possibly radar reflectors. The second type of geodetic satellite, known as the Passive Geodetic Satellite (or PAGOES), is simply a balloon, similar to Echo (§ 5.64 *et seq.*), in an almost circular, polar orbit at an altitude of about 2300 miles. This passive satellite will be tracked optically from 36 camera sites some 2500 to 2800 miles apart. By the use of triangulation, it should be possible to compute the distance of any two stations from one another and from Earth's center of mass to within about 10 meters (33 feet) of the exact values.

Chapter 6

THE SUN

GENERAL PROPERTIES OF THE SUN

IMPORTANCE OF SOLAR STUDIES

6.1. The study of the Sun is of interest for several reasons. In the first place, the Sun is a more-or-less average star with regard to its size, mass, and surface temperature. Although it is far from Earth in terms of terrestrial distances, namely, about 93 million miles, it is much closer than any other star, the next nearest star group (Alpha and Proxima Centauri) being nearly 300,000 times farther away. Consequently, the Sun can be studied in considerably greater detail than is possible for any other star. Because of the Sun's average nature, the knowledge gained about it can be utilized to understand the behavior of stars that are either larger or smaller, as well as of those of similar size and temperature.

6.2. Furthermore, the Sun is responsible for many of the phenomena on Earth, including the maintenance of life. Without solar radiations, there would be no plants on land or in the sea and no food for animals, birds, or fish. Long-range climatic changes, such as the occurrence of glacial periods, and also relatively short-range variations in weather, are probably related in some manner to the energy received by Earth's atmosphere from the Sun. In addition, magnetic storms, capable of disrupting long-range radio communication, and auroral displays, commonly visible in the polar regions, are associated with solar events.

6.3. As a consequence of developments in space exploration, there are additional reasons for needing to know more about the Sun. The path of a space vehicle is affected by the solar gravitational field as well as by that of Earth. For an Earth satellite, the Sun's gravitational attraction is essentially constant and is so small relative to that of Earth that it is not very significant. But for a space probe traveling away from Earth, the Sun's gravity field becomes increasingly important. The accurate calculation of the trajectory of a planetary or solar probe, and even of a vehicle making a journey to the Moon, requires a precise knowledge of the mass of the Sun and its distance from

292

Earth. Apart from the direct effect of solar gravity, there is an indirect effect in connection with the velocity of Earth in its orbit about the Sun. Because the orbit is slightly elliptical (see Chapter 7), the velocity will vary and this will affect the trajectory of a space probe.

6.4. An entirely different aspect of the Sun's behavior must be taken into consideration in connection with manned flight beyond Earth. At all times, the Sun emits electrically charged particles which travel millions of miles into space. These particles constitute a potential health hazard to human beings but, as a general rule, the space vehicle will provide ample protection. There are certain periods, however, when the Sun is especially active and the space-craft must be designed to allow for such situations (§ 13.119). More knowledge is needed about the factors that determine the Sun's activity and the magnitude of the hazard in order that steps may be taken to protect space travelers. Incidentally, on Earth and in satellites orbiting Earth at moderate altitudes, the terrestrial magnetic field prevents direct access of the electrically charged solar particles.

THE ASTRONOMICAL UNIT*

6.5. The basic physical properties of the Sun are its size, mass, and density and these will be examined first. But in order to do so, it is necessary to know the mean distance between Earth and the Sun; this distance is called the *astronomical unit.* According to the statement in § 2.61, it is essentially identical with the length of the semi-major axis of the slightly elliptical orbit in which Earth revolves about the Sun. The astronomical unit has been measured in several different ways; three basic procedures that were used before the development of radar techniques will be described.

6.6. The *orbital velocity method* involves the determination of the velocity of Earth in its orbit about the Sun by making use of the Doppler shift principle (§ 4.16). The light from a distant star, like that of the Sun, contains electromagnetic radiations of different wavelengths (or frequencies), as will be explained more fully in due course. An instrument called the spectrograph† (§ 6.54) spreads out the radiations according to their frequencies (or wavelengths) and makes it possible to measure these frequencies (or wavelengths). In the spectrograph, a radiation having a definite frequency then appears as a single line, referred to as a *spectral line.* Thus, in general, the light from a star exhibits a number of spectral lines; as will be seen shortly, these lines are determined by the elements present in the outer layers of the star.

6.7. Consider a distant star, a long way to the left of Fig. 6.1; the distance from the star to the Sun (or Earth) is so great that the light from the star

---

* The determination of the astronomical unit is treated at some length, because the same techniques are utilized in several other areas covered later in this book.

† The terms spectrum, spectra, spectral, spectrograph, etc., are derived from the Latin, *specere,* "to look," and *spectrum,* "appearance" or "image," cf., spectator, spectacle, specter.

may be assumed to travel along parallel lines to all parts of Earth's orbit. This situation is indicated by the parallel, dashed arrows. Suppose now that the frequency of a given spectral line in the light from the star is measured on Earth at different locations in its orbit about the Sun. If Earth is at the point A, it is traveling directly toward the star, as indicated by the arrow at A; as a result of the Doppler effect, the observed frequency of the line will be greater than the frequency as it left the star. If the latter is represented by f_0, the observed frequency will be

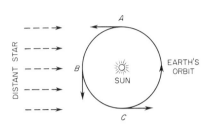

FIG. 6.1. Determination of Earth's orbital velocity by Doppler shift

$f_0 + f_d$, where f_d, the Doppler frequency shift, depends on the velocity of Earth at A relative to that of the star. Three months later, Earth will be at B and now its velocity relative to the star is zero because, as the arrow indicates, Earth is moving in a direction perpendicular to that of the star. The Doppler shift is then zero and the frequency of the given spectral line as measured at B will thus be f_0. Consequently, from the observations at A and B, the Doppler frequency shift, f_d, can be determined; this is related to the velocity of Earth in its orbit by equation (4.2) which, in the present case, may be written as

$$v = \frac{f_d}{f_0} c,$$

where v is Earth's orbital velocity and c is the velocity of light.

6.8. Confirmation may be obtained by repeating the measurement of the frequency of the spectral line after another three months, when Earth is at C in its orbit. The observed frequency is now $f_0 - f_d$, because Earth is moving directly away from the star. Again f_d can be evaluated by comparison with the observation made at B, and the orbital velocity calculated. The average value obtained in this manner for different points in the orbit, i.e., with different reference stars, is **29.77** kilometers (**18.50** miles) per second.

6.9. If Earth's orbit around the Sun were a circle, the circumference would be $2\pi a$, where a is the radius of the circle; thus a is the distance from Earth to the Sun, i.e., the astronomical unit. Since it requires **365.24** days (or 31.56×10^6 seconds) for Earth to complete an orbit, the velocity of Earth in a circular orbit would be $2\pi a/(31.56 \times 10^6)$ kilometers per second, if a is expressed in kilometers. If the orbital velocity is taken to be **29.8** kilometers per second, as given above, it follows that

$$\frac{2\pi a}{31.56 \times 10^6} = 29.8,$$

so that

$$a = \frac{29.8 \times 31.56 \times 10^6}{2\pi}$$

$$= 149.7 \times 10^6 \text{ kilometers}$$
$$= 92.9 \times 10^6 \text{ miles.}$$

Because Earth's orbit is slightly elliptical (eccentricity = 0.0167), the fore-going result is not completely accurate. The necessary corrections, which are relatively small, can be applied to yield a fairly good value of the astronomical unit.

6.10. Another approach to the determination of the average distance between the Sun and Earth, known as the *trigonometrical method,* involves as a first step the measurement of the distance of another planet from Earth. Before the development of radar reflection (echo) techniques for determining distances (§ 4.14), the *parallax method* was employed to obtain the distance of a planet from Earth. In Fig. 6.2, the point P represents the position of a planet with

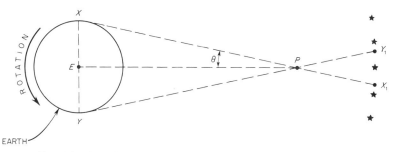

Fig. 6.2.   Parallax method for determining distance of a planet

reference to Earth and a background of fixed stars. The figure is not drawn to scale, but it will be adequate for illustrating the general principles. A particular diameter, XY, of Earth is chosen such that the line EP, where E is the center of Earth, is perpendicular to XY. At a certain time, e.g., in the early evening, an observer on Earth at X will see the planet in a particular direction, indi-cated by X_1, against the background of fixed stars. Twelve hours later, the observer will be at Y, because of Earth's rotation, and the planet will now appear to be in the direction Y_1. Both Earth and the planet will have moved to some extent in their orbits during the elapsed time and a correction can be applied to allow for this motion.

6.11. By utilizing the known directions of the fixed stars, as derived from an ephemeris (§ 1.11), the apparent shift in position X_1 to Y_1 of the (sta-tionary) planet can be determined, and from this the angle XPY can be evaluated. The angle XPE (or YPE), which is half the angle XPY, is called the *horizontal* (also *geocentric* or *diurnal*) *parallax** of the planet as it appears from Earth. The observations are generally made at an interval of less than 12 hours, and from these the horizontal parallax can be calculated. Since XE is the known radius of Earth, a knowledge of the angle XPE permits the distance EP, i.e., from the planet to Earth, to be computed. Thus, if θ is the horizontal parallax angle, then

$$EP = \frac{EX}{\tan \theta}.$$

If the radius of Earth, i.e., EX, is represented by R_0, and the distance of the planet, i.e., EP, by D, it follows that

$$D = \frac{R_0}{\tan \theta}.$$

Because the angle θ is small, very much smaller than indicated in Fig. 6.2, which is decidedly out of scale,

$$\tan \theta \approx \theta,$$

where θ is expressed in radians;† hence,

$$D = \frac{R_0}{\theta}. \tag{6.1}$$

6.12. With the distance of the planet from Earth known, the distance from Earth to the Sun is then calculated in the following manner. Suppose the points $E, P,$ and S in Fig. 6.3 represent the positions of Earth, the planet, and the Sun,

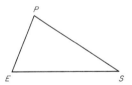

Fig. 6.3.   Determination of distance from
Earth to the Sun

respectively, at the time the parallax measurements are made. In order to determine ES, which is the required quantity, the astronomical unit, it is necessary to solve the triangle EPS. The distance EP is equal to D, as derived from equation (6.1), and may be regarded as known. Of the two other quantities that must be available, one is taken as the angle PES, which can be obtained from an ephemeris, and the other is the ratio of the distances ES and PS, which can be derived from Kepler's third law (§2.48). According to this law, as applied to planetary motion, the square of the orbital period of a planet, i.e., the duration of its year, is proportional to the cube of the average distance of that planet from the Sun.

---

* Parallax (from the Latin, *para*, "aside," and *allassein*, "to change") refers to the apparent displacement or change in apparent direction of an object as seen from two different positions.

† An angle of 360 deg is 2π radians; hence, conversion of an angle in degrees to the value in radians is achieved upon dividing by $360/2\pi$, i.e., 57.30. In other words 1 radian is equal to 57.30 deg and 1 deg to 0.01745 radian.

The orbital periods of Earth and the planet are known, and hence the ratio *ES/PS* can be evaluated. All the information is thus available for computing the distance *ES*, from Earth to the Sun.

6.13. The application of the trigonometrical method for determination of the astronomical unit is greatly simplified when the points *E*, *P*, and *S* lie in the same straight line with the planet between Earth and the Sun. As seen from Earth, the planet then passes directly in front of the Sun; this phenomenon is called a *transit*. The only planets for which transits are possible are Mercury and Venus, which lie between Earth and the Sun, but such transits are of rare occurrence. Furthermore, Mercury is too small and too far from Earth for its distance to be determined by the parallax method, although not by radar. Failing the opportunity to make observations during a transit, advantage may be taken of a *conjunction* when the planet, Earth, and the Sun all lie in a plane perpendicular to Earth's orbital plane (§ 7.14). The angle *EPS* in Fig. 6.3 can then be readily derived from the known inclination of the planet's orbit to that of Earth.

6.14. The best known use of the parallax method to determine the distance of a celestial object, in order to calculate the astronomical unit, is in connection with the minor planet or asteroid (§ 7.53) known as Eros. This travels around the Sun in a somewhat eccentric orbit between Earth and Mars and in 1931 came within about 26 million kilometers (16 million miles) of Earth.* At the time of close approach, the horizontal parallax is relatively large and can be measured with greater accuracy than is possible for Venus.

6.15. Since 1958, radar reflection techniques have been applied to determine the distance of Earth from the planets Mercury, Venus, and Mars. The measurements on Venus, in particular, made in the United States, in the United Kingdom, and in the U.S.S.R., are in satisfactory agreement and yield a value of 149,599,000 kilometers (92,950,000 miles) for the astronomical unit.

6.16. At this point, it may be wondered why the radar technique is not used for the direct determination of the Sun's distance from Earth. There are at least two reasons why accurate values cannot be obtained in this manner. First, the Sun itself is a strong emitter of radio waves (§ 6.172 *et seq.*) and so the radar reflection is difficult to detect against a background covering a wide range of radio frequencies. Furthermore, the extension of the Sun consists of an ionized gas or plasma at high temperature; consequently, there is no well-defined surface at which radar reflection occurs.

6.17. In theory, the parallax method described in § 6.10 could be utilized directly to obtain the distance of the Sun from Earth. All that would be necessary is to suppose that the point *P* in Fig. 6.2 represents the location of the Sun, and then to measure the horizontal parallax from Earth. The practical implementation of this conceptual procedure, however, encounters difficulties. In the first place, fixed stars are not visible in the vicinity of the Sun except

* The closest possible distance from Eros to Earth is 22.5 million kilometers.

during a total eclipse; and second, the parallax angle is so small that accurate measurement is almost impossible. Nevertheless, it is a common practice to express the astronomical unit in terms of the *solar parallax*, i.e., the horizontal parallax angle of the Sun as it would be observed from Earth (Fig. 6.4). The

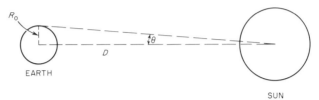

FIG. 6.4.   The solar parallax

average radius, R_0, of Earth is 6.378×10^6 meters and taking the average distance from Earth to the Sun to be 149.6×10^6 kilometers, i.e., 1.496×10^{11} meters, it follows from equation (6.1) that the solar parallax in radians is

$$\theta = \frac{R_0}{D} = \frac{6.378 \times 10^6}{1.496 \times 10^{11}}$$

$$= 4.263 \times 10^{-5} \text{ radian.}$$

The result is generally expressed in seconds (of arc), where 1 deg is 3600 sec; hence, 1 radian $= 57.30$ deg $= 57.30 \times 3600 = 2.0634 \times 10^5$ sec. Consequently, the solar parallax is

$$\theta = (4.263 \times 10^{-5})(2.063 \times 10^5)$$
$$= 8.795 \text{ sec (of arc).}$$

6.18. The third method, called the *dynamical method,* for deriving the astronomical unit is of particular interest in connection with the trajectories of space probes. When it comes fairly close to Earth, the orbit of a planet is influenced by the gravitational fields of both the Sun and Earth or, more exactly, the Earth-Moon system. From a study of the perturbation of the orbit, it is possible to calculate the ratio of the mass of the Sun to that of the Earth-Moon system. Since the latter may be regarded as known, the solar mass can be calculated. The astronomical unit (or solar parallax) can then be obtained from equation (2.28), which relates Earth's orbital period, i.e., 365.24 days, to the average distance from the Sun. The procedure is illustrated in § 6.20 in connection with the reverse calculation of the solar mass from the astronomical unit. The dynamical method has been applied to observations on the orbit of the minor planet Eros, and to perturbations by the Sun of the Moon's orbit around Earth. In both cases, the orbits were determined by optical telescope measurements of distances by the parallax principle.

6.19. A development of the dynamical method, for obtaining the astronomical unit with greater accuracy, involves the tracking by radar of a spacecraft in orbit about the Sun. Such a vehicle is essentially a planet whose trajectory is dependent on the gravitational forces of Earth and the Sun. If the spacecraft carries a radio beacon, its trajectory can be determined more precisely than was formerly possible for planets by means of conventional astronomical measurements. The first effort of this type was in connection with the space probe Pioneer V, launched on March 11, 1960, in a solar orbit lying between Earth and Venus. Better results were obtained, however, from the Mariner II probe which approached Venus and ultimately became a satellite of the Sun (§ 10.99). This spacecraft was tracked over a distance of some 60 million kilometers and from its trajectory the astronomical unit was calculated to be in almost exact agreement with the value obtained by radar methods. Just as the astronomical unit or, alternatively, the solar mass can be computed from trajectory observations so, conversely, accurate trajectories can be determined, and midcourse guidance adjustments made, by utilizing solar data.

SOLAR MASS, RADIUS, AND DENSITY

6.20. The mass of the Sun can be estimated from the perturbation of planetary (and other) orbits, as mentioned above. If the astronomical unit is known, however, the solar mass can be derived from Earth's orbital period, P, by utilizing equation (2.26) which can be written as

$$P^2 = \frac{4\pi^2 a^3}{G(M_s + M_e)}, \tag{6.2}$$

where M_s is now the mass of the Sun and M_e is that of Earth. If M_e is neglected in comparison with M_s, it follows that

$$M_s = \frac{4\pi^2 a^3}{GP^2}, \tag{6.3}$$

where a is the semi-major axis of Earth's orbit about the Sun and so may be taken as being equal to the astronomical unit; and G is the universal constant of gravitation defined in § 2.16. If mass is expressed in kilograms, distance in meters, and time in seconds, G is 6.673×10^{-11}. For the revolution of Earth about the Sun, the orbital period, P, is 31.56×10^6 seconds (§ 6.9) and a is 1.496×10^{11} meters; hence, from equation (6.3),

$$M_s = \frac{(4\pi^2)(1.496 \times 10^{11})^3}{(6.673 \times 10^{-11})(31.56 \times 10^6)^2}$$

$$= 1.99 \times 10^{30} \text{ kilograms.}$$

The *metric ton* is defined as 1000 kilograms, i.e., 2204.6 pounds; hence, the solar mass is 1.99×10^{30} kilograms or 1.99×10^{27} metric tons. In comparison, it may be noted that the mass of Earth is 5.98×10^{24} kilograms. The Sun thus has a mass greater than that of Earth by a factor of about 330,000.

6.21. In § 6.11, the distance between Earth and a planet was calculated from the known radius of Earth and the measured parallax angle. The general procedure can be reversed to obtain the radius of the Sun from the known average distance from the Sun to Earth and a determination of the angle subtended at a point on Earth by the Sun's radius. Thus, in Fig. 6.5, R_s is the solar radius, D

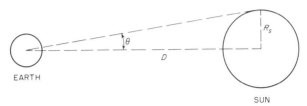

EARTH

SUN

FIG. 6.5.   Angular radius of the Sun from Earth

is the distance of the Sun's center from Earth's surface, and θ is called the *angular radius* of the Sun. The quantity usually quoted is the *angular diameter*, i.e., twice the angular radius. Since the angle θ is small, its value is given in radians by

$$\theta = \frac{R_s}{D}.$$

Consequently, the required solar radius is

$$R_s = D\theta, \qquad\qquad (6.4)$$

where, within the limits of accuracy of the measurements, D may be taken to be equal to the astronomical unit, i.e., 1.496×10^{11} meters.

6.22. The angle θ may be measured directly by means of a suitable telescope but a more accurate procedure is to observe the (transit) time required at noon for the Sun's image, as projected on a screen, for example, to pass a given point (or line) on the screen. The apparent motion of the Sun is, of course, due to the rotation of Earth about its axis. Earth rotates through 360 deg with reference to the Sun in 1 day, i.e., 86,400 seconds; a transit time of 1 second is thus equivalent to an angle of $360/86,400 = 0.004167$ deg. In this manner, the average value of the angular diameter of the Sun is found to be 32.0 min of arc; hence, θ is 16.0 min or 0.267 deg.* Since D is 1.496×10^{11} meters, it follows from equation (6.4) that

$$R_s = (1.496 \times 10^{11})(0.267)(0.0174)$$
$$= 6.96 \times 10^8 \text{ meters,}$$

where 0.0174 is the factor for converting the angle in degrees into radians. The radius of the Sun is therefore 6.96×10^8 meters or 6.96×10^5 kilometers (432,-

---

* The angular diameter of the Sun ranges from 31.5 min in July to 32.5 min in January. Thus, the Sun is closer to Earth during the winter than in summer in the Northern Hemisphere. The lower temperatures in winter are accounted for by the Sun being lower in the sky (cf. § 6.26).

500 miles). The solar radius (or diameter) is thus more than a hundred times that of Earth.

6.23. If the Sun is assumed to be spherical in shape, its volume is $(4/3)(\pi)(6.96 \times 10^8)^3$ cubic meters, i.e., 1.41×10^{33} cubic centimeters. Since the solar mass is 1.99×10^{30} kilograms, i.e., 1.99×10^{33} grams, the average density of the Sun is given by

$$\text{Average solar density} = \frac{1.99 \times 10^{33}}{1.41 \times 10^{33}}$$

$$= 1.41 \text{ grams per cubic centimeter.}$$

This may be compared with 5.52 grams per cubic centimeter for the mean density of Earth. The reason for the lower density of the Sun is the very much larger proportion of the light element hydrogen and, correspondingly, the smaller proportion of the heavier elements, including metals.

6.24. As a consequence of the lower solar density, the gravitational acceleration at the Sun's surface is not so much larger than that on Earth as the ratio of the masses would indicate, at first sight. According to equation (2.6), the acceleration due to the Sun's gravity is equal to GM_s/R_s^2; hence, the value at the solar surface, in meters per second per second, is obtained by setting G equal to 6.673×10^{-11}, M_s to 1.99×10^{30}, and R_s to 6.96×10^8; thus

$$\text{Acceleration} = \frac{(6.673 \times 10^{-11})(1.99 \times 10^{30})}{(6.96 \times 10^8)^2}$$

$$= 274 \text{ meters per second per second,}$$

compared with 9.83 meters per second per second at Earth's surface. The characteristic properties of the Sun are summarized for convenience in Table 6.1.

THE SOLAR CONSTANT

6.25. The problem of the apparent temperature of the Sun's surface will be treated in detail later, but one way in which this property can be calculated will be described here. The *solar constant,* i.e., the total amount of energy received from the Sun on a surface perpendicular to the Sun's rays 1 square centimeter in area in 1 minute at Earth's distance, has been determined experimentally by changing the energy into heat and measuring the accompanying rise in temperature of a body of known mass and specific heat.

6.26. The importance of the qualification that the surface must be perpendicular to the Sun's rays will be evident from a comparison of Fig. 6.6, I and II. In Fig. 6.6, I the rays fall perpendicularly on a 1-centimeter square surface, but in Fig. 6.6, II the same radiation, with a cross-sectional area of 1 square centimeter, is seen to fall on a larger area. Hence, the energy received from the Sun per unit area in a specified time is less in case II than it is in case I. It is this difference which explains why a given area of Earth's surface receives more

TABLE 6.1   CHARACTERISTIC PROPERTIES OF THE SUN

Distance from Sun to Earth (Astronomical Unit)	149,599,000 kilometers 92,950,000 miles
Solar parallax	8.795 sec
Angular diameter (average)	32.0 min
Radius (average)	6.96×10^8 meters 696,000 kilometers 432,500 miles
Mass	1.99×10^{30} kilograms 1.99×10^{27} metric tons
Density (average)	1.41 grams per cubic centimeter
Gravitational acceleration	274 meters per sec per sec 900 feet per sec per sec
Rotational period (approximate)	25.4 days at equator 33 days at 75° (N or S) latitude

solar energy is summer when the Sun is high in the heavens than it does in winter when the Sun is low in the sky. A secondary effect which tends to accentuate the difference is absorption of solar radiation by the atmosphere; the depth of atmosphere which the radiation must pass through before reaching Earth's surface is greater when the Sun is low (winter) than when it is high (summer).

6.27. Solar energy is received above Earth's atmosphere in the form of a

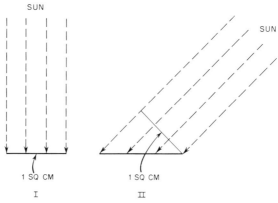

FIG. 6.6.   Solar radiation and orientation of surface: (I) perpendicular, (II) oblique

mixture of different radiations, including infrared, visible, and ultraviolet (Fig. 6.7).* A black surface has the ability to absorb these radiations almost completely and to convert their energy into heat. Hence, if a body with a blackened surface is exposed to the Sun, the increase in temperature is a measure of the

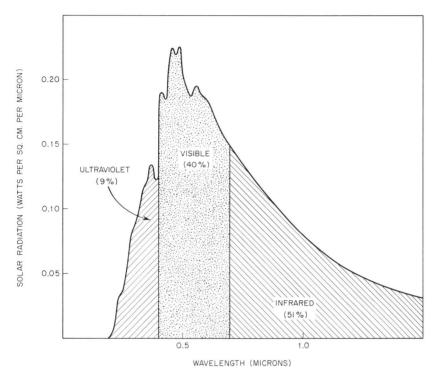

FIG. 6.7.　Solar radiation intensity above the atmosphere at Earth's distance from the Sun (after F. S. Johnson and J. C. New)

total energy in the solar radiation falling on the surface. From the known area of the exposed surface and the time of exposure, the solar constant can be evaluated after making appropriate corrections.

6.28. Three general procedures have been employed to determine the temperature increase. In the *thermocouple* (or *thermopile*) *method*, the (hot) junctions of a thermocouple system (§ 3.236) are attached to a blackened disc, while the other (cold) junctions are maintained at a constant temperature. The increase in temperature of the hot junctions is obtained from the measured potential difference (or voltage) developed between the two sets of junctions. In a second method, used in the *pyroheliometer*,† the actual rise in tempera-

* For an explanation of the significance of ultraviolet, infrared, etc., as applied to radiation, see § 6.45 *et seq.*

† From the Greek, *pyr, pyros,* meaning "fire" or "heat," and *helios,* "Sun."

ture of a blackened silver disc is observed by means of a sensitive thermometer. Alternatively, the heat absorbed may be calculated from the increase in temperature of water flowing past the disc at a known rate. Finally, in the *bolometer method*, the temperature increase of a blackened strip of platinum exposed to the Sun's radiations is evaluated from the accompanying increase in electrical resistance. The latter can be determined with considerable accuracy by comparison with a similar strip of platinum that has been protected from the radiation.

6.29. The measurements described above are generally made on Earth's surface and they must be corrected for the solar radiation that has been absorbed (or reflected) during its passage through the atmosphere. Unfortunately, this quantity is difficult to determine accurately because some of the radiations from the Sun, e.g., in the ultraviolet and part of the infrared, are absorbed almost completely, and so very little reaches Earth's surface. On the other hand, when the atmosphere is clear, only a small proportion of the visible radiation is absorbed. Strictly speaking, therefore, absorption measurements are required over the whole range of solar radiation wavelengths.

6.30. Since only a small proportion of the Sun's radiation above the atmosphere is in the form of ultraviolet (cf. Fig. 6.7), a reasonably satisfactory indication of the absorption correction may be obtained in the following manner. The solar radiation, consisting almost entirely of the visible and part of the infrared, is measured at Earth's surface on a clear day when the Sun is directly overhead, i.e., at point *A* in Fig. 6.8, and again when the Sun is lower in the sky, i.e., at *B*. In the latter case, more radiation is absorbed because it travels through a greater thickness of the atmosphere before reaching the observation point, *P*. From the ratio of the two sets of measurements, an estimate can be made of the atmospheric absorption and an appropriate correction can be derived.

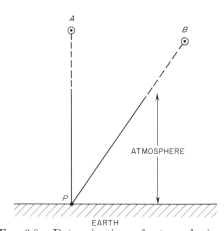

FIG. 6.8. Determination of atmospheric absorption of solar radiation

6.31. Apart from the uncertainty in estimating the atmospheric absorption, there is a possibility that the solar constant is not strictly constant but varies to some extent. It is known, for example, that certain features of the Sun's activity, e.g., sunspots, flares, prominences, etc., vary from year to year, and so it would not be surprising if there were some changes in the solar energy reaching Earth. It is not possible, therefore, to state the magnitude of the solar constant with any degree of precision. The value accepted at the present time, namely, 2.00 calories per square centimeter per minute, at a distance of 1 astronomical unit from the Sun, is believed to represent a reasonably good average, although it is possible that small changes occur from time to time.*

6.32. Since 1 calorie is equivalent to 4.18×10^7 ergs and 1 watt represents an energy rate of 10^7 ergs per second, i.e., 1 calorie per second is equal to 4.18 watts, alternative values of the solar constant are 8.36×10^7 ergs per square centimeter per minute or 1.39×10^6 ergs per square centimeter per second or 0.139 watt per square centimeter.

6.33. More accurate information concerning the solar constant and especially of its variation over a number of years would be of great value in the study of the Sun's behavior as well as of Earth-Sun relationships. It might possibly contribute to long-range weather prediction and it would throw light on the little understood problem of the development of glacial periods. It appears that the only way in which such reliable data could be obtained is by measurements in space above Earth's atmosphere. A station on the Moon would appear to be ideal for this purpose. The determination of the solar constant and its variation with time may represent one of the important future contributions of space science.

THE SOLAR SURFACE TEMPERATURE

6.34. If the Sun's radiation is emitted uniformly in all directions, then each square centimeter of a spherical surface of area $4\pi a^2$ around the Sun, where a is the Earth's distance from the Sun, i.e., the astronomical unit, will receive 2.00 calories of energy per minute. Since a is 1.496×10^{11} meters, i.e., 1.496×10^{13} centimeters, the total radiation received from the Sun over the whole area $4\pi a^2$ is $(4\pi)(1.496 \times 10^{13})^2(2.00) = 5.62 \times 10^{27}$ calories per minute; all of this energy is radiated from the Sun's surface. The radius of the Sun is 6.96×10^8 meters, i.e., 6.96×10^{10} centimeters, and so its surface area is $(4\pi)(6.96 \times 10^{10})^2 = 6.09 \times 10^{22}$ square centimeters. The rate of energy emission from the Sun is therefore

$$\text{Rate of solar energy emission} = \frac{5.62 \times 10^{27}}{6.09 \times 10^{22}}$$
$$= 9.23 \times 10^4 \text{ calories per sq cm per minute}$$
$$= 1.54 \times 10^3 \text{ calories per sq cm per second.}$$

6.35. According to the radiation law derived by the Austrian physicists Josef Stefan (1879) from experiments and by Ludwig Boltzmann (1884) from

---

* There is evidence of two types of significant periodic variations of solar energy in the past: (a) long-period changes occurring at intervals of several hundred million years, and (b) cyclic variations of a few tens of thousands of years, corresponding to glacial periods (ice ages).

theory, the total outward rate of energy emission by a perfect (or ideal) radiator (cf. § 6.61) is

$$E = 1.38 \times 10^{-12} \, T^4 \text{ calories per sq cm per second,} \qquad (6.5)$$

where T is the temperature of the radiating surface on the absolute (Kelvin) scale, as defined in § 3.19, footnote. For the Sun, E is 1.54×10^3 in the units given; hence,

$$T = \left(\frac{E}{1.38 \times 10^{-12}} \right)^{0 \cdot 25}$$

$$= \left(\frac{1.54 \times 10^3}{1.38 \times 10^{-12}} \right)^{0 \cdot 25}$$

$$= 5800° \text{ Kelvin, i.e., } 5800° \text{ K.}$$

Starting from the experimental value of the solar constant, it is thus found that the temperature of the radiating surface of the Sun is 5800°K, i.e., 5530°C or nearly 10,000°F. It will be seen shortly that this is a kind of average temperature because the solar radiation that reaches Earth is not emitted from a single surface of the Sun but rather from a layer a few hundred kilometers in depth.

6.36. At a temperature of about 5500°C (or 10,000°F), all known substances are converted into gases; no solids or liquids can exist at such high temperatures. Since other portions of the Sun are even hotter than the surface, it must be concluded that the Sun is completely gaseous in nature. In view of the average density of 1.41 grams per cubic centimeter, it is apparent that, in the solar interior, at least, the gases are under very high pressures; they are, nevertheless, still gases because of the extremely high temperatures. It has been estimated that, in the center of the Sun where its energy originates, the gases are about a hundred times as dense as water under normal terrestrial conditions (§ 6.198).

THE SOLAR ATMOSPHERE

6.37. The Sun is composed of a number of concentric regions, but all that can be observed by the eye or detected with instruments is the outermost envelope, sometimes referred to as the solar atmosphere. Nothing is known from direct observation about the Sun's interior; nevertheless, some inferences concerning its structure are possible, as will be seen in due course. The portion of the Sun that is visible or can be photographed under normal conditions is called the *photosphere* (Greek, *photos*, "light"). It is from this relatively thin part of the Sun's atmosphere, some 400 kilometers (250 miles) in depth, that nearly all of the heat and light reaching Earth is radiated. The radius of the Sun given in § 6.22 is actually the outer radius of the photosphere.

6.38. Examination of a photograph of the Sun's disc, taken with film having a sensitivity similar to that of the human eye, shows that the photosphere is somewhat darker at the edges, i.e., at the *limb*, than in the center (Fig. 6.9). The significance of the phenomenon of *limb darkening*, as it is called, may

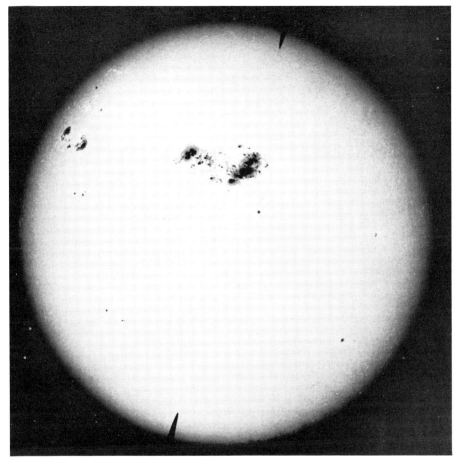

Fig. 6.9. Photograph of the Sun showing limb darkening and sunspots; an exceptionally large group of spots is seen at the top (south in the telescope image). (*Mount
Wilson and Palomar Observatories*)

be explained by the aid of Fig. 6.10, which is drawn out of proportion in order
to clarify the point at issue. An observer, e.g., a telescope or camera, on Earth
looking directly at the Sun can see a certain distance into the photosphere, as
indicated at A. Radiation coming from the lower levels cannot be seen because
of absorption in its passage through the photosphere. For radiation from the
region of the limb at B to traverse the same distance through the photosphere,
it must originate at a higher level, i.e., farther from the Sun's center, than A.
The fact that the limb appears to be darker means that the temperature at B
is lower than at A.

6.39. It is to be concluded, therefore, that the temperature of the photosphere
is not uniform, but decreases with increasing altitude. It has been estimated

that, at a depth of roughly 300 kilometers (200 miles) from the surface of the photosphere, which is about the lowest level from which direct solar radiation

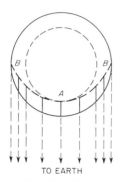

FIG. 6.10. Significance of darkening of the Sun's limb

can reach Earth, the temperature is close to 7500°K, i.e., 7230°C or 13,000°F, and it decreases steadily to approximately 4700°K, i.e., 4430°C or 7950°F, near the outer surface of the photosphere. Hence, the apparent surface temperature of 5800°K calculated from the solar constant is an average value, as already indicated.

6.40. At its lower depths, the photosphere blends into an opaque region known as the convective zone of the Sun (§ 6.205), and its upper layers merge into the *chromosphere,* an essentially transparent region of lower density extending beyond the photosphere. Very little of the Sun's radiation comes directly from the chromosphere which, being transparent, transmits nearly all the radiation originating in the photosphere. As a general rule, the chromosphere is visible only during a total eclipse of the Sun, when the photosphere is completely hidden by the Moon. Just before the instant of totality, the chromosphere is seen as a thin reddish crescent (or arc); the chromosphere (Greek, *chroma,* "color") owes its name to the bright color. Under normal conditions, the intense visible light from the photosphere makes it impossible to observe the much weaker radiation from the chromosphere. By means of special techniques, however, the chromosphere can be studied at times other than solar eclipses (§ 6.42).

6.41. The total thickness of the chromosphere is some 10,000 to 16,000 kilometers (6000 to 10,000 miles), depending on circumstances. Its temperature, unlike that of the photosphere, increases in the outward direction, from about 4700°K at its lowest level, where it adjoins the photosphere, to roughly 1,000,000°K (or 1,800,000°F) in its upper regions. The reason for the increase in temperature of the chromosphere with altitude is one of the major unsolved problems of solar physics.

6.42. Beyond the chromosphere lies the *corona* (Latin, *corona;* Greek, *korone,* "crown"); during a total eclipse of the Sun it is visible as a whitish halo surrounding the solar disc and extending outward for many millions of miles. The intensity of the radiation coming directly from the corona is very feeble, even less than that from the chromosphere; hence, the Sun's disc must be obscured, as in a total eclipse, before the corona can be observed. The invention of the *coronagraph,* a telescope with a polished central cone that reflects radiation from the photosphere, has made it possible to study the brighter, inner parts of the corona at other times. The best results are obtained when Earth's atmosphere is clear because light scattered from dust particles interferes with the faint light from the corona. Some observations have therefore been made from a coronagraph carried to high altitudes by a balloon or a satellite.

6.43. The temperatures of the corona are generally around **1,000,000°K**, although there appear to be regions in which they are much higher. The density is so extremely low, however, that the total energy content and the rate at which energy is radiated from coronal material are very small, compared with the energy coming from the photosphere.

6.44. The foregoing brief review has been presented in order to provide a general background for a more complete discussion of the structure of the Sun's atmosphere. But before undertaking a more detailed description of the three more-or-less independent regions mentioned above, it is necessary to consider the nature of the electromagnetic radiations whereby energy can be transferred from one body to another, even in a vacuum, and the origin of spectra. These topics have an important bearing on the interpretation of the phenomena occurring in the Sun.

ELECTROMAGNETIC RADIATIONS

SPECTRUM OF WHITE LIGHT

6.45. By passing a beam of sunlight through a glass prism, Isaac Newton in 1672 showed that white light could be spread out into a range (or spectrum) of colors, from red, through orange, yellow, green, and blue to violet (Fig. 6.11).

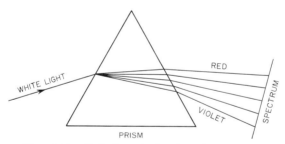

FIG. 6.11.   Splitting of white light by a prism

This was the first experimental indication that white light is composite in nature.* More than a century later, about the year 1800, the German-born musician turned astronomer William Herschel, then living in England, showed that invisible rays, capable of increasing the temperature of a thermometer, were present in sunlight just beyond the red end of the spectrum. This is now referred to as *infrared radiation* (Latin, *infra*, "below"). Then, in 1802, the

---

* A rainbow is equally good proof that white sunlight is actually a mixture of several colors.

English physicist William H. Wollaston proved that there were radiations outside the violet end of the visible spectrum which, like visible light, are capable of darkening silver chloride.* These radiations are now called *ultraviolet rays*.

6.46. By the early 1800's, therefore, it was realized that invisible radiations were present in sunlight, in addition to the visible rays ranging in color from red to violet. At about the same time, there was a revival of the theory, originally developed in the seventeenth century, that light is a form of wave motion. The difference between the various radiations was then ascribed to differences in their wavelengths, and this view is accepted at the present time. In the visible spectrum, the wavelength increases continuously from violet to red; infrared rays have even longer wavelengths whereas the wavelengths of ultraviolet radiation is shorter than that of the shortest visible (violet) light. It is because the waves of different wavelength are bent (or refracted) to different extents in their passage through matter that a transparent prism of glass or other material is able to split up white light into its constituent radiations, i.e., into its spectrum.

ELECTROMAGNETIC WAVES

6.47. A significant advance in the understanding of the nature of light and related radiations came in 1864 from the eminent Scottish mathematician James Clerk Maxwell. It was well known at the time that electrical and magnetic phenomena were closely related, e.g., an electric current is always associated with a magnetic field and a changing magnetic field can produce an electric current. Maxwell showed that certain electrical disturbances should result in the emission of electric waves and that these waves must be accompanied by magnetic waves of the same length. Physically, the terms electric waves and magnetic waves imply the existence of electric and magnetic fields, respectively, whose intensities vary periodically with distance (and time) in the same manner as the amplitude of a wave (cf. § 4.150). The wavelength is then the distance between successive points at which the variation in intensity repeats itself (Fig. 4.42).

6.48. The combination of electric and magnetic field variations constitutes an *electromagnetic wave;* such a wave can be transmitted through a vacuum and does not require the presence of a material medium. By making use of both theoretical considerations and experimental data, Maxwell found that all electromagnetic waves, no matter what their origin or wavelength, should be propagated through a vacuum with the same velocity, namely, the velocity of light. Consequently, he inferred that light is itself an electromagnetic wave phenomenon, i.e., a form of electromagnetic radiation.

6.49. Although no electromagnetic waves other than visible light and the adjacent infrared and ultraviolet radiations were known to Maxwell, he real-

---

* The darkening of silver chloride (or bromide) by visible and other radiations is the basis of photography.

ized that such radiations, with shorter and longer wavelengths, might be discovered. This expectation was fulfilled by Heinrich R. Hertz in Germany in
1887 when he produced the first radio waves by means of an oscillating electrical discharge obtained from an induction coil. The speed of propagation of these
waves is the same as the velocity of light, but their wavelength is considerably longer than that of visible light, e.g., on the order of meters as compared
with less than a thousandth part of a millimeter. Then, in 1895, the German
physicist W. C. Röntgen discovered the highly penetrating radiation he called
X-rays, and in 1900 Pierre Villard in France found that somewhat similar
radiations, now known as *gamma rays,* are emitted by certain radioactive substances. Soon afterward it was established that both X-rays and gamma rays
are electromagnetic radiations of very short wavelength, shorter than those of
ultraviolet rays.

The Electromagnetic Spectrum

6.50. The electromagnetic spectrum (or spread) of radiations has been found
to extend continuously from short gamma rays, of wavelength 10^{-11} centimeter
or less, to long radio waves, of 10^5 centimeters or more, as depicted in Fig. 6.12.

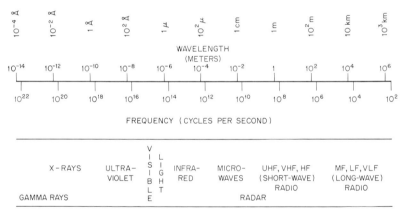

Fig. 6.12. The electromagnetic spectrum

It is seen that visible light occupies a very limited region of wavelengths, from
about 3.85×10^{-5} to 7.60×10^{-5} centimeter. Thus, by far the major part of
the electromagnetic spectrum consists of radiations that cannot be seen and
can be detected only by means of suitable instruments.

6.51. It should be understood that there is no sharp demarcation, but a
continuous gradation, between electromagnetic waves of the different types
indicated in Fig. 6.12. Thus, the shorter radio waves are indistinguishable from
the longer infrared rays, and the longer wavelength (*soft*) X-rays are identical
with the shorter ultraviolet radiation. Furthermore, *hard* (short wavelength)

X-rays and gamma rays frequently overlap; the name X-ray is commonly used, however, to describe the radiations when they originate from electronic energy transitions or interactions in which the electron is not annihilated. The X-rays accompanying the electrical interaction of free electrons with other charged particles, e.g., atomic nuclei, are frequently referred to as *bremsstrahlung* (German, "braking radiation"); such X-rays can cover a wide range of wavelengths. On the other hand, the term gamma rays is applied when the radiation is produced either in a nuclear reaction, e.g., radioactive decay, or in a process in which matter is annihilated and converted into energy. Because of the different ways in which the radiations originate, it is possible to have X-rays of shorter wavelength than some gamma rays, although the reverse situation, i.e., gamma rays with longer wavelengths, is the more common.

6.52. The properties of radiations comprising the electromagnetic spectrum have been considered above in terms of their wavelengths, but it is equally possible to use the *frequency* as a basis for comparison (§ 4.150). If λ is the wavelength in centimeters of a given electromagnetic radiation and c is the velocity of light in centimeters per second, the corresponding frequency, f, in cycles (or waves) per second is given by

$$f = \frac{c}{\lambda}.$$ (6.6)

Thus, a short wavelength corresponds to a high frequency and a long wavelength to a low frequency. The frequencies in cycles per second for the various wavelengths are indicated in Fig. 6.12.

6.53. Radio and similar radiations are commonly described by either wavelength or frequency; wavelengths are then generally expressed in meters or centimeters, and frequencies in terms of cycles, kilocycles, or megacycles per second (§ 4.150). Electromagnetic radiations in the infrared and shorter wavelength regions are generally identified by their wavelengths rather than their frequencies. In this connection, two units of length are commonly employed. One is the *micron*, i.e., 10^{-6} meter or 10^{-4} centimeter, represented by the symbol μ, which is generally used for infrared radiations (cf. § 5.18); thus, wavelengths in the infrared range from 0.76 micron, the limit of the visible region, to about 100 microns. The other unit is the *angstrom,* indicated by Å, named in honor of the Swedish spectroscopist, A. J. Ångström; it is equal to 10^{-8} centimeter or 10^{-4} micron (1 micron = 10^4 Å). The wavelength limits of visible light given in § 6.50 are thus 3850 to 7600 Å. Conventionally, ultraviolet radiation lies between 3850 and roughly 100 Å, whereas X-rays (and gamma rays) have wavelengths less than about 100 Å. X-rays and gamma rays are often characterized by the corresponding energies, as will be explained in § 6.75.

Spectrographic Instruments

6.54. An instrument for the visual examination of the spectrum of the Sun (or other body) is called a *spectroscope;* if it is modified in such a manner as to permit a photographic record of the spectrum to be obtained, as is generally the case in solar studies, the device is called a *spectrograph*. A telescope is used to form a concentrated image of the Sun and the light from this image passes through a narrow slit and a collimating lens or mirror system to produce a thin well-defined parallel (collimated) beam. In the spectrograph, this beam is spread out into the characteristic solar spectrum. The lines can be identified by comparison with the spectra of known terrestrial sources as obtained in the laboratory. There are various relationships among the wavelengths (or frequencies) of the lines of a given element, and sometimes among different elements, that facilitate the identification. In a complex spectrum, such as that of the Sun's photosphere, the procedure is a lengthy one and is still incomplete.

6.55. Two general types of spectrograph are in use for solar studies. The *prism spectrograph* is based on essentially the same basic principle as was used by Newton to demonstrate the composite nature of white light (cf. Fig. 6.11). The narrow (collimated) beam of light from the telescope falls onto a prism (or system of prisms) which refracts and disperses, i.e., spreads out, the light to produce a spectrum. By means of a suitable lens or mirror system, the spectrum is focused onto a photographic plate and recorded. For the study of spectra in the visual range, glass lenses and prisms can be used. But the transmission of radiation by ordinary glass begins to fall off at wavelengths less than about 3800 Å, and so quartz is employed for observations in the ultraviolet; this material is transparent down to roughly 1800 Å. For still shorter wavelengths, down to 1100 Å, lithium fluoride may be used. In infrared spectrographs, the prisms are generally made of rock salt (sodium chloride).

6.56. A desirable feature of a spectrograph is a high *resolving power* (or *resolution*), that is, the ability to produce good separation of lines having only slightly different wavelengths. In the prism spectrograph, increased resolution is obtained by increasing the size of the prism, but beyond a certain point this becomes prohibitively expensive. Consequently, preference is now being given to *grating spectrographs* in which the prism is replaced by a diffraction grating, made by engraving a large number of extremely thin parallel grooves on a highly polished metal surface. Light falling on the grating is reflected back in the form of a spectrum which can be focused and photographed in the usual manner. The number of grooves (or lines) per unit length of a grating depends to some extent on the region of the spectrum for which the grating is to be used. For radiations with wavelengths in the range from about 1500 Å (ultraviolet) to 10,000 Å (infrared), the gratings commonly have 10,000 to 30,000 lines per inch. By proper choice of the angle at which the radiation is incident, grating spectrographs can be employed over a considerable range of wavelengths. For a given wavelength and angle, the resolving power of the spectrograph is proportional to the total number of lines on the particular grating being used. For observations in the hard X-ray region, crystals serve as natural diffraction gratings.

6.57. When spectral studies are made from above the atmosphere by means of sounding rockets and recovery of the instruments is possible, the results are recorded photographically. But when it is desirable or necessary, e.g., when a satellite is the base of observation, to transmit the data by telemetry, the spectrum is continuously scanned by means of a suitable photomultiplier system. This serves as a transducer (§ 4.149) for converting radiations of various wavelengths into electrical signals which can be recorded on tape and transmitted to Earth upon command. Ultraviolet, X-rays, and gamma rays are capable of producing ionization in a gas, and this property has been utilized in ionization chambers, Geiger counters, and similar devices for recording the intensities of radiations of short wavelength. Other instruments, such as scintillometers and solid-state detectors, have been developed for the measurement of X-rays and gamma rays, but they have not been used extensively in spacecraft or sounding rockets.

RADIATION AND TEMPERATURE

6.58. All bodies emit radiations, their nature and intensity depending on the temperature and physical state of the body. These radiations arise from various types of electronic, atomic (or nuclear), or molecular motions within the material. At low temperatures, the quantity of radiation is so small as to be undetectable except with special instruments. Even at ordinary temperatures, materials which are invisible in the dark can be distinguished by the infrared radiation they emit; this is the basis of devices used for taking photographs in the absence of visible light. As the temperature of a material is raised, it may still be invisible in the dark, that is to say, it does not emit visible radiation, but the amount of infrared energy is increased. This is indicated by the warmth that can be felt at a distance. At about $1000°K$, i.e., $730°C$ or $1350°F$, a heated metal will begin to exhibit a red glow, indicating that it is emitting visible radiations, mainly those toward the red (longer wavelength) end of the spectrum.

6.59. As a result of a further increase in temperature, there is an accompanying increase in the rate at which energy is radiated, as is evident from the greater intensity of the light and heat emitted. Furthermore, the wavelengths extend to shorter values, as shown by the development of orange and yellow colors. Eventually, as the temperature approaches $3000°K$ ($2700°C$ or $4900°F$), the heated substance appears almost white, indicating that nearly all the colors of the visible spectrum are being produced, as well as the infrared radiation detected as heat. Although it is not obvious, there is also a significant amount of energy emission in the ultraviolet region of the electromagnetic spectrum.

6.60. There are two general conclusions to be drawn from the foregoing well-known facts. First, as the temperature increases, the rate at which energy is radiated by a given body of matter also increases; this is, of course, in agreement with the Stefan-Boltzmann law expressed by equation (6.5). Second, with increasing temperature, the radiation emitted extends farther and farther into regions of shorter wavelength, i.e., toward the violet, ultraviolet, and beyond, and also to longer (infrared) wavelengths, judging from the increased rate at which energy is radiated as heat. Both of these observed phenomena have been covered in a quantitative manner by the equation derived by the German physicist Max Planck in 1900, on the basis of the quantum theory of electromagnetic radiation (§ 6.74).

BLACK-BODY RADIATION

6.61. From Planck's equation it is possible to compute the rate at which a unit area of a body at a given temperature emits radiation energy at any specified wavelength. The results are applicable, however, only to an ideal (or perfect) emitter and absorber of radiation. This is called a *black body* because the nearest practical approach is a body that is completely black at ordinary temperatures. An ideal black body has the capacity to absorb 100 percent of the electromagnetic radiation falling upon it; since it reflects no radiation, visible or invisible, it is perfectly black.

6.62. The results of calculations utilizing the Planck equation are plotted in Fig. 6.13. Each curve corresponds to a particular temperature and indicates how the rate of emission of radiation energy, i.e., the *radiant power*, of a black body varies with the wavelength of the radiation. The area under any curve represents the total radiant power, that is, the total rate of emission of electromagnetic radiation of all wavelengths, at the given temperature. It is seen that the qualitative empirical conclusions stated above are in agreement with the results of Planck's theoretical treatment. Both the rate of radiation emission and and the range of wavelengths emitted increase with the temperature of a (black) body. It is of interest to note that the Stefan-Boltzmann law also follows directly from Planck's equation (see § 6.218).

SOLAR SURFACE TEMPERATURE

6.63. The curves in Fig. 6.13 provide various means for estimating the apparent surface temperature of the Sun (or of other celestial bodies). First, by combining a spectroscope with a device for measuring radiation energy, e.g., a bolometer or a photoelectric cell, the rate of energy emission can be determined at specific wavelengths over a range of values. It is then possible to plot a curve of the measured radiant power as a function of wavelength. Assuming that the photosphere behaves as a black body, the solar surface temperature can be estimated by comparison of the experimental curve with the theoretical curves in Fig. 6.13, in order to find the best match. The result obtained in this manner depends to some extent on the particular range of wavelengths chosen for the measurements. For the wavelength range from about 3000 Å (near ultraviolet) to 25,000 Å, i.e., 2.5 microns, the variation of the Sun's radiant power with wavelength corresponds fairly well to a black-body temperature of

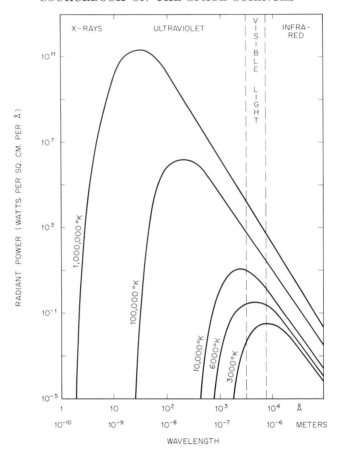

FIG. 6.13.   Energy distribution from a black body at various temperatures derived from the Planck equation

6000°K. This is in good agreement with that derived in § 6.35, namely, 5800°K, from the Stefan-Boltzmann equation and the solar constant.

6.64. Electromagnetic radiations of wavelength less than about 3000 Å are completely absorbed by Earth's atmosphere and were not included in the measurements referred to above. To study the Sun's radiation in the low wavelength region, it is necessary to make observations above the atmosphere and this has been achieved, so far to a limited extent, by the use of sounding rockets and satellites. Down to about 1500 Å, the radiation intensity is found to be roughly equivalent to a black body at 4500° K, but at shorter wavelengths higher temperatures are indicated because radiation is now being received from the chromosphere and corona.

6.65. A modification of the procedure in § 6.63 is to determine the radiant power within a narrow range about a particular wavelength and then to calculate the corresponding black-body temperature from the Planck equation. The result is called the *brightness temperature* for the particular wavelength (§ 6.220). This method for deriving surface temperatures has been applied to the Sun and also to the Moon and the planets, as will be seen in Chapters 9, 10, and 11. Because of their low surface temperatures, radiations from the Moon and planets are determined in the infrared region, where the radiant power is generally largest, or in the radio-frequency range where measurements are relatively simple.

6.66. Brightness temperatures of the Sun are about 5000°K for infrared radiation and roughly 6000°K for short (1 centimeter) radio waves (§ 6.175). The variations in the apparent temperatures arise partly because the radiations being measured do not always come from the same level in the solar atmosphere, and partly as a result of departure of the Sun from perfect black-body behavior.* In fact, since its density is so low, it would be surprising if the photosphere radiated as a black body. Consequently, it would be largely fortuitous if the rate of energy emission over the whole range of wavelengths was in agreement with that of a black body at a single temperature. Nevertheless, it is evident that 6000°K (5700°C or 10,300°F) is a good approximation to the average temperature of the photosphere.

6.67. Another method of utilizing Fig. 6.13 or the equivalent Planck equation to estimate the Sun's temperature is based on the form of the radiation distribution curves. It is seen that each curve in the figure exhibits a maximum and with increasing temperature this maximum moves toward shorter wavelengths; the mathematical relationship between the wavelength, λ_m, at which the radiant power is a maximum, and the black-body temperature is found from Planck's equation to be

$$\lambda_m = \frac{2.90 \times 10^7}{T}, \tag{6.7}$$

where the wavelength is in angstroms and the temperature, T, in degrees Kelvin. The relationship, known as *Wien's displacement law,* was derived by Wilhelm Wien in Germany in 1894, prior to the development of Planck's quantum theory. Observations show that the wavelength at which the solar radiant power is a maximum is close to 4700 Å; it follows, therefore, from equation (6.7) that the equivalent black-body temperature is

$$T = \frac{2.90 \times 10^7}{4700} = 6200°K.$$

This result is in general agreement with those derived earlier for the apparent surface (photosphere) temperature of the Sun.

---

* A distinction is made between the *kinetic temperature,* determined by the kinetic energy of the particles present, e.g., atoms, nuclei, ions, etc., and the *radiation temperature,* which is that computed from Planck's equation from the observed rate of radiation energy emission. For a black body, the two temperatures would be identical.

CONTINUOUS AND LINE SPECTRA

6.68. An examination of the electromagnetic radiations from a heated body by spectroscopic techniques shows that the resulting spectra fall into two broad categories, namely, continuous spectra and line spectra. The so-called band spectra produced by molecules actually consist of series of closely spaced lines that look like bands. In *continuous spectra*, the intensity varies in a continuous manner with the wavelength (or frequency); the intensity may increase, decrease, or even remain constant, but the changes, if any, are always gradual, never sharp. Heated (incandescent) solids and liquids, e.g., molten metals, and gases at high temperature and pressure emit continuous spectra of electromagnetic radiation.

6.69. Gases at normal or low pressure sometimes produce continuous spectra in a limited wavelength region, but these arise from a special situation to be considered shortly. As a general rule, the radiations from a gas at moderate pressures and temperatures are in the form of a *line spectrum*. The radiant energy is then emitted (and absorbed) only at specific wavelengths, each line in the spectrum corresponding to a particular wavelength (or frequency).

THE FRAUNHOFER SPECTRUM

6.70. Studies of the radiation from the Sun's photosphere indicate a spectrum that is basically continuous, i.e., a *continuum*, but is interspersed by thousands of sharp dark lines of different intensities (Fig. 6.14). These lines were first observed in 1802 by W. H. Wollaston (§ 6.45), but they are called *Fraunhofer lines*, after the Bavarian optician Josef von Fraunhofer who, in 1814, detected over 500 dark lines in the Sun's spectrum. In general, dark lines in a spectrum represent absorption of radiation energy, whereas the common bright lines, at the same wavelengths, are the corresponding emission lines, i.e., where radiation energy is emitted. Under suitable (gaseous) conditions, every element when heated produces a bright line spectrum that is characteristic of the element. At lower temperatures, the element can absorb radiation of exactly the same wavelengths as it emits at higher temperatures. The resulting dark absorption lines in the spectrum are just as characteristic of the element as are the normal bright emission lines.*

6.71. Electromagnetic radiations from the lower, hotter regions of the Sun's photosphere, where it adjoins the opaque convective layer (§ 6.205), are in the form of a continuous spectrum. As this radiation passes through the upper, cooler, and less dense layers of the photosphere and the lower levels of the chromosphere, the elements present absorb some of the radiation at the particular wavelengths corresponding to their normal line spectra. The radiation from the photosphere is thus observed as a bright continuous spectrum interrupted

---

* Some of the dark lines in the solar spectrum are due to absorption in Earth's atmosphere; these are called *telluric lines* (Latin, *tellus,* "Earth').

by the dark Fraunhofer lines. The existence is commonly postulated of a relatively cool "reversing layer," between (or including) the top of the photosphere
and the base of the chromosphere, where the dark lines are formed as a result
of radiation absorption. It is probable, however, that absorption occurs through-

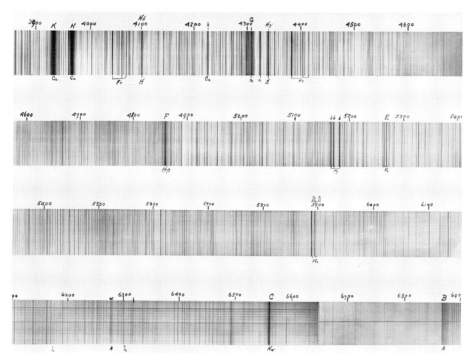

Fig. 6.14.   The Fraunhofer spectrum of the Sun from 3900 to 6900 Å wavelength.
(*Mount Wilson and Palomar Observatories*)

out much of the photosphere, in which the temperature falls gradually outward, as stated in § 6.39, and also in the lower levels of the chromosphere. It is
doubtful, therefore, if there is a well-defined reversing layer in which the
bright, continuous background changes to the dark-line (Fraunhofer) spectrum.

6.72. From the wavelengths at which the Fraunhofer lines appear in the
solar spectrum it is possible to identify the elements responsible for them. The
relative intensity of the dark lines is not a direct indication of the amount of
the given element present in the photosphere. In order to estimate this quantity,
it is necessary to take into consideration the probability that the atom will
absorb radiation of the particular wavelength and this depends on the temperature and other circumstances. These probabilities have been determined in a
number of instances, and from them and the width of the Fraunhofer lines, it
has been possible to make rough estimates of the relative proportions of various

elements in the photosphere. The results are inevitably approximate because radiation absorption occurs at different levels and the dark-line intensities will vary accordingly, quite apart from other considerations.

6.73. Observations in the ultraviolet region of the solar spectrum made by means of spectrographs carried above Earth's atmosphere in rocket-propelled probes indicate that the Fraunhofer lines become less distinct at short wavelengths and that they, and the continuous background, are no longer detectable below about 1850 Å (§ 6.125). The reason for this behavior is not known. At still shorter ultraviolet wavelengths, bright emission lines from elements in the hotter parts of the chromosphere begin to appear in the solar spectrum.

ENERGY AND WAVELENGTH

6.74. In order to interpret more completely the information that can be conveyed by the spectrum of a particular body, the mode of origin of various types of spectra must be considered. In general the emission (or absorption) of electromagnetic radiation is associated with an energy change in the emitter (or absorber).* According to the *quantum theory* of Max Planck (1900), the energy is given out (or taken up) as integral multiples of a definite amount known as a *quantum*. The energy quantum, E, for a particular radiation is related to its frequency, f, by

$$E = hf, \tag{6.8}$$

where h is a universal constant known as *Planck's constant*. In the centimeter-gram-second system of units, which is almost invariably employed in this work, the value of h is 6.625×10^{-27} erg-second. The frequency f may be replaced by c/λ, as given by equation (6.6), so that

$$E = \frac{hc}{\lambda} \quad \text{or} \quad \lambda = \frac{hc}{E}, \tag{6.9}$$

where c is the velocity of light, i.e., 2.998×10^{10} centimeters per second. Since both h and c are known constants, it is possible to write equation (6.9) in the form

$$E(\text{ergs}) = \frac{1.985 \times 10^{-16}}{\lambda(\text{cm})}, \tag{6.10}$$

thus relating the energy in ergs to the wavelength of the corresponding radiation expressed in centimeters. It follows from equation (6.10) that electromagnetic radiations of short wavelength, e.g., gamma rays and X-rays, are associated with large energy changes, whereas long wavelength radiations, e.g., radio waves, represent smaller energy changes.

6.75. It was stated in § 6.53 that gamma rays and X-rays are generally identified by their wavelengths; a common alternative practice, however, is to

---

* The only exceptions are the special cases in which matter (or mass) is converted into energy emitted as gamma rays.

characterize these radiations by the energy of the corresponding quantum. The energy unit employed in this connection is based on the *electron volt*, defined as the energy acquired by an electrically charged particle carrying a unit (electronic) charge when it falls through a potential difference of 1 volt. For the present purpose, more convenient units are the kilo (thousand) electron volt, abbreviated to keV, and the mega (million) electron volt, MeV. The electron volt is equivalent to 1.603×10^{-12} erg, and so it follows from equation (6.10) that

$$E(\text{keV}) = \frac{1.238 \times 10^{-7}}{\lambda(\text{cm})} = \frac{12.38}{\lambda(\text{Å})} \tag{6.11}$$

or

$$E(\text{MeV}) = \frac{1.238 \times 10^{-10}}{\lambda(\text{cm})} = \frac{1.238 \times 10^{-2}}{\lambda(\text{Å})}. \tag{6.12}$$

These expressions relate the energy quantum, in keV or MeV, to the wavelength of the radiation either in centimeters or in angstrom units. Thus, gamma rays or X-rays having a wavelength of 1 Å would be described as 12.38-keV (or 0.01238-MeV) radiation.

6.76. In an extension of the quantum theory, Albert Einstein (1905) suggested that electromagnetic radiations are not only emitted and absorbed as definite energy quanta, but are also transmitted through space as "particles," now called *photons*.* Each photon carries a single quantum of energy which is related to the frequency or wavelength of the radiation by the equations given above.

ENERGY LEVELS AND SPECTRA

6.77. It will be recalled from § 3.162 that all atoms consist of a central nucleus surrounded by a definite number of electrons; this number increases from 1 in the hydrogen atom, the lightest known atom, to 92 in uranium, the heaviest atom found on Earth. The line spectra in the visible, ultraviolet, and X-ray regions arise from energy changes involving the electrons. Gamma rays, on the other hand, are produced by changes in the energy of the nucleus; since these radiations are not of immediate interest, nuclear changes will not be considered here. Nevertheless, the general principles to be described for the relationships between spectra and electronic energy changes are also applicable to energy changes in the nucleus.

6.78. Provided an electron is part of an atom, its energy is restricted to certain particular values; these are referred to as the electronic *energy levels* of

---

* The view that radiation is carried through space by particles might appear to be incompatible with the wave concept of radiation used in earlier parts of this book. It is a basic aspect of modern physics, however, that all particles, including photons, electrons, protons, neutrons, etc., also exhibit wave properties. Thus, electromagnetic radiation can be treated either as particles or as waves, but not simultaneously as both, depending on the phenomenon under consideration.

the given atom. The energy levels are characteristic of the atomic species, i.e., of the given element, but they vary from one element to another. The lowest energy level is called the *ground level* and higher ones are referred to as *excited levels;* the atom is correspondingly said to be in its *ground state* or in an *excited state.* The difference in energy between the two levels (or states) is described as the *excitation energy* for the particular excited level (or state). When an electron is transferred from one energy level to another, a definite energy change is involved, and this will correspond to a spectral line of a specific wavelength, in accordance with equation (6.10). If a gas is heated, some of the electrons will gain energy and be raised to excited levels in the respective atoms; but in a short time the electrons will return to their normal (ground) levels, and in doing so the difference in energy is emitted as radiation of a definite frequency (or wavelength). This is how the bright lines are produced in the spectrum of an atom. Each atomic species (or element) has a different but definite series of electronic energy levels; hence it will yield its own characteristic spectrum from which the element can be identified.

6.79. The situation may be illustrated with the aid of Fig. 6.15, in which the horizontal lines represent the permitted electronic energy levels in a given atomic species. These energy levels are identified by the integers 1, 2, 3, etc., called the *principal quantum numbers* of the atom. Suppose a given electron acquires sufficient (excitation) energy, e.g., as a result of heating the atoms in a gas, to raise it to the fourth quantum level. In a short time, the electron will lose some or all of its excitation energy and will fall back to one of the lower levels, i.e., 3, 2, or 1. Each transition, e.g., $4 \rightarrow 3$, $4 \rightarrow 2$, $4 \rightarrow 1$, will be accompanied by a bright line in the atomic spectrum, its frequency (or wavelength) depending on the difference in energy of the two levels involved in the transition. An electron in level 3 can undergo the transitions $3 \rightarrow 2$ (followed by $2 \rightarrow 1$)

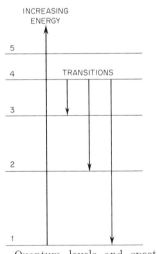

FIG. 6.15.   Quantum levels and spectral lines

and $3 \rightarrow 1$. Since there are several possible electronic energy levels, the number of transitions can be quite large, provided the excitation energy is sufficient for the electrons to be raised to high levels.

6.80. Although only a single electron is involved in an energy transition in a given atom, the spectrum of a particular element, in gaseous form, may consist of many lines corresponding to different electronic energy transitions occurring in the numerous atoms present. The number of lines generally increases with the temperature because excited states of higher and higher energy are occupied by electrons. Furthermore, the spectrum is often rendered complicated by the existence of two or more sublevels of slightly different energies associated with a given principal electronic level. As a result, each expected spectral line is actually a group of closely spaced lines. The splitting of lines in a magnetic field is also an important aspect of many spectra, as will be seen in due course.

6.81. In Fig. 6.15 the energy levels are drawn in such a manner as to indicate that the difference between successive levels decreases as the quantum numbers increase. The energy change from $2 \rightarrow 1$ (or $1 \rightarrow 2$) is thus larger than that from $3 \rightarrow 2$ (or $2 \rightarrow 3$), and so on. This means that electronic transitions involving the ground level, i.e., $1 \rightarrow 2$, $1 \rightarrow 3$, $1 \rightarrow 4$ (or the reverse), are associated with much higher energies than are corresponding transitions from (or to) higher levels, e.g., $2 \rightarrow 3$, $3 \rightarrow 4$, etc. Consequently, the spectral lines associated with transitions of the former type, called *resonance lines*, have shorter wavelengths than do other lines of the same element. The resonance lines of atomic hydrogen, for example, known as the *Lyman series* (T. Lyman, 1914), appear in the ultra-violet region. Their presence in the solar spectrum can thus be detected only by measurements made from sounding rockets or satellites above Earth's atmosphere. The transitions from the second level, i.e., $2 \rightarrow 3$, $2 \rightarrow 4$, $2 \rightarrow 5$, etc., in hydrogen atoms produce the lines of the *Balmer series* (J. J. Balmer, 1885) in the visible region which are readily observed from Earth.

6.82. When the atoms in the cooler regions of the Sun's atmosphere are exposed to the continuous radiation from the photosphere, the electrons absorb energy, just as if they were heated, and are thereby raised from lower to higher energy levels. Thus, an electron in the first energy level might undergo such transitions as $1 \rightarrow 2$, $1 \rightarrow 3$, etc., those in the second level could make the transitions $2 \rightarrow 3$, $2 \rightarrow 4$, and so on. For each transition, radiation having a specific energy quantum, and hence a given wavelength (or frequency), is removed from the continuous spectrum; the absence (or decrease) of that particular radiation thus leaves a dark line on the bright, continuous background. It is in this manner that the Fraunhofer spectrum of the Sun is formed. Since the electronic transitions occur between the same definite energy levels in both emission and absorption, the bright lines in the emission spectrum have exactly the same frequencies (or wavelengths) as the dark lines in the absorption (Fraunhofer) spectrum. Thus, both bright and dark line spectra are equally characteristic of the element producing them and either can serve to identify the element.

6.83. In the formation of the Fraunhofer dark-line spectrum, many of the atomic electrons will have been raised to higher energy levels as the result of the absorption of energy. As seen in § 6.79, such electrons will tend to lose the extra (excitation) energy in a short time and return to their initial, lower energy levels. In doing so, they will produce a bright-line, emission spectrum. Thus, it is to be expected that an emission spectrum will always accompany an absorption spectrum. In this event, it may be wondered why any effect is observed at all. The explanation of this apparent paradox is as follows. Light travels in straight lines through the photosphere and the absorption is observed in the direction from which the continuous radiation is coming. But in the associated emission, the radiation is *scattered,* that is to say, it is emitted more or less equally in all directions. Some is transmitted in the direction of observation, but this is only a small fraction of the total; hence, the darkness of the absorption lines is hardly affected. However, when the photosphere is obscured in a total eclipse of the Sun, the bright-line emission spectrum of the chromosphere becomes visible for a few seconds (§ 6.122).

6.84. In this discussion of the origin of spectra, it has been tacitly assumed that only neutral atoms are involved, i.e., the number of negatively charged electrons is equal to the number of positive charges on the nucleus. Exactly the same arguments are applicable, however, to atoms—other than hydrogen—that have lost one or more electrons, so that they are actually positively charged ions of the respective atoms (§ 3.188). The resulting spectra are frequently referred to as ionized (or stripped) atom spectra. Because the energy levels in the ionized atom are quite different from those in the neutral atom, the spectra are also different. The production of ions requires high energies for the removal of electrons, the ionization energy (or *ionization potential*) increasing with the number of electrons stripped from a given atom. The formation of ionized-atom spectra thus generally implies high temperatures; it is also favored by low pressures because the probability that ions and electrons will recombine to form neutral atoms is then small.

6.85. Since the hydrogen atom has only one electron, the hydrogen ion formed by the loss of this electron does not produce a line spectrum, but a continuous spectrum (§ 6.87). Thus, the element hydrogen yields only a neutral-atom line spectrum. The next element, helium, has two electrons, and so spectra exist for both neutral and singly-ionized atoms. Lithium, with three electrons, can form three spectral series, namely, neutral, singly ionized, and doubly ionized. The common convention is to use the Roman numeral I to designate the neutral-atom spectrum, II for the singly-ionized atom, III for the doubly-ionized atom, and so on. Since the tendency for an atom to lose electrons increases with increasing temperature, the presence of ionized-atom spectra can be used as a means for indicating temperatures. Thus, the emission spectra of highly stripped iron and calcium atoms have been observed in the Sun's corona where temperatures are on the order of a million degrees and the pressures are extremely low. In principle, both bright-line and dark-line spectra of ionized atoms are possible; but the dark-line spectra are uncommon because of the high temperatures which must be attained before stripping of electrons can take place to an appreciable extent.

6.86. Electronic transitions of various types in atoms and also in molecules are capable of producing line spectra ranging from the infrared to the X-ray region of the electromagnetic spectrum. Radiations of longer wavelengths, into the far infrared, can result from transitions in the vibrational and rotational energies of gaseous molecules. Such spectra do not arise from electronic transitions, but from quantum changes in the permitted energy levels of atomic vibrations within molecules and of the rotations of the molecule as a whole. Molecular spectra in the infrared region are commonly observed in absorption, rather than in emission. Absorption by Earth's atmosphere of part of the infrared radiation from the Sun is largely due to the presence of molecules of carbon dioxide, water, and ozone.

Formation of Continuous Spectra

6.87. A continuous emission spectrum (or continuum), such as that from the lower levels of the solar photosphere, can arise in several different ways. One of the simplest means of obtaining a continuous spectrum is to heat an opaque material to a high temperature. In heated solids, liquids, and high-pressure gases, interactions among the closely spaced atoms causes the individual energy levels to be broadened. Instead of sharp lines, the spectrum consists of broad lines having appreciable width. The overlapping of the broad lines then produces an apparently continuous spectrum. In a gas at high pressure, the Doppler frequency shifts, arising from the random motion of the molecules (or atoms), contribute to the line broadening.

6.88. Continuous spectra also result when there are no definite energy levels in one or both of the states involved in a transition. A case of particular interest is that of ionization, in which an electron is completely removed from an atom, and of the reverse process, called *recombination*, involving the return of a free electron to a positive atomic ion. Although the electron occupies a definite energy level when it is attached to the atom, there are no restrictions concerning its energy when it is in the free state, removed from the atom. Consequently, the energy change can have any value provided only that it exceeds the energy required to remove the electron in ionization, or gained by the electron in recombination. These two limiting energies are equal in magnitude for a given ionization-recombination process. Beyond the limit, i.e., below a certain wavelength, therefore, the spectrum—an absorption spectrum for ionization and an emission spectrum for recombination—consists of an infinite number of lines and is thus a continuum.

6.89. In another type of recombination, which involves hydrogen atoms, a free electron attaches itself to a neutral atom to produce a negative ion. Since the free electron has no specific energy level, the spectrum associated with this process is a continuous one. The formation of the negative hydrogen ion, i. e.,

$$H + e^- \rightarrow H^-,$$

results in an emission spectrum that is continuous at wavelengths less than 1.6

microns (infrared), whereas the reverse process, i.e., removal of an electron
from the negative hydrogen ion, yields a corresponding continuous absorption
spectrum.

6.90. A continuous emission spectrum as bremsstrahlung (§ 6.51) also results
when electrons lose energy in the form of radiation as a consequence of electrical
(electrostatic) interaction with other charged particles, e.g., atomic nuclei in
particular. There are no definite energy levels either before or after the interaction and so, in principle, all values of energy change are possible. Transitions of this type, called *free-free transitions* because the electrons are free both
before and after the electrostatic interaction, produce continuous spectra. The
minimum wavelength (or maximum frequency) is determined by the initial
energy of the electrons.*

6.91. The origin of the continuous emission spectrum of the Sun is not well
understood. But in view of the large proportion of hydrogen present (§ 6.101)
it is probable that important contributions are made by the recombination
processes

$$H^+ + e^- \rightarrow H \quad \text{and} \quad H + e^- \rightarrow H^-,$$

both of which might occur in the photosphere. In the lower regions of the
photosphere, and below, where the temperatures are much higher, the reverse
(ionization) reactions would be more probable. These processes would be accompanied by a continuous absorption spectrum, as already indicated. Although there is, on the average, only about one negative hydrogen ion to a
million hydrogen atoms, the presence of these ions is considered to be largely
responsible for the partial opacity of the lower photosphere.

OPTICAL AND RADIO WINDOWS

6.92. Because of its great distance and high temperature, the only conceivable
means of obtaining information about the Sun is by studying its radiations.
Until relatively recently, this work was handicapped by the limited regions of
the solar electromagnetic spectrum that have been accessible. Absorption of
the radiation by Earth's atmosphere takes place over wide ranges of wavelength, so that there are, in fact, only two "windows" through which the Sun
can be observed. Starting with the radiations of short wavelength, at the left of
Fig. 6.12, absorption by the atmosphere is almost complete up to a wavelength
of about 3000 Å in the near ultraviolet spectrum; in other words, Earth's atmosphere is opaque to all radiations of wavelength less than 3000 Å (0.3 micron).
From roughly 0.3 to 1 micron, in the near infrared, is the *visual* (or *optical*)
window where the atmosphere is essentially transparent; in this spectral range
the Sun can be studied by visual or photographic means, especially with the aid

---

* The bremsstrahlung X-rays described in § 6.51 are the result of free-free transitions involving electrons of sufficiently high initial energy. By equation (6.11), the minimum electron energy required to produce radiation of 100 Å, for example, is 0.12 keV.

of a telescope and spectrograph. Prior to the year 1942, all observations of the Sun were made through this window. Between the wavelengths of 1 and 24 microns, in the infrared spectrum, there are some narrow regions in which the atmosphere is transparent (cf. § 5.18), but absorption of radiation by carbon dioxide, water, ozone, and other molecules restricts their range.

6.93. From a wavelength of 24 microns to about 300 microns (0.3 centimeter), covering the far infrared portion of the electromagnetic spectrum, solar radiation is again completely absorbed by the terrestrial atmosphere. This region is followed by the *radio window*, extending to wavelengths of about 15 to 30 meters (20 to 10 megacycles per second) and sometimes beyond, through which observations can be made from Earth (Fig. 6.16). The long wavelength (low

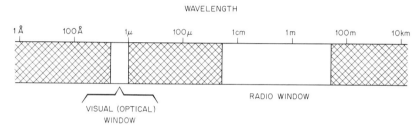

Fig. 6.16.   The visual (optical) and radio windows in the atmosphere

frequency) limit depends upon the condition of the ionosphere (§ 8.155) and since this is variable, so also is the long wavelength limit of the radio window. Solar electromagnetic radiations of wavelengths exceeding about 30 meters are mostly reflected back by the ionosphere and their energy is dispersed in space. Radiations which are absorbed, namely, X-rays, ultraviolet, and infrared, are eventually converted into heat and thus serve to warm Earth's atmosphere.

6.94. Important advances in understanding the nature of the Sun have been made, as will shortly be apparent, by observing it through the optical and radio windows. There are, nevertheless, wide ranges of the spectrum, as is apparent from Fig. 6.16, from which no data have been available until recently. The development of sounding rockets and, in particular, of satellites that permit observation from above the atmosphere, is making it possible to study solar radiation over an extended range of wavelengths. It is in the direction of the shorter wavelengths, i.e., X-rays and the far ultraviolet, in particular, that progress has already been made and more may be expected in the near future.

THE PHOTOSPHERE

GRANULAR STRUCTURE OF PHOTOSPHERE

6.95. The source of the Sun's energy lies in its interior, but what is known about this region is almost entirely speculative, being based largely on theoretical considerations rather than actual observations. Before discussing the interior of the Sun, a further, more detailed, description will be given of the three layers that constitute the solar atmosphere. It is by extrapolating data concerning the exterior regions of the Sun that some understanding has been gained of its interior.

6.96. It has long been known (P. Janssen, 1885) that the undisturbed surface of the photosphere, i.e., where there are no sunspots, has a granular appearance. Observations of the granules require high-resolution photography, i.e., pictures showing relatively small areas with a high degree of definition, and so are difficult to make. Although many telescopes are capable of taking good photographs of the Sun, the turbulence in Earth's atmosphere frequently obscures the details. Satisfactory results have been secured at certain times when the air was exceptionally clear, but some of the most striking pictures of the Sun were obtained with a telescope sent aloft in an unmanned balloon to a height of 80,000 feet. One of these photographs, which shows the granulation very clearly, and also the details of a sunspot (§ 6.103), is reproduced in Fig. 6.17.

6.97. A detailed examination of photographs similar to that in Fig. 6.17 shows that the base of the solar photosphere appears to consist of a large number of bright areas shaped like irregular polygons, roughly 300 to 1500 kilometers (200 to 1000 miles) across, separated by narrow darker regions. The difference in brightness indicates that the lighter areas have a temperature that is, on the average, about 200°C (390°F) higher than that of the darker areas. The bright granules are not stationary, but are continuously changing shape, the mean lifetime being about 4 minutes. A comparison of the Fraunhofer line spectrum of the lighter and darker regions shows a definite Doppler frequency shift, indicating that the regions are in motion relative to each other. The bright granular areas are apparently moving upward, i.e., outward from the Sun's center, while the intergranular regions are moving downward. The relative velocity varies from one granule to another, but an average value is somewhat in excess of 0.8 kilometer (0.5 mile) per second.

6.98. The granular appearance of the Sun's surface is regarded as evidence of convection currents in the opaque region just below the photosphere. Convection, in general, occurs when the lower layer of a fluid (liquid or gas) is heated and expands; as a consequence of the expansion, the density decreases and the heated layer rises through the fluid, under the influence of the gravitational field. At the same time, the upper, unheated layers, which have a higher density, sink through the fluid. The result is a kind of circulatory motion accompanied by the transfer of heat through the fluid from the lower (heated) to the upper (cooler) regions (§ 6.206). The bright granules on the solar surface evidently represent the tops of rising columns of gas which have been heated by energy from the Sun's interior. The darker, intergranular regions are then apparently the cooler portions moving downward.

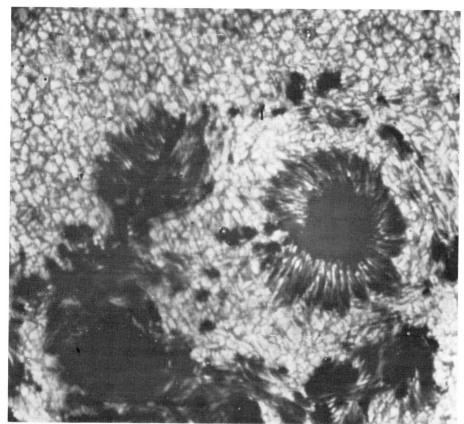

FIG. 6.17.   Portion of Sun's disc photographed from a balloon at an altitude of about 24 kilometers (80,000 feet). (*Project Stratoscope, Princeton University, Princeton, N.J. Sponsored by ONR, NSF, and NASA.*)

ANALYSIS OF FRAUNHOFER SPECTRUM

6.99. An important feature of the photosphere is, of course, the characteristic Fraunhofer spectrum of dark lines. The great majority of the absorption lines arise from electronic transitions in atoms, but there are also indications of the so-called band spectra of some 14 simple molecules (or quasi-molecules) each containing two atoms. Except for the spectra of CN, C_2, and CO, the molecular bands are very faint. As stated earlier, the Fraunhofer lines are characteristic of the elements present in the photosphere and in the lowest layers of the chromosphere.

6.100. A detailed analysis of the spectrum over a period of more than a hundred years has revealed the presence in the solar photosphere of between 60 and 70 of the 90 elements that exist on Earth. It is probable that many, if not all, of the others also occur in the Sun, but for one reason or another they have not yet been identified, e.g., because of the faintness of the lines, their occurrence at inaccessible wavelengths, the complexity of the Fraunhofer spectrum with its more than 25,000 lines, etc. By measuring the intensities of the various spectral lines and taking into consideration the transition probabilities, approximate estimates have been made of the relative amounts of many of the elements in the photosphere.

6.101. A comparison with the known chemical composition of Earth's crust shows that the proportions of the heavier elements, i.e., with atomic weight of 23 (sodium) or more, are much the same in the solar photosphere as on Earth. The lighter elements, hydrogen and helium, however, are much more abundant in the Sun.* In fact roughly 90 percent of the atoms (70 percent by weight) in the photosphere are hydrogen; helium constitutes some 9.9 atomic (28 weight) percent, whereas the heavier elements represent approximately 0.1 atomic (2 weight) percent. The high proportion of hydrogen and helium in the solar atmosphere is related, in some degree, to the strong gravitational field of the Sun which prevents the escape of the light atoms.

DENSITY AND PRESSURE IN PHOTOSPHERE

6.102. The variation in temperature with depth in the photosphere has been estimated from observations of the darkening of the Sun's limb (§ 6.38). Measurements of this type over narrow wavelength ranges in the continuous spectrum and studies of the shapes of Fraunhofer lines, have made it possible to calculate the densities and pressures in the photosphere. The density at the base of the photosphere is about 10^{-7} gram per cubic centimeter, compared with 10^{-3} gram per cubic centimeter for the density of air at Earth's surface, and the pressure is roughly one tenth of the normal pressure of Earth's atmosphere (§ 3.6). The pressure is the product of the mass of gas lying above a unit area of the surface and the gravitational acceleration. Since the force of gravity at the Sun's surface is nearly 30 times as great as that on Earth (§ 6.24), the total mass of gas above a unit area of the photosphere is less by a factor of almost 300 than over an equal area on Earth. But the Sun's surface is so large that the total mass of its atmosphere is about 1.5×10^7 metric tons; this is essentially the mass of the photosphere, since the densities of the chromosphere and corona are extremely low.

SUNSPOTS

6.103. The most obvious features of the disturbed surface of the photosphere are the *sunspots;* their existence had been suspected for some seventeen cen-

---

* The element helium was first identified from solar spectra obtained during a total eclipse in 1868; its name is derived from the Greek word *helios* for Sun. The presence of helium in Earth's atmosphere was not established until 1895.

turies before it was definitely confirmed by telescopic observations made in 1610 by Galileo and others. The spots appear in groups (Fig. 6.9), each spot consisting of a dark central area called the *umbra*, surrounded by a less dark region with a filament-like appearance known as the *penumbra* (cf. Fig. 6.17).*
Not only are sunspots darker than the surrounding surface, but they are also at a lower level. The spots vary in size, generally starting as small spots (or pores), about 2500 kilometers (1500 miles) in diameter, and increasing to a maximum in a week or two; they appear to remain steady for a time and then shrink gradually over a period that may last up to three months or more for large spots. An average spot is about 50,000 kilometers (30,000 miles) across at its maximum, but large spots may attain diameters up to 130,000 kilometers (80,000 miles).

6.104. Sunspots commonly form in groups, and a large group may contain as many as a hundred individual spots of different sizes and may extend for a total distance of some 300,000 kilometers (200,000 miles). On the average, equal numbers of spots appear in the northern and southern solar hemispheres, but at any given time the numbers may be very different. The dark appearance of the spots indicates that their temperature is lower than that of the undisturbed photosphere; thus, the umbra is estimated to be roughly 2000°C (3600°F) cooler than the main surface. Because of the lower temperature, the Fraunhofer spectrum of a sunspot differs from that of the undisturbed areas; absorption lines of molecules are stronger and more common and the atomic lines requiring larger excitation energies are weak.

6.105. A highly significant aspect of sunspots is their association with strong magnetic fields. In the course of laboratory experiments, the Dutch physicist Pieter Zeeman discovered in 1896 what is now known as the *Zeeman effect*. In a magnetic field, a single line in an atomic spectrum will frequently be split into a *multiplet*, as it is called, of closely spaced lines; the separation of the lines in the multiplet is proportional to the strength of the magnetic field. A doubling of some of the spectral lines in sunspots had been observed around the middle of the nineteenth century, but it was not until 1908 that such multiplet formation was interpreted by the astronomer George E. Hale in the United States as indicating the presence of magnetic fields in sunspot areas. The strength of these local fields may be as high as 3000 gauss or more, compared with about 1 gauss for the general magnetic field of the Sun at its surface and an average of roughly 0.5 gauss for Earth's field.†

6.106. Sunspots frequently, although not always, occur in related pairs (or a pair of groups) on a line roughly parallel to the solar equator. The more

---

* The terms *umbra* and *penumbra* (Latin, *umbra,* "shade") are commonly used in connection with shadows and eclipses (§ 9.40). Their use to describe sunspots is misleading, since they are not shadows in any sense.

† The *gauss* is a commonly used unit of magnetic field strength based on the centimeter-gram-second system of measurement.

westerly* (or *preceding*) spot (§ 6.109) is generally the larger of the two; it often appears prior to the other (*following*) spot, persists longer, and lies closer to the equator. When sunspots (or groups) form in pairs, the magnetic fields in the spots (or groups) often act in opposite directions, i.e., they have opposite magnetic polarity. It has been suggested that these *bipolar pairs* are formed when a toroidal (or ring-shaped) magnetic field in the interior of the Sun, roughly parallel to the equator, breaks through the surface. The magnetic field directions in bipolar spots are reversed in the two solar hemispheres; thus, if in one hemisphere the magnetic field in the more westerly of a pair of spots acts generally downward, then the field in the corresponding spot of a pair in the other hemisphere will usually be directed upward. It would appear, therefore, that the toroidal magnetic fields in the two solar hemispheres run in opposite directions. Furthermore, the directions change periodically, as will be seen in § 6.120.

6.107. It is generally accepted at the present time that strong local magnetic fields are the cause of sunspots. Little is known of the nature or source of these fields, but it has been speculated that they run around the solar interior in opposite directions in the northern and southern hemispheres. The production of the magnetic fields is probably associated with a flow of electricity (§ 8.211), and calculations indicate that enormous currents, on the order of 10^{12} amperes, would be required to generate the magnetic fields of large sunspots.

6.108. Because of its high temperature, the convective region of the Sun below the photosphere consists largely of electrically charged positive and negative hydrogen ions and electrons, so that it is, in effect, a plasma (§ 3.197). It is well known that a magnetic field can contain a plasma and prevent its escape; in other words, it is difficult for the charged particles to cross the magnetic field lines. Consequently, the presence of localized magnetic fields near the solar surface will interfere with the normal convection movements, such as those described earlier, that help in the transfer of energy from the Sun's interior to the photosphere. The result is that some of the surface areas in the vicinity of the strong magnetic fields receive heat energy at an appreciably lower rate than do other areas. The cooler regions produced in this manner are the sunspots, and there must presumably be associated areas which are correspondingly hotter than average. In view of this suggested mechanism for the formation of sunspots, it is not surprising that strong local magnetic fields are often detected at the solar surface before sunspots appear in those areas. In addition to these local fields, the Sun also has an overall (or general) magnetic field to which reference will be made later.

6.109. In the early years of the seventeenth century, Galileo had noticed that sunspots appear to move across the face of the Sun from east to west, i.e.,

---

* The directions east and west are used here, and later, in the common astronomical sense, i.e., as they would appear on a sky map held overhead in the Northern Hemisphere. That is to say, in facing the Sun, north is at the top, but east is to the left and west to the right.

from left to right as seen from Earth, and he interpreted the observation correctly as indicating rotation of the Sun in the same direction (Fig. 6.18). The

terms "preceding" and "following"
used in connection with sunspot pairs
arise from this apparent motion. The
view that the Sun rotates about a
north-south axis* has been confirmed
by measurements of the Doppler frequency shift of spectral lines from the
solar limb. As a result of rotation, the
easterly limb of the Sun has a relative
velocity toward Earth whereas the
westerly limb has an equal velocity
away from Earth. This is apparent
from Fig. 6.19 which is supposed to be
a view of the Sun and Earth as seen
from the north pole of the celestial
sphere (§ 9.38). Consequently, the

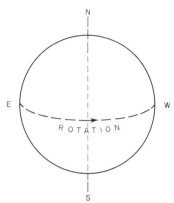

Fig. 6.18.   Rotation of the Sun

measured frequency of a given line should be higher in the spectrum from the
east limb than from the west limb. The difference in the two frequencies is
twice the Doppler shift corresponding to the velocity of rotation of the Sun.

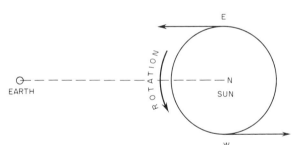

Fig. 6.19.   Determination of rotation of Sun by Doppler shift

6.110. Observations of sunspots and Doppler frequency shifts show that, unlike Earth, the Sun does not rotate about its axis in a uniform manner; the
rate of rotation is greatest near the equator and decreases steadily toward the
poles. The data from sunspots and Doppler shifts do not agree completely, because the sunspots are not actually stationary; the change in distance between
spots or groups of spots shows that they move in a longitudinal direction. It

---

* This axis is inclined so that the Sun's equator makes an angle of 7 deg with Earth's
orbital plane; as a result, sunspots generally appear to be traveling in a slanting direction
across the solar surface when viewed from Earth.

is reasonably certain, however, that the Sun's rotational period increases from 25.4 days at the equator, where the rotation rate is 1.98 kilometers (1.23 miles) per second, to 33 days at 75°(N or S) latitude. Obviously, the Sun, being gaseous, does not rotate like a solid body, and this may well cause internal distortions; these may be related to the changing solar magnetic fields which are associated with sunspots.

6.111. It has long been known that the number of sunspots varies from year to year, and in 1843 S. H. Schwabe, an amateur astronomer in Germany, showed that the variation is cyclic in nature; that is to say, it more or less repeats itself after a certain period. The concept of the *sunspot number*, as a quantitative measure of sunspot activity, was introduced by R. Wolf in 1849; thus,

$$\text{Sunspot number} = k(10g + f),$$

where g is the number of disturbed regions, i.e., groups of spots, f is the total number of individual spots, and k is a calibration factor for the observing instrument so as to make the results obtained with different instruments comparable with each other. The sunspot number defined in this manner is by no means a satisfactory indication of sunspot activity; it attributes excessive weight to groups as against individual spots and makes no allowance for the size of the spots. Nevertheless, because it has been used for such a long time, with almost complete data going back to 1745, and partial data to 1610, the sunspot number is still employed as a convenient index for recording variations in sunspot activity.

6.112. The total annual sunspot number exhibits a definite, although not completely regular, variation from year to year. Starting with a given year, the number increases to a maximum and then decreases; after reaching a minimum, it increases again to a maximum, and so on (Fig. 6.20). The average

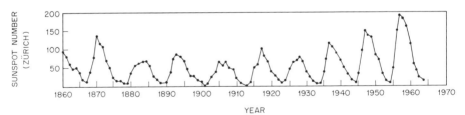

Fig. 6.20.   Sunspot numbers (Zürich) from 1860 through 1964

time from minimum to maximum is about 5 years and from maximum to minimum 6 years; hence the total length of a sunspot number cycle, from maximum to maximum or minimum to minimum, is, on the average, a little over 11 years. Actually, the periods between maxima have varied from 7.3 to 17 years and between minima from 8.5 to 14 years; consequently, the 11-year cycle must be regarded as being a broad average and not a precise period. It is possible that

the somewhat arbitrary nature of the sunspot number may be partly responsible for the lack of uniformity. Furthermore, there may be several superimposed cycles of activity which have not yet been identified; for example, there
is some evidence of an approximately 90-year period as indicated by the exceptionally large sunspot numbers for the years 1778, 1870, and 1957-1958.

6.113. It was stated earlier that the magnetic fields in bipolar sunspot pairs
are oppositely directed in the north and south solar hemispheres. It is of interest
that the polarities in the two hemispheres are reversed in successive sunspot
cycles, i.e., roughly every 11 years. Thus, taking magnetic field directions into
consideration, the sunspot cycle has a length of some 22 years. It is possible
that the reversal in the local sunspot magnetic fields has some relationship to
a reversal in the general magnetic field of the Sun, but this cannot be established
before about 1969 (see § 6.120).

6.114. Another regularity in sunspot behavior is concerned with the location
of the spots on the solar surface. At the beginning, i.e., at the minimum, of a
cycle the spot usually forms away from the Sun's equator, although very rarely
above 35°N or 35°S latitude. As the cycle develops, the spots originate closer
and closer to the equator and by the end of the cycle, i.e., just prior to the
next minimum, they are observed to form at about 5°N to 5°S latitude. Once
formed, the change in latitude of the spots is quite small. Generally, there is an
overlap between one 11-year cycle and the next, because spots of the expiring
cycle are observed to form near the equator at the same time as those of the
succeeding cycle are being generated at 30° to 35°N and 30° to 35°S latitudes.
This shows that the sunspot activity is not a simple cyclic phenomenon, since
one cycle is not quite complete before another is initiated.

6.115. It will be seen in due course that there are several forms of activity
which cause disturbances in the Sun's atmosphere. There is little doubt that
these effects, occurring at what are known as *centers of activity*, are related
to each other and to sunspots; that is to say, the same basic factor is responsible
for all types of activity. The sunspot activity is, however, the most obvious and
most easily observed indication of disturbances of the Sun as a whole. When
the solar surface exhibits many disturbances, as is the case at (or near) sunspot
maximum, the Sun is described as being *active;* the term *quiet Sun*, on the
other hand, refers to the Sun when completely free from disturbances. The year
1957-1958, the International Geophysical Year (IGY), was one in which the
Sun was very active; by contrast, the year 1964-1965 of sunspot minimum has
been designated the International Year of the Quiet Sun (IQSY) for making
studies of the undisturbed Sun.

Solar Faculae

6.116. When near the solar limb, sunspots are seen to be surrounded by irregular bright elevated areas called *faculae.** As the spots appear to move from

---

* The singular form, *facula,* is the diminutive of the Latin, *faces,* "torch."

the east limb toward the center of the disc, as a result of the Sun's rotation, the faculae become less conspicuous because of the brighter background. That they continue to exist, however, is indicated by suitable photographic observations (§6.139). Actually, faculae can often be detected in this manner prior to the observation of associated sunspots, and they may persist long after the sunspot ceases to be visible. Although sunspots are rarely seen at latitudes above 35°N and 35°S, isolated faculae have been observed in these regions. The formation of faculae is evidently a good indication, more sensitive than sunspots but more difficult to observe, of solar activity. In some instances, a facula has been detected when the disturbance was not serious enough for a visible sunspot to develop. In general, the brightness of a facula is related to the stage of development of the associated sunspot (or group of spots).

6.117. Faculae are about 10 percent brighter than the solar background; consequently, their temperatures exceed that of the photosphere and are certainly much higher than those of the sunspots themselves. The origin of faculae is not at all well understood, but they are undoubtedly formed as a result of magnetic disturbances. These cause some regions of the photosphere to be heated in excess of the average temperature and to rise for several miles above the surrounding level. It is possible that the restricted convection by magnetic fields, that leads to the formation of a relatively cold sunspot, is associated with enhanced convection in adjacent areas that thus become considerably hotter.

THE SOLAR MAGNETIC FIELD

6.118. In addition to the local fields that are presumably responsible for disturbances on the Sun, there is a general (or overall) solar magnetic field, somewhat similar to that of Earth. Because the main field of the Sun is relatively weak, e.g., about 1 gauss at the surface compared with the thousands of gauss in the sunspot regions, its existence was difficult to establish definitely, although it had been indicated by the streamers observed in the corona in the vicinity of the poles (§ 6.155).

6.119. In 1952, however, the American astronomers Harold D. Babcock and Horace W. Babcock, father and son, invented the *solar magnetograph*, which made possible a detailed quantitative study of the Sun's magnetic field in the region of the photosphere. In the magnetograph, the Zeeman splitting of the spectral lines of iron is measured and automatically converted into a magnetic field strength. By scanning the Sun along lines of latitude, the distribution of the magnetic fields over the surface and their strengths and directions can be determined.

6.120. The first observations, reported in 1953, showed that the Sun had a general magnetic field, apart from many local fields. At that time, the positive pole of the field was in the north and the negative pole in the south. In the succeeding years, the field strengths grew weaker and finally became undetectable.

Then, in the early part of 1957, the south polar field reappeared but with reversed polarity, and for over a year both north and south poles were weakly
positive, but in late 1958 the sign of the north pole changed from positive to
negative. Since the reversal of sign occurred at about the time of maximum
sunspot activity (1957-1958), there may well be another reversal around 1968
or 1969. There may be some connection between the reversal in sign of the
Sun's general field and that of the local fields in sunspots. But, it should be
recalled that, in sunspot fields, the sign reversal occurs close to sunspot minimum, when a new 11-year cycle is initiated, whereas the general solar field
apparently reverses nearer to sunspot maximum.

   6.121. It is obvious from the foregoing statements that the Sun's magnetic
field is not like that of Earth, which is a relatively simple dipolar field. The
fact that both north and south solar poles can have the same sign suggests that
the Sun has two types of magnetic field: a bipolar field that is responsible for
the general magnetism, and toroidal (or ring-like) fields, in opposite directions
in northern and southern hemispheres, which are related to solar disturbances.
The interactions among these fields could conceivably produce the observed
changes. Because of the fundamental connection of the solar magnetic fields
with disturbances in the Sun's atmosphere and the accompanying effects on
Earth, there is considerable scope for further study in this area of space
science.

THE CHROMOSPHERE

THE FLASH SPECTRUM

   6.122. The characteristic feature of the chromosphere is the reddish color of
the crescent of solar surface that is visible just prior to totality in an eclipse
of the Sun (§ 6.40). Spectroscopic examination shows that, at this time, the
dark-line, Fraunhofer spectrum suddenly changes to a bright-line, emission
spectrum; this is called a *flash spectrum* because it flashes out suddenly as the
solar disc is hidden by the Moon and lasts for only a few seconds. One of the
brightest lines in the flash spectrum is the red line of atomic hydrogen, designated H_α, at a wavelength of 6563 Å; it is this line that is largely responsible
for the observed color of the chromosphere. It may be noted that the H_α line
is the first (highest wavelength) line of the Balmer series of atomic hydrogen;
in emission, all electronic transitions in this series are to, and in absorption
from, the second quantum level of the hydrogen atom (§ 6.81). Other bright
lines in the flash spectrum are two lines of singly-ionized calcium (Ca II),
designated by the letters H (3968 Å) and K (3934 Å), respectively.

   6.123. The spectral emission from the chromosphere occurs, of course, at all
times, but it is only when the brilliance of the photosphere is obscured, during
an eclipse, that the bright emission lines can be detected from Earth (cf. § 6.40).
As is to be expected from the gradual transition from the photosphere to the

chromosphere, most of the bright lines coincide with the absorption lines of the normal Fraunhofer spectrum. But there are some significant differences between the two spectra. For example, certain lines of the neutral helium atom (He I), which are not found in the spectrum of the photosphere, and even some of singly-ionized helium (He II), appear in the flash spectrum of the chromosphere. Furthermore, a comparison of the lines of ionized metallic elements, e.g., calcium and iron, with those of the corresponding neutral atoms shows that the former are relatively more intense in the spectrum of the chromosphere than in that of the photosphere.

6.124. The increased proportion of ionized calcium and iron can be attributed partly to the much lower density in the chromosphere, which ranges from about 10^{-8}, at the base, to 10^{-15} gram per cubic centimeter. The frequency of collisions between ions and electrons is thus less than in the photosphere and, hence, so also is the rate of recombination to form neutral (or less ionized) atoms. The lifetime of a particular stripped (ionized) atom is thus greater in the chromosphere and the spectral lines would be enhanced relative to those of the neutral atoms. But density alone cannot account for the additional neutral helium (He I) lines and, especially, for those of singly-ionized helium (He II). It is known from laboratory experiments that, regardless of pressure, the former cannot be produced at kinetic temperatures much below about $10,000°$K ($9700°$C or $17,500°$F), and the latter below $20,000°$K ($19,700°$C or $35,500°$F). It is evident, therefore, that temperature in the chromosphere must increase considerably above the $4500°$K at its base, i.e., at the top of the photosphere. There is evidence that in the upper levels of the chromosphere, at a height of 10,000 to 16,000 kilometers (6000 to 10,000 miles), where it merges into the corona, the temperature approaches $1,000,000°$K.

6.125. An ultraviolet spectrum of the solar chromosphere, taken from above Earth's atmosphere, was first obtained in October 1946 by R. Tousey and his associates of the U.S. Naval Research Laboratory utilizing a V-2 rocket. It was observed that the radiation intensity fell off rapidly with decreasing wavelength, so that if spectra were to be obtained in the extreme ultraviolet, some means of pointing the spectrograph constantly at the Sun was necessary in order to provide the prolonged exposures. Such an instrument was flown in an Aerobee rocket by W. A. Rense and W. B. Pietenpol in 1952, and since that time similar devices have been used in several studies of ultraviolet radiations from the Sun down to wavelengths of less than 100 Å. It has been found that at wavelengths below 1850 Å, the normal (dark-line) Fraunhofer spectrum of the photosphere and the lower chromosphere fades out, and bright emission lines begin to appear. The most prominent line, as might be expected, is the Lyman-α (or first resonance) line of hydrogen at 1216 Å. At shorter wavelengths, the 584 Å line of ionized helium (He II) is very strong. Because of the relatively high temperatures in the chromosphere, the ultraviolet spectrum also contains emission lines of ionized as well as of neutral atoms of several other light elements, e.g., carbon (C I, II, III, IV), oxygen (O I, II, III, VI), nitrogen (N III, V), silicon (Si II, III, IV), etc. Lines of more highly stripped atoms are present in the spectrum, but they probably originate in the corona or in the upper chromospheric levels adjoining the corona where the temperatures are higher.

SPICULES

6.126. Ordinary photographs of the chromosphere, as seen in profile above the Sun's limb at the time of an eclipse, show it to consist of a roughly level region some 3200 to 5000 kilometers (2000 to 3000 miles) high, surmounted by a large number of excrescences, called *spicules** (Fig. 6.21). Spicules are a normal

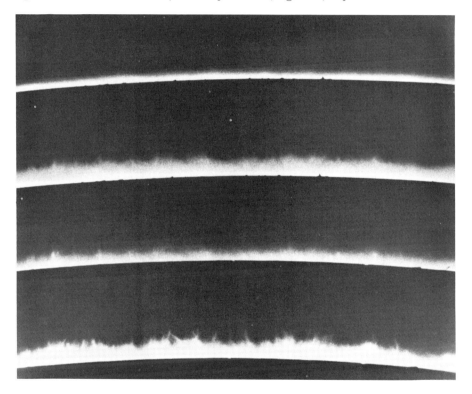

FIG. 6.21.   Coronagraph picture showing spicules from the solar chromosphere. (*Sacramento Peak Observatory, Air Force Cambridge Research Laboratories*)

phenomenon of the Sun since they occur in undisturbed regions and at all times. Because of the rarity of total solar eclipses a technique has been devised for taking profile (or projection) photographs of the chromosphere whenever the atmosphere is clear. This procedure makes use of a coronagraph (§ 6.42) in

* The Latin word *spiculum* is the diminutive of *spica,* "point" or "spike."

conjunction with a filter that cuts out all light except a narrow band, about 5 Å in width, around the H_α line of hydrogen which is so conspicuous in the flash spectrum. The photographs obtained in this manner are quite similar to those taken during an eclipse.

6.127. The spicules protruding from the main level of the chromosphere can be seen to ascend at speeds of 25 to 32 kilometers (15 to 20 miles) per second, reaching heights of 10,000 to 16,000 kilometers (6000 to 10,000 miles) from the base. The average diameter of the spicules is estimated to be about 500 miles. After attaining its maximum height, a spicule appears to remain stationary for a short period and then either fades away or seems to fall back. The total lifetime ranges from approximately a half minute to several minutes with an average of about 4 or 5 minutes. It has been estimated that, at any instant, there are roughly 100,000 spicules covering about 1 percent of the solar surface. Because the spicules over a large area are seen in profile, the photographs in Fig. 6.21 give the illusion that most of the surface of the atmosphere is punctuated by spicules of various sizes.

6.128. It is possible that the spicules are related in some manner to the bright granules in the photosphere, representing the upward-moving regions of the convective zone. The cross-sectional dimensions are certainly similar, but no other connection has been established. The spicules are observed to form in the chromosphere regardless of whether there is sunspot and related solar activity or not. It is not known, however, if the number of spicules varies with the extent or amount of such activity.

CHROMOSPHERE TEMPERATURES

6.129. Although it is widely accepted that temperatures in the chromosphere range from about 4500°K at the base to nearly 1,000,000°K at the top, there are differences of view regarding the manner in which the temperature varies with height. Some solar physicists are of the opinion that there is a more-or-less steady gradation in temperature with altitude, but others have suggested that there are both gradual and sharp increases, e.g., a gradual rise to 10,000°K, followed by a sudden increase to 40,000°K, then another gradual increase to 80,000°K, and finally a sharp rise to the vicinity of 1,000,000°K where the chromosphere merges into the corona. There is also some disagreement concerning the temperatures of the spicules; it is not known definitely whether they are hotter or cooler than the main chromosphere, and arguments have been presented for both points of view. Another complicating factor in the attempts to understand the chromosphere is that, in its lower levels, there appear to be considerable variations in temperature even at the same height. It has been suggested, in fact, that there are separate cells in which the temperature may be as low as 4000°K or as high as 30,000°K.

6.130. Regardless of the temperature distribution, the outstanding fact about the chromosphere is that its temperature is higher than that of the photosphere.

Energy must pass in some manner from the hotter convective layer, through the cooler photosphere, into the chromosphere, but how this happens is largely a matter for speculation. It is reasonably certain that the energy required to maintain the higher temperature in the chromosphere is not carried as radiation from the photosphere, for it is highly improbable that there will be a net transfer from a colder to a hotter region. The energy must, therefore, have a nonradiative origin.

6.131. A plausible suggestion is that the energy responsible for heating the chromosphere is directed kinetic energy, i.e., energy of directed motion. The rapid circulation of material in the convective zone is presumably capable of generating shock waves, i.e., high-pressure waves, traveling outward with a velocity equal to or greater than that of sound in the photosphere, estimated to be more than 10 kilometers (6 miles) per second. Shock waves are waves of material, not radiation, and in the solar atmosphere they consist largely of a hydrogen plasma. Their energy is thus mainly kinetic in nature. As the shock waves moved outward, they interact with the surrounding medium and thus raise its temperature. In other words, the directed kinetic energy of the shock wave is gradually converted into random kinetic energy of the atoms, ions, and electrons in the solar atmosphere.* The region where the gain in random kinetic energy exceeds the energy loss by radiation represents the base of the chromosphere, where the temperature starts to increase.

HYDROMAGNETIC WAVES

6.132. Another factor which may be involved in the energy transfer is the presence of variable magnetic fields. The lines of force of a magnetic field containing a plasma are in a state of tension similar to stretched elastic, because of the pressure exerted by the plasma. If a stretched elastic string is plucked at one point, a wave motion travels along the string. In the same way, if there is a displacement of plasma relative to a field line, either as a result of plasma motion or of a change in the field strength, a *hydromagnetic* (or *magneto-hydrodynamic*) *wave* will move along the lines of force. Such a wave is also called an *Alfvén wave*, after the Swedish astrophysicist Hannes Alfvén who first suggested their existence in plasmas. The velocity, v, in kilometers per second of an Alfvén wave in a proton-electron plasma is given by

$$v = \frac{1.7 \times 10^6 B}{\sqrt{n}}, \tag{6.13}$$

where B is the magnetic field strength in gauss and n is the number of electrons (or protons) per cubic centimeter. If the actual velocity of the plasma within

---

* It is of interest that the general mechanism is the reverse of that occurring in a rocket nozzle where the random kinetic energy of the hot gas in the combustion chamber is converted into directed kinetic energy of the exhaust gas, accompanied by a decrease in temperature (§ 3.59).

a magnetic field exceeds the Alfvén velocity, a hydromagnetic shock will develop, at the front of which there is an accumulation of energy. Such hydromagnetic shocks are capable of transferring energy from one location to another in a magnetic field.

6.133. In some respects the Alfvén velocity in a plasma is analogous to the velocity of sound in a more dense medium; motion of a body at supersonic speed in such a medium results in the development of a conventional shock wave with a high-pressure front. A similar effect occurs when a plasma in a magnetic field is moving faster than the Alfvén velocity for the existing conditions. There is, however, an important difference between a conventional shock wave and a hydromagnetic shock. In the former case, collisions among molecules play an essential role in the development of the shock front, but the density of a plasma is very low and collisions are so rare as to be virtually absent. The high-pressure front in the case of a plasma results from the interaction of waves rather than of particles; thus, successive hydromagnetic waves travel faster than the preceding ones so that they overtake and combine with each other. Hydromagnetic shock waves are thus referred to as *collision-free* (or *collisionless*) *shocks.* Such shock waves may very well be involved in the transfer of energy from lower to higher regions in the Sun's atmosphere.

MONOCHROMATIC PHOTOGRAPHS OF CHROMOSPHERE

6.134. Disturbances of the chromosphere have been identified from photographs of the Sun's disc taken in the light of a single wavelength or, more precisely, in a very narrow wavelength range. One instrument used for this purpose is the *spectroheliograph.* In an ordinary spectrograph, the light from a thin strip across the solar surface is dispersed into a broad spectrum; a narrow slit may then be located in the focal plane of the instrument in such a manner as to permit the passage of light of a particular wavelength only, the remainder of the spectrum being blocked off. Such a device, called a *monochromator,* because it selects light of a single color (or wavelength) and rejects all others, forms the basis of the spectroheliograph. In order to take a complete picture of the Sun's surface, the solar image may be allowed to drift across the spectroheliograph so that successive strips of the surface are exposed. A photographic plate is moved in unison, and the series of adjacent images join to produce a representation of the Sun in light of a selected wavelength. Alternatively, the instrument may be moved across the image of the Sun's disc while the photographic plate remains stationary.

6.135. Another form of monochromator is the *birefringent* filter. This consists of a series of alternating layers of plates cut in a special manner from a birefringent (doubly-refracting) crystal,* e.g., quartz or calcite, and of films

---

* A single ray of light passing through a birefringent material is split into two separate (refracted) rays. These rays are *polarized* at right angles to one another; that is to say, the electric field of the electromagnetic wave oscillates along a line (or a plane) in each case, and the two lines (or planes) are perpendicular.

of a polarizing material, such as Polaroid. Each plate of the birefringent material is twice as thick as the preceding one. A combination of this kind transmits electromagnetic radiations in a few narrow wavelength bands with wide spaces in between where the light is absorbed by the polarizing layers. From these narrow, essentially monochromatic bands, a particular one can be chosen and the others excluded, so that the whole constitutes a filter for a specific wavelength. The width of the transmitted band depends on the maximum thickness of the birefringent plate in the filter; the greater the thickness, the narrower is the bandwidth. For monochromatic observations of the solar surface, the bandwidth should be 0.5 to 1 Å, but for viewing the chromosphere in profile over the Sun's limb, a filter with a bandwidth of 5 Å is adequate.

6.136. With a birefringent, monochromatic filter and a suitable telescope, it is possible to photograph the whole of the solar disc in a single exposure. The filter has the advantage of much greater simplicity, both in design and operation, than the spectroheliograph. But it suffers from the drawback—a relatively minor one in the circumstances—that a separate filter is necessary for each wavelength, whereas the spectroheliograph can be readily adjusted, by moving the slit in the focal plane, to obtain photographs at any desired wavelength.

6.137. In taking monochromatic pictures of the chromosphere, the wavelength chosen must be one which appears in the flash spectrum but corresponds to absorption in, or is entirely absent from, the spectrum of the photosphere. It is then certain that what is being observed is the chromosphere and not the photosphere. Since the intensity of the chromospheric emission spectrum is relatively low, the most suitable lines are those which are the strongest in the flash spectrum. The ones most commonly employed are the Balmer atomic hydrogen H_α line and the H and K lines of singly-ionized calcium (Ca II) in the visible spectrum. Some photographs have been taken in the infrared, e.g., with a line of ionized calcium at 8542 Å (0.8542 micron) and a helium line at 10,830 Å (1.083 micron), and also, during rocket flights, in the ultraviolet and X-ray regions.

6.138. The photographs taken at the different wavelengths exhibit individual characteristics, presumably because they depict different levels in the chromosphere. Since higher temperatures are required to produce the Ca II lines than the Balmer H_α line, calcium photographs generally represent a higher level. There are also differences depending upon whether the wavelength lies in the center or toward the outer parts (or wings) of a broad, intense line. The radiation in the wings is expected to come from lower levels where the pressures are higher. It is of interest that, although sunspots can be observed as dark areas in the H_α photographs, they are generally not seen in those taken in the center of a Ca II line. In the latter, however, other evidence of chromospheric activity associated with sunspots is more marked, as will be seen in the next section.

DISTURBANCES OF THE CHROMOSPHERE: PLAGES

6.139. The monochromatic photographs of the chromosphere commonly show large, irregular bright areas called *plages* (Latin, *plaga*, "region" or "zone") in the sunspot regions (Fig. 6.22). In the light of the calcium lines, the plages seem to be larger and more intense than they do in H_α photographs; this sug-

 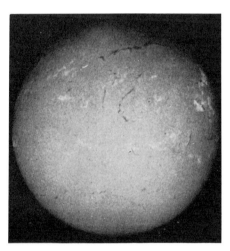

FIG. 6.22.   Photograph of the Sun taken in the K line of Ca II, showing calcium plages (left); simultaneous photograph in the Balmer H_α line (right). (*Official United States Navy Photograph*)

gests that the plages, described as *calcium plages,* develop more fully in the upper levels of the chromosphere. Where faculae are seen near the Sun's limb in the photosphere, plages are invariably observed in the chromosphere. Furthermore, plages, like faculae, are generally apparent before sunspots become visible and frequently persist for some time after the sunspots have faded away. But small plages may form and disappear before sunspots develop in the same areas. Plages can be observed across the whole solar disc in the sunspot latitudes, and so it is assumed that corresponding faculae are present in the photosphere although they cannot be detected against the bright background. The magnetic fields which produce faculae and their associated sunspots are presumably responsible for the plages.

SOLAR FLARES

6.140. Solar flares are not only the most spectacular disturbances seen on the Sun, but they are also the most significant from the terrestrial standpoint. Furthermore, the electrically charged particles emitted by some flares represent a potential hazard to man during space flights to the Moon and the planets (§ 13.119). For these reasons, in particular, solar flares have been the subject of extensive studies in recent years. Flares are sometimes seen in profile above the solar limb, but they are usually observed in monochromatic, e.g., H$_\alpha$-line, photographs and occasionally in ordinary (white light) photographs of the disc. A flare is apparent as a region of exceptional brightness that develops very suddenly in a plage area of the chromosphere; hence, flares generally form not too far from a sunspot group. They are thus observed in the equatorial band from about 40°N to 40°S latitude (cf. § 6.114). Flares are often associated with sunspot areas of long life and with groups that have complex magnetic fields, i.e., the polarities are distributed in an irregular manner among the spots in the group.

6.141. There are several different types of solar flares, as indicated by their appearance and behavior. The brightness, dimensions (area), and duration, for example, of flares vary over a wide range. These factors are taken into consideration in the system commonly used to classify flares according to their "importance." Flares of minor importance are designated 1⁻, whereas the largest flares of greatest importance are 3⁺, with obvious gradations in between. The dimensions and brightness of a flare increase rapidly, reaching a maximum in roughly 5 to 10 minutes; a brief period of extreme brilliance is then followed by a slow decay which may last from 1 to 3 hours or more, depending on the importance of the flare. Very large (Class 3⁺) flares are sometimes so bright that they can be detected against the background of the photosphere by conventional photographic methods. Radiations of several different types may be emitted from a flare, as will be seen shortly.

6.142. Although large flares are not very common, only a few per annum even when the Sun is active, there are often considerable numbers of small flares; thus, as many as a hundred have been seen on one day in the vicinity of a large sunspot group. There is a general correlation between the sunspot number and the frequency of flare formation, but the most important flares do not necessarily occur at sunspot maximum. Flares are seen most frequently during the period that a sunspot is growing, i.e., during the first week or two of its development. But there is evidence that some flares which produce the most marked effects near Earth are formed while the sunspot group is decaying. When flares are observed protruding above the solar limb, their heights are estimated to range mostly from about 2000 to 10,000 kilometers, with an average of about 7000 kilometers (4300 miles). The surface dimensions are usually from a few thousand up to 30,000 kilometers (20,000 miles) or so, but some of the most important flares are even larger.

6.143. From the radiations emitted, it is clear that solar flares are associated with the release of large amounts of energy. This energy probably arises from the rearrangement of complex magnetic fields or their interaction with the material in the chromosphere, although the mechanism of energy release is unknown. It is of interest in this connection that a large flare is often followed within a day or so by one or two more; there is thus a possibility that the formation of one flare may trigger the formation of others. In addition to luminous and ultraviolet radiations, flares may be accompanied by the emission of bursts of X-rays, by certain types of radio-frequency waves, and by electrically charged particles of high energy; these emissions may occur individually, together, or not at all. The positively charged particles are mainly protons (hydrogen nuclei) and some helium nuclei, with a small proportion of nuclei of heavier elements. These high-energy particles may have velocities ranging up to 100,000 kilometers (or more) per second; they are discussed more fully in § 8.252 *et seq.* Charged particles of somewhat lower energy are responsible for certain magnetic disturbances observed in the vicinity of Earth (§ 8.224).

6.144. The spectra of solar flares are very complex and there are clear indications that radiation equilibrium is not attained, i.e., the radiation is not typical of a black body at the existing temperature. In the visible region, the spectrum is not unlike that of the chromosphere, although there are some significant differences, e.g., considerable brightening and broadening of the H_α line of hydrogen and the presence of helium lines requiring high excitation energies. In general, the visible spectrum corresponds to temperatures in the range of 10,-000° to 20,000°K, i.e., roughly 18,000 to 36,000°F. But the emission of radiations of short wavelengths, i.e., X-rays and ultraviolet rays, from some flares is very much greater than would be expected at such temperatures. Some of the ultraviolet radiation is probably emitted from the corona, as will be seen in § 6.158.

6.145. The enhanced emission of X-rays at the time of a small solar flare was first detected in 1956 by H. Friedman, *et al.*, of the U.S. Naval Research Laboratory, by means of instruments carried to high altitude by a rockoon (§ 1.101). Subsequent studies of solar X-rays, in the wavelength range from about 1 to 15 Å, have been made with sounding rockets and with satellites, particularly Solar Radiation I (§ 6.211), the first Orbiting Solar Observatory (§ 6.212), and Ariel (§ 8.198). It has been established that many, but not all, flares are associated with an increase in X-ray emission. In the absence of flares, the X-ray intensity from the Sun is consistent with a temperature—although not a black-body temperature—of about 1,000,000°K at the top of the chromosphere or in the lower part of the corona. When a large X-ray flare occurs, however, the emission increases to such an extent as to indicate temperatures about a hundred times as great. It is doubtful if these high temperatures are actually attained in a flare, but it is evident that there must be intense electromagnetic activity to lead to the strong emission of radiation of short wavelength.

6.146. The marked enhancement of the X-ray and ultraviolet intensities at the time of certain solar flares results in a significant increase of the ionization in the lower layers of Earth's atmosphere. This sudden ionospheric disturbance, as it is called, has a striking effect on short-wave radio communication, as will be seen in Chapter 8. Not all flares, even among the larger ones, produce these ionospheric effects, presumably because they are not accompanied by the increased emission of short-wavelength radiations. Powerful emissions of radio waves, in the decimeter and meter regions, also often accompany large solar flares. In addition to a general noise background, there may be different types of radio bursts of relatively short duration. These and other radio-frequency emissions from the Sun are described in § 6.172 *et seq.*

SOLAR PROMINENCES

6.147. A striking feature of solar activity is the formation of *prominences.* They were first observed during total eclipses of the Sun as red streamers of a great variety of shapes ascending thousands of miles from the chromosphere into the corona (Fig. 6.23). By means of a coronagraph and a birefringent

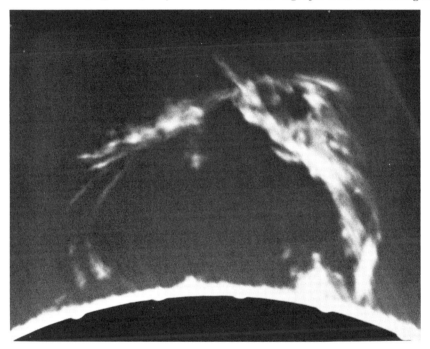

FIG. 6.23.   Solar prominence; the indentations in the circumference of the disc are 10 deg, i.e., about 120,000 kilometers (75,000 miles) apart. (*Mount Wilson and Palomar Observatories*)

filter, which transmits either the H$_\alpha$ line of hydrogen or the H or K calcium line, solar prominences can be observed extending from the Sun's limb, without waiting for an eclipse. Although they are treated here as a chromospheric disturbance, there is no doubt that the corona is frequently involved in the formation and behavior of prominences. In most cases, the material constituting the prominence appears to form in the corona and descend toward the chromosphere, but in some instances the internal motion is in the opposite direction. Whenever a major disturbance occurs, however, the whole mass of the prominence moves outward, away from the chromosphere, regardless of the direction of the internal motion.

6.148. Prominences vary widely in appearance and behavior, so that they may well represent phenomena of several different types. Efforts have been made to classify prominences on the basis of their shape, behavior, and apparent mode of formation, but for the present purpose it is adequate to consider two general types, namely, quiescent and active-region prominences.

6.149. A *quiescent prominence* develops slowly and may last for several months. It often originates close to a sunspot region and then moves away slowly toward the nearest pole; hence, after a time its association with sunspots is not obvious. As seen edgeways in a monochromatic photograph against the solar disc, a quiescent prominence has the appearance of a long dark *filament*. Filaments were at one time regarded as a separate type of solar disturbance, but observation as they passed across the Sun's limb showed that they are actually prominences seen from above.

6.150. From the dimensions of filaments, it appears that quiescent prominences may extend for distances often exceeding 150,000 kilometers (90,000 miles) in length; but they are only about 5000 kilometers (3000 miles) wide. The height, extending into the corona, as seen in profile above the Sun's limb is, on the average, about 40,000 kilometers (25,000 miles), some being higher than others. Long quiescent prominences have been referred to as "hedgerow" prominences because they consist of closely spaced and overlapping broad vertical streamers extending for great distances.

6.151. The spectra of quiescent prominences are similar but generally fainter than that of the chromosphere. The fact that the filaments appear dark against the background indicates that they have a lower temperature than the surrounding chromosphere. The temperature of quiescent prominences has been estimated to be about $10,000°K$ ($9700°C$ or $17,500°F$), which is very much less than that of the corona into which they penetrate. On the other hand, the density of the material, mainly ionized hydrogen, in a prominence is about a hundred times as great as in the corona, although it is less than in the bulk of the chromosphere. As a consequence of the lower temperature and higher density, the material in a quiescent prominence has about the same pressure as the surrounding corona.

6.152. On occasion, a quiescent prominence will suddenly become active and travel away from the solar surface at high speed. Such an eruption may last for some hours and may result in the apparent decay of part of the prominence; this phenomenon has been called *sudden disappearance*. After a few days, however, the quiescent prominence may appear in its original form, indicating that the basic activity of the Sun in that region still persists.

6.153. *Active-region prominences* are those that are formed in and remain associated with sunspot regions, and hence also with faculae, plages, and flares. As is to be expected, these prominences are most common at times when the Sun is active, i.e., at and near periods of sunspot maximum. The temperatures of active-region prominences are about 30,000°K (54,000°F) or more, and are thus much higher than those of the quiescent variety. Active-region prominences often appear as enormous loops or in some cases as arches which seem to bridge the gap between two sunspots with opposite magnetic fields. As is the case with other prominences, the material often appears to form by some kind of condensation in the corona and then stream downward.

6.154. Prominences sometimes ascend very rapidly and material is seen to be ejected upward at high velocity, e.g., 1000 to 2000 kilometers (600 to 1200 miles) per second, to form a *surge* or *surge prominence*. This is a large spear of luminous material which extends for 150,000 kilometers (90,000 miles) or more beyond the solar limit before finally falling back or fading away. Surges are probably related to flares because they often appear in nearby areas.

THE SOLAR CORONA

Spectrum of the Corona

6.155. The corona that can be seen extending for great distances beyond the solar disc during a total eclipse or by means of a coronagraph is generally somewhat irregular in form, the shape varying with the period in the sunspot cycle (Fig. 6.24). Around the time of sunspot minimum, the corona exhibits broad extensions (or streamers) in the equatorial region with shorter plumes

Fig. 6.24.   The Sun's corona photographed during the eclipse of February 25, 1952. (*Official United States Navy Photograph*)

(or brushes) at the poles. It was the appearance of the latter that led to the inference that the Sun possessed a general magnetic field. At the maximum of the sunspot cycle, the corona is brighter and appears to have a fairly symmetrical form with streamers in all directions.

6.156. In addition to the continuous background, which is attributed to the scattering of sunlight by electrons, the visible region of the (emission) spectrum of the corona exhibits some 30 or so bright lines. The line emission is at its strongest at sunspot maximum, indicating both higher temperature and density than the average values. For a long time, the origin of these lines remained a mystery and some scientists even attributed them to an unknown element, which was named coronium, that did not exist on Earth. In 1942, however, the Swedist physicist B. Edlén published evidence to show that the lines were produced by highly ionized (stripped) atoms of metals, especially calcium, iron, and nickel, and also of the element argon which had lost from 9 to 14 electrons.* These lines had not then been observed in the laboratory because they are excited only under conditions of high temperature and low pressure. The lines are what spectroscopists call "forbidden"; that is to say, the corresponding electronic energy level transitions are highly improbable in normal circumstances. Since 1963, however, special techniques have been developed in the United Kingdom and the United States to approach the conditions in the solar corona. In this manner, spectra have been obtained in the laboratory containing many of the forbidden lines of highly stripped atoms observed in the coronal spectrum.

6.157. Three of the most important lines in the visible spectrum of the corona are the green and red lines of iron, Fe XIV at 5303 Å and Fe X at 6347 Å, respectively, and the yellow calcium line, Ca XV at 5694 Å. The highly-ionized metal atoms should also produce spectral lines in the ultraviolet as well as in the visible region, but absorption by the atmosphere prevents their detection on Earth. Some of these lines, e.g., 284 Å of Fe XV and 335 Å of Fe XVI, have been identified, however, from spectral measurements made with instruments carried by rockets and by the Orbiting Solar Observatory (OSO) (§ 6.215). The presence of such highly stripped atoms as Fe XIV, Fe XV, and Fe XVI which have lost 13, 14, and 15 electrons, respectively, shows that the temperature in the corona must be in the vicinity of 1,000,000°K. The occasional appearance of the spectrum of Ca XV, i.e., calcium from which 14 electrons have been removed, suggests local temperatures of about 3,000,000°K.

6.158. The OSO observations indicated a sudden increase in the intensities of the coronal Fe XVI (335 Å) and Fe XV (284 Å) ultraviolet lines by a factor of three or four at the time of a flare. From the observations, it was calculated that the temperature in the corona was considerably above its normal value. An increase was also observed in the ionized helium (He II) line at 304 Å, but

---

* The total numbers of electrons per atom of these elements are as follows: argon, 18; calcium, 20; iron, 26; nickel, 28.

this was much smaller. Incidentally, plage activity of long duration, e.g., about two weeks, unaccompanied by flares, resulted in a gradual increase, followed by a slow decrease, in the intensity of the Fe XIV, Fe XV, and Fe XVI coronal lines in the ultraviolet.

6.159. Aside from the occurrence of the lines of highly stripped atoms, there is other evidence that high temperatures occur in the solar corona. If the observed Doppler broadening of the spectral lines is ascribed to the random motion of the ionized atoms in the coronal gas, the temperature must approach 2,000,000°K. Why this is higher than the temperature estimated above is not clear, but at least the general magnitude is the same.* Another argument is based on the emission of radio waves by the corona; the intensity of these electromagnetic radiations, in the meter wavelength band, from the undisturbed Sun are characteristic of a black body at a temperature of about 1,000,000°K. It is reasonably certain that the corona does not exhibit black-body behavior, because of its very low density, but the result is in harmony with the temperature values derived in other ways. Incidentally, preliminary measurements of spectra in the ultraviolet and the longer X-ray regions made from sounding rockets are consistent with a temperature of approximately 1,500,000°K. The foregoing data are applicable to the corona under average conditions; at times of considerable solar activity, higher temperatures undoubtedly occur.

6.160. Because of its high temperature, a large proportion of the energy of the corona is in the short wavelength (ultraviolet and X-ray) region. According to equation (6.7), a black body at a temperature of 1,500,000°K has a maximum rate of energy emission at a wavelength of about 20 Å (cf. Fig. 6.13). Although the corona is not an ideal radiator, most of its energy is, nevertheless, in the form of electromagnetic radiations of short wavelength. Such radiations are capable of causing ionization in gases and they are responsible for much of the ionization in the upper layers of Earth's ionosphere. Changes in the density of electrons (and ions) observed in these layers are closely related to variations in the temperature of the corona.

6.161. Striking evidence for the departure of the corona from ideal black-body behavior was obtained from measurements in the moderately high-energy (X-ray) region of 1 to 10 Å made from the OSO. During a period when the Sun was relatively quiet, the radiation from this region was about 360 times the theoretical value expected for a black-body temperature of 1,800,000°K. It is evident, therefore, that nonthermal processes accompanied by emission of radiations of high energy are important in the corona even under quiet conditions.

6.162. The cause of the high temperature of the corona is a matter for speculation. A number of different theories have been proposed, but the one most widely accepted at present is the same as that described in § 6.131 *et seq.*

* A possible explanation of the temperature difference may be excessive broadening caused by shock waves.

to account for the temperature of the chromosphere. The kinetic energy of material directed upward at high velocity as ordinary shock waves or as hydromagnetic waves (or both) is dissipated in the higher levels of the Sun's atmosphere. The variation in shape of the corona over a sunspot cycle is not understood, but the general solar magnetic field probably has some influence. The brushes (or plumes) observed near the poles, for example, clearly suggest the presence of magnetic lines of force.

DISTURBANCES OF THE CORONA

6.163. As seen earlier, chromospheric prominences may be regarded, to some extent, as being disturbances of the corona. In addition, there are coronal phenomena which are like loop prominences in general but differ in temperature. The *coronal loops* can be seen in photographs of the Sun's limb obtained with the aid of a birefringent filter which transmits only the green (5303 Å) line of Fe XIV. The emission of this line shows that the temperatures in the loops must be in the vicinity of 1,000,000°K, whereas the chromospheric prominences have much lower temperatures. On a few occasions, the distended loops have been seen to break open at the top and thus turn into long, whip-like streamers. This behavior seems to be connected with the occurrence of large flares.

6.164. Regions of the corona lying above active areas in the photosphere and chromosphere generally exhibit increased emission intensity and broadening of the spectral lines arising from highly ionized atoms. The observations suggest that the temperatures and densities in these regions are higher than in the surrounding corona. Of particular interest is the appearance of the yellow line of calcium (Ca XV) at 5694 Å in such *coronal condensations* or *hot spots,* wherein the temperatures are estimated by Doppler broadening to be in the vicinity of 4,000,000°K (7,200,000°F). These transient hot spots are closely associated with the appearance of flares in the chromosphere and with other solar disturbances. In one instance, the Ca XV line was even seen faintly in the coronal spectrum a few hours before the beginning of a flare. It is probable, therefore, that hot spots, flares, and other phenomena owe their origin to the same fundamental cause, namely magnetic field disturbances.

6.165. There are indications that the corona may contain regions that are cooler, as well as those that are hotter, than their surroundings. In spectrograms of the corona taken from an aircraft at high altitude during the total solar eclipse of July 20, 1963, A. J. Deutsch of the United States and G. Reghini of Italy detected the presence of lines of normal (nonionized) calcium atoms (Ca I). These atoms do not exist at temperatures above 20,000°K, and hence the corona must have *cool spots* in which the temperatures are less than this value. The suggestion has been made that the corona is threaded by magnetic fields which produce turbulence (or churning) in the plasma that results in uneven heating.

6.166. In the description of solar flares, it was mentioned that these disturbances are sometimes accompanied by greatly enhanced emission of X-rays. The total intensity or rate of energy emission in the X-ray region increases, and there is also a marked increase in the energy of the photons. Thus, at the time of a flare, the energy quanta may be as high as 100 kilo-electron volts (wavelength about 0.1 Å), compared with a maximum of a few kilo-electron volts (1 or 2 Å) in the X-rays from the quiet Sun.

THE DUST CORONA

6.167. Apart from the true corona described above, there is another coronal region called the *dust corona* or *F-corona*. It is more symmetrical than the solar corona and at considerable distances from the Sun it is also more readily visible. The spectrum of the dust corona differs markedly from that of the solar corona, in the respect that it resembles that of the photosphere, including the dark Fraunhofer lines. There is now little doubt that the F-corona is produced by the scattering of normal sunlight, i.e., from the photosphere, by fine particles of interplanetary dust that are spread throughout the solar system. It has been estimated that these particles range in size from a fraction of a millimeter down to about a one ten-thousandth (10^{-4}) of a centimeter in diameter and that there is, on the average, only a single particle in a volume of about 10^{13} cubic centimeters. Since the distance from Earth to the Sun is close to 1.5×10^{13} centimeters, there is less than one particle, on the average, in each square centimeter cross section of the intervening space. The zodiacal light phenomenon, which can be seen in the sky at certain times of the year soon after evening twilight or before morning twilight, is probably an extension of the dust corona (§ 7.157).

SOLAR PARTICLES AND SOLAR WIND

6.168. In addition to radiation, the Sun emits a plasma of electrically charged particles, consisting mainly of protons, i.e., hydrogen nuclei, as well as nuclei of some heavier elements in much smaller proportions, and their associated electrons. These particles can travel great distances, and as they approach Earth they interact with its atmosphere and magnetic field (Chapter 8). It must be noted here, however, that the solar particle emission is greatly increased following the appearance of some large flares (cf. § 6.143). The disturbance responsible for the flare may thus cause enhanced emission of material as well as of radiation from the Sun. Not only is there an increase in the total rate of charged particle emission, but the kinetic energies of many of the particles, e.g., protons, is extremely high; in fact, some apparently travel with velocities approaching that of light.

6.169. An interesting consequence of solar particle emission at the time of a large flare is the accompanying distortion of the Sun's magnetic field. Charged particles in a plasma can cross the lines of force of a magnetic field only as a result of collisions with other particles. Because of the very low pressures in the coronal region, such collisions are rare, and so the solar particles are unable to escape from a magnetic field. Consequently, when they are expelled from the Sun at high velocities, they tend to carry the solar magnetic field with them. The interaction of this field with that of Earth is of considerable interest, as will be seen in Chapter 8.

6.170. It is well known that certain comets develop tails when they come within one or two astronomical units of the Sun, and that the tails point away from the Sun (§ 7.65). For many years, it was widely accepted that the pressure of solar radiation (cf. § 3.224) was responsible for this aspect of cometary phenomena. It was realized in due course, however, that radiation pressure was insufficient to account for the observed effects, and so another factor must be operative. In the early 1950's, L. F. Biermann in Germany showed that the behavior of cometary tails could be accounted for in a satisfactory manner by postulating that a stream of high-speed particles, e.g., protons and electrons, was being emitted continuously from the Sun. The evidence indicated that the particle emission was enhanced during periods of high solar activity, i.e., when the sunspot number was large and there were many plages, flares, etc., but it persisted even when the Sun was in a quiet state.

6.171. In 1958, E. N. Parker in the United States reported an analysis of the conditions in the solar corona which provided confirmation of the foregoing views. The thermal conductivity of the corona, i.e., the ability to transfer heat from one point to another of the coronal gas, consisting largely of protons and electrons, is so high that the temperature of approximately **1,000,000°K** (or more) must extend out for a large distance into space. Beyond a certain range, the velocity of the particles, by virtue of their high kinetic energy, i.e., high temperature, is so large that it exceeds the velocity required to escape from the solar gravitational field.* Consequently, there must be a continuous outward flow (or expansion) of coronal gas in all directions; this flow has been termed the *solar wind*. Measurements made under relatively quiet Sun conditions, by means of instruments carried by the spacecraft Lunik II, Lunik III, Explorer X, and Mariner II, indicate that at approximately Earth's distance from the Sun the normal solar wind contains from 1 to 5 protons per cubic centimeter. The velocity of the wind, which is highly variable, ranges from about 350 to 700 kilometers (210 to 420 miles) per second. At the time of some Class 2 solar flares, the proton velocity was observed to increase to larger values. Further aspects of the solar wind are treated in Chapter 8.

---

* By means of equation (2.29) and the values of G, M_s, and R_s given earlier in this chapter, the escape velocity from the level of the photosphere is found to be 618 kilometers (384 miles) per second. At the distance of a solar radius in the corona it would be about 441 kilometers (274 miles) per second.

SOLAR RADIO WAVE EMISSION

THERMAL RADIO WAVES

6.172. Because of its high temperature, it is to be expected that the Sun will emit electromagnetic radiations of long wavelength, i.e., radio waves, as well as those of intermediate (infrared and visible) and short (ultraviolet and X-ray) wavelength (cf. Fig. 6.13). It was not until 1942, however, that J. S. Hey in England (published in 1946) and G. S. Southworth in the United States (published in 1945) definitely identified the solar radio-frequency waves. Since that time, considerable effort has been devoted to the study of these radiations both from the quiet (undisturbed) Sun and during periods of activity. The phenomena are quite complex but a tentative classification has made it possible to correlate the behavior with certain solar conditions.

6.173. Although the radio-frequency waves are electromagnetic radiations like visible light, X-rays, etc., they have an important advantage in connection with studies of the Sun. The plasma constituting the chromosphere and corona is essentially transparent to light in the visible and shorter wavelength regions of the spectrum. When observations of such radiations are made across the solar disc, it is not a simple matter to determine exactly the levels at which the radiations originate. Inferences can be made by comparing photographs obtained with monochromatic radiations at different wavelengths (§ 6.134), but the conclusions are approximate in nature. To obtain more precise information, it is necessary to study the profiles (or projections) that extend beyond the solar disc either during an eclipse or by means of a coronagraph.

6.174. With radio waves, however, the transparency of a plasma depends on the wavelength of the radio-frequency radiation and on the density of the electrons, i.e., the number per unit volume of plasma. A plasma of high electron density will transmit radio waves of short wavelength but will turn back those of longer wavelength; with decreasing electron density, radio waves of longer and longer wavelength can be transmitted. On the basis of these considerations and an estimate of the electron densities at various levels in the Sun, it has been possible to develop a connection between the solar radio wavelength and the depth from which it originated. The general nature of the results is depicted in Fig. 6.25, which shows the maximum wavelengths of radio waves that would be transmitted from various levels in the solar atmosphere. Thus, wavelengths of 1 centimeter received from the Sun must originate just above the photosphere, and those longer than 10 meters come from high up in the corona.

6.175. The undisturbed Sun emits radio waves over the range from about 1 centimeter to 15 meters (or more) in length, i.e., 30,000 to 20 megacycles per second. If these radiations are thermal in origin, that is to say, if they are emitted from a gas by virtue of its behavior as a black body at a certain temperature, then the intensities are such that the short wavelength end corresponds to a temperature of about 6000°K and that of the longer wavelength end to at least 1,000,000°K. From what has been stated above (Fig. 6.25), it would be reasonable to assign the lower temperature to the photosphere and the upper one to the corona. This would be in agreement with conclusions reached earlier

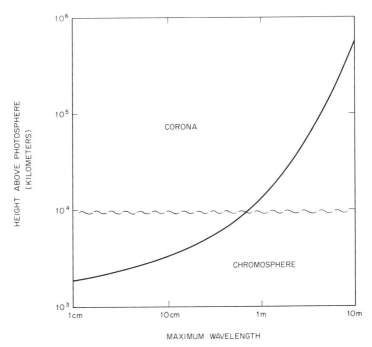

FIG. 6.25.   Maximum wavelengths of radio emission from approximate levels above the photosphere

concerning the temperatures in the Sun's atmosphere. Furthermore, the long-wave radio signals are received from regions well beyond the visible solar disc; hence, it may be concluded that the corona extends for considerable distances, as is known to be the case from other observations.*

Solar Radio Bursts

6.176. A number of transient radio phenomena have been correlated with various aspects of the Sun's activity and some of these will be described briefly here. Most of them are not related to the temperature of the region where they originate and so they are described as *nonthermal* radio emissions, but others appear to be truly thermal emissions. First, there is an effect called the *slowly*

---

* The shielding by the Sun of radio waves from the Crab Nebula (§ 12.166) indicates that the corona extends at least 22 million kilometers (13.5 million miles) in the solar equatorial plane.

varying component of the radio emission, represented by an increase in intensity in the wavelength range of very roughly 3 centimeters to 1 meter (10,000 to 300 megacycles per second). This is associated with the appearance of plages in the chromosphere and of sunspots in the photosphere, although the radiations appear to originate from what are called *radio plages* at the base of the corona. Radio emission may continue over a period of days to months, i.e., beyond the duration of the visible effects of the disturbance. The persistence is indicated by the roughly 27-day periodicity which is often observed, corresponding to the period of rotation of the Sun. Thus, the active areas may last through two or more solar rotations. The slowly varying component is believed to be thermal in origin, arising from local regions which have both a higher density and higher temperature than their surroundings. The general variation of the intensity of the slowly varying component over an extended period of time follows the changes in the sunspot number; the former, like the latter, thus provides a broad indication of solar activity.

6.177. Radio *noise storms*, in the 1- to 10-meter wavelength (300 to 30 megacycles per second) range, occur at times when the Sun is particularly disturbed; they may last for hours or even for days. Superimposed on the continuous noise storms are short bursts of several meters wavelength, known as *Type I bursts*, of relatively narrow bandwidth—about 5 to 30 megacycles per second—lasting from a fraction of a second to a few minutes. The emission apparently originates in the corona in regions above large sunspots. The bursts undoubtedly correspond to periods of unusual activity although the nature of the disturbance is not known. The intensity of the bursts is such that the radiation is unlikely to be of thermal origin. It is possible that Type I radio emission may be Čerenkov radiation; this is an electromagnetic radiation produced by high-energy electrons in their passage through a transparent medium when their velocity is greater than that of light in the medium. Both the background noise storm radiation and the Type I bursts are circularly polarized,* indicating that the electrons have acquired a circular motion presumably in a magnetic field.

6.178. *Type II (or slow-drift) bursts*, lasting from about 5 to 30 minutes, occur in a narrow-band of slowly decreasing frequency, i.e., increasing wavelength, in the range of less than 1 to about 10 meters.† The appearance of these bursts is closely correlated with that of large flares in the chromosphere, although the radio emission comes from the corona. The change in frequency indicates that the source is traveling outward, i.e., toward regions of low electron density, the estimated velocity being about 1000 kilometers (600 miles) per second.

---

* In circular polarization, the electric field does not oscillate along a single line, as it does in linear (or plane) polarization, described in § 6.135, footnote; the field magnitude remains constant, but its direction is continuously rotating in the manner of a radius moving round the circumference of a circle.

† Strong Type II bursts of long duration are often called *outbursts*.

6.179. Type II bursts often appear to be accompanied by the ejection of a stream of material from the Sun at high velocity. In fact, the outward velocity of the disturbance, as estimated from the decrease in frequency, is similar to that at which energetic particles are sometimes expelled at the time of a solar flare (§ 6.171). It has been suggested that the particles generate a shock wave which sets up (unpolarized) plasma oscillations in its passage through the corona. These plasma oscillations are believed to cause the Type II radio emission.

6.180. Varying frequency is also a characteristic of *Type III* (or *fast-drift*) *bursts* which, like those of Type II, are associated with solar flares and occur in the same wavelength range. The Type III bursts are of shorter duration, e.g., about 10 seconds, and often occur in groups. The frequency (or wavelength) changes about a hundred times as fast as in the slow-drift Type II bursts. The emission is possibly also due to plasma oscillations, at least in part, but the source is now traveling outward from the corona at a very high velocity, roughly a third the speed of light, i.e., 100,000 kilometers (60,000 miles) per second. A possible modification of the Type III burst is described as a *U-burst*, because the frequency increases again after decreasing; the plot of frequency against time is thus U-shaped.

6.181. A burst of Type II is sometimes followed by a *Type IV* (or *long-continuum*) *burst* in the event of a large solar flare. It consists of a fairly smooth emission over the range of 50 centimeters to 10 meters wavelength (600 to 30 megacycles per second) that may last from minutes to hours. There is a possibility that Type IV bursts may occur in two phases of different durations and in somewhat different wavelength ranges. The radiations of Type IV bursts are circularly polarized. They are attributed to *synchrotron radiation* produced when relativistic electrons, i.e., electrons with very high velocities, approaching the speed of light,* spiral about the lines of force in a magnetic field. Synchrotron radiation is known to cover a wide and continuous range of wavelengths, such as is characteristic of Type IV bursts. Normally, synchrotron radiation is linearly polarized, but if the waves pass through a plasma containing a magnetic field the polarization is changed to circular, as is the case for Type IV bursts.

6.182. Just as Type IV sometimes follow Type II bursts, so *Type V* (or *short-continuum*) *bursts* follow certain Type III bursts accompanying large flares. The Type V bursts are correspondingly of short duration, e.g., a few

---

* According to the theory of relativity, the effective mass of a particle moving with a velocity v is equal to $m_0/(1 - v^2/c^2)^{0.5}$, where m_0 is the mass of the particle when it is at rest and c is the velocity of light. As the particle velocity approaches that of light, i.e., as v/c approaches unity, the effective mass begins to exceed the rest mass by a significant amount. A *relativistic particle* is arbitrarily defined as one whose energy exceeds m_0c^2. A relativistic electron thus has an energy in excess of 0.51 million electron volts and a velocity that is more than 87 percent of the speed of light.

minutes. Little has been reported concerning these bursts, except that they are continuous and usually extend over a range of longer wavelengths, greater than a few meters, i.e., frequencies less than 100 megacycles per second. It is probable that, like Type IV bursts, those of Type V are a form of synchrotron radiation although they are sometimes elliptically polarized.

6.183. The phenomena associated with solar flares and with radio bursts are very complex, but there appears to be some correlation between them. The initial period of rapidly increasing brilliance of a flare is generally accompanied by one or more short, intense Type III bursts. Each radio burst appears to be associated with a brief but violent luminous outburst of the flare. The Type III bursts are then often, but not always, followed by a Type V burst. If the flare is large and intense, e.g., Class 3 or 3^+, a Type II burst occurs and this is sometimes followed by one of Type IV. For convenience, the characteristics of the five types of radio bursts are summarized in Table 6.2.

SOURCE OF SOLAR ENERGY

Fusion of Hydrogen Nuclei

6.184. The treatment so far has been concerned with the outermost, largely transparent (or atmospheric) regions of the Sun upon which observations can be made, although they may often be limited in nature. Some consideration must now be given to the solar interior and this must inevitably be conjectural to a great extent. A number of facts about the Sun have been established and the theories concerning its interior must be consistent with these facts as well as with the recognized laws of physics. Moreover, there must be a reasonable continuity between the conditions computed for various levels in the interior and those known to exist at the exterior of the Sun.

6.185. The basic solar data to be reconciled are the following: (a) the total rate at which energy is emitted as radiation, which is the same as the rate of energy production, (b) the temperature at the base of the photosphere, i.e., the temperature just outside the completely opaque interior, (c) the radius (or volume), and (d) the mass (or density). In addition, a reasonable assumption is made concerning the chemical composition, particularly of the amount of hydrogen present. In this manner, it has been possible to develop a model that provides a satisfactory interpretation of the Sun's characteristic properties.

6.186. The source of solar energy, as it is for all stars at a certain stage of development (§ 12.142), is the combination (or fusion) of four hydrogen nuclei—plus two electrons required to balance the electrical charges—to yield a helium nucleus. A hydrogen nucleus (or proton) is represented by the symbol $_1H^1$, which indicates that it has a mass of one unit (superscript) and a unit positive charge (subscript); a helium nucleus is denoted by $_2He^4$, i.e., mass 4, charge $+2$. Since an electron has essentially no mass but carries a unit negative

TABLE 6.2   CHARACTERISTICS OF SOLAR RADIO EMISSIONS

Designation	Duration	Wavelength	Origin	Polarization	Remarks
Slowly varying component	Days to months	Centimeter, decimeter, and meter range	Thermal	None	Associated with sunspots and plages
Noise storms	Hours or days	Meter range	—	—	Disturbed Sun
Type I bursts	Short bursts, seconds to minutes	Several meters	Čerenkov radiation (?)	Circular	Originate in corona above large sunspots; superimposed on noise storm
Type II (slow-drift) bursts	5 to 30 minutes	Decimeter, meter range; increasing slowly	Plasma oscillations	None	Associated with large flares; may be caused by shock waves
Type III (fast-drift) bursts	About 10 seconds, often succession of groups	Decimeter, meter range; increasing rapidly	Plasma oscillations (?)	Possible	Associated with large flares; may be caused by fast-moving particles
Type IV (long-continuum) bursts	Minutes to hours	Centimeter, decimeter, and meter range	Synchrotron radiation	Circular	Follows some Type II bursts; produced by high-energy electrons
Type V (short-continuum) bursts	Few minutes	Meter range	Probably synchrotron radiation	Sometimes elliptical	Follows some Type III bursts; produced by high-energy electrons (?)

charge, the appropriate symbol is $_{-1}e^0$. The overall nuclear fusion reaction can thus be written as

$$4\,_1H^1 + 2\,_{-1}e^0 \rightarrow\,_2He^4,$$

so that mass units and electrical charges are balanced.* The four protons taking part in this process must be associated with four electrons for electrical neutrality; of these, two are removed in the reaction written above, leaving two electrons to compensate for the positive charges on the helium nucleus. The effective result, as may be seen by adding two electrons to each side of the nuclear reaction equation, is

$$4\,H\ (\text{nuclei}) + 4\ \text{electrons} \rightarrow He\ (\text{nucleus}) + 2\ \text{electrons}.$$

In other words, four atoms of hydrogen are converted into an atom of helium, a process accompanied by the release of a large quantity of energy.

6.187. The amount of energy produced can be determined from the known masses of the hydrogen and helium atoms, the calculation being based on *Einstein's equation* expressing the equivalence of energy and mass, i.e.,

$$E = mc^2, \tag{6.14}$$

where E is the energy equivalent to a mass m, and c is the velocity of light. Any process in which there is a decrease of mass m, must be accompanied by the release of a quantity of energy, E, as given by equation (6.14). If m is in grams, and the value of 2.998×10^{10} centimeters per second is used for the velocity of light, the energy will be in ergs; hence,

$$E(\text{ergs}) = m(\text{grams}) \times 8.99 \times 10^{20}.$$

Making use of the fact that 1 calorie $= 4.18 \times 10^7$ ergs, an alternative form of the mass-energy relationship is

$$E(\text{calories}) = m(\text{grams}) \times 2.15 \times 10^{13}.$$

6.188. The mass of four hydrogen atoms on the conventional atomic mass scale is $4 \times 1.008145 = 4.03258$, and that of a helium atom is 4.00387; the decrease of mass in the reaction referred to above is thus 0.02871. In other words, for every 1 gram of hydrogen taking part in the process, the change in mass would be $0.02871/4.03258 = 0.00712$ gram. The corresponding energy release would be $0.00712 \times 2.15 \times 10^{13} = 1.53 \times 10^{11}$ calories. About 2 percent of this energy is carried away by neutral particles of essentially zero mass, called *neutrinos* (cf. § 12.240); hence, for each gram of hydrogen converted into helium, 1.50×10^{11} calories are released in the solar interior.

6.189. The total rate of energy emission from the Sun (§ 6.34), and hence the rate of energy generation, is 5.62×10^{27} calories per minute, i.e., 9.37×10^{25}

---

* The number of charges on a nucleus (subscript) is called the *atomic number,* and the number of mass units (superscript) is the *mass number.*

calories per second. The rate at which hydrogen would have to be consumed to provide this amount of energy is

$$\frac{9.37 \times 10^{25}}{1.50 \times 10^{11}} = 6.24 \times 10^{14} \text{ grams per second.}$$

Since there are 3.15×10^7 seconds in a year, the annual rate of hydrogen consumption would be close to 2.0×10^{22} grams, i.e., 2.0×10^{19} kilograms. Although this is a very large quantity of hydrogen, it is only a minute fraction of the total solar mass of about 2×10^{30} kilograms. Assuming hydrogen has been used up at the same rate during the whole of the approximately 5×10^9 years since the Sun was formed, the total mass of hydrogen consumed would be 10^{29} kilograms, i.e., about 5 percent of its present mass of 2×10^{30} kilograms. There is thus little danger of the solar hydrogen being exhausted within the next few billion years. The loss of mass resulting from conversion of the hydrogen into helium is about 1 part by weight in 140 of the hydrogen involved in the nuclear reaction, i.e., 1.4×10^{17} kilograms per annum or some 7×10^{26} kilograms since the formation of the Sun.*

MECHANISM OF FUSION REACTIONS

6.190. Although the overall nuclear reaction in the Sun can undoubtedly be represented by the combination of four hydrogen atoms to yield a helium atom, the probability that four protons will combine in a single step is vanishingly small. It is much more likely that the process takes place in stages and a study of nuclear reactions has indicated that there are two possible mechanisms to account for the energy release in stars in which hydrogen is converted into helium; these are known as the proton-proton chain and the carbon cycle, respectively.

6.191. In the *proton-proton* chain, the first step is the combination of two protons to form a deuteron, i.e., a nucleus of deuterium, the heavier isotope of hydrogen (§ 3.214), and a positron, i.e., an electron with a positive charge, represented by $_1e^0$; thus,

$$_1H^1 + _1H^1 \rightarrow _1D^2 + _1e^0.$$

It is in this step that the neutrino referred to in § 6.188 is formed. The deuteron then combines with another proton to yield a helium-3 nucleus, i.e.,

$$_1D^2 + _1H^1 \rightarrow _2He^3.$$

6.192. At temperatures somewhat below $13,000,000°K,$† the next step is

---

* It is estimated that during this period the Sun has lost about 2 percent of its mass as a result of particle emission. There has been some gain by the accretion of interstellar material, but this is much smaller than the total loss.

† In accordance with the common practice, all temperatures in this section are given in degrees Kelvin; the centigrade (Celsius) temperatures are 273° less, i.e., essentially the same. Temperatures on the Fahrenheit scale are obtained, with sufficient accuracy, by multiplying by 1.8.

believed to be the combination of two helium-3 nuclei; thus,

$$_2\text{He}^3 + {}_2\text{He}^3 \rightarrow {}_2\text{He}^4 + 2\,{}_1\text{H}^1,$$

a helium-4 nucleus being formed and two protons regenerated. To obtain the two helium-3 nuclei required for this process, the first two stages must be multiplied by two, and upon adding the resulting three equations, the overall reaction is found to be

$$4\,{}_1\text{H}^1 \rightarrow {}_2\text{He}^4 + 2\,{}_1e^0.$$

The two positrons are annihilated by two electrons with the release of energy and the final result is

$$4\,{}_1\text{H}^1 + 2\,{}_{-1}e^0 \rightarrow {}_2\text{He}^4,$$

as given in § 6.186. Some energy is liberated in each stage of the proton-proton chain, and the total is equal to that already calculated for the formation of a helium-4 atom from four hydrogen atoms.

6.193. Once helium-4 has been formed in the foregoing manner, the reaction

$$_2\text{He}^3 + {}_2\text{He}^4 \rightarrow {}_4\text{Be}^7$$

becomes possible at temperatures above about $13,000,000°$K. The beryllium-7 is unstable and captures a negative electron, represented by $_{-1}e^0$, to form lithium-7; the latter then interacts with a proton to generate two helium nuclei in the following manner:

$$_4\text{Be}^7 + {}_{-1}e^0 \rightarrow {}_3\text{Li}^7$$
$$_3\text{Li}^7 + {}_1\text{H}^1 \rightarrow {}_2\text{He}^4 + {}_2\text{He}^4.$$

The net reaction is then the same as before.

6.194. The *carbon cycle* differs from the proton-proton chain in the respect that it requires the presence of carbon; hence, it can occur only in stars in which this element is present in appreciable amounts. First, a carbon-12 nucleus captures a proton, i.e.,

$$_6\text{C}^{12} + {}_1\text{H}^1 \rightarrow {}_7\text{N}^{13},$$

but the product, nitrogen-13, is unstable, i.e., radioactive, and emits a positron to yield a stable carbon-13 nucleus; thus,

$$_7\text{N}^{13} \rightarrow {}_6\text{C}^{13} + {}_1e^0.$$

The carbon-13 nucleus then captures a second proton to form stable nitrogen-14 which, in turn, combines with a third proton to form radioactive oxygen-15; thus,

$$_6\text{C}^{13} + {}_1\text{H}^1 \rightarrow {}_7\text{N}^{14},$$
$$_7\text{N}^{14} + {}_1\text{H}^1 \rightarrow {}_8\text{O}^{15}$$

and the oxygen-15 emits a positron, i.e.,

$$_8\text{O}^{15} \rightarrow {}_7\text{N}^{15} + {}_1e^0,$$

the product being stable nitrogen-15. Finally, the latter captures a fourth proton,

$$_7N^{15} + {}_1H^1 \rightarrow {}_6C^{12} + {}_2He^4,$$

so that a helium-4 nucleus is produced and the carbon-12 is regenerated. Summation of the six stages represented above, and allowing for annihilation of the positrons by negative electrons, shows that the net result is again

$$4\ {}_1H^1 + 2\ {}_{-1}e^0 \rightarrow {}_2He^4.$$

The carbon-12 is not consumed and merely serves as a catalyst to permit the chain (or cycle) of nuclear reactions to take place.

6.195. A minor variation of the carbon cycle that occurs to the extent of at least 1 percent is the result of an alternative reaction arising from the capture of a proton by nitrogen-15, namely,

$$_7N^{15} + {}_1H^1 \rightarrow {}_8O^{16}.$$

The following reactions then ensue:

$$_8O^{16} + {}_1H^1 \rightarrow {}_9F^{17}$$
$$_9F^{17} \rightarrow {}_1e^0 + {}_8O^{17}$$
$$_8O^{17} + {}_1H^1 \rightarrow {}_7N^{14} + {}_2He^4.$$

The nitrogen-14 captures a proton to form oxygen-15, i.e.,

$$_7N^{14} + {}_1H^1 \rightarrow {}_8O^{15},$$

and the chain continues in the manner described above. At temperatures below about 14,000,000°K, however, the reactions are not able to go beyond nitrogen-14.

6.196. In order to proceed fast enough and release energy at a significant rate, the proton-proton chain and the carbon cycle require very high temperatures, on the order of several million degrees. They are, in fact, thermonuclear reactions of the type described in § 3.214. The relative probabilities of the two main mechanisms for converting hydrogen into helium depends on the actual temperature. At the lower stellar temperatures, the proton-proton chain predominates, but at higher temperatures, above about 20,000,000°K, the carbon cycle is the more important.

The Solar Interior

6.197. A representation (or model) of the Sun that is consistent with the basic requirements mentioned in § 6.185 has been developed by considering the solar interior to consist of a perfect (or ideal) gas mixture of hydrogen and helium. A point-to-point calculation, from the center outward, is then carried out in which the inward pressure due to the gravitational force at each radial distance, determined from the mass lying beyond that distance, is balanced against the kinetic pressure generated by the gas particles. In spite of the very high pressures (and densities), it is still reasonable to assume that the Sun behaves as a perfect gas because the temperatures are so high.

6.198. The model derived in this manner varies to some extent with the basic assumptions that are made, but there is general agreement in assigning a temperature of about 15,000,000°K to the central region (or core) of the Sun. In this event, most of the solar energy is produced by the proton-proton chain mechanism with very little, if any, arising from the carbon cycle. The density of the gas in the core, where the nuclear reactions occur, is estimated to be roughly 100 grams per cubic centimeter, i.e., a hundred times as dense as water under ordinary conditions. For a gas to attain such a density at the high core temperature, the pressure must have the enormous value of more than 10^{12} pounds per square inch. At the existing temperature the atoms of hydrogen and helium are completely stripped and the core contains only nuclei and free electrons.

6.199. The next matter to consider is how the heat energy generated in the central region of the Sun is conveyed to the surface where it is radiated away. There are three general methods whereby heat can be transferred from any region of higher temperature to one of lower temperature, namely, radiation, convection, and conduction. Of these, it appears that conduction is not very significant in the Sun, although it is in some other stars, and so it will not be considered further here.

6.200. In the immediate vicinity of the solar core, where the energy is generated, *radiative transfer*, i.e., heat transfer by radiation, is probably more important than convection; thus, it is considered that a *radiative zone* surrounds the nuclear reaction zone (or core) as indicated in Fig. **6.26**, which is drawn roughly to scale. In the radiative zone, energy is transferred from the hotter (inner) to the cooler (outer) layers by photons of radiation, each carrying an appropriate quantum of energy (§ **6.74**). The rate at which photons are emitted and the distribution of energy among the photons is determined by the temperature, in accordance with Planck's equation, as

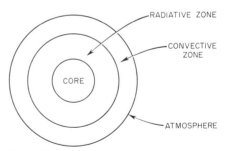

Fig. 6.26.   Zones in interior of the Sun

described earlier. Consequently, many of the photons leaving the core, which has a temperature of several million degrees, will have very high energies.

6.201. Consider a photon with a high-energy quantum that leaves the core and enters the radiative zone. It will be taken up by a material particle, e.g., atom, ion, or electron, in that zone, but after a short time, generally a small fraction of a second, the particle will emit one or more photons of lower energy than that of the absorbed photon. These emitted photons will subsequently be captured by other material particles and photons of still lower energy will be emitted in due course. In this manner, energy is transferred from one point to another. Of course, photons will move in both directions, i.e., some from the core to the radiative zone and others from the radiative zone to the core. But as a result of the higher temperatures in the core, the photons traveling outward will carry more energy than those moving in the opposite direction. The net result is the transfer of energy away from the core and through the radiative zone.

6.202. There are two important points to note in connection with the foregoing description of radiative energy transfer. In the first place, in passing through the radiative zone, the photons do not travel in straight lines. Because the photons are emitted in random directions, the succession of absorptions and emissions leads to what is known as a *random walk* for each photon. Consequently, although a photon moves with the velocity of light during the period that it is free, i.e., between emission and subsequent absorption, the net rate of progress in the outward direction is very slow. In the Sun, for example, calculations indicate that in the radiative zone a photon travels, on the average, only about a one-thousandth part (10^{-3}) of a centimeter before it is absorbed. Obviously, an extremely large number of absorptions and random emissions will occur before the energy carried by the photon eventually reaches the outer boundary of the zone. It has been estimated that it takes an average time of something like a million years before the energy produced in the nuclear reaction zone of the Sun finally escapes from the photosphere.

6.203. Because of the slow rate of energy transfer and the enormous mass of the Sun, changes, if any, taking place in the core should be largely damped out before becoming apparent at the surface. It is to be anticipated, therefore, that the solar constant would remain quite unchanged from year to year or that it might exhibit, at most, a very slight drift over a period of millions of years. But this argument does not take into consideration the possibility that large amounts of energy may be restrained temporarily by the complex solar magnetic fields. If short-term variations are found to occur in the solar constant, they could probably be explained in this manner. As mentioned in § 6.33, more and better information about the solar constant is badly needed.

6.204. The second point of interest in connection with the energy transfer mechanism described above is that, in passing outward from the Sun's core to (and through) the radiative zone, the photon energy is degraded; that is to say, photons of higher energy are gradually replaced by those of lower energy. This is, of course, in accord with Planck's theory (cf. Fig. 6.13), since the temperature must be highest in the core, where the energy is generated, and gradually decrease throughout the radiative zone. In the central region, at a temperature of 15,000,000°K, the maximum radiation intensity occurs at a wavelength of approximately 2 Å, i.e., in the X-ray range, according to equation (6.7). As the heat energy is transferred through the radiative zone, the maximum gradually shifts to longer wavelengths, i.e., lower energies, corresponding to the lower temperatures.

6.205. In the core of the Sun and in the lower levels of the radiative zone, the temperatures are so high that the only particles present are completely stripped nuclei and free electrons. With increasing distance from the center, as the temperature decreases, neutral and partially stripped atoms can exist. These can, however, become ionized, i.e., lose one or more electrons, as a result of interaction with (and absorption of) photons of sufficient energy. The result is that the medium becomes increasingly opaque to the passage of radiation. The average distance a photon travels before it is absorbed is considerably less than is the case closer to the core; as a consequence, the transfer of energy by radiation, i.e., by photons, is slowed down. At this stage, convection makes an important contribution to the mechanism of energy transfer. The radiative zone in the Sun is therefore followed by a *convective zone* (Fig. 6.26), its thickness being estimated to be some 80,000 kilometers (50,000 miles). There is no sharp demarcation between the radiative and convective zones, because energy transfer by both radiation and convection takes place to various extents in each zone.

6.206. The transfer of energy by convection involves the bodily movement, from one location to another, of material in which the energy is stored. This movement, as seen in § 6.98, depends on variations in density resulting from differences in temperature. The outward motion of hotter material and the inward movement of the cooler material cause heat to be carried through the convective zone. A contributory factor is the recombination in the outer layers of the ions and electrons that were formed by the interaction with photons in the lower layers as stated above. The recombination is accompanied by the liberation of energy that was absorbed in the reverse (ionization) process.

6.207. As a consequence of the decreasing pressure at increasing distance from the Sun's core, the density of the material also falls, in spite of the lower temperatures. This decrease in density becomes very significant toward the outer region of the convective zone, with the result that a condition is reached at which the material becomes much less opaque to black-body radiation at the existing temperature. At this point, the photosphere commences. Because the upper parts of this region are partially transparent, at least, to the solar radiation, subsequent emission of energy is almost entirely by radiation. Some energy is transferred from the convective zone to the chromosphere and corona in other ways, e.g., possibly as material and hydromagnetic shock waves (§ 6.131 *et seq.*), but this represents only a small proportion of the total energy emitted by the Sun. Thus, in the final stage, radiative transfer again becomes the dominant mechanism.

SOLAR STUDIES FROM SPACE

SOUNDING ROCKET OBSERVATIONS

6.208. The purpose of studying the Sun from above Earth's atmosphere is to permit extension of the observations into the short-wavelength, i.e., ultraviolet and X-ray, range of the electromagnetic spectrum. It is evident from the discussions in preceding sections of this chapter that there are many important areas in which the behavior of the Sun is not at all well understood. By obtaining more complete information on the nature of the solar radiations and especially of their variation with the Sun's activity, it is hoped that significant advances will be made. Such advances are of more than purely scientific interest because of the known, although not completely apprehended, connection between many solar and terrestrial phenomena.

6.209. As has been mentioned earlier in this chapter, the U.S. Naval Research Laboratory has pioneered in the use of sounding rockets to obtain spectra of the Sun at short wavelengths, i.e., in the ultraviolet and X-ray regions. The first ultraviolet spectra were obtained by R. Tousey, *et al.,* in 1946, and three years later H. Friedman, *et al.,* made the earliest measurement on solar radiations in the X-ray region. Subsequently, many studies with spectrographic sounding rockets have been carried out in the United States, in the United Kingdom, and in the U.S.S.R. In the earlier work, it was necessary to recover the instruments by means of a parachute, but the development of telemetry simplified matters by making recovery less important. Some of the results of the spectrographic observations on the Sun at short wavelengths have already been given, but specific mention may be made of remarkable photographs of the solar disc taken in Lyman-α and X-ray emissions to supplement the more familiar Balmer H_α and Ca II (H and K) representations (Fig. 6.27).

EARLY SATELLITE STUDIES

6.210. The ability to carry a spectrograph on board a satellite obviously represents a significant advance over the use of sounding rockets. By pointing the instrument at the Sun, observations can be made continuously over an extended period during the sunlit portion of the orbit and they could be repeated at regular intervals. Flare studies had been made with sounding rockets by launching them after a flare was detected. But instruments on a satellite would already be operational when a flare occurred, and measurements would be made automatically, provided the satellite was not in Earth's shadow at the time.

6.211. The first satellite to study radiation from the Sun was Explorer VII, launched on October 13, 1959; it carried spectrographic instruments to measure the solar ultraviolet and X-rays. The results were not too good, however, because of interference by electrically charged particles in the radiation belt surrounding Earth (§ 8.267). Much more successful was the Solar Radiation I

(or Greb I) satellite, launched simultaneously with the Transit II A navigational satellite on June 22, 1960.* It carried, among other devices, instruments
for measuring Lyman-α and X-ray (2 to 8 Å wavelength) emissions from the
Sun. During the course of a Class 1 flare, it was found that the X-ray intensity,

 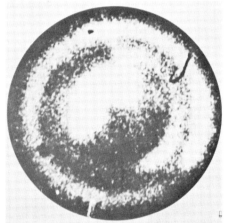

FIG. 6.27. Photograph of the Sun taken in the Lyman-α line of hydrogen (left); X-ray
pinhole camera photograph (right), smeared by rotation of rocket, taken on another
day. (*Official United States Navy Photograph*)

which had previously been very small, increased markedly; strangely, however,
the Lyman-α line of atomic hydrogen appeared to remain essentially unchanged.
This result was confirmed by observations from the OSO-I; the increase in the
intensity of the Lyman-α emission from hydrogen was very much less than for
Fe XVI, Fe XV, and He II (§ 6.158).

ORBITING SOLAR OBSERVATORY

6.212. Although it was not launched until more than three years later, planning was initiated in February 1959 for the first Orbiting Solar Observatory
(OSO). Structurally, the OSO consists of two parts: one is the "wheel," 92
inches in diameter, composed of nine sections arranged around a central hub,
and the other is the "sail," an approximately semicircular structure 37 inches
high (Fig. 6.28) The sail, which is covered with solar cells, is attached to the
wheel by a shaft that permits the two components to rotate freely with respect
to one another. To provide attitude stability, the wheel is kept spinning at a
rate of 30 revolutions per minute by means of jets, operated by nitrogen gas,
located at the ends of three arms. As a result of the gyroscopic action of the
spinning wheel, the spin axis, which is also the rotation axis of the sail about

* This is the first recorded case of the launch of two satellites by a single rocket vehicle.

the wheel, tends to remain fixed in inertial space. By means of photoelectric sensors, the plane of the sail is kept facing the Sun, within 1 or 2 minutes of arc, at all times during the sunlit period of each orbit.

6.213. In the center of the bottom of the sail is a gimbal that can move about the pitch axis with respect to the sail. Instruments which are to be kept pointed

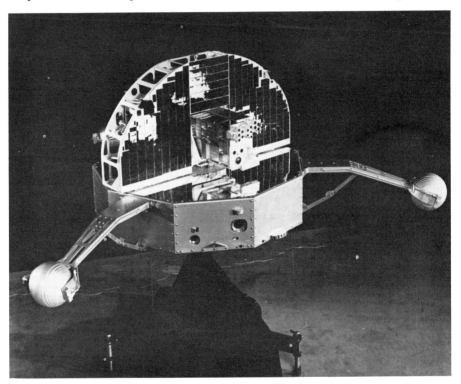

Fig. 6.28.   The Orbiting Solar Observatory

at the Sun are mounted on this gimbal. Small jets operated by signals from photoelectric devices alter the pitch of the gimbal so that the instruments point directly at the Sun, also within 1 or 2 minutes of arc. These instruments, weighing about 70 pounds, are contained in a space 38 inches in length with an 8-inch square cross section. OSO-I carried a spectrometer, which covered the spectral range from 30 to 400 Å, i.e., soft X-rays and far ultraviolet, and a monitor to determine the X-ray intensity in the energy range of 20 to 100 keV, i.e., 0.6 to 0.12 Å wavelength (§ 6.75). Another device, also pointed at the Sun, was designed to detect gamma rays of 0.51 MeV; these are produced by the mutual annihilation of ordinary (negative) electrons and positrons, such as are generated in the thermonuclear reactions occurring in the solar interior.

6.214. Of the nine sections of the wheel, four are occupied by the spacecraft's control, telemetry, and related systems; the remaining five contain about 150 pounds of instruments for various experiments to measure gamma rays, protons, neutrons, electrons, and the total solar radiation within certain broad energy ranges. Since the wheel spins at the rate of 30 revolutions per minute, each instrument sweeps across the Sun every 2 seconds. It is thus possible to compare solar emissions of various types with those from other regions of space. The spacecraft rolls slowly about the axis pointing at the Sun, and so the instruments in the wheel scan the entire celestial sphere in the course of time. Information from all instruments is recorded on tape and read out upon command from the ground in the usual manner (see Chapter 4).

6.215. The first OSO was launched on March 7, 1962 into an almost circular orbit, perigee 344 miles and apogee 370 miles, with a period of 96 minutes and an inclination of 33 deg to the equator. The total weight of the spacecraft in orbit was about 450 pounds. The useful life of the satellite, expected to be about 6 months, should have been determined by the quantity of nitrogen available for operating the spin rockets. But after less than 3 months, the recording and telemetry system developed difficulties which prevented continuous operation. Prior to that time, all instruments and telemetry of OSO-I operated satisfactorily and some of the results obtained have been described earlier in this chapter. In continuation of the OSO series, OSO-II was placed in an orbit similar to that of OSO-I on February 3, 1965. Among the instruments it carried were an ultraviolet spectrometer, X-ray and ultraviolet telescopes, gamma-ray detectors (solar and cosmic), and a coronagraph (§ 6.42).

ADVANCED ORBITING SOLAR OBSERVATORY

6.216. An Advanced Orbiting Solar Observatory (AOSO) is being planned for the purpose of obtaining more refined information about the Sun. Observations will be made in the infrared, visible, ultraviolet, and X-ray (or gamma-ray) regions of the solar spectrum. A telescope may be included to permit television recording of spectroheliograms in the short wavelength end of the spectrum. An important feature of the AOSO will be the ability to point instruments upon command at a particular area of the solar surface in order to study the behavior of active centers. The pointing accuracy will be 5 sec of arc, compared with 1 min in the OSO.

6.217. The spacecraft, which is expected to weigh about 900 pounds, including 250 pounds of instruments, is to be in the form of a cylinder some 10 feet long and 40 inches in diameter, apart from the solar-cell panels (Fig. 6.29). It will be placed in a near-polar orbit that will permit good visibility of the Sun on every orbit. Launching of the first AOSO is expected in the early part of 1969.

FIG. 6.29. The Advanced Orbiting Solar Observatory

APPENDIX

THE PLANCK EQUATION

6.218. On the basis of his quantum theory of the emission of radiation, Max Planck derived the equation

$$I_\nu = \frac{2\pi h}{c^2} \cdot \frac{\nu^3}{e^{h\nu/kT} - 1},$$

where $I_\nu \, d\nu$ is the amount of energy radiated by a black body per unit area per second in the frequency range from ν to $\nu + d\nu$; h is Planck's constant, k is Boltzmann's constant, i.e., the gas constant per molecule, c is the velocity of light, and T is the absolute temperature. The total energy emitted at all frequencies (or wavelengths) is obtained by integrating $I_\nu \, d\nu$ over all frequencies, from zero to infinity; thus,

$$E = \int_0^\infty I_\nu \, d\nu$$

$$= \frac{2\pi h}{c^2} \int_0^\infty \frac{\nu^3 \, d\nu}{e^{h\nu/kT} - 1} = \frac{2\pi k^4 T^4}{c^2 h^3} \int_0^\infty \frac{x^3 \, dx}{e^x - 1},$$

where $x = h\nu/kT$. The value of the integral is known to be $\pi^4/15$, so that

$$E = \frac{2\pi^5 k^4}{15c^2 h^3} T^4$$

$$= \sigma T^4,$$

where σ is a constant, which has the numerical value 1.38×10^{-12} calories per square centimeter per second. This is the Stefan-Boltzmann equation (6.5).

6.219. The Planck equation can be written in an alternative form in terms of the wavelength instead of the frequency; thus, since $\nu = c/\lambda$,

$$d\nu = \frac{c}{\lambda^2} d\lambda,$$

where λ is the wavelength of the radiation corresponding to the frequency ν. If the appropriate substitution is made, it is found that

$$I_\lambda = \frac{2\pi hc^2}{\lambda^5} \cdot \frac{1}{e^{hc/kT\lambda} - 1},$$

where $I_\lambda\, d\lambda$ is the energy radiated by a black body per unit area per second in the wavelength range from λ to $\lambda + d\lambda$. The quantity x defined above is equivalent to $hc/kT\lambda$, and so the expression for I_λ becomes

$$I_\lambda = \frac{2\pi k^5 T^5}{c^3 h^4} \cdot \frac{x^5}{e^x - 1}.$$

The wavelength λ_m at which the radiation emission is a maximum for a given temperature may be obtained from the condition that

$$\frac{dI_\lambda}{d\lambda} = 0.$$

The differentiation is simplified by recalling that

$$\frac{dI_\lambda}{d\lambda} = \frac{dI_\lambda}{dx} \cdot \frac{dx}{d\lambda},$$

and the result obtained may be written in the form

$$(5 - x)e^x = 5.$$

Apart from the trivial solution $x = 0$, this equation has only one solution, namely $x = 4.965$. It follows, therefore, that

$$x = \frac{hc}{kT\lambda_m} = 4.965$$

or

$$\lambda_m = \frac{hc}{4.965kT} = \frac{2.90 \times 10^7}{T},$$

with the wavelength expressed in angstroms. This is Wien's displacement law equation (6.7).

6.220. For radiations of long wavelength, x is small, and $e^x - 1$ may be replaced by x; the expression for I_λ then reduces to the form

$$I_\lambda = \frac{2\pi kc}{\lambda^4}\, T,$$

which is known as the Rayleigh-Jeans law. This result is commonly used in the derivation of brightness temperatures (§ 6.65) from radiation measurements at long wavelength, e.g., in the radio-frequency portion of the spectrum. It will be noted that under these conditions the brightness temperature is directly proportional to the rate of energy emission at a given wavelength (or small range about the given wavelength).

Chapter 7

THE SOLAR SYSTEM

THE PLANETS

INTRODUCTION

7.1. In addition to the Sun, which was described in the preceding chapter, the *solar system* consists of all those bodies whose motions are determined primarily by the gravitational attraction of the Sun. Thus, the solar system includes the nine principal planets, the asteroids (or minor planets), the comets, the meteoroids, and other particulate matter that revolves about the Sun. On the basis of the restricted definition given above, the various satellites of the planets, such as the Moon, will not be treated here. Although they are members of the solar system in its widest sense, the primary bodies about which they revolve are the respective planets and not the Sun.

7.2. In this chapter, the planets are considered as a system and their general characteristics are compared. A more detailed discussion of the properties of the individual planets is given later: Earth and its environment in Chapter 8, the other terrestrial planets in Chapter 10, and the major planets and Pluto in Chapter 11. The minor members of the solar system such as asteroids, comets, meteoroids, etc., however, are not treated elsewhere in the book. It may appear somewhat unbalanced, therefore, that most of the chapter is devoted to the discussion of these and related objects and phenomena. But this seemed to be the best way to organize and present the large volume of important but somewhat unrelated material on the various aspects of the solar system.

MOTION OF THE PLANETS

7.3. Some of the earliest observers of the sky realized that there was a difference between the planets and the other stars. Because of Earth's rotation about its axis, the stars, like the Sun, appear to move from east to west every night. But the motion of the so-called *fixed stars* is such that they always remain in essentially the same positions relative to each other. This constancy in the configurations of the stars led to the development of the largely artificial concept of *constellations* or groups of stars. Not only do the stars in each con-

stellation seem to have fixed locations within the group, but the various constellations always have the same orientations with respect to the others.

7.4. The planets also exhibit an apparent diurnal, i.e., daily, east-to-west
motion due to Earth's rotation, but otherwise their behavior differs from that
of the fixed stars. In the first place, the planets do not occupy definite positions
with reference to the fixed stars throughout the year. If a given planet is observed on successive days, its location will appear to move in a general west-to-
east direction among the constellations; this direct motion, as it is called, is a
result of Earth's orbital revolution about the Sun.* On some occasions, however, the planets exhibit retrograde motion for a few weeks; that is to say, they
seem to move from east to west against the background of the stars. It is because of their apparently erratic motion through the skies that they were named
planets, a word derived from the Greek *planetes,* meaning "wandering." Since
the Sun and the Moon also seem to move among the stars, they were considered
to be planets, and the Greek philosophers of over two thousand years ago
listed seven planets, namely, the Sun, the Moon, Mercury, Venus, Mars, Jupiter,
and Saturn, the last five being named for Greek gods.†

THE GEOCENTRIC AND HELIOCENTRIC SYSTEMS

7.5.   The Greek scholar Aristarchus of Samos, who lived in the third century
B.C., had suggested that the Sun was the center about which revolved all
celestial bodies, including the stars. But this view was not regarded with favor
because of the strongly entrenched opinion among the Greeks that Earth was
the fixed center of the universe. The planets, including the Sun and the Moon,
and the stars were believed to revolve around Earth. Consequently, it was the
geocentric (or *Earth-centered*) *universe* of the Greco-Egyptian astronomer
Claudius Ptolemaeus (Ptolemy), who lived in Alexandria during the second
century A.D., that was accepted for some 1400 years. But in 1543, after more
than 30 years of study, the Polish astronomer Nicolaus Copernicus published
his great work entitled *Revolutions of the Celestial Bodies,* in which he revived
the *heliocentric,* or Sun-centered, concept of Aristarchus. Although the views of
Copernicus were not universally accepted, because they did not account completely for the apparent motions of the Sun, the Moon, the planets, and the
stars, their publication marked a turning point in the development of astronomy.

7.6. One of those who was interested in the Copernican theory, although he
did not accept it, was the Danish astronomer Tycho Brahe. He died in 1601, be-

---

* It is appropriate to point out here the distinction that is made between rotation and
revolution; rotation is motion about an axis through the body, whereas revolution is motion
in a closed path about a point outside the body.

† A reminder of the seven planets of the Greeks is to be found in the names of the seven
days of the week, particularly in the Romance languages: Sunday (Sun), Monday (Moon),
Tuesday (French, *mardi,* Mars), Wednesday (*mercredi,* Mercury), Thursday (*jeudi,* Jove
or Jupiter), Friday (*vendredi,* Venus), and Saturday (Saturn).

fore the telescope was invented, but during his lifetime he developed and improved a number of instruments for observing the planets and the stars. With these, he was able to determine the positions and follow the motions of the planets with much greater accuracy then had been previously possible. From his observations, Tycho Brahe concluded that both Ptolemy and Copernicus were wrong, and he proposed a theory which combined features of both geocentric and heliocentric views of the universe. According to the Tychonic system, as it is known, the Sun and Moon revolve about Earth, but the planets revolve about the Sun. The theory certainly did not represent a step in the right direction, but the vast amount of data collected by Tycho Brahe was destined to play an important role.

7.7. In the year 1600, shortly before Tycho Brahe's death, Johannes Kepler (§ 1.31, § 2.48) became his assistant and thus had access to the astronomical data that had been accumulated over many years of careful observation. Kepler favored the Copernican theory of the universe, but realized, as Tycho Brahe had done, that in its original form it did not account for the motion of the planets. Copernicus, like his Greek predecessors, had assumed that celestial bodies move in orbits that were perfect circles; it did not seem reasonable that heavenly bodies, such as the Sun and the stars, could follow any other type of path. By postulating that the planets revolve about the Sun in elliptical orbits, with the Sun at one of the foci of the ellipse, Kepler was able to remove all objections to the heliocentric concept. The three laws of planetary motion, which he derived empirically from Tycho Brahe's observations and which were later developed from the universal theory of gravitation by Isaac Newton, are now completely accepted. As was seen in Chapter 2, they describe the orbits of satellites about any primary body, and the planets are in fact satellites of the Sun. The Moon is, of course, not a planet, since its motion is not determined primarily by the Sun, but a satellite of Earth, and Kepler's laws describe its motion about Earth.

DISCOVERY OF THE PLANETS

7.8. One of the consequences of Kepler's views was the acceptance of Earth as one of the planets, and so in the early years of the seventeenth century six planets were known; in order of increasing distance from the Sun, they were Mercury, Venus, Earth, Mars, Jupiter, and Saturn. These bodies are all visible with the naked eye and, in spite of the invention of the telescope, they remained the only known planets until 1781. In that year William Herschel (§ 6.45) discovered the planet Uranus, beyond Saturn. While studying the sky with a telescope of his own construction, Herschel detected an object that appeared to be larger than the fixed stars in its vicinity. At first he thought it might be a nebulous star or perhaps a comet, but observations of its motion established it to be a previously unidentified planet. It transpired subsequently that other astronomers had seen this celestial body but because of its relatively slow movement they had mistaken it for a star. Uranus is sufficiently bright to be detectable with the naked eye under favorable conditions.

7.9. Soon after the discovery of Uranus, it became apparent that its expected elliptical orbit was being perturbed, presumably by another planet which was then unknown. In 1845, John C. Adams in England and, in the following year, Urbain J. J. Leverrier in France independently completed calculations of the position of such a planet, beyond Uranus, which could account for the perturbations of the latter. At the suggestion of Leverrier, the German astronomer Johann G. Galle quickly sought and found the new planet, now called Neptune, very close to its predicted position in the sky.*

7.10. It developed in due course, however, that the mass and orbit of Neptune were inadequate to account for the observed perturbations in the orbit of Uranus. Among those who attempted to explain the situation was the American astronomer Percival Lowell. He postulated the existence of still another planet. Independent computations by William H. Pickering in the United States appeared to confirm Lowell's estimate of the orbit of the unknown planet. Before he died in 1916, Lowell tried to find what he called Planet X, but was not successful.

7.11. Following the death of Lowell, the search for the unknown planet was continued at the observatory which he had founded near Flagstaff, Arizona. In 1930, Clyde W. Tombaugh, a young assistant at the Lowell Observatory, detected an unknown object with a planet-like motion; this was identified with Planet X and named Pluto. A re-examination of older star charts, taken at the Lowell and Mount Wilson Observatories in 1914 and 1919, revealed the presence of the same planet. There were at least two factors that contributed to its discovery in 1930: first, in that year Pluto was much closer to Earth than in preceding years, and second, the invention of the "blink" microscope. With the latter, two photographs of the sky taken at different times could be compared and even the slight movement of an object (planet) with respect to the fixed stars was apparent by the change (or jump) in location. Although Tombaugh's discovery was directly connected with Lowell's calculations, some astronomers are of the opinion that the mass of Pluto is too small to produce the reported perturbations in the orbit of Uranus. If this is the case, the discovery of Pluto was at least partly accidental.

7.12. It is not at all impossible that there may be another planet (or planets) belonging to the solar system even farther from the Sun than Pluto. In fact, the discrepancy between the apparent diameter of Pluto, on the one hand, and its estimated mass, on the other hand (§ 11.100), has led to the suggestion that such a planet actually exists. An exhaustive search, however, made by Tombaugh between 1930 and 1945, has not brought it to light. Even if there were such a distant planet, it would be so faint that the only hope of finding it would

---

* Adams had earlier requested the assistance of astronomers in England in locating the planet but received a less enthusiastic response.

appear to be by means of reasonably accurate orbital computations. Since the data required for such calculations are not presently available, there appears to be little prospect of any further serious effort being made to find a planet that may not even exist.

SIDEREAL AND SYNODIC PERIODS

7.13. In order to obtain an overall picture of the Sun's planetary system, brief consideration will be given to the procedures for determining the periods of revolution, the orbital characteristics, and the size, mass, and density of the individual planets. The period of revolution of present interest is the sidereal period (§ 2.62), i.e., the time required to complete a single orbit (or revolution of 360 deg) about the Sun. For Earth, this period, the *sidereal year,* is determined by observing the time that elapses between successive passages (or transits) of the Sun past a given fixed star; it is equal to 365.256 sidereal days.* Because of Earth's orbital motion, the sidereal period of another planet cannot be measured directly from Earth, but must be calculated from the synodic

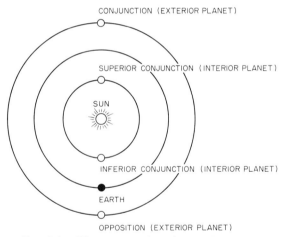

FIG. 7.1.   Planetary conjunctions and opposition

period, i.e., the apparent time of revolution about the Sun as seen from Earth. The synodic period of a given planet is obtained from observations of the time elapsing between two successive similar alignments of the Sun, Earth, and the planet.

---

* The sidereal day is the time interval between two successive transits of a fixed star past a given meridian on Earth, i. e., the exact time required for Earth to make a complete rotation about its axis. The length of the sidereal day is 23 hours 56 minutes 4.09 seconds. The solar day is the interval between two successive transits of the Sun past a given meridian. The length of the solar day varies with the time of the year but, on the average, it is 3 minutes 56 seconds longer than a sidereal day.

7.14. The hypothetical orbits of Earth and two other planets, one nearer to the Sun, i.e., an *interior planet,* and one farther away, i.e., an *exterior planet,* are depicted in Fig. **7.1.*** The alignments of the interior planet with the Sun and Earth are called *conjunctions;* when the planet is between the Sun and Earth, the planet is in *inferior conjunction.* A planetary transit of the Sun occurs on the rare occasions when an interior planet, at the time of its inferior conjunction, is so close to Earth's orbital plane that it passes directly in front of the Sun's disc as viewed from Earth. An exterior planet is said to be in conjunction when it is on the far side of the Sun and in a line with Earth, and in *opposition* when Earth lies between the planet and the Sun, as represented in Fig. 7.1.

7.15. The synodic period of an exterior planet is most conveniently obtained from the times of two successive oppositions, because of the proximity to Earth at these times; however, it can, in principle, also be determined from two conjunctions. In Fig. 7.2, E_1 is the position of Earth in its orbit at the time the exterior planet is in opposition at P_1. Because of its much larger orbit, the latter planet will have moved only as far as P_2 by the time of the next opposition, i.e., during its synodic period, while Earth will have traversed a complete orbit plus the extra distance from E_1 to E_2. If θ degrees is the angle subtended at the Sun by Earth and the planet at the times of successive oppositions, Earth will have traveled through a complete orbit of $360 + \theta$ deg, while the exterior planet moves through only θ deg in its orbit. During Earth's sidereal period, represented by E, it travels through 360 deg; hence, the synodic period, S, of the planet, is given by

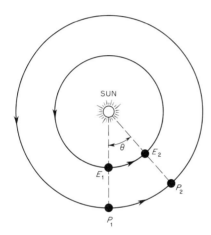

FIG. 7.2.   Determination of synodic period of a planet

$$S = \left(\frac{360 + \theta}{360}\right) E = E + \frac{\theta}{360} E. \qquad (7.1)$$

Upon rearrangement, this leads to

$$\frac{360}{\theta} = \frac{E}{S - E}. \qquad (7.2)$$

7.16. Since the planet revolves through θ deg during the synodic period, its

---

* The terms inferior and superior, respectively, are frequently used to describe these planets, but interior and exterior are less confusing. The interior planets are Mercury and Venus; the exterior planets are Mars, Jupiter, Saturn, Uranus, Neptune, and Pluto.

sidereal period, P, which is the orbital period defined in Chapter 2, i.e., the time required to make a complete revolution of 360 deg about the Sun, is expressed by

$$P = \frac{360}{\theta} S \qquad (7.3)$$

or

$$\frac{360}{\theta} = \frac{P}{S}.$$

Upon comparing this result with equation (7.2), it follows immediately that

$$P = \frac{SE}{S - E}. \qquad (7.4)$$

Earth's sidereal period, E, is known, i.e., 1 sidereal year as given above, and the synodic period, S, of the exterior planet can be obtained from the times of successive oppositions; hence, the sidereal period, P, of the planet can be derived from equation (7.4).

7.17. The result expressed by equation (7.4) is applicable to all cases in which Earth completes its orbit faster than does the other planet, i.e., when Earth's sidereal (or orbital) period is less than that of the planet. But if the sidereal period of the planet is less than that of Earth, as it is for the interior planets, Mercury and Venus, the planet revolves through $360 + \theta$ deg while the Earth moves through θ deg between successive inferior conjunctions. The equations corresponding to (7.1) and (7.3) are then

$$S = \frac{\theta}{360} E$$

and

$$P = \frac{360}{360 + \theta} S,$$

respectively. It follows, therefore, that

$$P = \frac{SE}{S + E}. \qquad (7.5)$$

The same expression could be obtained directly from equation (7.4) by interchanging E and P, since Earth and the planet merely exchange orbital locations.*

7.18. Since the mass of the primary, the Sun, is known, the orbit of a planet can be described in terms of six elements (or parameters) similar to those applicable to a satellite of Earth (§ 2.99). These parameters can be computed from

---

* Alternative forms of equations (7.4) and (7.5) are commonly found in astronomy texts. They may be combined and written as

$$\pm \frac{1}{P} = \frac{1}{S} \pm \frac{1}{E},$$

where the + signs apply to the interior and the − signs to the exterior planets.

measurement of the distances of the planet from Earth at several known times. The distances can be determined by the procedures described in Chapter 6, e.g., by parallax with reference to fixed stars (§ 6.10) or by radar reflection (§ 6.15). The planetary orbits are elliptical, but they are affected to some extent as a result of perturbations caused by other planets. Such perturbations vary with time because the distances between the planets are continually changing, and the orbital elements will vary accordingly. These variations are, however, now well established.

7.19. Since the mean distance of Earth from the Sun, i.e., the astronomical unit, is known (§ 6.5), it is not a difficult matter to calculate the average distance of the planet from the Sun if the distance from Earth to the planet has been measured at a convenient time, e.g., at a conjunction or opposition. A simple alternative procedure is based on a knowledge of the sidereal period. According to Kepler's third law, as given in § 2.48, the sidereal (or orbital) period, P, is related to the semi-major axis, a, of the elliptical orbit by

$$P^2 = \text{constant} \times a^3. \tag{7.5}$$

Since the difference between the semi-major axis of the planet's orbit and its mean distance from the Sun is insignificant, a in equation (7.5) may be taken as equal to the latter distance. If the sidereal period is expressed in terms of Earth's sidereal years, i.e., conventional years, and a in astronomical units (A.U.), it follows from equation (7.5) that, for Earth,

$$1^2 = \text{constant} \times 1^3,$$

so that, with the proposed units, the constant is unity. Consequently, for any planet revolving about the Sun,

$$P^2 \text{ (in years)} = a^3 \text{ (in A.U.)}$$

or

$$a \text{ (in A.U.)} = P^{2/3} \text{ (in years)}. \tag{7.6}$$

7.20. The sidereal period of Jupiter, for example, is known to be 11.862 years; its average distance from the Sun is thus $(11.862)^{2/3} = 5.201$ A.U. The astronomical unit was given in § 6.15 as 149.6 million kilometers (92.95 million miles); hence, the average distance from Jupiter to the Sun is 778.2 million kilometers (483.4 million miles).

7.21. In Table 7.1 there are summarized the important orbital data of the planets, the perturbations referred to in § 7.18 being neglected. It will be apparent that, except for Mercury and Pluto, the eccentricities of the orbits are quite small. From the discussion of eccentricity in § 2.44, it is evident that it may be taken as a measure of the departure of an elliptical orbit from a circular form. It follows, therefore, that, except for the innermost and outermost, the orbits of the planets are almost, but not quite, circular.

TABLE 7.1   ORBITAL DATA OF PLANETS

Planet	Average Distance from Sun		Orbital Eccentricity	Sidereal Period	Mean Velocity		Inclination (degrees)
	A.U.	10^6 kilom			kilom/sec	miles/sec	
Mercury	0.390	58.3	0.206	88 days	48	30	7.004
Venus	0.723	108.2	0.00679	224.7 days	35	21.8	3.39
Earth	1.000	149.6	0.0167	365.26 days	29.8	18.5	0
Mars	1.52	228	0.0933	687 days	24.1	15.0	1.85
Jupiter	5.20	778	0.0484	11.86 years	13.1	8.12	1.03
Saturn	9.53	1426	0.0557	29.46 years	9.65	6.0	2.50
Uranus	19.2	2870	0.0472	84.02 years	6.85	4.25	0.77
Neptune	30.0	4496	0.0086	164.8 years	5.47	3.4	1.79
Pluto	39.5	5900	0.249	248.4 years	4.84	3.0	17.2

THE ECLIPTIC PLANE AND THE ZODIAC

7.22. The inclinations given in the last column of Table 7.1 are the angles between the orbital planes of the respective planets and that of Earth. The orbital plane of Earth is called the *ecliptic plane* for the following reason. Ancient astronomers conceived of the fixed stars as lying on what they called the *celestial sphere*. Although this is now known to be incorrect, the concept of a hypothetical sphere of extremely large radius has been retained because it permits the location of any celestial body by means of angles, even when the distance from Earth is not known. The *ecliptic* is the apparent path of the Sun among the stars, as seen from Earth, projected onto the celestial sphere.* It will be evident from Fig. 7.3 that the ecliptic represents the intersection of Earth's orbital plane with the celestial sphere. The ecliptic plane is thus coincident with Earth's orbital plane.

7.23. Apart from Pluto, whose orbit is also exceptional in other respects, the orbits of the planets are inclined no more than a few degrees from the ecliptic plane. For Mercury, the inclination is as large as 7 deg, but for the other planets it is less than 3.4 deg of arc. This result is of considerable interest and undoubtedly has some relationship to the origin of the Sun's planetary system (§ 7.185 *et seq.*). Because of the small inclinations of their orbital planes, the planets are generally seen in the sky within a band extending about 8 deg on each side of the ecliptic. This band, known as the *zodiac*,† was divided into twelve equal sections, each of which was occupied by a constellation, repre-

---

* The name originates from the circumstance that all eclipses, of both the Sun and the Moon, occur on this imaginary circle (§ 9.44).

† From the Greek, meaning "circle of animals," derived from *zoidion,* diminutive of "animal," and *kyklos,* "circle."

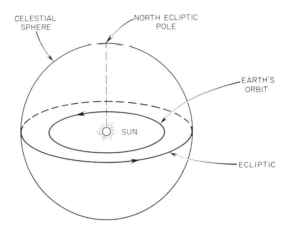

Fig. 7.3. Celestial sphere and ecliptic

sented by a characteristic sign, in most cases of an animal. It is in this manner
that the familiar signs of the zodiac originated.

Direct and Retrograde Motions

7.24. All the planets revolve in the same direction about the Sun in a
counterclockwise direction as seen from the north ecliptic pole of the celestial
sphere (cf. Fig. 7.3). With but relatively few exceptions, to which some reference will be made later, all the bodies and satellites in the solar system both
rotate about their axes and revolve about their primaries in the same (counterclockwise) direction; they are then said to exhibit direct (or progressive) motion. Thus, the rotation of Earth is counterclockwise and the Moon revolves
about Earth and rotates about its own axis in this same direction.

7.25. An approximate representation to scale of the orbits of the nine planets
is given in Fig. 7.4. In the main part of the figure, the smallest orbit shown is
that of Mars, whose semi-major axis (or mean distance from the Sun) is
1.524 A.U.; the inset shows the orbits of Mercury, Venus, Earth, and Mars on a
larger scale. It will be noted that the orbit of Pluto is abnormal in the respect
that part of it lies within that of Neptune. But there is no chance of a collision
between these two planets because, as a result of the large inclination of Pluto's
orbit (Table 7.1), it does not actually intersect that of Neptune.

7.26. Since the planets all revolve about the Sun in the same direction, it is
of interest to consider why they appear to exhibit retrograde motion, i.e., from
east to west with reference to the fixed stars, once during each synodic period.
This behavior can be readily understood by considering Fig. 7.5 which shows
the orbital locations of Earth and of an exterior planet, e.g., Mars, at successive
times, indicated by the numerals 1, 2, 3, . . . , 7. The apparent position of
the planet as seen from Earth at any instant is given by the point where the
line passing through the locations of Earth and the planet intersects the celestial

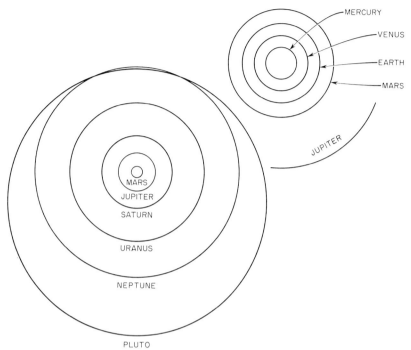

FIG. 7.4.   Relative dimensions of orbits of the planets

sphere. The results are indicated by the small crosses in Fig. 7.5. Thus, against the background of the fixed stars, the planet appears to an observer on Earth to move first from west to east, i.e., in the direct manner, then to reverse its direction exhibiting retrograde motion, and finally to return to direct motion. It can

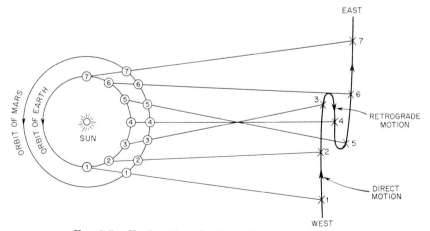

FIG. 7.5.   Explanation of retrograde motion of a planet

now be seen why the ancient astronomers regarded the planets as wanderers in the skies.

7.27. Consideration of Fig. 7.5 shows that the phenomenon arises from the different rates at which Earth and the planet revolve about the Sun, i.e., from their different sidereal periods. It occurs with interior as well as with exterior planets, as may be seen by exchanging the orbits of Earth and the planet and extending in the opposite direction the lines joining the simultaneous locations of the two bodies. The path of the planet among the stars in Fig. 7.5 is shown, for simplicity, to be Z-shaped. The actual appearance, however, depends, among other things, on the inclination of the planet's orbit to the ecliptic plane. Thus, in some cases, the path may be in the form of a loop or an S, as well as a Z (Fig. 7.6).

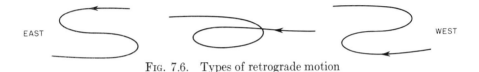

EAST   WEST

FIG. 7.6.   Types of retrograde motion

CONFIGURATIONS AND PHASES OF INTERIOR PLANETS

7.28. Another consequence of the difference in the orbital periods of Earth and the other planets is in their appearance and relative motion with respect to the Sun. Consider, first, the motion of an interior planet, e.g., Mercury or Venus. Since the orbital (sidereal) period of such a planet is shorter than that of Earth, it will always seem to travel ahead of and overtake Earth in its motion about the Sun. In other words, relative to a stationary Earth, the planet will always appear to move in a counterclockwise direction around the Sun, as indicated in Fig. 7.7. Shortly after superior conjunction, the interior planet will appear to a terrestrial observer to be east of the Sun; it is then an *evening star*. Since it is east of the Sun, it rises and sets somewhat later than the Sun; consequently, it is most readily visible in the evening after the Sun has set. At other times, the sky is generally, although not always, too bright to permit the interior planet to be seen.

7.29. Upon subsequent days, the planet appears to move farther east from the Sun and the angular distance or *elongation,* i.e., the angle subtended at Earth by the Sun and the planet, steadily increases until the location indicated as the *maximum eastern elongation* is reached.* At this point, a line to Earth is tangential to the planet's orbit. The elongation now commences to decrease, so that the planet appears to have reversed its direction of motion relative to the Sun, until inferior conjunction is reached. After inferior conjunction, the

---

* The points of maximum elongation and the conjunctions of an interior planet and the equivalent points, i.e., quadratures, conjunction, and opposition (§ 7.33), of an exterior planet are called the *configurations* or *aspects* of the planet.

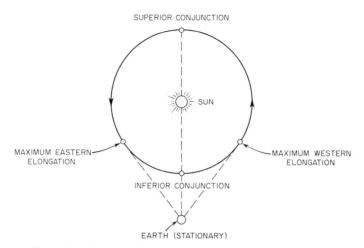

Fɪɢ. 7.7.   Configurations (or aspects) of an interior planet

interior planet as seen from Earth is to the west of the Sun, and it is now a *morning star;* it is readily visible in the east in the early morning, while the sky is still dark, just before dawn. The westerly elongation increases until a maximum is again attained, at the *maximum western elongation,* and then decreases to zero at superior conjunction; during this period the planet is a morning star.*

7.30. The maximum elongation of the planet Mercury varies between 18 and 28 deg of arc, because of the eccentricity of its orbit, whereas that of Venus is about 45 deg. Usually, however, the apparent angular distance from the Sun is much smaller than the maximum. Consequently, Venus is generally visible fairly close to the Sun, either in the east just before sunrise (morning star) or in the west shortly after sunset (evening star). The same considerations apply, of course, to Mercury, except that this planet is much more difficult to detect with the unaided eye.

7.31. The planets are too cold to radiate visible light by virtue of their temperatures (cf. § 6.58), and their luminosities, like that of the Moon, are entirely due to reflected sunlight. Furthermore, the interior planets exhibit *phases,* like the Moon. At superior conjunction, the fully illuminated face of the planet will be visible from Earth and this represents the full phase (Fig. 7.8). As the planet travels eastward, it passes through a gibbous phase (cf. § 9.9), when part of its surface is in shadow, and at maximum eastern elongation the interior planet is in its last quarter. A terrestrial observer then sees about half the

---

* Any planet, interior or exterior, is regarded as a morning star when it is west of the Sun and an evening star when it is east of the Sun. Thus an interior planet is a morning star between inferior and superior conjunctions and an evening star between superior and inferior conjunctions.

planet's surface to be illuminated. From maximum eastern elongation to inferior conjunction, the planet exhibits its crescent phase; the portion of the

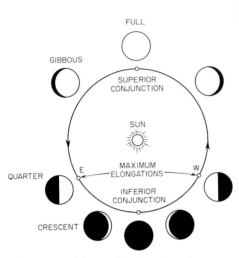

FIG. 7.8.   Phases of an interior planet

planet illuminated by the Sun diminishes in extent but the angular diameter increases because the planet is coming closer to Earth. As a result, the brightness increases to a maximum and then decreases as the planet approaches inferior conjunction where the sunlit side of the planet is not at all visible from Earth. The planet is then in its new phase, equivalent to the new moon. Subsequently, the planet goes through a further crescent and maximum brilliance, and has its first quarter at maximum western elongation. Then follows a gibbous phase, until the full phase is again attained at superior conjunction.

7.32. The angle subtended at the planet by Earth and the Sun is called the *phase angle*. At superior conjunction (full phase) the phase angle of an interior planet is 0 deg; at the maximum elongations (quarter phases) it is 90 deg and at inferior conjunction (new phase) it is 180 deg. If the phase angle is divided by 180 deg, the result gives the fraction of the planetary hemisphere turned toward Earth that is not illuminated by the Sun.

CONFIGURATIONS OF EXTERIOR PLANETS

7.33. To an observer on Earth, the behavior of the exterior planets with regard to their apparent motion relative to the Sun is quite different from the interior planets. Since the orbital periods of the exterior planets are longer than that of Earth, they always appear to be moving in a clockwise direction around the Sun relative to a stationary Earth, as represented in Fig. 7.9. Consequently, shortly after conjunction, the exterior planet is seen just west of the Sun, and it is then a morning star. On subsequent days, the planet appears farther and farther to the west of the Sun. The elongation, which is zero at conjunction, increases to 90 deg of arc at the point called the *western quadrature* and then to 180 deg at *opposition*. Thus, at western quadrature the planet would be in the south when the Sun is in the east in the early morning, and at opposition the planet is in the south at midnight. At *eastern quadrature*, when the elongation is 270 deg, the planet is in the south at sunset and is an evening star. After eastern quadrature, the planet appears to move westward as it works its way around to conjunction again.

7.34. The phases of an exterior planet are different from those of the interior planets (and of the Moon) in the respect that there are no new, crescent, or quarter phases. Moreover, it is apparent from Fig. 7.9 that full phases occur at both conjunction and opposition, when an observer on Earth can see the

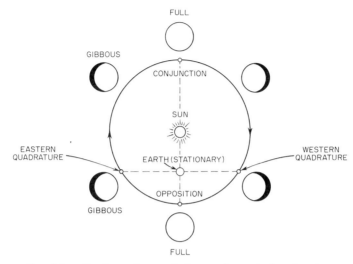

FIG. 7.9. Configurations and phases of an exterior planet

fully illuminated surface of the planet. At all other times, the phases are gibbous, with the maximum proportion of the planet in shadow at the quadratures, since the phase angle is then a maximum. The maximum phase angle, which can never be as large as 90 deg for an exterior planet, diminishes with increasing angular distance of an exterior planet from the Sun. Thus Jupiter, with a maximum phase angle of 12 deg, and the more distant planets, with even smaller maximum phase angles, always appear either in full phase or very close to it. The nearest exterior planet to Earth, namely Mars, with a maximum phase angle of 47 deg, does exhibit a distinct gibbous phase near quadrature; at this time 47/180, i.e., a little more than a fourth, of the surface is in darkness.

ROTATION OF THE PLANETS

7.35. Every planet undergoes some form of rotation about its axis, although the rotations of Mercury and Venus are somewhat unusual in character, as will be explained more fully in Chapter 10. There are various methods for studying planetary rotation. Perhaps the simplest procedure is to utilize telescopic observations of characteristic, permanent markings on the surface, such as can be seen on Mercury and Mars. Alternatively, features of relatively long duration, such as certain cloud formations on Jupiter and Saturn, may be used to study the rotation of the planet. For planets of moderate or large angular dimensions, measurement of the Doppler frequency shift of spectral lines, as observed from opposite edges of the planet, can be employed in the manner described in § 6.109 for determining the rotation of the Sun. When the angular dimensions are small, e.g., for Pluto and the asteroids, rough observations of rotation can sometimes be made by noting the periodic appearance of brighter surface areas. These serve as identifications, similar in nature to, but less precise than, the characteristic features of Mars, Jupiter, etc. The planet Venus represents a special case to which reference will be made shortly.

7.36. From observations of the type described above it is possible to derive both the period of rotation and the direction of the rotational axis. The rotational velocity at the equator can then be evaluated from the radius, r, of the planet; it is equal to $2\pi r/P$, where P is the rotational period, assuming a circular cross section. The best available data for all the planets are summarized in Table 7.2. The last column in the table gives the angle which the axis of rota-

TABLE 7.2   ROTATIONAL PARAMETERS OF THE PLANETS

Planet	Rotation Period	Rotation Velocity at Equator		Direction of Axis (degrees)
		kilom/sec	miles/sec	
Mercury	88 days	0.0020	0.0012	7 (approx)
Venus	247 days (approx)	0.0018	0.0011	6 (approx)
Earth	23 hours 56.07 min	0.47	0.29	23.45
Mars	24 hours 37.4 min	0.26	0.16	25.0
Jupiter	9 hours 55 min	12	7.3	3.01
Saturn	10 hours 30 min	9.5	5.8	26.7
Uranus	10 hours 50 min	3.8	2.5	98.0
Neptune	16 hours	2.5	1.5	28.8
Pluto	6.4 days	0.032(?)	0.019(?)	?

tion makes with a line perpendicular to the orbital plane of the planet. As seen from the north celestial pole, the direction of rotation of Uranus is retrograde, i.e., clockwise, and probably so also is that of Venus.

7.37. It will be noted, by comparing with the data in Table 7.1, that the rotational periods of the two interior planets, Mercury and Venus, are essentially the same as their orbital periods. As far as is known, the motion of Mercury is direct, i.e., counterclockwise; hence, it always presents the same face toward the Sun. The Moon behaves in this manner in its revolution about Earth, as will be seen in Chapter 9, where the reason for the phenomenon will be considered. It may be mentioned here, however, that it is the result of tidal forces arising from the proximity of a satellite to a heavier primary. The rotation of Venus has been difficult to study because of the thick cloud cover of this planet, but radar investigations (§ 10.41) indicate that the direction of rotation is retrograde. The rotational period is known only approximately, but it appears to be close to the orbital period. As a result of the retrograde rotation, the surface of Venus facing the Sun changes continuously.

7.38. Earth and the planets more distant from the Sun have relatively short periods of rotation and Jupiter, the largest planet, has the shortest period. The rate of rotation of Jupiter at the equator, i.e., $2\pi r/P$, expressed in kilometers (or miles) per second, is thus about **27** times greater than that of Earth.* Actually, the rotational periods of the larger planets, Jupiter and Saturn, vary somewhat with the latitude. The periods given in Table **7.2** apply to the equator and those at high latitudes are longer by several minutes.

7.39. Another point of interest is in connection with the inclination of the rotational axis of a planet to a line perpendicular to its orbital plane or, in other words, the angle between the equatorial and orbital planes (Fig. **7.10**).

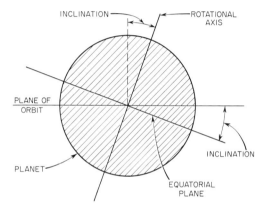

FIG. 7.10. Angle of inclination of rotational axis

In most cases, this angle is not very large, e.g., **23.5** deg of arc for Earth, but for the planet Uranus, it is **98** deg. The fact that the angle of inclination is greater than **90** deg makes the rotation about its axis retrograde. The peculiar nature of the situation is apparent from Fig. **7.11**, which shows the directions of the rotational axes of eight planets relative to the respective orbital planes. The tilt of the rotational axis to the orbital plane determines the changes of season, i.e., spring, summer, etc., during the course of the year; thus, the annual variations on Uranus would be very different from those on Earth (§ **11.89**).

DIMENSIONS AND MASSES OF THE PLANETS

7.40. The diameter (or radius) of a planet is best determined by measuring the angular diameter (or radius) at a time when the distance of the planet from

---

* The angular velocity of rotation, i.e., the rate of change of angle, expressed in radians per second, is equal to $2\pi/P$. The value for Jupiter is then only about 2.5 times that of Earth.

Earth is known, e.g., by the parallax method (§ 6.10). The procedure is the same as that described in Chapter 6 for estimating the diameter of the Sun. Since the planets are so much smaller, however, the angular diameters are less than that of the Sun, even for the closer planets. In order to make reason-

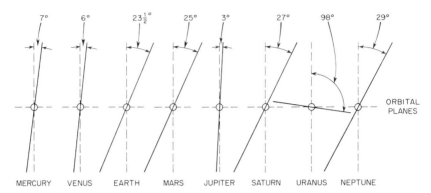

FIG. 7.11.   Inclinations of the rotational axes of eight planets

ably accurate measurements, a special micrometer device is employed in conjunction with a telescope. Large-scale photographs of the planets can be used to determine the angular diameter by comparison with a celestial body, e.g., another planet, whose angular diameter is known. Once the angular diameter has been determined, the actual diameter is readily derived from equation (6.4).

7.41. If the planet has one or more natural satellites, i.e., moons, the calculation of its mass is a relatively simple matter. The sidereal period of the satellite as it revolves about the planet is computed from telescopic observations, and the distance between the two bodies can be obtained from angular measurements. Provided the mass of the satellite is small in comparison with that of the primary body, i.e., the planet, the mass of the planet can be calculated from equation (2.26) in the manner described in § 6.20 for computing the mass of the Sun. The planets Mercury, Venus, and Pluto have no satellites, and the only means for determining their masses is by a study of the perturbations they produce in the orbits of other planets and, occasionally, of comets. Because of the great distance of Pluto from Earth, as well as from the nearest planet, Neptune, accurate evaluation of the mass of Pluto from the perturbation of the orbit of Neptune has not been possible. Hence, the mass of Pluto is uncertain. The masses of Mercury and Venus, however, are known with a fair degree of accuracy.

7.42. From the measured radius (or diameter) of a planet, it is a simple matter to obtain its volume and then, knowing the mass, to determine its density. Furthermore, from the mass and radius, the gravitational acceleration at the planet's surface is obtainable, employing the procedure given in § 6.24.

Other quantities of interest which can be calculated from the available data are the circular orbital velocity of a satellite close to the planet's surface, as given by equation (2.16), and the escape velocity, which is $\sqrt{2}$ times the circular velocity (§ 2.69). Thus, the circular velocity is given by $\sqrt{K/R}$, where R is the radius of the circular orbit; and, according to equation (2.12), K is equal to GM, where M is the mass of the planet and G is the universal gravitational constant (§ 2.16).

7.43. The (average) radius, volume, and mass of each of the planets, relative to the corresponding properties of Earth, are summarized in Table 7.3; also included are the actual density and escape velocity. The latter is of interest in connection with the landing of a spacecraft on and its take-off from the planet, and has a bearing on the nature of the planetary atmosphere, if any. The radii are average values which are generally larger than the polar radii; with the possible exception of Mercury and Venus, all the planets are somewhat flattened, like Earth. Since it has a dense cloud cover, the shape and exact dimensions of Venus are not known. For Saturn, the values given in Table 7.3

TABLE 7.3　DIMENSIONAL AND MASS PARAMETERS OF THE PLANETS

Planet	Average Radius (Earth = 1)	Volume (Earth = 1)	Mass (Earth = 1)	Density grams/cm³	Escape Velocity	
					kilom/sec	miles/sec
Mercury	0.380	0.0549	0.0536	5.4	4.2	2.5
Venus	0.958	0.879	0.816	5.1	10	6.2
Earth	1.000	1.000	1.000	5.52	11.2	6.95
Mars	0.53	0.149	0.108	4.05	5.0	3.1
Jupiter	10.8	1260	318	1.35	61	38
Saturn	9.02	734	95.2	0.71	37	23
Uranus	3.77	536	14.6	1.56	22	13.7
Neptune	3.38	391	17.2	2.47	25	15.5
Pluto	0.45(?)	0.09(?)	?	?	?	?

refer to the main body of the planet, i.e., apart from the rings (§ 11.69). Because of its great distance, the physical characteristics of Pluto are not well known, so that the data in Table 7.3 are to be regarded as approximate; the matter will be considered further in Chapter 11. In order to permit calculation of the actual (average) radius, volume, and mass of any planet, the values for Earth are as follows:

Average radius of Earth = 6371 kilometers (3959 miles)
Volume of Earth = 1.082×10^{21} cubic meters (3.825×10^{22} cubic feet)
Mass of Earth = 5.975×10^{24} kilograms (5.975×10^{21} metric tons).

7.44. The relative sizes of the planets, on the same scale, are shown in Fig. 7.12. For comparison purposes, it may be mentioned that the diameter of the Sun is ten times as great as that of Jupiter, the largest planet. Although Jupiter is large in comparison with Earth, it is still small relative to the Sun. In spite of its low average density, the Sun in fact contains 99.9 percent of the mass of the whole solar system.

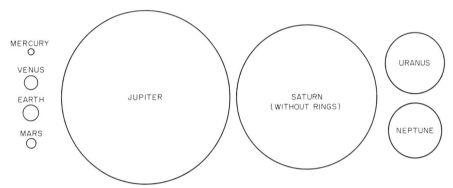

FIG. 7.12. Relative dimensions of the planets; Pluto has been omitted because its size is uncertain

7.45. An examination of Fig. 7.12 shows that, apart from Pluto, the other eight planets fall into two groups. In the first group are the planets Mercury, Venus, Earth, and Mars, all of which have diameters and densities that are not very greatly different from those of Earth; they have consequently been called the *terrestrial planets.* The second group consists of Jupiter, Saturn, Uranus, and Neptune; these are all large (and massive) planets, the diameter of the smallest, Neptune, being about 3.4 times that of Earth. As will be seen in due course, their low densities are probably related to the large diameters. This group of large planets is referred to as the *major planets,* or the *Jovian planets.**

7.46. It is somewhat strange that Pluto, lying beyond the major planets, more closely resembles the terrestrial planets in size and mass. The unusual orbit and the large inclination of Pluto's orbital plane with the plane of the ecliptic are also exceptional. It has been suggested that the reason for these exceptional characteristics is that Pluto was originally a satellite (or moon) of Neptune but escaped from this primary to become a satellite (or planet) of the Sun. In later chapters, in which the properties of the individual planets will be examined in some detail, Pluto will be included with the Jovian planets simply on the basis of the position of its orbit in the solar system.

* Jove is an alternative Roman name for the god Jupiter.

THE ASTEROIDS

BODE'S RULE

7.47. The *asteroid* (Greek, *asteroeides*, "starlike"), also known as the *minor planets* or *planetoids*, constitute a group of bodies, ranging from 470 miles (760 kilometers) to a mile or two in diameter, that revolve about the Sun in orbits lying mainly between those of Mars and Jupiter. It has long been known that, when comparing the orbits of the planets, there appears to be an exceptionally large gap separating Mars and Jupiter. In fact, Kepler had suggested that a planet might be found in this region of the solar system. If the average distance of any planet from the Sun, starting with the most distant, Pluto, is compared with that of the next planet, i.e., closer to the Sun, the ratios are found to have the following approximate values: 1.3, 1.6, 2.0, 1.8, 3.4, 1.5, 1.4, 1.8 (see Table 7.4). It is evident that the Jupiter/Mars ratio is much larger

TABLE 7.4   AVERAGE DISTANCES OF PLANETS FROM SUN

Planet	Astronomical Units Bode's Rule	Actual	Ratio
Mercury	0.4	0.39	
			1.8
Venus	0.7	0.72	
			1.4
Earth	1.0	1.0	
			1.5
Mars	1.6	1.52	
—	2.8	—	
			3.4
Jupiter	5.2	5.2	
			1.8
Saturn	10.0	9.5	
			2.0
Uranus	19.6	19.2	
			1.6
Neptune	38.8	30.1	
			1.3
Pluto	77.2	39.5	

than any of the others; that is to say, the spacing between Mars and Jupiter is greater than would be expected for adjacent planets.

7.48. Before the discovery of Uranus, J. D. Titius, a German astronomer, had developed a numerical relationship to represent the distances from the Sun of the six known planets; this empirical rule has become known as *Bode's law*,

after another German astronomer, J. E. Bode, who was responsible for bringing it to public attention in 1771. According to what should preferably be
called Bode's rule, since it does not yet have the validity of a natural law, the
distances, in astronomical units, of the successive planets from the Sun are
obtained by adding 0.4 to each of the following numbers: 0, 0.3, 0.6, 1.2, 2.4,
4.8, etc. Apart from the first number, i.e., zero, the others constitute a geometrical progression in which the ratio of successive terms is two. In Table
7.4, the distances derived from this formula are compared with the actual
values in astronomical units. It is evident that there is a gap between Mars
and Jupiter which should perhaps have been occupied by an unknown planet.
The large discrepancies for Neptune and particularly for Pluto may well be
due to the unusual relationship between these planets mentioned earlier.

DISCOVERY OF THE ASTEROIDS

7.49. The discovery of Uranus in 1781 and the determination of its orbit
appeared to provide confirmation of Bode's rule. Consequently, toward the
end of the eighteenth century plans were made by a group of astronomers to
look for a planet between Mars and Jupiter. Before a systematic search began,
however, the first asteroid was discovered early in 1801 by an Italian, Giuseppe
Piazzi, in the course of his work on the preparation of a star catalog. Piazzi
observed an object that moved against the background of fixed stars and he
thought it might be a comet. But the famous German mathematician Karl F.
Gauss, for whom the unit of magnetic field is named (§ 6.105, footnote), calculated its orbit and showed that it resembled the orbits of the planets. The
average distance from the Sun of this new member of the solar system, which
was called Ceres, was found to be 2.77, compared with the 2.8 predicted by
Bode's rule for the missing planet between Mars and Jupiter (Table 7.3).

7.50. The discovery of Ceres appeared to fill the gap in the solar system, but
by 1807 three other similar bodies—Pallas, Juno, and Vesta—had been discovered with orbits in the same general region. These were the first four, and
incidentally the largest, of the asteroids (or minor planets) to be identified.
No further asteroids were observed until 1845 when a fifth was added, but
subsequently the number has increased steadily almost from year to year. It is
estimated that perhaps 30,000 or more asteroids, down to a mile or so in
diameter, have now been detected photographically by means of large telescopes; of these, the orbits of some 1600 have been established and recorded.

7.51. The great majority of the asteroids move in orbits which lie within a
range of 2.1 to 3.5 A.U. from the Sun, so that the approximate average of 2.8
is an agreement with the requirement of Bode's rule. However, there are some
striking exceptions, as will be seen shortly. The orbital periods vary, in general,
between 3.3 and 6 years, with a weighted average of 4.5 years, compared with
1.88 years for Mars and 11.86 years for Jupiter. On the whole, the orbits of
the asteroids are somewhat more eccentric than those of the principal planets

and the orbital planes are also more highly inclined to the plane of the ecliptic. Thus, most of the eccentricities lie between 0.02 and 0.3, and the weighted average is roughly 0.15; the orbital inclinations range from less than 1 to 25 deg, in the great majority of cases, with an average of about 10 deg of arc.

7.52. Among the relatively few asteroids whose orbital characteristics are outside the range given above, two are worthy of mention. One is Icarus which has the unusually high orbital eccentricity of 0.83; its perihelion distance, i.e., the closest approach to the Sun (cf. § 2.49), is only 0.19 A.U., so that it is then nearer to the Sun than is Mercury. At aphelion, it is 1.97 A.U. from the Sun, i.e., beyond the orbit of Mars (Fig. 7.13). The orbit of Icarus is inclined at an

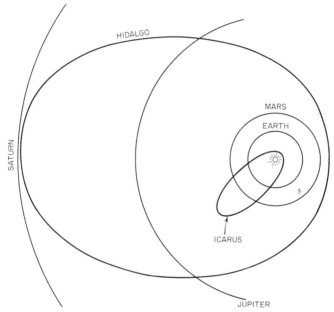

Fig. 7.13.   Orbits of the asteroids Icarus and Hidalgo relative to the orbits of the planets

angle of 23 deg to the ecliptic plane. Whereas Icarus approaches the Sun closely, at the other extreme the orbit of the asteroid Hidalgo at aphelion extends almost as far out as Saturn's orbit. The orbital eccentricity of Hidalgo is 0.65 and the inclination of its orbital plane, the largest recorded, is 42.5 deg.

7.53. Some of the asteroids cross Earth's orbit and, from time to time, come fairly close to Earth. Of these, Eros, which can approch within about 14 million miles of Earth, was at one time of special interest for determining the astronomical unit (§ 6.14). The development of radar techniques has now made Eros less significant in this respect. The closest recorded approach of an asteroid to Earth occurred in October 1937 when the small asteroid Hermes, whose orbit has an eccentricity of 0.48, came within about 800,000 kilometers (500,000 miles), i.e., about twice the distance of the Moon. In spite of their relatively close approach, the probability of a collision between Earth and an asteroid is quite small. It has been estimated that the average time between collisions of Earth with an asteroid of appreciable size is more than 100,000 years. The relatively few meteorite craters known on Earth were probably formed by collisions with quite small asteroids (§ 7.119).

THE ASTEROIDS AND JUPITER

7.54. The orbits of the asteroids are affected mainly by the gravitational field of the Sun, but there is no doubt that, because of its proximity and large mass, the planet Jupiter has an important influence. For example, consider the numbers of asteroids having various orbital periods between 3 and 7 years, as depicted in Fig. 7.14. It is seen that there are no asteroids with periods of ap-

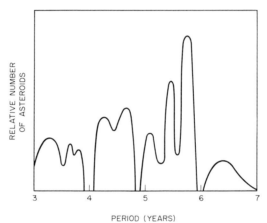

PERIOD (YEARS)

Fɪɢ. 7.14.   Asteroids with periods from 3 to 7 years

proximately 4.0, 4.8, and 6.0 years; the spaces are called *Kirkwood gaps,* after the American astronomer Daniel Kirkwood who drew attention to their existence in 1866. The missing values are $\frac{1}{3}$, $\frac{2}{5}$, and $\frac{1}{2}$, respectively, of the period of Jupiter, which is close to 12 years. Calculations indicate that the attraction of Jupiter would tend to force the asteroids out of these *resonant orbits,* i.e., orbits that are simple fractions or multiples of the attracting body. If these orbits were occupied by asteroids at some distant time in the past, as they probably were, they would have been perturbed over the course of years so that they are no longer in resonance with Jupiter's orbit. It is of interest that, by contrast, for asteroids with periods longer than 7 years, the values tend to cluster around $\frac{2}{3}$, 1, $\frac{4}{3}$, and $\frac{3}{2}$ times Jupiter's period (cf. § 7.63).

7.55. In 1772, when developing a solution of a special case of the mathematically difficult three-body problem, the French mathematician and astronomer Joseph L. Lagrange considered a hypothetical case of a body of relatively small mass, e.g., an asteroid, revolving about the Sun in the same orbit as a heavy planet (cf. § 9.45). He showed that if the Sun, the planet, and the asteroid were located at the corners of an equilateral triangle, the position of the asteroid with respect to the planet would remain essentially unchanged. An asteroid which satisfied the requirement of having an orbit close to that of the planet Jupiter was discoverd by Max Wolf in Germany in 1906 and was called Achilles. In later years, some 15 such asteroids, with orbits close to Jupiter's, have been characterized, and others undoubtedly exist. They have all been named for the mythical heroes of the Trojan War between Greece and Troy, and are consequently referred to as the *Trojan asteroids,* or, in brief, as the *Trojans.*

7.56. The Trojans fall into two groups: one group of five asteroids precedes Jupiter in its orbit by 60 deg of arc, and the other group of ten follows it by the same angle (Fig. 7.15). Thus, the Sun, Jupiter, and each asteroid group

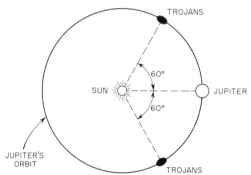

Fɪɢ. 7.15. Jupiter's orbit and the Trojan asteroids

are located at the corners of an approximate equilateral triangle. Because the orbits of the Trojans differ to some extent in both eccentricity and inclination from the orbit of Jupiter, they are often at a distance from their theoretical (Lagrangian) locations. Although their motion is mainly influenced by Jupiter and the Sun, it is actually more complicated than is implied by the simple representation in Fig. 7.15. The planet Saturn also causes perturbations of the Trojan orbits and it is expected that, as a result, a Trojan asteroid will occasionally be removed entirely from the group. On the other hand, it is probable that the strong gravitational field of Jupiter causes an asteroid to be captured into one of the Trojan groups at infrequent intervals.

SIZE AND MASS OF ASTEROIDS

7.57. The sizes of a few of the larger asteroids have been determined by measuring their angular diameters with the aid of a telescope and micrometer (§ 7.40); these include the first four to be discovered, the diameters of which are as follows:

Ceres	760 kilometers	470 miles
Pallas	490 "	300 "
Vesta	390 "	240 "
Juno	190 "	120 "

7.58. The dimensions of some smaller asteroids have been estimated from their brightness, together with an average value of their surface reflectivity or albedo (§ 5.18). If the diameter of a body is known, as is the case with the four largest asteroids, as well as the distance from the Sun, a comparison can be readily made between the observed brightness and the amount of visible radiation received from the Sun. The ratio of these quantities gives the albedo, and the average value found for the asteroids is 0.16. By reversing the procedure, i.e., by using the observed brightness and the average albedo, to calculate the amount of solar radiation received, the dimensions of an asteroid can be computed, provided its distance from the Sun has been determined. Of the asteroids that have been studied in this manner, probably **90** percent, at least, have diameters of **80** kilometers (50 miles) or less.

7.59. The two largest asteroids, Ceres and Pallas, are apparently spherical or approximately so. But most, if not all, of the others have irregular shapes; this is indicated by the large variations in brightness observed as the asteroid rotates and reflects sunlight from different regions on its surface. From the fluctuations in brightness of Eros, for example, it has been estimated that it is about **24** kilometers (15 miles) long and roughly **8** kilometers (5 miles) in each of the other two dimensions. Its period of rotation is a little over 5 hours; rotational periods of a few hours are typical of most asteroids.

7.60. The masses of even the largest asteroids are too small to be determined by the conventional methods, described earlier, for obtaining the masses of the planets. The best that can be done, therefore, is to make a rough estimate from the observed dimensions, and assuming the density to be the same as that of the Moon, namely, about 3.3 grams per cubic centimeter. On this basis, the mass of Ceres, the largest asteroid, is found to be 7.5×10^{20} kilograms (7.5×10^{17} metric tons), which is about a one-hundredth part (10^{-2}) of the mass of the Moon; the total mass of all the asteroids is estimated to be little more than one tenth that of the Moon.

7.61. Because of their low masses, the force of gravity at the surfaces is very small. It is highly probable therefore that, like the Moon, the asteroids have no atmospheres. Any atmospheric gases that may have been associated with the asteroids must have escaped long ago. The polarization of the light (§ 6.135) reflected by some of the asteroids is similar to that of moonlight. It would appear, therefore, that the surface characteristics are very much the same. It will be seen in Chapter 9 that the nature of the lunar surface is a highly controversial matter; some think it is fairly rigid but highly porous, whereas others consider that it is covered with a layer of dust.

Origin of Asteroids

7.62. Because they are mostly found in the region where Bode's rule predicted the presence of a planet, it has been suggested that the asteroids were formed by the disruption or explosion of such a planet, perhaps while the solar system was evolving. There is a distinct possibility, however, that the proximity and large mass of Jupiter may have prevented the formation of a single planet, so that several smaller planetoids were formed. Of these, Ceres and Pallas, which are spherical, presumably still remain whereas the others were shattered as a result of mutual collisions. Because of their small masses, the orbits of the planetoids would be readily perturbed, particularly by Jupiter, so that occasional collisions might be expected. As a result, the many thousands of asteroids of various sizes and shapes would be formed. It is conjectured that the smaller bodies which pass through Earth's atmosphere and are found on (or below) its surface as meteorites were produced at the same time.

7.63. It is of interest to mention that there are at least five groups of asteroids, each consisting of a large number of bodies having similar orbits. This suggests that the asteroids in each group have a common origin, namely, the disintegration of a larger body, possibly in a collision. Such collisions must have occurred in relatively recent times, otherwise perturbations would probably have destroyed the regularity of the orbits.

THE COMETS

Characteristics of Comets

7.64. When first seen, at a great distance from the Sun, a *comet* appears as a celestial body with a fuzzy (or nebulous) luminosity moving fairly rapidly against the background of fixed stars. As a general rule, a comet remains visible for a period of days or a few weeks at most. Telescopic observation usually reveals the presence in the interior of the nebulous mass, called the *coma* (Latin, *coma;* Greek, *kome,* "hair"), of a small, starlike region known as the *nucleus.* The coma and the nucleus together constitute the *head* of the comet. In some comets the nucleus is not clearly evident whereas in others it appears to be split into parts so that two or three separate nuclear bodies can be seen. This splitting has sometimes been observed to occur when the comet comes close to the Sun or to Jupiter. Subsequently, the two (or more) nuclei may break away and form individual comets.

7.65. As it approaches within one to two astronomical units, i.e., 150 to 300 million kilometers (100 to 200 million miles), of the Sun, a comet may develop a *tail*, which is directed away from the Sun. Because of the rapid motion of the comet, the tail generally appears to be curved. The characteristics of cometary tails vary, however, and several different types have been observed. Comets that do not come within two astronomical units of the Sun do not develop tails.

7.66. The dimensions of cometary heads vary over a wide range, e.g., from about 16,000 to 2,500,000 kilometers (10,000 to 1,500,000 miles) across, with an average of approximately 160,000 kilometers (100,000 miles). For a given comet, the diameter often increases when it is near the Sun; it is frequently a maximum just prior to and soon after, but not at, perihelion. The size of the nucleus is not known with any degree of certainty, but is believed to range from 1 to 100 kilometers (0.6 to 60 miles) in diameter, with an average value of probably a few kilometers (or miles). After the tail has developed, it becomes a conspicuous feature of a comet, sometimes extending to a length of 80 to 160 million kilometers (50 to 100 million miles). As the comet passes through its perihelion point and moves farther away from the Sun, the dimensions of the tail gradually decrease; it finally disappears at about the same distance as that at which it was first observed. Cometary tails are evidently formed by the impact of charged particles expelled from the Sun, i.e., by the solar wind; in fact it was the study of the tails of comets that represented the first step in the development of the concept of the solar wind (§ 6.170).

7.67. The mass of even the heaviest comet is too small to produce a detectable perturbation in the orbit of any adjacent celestial body. Consequently, all that can be done is to estimate the mass that would have caused a noticeable perturbation in a particular case and then to state that the mass of the comet is less than this amount. From such calculations, it appears that the masses of comets are, on the average, roughly 10^{-9} of Earth's mass. Although small in comparison with Earth or even the Moon, the mass of a comet may still be something like 10^{13} kilograms (10^{10} metric tons) or more; the mass is thus of the same order of magnitude as that of the smallest asteroids. This is, of course, not surprising because the latter are not more than a mile or so across.

ORBITS OF COMETS

7.68. The orbits of comets frequently undergo changes, in some cases quite small but in others fairly large, and so it is difficult to establish their parameters with any precision. Furthermore, it is only when a comet is near Earth—and the Sun—that observations can be made; the path may have been perturbed by the Sun to such an extent that it is not representative of the whole orbit. The orbits of some five or six hundred comets have been computed with reasonable accuracy and they have been found to fall into two categories. In the larger of the categories, the orbits are highly eccentric and the periods are long, many of them being several hundred and possibly up to a million years. These are known as the *long-period comets*. Their orbits are highly inclined to the ecliptic plane, and roughly half revolve about the Sun in direct orbits, i.e., in the same (counterclockwise) direction as the planets and asteroids, whereas the others have retrograde orbits, i.e., in a clockwise direction.

7.69. The orbital eccentricities of many of the long-period comets are very close to unity; that is to say, the orbits are almost parabolic. In some cases, the eccentricities as determined from the paths near Earth (and the Sun) exceed unity by a small amount, so that the orbits are apparently hyperbolic (§ 2.44) with reference to the Sun. Were the orbits truly hyperbolic, however, and not perturbed by the planets or the Sun, it would mean that the comet came from outside the solar system and would presumably leave the solar system again. In this event, it is to be expected that the eccentricity would be appreciably greater than unity, whereas in all known instances it is only very slightly more than unity, the largest being 1.013.

7.70. The general conclusion is, therefore, that the long-period comets are actually members of the solar system but that the eccentricities of their unperturbed elliptical orbits about the Sun probably approach unity, so that at aphelion they may be well beyond Pluto. The apparent eccentricities exceeding unity are then due to perturbations caused by the major planets Jupiter and Saturn. These perturbations occur near perihelion, i.e., when the comets are closer to the Sun. If, as a result of such perturbations, the eccentricity exceeds unity, it means that the comet may possibly leave the solar system. Because of the uncertainties in their orbits, the periods of long-period comets are not generally known.

7.71. Less than 40 percent of the cometary orbits that have been computed fall into the second category, that of the *short-period* (or *periodic*) *comets;* these have definitely elliptical orbits about the Sun and their orbital periods range from 3.3 to roughly 200 years. The perihelia of these comets are all moderately close to the Sun, and so they can be observed from Earth; but their eccentricities, which average about 0.5, have values from 0.1 to 0.99. If the eccentricity is small, the orbit of the comet may be completely between the orbits of two planets, e.g., the orbit of Comet 1925 II is between Jupiter and Saturn and that of Comet Oterma 1943 is between Mars and Jupiter. For high eccentricities, the cometary orbits cross those of the planets. Thus, in some instances the perihelion is fairly close to the Sun but the aphelion may be beyond Pluto.

7.72. The orbital planes of the periodic comets are generally fairly near the plane of the ecliptic, with inclinations of less than 20 deg in most cases. Furthermore, the great majority of these comets revolve about the Sun in the same direction as do the planets. A notable exception is Halley's comet, the first identified periodic comet. From calculations based on Newton's theory of gravitation, the British astronomer Edmund Halley predicted in 1705 that the great comet of 1682 would return in 1759, as it indeed did. This comet revolves about the Sun in a retrograde direction with an orbital period of about 76 years; another exceptional feature is that its orbital plane is highly inclined to the ecliptic plane.

7.73. Almost half of the periodic comets have aphelia close to the orbit of Jupiter. This circumstance is more than mere coincidence and undoubtedly arises from perturbations by Jupiter's gravitational field of the orbits of highly eccentric, perhaps long-period, comets as they approach this large planet. Incidentally, in addition to this process of capture, as it is called, it has been shown theoretically that Jupiter can perturb the orbit of a comet to such an extent as to cause it to escape from the solar system altogether. Although there are few, if any, recorded instances of actual escape, there is evidence that Jupiter produces large sudden changes, as well as progressive small ones, in the orbits of comets.

Spectra of Comets

7.74. Much of the luminosity of a comet arises from reflected and scattered sunlight, as is evident from the spectrum, particularly of the radiation from the nucleus; this has a continuous background with indications of dark Fraunhofer lines (§ 6.70). In addition, however, the coma and the tail exhibit the emission spectra of a number of unstable molecules and ionic species not present in the solar spectrum. They consist of many closely spaced bright lines that constitute the so-called band spectra (§ 6.99).

7.75. In the spectrum of the coma, the bands of the diatomic carbon molecule C_2, in the visible region, and of the cyanogen radical CN, in the ultraviolet, are the most conspicuous; in fact, the C_2 bands are mainly responsible for the luminosity of the comet's head. There are also present the spectra of the radicals CH, CH_2, NH, and OH, and of the ions CH^+, OH^+, CO^+, CO_2^+, and N_2^+. The most significant spectral lines in the tail of a comet are apparently those of the ions CH^+, CO^+, CO_2^+, and N_2^+, but other species are also present. The characteristics of the band spectra of both the coma and the tail may change as the comet comes nearer to the Sun, indicating that the latter has a significant influence on the constituent molecules, radicals, and ions. Besides the band spectra, bright lines, produced by excited atoms of sodium, iron, and possibly chromium, manganese, and other elements have been detected in some instances.

7.76. In order to account for the molecular and ionic band spectra, it is postulated that the heads of comets contain the normally stable compounds methane (CH_4), ammonia (NH_3), water (H_2O), carbon dioxide (CO_2), and perhaps cyanogen (C_2N_2). As a result of absorption of solar radiation of short wavelength, i.e., ultraviolet and X-rays, these molecules are broken up into various radicals, e.g., CH, CH_2, NH, NH_2, OH, and CN, and simple molecules, e.g., CO and N_2. Moreover, the same radiation can cause ionization, i.e., ejection of an electron from some of the radicals and molecules, so that positive ions are produced.

7.77. Normally, the radicals might be expected to recombine with each other or with hydrogen atoms, which must be present, to regenerate molecules. Also, the ions would capture electrons and become neutral species. Evidently these processes do not take place very rapidly in the comet and so it is concluded that the pressures are extremely low. Encounters between pairs of particles that would lead to recombination are not frequent and the unstable radicals and ions exist for a sufficiently long time to produce emission spectra.

7.78. Excited, high-energy states (§ 6.78) of these species may be generated directly in the breakup of the molecules or they may result from the absorption of energy from the Sun's radiation by the radicals and ions after they are formed. The transition from the excited states to states of lower energy is then accompanied by the production of a bright, emission (band) spectrum. In effect, the net result is that the cometary material has absorbed energy in the short wavelength region of the spectrum and subsequently emitted much of it at other, longer wavelengths. Behavior of this type, which is well known in the laboratory, is called *fluorescence;* thus the light from the head and tail of a comet is *fluorescence radiation.*

STRUCTURE OF COMETS

7.79. A theory of cometary structure, proposed by the American astronomer Fred J. Whipple in 1950, has been widely accepted. It is postulated that the nucleus is very cold and consists of a conglomerate of solidified methane, ammonia, and carbon dioxide, which are normally gases, and water. Since these solids resemble crystals of ice or snow in some respects, they are often referred to as "ices." Within the mass of ices there are inclusions of particles of mineral (stony) material of various sizes, ranging from microscopic dimensions up to perhaps a few inches across. The total mass of this included material may be only 20 or 30 percent of the mass of the comet. As the comet approaches the Sun, the ices warm up and vaporize and the resulting gases produce the coma. At distances of one or two astronomical units, the pressure of solar radiation and the impact of the electrically charged particles in the solar wind (§ 6.170) blow part of the coma away to form the comet's tail.

7.80. Since methane (CH_4) is the most readily vaporized of the comet's constituents, the species present in the coma at a considerable distance from the Sun should be CH_4 and the products of its decomposition, e.g., C_2, CH, and CH_2. Closer to the Sun, where the temperature is higher, gaseous carbon dioxide (CO_2) and ammonia (NH_3) are released and then these molecules and related species, e.g., NH, NH_2, CO, N_2, etc., and their ions begin to appear. Finally, solid water (H_2O) and possibly cyanogen (C_2N_2) are converted into vapor and produce OH and CN radicals and ions. The changes observed in the spectrum of a comet as it approaches the Sun are in general agreement with the series of events described above.

7.81. It will be recalled that the spectrum of a comet's tail indicates that the main components are ions of normally stable molecules, e.g., CO^+, CO_2^+, and N_2^+, whereas the coma also contains substantial proportions of free radical ions. By the time the gases have traveled from the coma to an appreciable distance down the tail, a process requiring a period on the order of several hours, the radicals will have combined to form molecules. Hence, the latter, either in the neutral or ionized state, may be expected to predominate in the tail of the comet.

7.82. Each time a comet comes near the Sun in the course of its revolution, i.e., near perihelion, the ices in the nucleus partially evaporate. They apparently do so in a semi-explosive manner and thus carry with them some of the particulate mineral matter in the coma. This material is then dispersed in space either directly or through the comet's tail, if one develops. As will be seen shortly, such particles are mainly responsible for the familiar streaks of light, known as meteors, that appear in the sky from time to time. The vaporization of the ices in the nucleus is inhibited to some extent because some of the mineral matter, which is a relatively poor conductor of heat, provides partial protection from the Sun's radiation. Ultimately, sufficient heat penetrates into the interior and the ices are converted into gas (or vapor) which is expelled at high velocity. The rapid expulsion of gas produces a reaction (or rocket action) which can affect the comet's orbit. Regular orbital changes observed to occur with some comets can be accounted for in this manner.

7.83. Comets offer an interesting and feasible possibility for investigation by means of spacecraft. It has been suggested that an instrumented probe be launched to pass through a comet's tail or even through its head. A convenient object for this purpose would be Encke's comet which has a period of **3.3** years. At perihelion it approaches within 0.3 A.U. of the Sun and so it develops a substantial tail. The instruments which might be carried by such a probe are an ordinary (optical) spectrograph to obtain detailed spectra, a mass spectrometer to determine the masses of the ions present, a plasma probe to investigate the charged particle concentration, and a magnetometer to study the magnetic field.

ORIGIN OF COMETS

7.84. Calculations indicate that roughly about one part in 200, i.e., 0.5 percent, of the mass of a comet is lost, by vaporization of the ices and dispersion of the mineral matter in the nucleus, upon each approach to the Sun. As the comet gets smaller, the proportional rate of loss will tend to increase, and a point may be reached when the comet disappears as a result of complete disruption, rather than of gradual attrition. In general, a comet may not be expected to survive a hundred or so passes through its perihelion. That comets do disappear from time to time, there is no doubt. A rough estimate would indicate that comets, even long-period comets, which approach at all near to the Sun at perihelion would have a lifetime of certainly not more than a million years. Since many such comets still exist, in spite of the several thousand million years age of the solar system, it is evident that new comets must be continuously moving into the vicinity of the Sun.

7.85. In order to be capable of detection, a comet must come within about 5 A.U. of Earth or (approximately) the Sun. It is not improbable, therefore, that many comets exist whose perihelia are farther than 5 A.U. from the Sun. Actually, a correlation of the numbers of comets and their respective perihelion distances indicates that the number increases with distance. On this basis, it has been estimated that there are roughly five million comets with perihelia within 30 A.U., i.e., between the Sun and the orbit of Neptune, and many more still farther away.

7.86. According to the calculations of the Dutch astrophysicist Jan H. Oort published in 1950, a consistent picture of the origin of comets can be obtained by postulating that a cloud containing about 200 billion (2×10^{11}) comets circulates around the Sun with aphelia as far away as 150,000 A.U. or more. In spite of this enormous number, the total mass of the comets would be only 10 to 100 times that of Earth, so that it is not unreasonable. The material constituting these comets was probably originally very much nearer the Sun, and may perhaps have been part of the debris resulting from the planetary disruption that led to the formation of the asteroids. As a result of the perturbing action of the Sun and the planets, this material must have been driven farther and farther out. The distance of roughly 150,000 A.U., approximately half the average separation of stars in the Milky Way, may be regarded as the theoretical limit of the solar system. At greater distances, the comets would be perturbed by other stars, so that some might depart from the solar system permanently.

7.87. Occasionally one of the distant comets will pass moderately near to a star; its orbit may then be perturbed in such a manner as to bring it within the planetary region at perihelion. It then becomes a long-period comet. In due course, this comet will be captured by Jupiter, as described in § 7.73, when it will enter the category of periodic comets and be visible from Earth at regular intervals. Eventually, it will lose its material and cease to exist. But by this time another comet will probably have come within reasonable perihelion distance to be affected by Jupiter, and so on. Oort has estimated that during the lifetime of the solar system, not more than 20 percent of the very distant comets have been lost in the manner described. There is thus an ample supply for many billions of years to come, even if no new material is accumulated from the cosmic dust in space (Chapter 12).

METEORS, METEORITES, AND TEKTITES

SPORADIC AND SHOWER METEORS

7.88. A *meteor** is a celestial phenomenon associated with a streak of light of short duration; it is commonly known as a "shooting star." The bright streak, referred to as the *meteor trail*, results from the heat generated when a particle (or piece) of matter traveling with a high velocity in space enters Earth's atmosphere. The particle itself is sometimes also called a meteor, but it is preferable to designate it as a *meteoroid;* a meteoroid then produces a meteor when it encounters and interacts with Earth's atmosphere. A very bright meteor is known as a *fireball*, and a large fireball, particularly one accompanied by sparks and explosive noise, is called a *bolide* (Greek, *bolis*, "missile").

7.89. Most meteoroids which become incandescent when they pass through the atmosphere and produce visible meteors are probably disintegrated into small particles or dust. There is then no detectable residue on the ground. Large meteoroids and the objects that produce fireballs, on the other hand, are not consumed completely and the name *meteorite* is given to the material, stony or metallic in nature, that survives passage through the air and is recovered from Earth's surface. Although the terms "meteoroid" and "meteorite" are similar, they must not be confused. It is probable that in many cases, but not necessarily always, they represent bodies of different origin and structure. The estimated density of average meteoroid material, for example, is appreciably lower than the densities of known meteorites. Furthermore, the meteoroids are believed to be porous and fragile, whereas meteorites have sufficient strength to withstand high-velocity impact with the ground.

7.90. Meteors are of common occurrence and, away from cities, they can be observed on most clear nights, the frequency of appearance increasing after midnight; on the average, three or four times as many meteors can be seen during a given interval just before dawn than at dusk. As a general rule, meteors are seen singly in various parts of the sky and coming from different directions; these are called *sporadic meteors*. At certain periods, however, which often recur annually, *meteor showers* are observed; the meteors then appear in large numbers and essentially all originate from a particular region in the sky. As will be seen shortly, such showers are commonly named for the constellation from which they seem to radiate. There are probably twice as many sporadic as shower meteors, but their nature is less well understood because of their random appearance.

7.91. The greater frequency of sporadic meteors after than before midnight is due basically to Earth's orbital motion with a velocity that is of the same

---

* The word meteor is derived from the Greek *meteoros,* meaning "high in the air," from *meta,* "beyond," and *aeros,* "air." Although meteorology (see Chapter 5) is not concerned with meteors, the term has the same origin.

order as that of the meteoroid particles. Between midnight and dawn an observer is facing in the same direction as Earth is moving (Fig. 7.16) and he can see all the meteors formed by meteoroids traveling towards him, i.e., from the left, no matter what their velocity. Between dusk and midnight, on the

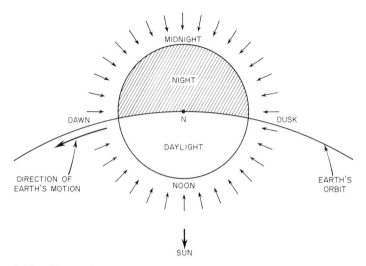

FIG. 7.16.   Greater frequency of meteors observed after midnight than before

other hand, the only meteors that are visible are those produced by meteoroids coming towards him, i.e., from the right, with sufficient velocity to overtake Earth. Since only a small proportion of meteoroids have velocities exceeding Earth's orbital speed of 29.8 kilometers (18.5 miles) per second, the number of meteors seen between dusk and midnight is considerably less than can be seen between midnight and dawn.

METEOR OBSERVATION TECHNIQUES

7.92. Some information concerning the trajectories of meteors have been obtained with the unaided eye by reliable observers, but photographic and radar (or radio echo) techniques have given data of much greater precision.* The photographic procedure makes use of wide-angle cameras with rapidly rotating shutters, giving up to 60 exposures per second, similar to those employed for tracking satellites (§ 4.134). Two such cameras are located at a known distance, 30 to 100 kilometers (20 to 60 miles), apart and focused upon the same region of the sky. In this way, a meteor passing across the field of vision is photographed simultaneously against a background of stars from two

---

* A distinction is sometimes made between the trajectory of a meteor, i.e., the actual three-dimensional line of motion, and its path, i.e., the two-dimensional projection on the celestial sphere that the observer actually sees.

separate points. From the photographic records, the height, velocity, and direction of motion of the meteor can be computed.

7.93. The radar method of studying meteors has proved to be remarkably fruitful; first, because it can detect meteors in daylight, when the photographic procedure is ineffective, and second, it is sensitive to meteors with trails whose luminosity is too feeble to affect a photographic plate. However, it is not capable of the precision possible by the photographic method. The radar technique depends on the fact that the passage of a meteor is accompanied by ionization, i.e., the formation of positive and negative electrical charges (§ 3.188), in the atmosphere. The resulting ionized region has the ability to reflect radio waves (§8.180). In order to penetrate Earth's ionosphere, into the region where meteoroids interact with the atmosphere, radio waves in the frequency range of about 30 to 80 megacycles per second (wavelength 10 to 4 meters) are employed.

7.94. Two general types of radio reflection techniques have been applied to the study of meteors. In the first, the reflection occurs from an ionized region at the head of the meteor; the distance can then be determined in the usual manner from the time delay in receipt of the return signal (§ 4.14). The radial velocity (or range rate) can be obtained from the Doppler frequency shift (§ 4.17). Velocities, however, are usually obtained by the second technique which makes use of the reflection from the ionization trail that accompanies the visible trail of the meteor. From variations in the oscillations of the reflected signal over a period of time as the trail develops, it is possible to calculate the meteor's velocity. Furthermore, the intensity of the reflected signal varies with time and is a maximum when the trail is perpendicular to the radio beam. Observations from three stations are required to establish the orbital elements of the meteoroid that produced the given meteor.

7.95. Both photographic and radio echo methods indicate that meteors begin to appear at heights of 60 to 130 kilometers (37 to 80 miles) and that they are visible down to about 40 to 100 kilometers (25 to 60 miles), respectively. As a general rule, meteors which eventually produce the most luminous trails are seen at greater altitudes than those having the fainter trails. Shower meteors appear to begin and end somewhat higher in the atmosphere than do sporadic meteors. In a meteor shower, the trajectories all seem to come from the same point in the sky, called the *radiant point* or *radiant*. This effect is due to perspective and indicates that the shower meteoroids actually follow parallel paths before they enter Earth's atmosphere. It is probable, therefore, that the meteoroids responsible for the shower are traveling together as a group in space. Meteor showers are commonly named for the star constellation in which the radiant appears to fall on the celestial sphere; examples are the Draconids (Constellation Draco), Geminids (Gemini), Perseids (Perseus), and Orionids (Orion).

VELOCITIES OF METEOROIDS

7.96. The measured velocity of a meteor (or meteoroid) may be treated as a combination of three components: first, the *heliocentric velocity*, i.e., the velocity within the solar system or with respect to the Sun; second, the velocity of Earth in its orbit around the Sun; and third, the velocity resulting from Earth's gravitational attraction. It is the general practice to subtract the latter component, and the remainder then represents what is called the *geocentric velocity*.

7.97. Just as an object must have the escape velocity (§ 2.67) if it is to overcome Earth's gravity, so it will gain this same velocity when it enters the region where Earth's gravitational field is dominant. A body originating from outside Earth's environment will, therefore, acquire an additional velocity equal to the escape velocity when it approaches Earth. At a height of 80 to 100 kilometers (50 to 60 miles), for example, where meteoroid velocities are determined, the escape velocity is about **11.2** kilometers (**6.95** miles) per second, and this is the gravitational component of the measured meteoroid velocity. If this velocity is v_m kilometers per second, then the geocentric velocity, v, in these units is given by

$$v^2 = v_m{}^2 - (11.2)^2,$$

so that v may be evaluated.

7.98. With but rare exceptions, the observed geocentric velocities of meteoroids range between the extremes of **12** and **72** kilometers (**7.5** and **44.5** miles) per second, with the great majority of values being from **16** to **50** kilometers (**10** to **30** miles) per second. The maximum velocity is important because it shows that meteoroids must originate in the solar system, and that they do not come from outer space. Since the average orbital velocity of Earth is nearly **30** kilometers per second, the maximum heliocentric velocity of a meteoroid striking Earth's atmosphere head-on is close to $72 - 30 = 42$ kilometers (**26** miles) per second. Although the numbers are not exact, it is reasonably certain that the heliocentric velocities of meteoroid particles do not exceed about **42** kilometers (**26** miles) per second.

7.99. Earth's orbit is not quite circular, but the average orbital velocity of **29.8** kilometers per second is a good approximation to the circular velocity of Earth as a satellite of the Sun. In other words, the (heliocentric) circular velocity, i.e., with respect to the Sun, at Earth's distance is **29.8** kilometers per second; consequently, the escape (or parabolic) velocity is $\sqrt{2}$ times this value, i.e., **42.1** kilometers (**26.2** miles) per second. It is evident, therefore, that although the maximum heliocentric velocities of meteoroids observed in the vicinity of Earth approach the parabolic velocity with respect to the Sun at Earth's distance, they never (or very rarely) exceed it; this means that the meteoroids cannot originate outside the solar system. The conclusion to be drawn is that meteoroids belong to the solar system and consist of objects that orbit about the Sun, just as do other members of the system, namely, planets, asteroids, and comets.

METEORS AND COMETS

7.100. A review of the orbits of shower meteors shows that in several cases they coincide almost exactly with the orbits of known comets. The most conspicuous and regular of the annual showers, the Perseids, which are visible in the Northern Hemisphere for a week or two before and after August 12th every year, have the same orbit as a well-known comet designated Comet 1862 III. The Orionids, observed annually around October 22nd, are in the orbit of Halley's comet. It is reasonably certain, therefore, that the meteoroids that produce shower meteors when they enter Earth's atmosphere are debris left behind by evaporation of the ices present in comets. Some of the better known meteor showers and the comets with the same orbits are listed in Table 7.5. Showers

TABLE 7.5   METEOR SHOWERS AND RELATED COMETS

Shower	Date of Maximum	Comet
Lyrids	April 21	1861 I
Eta Aquarids	May 4	Halley (probably)
Beta Taurids		
(daytime)	June 30	Encke
Perseids	August 12	1862 III
Draconids	October 10	Giacobini-Zinner
Orionids	October 22	Halley (probably)
Taurids	November 1	Encke
Andromedids	November 14	Biela
Leonids	November 17	1866 I

that are associated with comets are sometimes named after the related comets; thus, the Andromedids are also called the Bielids (after Biela's comet) and the Draconids are referred to as the Giacobinids (after the Giacobini-Zinner comet).

7.101. Although there are some meteor showers that are not associated with known comets, it is probable that the parent comets have either been perturbed into new orbits or that they have now ceased to exist as coherent units. An interesting case in point is that of Biela's comet, one of those associated with Jupiter, having a period of 6.6 years. During the course of its passage near the Sun in 1846, the nucleus of this comet split into two parts; the resulting double comet reappeared at near its regular time in 1852, but it presumably disintegrated during its next orbit, as it has not been seen since. However, in 1872 and 1885, extensive meteor showers, the Andromedids (or Bielids), were observed with orbits almost identical with that of Biela's comet. Lesser displays occurred in 1892 and 1899, but after that the Bielids have not been seen again. Presumably the orbit of the debris has been perturbed to such an extent that it no longer approaches within a reasonable distance of Earth.

7.102. Shower meteors fall into two categories, depending upon whether they reappear annually or at longer intervals. The annual showers would occur if the cometary debris were spread out more or less evenly throughout the whole of its orbit; this is referred to as a *meteoroid stream* (Fig. 7.17, I). That the

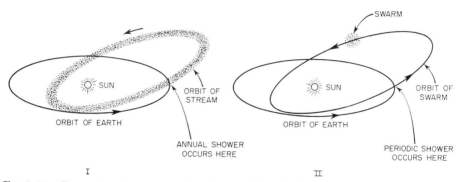

FIG. 7.17.   Formation of annual meteor showers (I) and of periodic meteor showers (II)

distribution along the stream is not uniform is shown by the variations in the shower intensity from year to year. When Earth's orbit crosses the stream, which may or may not be in the orbit of an existing comet, a meteor shower is seen. In some instances, Earth crosses the meteoroid orbit twice a year; a nighttime shower then occurs at one time of the year and a daytime shower is observed, by radar, some months later. An example of this behavior is provided by the Taurids, which are at a maximum at night near the beginning of November and in the daytime toward the end of June each year. The orbits are essentially identical with that of Encke's comet. The width of a meteoroid stream can be estimated from the length of the shower period and the measured velocity of the meteors. The values range from 0.8 to 80 million kilometers (0.5 to 50 million miles), with an average around 16 million kilometers (10 million miles). Thus, an approach of Earth within a few million kilometers (or miles) of the comet's orbit is necessary if a meteor shower is to be observed.

7.103. When meteor showers are periodic but not annual, it is probable that the cometary residues occur mainly in a relatively small region of the orbit; they then form a *meteoroid swarm*, rather than a stream, moving around the Sun (Fig. 7.17, II). It is only when Earth passes through the swarm that a meteor shower occurs. A small number of Leonids, for example, appear every year, but from at least as far back as 902 A.D. until 1866 they were exceptionally strong every 33 years. Between 1866 and 1899, the swarm passed near both Jupiter and Saturn, so that its orbit suffered some perturbation. Hence, in 1899 and 1932 the shower displays were relatively feeble. Mention may also be made of the Draconids (or Giacobinids); they have the same orbit as the Giacobini-Zinner comet discovered in 1900, although the meteor showers have been known for hundreds of years. A strong nighttime shower was observed in October 1933 and again in 1946, but not in between. It had been estimated that the showers would recur at intervals of about 13 years, i.e., twice the orbital period of the parent comet. An unexpected Draconid shower was observed in the daytime in October 1952, however, which may have escaped detection in 1939 because the radio echo technique had not been developed at that time. It is probable that all meteor streams started originally as swarms, which were at first close to the parent comet, and that the debris eventually spread out over the complete orbit.

7.104. As stated earlier, sporadic meteors exceed shower meteors in total number, but less is known about them. Some astronomers have suggested that they are produced by asteroids rather than comets. But this view is not generally accepted because the majority of sporadic meteoroids have orbits similar to the short-lived comets lying between Mars and Jupiter. Most of the orbital inclinations are less than 35 deg and the angles tend to increase with the estimated orbital period. These facts appear to argue in favor of a cometary origin for at least 85 to 90 percent of the sporadic meteors. It will be seen in § 7.175 that such meteors might be formed from meteoroid streams in which nearly all the particles are too small to produce visible meteors.

The Poynting-Robertson Effect

7.105. There is evidence from the brightness of the meteor trails in a shower that particles of similar size tend to travel in orbit together. There thus appears to be a sorting process taking place in space. An important contribution to this action is made by the *Poynting-Robertson* effect, which arises from the absorption and emission of radiation by the particles. The British physicist J. H. Poynting published an approximate solution to the problem of the motion of a body in a radiation field in 1903, and this was refined, with the aid of the theory of relativity, by H. P. Robertson in the United States in 1937.

7.106. A body revolving about the Sun is subjected to gravitational forces and the action of solar radiation. For bodies of appreciable size, the influence of the radiation is insignificant, but for small particles, the situation is different. In addition to the normal force directed away from the Sun due to solar radiation pressure, as described in § 3.224, another factor must be considered. A particle absorbs radiation energy from the Sun coming from one direction, but it reradiates energy in all directions. Calculations show that as a result a tangential drag acts on the particle and decreases its angular momentum. Consequently, the particle follows a spiral path, drawing steadily closer to the Sun.*

---

* For a particle of mass m moving with a velocity v in a circular orbit of radius R, the angular momentum is mvR (§ 2.51). The velocity, according to equation (2.16), is pro-

This is the Poynting-Robertson effect, the magnitude of which is inversely related to the radius and density of the particle. It is, therefore, most significant for particles of low density and small size (and mass).

7.107. As a result of the Poynting-Robertson effect, there is a tendency for particles of various sizes revolving about the Sun to become sorted out into different orbits. The smallest particles will be closest to the Sun and the largest farther out, provided the densities are approximately the same. In the course of millions of years, the particles will fall into the Sun, first the smaller ones and then those of larger diameters.* The oldest meteoroid streams thus contain the larger, more massive particles and produce the brightest meteors. The removal of particles from solar orbit as a result of the Poynting-Robertson effect does not necessarily mean that the total number is decreasing. The loss is being replaced continuously by material from the breakup of comets.

PROPERTIES OF METEOROIDS

7.108. The mass and dimensions of a meteoroid cannot be measured directly, because the material is entirely (or almost entirely) dispersed as it passes through the atmosphere. These properties must therefore be inferred from the observed luminosity and velocity of the meteor. The brightness of the trail is related to the kinetic energy of the meteoroid, and this is proportional to its mass and the square of the velocity. Hence, if the velocity has been measured, the mass of the meteoroid can be estimated from its brightness. The somewhat surprising conclusion has been reached that the most brilliant meteors, excluding fireballs, originate from particles weighing no more than a few grams, i.e., on the order of one tenth of an ounce or so. For the great majority of meteoroids, the masses are small fractions of a gram, perhaps a few milligrams, i.e., thousandths of a gram. The largest meteoroids are probably less than half a centimeter (one fifth of an inch) across, and the smaller ones, which produce most meteors, may be less than a millimeter in diameter, i.e., smaller than the head of an average pin.

7.109. Estimates of the density of meteoroids indicate that for the great majority the values lie between 0.01 and 0.7 gram per cubic centimeter, and F. L. Whipple (1963) has adopted a density of 0.44 gram per cubic centimeter for calculational purposes. A similar result has been derived for micrometeoroids, which do not produce visible meteors (§ 7.170). The density of mineral matter is close to 3 grams per cubic centimeter, and so it must be concluded that meteoroids are commonly porous in nature. This is in agreement with their

---

portional to $1/\sqrt{R}$; hence, the angular momentum varies as $m\sqrt{R}$. Since m is constant, a decrease in angular momentum must be accompanied by a decrease in the orbital radius, i.e., the distance of the particle from the Sun. The same general conclusion is applicable to an elliptical orbit.

* According to Robertson's calculations, the time required for a particle of radius r centimeters and density ρ grams per cubic centimeter to spiral into the Sun is $7.0 \times 10^6 r\rho R^2$ years, where R is the initial distance in astronomical units.

probable origin as cometary residues; rapid conversion of the ices in the nucleus of the comet into gas might be expected to lead to the formation of porous material. Because of its low strength, such material would be readily broken up into the small particles that constitute almost all meteoroids.

7.110. On the average, something like ten meteors per hour can be seen by a single observer. Allowing for the limitations of the field of view and the altitude at which the trail appears, calculations indicate that 24 million meteoroids, producing visible trails, enter Earth's atmosphere each day. From a comparison of the frequency of meteors of different brightness, it has been concluded that the number of meteoroids increases with decreasing particle size. A rough rule is that the number increases by a factor of 100 for a decrease in diameter by a factor of five. That is to say, there are roughly 100 times as many meteoroids 0.1 cm across as there are 0.5 cm across; it is apparent, therefore, that very bright meteors constitute only a small proportion of the total. For very small particles, less than 0.01 cm in diameter, the number appears to be even larger than given by this rule (§ 7.171).

7.111. It was thought at one time that the heating of a meteoroid upon entering the atmosphere, and the consequent production of a visible and ionized meteor trail, resulted mainly from compression of the air in front of the fast-moving object. It is now realized, however, that the small dimensions of the meteoroid particles and the very low density of the air, i.e., the great distances between molecules, at the altitudes of 80 kilometers (50 miles) or so where the meteor luminosity is observed, make this explanation unsatisfactory.

7.112. The view now commonly held is that the individual molecules and atoms of the atmosphere bombard the surface of the meteoroid and their kinetic energy is converted into heat. The temperature of the solid is thereby raised to the point where its surface begins to vaporize. The vaporized meteoroid atoms move into the surrounding atmosphere at about the same high velocity as the solid particle from which they originated and collide, from time to time, with atoms and molecules of the air. In these collisions, the directed kinetic energy of the evaporated atoms is converted into heat, i.e., random kinetic energy. This heat produces both light and ionization, the two phenomena whereby meteors are detected. The disintegration of the original meteoroid into two or more particles generally takes place in the first stage of its interaction with the atmosphere, i.e., when it is bombarded by the molecules and atoms of the air.

7.113. Relatively few spectra of meteors have been recorded and these do not reveal anything at all unusual or significant. When the particle velocities and, consequently, the temperatures are high, the bright-line emission spectra include the H and K lines of ionized calcium, i.e., of Ca II (§ 6.122); when the temperatures are probably lower, only the neutral atom lines are observed. In addition, meteor spectra reveal the presence of neutral iron atoms and also of magnesium, manganese, silicon, aluminum, and sodium. The general impression is that meteoroids are largely stony in character, consisting possibly of alumino-silicates and ferrosilicates of calcium, magnesium, sodium, etc. But the available data are insufficient to make any definite identification possible.

METEORITES

7.114. A meteorite is an extraterrestrial object that survives passage through the atmosphere and reaches Earth's surface. There are several hundred cases on record of the discovery of meteorites associated with fireballs (or bolides) and it is highly probable that all the 1700 or so known meteorites fell to Earth in this manner. A distinction is sometimes made between meteorite *falls*, which are observed, and *finds*, which are discovered independently. There is no recorded instance of a meteorite coming either from a meteor shower or from a sporadic meteor of normal intensity, i.e., not a fireball. It is generally concluded, therefore, that meteorites do not necessarily come from the same source as do meteoroid particles that form meteors upon entering the atmosphere.

7.115. Although meteorites leave an intensely bright (fireball) trail in their passage through the air, the luminosity arises from a thermal ablation mechanism (cf. § 3.76) somewhat different from that described in § 7.112. Because a meteorite body is generally much larger than the particles that produce ordinary meteors, it is able to trap and compress the air in front of it, as it travels with high velocity. As a result of the compression, the temperature of the air is increased to the point at which it can cause melting of the adjacent meteorite surface. The incandescent drops of the liquid are then swept off by the streaming air to form the luminous trail of the fireball. Aerodynamic drag (§ 3.128) causes the velocity of the meteorite to decrease and the temperature of the air falls correspondingly. In due course, the molten surface layer solidifies to form a smooth—often glass-like—coating that is characteristic of meteorites. Part of a meteorite body is removed as it passes through the atmosphere, but the remainder is usually large enough to be found on Earth.

TYPES OF METEORITES

7.116. The great majority of meteorites are of two types: the *stony meteorites* (or *stones*), like terrestrial stones, consist mainly of silicates of calcium, magnesium, iron, aluminum, etc., and the *iron meteorites* (or *irons*), which are metallic in nature and are made up largely of iron with various proportions of nickel. The stones constitute about 61 percent of known meteorites and the irons represent some 35 percent. The remaining 4 percent are the *stony-irons*, which are intermediate in character. The largest meteorites discovered are of the iron type; this is partly, at least, because the stones are more brittle and break up to some extent during their passage through the air or when they strike the ground. Fireballs have been seen to disintegrate in flight and frequently several meteorites are found close together.

7.117. The largest known iron meteorite, which was discovered at Hoba in the southwest of Africa, is roughly 3 meters by 3 meters (10 feet by 10 feet) across the top and about 0.5 to 1 meter (20 to 40 inches) thick; it is estimated to weigh about 60 tons, apart from some 20 tons of surrounding material that has separated from the main body. The largest stony meteorite, weighing about 2300 pounds, fell in Kansas in 1948. It was observed to burst twice during its descent through the atmosphere and many smaller fragments have been found in addition to the large single piece.

METEORITE CRATERS

7.118. There is little information available concerning the velocities and orbits of the meteorite bodies (see § 7.131). That they travel at high speed, with geocentric velocities around 40 kilometers (25 miles) per second, is indicated by the occasional formation of craters, called *meteorite craters* although they are often referred to as *meteor craters*. Nearly all the meteorite craters are associated with iron meteorites and a small number with stony-irons. By the time they reach the ground, stony meteorites are rarely massive enough to form large craters. The study of meteorite craters is of interest because there is a possibility that the numerous craters on the Moon may have resulted from meteorite impacts, as will be seen in Chapter 9.

7.119. A well known meteoritic crater is the Barringer Crater (or Meteor Crater) near Winslow, Arizona, which averages approximately 1.3 kilometers (4000 feet) across. It has been estimated that the meteorite (or meteorites) which produced this crater weighed between 10 and 100 thousand tons, and fell some 30,000 years ago. There are at least two pieces of evidence that throw light on the origin of the Barringer Crater. First, large numbers of iron meteorites have been found in and around the crater, and second, the discovery by E. C. T. Chao, E. M. Shoemaker, and B. M. Madsen in 1960 of the mineral coesite in many rock fragments. This mineral is a dense form of silica (SiO_2) previously known only in the laboratory, where it had been made by the action of very high pressure, in excess of 300,000 pounds per square inch. Subsequently, an even more dense modification of silica, known as stishovite, the formation of which requires still higher pressures, was found in fragments from Meteor Crater. It is probable that the coesite and stishovite were produced by the high-pressure shock wave that resulted from the hypervelocity impact of a massive meteorite.

7.120. It is of interest that, since 1960, coesite and sometimes stishovite have been found in other craters, which are presumably meteoritic in origin. Notable among these is the Ries Kessel (or Ries Basin), not far from Stuttgart, Germany. This crater was originally at least 30 kilometers (18 miles) in diameter and its age is estimated to be between 15 and 20 million years. The fact that such a large crater was apparently formed by impact may be of significance in connection with the problem of the origin of the large lunar craters.

7.121. Two moderately large crater groups are known to have been produced in Russia by impact with extraterrestrial objects in relatively recent times. One, near the Sikhote-Alin mountains in southeast Siberia, formed in 1947, is undoubtedly meteoritic in character because several tons of iron meteorites were found in its vicinity. On the other hand, the Tunguska River craters in central Siberia may have resulted from impact with a cometary body in 1908. As far as is known, there is no significant quantity of meteoritic material associated with these craters.

CHONDRITES AND ACHONDRITES

7.122. Most (over 90 percent) of the stony meteorites have small spheroidal inclusions, a millimeter or two in diameter, called *chondrules* (Greek, *chondros*, "grain of wheat"). These meteorites are referred to as *chondrites*, whereas those that do not include chondrules are known as *achondrites*. Some chondrites contain very few chondrules per unit volume, but in others the number is large. The chondrules are composed of magnesium-iron silicates and the appearance of many suggests that they were formed from a melt which had been subjected to rapid cooling. In the chondrite meteorites, the chondrules are imbedded in a matrix consisting of irregular masses, mainly of magnesium-iron silicates, olivine and pyroxene in particular, together with pieces of broken chondrules. Appreciable quantities of metallic iron, containing nickel in small proportions, and of iron sulfide are often present as inclusions in chondrites.

7.123. The minerals in chondrites are all well known, but the structure is different from that of any rocks found on Earth. The overall chemical composition is fairly constant, with about 36 percent silica and 22 percent magnesia, except for variations in the iron content. The proportions of many elements in chondrites differ from those in terrestrial rocks; there is, however, a general similarity between chondrites and the material constituting the Sun and the stars. This is seen in Fig. 7.18, which shows the average abundances of some of the heavier elements relative to silicon, the abundance of which is arbitrarily taken as unity. The inference is that chondrites were formed from the primordial material which ultimately accumulated to produce the planets (§ 7.192).

7.124. The only significant variation in chemical composition of the chondrites is the proportions of iron and of associated small quantities of nickel and cobalt. The amount of iron in different chondrites ranges from about 20 to 35 percent, but many fall into two groups containing 22 and 28 percent, respectively. It is of interest that the free, metallic iron is only about 7 percent, on the average, in the former case but nearly 18 percent in the latter. The remaining iron is chiefly present as sulfide or in the oxidized form as an iron silicate.

7.125. The achondrites, which contain about 50 percent of silica, also consist mainly of silicates, but their chemical compositions are much more variable than are those of the chondrites. Some achondrites are high in calcium and low in magnesium, whereas for others the situation is reversed in this respect. In general, many achondrites resemble terrestrial igneous rock, such as basalt, but their sodium and potassium contents are lower. Possibly the oxides of these elements were vaporized when the material was at a high temperature. It is unlikely that any changes, except to the outermost layers, took place to meteorites

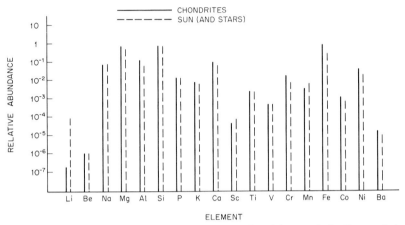

FIG. 7.18.   Comparison of relative compositions of chondrites and the Sun and similar stars (adapted from D. L. Chapman and H. K. Larson)

during their descent through the atmosphere. The interiors of meteorites observed soon after falling to Earth have always been found to be quite cold.

IRON AND STONY-IRON METEORITES

7.126. Three general categories of iron meteorites have been identified; they contain less than 6 percent, between 6 and 14 percent, and more than 14 percent of nickel, respectively. In some cases they have inclusions of small quantities of silicate. The iron meteorites with between 6 and 14 percent of nickel are the most common. After polishing and etching, they exhibit a typical geometrical structure well known to metallurgists as a Widmanstätten pattern. The formation of such a pattern is characteristic of systems consisting of two solid metallic alloys of different composition—in the present case with low and high nickel contents, respectively—that have separated slowly from the molten state upon cooling. The presence of large crystals in iron meteorites is also regarded as evidence of slow changes occurring in the metal over a long period of time.

7.127. A small proportion of meteorites are of the stony-iron type; in some, the metal appears to have a continuous form and to surround the stony minerals, whereas in others the metal is in small pieces imbedded in the silicate stone. Both stony and metallic constituents are quite similar to those found in stony and iron meteorites. It seems probable, therefore, that the stony-iron are a true intermediate forming a link between the stony meteorites, on the one hand, and the iron meteorites, on the other hand. There is thus a continuity, suggesting that some meteoritic materials, at least, were formed in a single body (or bodies) which subsequently disintegrated.

CARBONACEOUS CHONDRITES

7.128. Of the meteorites that have been recovered after being seen to fall, some 3 or 4 percent are black, friable chondrites, containing roughly 2 to 4 percent of carbon, partly in the form of the element but mainly as complex organic compounds. These remarkable objects are called *carbonaceous chondrites*. The proportion of water in these meteorites is also substantially higher than normal. This water is, of course, not present as liquid but in various combined forms. The true proportion of carbonaceous meteorites is probably higher than the few percent indicated above because they are difficult to recognize, even if their fall is actually observed. Furthermore, they disintegrate fairly rapidly as a result of weathering, so that chance finds are rare. When found, they are usually less than 20 centimeters (8 inches) across and have a thin black crust formed by the solidification of material that was melted while traversing the atmosphere.

7.129. Analysis of the organic material extracted from carbonaceous chondrites has revealed the presence of various hydrocarbons of high molecular weight, similar to those found in crude petroleum and in some ancient terrestrial sediments. In addition, the identification has been reported of small proportions of other types of complex organic structures, such as amino acids, sugars, and unidentified compounds that absorb radiation and fluoresce in the ultraviolet region of the spectrum. It is reasonably certain that the organic compounds were actually in the meteorites before falling to Earth, and this may be of great significance. Although it is improbable that the material was produced by extraterrestrial living matter, the presence of complex organic (carbon) compounds which have played a role in the development of life on Earth indicates their chemical synthesis elsewhere in the solar system.

7.130. In 1961, G. Claus, and B. S. Nagy, in the United States, reported that they had discovered what they called small *organized elements* resembling fossil algae* in two carbonaceous chondrites. Detailed examination of photomicrographs showed several features characteristic of living cells; for example, some of the constituents reacted to stains in a manner that is deemed to be specific for certain biological compounds. Because of its tremendous significance, the question of whether or not the organized elements, of which examples are shown in Fig. 7.19, are indeed the remains of extraterrestrial life has become the subject of intense controversy. Some scientists are convinced that the organized elements are of biological origin, but most consider that they are either ter-

* The algae are simple plants, the most elementary consisting merely of single cells.

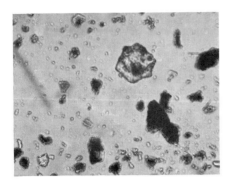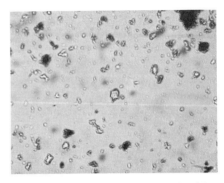

Fig. 7.19. Microstructures in carbonaceous chondrites: left, from South Africa (× 630); right, from the United States (× 400). (*Courtesy Jet Propulsion Laboratory, California Institute of Technology*)

restrial contaminants or crystals of inorganic or organic compounds and are not associated with any form of life.*

Origin of Meteorites

7.131. It is commonly, but not universally, accepted that meteorites are residual fragments of a planet-like body (or bodies), possibly the same body (or bodies) from which the asteroids originated. In other words, in the disruptive process that led to the formation of the asteroids, described in § 7.62, fragments of various sizes were produced; the largest ones are still revolving about the Sun, whereas many of the smaller pieces have had their orbits perturbed and have fallen to Earth as meteorites. There is only one case on record of a reasonably accurate calculation of the orbital elements of a meteorite; the results indicate an asteroid-like orbit, lying between Mars and Jupiter at aphelion and between Venus and Earth at perihelion. More information on meteorite orbits is needed and this should be available in the future from the new photographic network in the United States (§ 7.137).

7.132. Disregarding for the present the somewhat unusual carbonaceous chondrites, there is a sequence in the characteristics of meteorites, from stones through stony-irons to irons, that is suggestive of a common origin. A possible explanation is that the primodial material, from which the solar planetary system developed, accumulated to form a body of appreciable size. As a result of the decay of various radioactive isotopes present, the interior of the mass became sufficiently hot for melting to occur. Upon cooling, the silicates would crystallize out first and rise to the top of a layer of molten ferrous metals. Subsequently, an intermediate region would form, containing both silicate (stony)

---

* Toward the end of 1964, it was discovered that some specimens of the Orgueil meteorite, one of the best known carbonaceous chondrites, which fell in 1864, had been deliberately contaminated with organic matter. The general conclusions given above are, however, unaffected.

material and metal, and finally the liquid metal in the center would solidify when the temperature and pressure dropped to a sufficient extent.* The disruption of such a body might be expected to yield masses which were either stony or metallic or a combination of the two forms.

7.133. The foregoing provides a broad outline of the origin of meteorites, but it does not account for their many structural details, e.g., the formation and inclusion of chondrules, the complexity in structure of the stones and of the chondrites in particular, the large crystals and Widmanstätten structure in the irons, etc. Obviously, meteorites have had a complex history, but there is little definite that can be said about either its nature or the underlying causes. In recent years, efforts have been made to throw light on the situation by determining the relative amounts of the isotopes of different elements present § 7.201). This promising technique may be expected to provide useful information in due course.

7.134. The carbonaceous chondrites may have an important bearing on the origin of meteorites. Different suggestions have been put forward to account for these carbon-bearing stones. One theory is that the composition is representative of the primordial material which constituted the original solar nebula (§ 7.192). As a result of various processes involving high temperatures, the carbonaceous material would have been mostly driven off, thus leaving the noncarbonaceous stones. A modification of this view is that the carbonaceous chondrites are derived from specific regions of one or more asteroidal (or planetary) bodies formed by the aggregation of dust, etc., from the solar nebula. These regions would lie between the hot interior, where silicates are formed, and the cold exterior, where organic compounds could exist. The resulting rocks would be carbonaceous stones, just as the stony irons are intermediate between silicate and metallic bodies.

7.135. An entirely different hypothesis is that the carbonaceous material is not a primary component of chondrites, but is entirely secondary in nature. The suggestion is that it has been produced by the infiltration into the chondrites of carbon compounds, hydrogen sulfide, and moisture from outside sources. A resolution of the conflicting theories might not only throw light on the history of the solar system but also on the origin of life on Earth and perhaps elsewhere.

7.136. Until samples are collected from the Moon, meteorites are the only materials accessible to man that are definitely of extraterrestrial origin. In spite of their complexity, meteorites may in time provide information concerning the development of the solar system. Further studies with improved techniques, e.g., isotopic analysis, and a comparison with the characteristics of rocks obtained from the Moon will undoubtedly open up new areas of understanding.

---

* It is generally agreed that the interior of Earth, consisting of an iron-nickel core surrounded by a mantle and crust of silicates, was formed in an analogous manner.

THE PRAIRIE NETWORK

7.137. In order to obtain more information about meteorites and their orbits, there has been established in the United States an extensive, organized program for photographing bright meteors (fireballs) and the recovery of associated meteorites. The Prairie Network, as it is designated, consists of 16 unmanned stations in seven midwestern states, namely, Illinois, Iowa, Kansas, Missouri, Nebraska, Oklahoma, and South Dakota. Each station is equipped with four automatic wide-angle cameras having rotating shutters. The cameras are pointed toward north, south, east, and west, respectively, and effectively cover the entire sky, from horizon to horizon. The distance between adjacent stations is about 250 kilometers (150 miles).

7.138. From photographs of the fireball trails obtained at two or more stations simultaneously, it will be possible to derive the orbital elements of the trajectory. Data of this kind will help to determine from where in space the material came. In addition, from the direction of motion through the atmosphere an accurate prediction can be made of the point of impact with Earth. An immediate search can then be instituted with a good chance of recovering the meteorite. Laboratory studies and analysis will follow without delay.

TEKTITES

7.139. The glassy materials called *tektites* (Greek, *tektos,* "molten") are objects, possibly of extraterrestrial origin, which may be related in some manner to meteorites. Tektites are commonly about 2 or 3 centimeters, i.e., roughly an inch, across, although many are either smaller or larger. A few are as much as 10 centimeters (4 inches) in diameter. Tektites have various shapes, but they are invariably rounded and often spheroidal in form; their glassy nature and general appearance suggest very strongly that they were formed by the melting of mineral matter (Fig. 7.20). Some tektites exhibit markings which have been attributed to subsequent surface melting and aerodynamic ablation of the solid caused by rapid motion through the atmosphere.

7.140. Unlike meteorites, which are more or less uniformly distributed over all parts of Earth, tektites are largely restricted to a few regions. The most extensive areas where tektites have been found are in the *strewn fields,* as they are called, of the countries surrounding the South China Sea and in most of Australia and the adjacent island of Tasmania. Smaller strewn fields are in the Ivory Coast (Africa), Czechoslovakia, and Texas and Georgia in the United States.* A single tektite has also been found in Martha's Vineyard, Massachusetts.

7.141. The tektites are true glasses, that is to say, they are noncrystalline solids, and contain 68 to 80 percent of silica as their main constituent, together

---

* Glassy materials found in Colombia and Peru are sometimes, but probably erroneously, described as tektites.

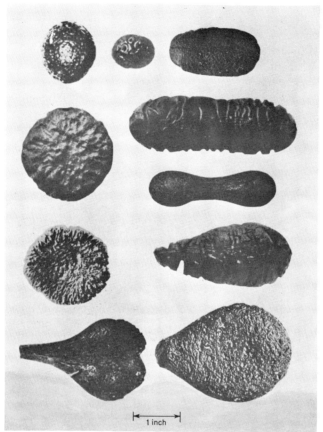

F<small>IG.</small> 7.20.   Tektites from the South China Sea area, Australia, and Czechoslovakia

with 10 to 16 percent of aluminum oxide (alumina); in addition, there are small amounts of iron, calcium, sodium, potassium, titanium, and other oxides. In their major chemical constituents, tektites resemble typical rocks of Earth's crust, such as granite, except for the volatile oxides of hydrogen (water), sodium, and potassium. The densities of all known tektites are within the range of approximately 2.3 to 2.5 grams per cubic centimeter. In chemical composition, density, and glassy nature they somewhat resemble the terrestrial volcanic substance known as obsidian, although they differ in the nature of the inclusions and in other ways. Most tektites are dark brownish in color, but some are green or yellow; many are quite clear, but others have small inclusions, particularly of fused quartz.

7.142. In addition to the relatively small variations in overall composition and density, tektites are remarkable in the constancy of the ratios of certain isotopes. The ratios of oxygen-18 to oxygen-16 and of strontium-87 to strontium-86 in tektites found in different parts of the world fall within a very narrow range in each case. The situation is quite different from that in normal terrestrial rocks; in the latter, the isotope ratios exhibit a relatively large variation.

7.143. Small metallic spherules, about 1.5 millimeters diameter on the average, were found in some Philippine tektites, and were shown to consist of an alloy of iron containing a few percent of nickel, called kamacite. Spherules of similar form and composition sometimes occur in the ejecta, i.e., material thrown out, from meteoritic craters on Earth. The mineral kamacite is also present in iron meteorites but, as far as is known, it does not exist in any other natural terrestrial material. This fact suggests very strongly that meteorites played some role in the formation of tektites.

7.144. Two methods in particular have been used to determine the ages of tektites, since they were last in a molten state. One, depending on the measurement of the ratio of potassium-40 to argon-40, is described in § 7.204. The other, developed in the United States by P. B. Price and R. M. Walker in 1963, is applicable to materials, especially if they are transparent, containing small amounts of uranium, as tektites do. The tracks produced by the fission fragment nuclei resulting from the spontaneous fission of the uranium-238 isotope can be made visible by etching the mineral with hydrofluoric acid. From the number of such tracks present and the concentration of uranium-238, which is determined by radioactive techniques, it is possible to calculate the age of the material. Both procedures agree in giving the following ages: North American tektites, about 34 million years; Czechoslovakian tektites, roughly 14 million years; and Far Eastern (Australia, Philippines, and Indo-China) tektites nearly 700,000 years. It should be noted that these ages are the elapsed periods since the tektite was last in a molten stage. The age at which the material was differentiated (or separated) from its source, as calculated from the rubidium-strontium isotope ratios, is estimated to be a few hundred million years.

ORIGIN OF TEKTITES

7.145. Although tektites are considered here in connection with meteorites, it is possible, but by no means certain, that they are actually made of terrestrial material. Nevertheless, it is generally believed that an object from space was responsible for their formation. At one time it was thought that tektites were the result of heating by lightning or by volcanic action, but such explanations of their origin appear to be inadequate.

7.146. The view generally held is that tektites were produced by the impact of large meteorites, possibly on igneous rocks, i.e., solid materials which were formed upon cooling of a molten mass called a *magma*. The ejecta, which were melted by the heat of impact or in other ways, then landed as tektites at a considerable distance away. Some authorities consider that the meteorite impacts occurred on Earth whereas others think that they were on the Moon. The presence of spherules of kamacite in certain tektites, as mentioned earlier, is regarded as strong evidence of their meteoritic origin, no matter where the actual impact took place.

7.147. The restricted distribution of tektites on Earth's surface, limited to a few large areas in Australia and Southeast Asia and some smaller ones in North America, Central Europe, and East Africa, is consistent with the relative scarcity of large meteorites. The tektite deposits in the Ivory Coast and Czechoslovakia have been referred to nearby meteoritic craters, but similar craters are not known to be associated with the extensive finds in Asia and Australia. Since the Far Eastern tektites are known to have been formed much more recently than the others, it is surprising, if these tektites were formed on Earth, that no corresponding crater has been found.

7.148. One of the points in favor of the lunar origin of tektites is the narrow range of their chemical composition and of certain isotopic ratios. If they had been formed from igneous rocks on Earth, it is expected that the variations would be much greater. Those who favor the terrestrial origin of tektites claim that the only material involved was the sedimentary material (or soil) near the surface which has a fairly constant average composition to a depth of a few feet all over the world. It would appear, however, that a meteorite large enough to form the extensive tektite deposits in Australia, for example, would have produced ejecta from much greater depths. On the Moon, changes of the type that have altered Earth's crust were apparently absent and large areas of the lunar surface, the maria in particular (§ 9.82), probably have the same (or similar) composition.

7.149. The striking physical characteristics of the Australian "button" tektites (Fig. 7.21) is the basis of another argument for their lunar origin. In the first place, these tektites show marked evidence of aerodynamic ablation and surface melting; these changes were probably caused by an extensive journey through Earth's atmosphere. It is perhaps significant that D. R. Chapman in the United States (1962) has made objects bearing a decided resemblance to Australian tektites by exposing glass-like materials to a high-velocity stream of hot air in a wind tunnel. Calculations indicate that to produce the observed shapes, the tektites (or their precursors) must have entered Earth's atmosphere at a velocity in the vicinity of 11 kilometers (6.8 miles) per second. This is too close to Earth's escape velocity for the tektites to have originated from a terrestrial impact, but it is too low for an object coming from a large distance away. It is, however, consistent with a lunar origin of the material. The essential absence of the isotope aluminum-26, which would have been formed in space by the action of cosmic rays, also indicates that tektites did not travel far from Earth.

7.150. One of the unusual properties of tektites is their extremely small water content, namely 10 to 150 parts (by weight) per million, compared with 5000 or more for terrestrial igneous rocks which were formed at high temperature. It seems unlikely, therefore, that tektites were produced by meteorite (or cometary) impact on Earth, especially as the removal of water from molten glass is known to be very difficult. A possible explanation, offered by John A.

FIG. 7.21.   Front, side, and back views of Australian button tektite (top row); artificial tektite prepared by D. R. Chapman from molten glass in a wind tunnel (lower row). (*National Aeronautics and Space Administration, Ames Research Center, Moffett Field, California*)

O'Keefe (1964), is that the tektites originated on the Moon, where the very low atmospheric pressure would facilitate the loss of water.

7.151. Regardless of the manner in which the tektites were formed, the theory of their lunar origin has some interesting corollaries. First, it is expected that other ejecta of meteorite impacts on the Moon probably exist on Earth, but have not been recognized as such. It may be significant that glassy materials, believed to have been formed by impact melting, i.e., impactites, have been found in Libya, Bavaria, and Tasmania; these have the same ages, as determined by the fission-track method, as adjacent tektites from North America, Czechoslovakia, and the Far East, respectively.* Second, the view that tektites are lunar material has an important bearing on the problem of the structure of the Moon; this will be discussed in Chapter 9.

7.152. The suggestion has also been made that tektites may have resulted from interaction of Earth with the nucleus or the head of a comet. In this event, it would be difficult to account for the presence of iron-nickel particles

---
* The correspondence in age since last melting of tektites and impactites could also be interpreted as favoring a common terrestrial origin.

in some tektites. Furthermore, there is the matter of the fairly uniform composition of tektites which applies to any theory based on a terrestrial impact. On the other hand, the impact with Earth of a comet of moderate size might not produce a conspicuous crater, and so the absence of such craters, e.g., in the Far East, would not be a serious objection. The general conclusion to be drawn at present is that the origin of tektites is still uncertain.

MICROMETEOROIDS

INTRODUCTION

7.153. By means of optical and radar techniques, it has been possible to observe and count meteoroids down to about a one ten-thousandth part (10^{-4}) of a gram in weight or roughly three tenths (0.3) of a millimeter in diameter, i.e., about one fifth the diameter of a pin's head. Particles smaller than this cannot be detected because they leave no luminous or ionized trail when they pass through the atmosphere. The reason is that the ratio of the surface area of a particle to its volume (or mass) increases as the size decreases.* The heating of a meteoroid that results from interaction with the atmosphere is related to the kinetic energy and, hence, to the mass, assuming a given velocity. The loss of heat by radiation, on the other hand, increases with increasing surface area of the particle. Since the ratio of area to mass increases with decreasing particle size, it is evident that the loss of heat by radiation, relative to that produced by interaction with the atmosphere, must increase correspondingly. Thus, as the particle size decreases, a point is reached at which the temperature attained by the meteoroid is insufficient to produce either a luminous trail or ionization. Detection by either optical or radar methods is then no longer possible.

7.154. Meteoroids too small to be observed by the conventional techniques are called micrometeorites or micrometeoroids. They are of special interest because they survive passage through the atmosphere, whereas the somewhat larger meteoroids do not. The very small particles reach Earth ultimately, at the estimated rate of 10^7 kilograms (10,000 metric tons) per day, and so they are in a sense meteorites, although they are too minute to be recognized as such. Since the particles are generally studied while still far from Earth and are probably more closely related to the meteoroids than to the larger bodies that fall as meteorites, they will be referred to here as *micrometeoroids*. In Chapter 9, however, where impact of the small particles with the lunar surface is under consideration, the term micrometeorite will be used.

7.155. It will be seen later that the number of micrometeoroids increases

---

* Assume, for simplicity, that the particle is spherical; then, if r is the radius, the surface area is proportional to r^2 and the volume and mass to r^3. The ratio of area to volume (or mass) is thus proportional to r^2/r^3, i.e., to $1/r$; consequently, the ratio increases as r, i.e., the size, decreases.

rapidly as the particle size decreases. The space density* of the micrometeoroids is therefore much larger than of meteoroids. Although the masses of the micrometeoroid particles are extremely small, namely, less than a millionth part (10^{-6}) of a gram, they travel in space with high geocentric velocities, presumably on the same order as the observed velocities of the meteoroids, i.e., 12 to 72 kilometers (7.5 to 44.5 miles) per second. It is possible that these hypervelocity particles may represent a hazard in space flight because of their ability to erode and possibly to penetrate thin-walled vessels, such as fuel tanks, radiators for power supplies (§ 3.231), and even manned space capsules.

7.156. In the interest of minimizing the total weight, spacecraft materials are made as thin and light as is compatible with mechanical strength and safety. Consequently, the hazard arising from the impact of meteoroids and micrometeoroids must be taken into consideration. The space density of the larger particles is relatively so small that the probability of a collision with a spacecraft may not be significant, unless the vehicle passes through a meteoroid stream or swarm. Of course, precautions would be taken against such a circumstance. If a collision with a relatively large meteoroid did occur, however, the results might be serious. Since the particle density in space increases with decreasing particle size, the probability of impact with a spacecraft increases correspondingly. The problem of collisions with micrometeoroids is thus the subject of an extensive study, as will be seen shortly.

THE ZODIACAL LIGHT

7.157. The presence of micrometeoroid particles in space, down to 1 micron (§ 6.53) in diameter, has been inferred from a study of the *zodiacal light*. Under suitable conditions, especially when the plane of the ecliptic is almost perpendicular to the horizon, this light is seen as a dome-shaped (or pyramidal) region of faint luminosity in the western sky soon after sunset or in the east shortly before sunrise (Fig. 7.22). As the Sun sets farther or rises, respectively, the pyramidal cloud of zodiacal light appears to sink below the horizon and fade away. At its maximum, the luminosity is about the same as that of the Milky Way.

7.158. The zodiacal light owes its name to the fact that the light is observed for some distance in the region of the zodiac (§ 7.23), i.e., it extends for several degrees on each side of the ecliptic plane. In the Northern Hemisphere, the most favorable periods for seeing the zodiacal light are after twilight during March and April and before dawn in September and October. At other times the ecliptic plane is closer to the horizon and the glow is obscured by haze and by absorption in the denser parts of the atmosphere near Earth. In equatorial

---

* The space density is the number of particles per unit volume of space, and should be distinguished from the ordinary (or mass) density, which is the mass of unit volume of the particulate material.

regions, the zodiacal light is visible throughout the year whenever the air is clear.

7.159. It is agreed that the zodiacal light is sunlight that has been scattered and refracted (bent) on its way to Earth, but there has been a difference of opinion as to whether most of the scattering is caused by electrons or by very

Fig. 7.22.   Zodiacal light; the streaks were produced by stars during the long exposure required to photograph the faint zodiacal light. (*Photograph by D. E. Blackwell and M. F. Ingham. Monthly Notices of the Royal Astronomical Society* **122**, 113 (1961))

small particles of dust, i.e., micrometeoroids, orbiting around the Sun. In recent years, several observations have helped to resolve the controversy in favor of the latter viewpoint. For example, light scattered by electrons is strongly polarized (§ 6.135, footnote), but the zodiacal light shows no more than about 20 percent polarization. Moreover, if electrons were responsible for most of the scattering, the Doppler effect due to random motion of the electrons would cause considerable broadening of the spectral lines, so that a continuous spectrum would be obtained. Solid particles have lower velocities and produce much less broadening. The spectrum of zodiacal light is essentially the same as that of sunlight, i.e., from the photosphere, with its dark Fraunhofer lines. There are also some bright emission lines (or bands) of ionized nitrogen molecules (N_2^+), but these are atmospheric in origin. It is thus accepted that the zodiacal light is mainly sunlight scattered by very small solid particles suspended in space between the Sun and Earth, and presumably orbiting throughout the whole of the solar system.

7.160. It will be recalled from § 6.167 that the F-corona (or dust corona) of the Sun is attributed to the scattering of light from the photosphere by interplanetary dust particles with diameters down to about 1 micron, i.e., 10^{-4} centimeter. There is now little doubt but that the zodiacal light phenomenon is actually an extension of the F-corona. In Fig. 7.23 there are shown a number

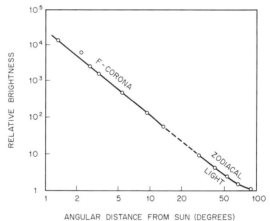

Fɪɢ. 7.23.   Relative brightness of F-corona and zodiacal light (after D. E. Blackwell).

of points, on a logarithmic scale, representing the relative brightness of the F-corona, at one extreme, and the zodiacal light, at the other extreme, as a function of the distance from the Sun expressed as an angle seen by an observer on Earth. Although there is a gap between the angular distances of about 12 deg, where measurements on the F-corona end, and 28 deg, where those on the zodiacal light commence, it is clear that the points fall on a single curve. This is strong presumptive evidence of the continuity between the F-corona and the zodiacal light.

7.161. There are no definite data that provide information on the size of the particles responsible for the zodiacal light. But the observations are consistent with dimensions ranging from about 300 microns, i.e., 3×10^{-2} centimeter, down to 1 micron, i.e., 10^{-4} centimeter. In other words, the particles are within the category described earlier as micrometeoroids. Provided such particles were not far from the Sun, e.g., not farther out than Jupiter, they would be swept into the Sun in the course of a few million years as a result of the Poynting-Robertson effect (§ 7.105). It follows, therefore, that the interplanetary micrometeoroids responsible for the zodiacal light and the F-corona are being continuously replaced; the most likely source is the same as that which replenishes the supply of most meteoroids, namely, cometary debris. Attention may be drawn to the statement in § 6.167 that the space density of the interplanetary dust is as small as 1 particle in a volume of 10^{13} cubic centimeters. It is only because of the large distances (and volumes) involved that there are enough particles to cause sufficient scattering of sunlight to be seen as the F-corona of the Sun or as the zodiacal light.

DIRECT OBSERVATIONS OF MICROMETEOROIDS

7.162. From studies of the zodiacal light as well as from photographic and radar observations of meteors, relationships have been established between the size of the interplanetary dust particles and their space density (cf. § 7.155). By extrapolation with the aid of such relationships, estimates have been made of the space densities of micrometeoroid particles of extremely small diameter and mass, even smaller than those responsible for the zodiacal light. With the development of sounding rockets and satellites, it has become possible to send instruments into space and to measure directly the numbers of such particles of different sizes. The results can then be compared with those derived indirectly from extrapolation of zodiacal light and meteoroid measurements.

7.163. The instrument most widely used for the study of dust particles from spacecraft has been a *microphone detector*. It is a form of transducer consisting basically of a piezoelectric crystal, e.g., of lead zirconate,* attached to a metallic sounding board (or diaphragm) that may be the wall of the space vehicle. A particle striking the sounding board causes a pressure to be exerted on the crystal and the resulting electrical pulse can be amplified and recorded. The information can be transmitted directly to a ground station by telemetry or it can be recorded on tape for transmission at a later time.

7.164. The size of the output pulse from the crystal microphone is related to the momentum of the particle striking the sounding board. The relationship is determined in laboratory experiments by dropping beads with known momenta onto a sounding board and observing the magnitude of the output voltage pulse. Momentum is the product of mass and velocity; hence, if the velocity of the particles is known, it should be possible to derive the rate at which particles of different masses strike the detector. The geocentric velocities of the micrometeoroids are presumably, on the average, similar to those of the larger meteoroids. It is the common practice, therefore, to assume that the dust particles producing signals in a microphone detector in space have an

---

* A piezoelectric material (Greek, *piezein,* "to press") produces an electrical voltage pulse when subjected to pressure.

average velocity of 30 kilometers (18 miles) per second. This is, of course, an approximation, but it is the best that can be done pending the development of instruments capable of measuring the velocities of the individual particles.

7.165. The microphone detector can count particles in the low mass range from 10^{-7} down to 10^{-10} gram. To extend the measurements to still smaller masses, down to 10^{-13} gram,* a *photomultiplier detector* is employed. If certain transparent materials, such as quartz or Lucite, are struck by a particle moving at high velocity, a faint flash of light is produced; this can be detected and amplified by a photomultiplier tube (§ 4.116), giving an electrical output signal proportional to the kinetic energy of the particle. The kinetic energy is equal to half the product of the mass and the square of the velocity; consequently, if the velocity is assumed to be 30 kilometers per second, as before, the numbers of particles of different masses striking the detector can be determined from the photomultiplier signals.

7.166. The first direct measurements of micrometeoroids in space were made in 1949 with a sounding rocket using a V-2 carrier. Subsequently, other sounding rockets (Aerobee and Nike-Cajun) were employed, and since 1958 several satellites and space probes launched by the United States, e.g., Explorers I and VIII, Vanguard III, Pioneer I, and Ranger I, and by the U.S.S.R., e.g., Sputnik III, Luniks I, II, and III, have carried instruments for the study of micrometeoroids in space. Another technique is to collect samples of interplanetary dust in recoverable sounding rockets and to examine under a microscope the particles and the holes they produce in a plastic membrane. The device is referred to as the Venus Fly Trap.†

MICROMETEOROIDS NEAR EARTH

7.167. The results of various rocket measurements are summarized in Fig. 7.24; it shows the influx rate of particles, expressed as the number of particles striking a square meter of surface per second, as a function of the particle mass, both scales being logarithmic. The curve represents an approximate average of the results of measurements that were not always in complete agreement with each other; variations can arise from different measuring and calibration techniques, from differences in altitude at which observations are made, and from actual variations, both in time and space, of the space density of the dust particles. Nevertheless, it is probable that Fig. 7.24 indicates, to a fair approximation, the average influx rate of micrometeoroids of different masses in space at an altitude of a few hundred miles. It will be seen later that the rate sometimes changes markedly from day to day, but this does not affect the general discussion presented below.

---

* The small size of such particles may be appreciated by noting that it would require about 500,000 to form a single layer on the head of a pin (1.5 millimeters diameter).

† It is named for the insectivorous plant, Venus's flytrap, that catches (and consumes) small insects.

7.168. In spite of the limitations of the data, there are two important con-clusions that can be drawn from them. First, it will be noted that the curve in Fig. **7.24** tends to flatten out when the micrometeoroid masses fall below about 10^{-11} gram; this means that the extremely small particles do not in-

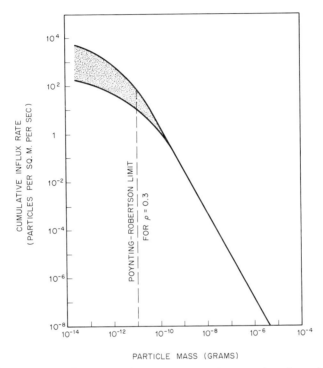

Fɪɢ. 7.24. Cumulative influx rate of micrometeoroids as a function of mass, with uncertain area shaded. (The cumulative rate is the total for all masses up to and in-cluding the given mass)

crease in number as fast as might be expected. The reason is that these very small particles tend to be removed from the solar system as a result of the Poynting-Robertson effect (§ **7.107**).

7.169. Provided the gravitational attraction of the Sun exceeds the repulsive action due to the normal solar radiation pressure, the Poynting-Robertson effect is of no consequence. It becomes significant, however, when the gravita-tional force is equal to or less than that caused by the radiation pressure. For a particle that absorbs, rather than reflects, solar radiation, the pressure at Earth's distance is half the value given in § 3.225, i.e., 4.65×10^{-5} dyne per square centimeter. If r centimeters is the radius of a particle, the effective area is the cross-sectional area πr^2, and the force due to solar radiation is

$4.65 \times 10^{-5} \times \pi r^2$ dynes. The mass of the particle is $4\pi r^3 \rho/3$, where ρ is the density of the material in grams per cubic centimeter. The solar gravitational attraction, as calculated from equation (2.1), using the known mass of the Sun, is then found to be $0.80 \times \pi r^3 \rho$ dynes. The condition for the Poynting-Robertson effect to be of significance is consequently

$$0.80 \times \pi r^3 \rho \leqslant 4.66 \times 10^{-5} \times \pi r^2$$

or

$$r\rho \leqslant 5.8 \times 10^{-5},$$

that is, when the product of the particle radius in centimeters and the mass density in grams per cubic centimeter is equal to or less than 5.8×10^{-5}.

7.170. According to Fig. 7.24, the particle mass for which the Poynting-Robertson effects begins to influence the micrometeoroid flux is about 10^{-11} gram. There are thus two equations relating the particle radius and mass density, namely,

$$\tfrac{4}{3}\pi r^3 \rho = 10^{-11} \quad \text{and} \quad r\rho = 5.8 \times 10^{-5}.$$

From these, it is readily found that ρ is nearly 0.3 gram per cubic centimeter. In view of the approximate nature of the data in Fig. 7.24 for particles of very small mass, it is probably not justified to conclude any more than that the mass density of many micrometeoroid particles is on the order of roughly 1 gram per cubic centimeter. If this value is confirmed by more reliable measurements, it will provide support for the view presented in § 7.109 that meteoroid (and micrometeoroid) material is somewhat porous in nature.*

7.171. A comparison of the curve in Fig. 7.24 with the influx of particles of small mass derived by extrapolation from zodiacal light and meteor observations has revealed the somewhat surprising and disturbing fact that the observed rates are larger than the extrapolated values by a factor of 1000 or more. At first, it was thought that the direct measurements were in error, but it is now agreed that the discrepancy is real. In other words, there are many more micrometeoroid particles in the vicinity of Earth than would be expected from the rate of influx of the larger, meteoroid material.

7.172. This conclusion is supported by the results obtained from a microphone detector carried on the Venus probe, Mariner II (§ 10.94). During 129 days of flight between Earth and the planet Venus and beyond, the number of micrometeoroid particles recorded was less by a factor of about 10,000 than would have been encountered near Earth. The space density of the very small interplanetary dust particles at a distance from Earth is thus in general agreement with the extrapolated values based on zodiacal light and meteor observa-

---

* Some micrometeoroids are metallic and consequently have much higher densities (cf. § 8.100).

tions. It is apparent, therefore, that there is a much higher concentration of such small particles within a few hundred miles of Earth than in the interplanetary regions of the solar system.

7.173. Four different mechanisms have been proposed to account for the accumulation of micrometeoroids in the vicinity of Earth, but there are no compelling arguments which would appear to make any one more probable than the others. In outline, they are as follows: (a) the gravitational effect of the Earth-Moon system; (b) breakup of fragile meteoroid particles into micrometeoroids near Earth as a result of electrostatic repulsion of electrical charges accumulated in or near the radiation belt (§ 8.267 et seq.); (c) capture of small particles into temporary orbits around Earth as a result of slowing down by electrostatic forces or aerodynamic drag; and (d) impact of meteorites on the Moon producing fine dust that escapes readily because of the absence of an atmosphere and the small gravitational attraction.

7.174. In connection with the last of these mechanisms, it may be noted that the space density of dust particles in the vicinity of the Moon is believed to be high, probably higher than near Earth. The problem of the micrometeoroid concentration around the Moon and also in cislunar space,* i.e., in the region between Earth and the Moon, is of vital importance in evaluating the hazards that might be encountered in a manned flight to the Moon.

7.175. It was mentioned earlier that significant variations are sometimes observed in the micrometeoroid influx rate. During a 10-hour flight, for example, on February 2, 1958, the microphone detector on the Explorer I satellite recorded a rate that was 10 to 100 times the average value during the preceding (and subsequent) days. Evidently, the spacecraft was exposed to a micrometeoroid stream (or swarm) which did not correspond to any known meteoroid system. Presumably, there were not enough larger particles present to be capable of producing a significant number of visible meteor trails. The enhanced influx rate of micrometeoroid has been attributed to a *sporadic shower*, because it is apparently not periodic and does not correspond to any of the established meteor showers. It is possible that such sporadic showers, consisting mainly of very small particles, may be responsible for some sporadic meteors, and there is some evidence for this from radar observations.

7.176. The micrometeoroid shower of February 1958, referred to above, has not been detected in succeeding years, but an apparent annual shower occurs around the middle of November. This period coincides with the appearance of the annual Leonid showers and the micrometeoroids are evidently part of the same stream. Whether other known periodic meteor showers are also associated with an increase in the micrometeoroid flux has not been established. It is evident that much still remains to be done in the observation of the small dust particles in the vicinity of Earth as well as in interplanetary space.

* The Latin preposition *cis* means "on this side."

PARTICLE PENETRATION STUDIES

7.177. In addition to determinations of micrometeoroid influx by counting particle impacts, several satellites have carried instruments for recording penetration of various materials of different thicknesses by the particles in space near Earth. The most comprehensive study of this kind was that made with the orbiting spacecraft designated Explorer XVI, sometimes known as the Micrometeoroid Satellite (Fig. 7.25). It was launched on December 16, 1962

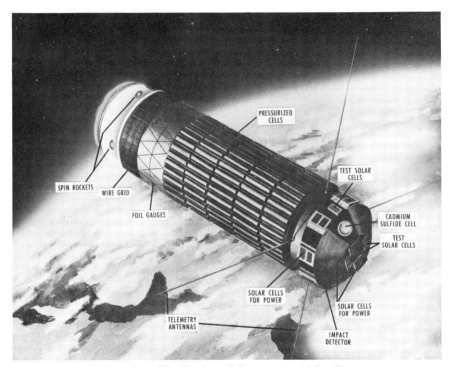

FIG. 7.25.   The Explorer Micrometeoroid Satellite

into an orbit inclined 52 deg to the equator, with a perigee of 469 miles and an apogee of 728 miles. The cylindrical spacecraft was 6 feet 4 inches long and 2 feet in diameter, and weighed just over 200 pounds. The total area of Explorer XVI covered with detectors and sensors was 25 square feet.

7.178. In addition to impact detectors, such as those already described, Explorer XVI carried four different devices for observing the penetration of materials by micrometeoroid particles in space. One instrument consists of a number of cells with thin walls, made of a beryllium-copper alloy, containing helium gas under pressure; penetration of a cell wall by a micrometeoroid causes the gas to escape and the accompanying pressure decrease is recorded. The rate at which the gas escapes and the pressure drops is related to the size of the hole and, hence, to the dimensions of the penetrating particle. In another sensor, called a *foil gage*, a continuous strip of gold (foil), deposited on a silicone plastic base, can move past two electrical contacts. A thin sheet of stainless steel is mounted in front of the foil gage but is separated from it by Mylar insulation. If a particle penetrates the steel, it will fracture the gold foil and thus increase the resistance between the electrical contacts. A drop in current (or voltage) thus indicates that penetration has occurred.

7.179. A third type of penetration sensor is made of a grid of thin copper wires mounted in a Melamine (plastic) insulator. Should a micrometeoroid break one of the wires, the increase in electrical resistance is noted by an accompanying decrease in current. Finally, in the cadmium sulfide cell detector, a cadmium sulfide layer is shielded by means of a Mylar film made opaque by evaporating a coating of aluminum on both sides. If the film is punctured by a small particle, sunlight is admitted to the cell and the electrical resistance of the cadmium sulfide, which is affected by light, decreases. The extent of the change can be related to the intensity of the light falling on the cadmium sulfide and consequently to the size of the hole produced by the particle.

7.180. During some 30 weeks of operation, over 15,000 impacts were recorded by the microphones which covered about one tenth of the exposed area of Explorer XVI. There were 44 penetrations of 1-mil (one thousandth of an inch) thick beryllium-copper foil, 11 penetrations of 2-mil beryllium-copper, six of 1-mil stainless steel, and one each of 2-mil and 3-mil copper. There were no punctures of the thicker foils. Furthermore, no two sensors were penetrated simultaneously, which is not surprising in view of the low space density of the particles. If the average is assumed to be 1000 times the interplanetary particle density estimated from studies of the F-corona, there will be 1 particle in 10^{10} cubic centimeters. The average distance between particles is then the cube root of this volume, namely, over 2000 centimeters, i.e., approximately 65 feet. Since this is much larger than the dimensions of the Explorer XVI satellite, it is very highly improbable that two particles will strike it simultaneously, even in the vicinity of Earth.

7.181. Although Explorer XVI has provided useful information about the smaller micrometeoroids, its surface area of 25 square feet was too small to yield satisfactory data concerning larger particles. The latter are, of course, less numerous but because they have a greater mass they are capable of penetrating thicker materials. In this respect, therefore, they may represent a more serious hazard, from the practical standpoint, than do the very small micrometeoroids. In order to study this problem, a large Micrometeoroid Detector Satellite, named Pegasus,* weighing nearly 2 tons, has been constructed for launching into a 300- to 800-mile orbit by means of a Saturn I rocket. When in space, the two large flat wings, 14 feet wide and having a total span of 96

* Pegasus is the flying horse of Greek mythology.

feet, open out from the satellite to produce an exposed area of about 2500 square feet (Fig. 7.26). Pegasus I was placed in orbit on February 16, 1965, and its wings spread out as planned; it was the first scientific spacecraft to be launched by a Saturn I rocket.

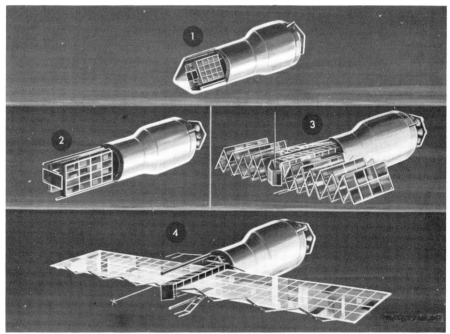

FIG. 7.26.   The Pegasus micrometeoroid detection satellite; (1) represents the spacecraft folded for launching, and (2), (3), and (4) show stages of its opening up in orbit

7.182. The wings consist of a foamed plastic material, about 1 inch thick, and on each face is mounted a sandwich made up of an outer sheet of aluminum, with a thickness of 1.5, 8, or 16 mils, a central layer of Mylar plastic, and a thin inner coating of copper. The two sandwiches are each divided into 208 rectangular (20 inches by 40 inches) panels which act as the micrometeoroid detectors, making 416 in all. A potential of 40 volts is placed between the aluminum and copper, so that each panel constitutes a separate charged electrical capacitor. If the aluminum sheet is penetrated by a particle, the material removed is vaporized forming a conducting gas; this permits the capacitor to discharge. The discharge in the particular panel is recorded and indicates the penetration of aluminum of known thickness. The vapor dissipates very rapidly, and the capacitor becomes recharged and is ready to record another penetration.

7.183. Several ground-based activities are being pursued in support of the space program to study the penetration of thin materials by small particles traveling at extremely high speeds. These include the firing of such particles from a gun at sheets of different materials with various thicknesses. The experiments provide information on the types of materials and structures which might be expected to withstand micrometeoroid and meteoroid impacts in space.

7.184. A possibility that is being examined for the inhibition of penetrations is the use of a *meteoroid bumper*, originally proposed by F. L. Whipple (§ 7.79) as far back as 1946. Such a bumper consists of a thin shield placed a short distance from the outer wall of a space vehicle or other structure. It has been found that a shield of this kind can shatter a projectile, e.g., a meteoroid, into a number of small fragments, each of which is much less penetrating than the original impacting particle. Except for the unlikely event of two meteoroids striking at exactly the same point, the bumper may provide protection from many impacts.

ORIGIN OF THE SOLAR SYSTEM

OCCURRENCE OF PLANETARY SYSTEMS

7.185. A number of theories have been proposed to account for the formation of the solar system and for some of its characteristic features. But, none of these is convincing or complete enough to have found wide acceptance. The discussion here will, therefore, be devoted less to details than to an emphasis on certain general principles of basic significance. Views concerning the origin of the Sun's planetary system fall broadly into two categories: The *collision* (or *tidal*) *theories* postulate that a grazing collision or close encounter of the Sun with another star caused a quantity of the solar material to be pulled out, by gravitational attraction somewhat like a tide; this material subsequently condensed to form the planets. In the alternative, *nebular theories,* the planets are regarded as being formed by localized condensation, in some manner, from a nebula of gas and dust that surrounded the Sun when it was first formed.

7.186. The difference between these two points of view is more than of pure scientific interest; it has, in addition, other implications of great significance. From the known average distances between the stars in the Milky Way galaxy and their velocities relative to each other, it has been calculated that, during the lifetime of the galaxy, there would have been less than ten close encounters between a pair of stars. In other words, if the collision hypothesis of the formation of a planetary system is correct, it is very unlikely that there are any more than ten such systems, similar to the solar system, among the 100 billion (10^{11}) or so stars in the Milky Way.

7.187. Several arguments have been presented against the theory. First, it has been shown that matter drawn out of the Sun would probably not condense but would tend to expand and form a gaseous nebula. Furthermore, the distribution of angular momentum between the Sun and the planets, to which further reference will be made shortly, appears to be quite incompatible with the collision theory of the origin of the solar system. This theory could be most readily refuted by direct astronomical evidence of the existence of an appreciable number of planetary systems in the Milky Way. Unfortunately, even large planets, as large as Jupiter, are too small to be seen in the vicinity of a distant star with the most powerful of existing telescopes. There is, however, indirect evidence that the development of a planetary system represents a natural stage in the evolution of certain stars. If this is the case, the postulate of a collision or close encounter is unnecessary.

7.188. It was seen in § 6.109 that the Sun rotates, and a study of the spectra of many stars has shown that this behavior is quite general. Upon comparing the equatorial velocities of rotation of a number of stars of different spectral types, i.e., with different surface (and probably internal) temperatures, belonging to the main stellar series (§ 12.106), an interesting situation becomes apparent. The majority of stars hotter than the Sun are rotating rapidly, at from about 100 to 500 kilometers (60 to 300 miles) per second, but most of the stars having a temperature about the same as (or lower than) that of the Sun rotate at a much slower rate. The transition from one group to the other is not gradual, but appears to be quite sharp.

7.189. The present rate of rotation of the Sun at its equator is known to be 1.98 kilometers (1.23 miles) per second (§ 6.110). But if the angular momentum of the planets, associated with their revolutions about the Sun, were combined with that of the Sun itself, as was probably the case before the solar system developed, the rate of rotation would be increased by a factor of roughly 50, i.e., to 100 kilometers (60 miles) per second. If there had been interaction between the magnetic field of the Sun and surrounding ionized gas (plasma) which would decrease the angular momentum, the initial velocity of rotation could have been considerably larger. It would appear, therefore, that the Sun originally rotated at about the same velocity as the hotter stars and that the slowing down has resulted largely from the distribution of its angular momentum among the planets. It is consequently possible, but not certain, that other stars which resemble the Sun in their surface temperature rotate slowly because they also have planetary systems (cf. § 13.144).

General Requirements of Solar System Theories

7.190. Before attempting to outline a few basic ideas of the nebular hypothesis, it is of interest to review some of the essential features of the solar system which must be accounted for by any complete theory of its origin. One of the most significant of these appears to be the division of the planets, apart from Pluto, which may well be a displaced satellite of Neptune, into two groups; one in which the masses are relatively small and the densities high, and the other in which the masses are large but the densities low. In between these two groups of planets lie the orbits of the asteroids. Then there is the almost complete uniformity in the counterclockwise directions of revolution of the planets about the Sun and of the various satellites (moons) about their respective planets, and of rotation of planets and satellites about their axes. The relatively few exceptions, in the retrograde rotation of Uranus and possibly Venus and in the revolution of some of the satellites of the major planets, are probably to be regarded as special cases. Ultimately, of course, these apparent exceptions will have to be explained. Finally, again disregarding Pluto, the orbital planes of the planets are all close together and their axes of rotation, aside from Uranus, are approximately perpendicular to this universal plane of the solar system.

7.191. In addition to these more obvious considerations, a theory of the origin of the solar system must take into account the uneven distribution of angular momentum between the Sun and the planets. Although the Sun constitutes 99.9 percent of the total mass of the solar system, it has only 2 percent of its angular momentum; this is another way of saying that it rotates relatively slowly. The planet Jupiter alone has over 60 percent of the angular momentum and the other three major planets have some 37 percent or more between them. If the argument presented earlier concerning the rate of rotation of stars and the existence of planetary systems has any validity, then the same general type of unequal distribution of angular momentum, as between the central body and its planets, must be fairly general.

The Nebular Theory

7.192. The nebular hypothesis of the formation of the solar system was proposed by the German philosopher Immanuel Kant in 1755 and a related concept was presented independently by the French astronomer and mathematician Pierre S. Laplace in 1796. The basic premise of the theory is that the Sun was originally surrounded by a large, rotating nebular disc of gas and dust. Laplace suggested that, as the gas cooled, the nebula contracted and hence, in accordance with the requirements of the conservation of angular momentum (§ 4.30), it had to rotate faster. The angular momentum of a rotating body is equal to the sum (or integral) of the mvr terms for all the particles of which the body is made up, m being the mass, v the rotational velocity, and r the distance of the particle from the axis. When contraction occurs, r decreases and since the mass is unchanged, the velocity, v, must increase to maintain the product mvr constant.

7.193. As a result of the increased rate of rotation, the outward centrifugal effect of inertia at the edge of the nebula would ultimately overcome the inward gravitational attraction; a ring of material would then separate from the nebular disc and would coalesce to form a planet. The process would continue, with planets being formed, as long as the conditions for separation of a ring could be achieved. This simple theory was commonly accepted until the beginning of the twentieth century when several difficulties were pointed out. In particular, it was shown that the total angular momentum (or rate of rotation) of the nebula that would have been required to permit formation of the planets in this manner was far greater than appeared reasonable.

7.194. One of those who objected to the Laplace hypothesis was the distinguished British mathematician James H. Jeans and over a period of years, in the first two decades of this century, he and astronomer Harold A. Jeffreys, in particular, developed the tidal (or collision) theory already described. This view has now been discarded, however, and there has been a revival of the nebular hypothesis. The formation of a solar nebula is consistent with modern views relating to the development of the stars by the collapse of clouds of interstellar gas and dust (see Chapter 12). Several different ideas have been proposed to account for the breakup of the nebular cloud into planets. Although these theories provide a general picture of the development of the solar system, they apparently fail when quantitative tests are applied. There is thus, at present, no completely satisfactory theory of the formation of the planets.

7.195. According to some theories, the planets were formed by a process of accretion from very small bodies called *planetismals* (T. C. Chamberlin and F. R. Moulton, 1900); these gradually accumulated solid particles and gases, chiefly by gravitational attraction. On the other hand, it has been postulated that the nebular cloud broke up into larger masses, named *protoplanets* (G. P. Kuiper, 1949), as a result of turbulence (C. F. von Weizsäcker, 1945) or gravitational attraction (or both). The protoplanets are thought to have been very much larger and more massive than the planets are now. The excess mass was then lost in the course of the development of the solar system.

7.196. A qualitative indication of the factors which determined the present characteristics of the individual planets may be obtained by considering the variations with increasing distance from the Sun of the nebular cloud density, of the gravitational forces leading to tidal action, and of the temperature. It is to be expected that solid matter of relatively high density would collect near the Sun, where the gravitational attraction is large. On the other hand, the disruptive effect of the solar tidal forces would also be large. Consequently, the inner planets would have fairly high densities, but they would be comparatively small. The moderately high temperatures in this region would prevent the condensation of volatile substances like ammonia and methane, such as occurs on the more distant planets.

7.197. Much farther from the Sun, where the solar tidal forces are smaller, it is possible for large planets to exist; this would account for the formation of the Jovian planets. These bodies have low densities, mainly because they contain large quantities of hydrogen, helium, ammonia, methane, and probably water, all of which are light substances. The low temperatures of the major planets, due to their great distances from the Sun, make it possible for normally volatile substances to exist in the liquid, and even in the solid, state. As the distance from the Sun increases, the solar nebula would thin out and the quantity of material available for planet formation would decrease. Hence, the dimensions of the planets do not increase with distance from the Sun but reach a maximum with Jupiter.

7.198. The large angular momenta of the Jovian planets, and of Jupiter in particular, are an indirect consequence of their locations. The velocity, v, of a satellite (planet) in orbit about a primary body (Sun) is determined by its distance, r, from the primary (Sun), as seen in Chapter 2. Furthermore, according to the views presented above, the mass, m, of a planet is also dependent on the distance from the Sun at which it is formed. Hence, the angular momentum, mvr, of Jupiter, for example, is a result of the circumstances that caused a massive planet to grow at a particular radial distance in the solar nebula. This argument can account for the large angular momenta of the Jovian planets, but it does not explain why the angular momentum, i.e., rotational velocity, of the Sun is so comparatively small. Magnetic forces have been invoked in this connection, but the situation is not at all clear.

7.199. The disc-like shape of the solar nebula, which would probably be a result of its initially rapid rotation, can account for the situation that all the planetary orbits lie close to a single plane. The uniform direction of revolution of the planets is a consequence of the direction of rotation of the nebula. Furthermore, the rotation of the planets about their axes would be determined by the motion of the accreted material, which might well be related to the direction of rotation of the nebula. This would lead to the general counterclockwise (direct) rotation of the planets.

7.200. It must be emphasized that the foregoing is intended only as a somewhat general, qualitative interpretation of the development of the planetary system of the Sun. Its purpose is merely to present a rough working hypothesis that provides, at least, a conceptual picture of how the planets might have been formed from a large nebula of gas and dust. The question of the origin of comets was discussed in § 7.84. Although these are members of the solar system, they are not planets and were undoubtedly formed in a different manner. The two problems can thus be treated independently, as they have been in this chapter.

AGE OF THE SOLAR SYSTEM

7.201. The most reliable information concerning the age of the solar system has been derived from various applications of the radioisotope dating technique. Every radioactive isotope undergoes disintegration (or decay) at a characteristic rate that is independent of its chemical state, i.e., element or compound, or its physical condition, i.e., temperature or pressure. The characteristic decay rate is commonly expressed in terms of the half-life of the particular radioisotope, defined as the time required for half the amount present at any time to suffer disintegration (§ 3.242). Because of the nature of radioactive decay, the

half-life is independent of the absolute quantity of material under consideration. It is this property that makes the half-life convenient for expressing decay
rates. As a result of one or more stages of radioactive disintegration, the radioisotope is eventually transformed into a stable isotope of a different element.
Consequently, the quantity of the stable isotope increases steadily, as the unstable species decays; the total amount of the former produced in a given
material thus depends on the time the unstable isotope has been present in that
material.

7.202. If A^* represents the radioisotope and B is the stable decay product in
a specimen of material, e.g., a mineral or rock, the length of the decay period
can be calculated from a knowledge of the half-life of A^* and the ratio A^*/B of
the quantities in the given mineral at the present time. For the dating of materials of considerable age, such as meteorites and terrestrial rocks and minerals,
the isotope A^* must have a long half-life, on the order of billions of years.
Among those which have been commonly employed in this connection are the
following; the stable end-product B is given in parentheses in each case: ura-
nium-238 (lead-206); uranium-235 (lead-207); rubidium-87 (strontium-87);
potassium-40 (argon-40).

7.203. The foregoing simple procedure is based on the supposition that the
mineral originally contained none of the isotope B. Since this may not be the
case, an appropriate correction must be applied; it is determined from an
examination of material in which B is not of radiogenic origin, i.e., it contains
B but no A^*. The correction is somewhat uncertain and it can be avoided entirely if B is a gas, e.g., argon-40. In this event, it is known that any B that may
have existed in the material before it solidified will have escaped. The quantity
that has been accumulated will then have resulted from the decay of A^* since
the original formation of the substance in its present form. This period is generally referred to as the age of the material.

7.204. Radioisotope dating techniques, based on uranium-238, uranium-235,
rubidium-87, and potassium-40, have been applied to the determination of the
ages of meteorites. The last of these radioisotopes is particularly suitable because one of the decay products of potassium-40 is the gas argon-40; hence,
measurement of the potassium-40/argon-40 ratio has been extensively used in
the work on meteorites. It is a striking fact that all the experiments agree in
giving a maximum age of close to 4.5 billion (4.5×10^9) years for these substances. This is also the greatest age estimated for any rock or mineral of
terrestrial origin. It seems reasonable to conclude, therefore, that Earth and the
planet (or other body) from which meteorites were formed became coherent
members of the solar system at the same time, some 4.5 billion years ago. Consequently, this is generally accepted as the age of the solar system.

7.205. Further light has been shed on the history of the system by a study of
the relative amounts of the isotopes of the gas xenon in meteorites. In several
specimens, the proportion of the stable xenon-129 isotope, as compared with

that of xenon-122, has been found to be appreciably larger than in atmospheric xenon. The excess of xenon-129 has been attributed to its production by the radioactive decay of iodine-129. The latter no longer exists in nature, but it has been made artificially in the laboratory and its half-life determined to be 17 million years. As a result of this moderately short half-life, compared with the age of the meteorite, iodine-129 has now ceased to exist. But from the excess of xenon-129 in a meteorite, it is possible to calculate how much iodine-129 was present when the meteorite solidified and started to accumulate xenon gas.

7.206. By making a reasonable assumption concerning the amount of iodine-129 that was produced when the various elements were first formed, it is possible to calculate the time that has elapsed between nucleogenesis, i.e., the formation of atomic nuclei, and the solidification of the meteorite, which occurred 4.5 billion years ago. The elapsed time is somewhat dependent on the proportion of iodine-129 assumed to have been formed initially, but it is evidently in the range from 120 to 300 million years. It is not known whether the process of nucleogenesis occurred over a long period or over a short time. It appears, however, that the formation of elements present in meteorites, and presumably also in Earth's crust, was completed some few hundred million years before coherent material, subsequently unchanged, came into existence in the solar system.

7.207. Another type of age dating has been performed with meteorites. It depends on the fact that space is pervaded by the high-energy particles of cosmic rays (§ 8.245); when these particles strike the nuclei of heavy and moderately heavy elements, they are able to eject lighter nuclei. Among the latter, helium-3 is of special interest. By combining assumptions concerning the distribution of the particle energies in cosmic rays with laboratory experiments, the amount of helium-3 formed can be related to the time of exposure to cosmic rays. Thus, by measuring the quantity of helium-3 in a given material, this exposure time (or *cosmic-ray age*) can be computed.

7.208. All planets and other members of the solar system (and elsewhere) are being continuously bombarded by cosmic rays. As a general rule, the particles are removed or slowed down by interaction with the atoms in the atmosphere or outermost regions of the planet or asteroid. The interior is then unaffected by cosmic rays, and because of the large mass of the planetary body relative to its exposed area, the effect of the cosmic rays is negligible. But if a planet or asteroid breaks up into smaller bodies, such as meteoroids, there is a significant effect, especially on the outer layers, caused by the cosmic ray particles in space where there is no atmosphere. Consequently, by measuring the proportion of helium-3, relative to the common helium-4, in meteorites, it is possible to determine how much time has elapsed since the breakup of the parent body. Because the debris from the original collision may well have suffered further breakup in subsequent encounters, the date derived by the helium-3 technique presumably represents that of the most recent collision.

7.209. The results indicate that iron meteorites, in their present form, were produced from a larger body (or bodies) some 100 million to 1.5 billion years ago. Stony meteorites, on the other hand, have a cosmic-ray age of only four to 500 million years, mostly about 20 million years. This difference may well be accounted for by the fragile nature of the latter as compared with the irons. The stony meteorites would undoubtedly continue to break up into smaller pieces long after the iron meteorites ceased to do so to any extent. The only definite conclusion to be drawn at present is that the disruption leading to meteorite formation started at least 1.5 billion years ago, but continued for millions of years thereafter.

Chapter 8

EARTH AND ITS ENVIRONMENT

EARTH'S GRAVITATIONAL FIELD

INTRODUCTION

8.1. Although the study of Earth itself does not strictly fall within the scope of space science, certain properties of Earth, namely, gravitation and magnetism, called *field properties,* are associated with forces which extend for a considerable distance into space. The present section will be concerned with some aspects of gravity that are related to space science; the characteristics of Earth's magnetic field and its influence on the environment will be described later in this chapter.

8.2. Apart from the perturbing effects of atmospheric drag and solar radiation pressure, the orbit of a satellite is determined by the gravitational field of Earth, with minor contributions from the Sun and the Moon. The accurate prediction of the orbits of satellites and, to some extent, of the trajectories of lunar and interplanetary probes requires a precise knowledge of the distribution of the force of gravity over Earth's surface. This information has not been available in the past, so that calculated orbits and trajectories were not exact. By studying the orbits of existing satellites, however, it has been possible to reverse the procedure and to determine the gravitational field of Earth; the information thus obtained can be used to make more precise calculations of future orbits and trajectories.

EARTH AS AN ELLIPSOID

8.3. It has been realized for nearly three hundred years that Earth is not a sphere, but is flattened somewhat at the poles and, consequently, bulges correspondingly at the equator; such a shape is called an *oblate spheroid.* In fact, in 1687 Isaac Newton showed that the centrifugal (inertial) effect due to Earth's daily rotation about the polar axis would cause its diameter to be greater at the equator than at the poles. By assuming hydrostatic equilibrium, i.e., by postulating that the pressure produced at the center of Earth by a column extending to either of the poles was the same as one to the equator,

Newton made an approximate estimate of the extent to which Earth departed from a spherical shape.*

8.4. If Earth's interior is plastic, that is to say, if it has the ability to accept a certain amount of deformation without resistance, as might be expected in view of the high temperatures and pressures, an approach to hydrostatic equilibrium could be possible. It can be shown mathematically that Earth should then be an *ellipsoid of revolution*, i.e., the shape resulting from the rotation of an ellipse about its minor (shorter) axis. A section of Earth through the poles would thus be an ellipse whereas one through the equator would be circular. The departure from the spherical shape is expressed by a quantity, f, variously called the *flattening*, the *oblateness*, or the *ellipticity*, which is defined by

$$f = \frac{r_e - r_p}{r_e},$$

where r_e and r_p are the equatorial and polar radii, respectively, of Earth. If hydrostatic equilibrium existed, then the flattening, based on the present rate of Earth's rotation, has been calculated to be 1/299.8.† The actual value, as will be seen shortly, is somewhat larger.

8.5. In the science of geodesy (§ 5.136), it has been useful to define a reference ellipsoid as a mathematical surface which is an idealized approximation to Earth's actual surface. The flattening of the ideal ellipsoid has been estimated in several ways. One, for example, is based on the determination of the gravitational acceleration at as many locations as possible on Earth's surface. The other involves the measurement of the distance corresponding to one degree of latitude, at constant longitude, at various latitudes; the actual latitudes can be determined from observations of Polaris, the polestar, and so are independent of any terrestrial considerations. The degree of latitude has been found to be equivalent to 110.6 kilometers (68.7 miles) at the equator and 111.7 kilometers (69.4 miles) at the poles; as is to be expected for an oblate spheroid, the distance at the poles is greater than at the equator. From various observations of gravity, degree of latitude, etc., the International Union of Geodesy and Geophysics recommended in 1930 that the flattening of Earth's ellipsoid be taken as 1/297.0, and this value was accepted for nearly 30 years.

8.6. The study of satellite orbits in recent years has made possible another procedure for evaluating Earth's flattening. The method has been applied in the past to the Moon, but the results were not very accurate; one reason is the

---

* The hydrostatic pressure is the sum (or integral) of a series of products of length, density, and gravitational acceleration over the whole column. Because of the centrifugal effect due to rotation, gravity at the equator is less than at the poles (cf. § 2.20); if the average density of Earth's interior is assumed to be the same in all radial directions, i.e., outward from the center, the column length, and hence Earth's radius (or diameter), at the equator must exceed that at the poles.

† Because f is a very small fraction, it is the general practice to express it, as here, in the form of a reciprocal of a fairly large number.

relatively large distance from Earth to the Moon, and another is that it is difficult to make allowance for perturbations that do not depend on Earth's shape. It was seen in § 2.88 that Earth's equatorial bulge causes a rotation of the line of the apsides of a satellite's orbit, provided the angle of inclination, i, of the orbit to the equator is such that $4 - 5 \sin^2 i$ is not zero, i.e., provided i is not 63 deg 26 min. From a measurement of the rate at which the line of the apsides rotates about Earth, it is possible to calculate the flattening of the ellipsoid; for this purpose, Earth's equatorial radius, the average distance of the satellite from Earth's center, and the eccentricity and inclination of the orbit must be known.

8.7. Soon after the launching of the first U.S. Satellite (§ 1.114), F. O. Diercks and his associates in the United States called attention to the fact that the orbit of this satellite was not compatible with the international value of $1/297$ for the flattening of the terrestrial ellipsoid, but required a value closer to $1/298$. Subsequent observations of the orbits of several satellites confirmed this conclusion and the flattening accepted at the present time is $1/298.24$. According to this new datum, the difference between the equatorial and polar radii of the ellipsoid is **21.4** kilometers (**13.3** miles).

THE GEOID

8.8. Another surface that is commonly used in geodesy is the *geoid* or the "figure" of Earth. This is defined as the equipotential surface of gravity, i.e., a hypothetical surface on which no work (or force) is required to move a mass from one point to another. The shape of the geoid is not smooth, like that of the ideal ellipsoid, but it has many undulations which are determined by the mass distribution in Earth below the surface (Fig. 8.1). The essential charac-

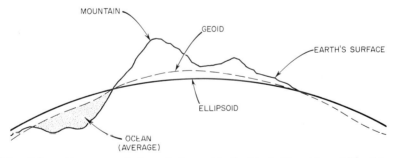

FIG. 8.1.   Schematic representation of the geoid, the ideal ellipsoid, and Earth's actual surface

teristic of an equipotential surface, such as the geoid, is that the same amount of energy is required to move a given mass to infinity from any point on this surface. In the language of satellite orbits (§ 2.67), the escape velocity is precisely the same at all locations on the geoid. Another property of an equipotential surface of gravity is that the direction of the force, i.e., the direction of a plumb line at any point, is always perpendicular to the surface (or geoid) at that point.

8.9. All the points on an equipotential surface are at the same potential, but the surface is not defined completely until the value of that potential is specified. For the geoid, the potential chosen is that corresponding to the average sea level of the oceans. Thus, in physical terms, the geoid represents the continuation of the mean sea level over the whole surface of Earth. In other words, if Earth were completely covered by a layer of water, which could percolate through mountains, the mean level would correspond to the geoid surface.

THE "PEAR-SHAPED" EARTH

8.10. A detailed study of the orbits of satellites provides a very useful method for determining the form of the geoid or the figure of Earth. Before the advent of artificial satellites, it was generally accepted that, except for relatively small variations resulting from the presence of mountains or deep valleys, the geoid could be regarded as approximately an ellipsoid. In 1959, however, J. A. O'Keefe, A. Eckels, and R. K. Squires in the United States reported some observations on the satellite Vanguard I which brought about a significant change in the views concerning the form of the geoid. Vanguard I, weighing only $3\frac{1}{4}$ pounds (§ 1.115), carried no instruments other than two radio beacons for tracking purposes. One of the latter has been transmitting for several years, so that accurate determination of the orbital elements has been possible. In studying the data, after applying necessary corrections, it was observed that the perigee of the orbit changed in a regular manner, over a range of about 8 kilometers (5 miles), during successive periods of about 80 days, the time of rotation of the line of the apsides. Utilizing this result, O'Keefe and his collaborators showed that the geoid was not symmetrical about the equatorial plane; the distance from Earth's center to the north pole was calculated to be something like 25 meters (80 feet) more than to the south pole. This conclusion has subsequently been confirmed by means of orbital data from other satellites.

8.11. Because of the difference in the north and south polar radii of the geoid, there has developed the somewhat loose description of Earth as being "pear-shaped," with the stem of the pear at the north pole and the base at the south pole. There are some reservations, however, with regard to this description which should be pointed out. In the first place it is the geoid, i.e., the mass distribution, which has the so-called pear shape; only if the average density in Earth's interior is the same in all radial directions will the actual (physical) shape have the same form as the geoid. Moreover, there are modifications of the pear shape, as will be seen from the following simplified interpretation of the mathematical aspects of Earth's gravitational potential (cf. § 8.363).

8.12. In general a complex shape which may be regarded as a somewhat distorted sphere, such as the geoid, representing a surface of constant gravita-- tional potential, can be expressed in terms of a series of quantities known to mathematicians as *spherical harmonics*, each of which makes a contribution, positive, negative, or zero, to the total. The contribution of any harmonic is determined by a factor, usually represented by the symbol J and commonly referred to as the "value" of the particular harmonic. The important point in the present context is that, in principle, the J values for Earth's gravitational field can be determined from observations on satellite orbits and they can be related to the shape of the geoid.

8.13. A large number of harmonics may be required, in theory, to provide an accurate representation of the gravitational field, especially if it departs ap- preciably from spherical symmetry. But in practice the higher harmonics make such a small contribution that they can be neglected, at least to a first approxi- mation. In any event, the higher harmonics cannot be evaluated with any degree of accuracy unless extremely precise orbital data are available. If variations in the geoid with longitude are neglected, that is to say, if it is assumed that sections through the geoid from pole to pole always have the same shape regardless of longitude,* the appropriate (zonal) harmonics may be written simply as J_0, J_1, J_2, J_3, etc.

8.14. The zonal harmonic of zero order, i.e., J_0, expresses the overall size of the geoid, and J_1, the first degree harmonic, determines the center point of the geoid in the north-south direction. The other harmonics represent deviations from the spherical form, as shown by the illustrations in Fig. 8.2. It is seen that

FIG. 8.2.   Qualitative representation of the harmonics of the geoid from J_2 through J_5

the contributions of the even harmonics are symmetrical about the equatorial plane of the geoid, whereas the odd harmonics correspond to contributions that are different in the Northern and Southern Hemispheres. The degree of the harmonic gives the number of undulations or waves in the shape of the surface. It should be pointed out that the various forms represented in Fig. 8.2 have been greatly exaggerated for the sake of clarity. For example, the value of the third degree harmonic, J_3, for the geoid corresponds to a deviation of only about 16 meters at the peaks of the undulations and 8 meters in the valleys.

---

* This is not strictly correct, as will be apparent shortly, but the assumption made here does not affect the main argument.

8.15. A detailed examination of the orbits of several satellites has made possible the evaluation of the zonal harmonics J_2, J_3, . . . , J_{10}, and J_{12}. The actual shape of the geoid is thus determined by a combination of all these, and probably other, harmonics weighted according to the respective J values. The value of J_2, as may be expected, is by far the largest, namely, 1082.47, compared with the next largest, J_3, which is -2.48; the contributions of the other harmonics are all smaller still. The deviation of the geoid from an ellipsoid is thus not very great, although it is significant. Incidentally, it is from the value of J_2 obtained in this manner, with minor corrections for J_3, J_4, etc., that the flattening of the ellipsoid given in § 8.7 was determined. The conclusions to be drawn from combining all the J values together with other (tesseral) harmonics will be given shortly.

8.16. The difference between the flattening of Earth calculated on the assumption that hydrostatic equilibrium exists, i.e., 1/299.8, and the actual value of 1/298.24, and the difference in the form of the geoid in Northern and Southern Hemispheres, as indicated by the significant value of J_3, show that Earth's interior is not in a state of hydrostatic equilibrium. It follows, therefore, that the interior of Earth is not plastic; that is to say, the material does not accept deformation without resistance. In fact, the interior must have considerable mechanical strength to withstand the stresses resulting from uneven, random irregularities in the density (or mass) distribution implied by the markedly unsymmetrical form of the geoid. This uneven distribution is believed to be deep-seated in character and thus has important implications for the structure of Earth's interior.

8.17. It should be noted that, although Earth is not plastic, it is probably not completely rigid. Since the observed flattening is larger than the value calculated from the present rate of Earth's rotation, it follows that the actual flattening corresponds to hydrostatic equilibrium at a more rapid rate of rotation. The Moon produces tidal waves in Earth's crust, just as it does in the oceans, but of smaller magnitude. The dissipation of the energy, i.e., the conversion into heat, resulting from the frictional effect of Earth tides, causes a slowing down in the rate of rotation (cf. § 9.21). It has been estimated that the present flattening corresponds to the rate of rotation that a plastic Earth would have had some 50 million years ago, and this is only a small fraction of the 4500 million years since Earth was formed as a separate entity (§ 7.204). It would appear, therefore, that there may have been some plastic flow, although it is restricted by Earth's internal strength.

ELLIPTICITY OF THE EQUATOR

8.18. The results described above have been based on the values of the zonal harmonics which are independent of longitude and indicate only north-south variations in the geoid. Thus, they do not provide any information concerning the shape of the cross section of the geoid through (or parallel to) the equator. By considering the tesseral harmonics, which depend on longitude and give east-west deviations from symmetry, I. G. Izsak in the United States concluded in 1961, from data on the optical tracking of the satellites Vanguard II and Vanguard III, that the equator of the geoid is slightly elliptical, rather than circular. Observations on other satellites, e.g., Transit 4A (§ 5.128), have confirmed this general conclusion.

8.19. It appears that the longest equatorial diameter of Earth runs from approximately 33°W to 147°E longitude; it is about 400 meters (1250 feet) longer than the shortest diameter in the direction at right angles. This small difference would seem to be negligible in comparison with the 12,750-kilometer (7900-mile) diameter of the geoid. It is, nevertheless, of sufficient significance to affect the orbit of a satellite.

THE COMBINED GEOID

8.20. The best available values of the zonal and tesseral harmonics have been combined by W. M. Kaula (1963) in the United States, and the results are shown in the form of a series of contours in Fig. 8.3. The numbers repre-

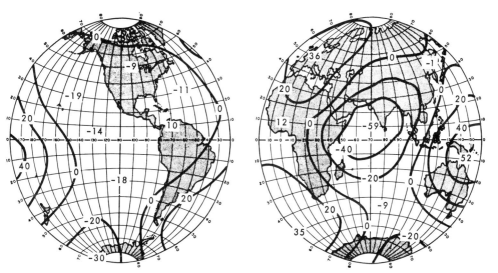

FIG. 8.3.   Contours of the geoid (*Courtesy NASA, Goddard Space Flight Center*)

sent the differences in meters between the level of the geoid surface and an ellipsoid with a flattening of 1/298.24. It is seen that the geoid surface rises above the ellipsoid (positive anomaly) just southwest of the north pole, but is below it (negative anomaly) northeast of the south pole, roughly in accordance with the so-called pear shape. Furthermore, the geoid is strongly depressed in the Indian Ocean, with an almost equivalent elevation in the extreme western Pacific Ocean around New Guinea.

8.21. A possible interpretation of these results has been proposed on the basis of the transport of material by convection from the deep interior of Earth in the anomalous regions. It will be recalled that the geoid is an equipotential surface of gravity, and consequently theory requires that, where the elevation is above the ellipsoid, the material below the surface at that location, down into Earth's interior, should have a higher density than the average; on the other hand, where the geoid is below the ellipsoid the density should be lower than average. The difference in the elevations could thus be accounted for if warmer, less dense material were rising from the interior of Earth toward the surface in the areas of Antarctica and the Indian Ocean where the anomalies are negative; correspondingly, cooler, more dense material would be sinking into the interior below such regions as Europe and the western Pacific Ocean where the anomalies are positive. This interpretation finds support from independent observations which show that the heat flow outward from the body of Earth is greater in the regions of negative anomaly than in those of positive anomaly.

Importance of the Geoid

8.22. An extremely accurate knowledge of the geoid is of great importance for the calculation of Earth satellite orbits, especially in connection with rendezvous operations, and of the trajectories of space probes. Furthermore, as already indicated, it should ultimately make possible a better understanding of the structure of Earth's interior. In order to achieve this objective, it is desirable to utilize satellites in special orbits; of these three are of particular interest. A satellite in polar orbit would provide good data on the zonal harmonics, i.e., those dependent only on longitude, and one in equatorial orbit would give only the latitude-dependent (sectorial) terms. If the orbital inclination is 63 deg 26 min, the contributions of the even harmonics, i.e., J_2, J_4, etc., to the rotation of the line of the apsides are all zero; analysis of the data for evaluation of the odd terms, i.e., J_3, J_5, etc., would then be simplified.

8.23. In selecting the characteristics of the satellite orbit, two opposing factors must be borne in mind. If the orbit has a relatively low altitude, the larger value of Earth's gravity should enhance the accuracy of calculations based on the observed orbital data. On the other hand, at higher altitudes, aerodynamic drag effects are less significant, but the perturbations associated with higher harmonics of the gravitational field will also be smaller and more difficult to determine with any degree of precision. The actual orbit should, therefore, not be too high or too low; an altitude of about 800 kilometers (500 miles) is regarded as a satisfactory compromise.

THE ATMOSPHERE

INTRODUCTION

8.24. The *atmosphere* is defined as the layer of gas that surrounds Earth. There is, however, no definite upper limit to the atmosphere because at great heights it blends imperceptibly into the low-density gas (or plasma) that pervades interplanetary space. The study of the upper atmosphere, particularly the regions in which solar radiations cause ionization and dissociation of molecules into atoms, is called *aeronomy;* it represents an important and interesting area of the space sciences.

8.25. Most properties of the atmosphere change gradually with altitude but it is, nevertheless, convenient to consider the atmosphere in terms of a number of regions according to certain characteristic features, e.g., temperature, composition, ionization, chemical reactions, magnetic field, etc. The thermal and related properties of the atmosphere will be considered first and the remainder of the chapter will be devoted to a discussion of the regions in which other aspects are dominant.

THERMAL STRUCTURE OF THE ATMOSPHERE

8.26. The lowest thermal layer of the atmosphere, in which the temperature decreases steadily with increasing altitude, is called the *troposphere* (Greek, *trope,* "turning"). It extends from Earth's surface to a height of 8 to 16 kilometers (5 to 10 miles), depending on the latitude and the time of the year. Most of the visible phenomena associated with the weather occur in the troposphere and it is in this region, too, that nearly all clouds are formed. The *lapse rate,* i.e., the rate of decrease of temperature with altitude, is almost constant at roughly 6.5°C per kilometer (10°C or 18°F per mile).* At the top of the troposphere is the *tropopause,* where the temperature is close to −60°C (−76°F).

8.27. Above the tropopause lies the *stratosphere* (Latin, *stratum,* "a covering") reaching up to an altitude of roughly 30 kilometers (19 miles). In this region the temperature generally increases slightly, attaining about −40°C (−40°F) at the top, in the *stratopause.* Compared with the troposphere, the stratosphere is a relatively quiet part of the atmosphere, although it is definitely known to have some influence on the weather.

8.28. The portion of the atmosphere from 30 to 80 kilometers (19 to 50 miles)

---

* The theoretical *adiabatic lapse rate,* based on the supposition that the temperature decrease with altitude is due entirely to the expansion accompanying the decreasing pressure, is numerically equal to g/c_p, where c_p is the specific heat of the gas at constant pressure and g is the gravitational acceleration in appropriate units (§ 8.366). For air, the adiabatic lapse rate is 9.6°C (or °K) per kilometer. The observed value given above is lower because the condensation of water to (liquid or solid) in the upper atmosphere contributes heat to the surroundings.

is known as the *mesosphere* (Greek, *mesos*, "intermediate"). There the temperature increases at first to a maximum around 10°C (50°F) and then decreases to about −90°C (−130°F) or less, depending on the latitude and the season; the upper limit of the mesosphere, where the temperature has the lowest value in the atmosphere, is called the *mesopause*. Ionization and molecular dissociation processes and various chemical reactions induced by the Sun's radiations become significant in the mesosphere.

8.29. At altitudes above some 80 kilometers (50 miles) is the *thermosphere*, where the temperature increases up to a height of roughly 320 to 400 kilometers (200 to 250 miles). Subsequently, the temperature appears to be independent of altitude for several hundred kilometers, although it must increase again at greater distances from Earth. The temperature attained in the thermosphere is highly variable because it changes with time of day and, to some extent, with the latitude; it is also dependent on solar activity. At the minimum of a sunspot cycle, for example, the highest average temperature in the thermosphere at middle latitudes is about 750°C (1380°F), but at the time of sunspot maximum it is considerably higher, around 1250°C (2280°F). Corresponding with some solar flares (see Chapter 6), the temperature may reach over 1700°C (3090°F).

8.30. The approximate temperature variations with altitude during the daytime are summarized, for convenience, in Fig. 8.4. The solid curve refers to low and temperate latitudes in summer or winter and to high latitudes in summer; the curve made up of short dashes, on the other hand, applies to high latitudes in winter. The two curves with the longer dashes give the temperatures in the thermosphere under the extreme conditions of sunspot minimum and maximum, respectively.

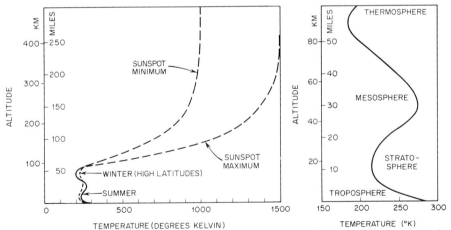

FIG. 8.4.   Temperature of the atmosphere at different altitudes (after F. S. Johnson); the temperatures in the lower atmosphere are shown at the right

8.31. Attention should be called to the significance of the temperatures, especially in the upper regions of the atmosphere where the gas densities are very low.* The temperatures referred to are the kinetic temperatures; that is to say, they are an indication of the average kinetic energy of the gaseous molecules (or atoms) present in the atmosphere. Because of the extremely low densities at high altitudes, the distances that separate the molecules are very large. Thus, at a height of 320 kilometers (200 miles), a gas molecule (or atom) will travel, on the average, a distance of 1.6 kilometers (1 mile) or so before it encounters another molecule; in other words, its *mean free path* is about 1.6 kilometers in length. A body, e.g., a spacecraft, in such an environment does not acquire the temperature of its surroundings as indicated by the molecular kinetic energy. The actual temperature of the body is determined by the absorption of heat from the Sun and its reradiation; both of these factors are dependent on the shape and constructional material of the spacecraft.

COMPOSITION OF THE ATMOSPHERE

8.32. From the standpoint of its composition, the atmosphere can be divided into two fairly distinct regions. In the *homosphere* (Greek, *homos,* "same"), which extends up to an altitude of about 100 kilometers (60 miles), general circulation of the air, local turbulence, and various winds cause a continuous mixing of the gaseous components of the atmosphere. The composition and average molecular weight of the air in this region are thus essentially constant, with the same values as at sea level.

8.33. Sounding rocket measurements have shown that the character of the atmosphere changes at a height of roughly 100 kilometers (60 miles); above this level is the *heterosphere* (Greek, *heteros,* "different"), where there is little mixing and the composition changes with altitude. This is commonly referred to as the region of *diffusive separation* (or *diffusive equilibrium*). The molecules (and atoms) are now distributed vertically, in accordance mainly with their masses, as determined by gravity. In other words, the molecules (and atoms) tend to separate out in such a manner that the heavier species, e.g., molecular oxygen and nitrogen, tend to predominate at the lower levels whereas the lighter ones, e.g., atomic oxygen, helium, and hydrogen, are the main constituents at the higher levels.

8.34. The upper part of the heterosphere is sometimes treated as a special region called the *exosphere* (Greek, *exo,* "outside"). At sufficiently high altitudes in the atmosphere the gas density is so low that the mean free path is extremely long. At a height of 800 kilometers (500 miles), for example, the mean free path of the atmospheric particles is on the order of 160 kilometers (100 miles). A molecule (or atom) having the necessary velocity can thus

---

* The atmospheric density decreases steadily with increasing altitude, in spite of the irregular temperature variations (see Fig. 8.8).

escape completely from Earth's gravitational environment without colliding with another molecule. It is this possibility of escape that characterizes the exosphere. Light atoms and molecules can escape more readily than the heavier ones because, at a given temperature and density, the former have longer mean free paths. Consequently, the lower level of the exosphere is somewhat indefinite, but it is generally thought to be from 500 to 1000 kilometers (300 to 600 miles). The concept of the exosphere is restricted to neutral particles, i.e., without electrical charge; charged particles are affected by Earth's magnetic field as well as by gravity (§ 8.267 *et seq.*).

8.35. The main constituents of dry air* in the homosphere are as follows: molecular nitrogen (N_2), 78.08 percent by volume; molecular oxygen (O_2), 20.95 percent; and argon, 0.93 percent. In addition, there are at least 15 minor constituents, the amounts of which are somewhat variable; in total, they represent only 0.036 percent by volume of the homosphere. Several of these substances are of industrial origin, e.g., carbon monoxide, sulfur dioxide, nitric oxide, and nitrogen dioxide, and hence vary in amount; others, e.g., methane and nitrous oxide, are produced by biological processes. Carbon dioxide, the most abundant of the minor constituents of the homosphere, represents 0.033 percent by volume. It can arise from both industrial and biological sources, but it is removed by green plants in photosynthesis; moreover, large quantities of carbon dioxide are dissolved in the water of the oceans. Among the other minor constituents of interest, in addition to water vapor and carbon dioxide, are ozone, helium, and hydrogen. Reference to these substances will be made in due course.

8.36. In the heterosphere, interaction of solar radiation with various molecules, oxygen in particular, has a significant influence on the composition of the atmosphere. Data from mass spectrometers, i.e., instruments that determine the quantities of atoms and molecules according to their masses, carried aloft by sounding rockets and satellites indicate that there are significant amounts of atomic oxygen at a height of about 100 kilometers (60 miles), near the top of the homosphere. The proportion increases with altitude and these atoms represent an important constituent of the heterosphere up to levels of several hundred miles.

8.37. Oxygen atoms are produced in the atmosphere by photochemical (Greek, *photos*, "light") dissociation, i.e., a breaking up under the influence of solar (ultraviolet) radiation, of molecular oxygen. Apart from mass spectrometer data, evidence for the presence of atomic oxygen in the upper atmosphere was obtained when 18 pounds (8 kilograms) of nitric oxide gas were released from a rocket during the night in March 1956 at an altitude of roughly 110 kilometers (65 miles). Immediately a yellowish-red glow appeared in the sky to be followed by a silver-gray luminosity lasting about 10 minutes.

---

* The composition of the atmosphere is always given for dry air because the amount of moisture is variable, e.g., from 0.1 to 2.8 percent by volume.

The light was believed to be produced in the reaction between nitric oxide and atomic oxygen to form nitrogen dioxide, i.e.,

$$NO + O \rightarrow NO_2 + radiation,$$

accompanied by the emission of a continuous spectrum of radiation covering much of the visible region. The nitrogen dioxide reacts with another oxygen atom and an oxygen molecule is produced in a high-energy (excited) state; thus,

$$NO_2 + O \rightarrow NO + O_2{}^*,$$

the excited molecule, $O_2{}^*$, then reverting to its normal (ground) state by emitting its excess energy as radiation (§ 6.78). The latter may also contribute to the observed luminosity. It is seen that in the second reaction the nitric oxide is regenerated, so that it can react with more oxygen atoms, and so on.

8.38. At the base of the heterosphere, the main components of the atmosphere are molecular nitrogen and molecular and atomic oxygen. As a result of diffusive separation and photochemical dissociation, the proportion of atomic oxygen, the lightest of the three species, increases with altitude. Above about 230 kilometers (140 miles), there is relatively little molecular oxygen and the atmosphere then consists mainly of oxygen atoms with smaller and smaller proportion of nitrogen molecules. Although these molecules can absorb solar ultraviolet radiation of sufficient energy to produce photochemical dissociation into atoms, the probability of the absorption occurring is very small.† Consequently, atomic nitrogen is a relatively minor constituent of the upper atmosphere, although the proportion increases somewhat with altitude. There is no direct information concerning the concentration of neutral nitrogen atoms present, but there is evidence from satellite measurements that the relative amount of atomic nitrogen ions (N^+) increases up to some 720 kilometers (450 miles) altitude where the ratio of nitrogen to oxygen ions, i.e., N^+/O^+, attains a maximum value of 0.07.

8.39. At higher levels in the heterosphere, above about 1000 kilometers (600 miles), two atmospheric constituents, previously of minor significance, begin to become important; these are helium and atomic hydrogen (Fig. 8.5). Helium is normally present in the lower atmosphere to the extent of approximately 5×10^{-4} percent, i.e., five parts per million. But since its atomic weight is only 4,‡ compared with 16 for atomic oxygen (or 14 for atomic nitrogen), it will tend to rise above the oxygen atoms in the region of diffusive separation. That there is a layer in which helium is the predominant component of the atmosphere was

† In the appropriate technical language, it is said that the *cross section* of the absorption process is small; the cross section of any process is a measure, expressed as an area per molecule (or atom), of the probability that this process will occur.

‡ The molecule of helium is monatomic, i.e., the atom and molecule are the same, and hence the atomic and molecular weights are identical. There is, consequently, no question of dissociation.

suggested by the Belgian aeronomist Marcel Nicolet in 1961; he showed that its existence would account for certain features of the orbit of the Echo balloon satellite. Subsequently, a study of the variation of electron density with altitude (§ 8.143), as well as determination of the ion masses by instruments on

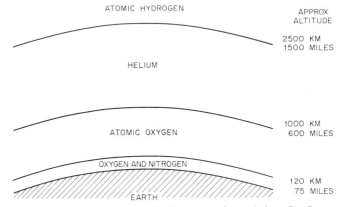

Fig. 8.5. Chief components of the atmosphere (after R. Jastrow)

satellites, revealed the presence in the atmosphere of a region in which helium ions are an important constituent. More recently, the presence of neutral helium was established by means of a mass spectrometer carried on the Explorer XVII satellite, launched on April 2, 1963. The existence of a *heliosphere* may thus be regarded as a feature of the heterosphere. It is particularly important at times when sunspot activity is low.

8.40. The helium layer in the atmosphere lies within the exosphere, from which atoms having sufficient velocity can escape into interplanetary space. There must, consequently, be a continuous replacement of helium, presumably from below. The source is the radioactive matter containing uranium, thorium, etc., that is present in Earth's crust. Many radioactive species continuously emit alpha particles and these are, in fact, identical with helium nuclei (or ions). By picking up two electrons, which are readily available, the alpha particle becomes a normal helium atom.

8.41. Finally, above the helium layer is a region where atomic hydrogen, the lightest atomic species, is the main constituent. The chief source of these atoms is considered to be the photochemical decomposition, by solar ultraviolet radiation, of molecules of water vapor, methane, and hydrogen normally present in the homosphere. Some hydrogen atoms (or hydrogen nuclei) also come into the atmosphere from the solar wind (§ 6.168). Hence, means are available for maintaining a fairly constant concentration of atomic hydrogen, in spite of the inevitable loss into space. The hydrogen atoms are ionized by solar radiation to a certain extent, so that many positive hydrogen ions (and electrons) are present. Since hydrogen ions are identical with hydrogen nuclei or protons, the name *protonosphere* has been applied to this region. The protonosphere extends more or less indefinitely into space, the density decreasing but the degree of ionization increasing with distance. At an altitude of 6500 kilometers (4000 miles), the estimated particle density of atomic hydrogen is about 4000 atoms per cubic centimeter, of which probably more than 50 percent is in ionic form; at a distance of 65,000 kilometers (40,000 miles), the density is something like 30 to 60 atoms per cubic centimeter, nearly all being ionized. In interplanetary space, the normal density ranges from 1 to 5 hydrogen nuclei per cubic centimeter (§ 6.171).

8.42. There is no definite information concerning the altitudes of the layers in which helium and atomic hydrogen, respectively, predominate. The only evidence available is from the distribution of the corresponding ions obtained both by direct determination of the masses and by an indirect analysis of the variation of electron density with altitude. The data indicate that the levels vary with the atmospheric temperature and this is subject to many changes. In any event, the formation of oxygen atoms below the helium layer and of hydrogen atoms above depend on photochemical processes brought about by ultraviolet radiation from the Sun. It is evident, therefore, that the lower and upper levels of the heliosphere may be expected to vary daily, seasonally, and with the degree of solar activity. The distribution of ions is more directly related to the structure of the ionosphere and the subject will consequently be treated further in § 8.141 *et seq.* It may be mentioned here, however, that the layer in which helium is an important component commences at an altitude of about 1000 to 1150 kilometers (600 or 700 miles), on the average, whereas the protonosphere lies above 2000 to 2500 kilometers (1200 to 1500 miles) or thereabouts.

TEMPERATURES AND DENSITIES IN THE ATMOSPHERE

8.43. Before the development of sounding rockets and satellites, the measurements of atmospheric temperatures and densities at high altitudes were made with instruments carried by balloons up to heights of about 32 kilometers (20 miles). But at greater altitudes, approximate estimates only were possible from observations on meteor trails and on the reflection of sound waves by the mesopause. Since 1946, when rocket sounding was initiated in the United States, significant progress has been made in knowledge of the physical properties of the upper atmosphere. Ambient pressures and densities can be determined with fair accuracy by rocketborne instruments and radiosondes, as described in § 5.47 *et seq.* The direct temperatures indicated by instruments on sounding rockets and satellites are, however, not representative of the surroundings because they are affected by the motion through the air. Furthermore, at very high altitudes, where the air molecules and atoms have long mean free paths, the situation referred to in § 8.31 arises.

8.44. For the determination of temperatures in space it is necessary, therefore, to employ indirect methods. One such technique, which has been widely used, is based on the rocket grenade procedure for measuring the velocity of sound, as outlined in § 5.48. Another approach, which will be considered here, depends on the rate of change of atmospheric density with altitude; then, if the average molecular weight of the gases in the atmosphere is known, as is certainly the case in the homosphere, i.e., up to a height of 100 kilometers (60 miles) or so, the kinetic temperatures at different altitudes can be calculated.

8.45. The temperature of the atmosphere varies with altitude, as was seen earlier in this chapter, but a relatively narrow region may be selected in which the temperature does not change very greatly, and so may be assumed to have a constant value, $T°$ Kelvin (§ 3.19, footnote). If n_1 is the atmospheric density at a height h_1 in this region, and n_2 is the density at height h_2, then it can be shown that (cf. § 8.364)

$$\ln \frac{n_1}{n_2} = -\frac{mg}{kT} (h_1 - h_2),^*$$

where ln, sometimes represented by $\log_e$, is the symbol for natural logarithms; m is the average mass of the atmospheric molecules (and atoms), g is the acceleration of gravity, and k is the Boltzmann constant, i.e., 1.38×10^{-16} erg per degree. The negative sign on the right side of the equation indicates that the atmospheric density decreases with increasing altitude. Since g varies with altitude, it is convenient to use g_0, the sea-level value, and then to replace the geometric altitude, h, by the *geopotential altitude, h'*, i.e.,

$$h' = \frac{R_0 h}{R_0 + h},$$

where R_0 is the radius of Earth (§ 8.365). The appropriate form of the equation given above is then

$$\ln \frac{n_1}{n_2} = -\frac{mg_0}{kT} (h'_1 - h'_2). \tag{8.1}$$

8.46. It is evident that if the gas density is measured at two different altitudes, it is possible to calculate the temperature, T, from equation (8.1), since the quantities m, g_0, and k may be regarded as known. In practice, more accurate results are obtained by plotting the geopotential altitude as ordinate on a linear scale against the density on the common logarithmic scale. The (negative) slope of the resulting curve at any geomagnetic altitude is then equal to 2.30 kT/mg_0, where 2.30 is the factor for converting natural logarithms to common logarithms; thus, the temperature at the given altitude can be calculated.

8.47. A modified form of equation (8.1) is obtained by defining the *geopo-*

---

* This expression is commonly known as the *barometric equation.*

tential scale height, H, in any region of approximately constant temperature and (average) molecular weight, by

$$H = \frac{kT}{mg_0},\tag{8.2}$$

so that the slope referred to above is $2.30\ H$. If the vertical difference between the geopotential altitudes h'_1 and h'_2 is represented by d, equation (8.1) is now

$$\ln \frac{n_1}{n_2} = -\frac{d}{H}.\tag{8.3}$$

A physical significance can be given to the scale height by setting the level difference d equal to H; it follows then from equation (8.3) that, in these circumstances, $\ln (n_1/n_2) = -1$ and, hence, n_1/n_2 is equal to $1/2.72$. Thus, in a region of constant temperature and molecular weight, the scale height is the vertical (geopotential) distance within which the density changes by a factor of 2.72.

8.48. In the homosphere, up to an altitude of about 100 kilometers (60 miles), the scale height is very roughly constant at 6.9 kilometers (4.3 miles).* Within this range, too, the geopotential altitude difference, d, is virtually equal to the actual (measured) level difference, so that d may be taken as the geometrical distance. A simple form of equation (8.3) may be obtained if altitudes are expressed in miles; thus, if H is set equal to 4.3 miles, this equation becomes

$$\ln \frac{n_1}{n_2} = \frac{d}{4.3},\tag{8.4}$$

where d is now the actual distance in miles. A useful modification of the scale height is the distance within which the density changes by a factor of ten; this can be derived from equation (8.4) by setting n_1/n_2 equal to 10, i.e.,

$$\ln 10 = -\frac{d_{10}}{4.3},$$

where d_{10} is the required distance. Since $\ln 10$ is 2.30, it follows that

$$d_{10} = 2.3 \times 4.3 \approx 10 \text{ miles.}$$

8.49. From sea level up to some 60 miles (100 kilometers), the atmospheric density thus decreases by a factor of approximately 10 for every 10 miles (16 kilometers) increase in height. The mass density of air at sea level is about 1.2×10^{-3} gram per cubic centimeter and the particle density is 2.5×10^{19} molecules per cubic centimeter. With these data, it is possible to obtain in a simple manner a rough estimate of the air density at any altitude up to 60 miles (100 kilometers). For example, at 30 miles (50 kilometers), the value

---

* It cannot be a true constant because the temperature varies, although m remains essentially unchanged in this altitude range.

will be less than at sea level by a factor of 10^3, i.e., about 1.2×10^{-6} gram (or 2.5×10^{16} molecules) per cubic centimeter. Above 60 miles (100 kilometers), in the heterosphere, both the temperature and the average molecular weight change with altitude; hence, so also does the scale height. Values of the air density at these heights will be given later.

ATMOSPHERIC DENSITY FROM SATELLITE ORBITS

8.50. Sounding-rocket techniques for determining air densities are adequate up to altitudes of about 160 kilometers (100 miles), but beyond this level they are not too satisfactory. It is in this upper part of the atmosphere that Earth satellites play a highly important role. The procedure is based on the computation of the aerodynamic drag on the satellite; according to the footnote in § 3.128, this is related to the ambient density. The quantity measured is the change in orbital period of the satellite over an interval of time. From the rate at which this period decreases, the density of the surrounding air can be calculated provided the mass and cross-sectional (frontal) area of the satellite are known. If the eccentricity of the orbit is relatively small, i.e., the orbit does not deviate greatly from a circle, the density may be regarded as applying to the average orbital altitude. For a highly eccentric orbit, however, most of the drag occurs near the perigee where the air density is relatively high, because of the low altitude, and where the velocity is also high.* The atmospheric density obtained from the rate of change of the orbital period is then essentially that for an altitude somewhat above that of the perigee.

8.51. There are a number of factors that affect the accuracy of the density calculated from satellite drag measurements. In the first place, unless the satellite is spherical, as is rarely the case, the frontal area and drag coefficient are uncertain. Moreover, it is questionable if the conventional expression for the drag force, which applies when the gas densities are moderately high, is appropriate at high altitudes where the densities are low and the molecules are far apart. Consequently, it is doubtful whether the results from satellite drag measurements are accurate to better than ± 20 percent; they are, nevertheless, more reliable than those obtainable in any other manner. At an altitude of 320 kilometers (200 miles), for example, a widely accepted value of the air density before satellite data were available turned out to be almost ten times too large. The most recent results for the density of the atmosphere as a function of altitude will be given in Fig. 8.8.

8.52. In order to determine temperatures from density data, the average molecular weight of the air is required. Up to 100 kilometers (60 miles) altitude the value is essentially constant at 29.0, but at higher levels it changes continuously because the composition of the atmosphere varies with altitude in the heterosphere. Between 100 and 1000 kilometers (60 and 600 miles) the molecu-

---

* It will be recalled that the aerodynamic drag is proportional to the square of the velocity.

lar weight decreases steadily from 29.0 to 16, the value for atomic oxygen; then, in the heliosphere, up to 2000 or 2500 kilometers (1200 or 1500 miles), it falls to 4, the molecular (or atomic) weight of helium. Subsequently, the value decreases to 1 (for atomic hydrogen) and to 0.5 (for a fully ionized atomic hydrogen plasma). Because of the uncertainty in the molecular weights at different altitudes, the temperature values calculated from satellite densities may be in error to some extent. The situation is now being improved by utilizing satellite-borne mass spectrometers to permit determination of average molecular weights concurrently with the density measurements.

ATMOSPHERIC DENSITY VARIATIONS

8.53. In addition to demonstrating that the values of atmospheric densities (and temperatures) previously adopted were somewhat in error, satellite observations revealed the existence of several unexpected temporal, i.e., occurring over a relatively short time, variations of great significance. Analysis of the orbital period of the U.S.S.R. satellite Sputnik II (perigee 140 miles),* made independently by Luigi G. Jacchia in the United States and by Desmond G. King-Hele in the United Kingdom during the winter of 1957-1958, indicated somewhat irregular variations in the atmospheric density that appeared to recur at intervals of about 30 days. By early 1959, this behavior had been confirmed by observations on both Vanguard I (perigee 400 miles) and Sputnik III (perigee 140 miles). It was apparent that the density of the air at high altitudes was changing in such a manner as to exhibit a maximum every 27 or 28 days. It will be recalled that this is approximately the period of solar rotation (§ 6.110) and Jacchia suggested that the variations in density were caused by an active region (or regions) on the Sun.

8.54. The explanation proposed for this phenomenon is the following. When a region of activity on the Sun is facing toward Earth, there is an increase in the emission of radiation. Such radiation is partly electromagnetic in nature, i.e., X-rays and ultraviolet, and partly corpuscular, i.e., mainly protons and electrons. As they pass through the atmosphere, nearly all the energy of these radiations is transferred to the air molecules (and atoms), mainly in the altitude range of 160 to 240 kilometers (100 to 150 miles). As a result, the air is heated and it expands. In expanding, air of higher density is pushed up from below into the upper levels where the density is extremely low; an increase in density is consequently observed at the higher altitudes. As the Sun rotates, the active region becomes hidden from Earth but reappears after 27 days or so, during the lifetime of the activity.

8.55. A definite correlation between solar activity and air density in the upper atmosphere was brought to light by Wolfgang Priester in Germany in 1959. He showed that the changes in the orbital period of Sputnik II coincided

_____
* Since the orbital characteristics of satellites are usually quoted in miles in the United States, this unit of length is retained here; for conversion into kilometers, multiply by 1.61.

almost exactly with the recorded 20-cm radio wave emission received from the Sun. These waves are part of the slowly-varying component described in § 6.176 and constitute a good indication of general solar activity. Subsequently, Jacchia found that there was a correlation between 10.7-cm radio emission from the Sun and the atmospheric drag on Sputnik II, as well as on the satellites Vanguard I (Fig. 8.6) and Sputnik III.

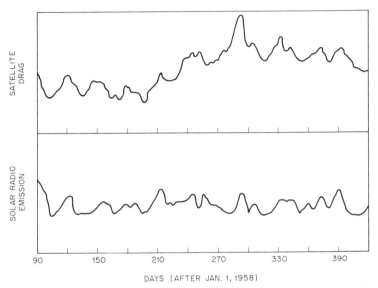

DAYS (AFTER JAN. 1, 1958)

FIG. 8.6. Atmospheric drag on Vanguard I and 10.7-cm solar radio emission (after L. G. Jacchia)

8.56. Some evidence that there is an increase in air density about the times of solar flares was obtained from the orbital periods of Sputnik III, but a striking correspondence was found with two major (Class 3⁺) flares that occurred between November 11 and 15, 1960 and with one on December 4, 1960. A day or so after the flares were seen, marked changes were observed in the orbits of seven satellites, which were being tracked at the time, at altitudes ranging from 130 miles (Discoverer V capsule*) to 700 miles (Echo I). It is of interest that the 10.7-cm solar radio emission showed little change at the times of the flares. This is not altogether surprising because that particular radiation is part of the slowly-varying component which corresponds more to the overall activity of the Sun than to sudden increases associated with solar flares.

8.57. The foregoing results have a bearing on the question of whether heating

---

* Discoverer V, launched from California on August 13, 1959 into a near-polar orbit, carried a capsule which was to be ejected in a proper location for return to Earth and subsequent recovery. Ejection did not take place at the right time, however, and the capsule remained in an approximately polar elliptical orbit.

of the atmosphere is caused by the absorption of short-wave (X-ray and ultra-violet) electromagnetic radiation from the Sun or by the electrically charged particles that are emitted in especially large numbers at the times of intense local solar activity. The electromagnetic radiation, traveling with the velocity of light, would reach Earth's vicinity in about 8 minutes but the particles, traveling as fast as 1600 kilometers (1000 miles) per second, might require 26 hours to make the journey from the Sun. Since the change in air density always occurred a day or so after a strong solar flare, it appears that most of the heating of the atmosphere was the result of collisions of the fast-moving (high-energy) protons and electrons with the atoms and molecules in the air.

8.58. Although the X-rays (and possibly ultraviolet radiation) from the Sun are enhanced at the time of a flare, they apparently contribute relatively little to the observed increase in air density at high altitudes. At other times, how-ever, when the regular but smaller 27-day variations in density are apparent, it is probable that short wavelength electromagnetic radiation is largely respon-sible for the additional heating of the atmosphere. It is perhaps significant in this connection that the 10.7-cm radio emission correlates with the intensity of the solar helium I (584 Å) and helium II (304 Å) lines in the extreme ultra-violet. Electromagnetic radiations of short wavelength interact with atoms and molecules in the atmosphere by causing ionization (photoionization) and dis-sociation (photodissociation). Recombination of the ions and electrons and various chemical reactions among the dissociation products (and ions) is ac-companied by the liberation of heat. In this manner, the energy of the electro-magnetic radiations is utilized in heating the atmosphere. Most of the longer wavelength radiations from the Sun, i.e., in the optical and radio windows (§ 6.92), are unable to produce ionization or dissociation* and so they are transmitted to and absorbed by Earth's surface.

8.59. If upper atmosphere densities and temperatures are related to the Sun's activity, then it is to be expected that the average temperatures would exhibit an approximately 11-year cycle corresponding to the sunspot cycle, just as does the 20-cm solar radio emission. There is definite evidence that the average temperature at high altitudes has decreased considerably since 1958, i.e., about the time of sunspot maximum, when the first satellite observations were made. During the quiet Sun period around 1964 and 1965, the average temperature of the atmosphere attained a minimum value to be followed by a subsequent increase.

8.60. Many meteorologists hold the opinion that the phenomena associated with solar activity have an effect on the weather. Be that as it may, a definite correlation has been established between the 11-year sunspot cycle and the widths of tree rings. It seems, therefore, that there is a connection between the activity of the Sun and the growth of trees, the latter being primarily de-

---

* The reason is that at the longer wavelengths, i.e., lower frequencies, the energy quanta (§ 6.74) are not large enough to cause these reactions to take place.

pendent on the extent of rainfall. Since the amount of energy released in sunspots, solar flares, etc., represents a very small fraction only of the energy radiated by the Sun, it is somewhat surprising that it should have any effect on the climate. The large temperature changes at high altitudes that accompany solar activity presumably have an influence on the general structure of the atmosphere and, hence, on the meteorological conditions in the vicinity of Earth. It is evident that this aspect of Earth-Sun relationships merits additional study, for both scientific and practical reasons.

8.61. Two further periodic variations have been reported in the density of the atmosphere, as determined from observations on Vanguard I and Vanguard II. First, at high altitudes, at least between 350 and 660 kilometers (220 and 410 miles), there is a regular diurnal variation in the air density (and temperature). A typical example is given in Fig. **8.7** for an altitude of 600 kilometers (370

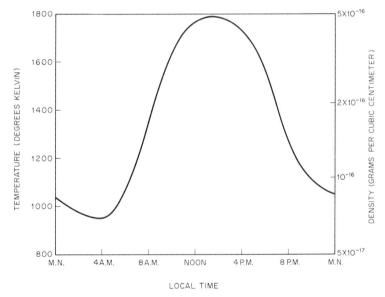

FIG. 8.7.   Diurnal variation of atmospheric density and temperature at an altitude of 600 kilometers (after I. Harris and W. Priester)

miles); the density passes through a maximum every day about 2 P.M. local time, when it is about eight times as large as the minimum density around 4 A.M. Calculations show that solar ultraviolet radiations alone cannot account for the observed density changes and some other type of radiation, possibly corpuscular, must be involved.

8.62. The second type of variation is a semiannual effect; the average atmospheric density has a maximum value in March followed by a minimum around June or July, with a second maximum in September and another minimum in December or January. These fluctuations correspond to a well-known periodicity in the variations of Earth's magnetic field that are caused by corpuscular radiations from the Sun.

8.63. In view of the continuous changes taking place in the upper atmosphere, it is obviously impossible to represent the density data in a simple manner. An approximate indication of the average density as a function of altitude, at about the time of sunspot maximum, is shown in Fig. 8.8. At heights of over

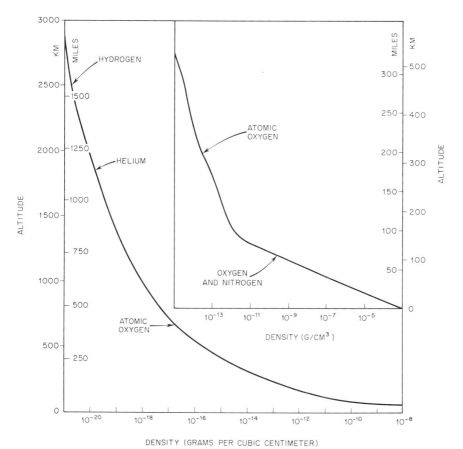

FIG. 8.8. Mass density of the atmosphere at different altitudes; the densities up to altitudes of 500 kilometers are shown in the inset.

160 kilometers (100 miles) or so, the densities would be lower when the solar activity is less. The extremely low densities at great heights should be noted; at an altitude of 800 kilometers (500 miles) the average mass density is only 10^{-17} gram (or about 4×10^5 oxygen atoms) per cubic centimeter, and at 2000 kilometers (1250 miles) the density is 10^{-20} gram (or some 1500 helium

atoms) per cubic centimeter. The respective sea-level values were given in § 8.49.

8.64. The temperatures at high altitudes are just as variable as the densities. The average daily variation at an altitude of 600 kilometers (370 miles) is shown in Fig. 8.7. In general, temperatures above 400 kilometers (250 miles) are about 300°C (540°F) higher in the early afternoon and the same amount lower before sunrise than the mean daily value. There are also variations with latitude and with the general activity of the Sun (cf. Fig. 8.4). Other aspects of atmospheric temperatures will be treated in connection with the ionosphere (§ 8.145), because interesting information has been obtained from observations made in this region of the atmosphere.

8.65. The considerable temperature fluctuations in the upper atmosphere during the course of a day, often amounting to 600°C (1080°F) or more, are perhaps somewhat surprising, at first sight. It must be remembered, however, that the air densities are extremely low. Thus, the quantity of solar energy required to increase the air temperature by 600°C at an altitude of 400 kilometers (250 miles) would cause an increase of only a minute fraction of a degree at sea level.

Improvements in Density Measurements

8.66. One of the main uncertainties in the determination of densities from observations on the orbital periods of satellites is the effective shape of the spacecraft. Most satellites have irregular structures and both the effective frontal area and drag coefficient depend on the often unknown aspect in the direction of motion. It would be advantageous, therefore, if spherical satellites were used for atmospheric density measurements. A sphere always has a definite frontal area and, in addition, experience has shown that its drag coefficient can be predicted quite accurately. Thus, two important sources of error would be largely eliminated by the use of a spherical spacecraft.

8.67. Furthermore, the actual observations could be made more reliable by increasing the magnitude of the drag force relative to the mass of the satellite. The difference in length of successive orbital periods would then become larger, and more precise measurement of the rate of change would be possible. A compromise is necessary, however; if the aerodynamic drag is too large, the satellite would lose altitude so rapidly that it would spiral to Earth after a few orbits. Obviously, it is desirable for the satellite to remain aloft long enough, e.g., three months or more if possible, to permit a sufficient number of observations to be made.

8.68. Calculations and laboratory tests indicated that a sphere 12 feet (3.7 meters) in diameter and weighing 10 to 15 pounds (4.5 to 7 kilograms) would be suitable for air density determinations. An inflatable sphere of this type was made of a four-ply laminate of alternate layers of aluminum foil and Mylar plastic film; it could be folded for launching and inflated in space by means of compressed nitrogen gas contained in a small steel reservoir. When inflation is completed, the gas reservoir is disconnected and jettisoned in space.

8.69. After several failures, such a spherical satellite, entitled Explorer IX, was launched on February 16, 1961, from Wallops Island, Virginia, into an orbit with an initial perigee of 393 miles and apogee of 1607 miles. The total weight, including a radio beacon for tracking, was close to 15 pounds (7 kilograms). Unfortunately, the radio transmitter on the satellite failed during the first orbit, and so subsequent tracking was performed optically by the Baker-Nunn cameras of the Smithsonian Astrophysical Observatory Network (§ 4.133). Although more accurate than radio tracking, the optical method suffers from the drawback that it can be used only at certain times, whereas with radio continuous tracking is possible. Another balloon satellite, Explorer XIX, was launched from California on December 19, 1963; the initial orbital perigee and apogee were approximately 370 and 1490 miles, respectively. Radio contact was soon lost, but the satellite was tracked optically. The observations from Explorers IX and XIX served to confirm the results already given. A third air-density satellite, Explorer XXIV, placed in orbit on November 21, 1964, appears to be operating satisfactorily.

8.70. An entirely different and promising approach to the determination of air densities is being explored in the San Marco spacecraft designed and constructed by Italian scientists, as part of the U.S. program for international cooperation in space projects. Instead of depending on orbital period data to determine the drag force, the satellite carries a novel *drag balance* to measure the force directly. The outstanding advantage of this technique is that changes in drag, and hence in density, will be recorded immediately they occur, whereas in the procedure described above the values are inevitably averaged over at least two orbits.

8.71. The spacecraft consists of a sealed outer shell, essentially spherical in form, within which is supported a disc-like structure that carries the instruments; in the center is the drag balance. As the satellite moves through the atmosphere, the outer shell is continuously subjected to drag forces and is thus being decelerated. The inner structure, however, is not exposed to the air and its inertia tends to keep it moving at a constant speed. The resulting differential motion is sensed by the drag balance consisting basically of three accelerometers to measure the components of motion along three rectangular axes (§ 4.55). The relative deceleration is proportional to the drag force on the satellite, and is thus related to the ambient atmospheric density.

8.72. The San Marco satellite, weighing 250 pounds (115 kilograms), is to be placed deliberately in a relatively low-altitude orbit, between 175 and 350 kilometers (110 and 220 miles). This region is above the useful range of sounding rockets but below that at which most previous satellite observations have been made. In order to achieve a reasonable lifetime, about 4 to 6 months, at low altitude the spacecraft has been designed so as to have a large ratio of mass to frontal area, namely, about 60 pounds per square foot (290 kilograms per square meter). The San Marco system is to be launched, with the assistance of the United States, into an equatorial orbit from a platform erected in the Indian Ocean. To provide a qualification test of the spacecraft and its instrumentation and a training exercise for the Italian launch crew, a San Marco satellite was placed in an elliptical orbit, inclination about 38 deg, on December 15, 1964, from Wallops Island, Virginia.

THE CHEMOSPHERE

Ozone in the Atmosphere

8.73. A minor constituent of the atmosphere, but one of great significance in spite of its small concentration, is ozone; its proportion probably never exceeds ten molecules per million air molecules, i.e., 0.001 percent by volume.* The first stage in the formation of ozone (O_3) is the photochemical dissociation (photodissociation) of oxygen molecules into atoms. There are two wavelength regions in the solar ultraviolet where molecular oxygen can absorb radiation leading to dissociation: one is the Schumann-Runge continuum, at wavelengths shorter than 1760 Å, and the other is the Herzberg continuum, lying below 2420 Å.† Radiation from the 1760 Å continuum is the more strongly absorbed and hence solar radiation in this region does not penetrate to levels in the atmosphere below about 100 kilometers (60 miles), but radiation in the more weakly absorbed 2420 Å continuum extends down to an altitude of roughly 40 kilometers (25 miles).

8.74. As a result of the absorption of radiation in either of the two specified spectral regions, oxygen molecules are dissociated into atoms, i.e.,

$$O_2 + \text{radiation} \rightarrow O + O.$$

These atoms can either remain free or they may undergo certain chemical reactions, depending upon circumstances. The reaction of present interest is the combination of an oxygen atom with a molecule of oxygen to form ozone; this process requires the presence of a so-called *third body*, so that it may be written as

$$O + O_2 + M \rightarrow O_3 + M',$$

---

* If breathed over long periods of time, air containing 0.1 part per million of ozone can be toxic. At sea level, the normal concentration, in the absence of smog, is about 0.01 to 0.03 part per million; under conditions that favor smog formation, however, the ozone may attain 0.5 part per million for short periods.

† A *continuum* is a spectral region in which absorption (or emission) is continuous, with no discrete lines (cf. § 6.87); the presence of an absorption continuum in a molecular spectrum implies either dissociation or ionization of the molecule. An emission continuum is produced as a result of recombination, either of the components of the molecule or of the ion with an electron.

where M is the third body, which may be any available atom or molecule. The purpose of the third body, in this and other reactions, is to carry off part of the energy liberated in the chemical reaction; for this reason the product is indicated as M′, the prime implying that it has more energy than it had initially. In the absence of a third body, all the energy liberated would remain in the ozone molecule, with the result that it would tend to break up immediately into an oxygen atom and molecule. By removing part of the energy released, the third body increases the probability that the ozone molecule will survive.

8.75. Instead of reacting with oxygen molecules, there is a possibility that two oxygen atoms will recombine, also in the presence of a third body, i.e.,

$$O + O + M \rightarrow O_2 + M'.$$

The net effect of the photochemical dissociation followed by recombination is that the energy of the radiation absorbed from sunlight in the dissociation stage is released as heat in the recombination process.

8.76. At an altitude above 100 kilometers (60 miles), where oxygen molecules absorb in the Schumann-Runge continuum, the concentration (or particle density) of oxygen molecules is low, and so also is the total density upon which the third-body concentration depends. Consequently, the rate of formation of ozone must be relatively small. For the same general reasons, the rate of recombination of oxygen atoms is not large. Hence, at levels of over 100 kilometers, absorption of solar radiation will lead to the presence of oxygen atoms in the atmosphere. This accounts for the situation described in § 8.52.

8.77. Where radiation absorption takes place in the Herzberg continuum, mainly at a height of about 40 to 50 kilometers (25 to 30 miles), both the total gas density and that of molecular oxygen are sufficiently high to permit the rapid formation of ozone. But not all of the latter produced remains in the atmosphere. The ozone molecule itself absorbs ultraviolet radiation strongly in the region from about 2100 to 3000 Å and this leads to photodissociation, i.e.,

$$O_3 + \text{radiation} \rightarrow O_2 + O.$$

Subsequently two oxygen atoms may recombine to form molecular oxygen, as described above, or an oxygen atom may react with an ozone molecule; thus,

$$O_3 + O \rightarrow O_2 + O_2,$$

so that the final product is always molecular oxygen. There are other reactions whereby ozone is removed, but these two are of major importance in the atmospheric region of interest.

8.78. The variation of the ozone concentration with altitude is determined by a combination of opposing factors. The radiation intensity, upon which the rate of oxygen atom—and hence ozone—formation depends, increases with altitude, but the concentrations of molecular oxygen and of the third body, which are also involved, decrease. Moreover, the relative rate of loss of ozone by photodissociation and by interaction with oxygen atoms may also be expected to increase with altitude. In view of these considerations, it is not surprising that the ozone concentration increases to a maximum and then decreases (Fig. 8.9). At an altitude of 10 kilometers (6 miles), the concentration is usually less

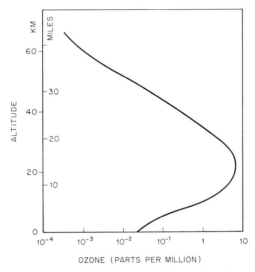

FIG. 8.9.   Ozone concentration versus altitude in the atmosphere

than one part per million; it then increases to a maximum of about five to ten parts per million at a level of 25 kilometers (16 miles). At greater heights, the ozone concentration decreases again and is quite small at 65 kilometers (40 miles).

8.79. The atmosphere between the altitudes of about 15 and 35 kilometers (10 and 20 miles), where most of the ozone is found, is called the *ozonosphere*. This is actually part of a considerably larger region, extending up to a height of 200 kilometers (120 miles) or beyond, known as the *chemosphere*. It is here that a number of chemical processes occur; these are usually initiated by the absorption of ultraviolet radiation from the Sun which produces either ionization or dissociation. In later sections, the role of these chemical reactions will be described in connection with the airglow phenomena and with certain properties of the ionosphere.

8.80. Prior to 1948, the distribution of ozone in the upper atmosphere was determined either by ingenious but relatively involved methods utilizing measurements made from Earth's surface, or by means of balloons carrying suitable spectrographs. The strong absorption of ultraviolet radiation by ozone, as mentioned earlier, lends itself particularly to the determination of its concentration by spectrographic techniques. In this connection, sounding rockets have proved to be very effective for determining the variation in the atmospheric concentration of ozone with altitude. The United Kingdom satellite UK-2 (or Ariel II), launched from Wallops Island, Virginia, on March 27, 1964, carries an instrument for the determination of ozone in the atmosphere by measuring the absorption of certain wavelengths of the solar radiation when the Sun is in a suitable position relative to the spacecraft.

8.81. In spite of its small concentration, ozone plays an important role in the atmosphere. First, the reactions leading to the decomposition of ozone into oxygen molecules are accompanied by the liberation of energy as heat. The resulting warming of the atmosphere is considered to be responsible for the increase in temperature that occurs in the mesosphere at altitudes between roughly 30 and 50 kilometers (20 and 30 miles). In addition, the absorption by ozone of radiations with wavelengths greater than about 2100 Å prevents harmful amounts of ultraviolet radiation from penetrating to Earth's surface. Oxygen molecules, and to a lesser extent nitrogen, absorb essentially all the solar ultraviolet having wavelengths below 2100 Å, but none of the normal constituents of the atmosphere absorbs between 2100 Å and the visible region. Except for the narrow range between 3000 and 3400 Å, the gap is filled by absorption in ozone. Were it not for the formation of ozone in the upper atmosphere, even though the concentration is very low, life as it presently exists on Earth would not be possible because of the deleterious effect of ultraviolet radiation on most living organisms.*

The Greenhouse Effect

8.82. Ozone and two other minor components of the atmosphere, namely, water vapor and carbon dioxide, contribute to what is known as the *greenhouse effect*. Solar radiation, mostly in the visible with a little in the ultraviolet and infrared regions, penetrates the atmosphere and is absorbed by the ground and by the oceans. Earth's surface is thus warmed, and as a result it emits radiation but almost entirely in the infrared. The three molecular species mentioned above, however, absorb radiation strongly in this region of the spectrum in the wavelength range from about 5 to 17 microns (cf. § 6.53). Hence, instead of being dissipated in space, the radiated energy serves to increase the temperature of the atmosphere. The phenomenon is called the greenhouse effect because it is similar to the trapping of the Sun's heat in a greenhouse.

8.83. Were it not for the infrared absorbing molecules in the lower atmosphere, the temperatures at Earth's surface would be considerably lower than they are actually. It has been estimated, in fact, that the greenhouse effect is responsible for an average increase of about 45°C (81°F) in the temperature near the ground. Some of the consequences are often particularly evident at night when Earth's surface, which has been warmed in the daytime, radiates

---

* Life in the oceans would be possible, however, because most of the ultraviolet radiation is absorbed by the deep water.

but receives no energy from the Sun. One result is that the presence of clouds frequently prevents appreciable cooling of the atmosphere because the heat is absorbed by the water molecules. On the other hand, in the absence of clouds, there will be a greater drop in temperature. An extreme example of this situation arises in regions where the atmosphere is exceptionally dry, e.g., in desert areas; although the days are hot, they are generally followed by moderately cool nights.

THE NIGHTGLOW

8.84. An interesting but not completely explained atmospheric phenomenon is the *airglow*. Its spectrum confirms the existence of atomic oxygen at high altitudes and indicates the presence of traces, at least, of other species. The airglow probably occurs in some form at all times, both day and night, but it is most readily observed and studied at night when the sky is dark. It is then called the *night* (or *nocturnal*) *airglow* or, in brief, the *nightglow*. On a clear moonless night, it can be detected as a very faint general luminosity in the sky. The nightglow spectrum has some features in common with those of auroras, as will be seen later, but the phenomena differ in several important respects. The auroras are largely dominated by Earth's magnetic field and are generally observed within restricted latitudes near the poles; furthermore, their occurrence is related to activity in the solar atmosphere. The nightglow, on the other hand, does not depend greatly on latitude or on exceptional solar activity. Nevertheless, the Sun's normal radiations are ultimately responsible for the observed luminosity, and so it often exhibits hourly, seasonal, and cyclic variations; they are, however, of a minor character.

8.85. The nightglow is faintest at the zenith, i.e., overhead, and increases in intensity toward the horizon, with its maximum about 10 deg above the horizon. The increase in intensity as increasing thicknesses of the atmosphere are penetrated, in going from the zenith to the horizon, indicates that the nightglow is an atmospheric phenomenon. By comparing the intensities at different angles, rough estimates have been made of the altitude at which the luminosity originates. The values obtained in this manner are not too reliable, but the general indication is that most of the nightglow comes from the region 100 to 160 kilometers (60 to 100 miles) above Earth's surface. This conclusion is in general agreement with the results obtained from photometers, i.e., instruments for measuring light intensity, carried aloft by sounding rockets.

8.86. The nightglow is commonly studied by prolonged spectrographic observations of the night sky made from the ground. Characteristic features of the spectrum are the green (5577 Å) and red (6300, 6364, and 6391 Å) lines of atomic oxygen which also appear in auroral spectra, and a continuum in the visible region due, in all probability, to the reaction between oxygen atoms and nitric oxide (§ 8.37). Sounding rocket studies show that the green line of atomic oxygen is emitted at levels between about 100 and 120 kilometers (60 and 75 miles), but the red lines originate at higher levels, around 160 kilometers (100 miles) altitude. The intensity of the green radiation in the nightglow increases toward midnight and decreases at later times, but the red lines are brightest in the early evening and at dawn. This behavior is difficult to explain but the emission of the lines of atomic oxygen from the nightglow is further confirmation of the existence of this species at altitudes above 100 kilometers (60 miles). The nightglow spectrum also contains fairly strong emission bands of molecular oxygen, mainly in the near ultraviolet and infrared. But the spectra of nitrogen molecules and atoms are either very weak or completely absent. Among the somewhat unusual spectra of the nightglow are those of hydroxyl (OH) radicals, mainly in the infrared, and of sodium; further reference to these spectra will be made shortly.

8.87. One of the striking features of the ultraviolet spectrum of the night sky, at altitudes above 80 kilometers (50 miles), is the surprisingly strong Lyman-α (1216 Å) emission of atomic hydrogen discovered in 1955 by H. Friedman, *et al.* (§ 6.145). The radiation appears to come with more-or-less equal intensity from all directions over the upward hemisphere. In order to account for this phenomenon, it has been suggested that Earth is surrounded, out to a distance of about 10 Earth radii, by a *geocorona* containing neutral hydrogen atoms. The density is estimated to be about 2×10^4 atoms per cubic centimeter at a distance of 550 kilometers (340 miles) from Earth, but it decreases fairly rapidly with increasing distance.

REACTIONS OF THE NIGHTGLOW

8.88. The radiation energy emitted by the airglow during the night must have been stored in the atmosphere during the daytime. In view of the altitudes at which the nightglow is observed, the most probable main source of this energy is the atomic oxygen formed by absorption of solar ultraviolet radiation as already explained. The other aspect of the nightglow problem is to account for the particular excited states, especially of oxygen molecules and atoms, responsible for the emission of the characteristic radiations. Recombination of two oxygen atoms could result in the formation of an excited oxygen molecule, i.e.,

$$O + O \rightarrow O_2{}^*,$$

where the asterisk is used to indicate a high-energy (or excited) state with sufficient energy to produce a spectrum of molecular oxygen by reverting to its normal energy (or ground) state. This is a simple and straightforward mechanism, but an explanation of the formation of the excited oxygen atoms that emit the red and green lines is more complicated.

8.89. One suggestion is that three oxygen atoms interact to form a molecule of oxygen and an excited atom; in a sense, the latter acts as the third body to carry off part of the energy produced in the recombination of the other two atoms, i.e.,

$$O + O + O \to O_2 + O^*.$$

Such a triple-collision process would be rare and only possible where the atomic oxygen concentration (or particle density) is relatively high, namely, at an altitude of around 100 kilometers (60 miles).† The excited oxygen atoms that emit the green line, which comes from this level, may thus have been formed in the manner described.

8.90. There is a possibility, based on laboratory observations, that the rate at which three oxygen atoms interact would be insufficient to account for the intensity of the auroral green line (5577 Å) in the night airglow. If this is the case, an alternative mechanism might be the combination of two oxygen atoms in the presence of any other atom or molecule, M, as the third body. The reaction would then be the same as in § 8.75, except that it is postulated that the oxygen molecule is formed in an excited state, i.e.,

$$O + O + M \to O_2^* + M'.$$

The excited oxygen molecule then interacts with a normal oxygen atom and transfers part of its excitation energy to the latter, i.e.,

$$O_2^* + O \to O_2 + O^*,$$

thereby producing an excited oxygen atom which can emit the green line.

8.91. Since the lower energy level of the green-line transition is the upper level for the formation of the red spectral lines of atomic oxygen (Fig. 8.10), it is necessary to explain why the red lines are not produced at the lower altitudes. The conditions for the formation of the red and green oxygen lines, which are significant in the auroral spectrum, are discussed more fully in § 8.341. It will then be seen that oxygen atoms in the intermediate energy state shown in Fig. 8.10 have a relatively long lifetime, i.e., a significant time elapses, on the average, between the formation of the excited atoms and the emission of the excess energy. Consequently, there is a considerable probability that the atom will lose all or part of its excitation energy in a collision, most likely with an oxygen molecule, before it can pass into the lower-energy (ground) state by the emission of the red-line radiation.‡

8.92. At an altitude of about 160 kilometers (100 miles), where the red lines actually appear in the nightglow, the concentration of atomic oxygen is too small for triple collisions to be significant. The excited oxygen atoms must, therefore, be produced in another manner, but the nature of the process is not

† Although the *proportion* of atomic oxygen in the atmosphere is higher above 60 kilometers, the concentration, i.e., the number of atoms per unit volume of air, is lower because of the steady decrease in density.

‡ The ground state of atomic oxygen is a triplet, i.e., it consists of three related levels with energies that differ by small amounts. Consequently, there are three red lines with wavelengths lying in a narrow range (§ 8.86).

clear. One possibility is the interaction of normal oxygen atoms with excited molecules, the latter being formed by recombination of two atoms, as mentioned above. Another suggestion is that atomic oxygen ions, formed in the daytime at

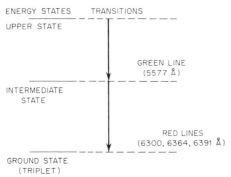

FIG. 8.10.   Energy levels of atomic oxygen

the altitude under consideration (§ 8.137), exchange with molecules to form molecular oxygen ions, i.e.,

$$O^+ + O_2 \rightarrow O + O_2^+.$$

The O_2^+ ion then captures an electron and the energy liberated in the electrical neutralization process is sufficient to dissociate the molecule into a normal and an excited oxygen atom, i.e.,

$$O_2^+ + e^- \rightarrow O + O^*.$$

8.93. The foregoing reactions all satisfy the requirement that the energy released be sufficient to produce the appropriate (intermediate) excited state of atomic oxygen. Because of the small particle density at high altitudes, the probability that the excited atom in the intermediate energy state will transfer its energy to another species in a collision is very much less than at lower levels; hence, the emission of the red-line radiation becomes possible.

8.94. One of the peculiar aspects of the nightglow is the presence of the band spectrum of the hydroxyl (OH) radical; this portion of the spectrum, which is very strong in the infrared and extends, although more faintly, into the visible region, contains most of the energy of the nightglow. It is suggested that excited hydroxyl radicals are formed by interaction of ozone with atomic hydrogen, i.e.,

$$O_3 + H \rightarrow O_2 + OH^*,$$

and the band spectrum is then produced as the excited radical emits its excess energy. Although ozone and, in particular, hydrogen atoms are present in very small concentrations at the nightglow altitude, there are two factors that contribute to the formation of OH radicals in appreciable amounts. First, the reaction between ozone and atomic hydrogen is extremely rapid, and second, the OH in the ground state remaining after the emission of radiation can interact with oxygen atoms to regenerate hydrogen atoms, i.e.,

$$OH + O \rightarrow O_2 + H.$$

As a consequence of these processes, a very small concentration of hydrogen atoms, together with the ozone formed during the daytime, can maintain a significant density of hydroxyl radicals in the upper atmosphere.

Sodium Lines in the Nightglow

8.95. Another strange feature of the nightglow spectrum is the presence of the well known pair of yellow D-lines (5890 and 5896 Å) of sodium. The intensity of these lines varies during the night in a manner similar to the red line of oxygen; that is to say, it is brightest near sunrise and sunset. The increase in intensity of the sodium lines at these times has been ascribed to *resonance scattering*. The normal sodium atoms absorb solar radiation and are thereby raised to the first excited electronic energy state; the return to the ground state is then accompanied by the emission, in all directions, of the resonance (D-line) radiation.* The stronger emission at dusk and dawn can then be accounted for by the greater intensity of the solar radiation at these times than during the night; as is to be expected, the sodium emission is strongest in the daytime when the intensity is about ten times as great as at twilight. The question of the origin of the sodium in the atmosphere is discussed below in connection with the twilight glow.

Twilight Glow, Noctilucent Clouds, and Dayglow

8.96. The airglow in the early evening is called the *twilight glow* or the *twilight flash* because of its short duration. Its spectrum is especially strong in the sodium D-lines and in the red lines of atomic oxygen, but the green line is not enhanced. The strengthening of the sodium lines can probably be ascribed to resonance scattering, as explained above, but it is not clear why the red lines of oxygen are stronger whereas the green line is not affected. Some nitrogen spectra are also present in the twilight glow, especially the blue-violet band (from 3914 Å) of ionized nitrogen molecules, N_2^+, and a line (5200 Å) of atomic nitrogen which is either absent from or extremely weak in the nightglow.

8.97. Sodium is by far the most abundant metallic element whose lines have been observed in the spectrum of the twilight glow; in addition, there are smaller amounts of potassium and lithium. The peak of the sodium and potassium concentrations is at an altitude of about 95 kilometers (58 miles), but the lithium peak is reached some 10 or 12 kilometers (7 miles) lower. The

---

* The general phenomenon is called *fluorescence scattering*, but when the excited atom reverts to the lowest energy (ground) state after emission of radiation, the term resonance scattering is used (cf. § 6.81).

lines of ionized calcium have been observed on occasion, but they are so weak as to be on the threshold of detectability. Russian scientists, however, have reported the detection of calcium and magnesium ions at levels of 90 to 200 kilometers (55 to 120 miles) by means of mass spectrographs carried aloft by sounding rockets.

8.98. Two possible sources have been suggested for the metallic elements in the upper atmosphere, namely, salt from the oceans and meteoroid material from space. The fact that the ratio of sodium to potassium found from the spectrum of the twilight glow is similar to the ratio of these elements in sea water indicates that they are mainly of oceanic origin. The seasonal variation in the abundance of sodium, which is a maximum in the local winter and a minimum in the summer in both Hemispheres, suggests that it is carried upward from the sea by large scale circulations in the atmosphere that correspond with the seasons. The variations in the lithium content of the atmosphere are sporadic, rather than regular, and it has been suggested that this element is brought in by meteoroids (or micrometeoroids). The detonation of thermonuclear weapons at high altitudes has been accompanied by an increase in the intensity of the lithium spectrum in the twilight glow, but it is only of a temporary nature. Meteoroids are also probably the source of calcium and magnesium, since the mass spectrograph measurements indicate a larger proportion of magnesium, as in most stony meteorites.

8.99. The spectral lines of atomic sodium, potassium, and lithium, at least, imply that these substances must exist in the elemental form. But when they enter the atmosphere, either from the sea or from space, they must be present as compounds. The latter are then evidently dissociated into their constituent elements by sunlight or by reaction with oxygen atoms.

8.100. Evidence for the existence of mineral material in the atmosphere at a height of about 80 kilometers (50 miles) has been obtained from a study of *noctilucent clouds.** These tenuous clouds can sometimes be seen, generally at high latitudes in the summer, glowing faintly in the sky soon after sunset. They owe their luminosity to the scattering of sunlight which still reaches them at an altitude of 80 kilometers, although the Sun is below the local horizon at the time. Samples have been obtained from noctilucent clouds over Sweden by means of recoverable collectors attached to rockets provided by the United States. Analysis of the samples showed the presence of very fine particles, 5×10^{-6} to 5×10^{-5} cm in diameter, which contain appreciable amounts of nickel.† The presence of this element suggests that the particles are not of terrestrial, but of meteoroid, origin.

8.101. There are indications, somewhat surprising at first thought, that the particles in the noctilucent clouds are coated with a thin layer of ice. It should

* Noctilucent, from the Latin, *noctis,* "night," and *lucere,* "to shine," meaning "luminous at night."

† The smallest micrometeoroids detected by satellite-borne instruments have an estimated diameter of about 3×10^{-5} cm.

be noted, however, that the clouds form at a height of some 80 kilometers, i.e., near the mesopause (§ 8.28). At this level, the atmospheric temperature is at its lowest, i.e., about $-100°C$ ($-148°F$), in the summer at high latitudes (cf. Fig. 8.4).* This may explain why noctilucent clouds are most frequently observed in these circumstances. Although the concentration of water vapor at the top of the mesosphere is extremely small, the temperature is low enough for ice formation to be possible.

8.102. Since the airglow is enhanced at twilight, it seems probable that there is an even stronger *dayglow*, but it cannot normally be observed from Earth because of the background of scattered sunlight. It should be possible, however, to study the dayglow from altitudes above about 100 kilometers (60 miles) where the sky is always dark, except in the direction of the Sun. Spectroscopic observations with sounding rockets have indicated the presence of emission radiation in the ultraviolet. The most important component is the Lyman-α (1216 Å) line of atomic hydrogen, possibly produced by resonance scattering; there is also a less intense atomic oxygen triplet centered at 1304 Å. In 1964, C. A. Barth, in the United States, announced the discovery in the dayglow of one of the bands in the spectrum of nitric oxide molecules in the ultraviolet range from 1730 to 2730 Å. This represents the first positive identification in the atmosphere of neutral nitric oxide, a minor constituent of considerable importance; the presence of nitric oxide (positive) ions has been known for some time. The spectrum of OH radicals, mainly in the infrared, has also been found in the dayglow by means of an instrument carried in a balloon.

8.103. In February and May 1962 John H. Glenn and M. Scott Carpenter, respectively, described a luminous haze just above the horizon, as seen from their Mercury space capsules. This was later identified as the airglow, and rough measurements made by Carpenter indicated that the height was about what was to be expected. During the course of his 22-orbit flight on May 15 and 16, 1963, L. Gordon Cooper obtained color photographs of a sharply defined green band in the sky; it was approximately 25 kilometers (16 miles) thick and the altitude of its base was estimated to be 110 kilometers (68 miles). In addition, Cooper reported that he obtained a glimpse of a faint, thin rust-colored layer about 120 kilometers (74 miles) higher. This might well be the region in which the red lines of oxygen are excited.

THE IONOSPHERE

DISCOVERY OF THE IONOSPHERE

8.104. In 1882, the Scottish physicist Balfour Stewart suggested that the continuous but minor variations in Earth's magnetic field might be caused by

---

* The lowest recorded atmospheric temperature is $-143°C$ ($-226°F$) observed over northern Sweden in 1963 during a sounding-rocket study of noctilucent clouds.

the presence in the upper atmosphere of a layer of air capable of conducting electricity. Movement of this layer in the terrestrial field could produce electric currents by the *dynamo effect;** these currents would, in turn, generate magnetic fields which would be superimposed upon the normal magnetic field observed at Earth's surface. Stewart's suggestion attracted little interest until after December 1901 when the Italian radio pioneer Guglielmo Marconi succeeded in transmitting "wireless" signals a distance of about 2000 miles across the Atlantic Ocean. Physicists had previously regarded this feat as "impossible" because radio waves, like light, travel in straight lines; detection on Earth's surface should thus not be possible beyond the line of sight. The explanation, proposed independently in 1902 by Oliver Heaviside in England and Arthur E. Kennelly in the United States, of Marconi's unexpected achievement was that there exists an electrically conducting layer in the atmosphere at a height of about 80 kilometers (50 miles). Such a layer would reflect radio waves, like a passive repeater station, and return them to Earth at a considerable distance beyond the horizon.

8.105. The concept of the conducting *Kennelly-Heaviside layer,* as it was called, was generally accepted, but for more than two decades there was no direct evidence of the manner in which it functioned. In 1924, Edward V. Appleton and M. A. F. Barnett in England, using directional antennas, were able to relate the angles with the vertical made by transmitted and received continuous radio wave signals. In this way they showed that the signal received at a distance was indeed a reflection, high in the atmosphere, of the transmitted wave.

8.106. The following year, Gregory Breit and Merle A. Tuve in the United States devised a technique for determining the height of the reflecting (conducting) region. They transmitted a short pulse of radio waves upward and, by means of an oscilloscope, determined the time taken for the pulse to be reflected back to a receiver a few miles away on Earth's surface. Since the electromagnetic radio waves travel with the speed of light, the height of the reflecting layer in the atmosphere can be calculated from the time delay.† It will be seen shortly that the radio waves travel somewhat more slowly than light in the conducting region but allowance can be made for the retardation.

8.107. The altitude of the Kennelly-Heaviside layer was found to be some 80 or 100 kilometers (50 or 60 miles) and subsequently, in the course of investigations with radio waves of shorter wavelength, i.e., higher frequency, Appleton discovered another reflecting region, at a height of roughly 200 to 400 kilometers (120 to 250 miles), which was at one time known as the *Appleton layer.* To simplify the identification of the conducting layers in the atmosphere,

---

* In a dynamo, an electric current is produced by rotation of a conductor in a magnetic field. In general, any relative motion of an electrical conductor and a magnetic field will produce an electromotive force capable of causing a flow of current.

† It is of interest to note that this is the first known application of the radio reflection (or echo) principle for determining distances (cf. §§ 4.14, 6.15).

Appleton proposed the nomenclature now universally employed; he called the lower of the two layers the *E layer* and the upper one the *F layer*. In the daytime, the latter is split into two parts designated by the symbols F_1 and F_2, respectively. A layer below the E layer discovered later, became known as the *D layer*.

8.108. The ability of the conducting layers to reflect radio waves is dependent upon the presence of electrically charged particles, especially electrons; in other words, the air in these layers is ionized. The name *ionosphere* was therefore proposed for the whole ionized region in the atmosphere by R. Watson Watt, the British engineer who contributed greatly to the development of radar. The ionization is a result of the absorption of radiations of various kinds from the Sun, and it is a combination of air density and composition and radiation intensity that leads to formation of the ionosphere region of the atmosphere extending upward from an altitude of about 60 kilometers (35 miles).

8.109. Because of its great importance in radio communication, as well as on account of its intrinsic scientific interest, the ionosphere has been the subject of extensive study during the past 40 years. For a long time it was thought that there were actual finite layers of ionization in the upper atmosphere, but it has become clear that the so-called layers have a considerable depth. It is thus current practice to refer to the D, E, F_1, and F_2 *regions*, rather than layers, of the ionosphere.

8.110. The structure of the ionosphere is continually changing, so that an exact description is not possible. It varies from day to night, with the season of the year, and with latitude; furthermore, it is highly disturbed by solar radiations at periods when the Sun is especially active. Nevertheless, in spite of the many fluctuations, the regions appear to maintain some kind of individual identity, as indicated by the manner in which the electron density, i.e., the number of electrons per unit volume, changes with increasing height above Earth's surface. On this basis, the altitudes of the various regions during the daytime may be defined, on the average, by the values in Table 8.1. In principle, the F_2 region extends upward more or less indefinitely, but an arbitrary limit is sometimes set at an altitude of about 1000 kilometers (600 miles);

TABLE 8.1   APPROXIMATE AVERAGE ALTITUDES OF IONOSPHERIC
REGIONS IN THE DAYTIME

Altitude

Region	Kilometers	Miles
D	60 to 90	35 to 55
E	90 to 150	55 to 90
F_1	150 to 250	90 to 150
F_2	above 250	above 150

at this level the composition of the atmosphere begins to change from atomic oxygen to helium and then hydrogen, and Earth's magnetic field has an effect on the charged-particle distribution.

Electron Density Profile of the Ionosphere

8.111. The experimental techniques for determining the *electron density profile* of the ionosphere, i.e., the variation of the electron density with altitude, will be described later (§ **8.167** *et seq.*), but the general nature of the results obtained will be considered here. The ionosphere exhibits a great variability, but the essential features are quite definite except at times of unusual disturbances. The form of the electron density profile, during the summer at middle latitudes around the time of sunspot maximum, is indicated by the curves *A* (day) and *B* (night) in Fig. 8.11. The data are derived from a wide variety of

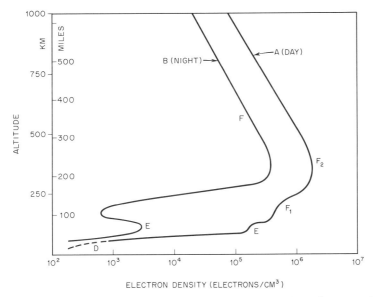

Fig. 8.11.   Electron density profiles during summer at middle latitudes around sunspot maximum (after W. B. Hanson)

ground-based, sounding rocket, and satellite measurements which are in satisfactory agreement. The electron densities vary with the solar conditions, e.g., time of day, season and solar activity, and with latitude; thus, the numbers must not be regarded as definitive, but they do provide some indication of how the electron density in the atmosphere varies with altitude. Because the D region is not too well defined, even in the daytime, the curve is shown as a broken line.

8.112. With regard to normal fluctuations in the ionosphere, some general observations can be made. At night, the D region disappears and so also does the distinction between the F_1 and F_2 regions; at the same time, there is a marked decrease in the maximum electron densities in the E and F regions, by a factor of at least 10 and possibly as much as 100. The daytime ionizations in the E and F_1 regions are larger in the summer than in the winter, but the reverse is often true for the F_2 region. Similar variations also occur with latitude, e.g., the electron densities in the E and F_1 regions are higher at the equator than near the poles, but in the F_2 region the ionization may increase with the latitude. There is a definite relationship between solar activity and the electron density of the ionosphere. At sunspot minimum, for example, the electron densities are lower by a factor of about 2 to 4 than the values shown in Fig. 8.11, especially in the F_1 and F_2 regions (or the F region at night). Furthermore, the maximum electron density in the F_2 layer at noon exhibits an 11-year cycle which closely parallels the sunspot cycle.

8.113. The electron density curves in Fig. 8.11 are given up to an altitude of 1000 kilometers (600 miles). Measurements have been made, however, particularly of positive ion densities, up to 5500 kilometers (3300 miles). Since at levels above about 100 kilometers (60 miles) or so there are few negative ions, the variation of positive ion density with altitude also represents the electron density profile. As will be seen in § 8.143, the electron density decreases steadily with increasing altitude, although there are changes in the slope of the curve as oxygen ions are replaced by helium ions and the latter in turn by protons as the dominant ions in the ionosphere. There is evidence, however, that, at a height of approximately 4200 kilometers (2600 miles), the ion (and electron) density begins to increase with altitude. The significance of this observation will be more clearly understood in connection with the discussion of the trapping of electrically charged particles by Earth's magnetic field (§ 8.303).

MINOR IONOSPHERIC DISTURBANCES

8.114. Some fairly regular variations in the electron density profile of the ionosphere result from atmospheric tides produced by the Sun and the Moon. The vertical motions of the atmosphere are accompanied by similar motions of the electrically conducting, ionized regions. Such movement of a conducting medium in Earth's magnetic field causes an electric current to flow by the familiar dynamo action (§ 8.104). The phenomenon is consequently referred to as the *atmospheric dynamo*. The flow of current in the magnetic field will, in turn, produce motion in the conducting (ionized) medium in which the current flows as a result of what has been called an *atmospheric motor*. It is believed that the E region of the ionosphere constitutes the dynamo and the F region the motor. Movements in one region due to tidal action will thus be accompanied by similar motion in the other. The general result is that there are regular, although minor, changes in the structure of the ionosphere.

8.115. In addition to the regular fluctuations, there are many of an erratic nature, some of them being of special interest. The phenomenon called *sporadic-E*, for example, is detected as a marked but irregular and rapidly varying increase in the electron density in the E region. It is most frequently observed in the daytime near the equator and at night at high (polar) latitudes; in these locations there is little seasonal variation in the occurrence of sporadic-E ionization. At middle latitudes, however, the increase in electron density is less marked, the time of day has little influence, but the fluctuations are definitely seasonal, occurring most frequently in the summer. Sounding measurements indicate that one or more fairly sharply defined layers of high electron density, extending over several hundred kilometers, are found within the E region when the sporadic-E phenomenon occurs. The variable character may be due to movement of the layers by high-altitude winds or by ion-electron combination leading to a decrease in electron density. The sporadic-E effect is not sufficiently well understood for a reasonable explanation to be offered for its origin and behavior.

8.116. Another type of disturbance that occurs mainly in the E region is caused by meteors. Most meteor trails are visible at an altitude of 80 to 115 kilometers (50 to 70 miles) and it is here that the associated ionization takes place (§ 7.94). The radar method for observing meteors depends on the reflection of the high-frequency waves by the trail of high electron density produced in this manner; under normal conditions radar waves pass through the E region without reflection. Advantage has been taken of the high electron densities in meteor trails to transmit information by reflected radio waves over long distances on Earth.

8.117. A turbulent situation in the ionosphere that, like sporadic-E, is accompanied by rapid changes of electron density in space and time, and may last from a few minutes to several hours, is known as *spread-F*. It was given this name because, in a method for the study of the ionosphere based on the reflection of radio waves, the oscillograph trace, called an ionogram (§ 8.167), obtained from the F region is then spread out, instead of being a single, well-defined curve. This indicates that several reflections, rather than one only, are occurring at different levels. Unlike the situation in sporadic-E, the areas of abnormal density apparently do not extend over great distances horizontally. At night, the ionospheric disturbances responsible for spread-F are located at altitudes around 225 kilometers (140 miles). It is then most common at latitudes greater than 40° and particularly near the poles. In the daytime, however, spread-F originates at lower altitudes and the areas of high ionization are smaller than at night; furthermore, it is observed more or less equally at all latitudes. The cause of this erratic ionospheric phenomenon is not known, but it is significant in connection with long-distance radio transmission at high latitudes.

8.118. One of the consequences of spread-F and similar ionospheric turbulence is the irregular fluctuations in the strength of radio signals from satellites; this effect is referred to as *scintillation*. A similar and presumably related phenomenon is the scintillation of signals received from distant cosmic radio sources (§ 12.217). Since the radio waves coming from a satellite or a distant source enter the ionosphere from above, they provide a means of studying the spread-F type of behavior above the F_2 (daytime) or F (night) maximum.

MAJOR IONOSPHERIC DISTURBANCES

8.119. The major disturbances in the ionosphere are generally divided into two categories, namely, sudden ionospheric disturbances and ionospheric storms; furthermore, two different types of the latter have been recognized. A *sudden ionospheric disturbance* (or *SID*) manifests itself within a few minutes of the appearance of some strong solar flares as a sharp fadeout of long-distance, short-wave, i.e., high-frequency, radio communication on the sunlit side of Earth. The short-wave fadeout effect is often abbreviated to *SWF*. This fadeout is caused by a marked increase in the electron density in the D region and the lower E region. As a result, high-frequency radio waves which would normally pass through the D region and be reflected at higher levels are now absorbed (§ 8.153). Long distance radio communication that depends upon reflection in the ionosphere is therefore suddenly and completely disrupted for a period of about 15 minutes to an hour or so.

8.120. Since the SID is experienced very soon after observation of the solar flare, the enhanced ionization in the lower levels of the ionosphere is undoubtedly caused by the greatly increased emission of electromagnetic radiation from the Sun. As is to be expected, the period of radio fadeout corresponds roughly to the duration of the more active phase of the flare plus the time required for the additional ionization to decay. The absence of any SID effect on the night side of Earth is largely due to this decay, which is a result of the rapid recombination of electrons and ions. It is the same factor that is responsible for the disappearance of the D region after sunset under normal circumstances (§ 8.133).

8.121. *Ionospheric storms* are characterized, as a general rule, by more gradual onset and longer duration than the SID. One type of storm which has been the subject of considerable interest in recent years is called *polar cap absorption* (or *PCA*). As the name implies, the PCA phenomenon is observed only in high latitudes, and is accompanied by a blackout of long-range radio communication in these regions by the absorption of high-frequency radio waves. The degree of absorption is conveniently determined by a simple, automatically operating device called a *riometer,* an acronym for relative ionospheric opacity meter. Its operation is based on the fact that the intensity of cosmic radio noise, in the frequency range of about 10 to 30 megacycles per second, is normally fairly constant. But when a PCA event occurs, the waves are partly or completely absorbed as they pass through the ionosphere and the signal strength on the ground is decreased; the relative extent of the decrease is thus a measure of the absorption. In the riometer, a selected frequency in the radio noise signal, generally about 20 to 30 megacycles per second, is continuously balanced automatically by a signal of the same frequency generated locally. The strength of the latter is recorded and the variation from its normal value provides a direct measure of the absorption in the ionosphere.

8.122. The PCA phenomenon is caused by an increase in the electron density in the lower ionosphere, at altitudes between about 55 and 90 kilometers (35 and 55 miles). It is associated with some solar flares, but may commence either fairly rapidly, within 20 minutes to an hour or so after the flare, or more gradually, about a day later. The electron density and radio wave absorption increase steadily for a few hours, level off at a maximum for several hours, and then decrease slowly over the course of days. There is a fairly regular diurnal variation, the effect being greater during the day than at night. The phenomena take place simultaneously in both Hemispheres, and such differences as exist can be ascribed to the different exposures to the Sun.

8.123. It is very probable that the increase in ionization associated with PCA is caused by high-energy protons expelled from the Sun at the time of certain solar flares. In fact, an increase in the intensity of high-energy protons has been observed in polar regions soon after a flare. If the flare is an isolated one, the protons are temporarily trapped by a distended region of the solar magnetic field.* Consequently, several hours may elapse before the protons reach Earth; because of the terrestrial magnetic field, they can enter the atmosphere only in the polar regions. On the other hand, if two flares occur within a day or so of one another, the high-energy protons from the second flare can travel much more rapidly along the Sun's magnetic field lines and may reach the vicinity of Earth within 20 minutes or less. In this manner it is possible to explain the different ways in which PCA events can start. The trapping of the protons and their gradual escape account for the duration of the PCA event for some days after the solar flare (or flares).

8.124. The second type of ionospheric storm is the *auroral storm;* it is also associated with increased electron density in the lower ionosphere and an increase in absorption of radio waves. Auroral storms occur at the times of special auroral activity, when there are also disturbances (geomagnetic storms) in Earth's magnetic field (§ 8.224). They commence, on the average, about 21 hours after some solar flares and may persist for a few days. Auroral storms, like the aurora themselves, are more intense at night. They differ in this respect from the storms causing the PCA phenomenon in which absorption is greater in the daytime. Although they are most frequent at high latitudes, the stronger of the auroral storms are accompanied by an enhanced radio wave absorption at lower latitudes.

* A fuller discussion of this whole subject is given in § 8.235 *et seq.,* in connection with the treatment of the interaction of solar and terrestrial magnetic fields.

8.125. The increase in ionization responsible for the auroral storms is apparently caused by solar protons. They are probably of lower energy than those which produce the PCA phenomenon. Many protons emitted from the Sun at the time of a flare travel with a velocity of about 1600 kilometers (1000 miles) per second and these would require about a day to reach Earth. This is approximately the elapsed time between observation of the solar flare and the onset of an auroral storm. Why such storms should be accompanied by more absorption at night than in daylight is not clear.

PRODUCTION AND REMOVAL OF ELECTRONS IN THE IONOSPHERE

8.126. The electron density in the ionosphere is the result of many interactions, varying with altitude, in which electrons are produced or removed. The ionization process, i.e., the removal of an electron (or electrons) from an atom or molecule of air, can result from the action of either electromagnetic radiation of short wavelength (photoionization), i.e., X-rays and ultraviolet rays, or of corpuscular radiation, i.e., mainly protons and electrons, from the Sun.

8.127. For each atom or molecular species, a particular amount of energy is required if ionization is to be possible; only if this energy is available can electrons be removed from the given species. Furthermore, the rate at which ionization takes place, even when the energy is available in the radiation, depends on the identity of the atom or molecule to be ionized, its particle density, and the nature and intensity of the radiation. It is evident, therefore, that mathematical relationships for the processes resulting in the formation of electrons in the atmosphere cannot be expressed in a simple manner. In addition, many of the basic constants (cross sections) which determine ionization rates are not known.

8.128. Somewhat the same situation holds for the loss of electrons. There are two main ways in which this can occur, namely, by recombination or by attachment. In *recombination,* a positive ion and an electron recombine to form a neutral atom or molecule (§ 6.88); thus, if the ion is represented by A^+, where A may be a molecule or atom, the recombination process is

$$A^+ + e^- \rightarrow A,$$

where e^- is an electron. This is actually the simplest type of recombination but other types, that are more complex and involve the intervention of another species, are possible.

8.129. A special form of recombination, which apparently occurs to some extent in the ionosphere, is *dissociative recombination;* an ionized molecule, e.g., BC^+, combines with an electron and, as a result, enough energy is released to dissociate the molecule into its constituent atoms; thus, the overall reaction is

$$BC^+ + e^- \rightarrow B^* + C^*,$$

the asterisks indicating that the products are (or may be) formed in excited (high-energy) states. If the number (or density) of positive ions is assumed to be equal to the number (or density) of electrons taking part in recombination reactions, the rate is proportional to the square of the electron density; it increases very rapidly, therefore, with increase in this density.

8.130. In the *attachment* process, an electron attaches itself to a neutral atom or molecule to form a negative ion, e.g.,

$$D + e^- \rightarrow D^-.$$

Although the extent of ionization is not changed by the attachment, since it merely replaces a negative electron by a negative ion, the effect of the ions on the reflection (and absorption) of radio waves is negligible. As far as the characteristic properties of the ionosphere are concerned, therefore, the effect is the same as in recombination. The rate of the attachment process depends on the electron density and on the density of the neutral species. Consequently, it is likely to predominate over recombination under such conditions that the atmospheric density, and hence the neutral particle density, is comparatively high and the electron density is moderately low.

8.131. An interpretation will now be given of some of the behavior of the several regions of the ionosphere in the light of the foregoing review of the essential electron formation and loss mechanisms. It should be noted, however, that the processes occurring in the ionosphere are very complex and, in any case, not completely established. The following discussion is intended, therefore, to provide only a general outline, with many details still remaining to be filled in.

THE D REGION

8.132. Most of the short-wavelength electromagnetic radiation from the Sun entering the atmosphere is absorbed as a result of photochemical reactions and photoionization involving the atoms and molecules in the upper layers of the ionosphere. Only the Lyman-α radiation (1216 Å) of atomic hydrogen can penetrate to the D region, at an altitude below 90 kilometers (55 miles). This particular radiation, however, cannot cause photoionization of any of the common atmospheric species. The only molecules that can be ionized are those of nitric oxide (NO); the NO^+ ions are known to be present in the E region, but they have not been detected at lower levels. It is of special interest to recall, therefore, that neutral nitric oxide has been identified by its ultraviolet spectrum in the dayglow (§ 8.102) at altitudes between 75 and 125 kilometers (47 and 80 miles). Ionization of nitric oxide by Lyman-α radiation can account for the electron density in the upper part of the D region, but at the lower levels, where this radiation does not penetrate, it is necessary to invoke the action of cosmic rays (§ 8.245). These rays and the products of their interaction with the atmosphere undoubtedly pass through the D region and cause some ionization, possibly of oxygen molecules.

8.133. Because of the relatively high density of neutral species in the D region and the low electron density, it is probable that removal of electrons occurs mainly by attachment to either oxygen or nitrogen molecules. In the daytime, the rate of formation of electrons by ionization of nitric oxide exceeds the loss by attachment. Moreover, sunlight, even in the visible region, has enough energy to remove the electrons from the negative ions produced by attachment. Hence, in daylight the loss of electrons, from both recombination and attachment, is small. The D region, therefore, acquires a modest density of electrons. But after sunset, electron formation ceases whereas removal by attachment becomes significant, and so the D region disappears at night. Next morning, solar radiation removes the electrons from the negative ions and the electron density is rapidly restored to its daytime value.

8.134. When a sudden ionospheric disturbance occurs, the electron density in the D region increases sharply. Because of the short time interval between a solar flare and the onset of the SID, it is apparent, as already seen, that electromagnetic radiation from the Sun must be responsible for the enhanced ionization. There is some evidence that the Lyman-α radiation of atomic hydrogen does not change very much at the time of a solar flare, but the intensity of X-rays (2 to 8 Å) is often greatly increased (§ 6.211); furthermore, sounding rocket measurements have shown that these X-rays can penetrate into the D region. In this event, the radiation may have sufficient energy to ionize nitrogen and oxygen molecules, but it is not known whether N_2^+ and O_2^+ ions are formed at low altitudes. The increase in electron density associated with ionospheric storms is due to high-energy protons, but the nature of the ions produced is in doubt.

The E Region

8.135. In the normal E region, photoionization is caused mainly by X-rays (10 to 100 Å) and perhaps also by short-wave ultraviolet radiation. It is to be expected that oxygen, nitrogen, and nitric oxide molecules and oxygen atoms will be ionized. Direct observations with sounding rockets have revealed that NO^+ is the dominant ion in the E region with about one third as many O_2^+ ions; there are some O^+ ions at the upper levels, but few, if any, N_2^+ ions.[*] The absence of ionized nitrogen molecules is attributed to the dissociative recombination process

$$N_2^+ + e^- \rightarrow N^* + N^*,$$

the nitrogen atoms subsequently recombining in a three-body collision to form neutral molecules. The nitric oxide ions are probably formed by the chemical reaction between nitrogen molecules and atomic oxygen ions, i.e.,

$$N_2 + O^+ \rightarrow NO^+ + N,$$

thus accounting, partly at least, for the low concentration of O^+ ions.

[*] The occurrence of N_2^+ ions has been reported in a region of sporadic-E during the night.

8.136. During the daytime, the electron density in the E region is considerably higher than in the D region because of the greater intensity of high-energy (short-wavelength) radiation available to produce photoionization. At night, electrons are lost, presumably as the result of various recombination and attachment processes; hence, the electron density decreases, but since it is considerably larger in the daytime, it never falls to zero as it does in the D region.

The F Region

8.137. Above the E region, the proportion of atomic oxygen in the atmosphere increases and at certain altitudes it is the main constituent (§ 8.38). Consequently, in the F_1 region, the proportion of NO^+ and O_2^+ ions decreases whereas that of O^+ ions increases steadily with altitude; again, the expected N_2^+ ions are presumably removed by dissociative recombination. In the upper F_1 region and in the F_2 region up to an altitude of 800 or 1000 kilometers (500 or 600 miles), i.e., well above the electron density maximum, O^+ is the predominant ion.

8.138. The formation of electrons in both F_1 and F_2 regions is chiefly due to photoionization of oxygen atoms by short-wavelength, ultraviolet rays in the range from about 100 to 900 Å. The most significant loss mechanism proposed for both regions involves *charge exchange* between atomic oxygen ions and molecular oxygen as the first step, i.e.,

$$O^+ + O_2 \rightarrow O + O_2^+,$$

followed by dissociative recombination,

$$O_2^+ + e^- \rightarrow O^* + O^*.$$

The small increase in electron density which distinguishes the F_1 and F_2 regions may be due to the decrease in the ratio of oxygen molecules to oxygen atoms with increasing altitude. It has been shown that, as a result, the rate of electron loss should decrease to some extent, and so the electron density will increase accordingly. The approximate boundary between the F_1 and F_2 regions, which disappears at night, is where a significant change occurs in the overall electron loss rate.

8.139. Calculations indicate that, because the atmospheric density decreases with increasing altitude but the solar radiation intensity increases, there should be a maximum rate of electron production between the altitudes of 100 and 200 kilometers (60 and 120 miles). Consequently, a decrease in the electron density would be expected somewhere near 200 kilometers; but the maximum of the F_2 region, above which the electron density decreases, is something like 100 kilometers (60 miles) higher. A possible explanation for this difference in altitude has been proposed along the following lines. Although the rate of electron production decreases above 200 kilometers, the loss rate decreases more rapidly; hence, the electron density continues to increase above the level at which the production rate is a maximum. Eventually, with increasing altitude, another loss mechanism becomes more and more effective, and then the electron density decreases. This second loss process has been attributed to the downward diffusion of the relatively heavy positive ions under the influence of gravity. As a result of electrostatic attraction, the ions tend to pull the lighter negative electrons down with them, thus decreasing the electron density at higher altitudes. From about 400 to 4000 kilometers (250 to 2500 miles), the variation of electron density with altitude is apparently determined only by diffusive separation of the positive ions.

8.140. Although the properties of the ionosphere are dependent on the electron densities, it is of interest to note that the ions (and electrons) are only a minor atmospheric constituent, at least up to altitudes of several hundred kilometers. The maximum electron density, which is attained in the F_2 region, is about 2×10^6 electrons per cubic centimeter, and the density of positive ions is approximately the same. The total particle density at the level of the F_2 maximum is roughly 10^9 atoms (and molecules) per cubic centimeter. Hence, at this altitude, about 300 kilometers (180 miles), only two atoms in a thousand, i.e., 0.2 percent, are ionized. At lower levels, where the electron density is less but the particle density is greater, the degree of ionization is still lower. At higher altitudes, however, the proportion of ions increases and at several thousand kilometers from Earth there are probably few neutral atoms (cf. § 8.41).

Helium Ions and Protons

8.141. The ionospheric electron density profile shows that at a height of about 1000 kilometers (600 miles) or so, there is a change in the slope of the curve; this change is of considerable significance. The distribution of (positive) ion density with altitude, as determined by gravity in the region where diffusive separation occurs, is given by a modification of equation (8.1) as

$$\ln \frac{n_1}{n_2} = -\frac{m_i g_0}{k(T_i + T_e)} (h'_1 - h'_2), \tag{8.5}$$

where n_1 and n_2 are now the *ion* densities at the geopotential altitudes h'_1 and h'_2, respectively; m_i is the mass of the ion, and T_i and T_e are the ion and electron temperatures, respectively. Since the temperatures are merely an indication of particle kinetic energies, they can be, and frequently are, different for the ions and electrons (§ 8.146). Basically, equation (8.5) represents the distribution of positive ion densities, but the numbers of positive ions and electrons are essentially identical at the higher altitudes, at least in the daytime; consequently, the equation may be taken as expressing the variation of electron density with altitude.

8.142. Electron density profiles are invariably plotted with the ordinates (altitudes) on a linear scale and abscissae (densities) on a logarithmic scale. Consequently, according to the arguments in § 8.46, the (negative) slope of the plot of geopotential altitude against the logarithm of the electron density is equal to $2.30 \, k(T_i + T_e)/m_i g_0$. If the sum of the temperatures is assumed to be constant within a limited altitude range, it follows that this slope is inversely proportional to the mass of the ionic species. A geopotential scale height for ions (or electrons) can be defined, by analogy with equation (8.2), as

$$H_i = \frac{k(T_i + T_e)}{m_i g_0}, \tag{8.6}$$

and the slope of the geopotential electron density profile is $2.30 \, H_i$.

8.143. A plot of observed electron densities, at levels above 450 kilometers (280 miles), as a function of geopotential (and actual) altitude is shown in Fig. 8.12. There is clearly a marked increase in the (negative) slope of the

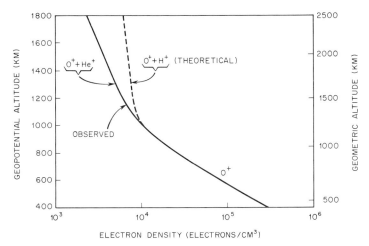

FIG. 8.12.   Electron density as a function of geopotential and geometric altitudes above 450 kilometers (after S. J. Bauer and J. E. Jackson)

curve at about 1000 kilometers (600 miles), indicating that the mass of the predominant ions decreases at about this level. Below 1000 kilometers (600 miles), the ions present are mainly O+ (mass 16 units) and the change of slope shows that at higher altitudes helium (He+) ions (mass 4 units) become increasingly important. The dotted curve is the expected form of the electron density profile if hydrogen ions, i.e., protons (H+), had been formed at 1000 kilometers geopotential altitude. It is evident, therefore, that the oxygen ion layer is followed by one of helium ions and not of protons, as was at one time assumed. This conclusion is in agreement with the accepted views on the distribution of neutral atoms in the upper atmosphere (§ 8.39). At still higher levels, the helium ions give way to protons, i.e., in the protonosphere, which extend indefinitely into interplanetary space.

8.144. The altitude at which helium ions begin to predominate over oxygen ions increases with the temperature of the atmosphere. At the same time, the boundary between the helium ion layer and the protonosphere increases more rapidly. Consequently, when the air temperature is low, as it is at night, the helium ion layer is fairly shallow, perhaps a few hundred kilometers, but in the daytime, when the atmospheric temperature is higher, it may be over 1600 kilometers (1000 miles) deep. Thus, the base of the protonosphere may range in altitude from about 1000 kilometers (600 miles) at night to as high as 3200 kilometers (2000 miles) in the daytime (Fig. 8.13).

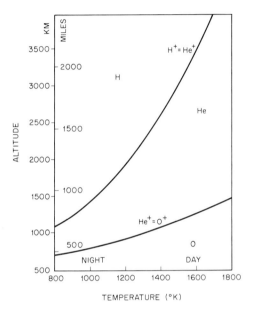

FIG. 8.13.   Transition altitudes ($O^+ = He^+$ and $He^+ = H^+$) as functions of temperature; the predominant species in the regions between are indicated (after S. J. Bauer)

TEMPERATURES IN THE IONOSPHERE

8.145. Another property of the atmosphere that can be calculated from the electron (or ion) density profile is the kinetic temperature at high altitude. If the ions are assumed to be in kinetic equilibrium with electrons and neutral particles, the temperature, T, of the latter can be derived by replacing $T_e + T_i$ in equations (8.5) and (8.6) by $2T$. It follows, therefore, that the (negative) slope of the geopotential electron density profile is equal to 4.60 $kT/m_i g_0$, and so the temperature of the neutral particles can be determined from the slope. The principle is exactly the same as that described in § 8.46. Alternatively, if $2T$ is substituted for $T_i + T_e$ in equation (8.6), the result is

$$T = \frac{H_i m_i g_0}{2k},$$

where H_i is the scale height derived from the slope of the curve of geopotential altitude against the logarithm of the electron density, e.g., from Fig. 8.12.

8.146. The atmospheric temperatures determined from electron density profiles at altitudes below about 150 kilometers (90 miles) and above some 400 kilometers (250 miles) are in fair agreement with the values calculated from observations of satellite drag, especially at low and medium latitudes. Furthermore, they are approximately equal to the electron temperatures that have been determined directly by measurements with instruments carried on sounding rockets and satellites, e.g., Explorer VIII and Ariel.* Between the altitudes mentioned above, however, i.e., in the F_1 and F_2 regions, the electron temperatures are considerably higher than the neutral gas temperatures derived from satellite drag data. At an altitude of about 200 kilometers (125 miles), for example, a difference of nearly 900°C (1600°F) was reported at mid-latitudes under quiet Sun conditions. At levels above 400 kilometers (250 miles), the difference between electron and neutral temperatures decreases considerably, but it still appears to be significant at higher altitudes (Fig. 8.14).

8.147. Electron temperatures show a diurnal variation, somewhat similar to that exhibited by neutral gas temperatures in Fig. 8.7, except that the maximum is more pronounced and occurs earlier in the day, near sunrise. There is also a marked dependence on latitude; thus, near the equator, the differences between electron and neutral temperatures are not great, but at middle and higher latitudes, approaching the poles, the differences may approach 1000°C (1800°F). The sunspot and related solar activities also appear to have some effect on the difference between electron and neutral gas temperatures.

8.148. A knowledge of the relationship between electron and gas temperatures is required for a complete understanding of the processes taking place in the ionosphere. When ionization occurs, as a consequence of the absorption of X-ray, ultraviolet, and corpuscular radiation by oxygen atoms (or other species), most of the available energy is acquired by the electrons. This is largely in the form of kinetic energy, and so the electrons initially have a high temperature (cf. § 8.31). In collisions with ions, with neutral atoms, and with other electrons, the high-temperature electrons share their excess energy with other particles in the ionosphere. Hence, if a condition of thermal equilibrium were attained, the electrons, positive ions, and neutral gas atoms would have the same temperature. Because the masses of the ions and neutral atoms are essentially equal, it is expected that these particles will have the same temperature (and energy) whether thermal equilibrium is established or not.

8.149. The differences between electron and gas temperatures reported above indicate that the F_1 and F_2 regions, in particular, of the ionosphere are not in thermal equilibrium. Calculations show that, at these altitudes in low and

---

* Electron temperatures are generally obtained by means of a form of Langmuir probe with which electron current is measured as a function of the voltage applied between the probe and the wall of the carrier vehicle.

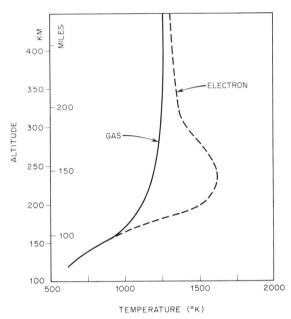

F<small>IG.</small> 8.14.   Atmospheric gas and electron temperatures at various altitudes (after R. E. Bourdeau)

middle latitudes, the discrepancy can be accounted for fairly well on the basis of the ionization of oxygen atoms by ultraviolet radiation of short wavelength. It appears, however, that this is not the only way in which electrons are produced. Corpuscular radiation is evidently involved, to some extent at least, at high altitudes, e.g., above about 450 kilometers (280 miles). There are indications that the electron temperature exceeds the gas temperature even at night, when there is no solar radiation but some form of corpuscular radiation might be present to cause ionization. Furthermore, the very high electron temperatures observed at high latitudes cannot be accounted for by the absorption of solar radiation alone. It has been suggested that electrons of moderately high energy, which have been trapped in the corpuscular radiation belts that surround Earth (§ 8.294), enter the atmosphere at the higher latitudes and thus increase the electron temperature. It will be seen in due course that only at high latitudes is the significant escape of such particles possible.

INTERACTION OF RADIO-FREQUENCY WAVES WITH THE IONOSPHERE

A<small>TTENUATION OF</small> R<small>ADIO-FREQUENCY</small> W<small>AVES</small>

8.150. An ionized region in the upper atmosphere can affect the transmission of radio (or radar) waves in at least two ways. First, under suitable conditions, the charged particles can remove energy from an electromagnetic wave and thus attenuate the signal; in the limiting case, the energy of the wave can be absorbed completely. Second, a wave traveling from one place to another in which the electron density is different will undergo a change in its direction of propagation. In certain circumstances, to be explained shortly, the radio wave can be reflected back, as in the various situations considered earlier. These two effects of an ionized medium on electromagnetic, radio-frequency waves will be examined in turn.

8.151. When a radio-frequency wave enters the ionosphere and encounters a significant concentration of free electrons, some of the wave energy is transferred to the electrons which are thus set into oscillation at the frequency of the electromagnetic wave. The electrons can lose some of this energy as a result of collisions with neutral particles (atoms or molecules) in the air. But, if there are no such collisions, the oscillating electrons will reradiate electromagnetic waves at the same frequency. In this event, the energy of the original radio-frequency signal is restored without loss.

8.152. If, however, the air density is appreciable, e.g., more than one ten-thousandth (10^{-4}) of the sea-level value, as it is at altitudes below 65 kilometers (40 miles), the atmosphere contains such a relatively large concentration of neutral particles that collisions with electrons will occur at a significant rate. In these collisions much of the oscillation energy the electrons have acquired from the radio wave is transferred to the neutral molecules and appears as random kinetic (heat) energy. Less energy is therefore available for re-radiation by the electrons as electromagnetic waves; consequently, the radio-frequency signal is attenuated. If the rate of collisions between electrons and neutral particles is sufficiently large, essentially all of the energy of the radio-frequency wave is transferred to the atmospheric molecules in the manner described; the signal is then said to be absorbed completely.

8.153. For marked loss of signal strength to occur in the atmosphere, there must obviously be a sufficient concentration (or density) of both electrons and neutral particles—the electrons to take up the energy from the electromagnetic waves and the neutral particles to remove the energy from the oscillating electrons in collisions. This situation arises in the D region of the ionosphere. The density of neutral molecules is about 10^{-4} to 10^{-5} of that at sea level and the electron density, while not as large as in the E and F regions, is sufficient to permit considerable interaction with radio-frequency waves. Consequently, appreciable attenuation of radio signals can occur in the D region. Other conditions being equal, the attenuation is greater the lower the frequency, i.e., the longer the wavelength, of the electromagnetic wave. In the E and F regions, the atmospheric density is much less than in the D region, and although the electron density is greater the number of collisions is decreased. As a general rule, therefore, radio waves suffer little loss of signal strength in passing through the higher levels of the ionosphere. Most of the attenuation that does occur takes place at the lower altitudes, i.e., in the D region.

8.154. The foregoing discussion has been based on the interaction between electromagnetic waves and electrons. Actually, both positive and negative ions can, in principle, also be set into oscillation by the radio-frequency waves and so can take up energy from the latter. This energy may then be transferred by collisions to neutral particles. Because of their much greater mass,* however, the ions do not oscillate as readily as do electrons and are thus much less effective in removing energy from the radio-frequency wave. Consequently, the attenuation due to the ions in the ionosphere can be ignored.

REFLECTION OF RADIO-FREQUENCY WAVES

8.155. The second effect of the ionized region of the atmosphere on radio waves, namely the change in direction of propagation, arises from the effect of free electrons on the velocity of an electromagnetic wave. For radio-frequency waves traveling in a vertical direction through the ionized medium, the phase velocity, u,† is related to the velocity of light in a vacuum, c, by

$$u = c\left(\sqrt{1 - \frac{ne^2}{\pi m f^2}}\right)^{-1}, \tag{8.7}$$

where n is the number of electrons per cubic centimeter, e is the magnitude of the charge carried by an electron, and m is its mass; f is the frequency of the electromagnetic waves. At a given frequency, the phase velocity thus increases with the electron density of the medium. Equation (8.7) is a form of the *Appleton-Hartree equation*, which was derived in different ways by E. V. Appleton (**1927**) and D. R. Hartree (**1928**). By inserting the known values of e, m, and π, and expressing the wave frequency, f, in megacycles per second, equation (8.7) becomes

$$u = c\left(\sqrt{1 - \frac{8.1 \times 10^{-5} n}{f^2}}\right)^{-1}. \tag{8.8}$$

8.156. The phase refractive index, r, of the ionized medium for radio-frequency waves is equal to c/u; hence,

$$r = \sqrt{1 - \frac{ne^2}{\pi m f^2}}$$

$$= \sqrt{1 - \frac{8.1 \times 10^{-5} n}{f^2}}. \tag{8.9}$$

It is evident from this equation that, for waves of a given frequency, the re-

---

* The mass of the lightest ions, namely the hydrogen (H^+ or H^-) ions, is some 1840 times as great as that of an electron.

† The phase velocity, i.e., the velocity with which planes of constant phase are propagated in a given medium, is equal to the product of the frequency and the wavelength in that medium.

fractive index decreases in passing from a medium of lower to one of higher electron density. Hence, a beam of radio waves will be refracted in the manner shown in Fig. 8.15, i.e., the angle with the vertical increases when the electron density increases. The same conclusion can be drawn from the fact that the

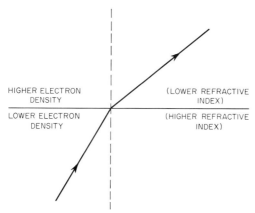

HIGHER ELECTRON
DENSITY

(LOWER REFRACTIVE
INDEX)

LOWER ELECTRON
DENSITY

(HIGHER REFRACTIVE
INDEX)

FIG. 8.15.   Refraction of radio waves by increase in electron density of medium

phase velocity of the waves increases with the electron density, as seen above. For a given electron density, a high-frequency wave will suffer less refraction than one of lower frequency since r is larger in the latter case. It should be mentioned that equations (8.7) and (8.9) have been derived from electromagnetic theory on the assumption that the electrons undergo essentially no collisions and that there is no magnetic field present. Neither of these conditions is satisfied in practice, but the general conclusions to be drawn from the equations are not greatly affected.

8.157. Consider the situation in which an electromagnetic wave of definite frequency, f, enters the ionosphere in which the electron density increases with altitude. At first, n in equation (8.8) is small, and the velocity with which the wave travels is not very different from that of light in a vacuum. But, as n increases with altitude, with f remaining constant, it is seen that the phase velocity, u, must increase while the refractive index decreases. Eventually, when the quantity under the square-root sign in equation (8.9) becomes zero, the refractive index is zero, i.e., when

$$1 - \frac{8.1 \times 10^{-5}n_c}{f^2} = 0$$

or

$$n_c = \frac{f^2}{8.1 \times 10^{-5}} = 1.2 \times 10^4 f^2. \tag{8.10}$$

At this value of the electron density, represented by n_c and called the *critical electron density*, the radio-frequency wave can no longer be propagated in the forward (upward) direction and so it is reflected back to Earth.

8.158. In the foregoing, the frequency has been taken as fixed and the corresponding critical electron density calculated. The procedure can be reversed and the *critical* (or *penetration*) *frequency* derived; this is the highest frequency that can be reflected by a given electron density or the lowest frequency that will pass through.* The critical frequency, f_c, is obtained from equation (8.10) as

$$f_c = 9 \times 10^{-3}\sqrt{n}, \tag{8.11}$$

for an electron density of n. In the D region, for example, the largest value of n is about 10^3 electrons per cubic centimeter; the highest frequency that can be reflected is thus about 0.28 megacycle (or 280 kilocycles) per second. The maximum electron density in the F_2 region, on the other hand, is roughly 2×10^6 and so radio waves with frequencies up to 13 megacycles per second are reflected. Thus, waves of sufficiently high frequency will pass through the D region but may be reflected in the higher regions where the electron densities are greater.

REFLECTION OF RADIO WAVES BY THE IONOSPHERE

8.159. In experimental work on the ionosphere, e.g., in the determination of the electron density at different altitudes, the radio waves are generally transmitted in a vertical (or almost vertical) direction, and then equations (8.10) and (8.11) give the appropriate critical density and critical frequency, respectively. For communication purposes over long distances, however, the radio signal must have a relatively large angle with the vertical, i.e., a large angle of incidence, in order for the reflection from the ionosphere to be received at a considerable distance away. In these circumstances the equations given above require modification.

8.160. The reason is that, in passing through a region of gradually increasing electron density, such as the ionosphere, the radio wave is not reflected sharply as light is reflected by a mirror; instead, it is continuously refracted or bent away from the vertical, and the actual path is somewhat like that represented in Fig. 8.16. The refractive index is thus decreased to zero at a lower electron density than would be the case for vertical incidence. If i is the angle of incidence of the transmitted beam, equation (8.10) now takes the form

$$n_c = 1.2 \times 10^4 f^2 \cos^2 i. \tag{8.12}$$

Except when i is zero, i.e., for vertical incidence, $\cos^2 i$ is always less than unity; hence, n_c in equation (8.12) is less than for vertical transmission. The corresponding form of equation (8.11) is

$$f_c = \frac{9 \times 10^{-3}}{\cos i} \sqrt{n}, \tag{8.13}$$

* In plasma physics, the critical frequency is called the *plasma frequency*.

so that the critical frequency is increased when i is less than 90 deg. If i is 60 deg, for example, cos i is 0.5 and the critical frequency for reflection by the F_2 region is increased from 13 to 26 megacycles per second.

8.161. Unless it is absorbed, a radio wave of given frequency beamed upward will continue to travel through the ionosphere until it reaches a level in which

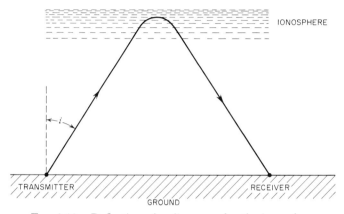

FIG. 8.16.   Reflection of radio waves by the ionosphere.

the electron density has the critical value, as given by equation (8.12). Then, the wave will be turned back. The higher the frequency, the greater is the electron density at which reflection occurs. As seen in Fig. 8.11, the electron density increases more or less continuously up to an altitude of roughly 300 kilometers (180 miles), after which it decreases. Consequently, the higher the frequency of the radio waves, the farther the distance they can travel into the ionosphere, up to a height of 300 kilometers or so, before undergoing reflection. The limiting frequencies for which reflection is possible at any particular level is given by equation (8.13).

RADIO COMMUNICATION AND THE IONOSPHERE

8.162. For long-range radio communication, where it is desired to take advantage of the reflection by the ionosphere, the so-called high-frequency (HF) band is used; the frequencies are in the range from 3 to 30 megacycles per second and the corresponding wavelength range is from 100 to 10 meters. Waves of lower frequency (longer wavelength) are too greatly attenuated in passing through the D region, whereas those of higher frequency (shorter wavelength) will not be reflected because the maximum critical frequency, i.e., for the F_2 region, is exceeded.

8.163. Because the electron density distribution in the ionosphere is likely to undergo changes, the altitude at which the incident wave is turned back will also vary. If the angle of incidence of the radio beam remains unchanged, there will consequently be a change in the location at which the reflected signal is received on Earth, as will be evident from Fig. 8.16. Radio communication between two given points will then be disrupted. This situation can be overcome in two ways: by changing either the angle of incidence of the beam or the frequency of the transmitted waves. In both cases, the altitude at which reflection occurs will be altered. Since the adjustment of the frequency is simpler, this is the procedure generally adopted. A special type of disturbance occurs at the time of a magnetic storm; there is then a great increase in the electron density in the D region, so that even high-frequency waves are absorbed.

8.164. For transmissions requiring a considerable bandwidth (§ 4.155), e.g., television, frequency-modulated radio, and multichannel telephone communication, it is necessary to employ frequencies above the HF band, e.g., in the range from 30 to 300 megacycles per second in the very-high-frequency (VHF) band. Under normal conditions, these waves are not reflected in the ionosphere, because the electron densities are not high enough. It is well known, however, that occasionally "freak" reception of television signals can occur from transmitting stations at a considerable distance. This effect arises from the *ionospheric scattering* phenomenon.

8.165. The distribution of electrons in the ionosphere, even within a fairly narrow altitude range, is not uniform. Quite frequently, small regions exist in which the electron density is larger than in the surrounding atmosphere. Such regions of higher than average electron density can scatter electromagnetic waves of very high frequency, much as particles of dust, moisture, etc., and even molecules cause scattering of a beam of light. If the dimensions of the high-density regions are greater than the wavelength of the radio waves, there will be a tendency for preferred scattering to take place in the forward direction, i.e., in the direction in which the waves are traveling. The result is that the range of reception of the transmitted signal is increased. Although exceptional television reception caused by ionospheric scattering is of little value, practical communications systems have been developed for transmission of VHF radio waves over distances of 1000 to 2000 kilometers (600 to 1200 miles). The chief drawback is the somewhat erratic behavior arising from fluctuations in the nonuniformities in the ionospheric electron densities.

8.166. In the cases considered above, it has been the purpose to take advantage of the reflecting (or scattering) properties of the ionosphere. A completely opposite situation arises in connection with the transmission of radio beacon signals or in telemetering information from a satellite or space probe to Earth. The problem is now to avoid reflection, so that the signal passes downward through the ionosphere and reaches the receiving station on the ground. It is then necessary to use waves of very high frequency, i.e., above the critical frequency of the F_2 layer, so that they are not reflected back into space from the ionosphere. For this reason, frequencies of over 100 megacycles per second are almost invariably employed for tracking and telemetry.

DETERMINATION OF ELECTRON DENSITIES

THE IONOGRAM

8.167. The procedure commonly used for determining electron densities from ground stations is based on the time-delay (or radio echo) technique described in § 8.106. The instrument employed for the purpose is called a vertical incidence *ionospheric sounder* or *ionosonde*.* A radio pulse of known frequency is transmitted vertically upward and the time elapsing before the receipt of the return (echo) signal is indicated by an oscillograph attached to a receiver tuned to the same frequency. This pulse is followed in rapid succession by others of higher and higher frequency, covering a range from about 1 to 20 megacycles per second. A device in which the frequency of both transmitter and receiver is steadily changed in this manner is known as a *sweep-frequency sounder*. The resulting *ionogram*, obtained by recording the output of the oscillograph on a moving photographic film, is a series of curves, as in Fig. 8.17, giving the delay time (ordinate) as a function of the frequency (abscissa) of the incident radio wave.

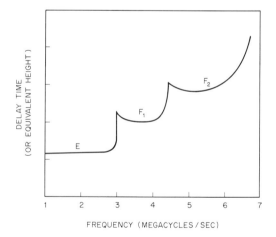

FIG. 8.17.   Typical ionogram

8.168. If the signal traveled all the way with the velocity of light, as it does in the nonionized region below the ionosphere, the delay time would be a direct measure of the height at which reflection occurred at each frequency. But since the radio pulses are slowed down in the ionized region, the average

---

* There are some 150 ground-based ionospheric sounding stations over the globe for determining the maximum usable radio frequencies for long-range communication.

velocity is less than that of light in a vacuum.* The actual height of the reflection layer is thus somewhat less than the equivalent height derived directly
from the observed time delay. From the frequency of the transmitted (and
reflected) pulse, the electron density at which reflection takes place is determined from equation (8.10) and the corresponding equivalent height can
be corrected to give the true height for this density. It is thus possible to obtain
the electron density profile of the ionosphere, such as is shown in Fig. 8.11.

8.169. Often ionograms show, in addition to the curves depicted in Fig. 8.17,
fainter curves at about twice the equivalent height for each frequency. The
fainter curves are the result of a ground echo effect; when it reaches Earth's
surface, the initial reflected radio wave is reflected back by the ground and
then suffers a second reflection from the ionosphere. The total delay time, and
hence the effective equivalent height, is thus twice the true value. Another set
of faint curves is occasionally seen at the proper equivalent height but displaced
toward higher frequencies. This effect is caused by Earth's magnetic field which
makes the ionosphere birefringent, i.e., doubly refracting (§ 6.135), to radio
waves; the motion of the electrons in the magnetic field produces an apparent
change in frequency. From the frequency shift, the strength of the terrestrial
magnetic field at the corresponding altitude can be calculated.

8.170. The chief drawback to the ground-based ionosonde method for investigating the ionosphere is that it is not possible to probe beyond the altitude
of maximum electron density in any region. For the incident radio wave to
penetrate into a region of lower density lying above a maximum, it must have
a smaller frequency than corresponds to the maximum density. But waves of
such a frequency will be reflected at a lower level, i.e., below the maximum.
They obviously cannot reach to a higher altitude, above that at which the
maximum electron density occurs.

8.171. Fortunately, this limitation has not been too serious for the D, E, and
F_1 regions, because the decreases in electron density following the maxima, if
they occur at all, are very slight. For the F_2 region, however, there is a very
definite maximum and the sounding method can provide no information concerning the decrease in electron density above the level of this maximum. From
the standpoint of radio transmission, this is of little concern because the
maximum of the F_2 region, at about 300 kilometers (180 miles), is the highest
altitude at which reflection can take place. However, the electron densities at
greater heights are important in connection with studies of the atmosphere.

INCOHERENT BACKSCATTERING

8.172. A modified, ground-based sounding technique, the extensive development of which has awaited the construction of suitable antennas, makes it
possible to probe the ionosphere both below and above the maximum of the F_2

---

* The pulses travel with the *group velocity* which decreases with increase in electron
density.

region. If a short but strong radio pulse is directed upward from the ground, the electromagnetic waves suffer weak incoherent scattering by individual electrons in the ionosphere.* The result is that a small amount of the radio energy is scattered back to the ground; the weak signal received is called an *incoherent backscatter echo.* The strength of the echo signal is proportional to the electron density, and the elapsed time between transmission of the pulse and receipt of the echo signal on the ground is a measure of the altitude at which the scattering occurred. The oscillograph trace on the receiver shows the backscattered echo signal strength as a function of delay time, and from this can be derived the variation of electron density with altitude.

8.173. By using radio (or radar) waves of high frequency, i.e., well over 30 megacycles per second, the pulse can penetrate the F_2-region maximum and scattering can occur from all altitudes up to great heights. In fact, the only limitations are the energy of the transmitted pulse and the sensitivity of the receiver; the strength of the backscattered signal decreases with altitude of the scattering electrons.

8.174. The radar telescope at the Arecibo Ionospheric Observatory, Puerto Rico, completed by the Advanced Research Projects Agency of the U.S. Department of Defense during 1963, consists of a bowl-shaped antenna, 300 meters (1000 feet) in diameter, located in a natural depression between surrounding hills. It was because of this topographical situation and its location near the equator that the particular site was chosen. The transmitter has a peak power of 2.5 megawatts for pulses and operates at a frequency of 430 megacycles per second; observations will also be made at 40 megacycles per second, and perhaps at a much higher frequency, to determine what effect, if any, the radio-frequency has on the results. A different system is being used by the U.S. National Bureau of Standards at a station in Jicamarca, Peru. The peak power of the transmitter is 6 to 8 megawatts and the frequency 50 megacycles per second. The receiving antenna is a linear array of dipoles covering an area of about 20 acres.

Whistling Atmospherics

8.175. An unusual procedure for determining electron densities at distances of thousands of miles above Earth, from observations at a ground station, is based on a curious atmospheric phenomenon. It has been known since about 1918 that when a radio receiver, attached to a long antenna, is tuned to very low frequencies there is occasionally heard a whistling sound, starting at a high pitch and falling steadily for a second or so, at first rapidly and then more slowly. The whistle is sometimes preceded by a loud click, and may be followed by further whistles becoming successively fainter and of somewhat longer duration.

---

* The adjective "incoherent" as applied to scattering means that each scattering particle acts independently of the others and the various scattered waves do not, in general, interfere with (or enhance) each other.

8.176. The explanation of these *whistling atmospherics,* commonly called *whistlers,* is that the phenomenon originates in lightning which may have occurred thousands of miles away. The discharge of lightning is accompanied by a wide range of electromagnetic radiations varying in frequency from high to extremely low. In some instances, much of the energy, however, is in the low range of about 1000 to 10,000 cycles per second, the same as the frequencies of audible sound waves. The radiations cannot be heard directly because they are electromagnetic vibrations, but they are readily convertible into sound, i.e., air vibrations, by means of a conventional audio-frequency amplifier and loud speaker. As the electromagnetic disturbance from the lightning discharge moves outward, some of the waves reach the ionosphere and there the low-frequency oscillations tend to follow the lines of Earth's magnetic field. In an ionized medium containing free electrons, the waves of higher frequency travel faster along the field lines than do those of lower frequency.* Consequently, the arrival of the radiations at a distant point will be spread out (or dispersed) over a short period of time.

8.177. Suppose lightning is discharged at the point on the globe indicated by *A* in Fig. 8.18, I; an antenna, amplifier, and loud speaker are located at *B,* at

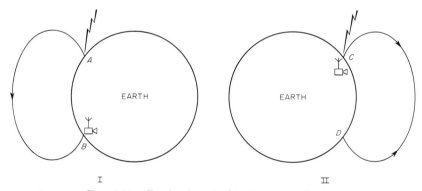

FIG. 8.18.   Production of whistling atmospherics.

the other end of a line of force of Earth's magnetic field. Since *A* and *B* are in different hemispheres, they may be several thousand miles apart. The lower frequency radio waves travel from *A* to *B* along the line of force, as described above, but are dispersed in time. At *B,* the audio-amplifier converts the electromagnetic oscillations into sound waves of the same frequency, and so what is heard is a whistle, starting at a high sonic frequency and falling in pitch during the course of a second or so. When the electromagnetic signal reaches *B,* it may be reflected back to *A* along the line of force, and then again to *B;* a second, fainter whistle is then heard. The second (or echo) whistle is of longer

* The appropriate velocity is the group velocity (§ 8.168, footnote) which, unlike the phase velocity, increases with increasing wave frequency.

duration than the first because the frequencies have suffered additional dispersion in traveling from B to A and back to B.

8.178. If the lightning discharge takes place close to the receiver, e.g., at the location C in Fig. 8.18, II, the first sound heard is a loud click, the familiar atmospheric "static," representing a mixture of all the frequencies produced by the nearby discharge. The waves then follow the line of force of Earth's magnetic field to D and back to C; by this time, dispersion has occurred twice and the sound is heard as a whistle of decreasing pitch lasting twice as long as the first whistle heard at B from a discharge at A (Fig. 8.18, I). Successive whistles of decreasing intensity and increasing duration may follow as the electromagnetic waves are reflected back and forth between the points C and D.

8.179. From the times of arrival of successive whistles or the elapsed time between the click and arrival of the whistle, the *transit time*, t_f, of a whistler component of frequency f can be determined. The quantity $t_f\sqrt{f}$ is called the *dispersion* of the whistler, and theoretical treatment shows that it can be related approximately to the electron density at the maximum height of the line of force joining the points A and B or C and D, in the respective cases. Estimates have been made in this manner of electron densities at altitudes up to about 30,000 kilometers (19,000 miles). The results obtained by different investigators are not in complete agreement, indicating that there are still some unresolved problems.

8.180. The foregoing description has referred to whistlers of the simplest type, but there are others of varying complexity. One of these of special interest is the so-called *nose whistler*, in which the normal descending tones of the simple whistler are followed by rising tones; the minimum frequency is termed the *nose frequency*.* This frequency can be determined and timed quite accurately, so that it is particularly useful for the evaluation of electron densities.

MEASUREMENTS FROM SPACE: TOPSIDE SOUNDER

8.181. Both sounding rockets and satellites have been employed in recent years to study the electron density and other properties of the ionosphere. Sounding rockets are useful for determining electron profiles at a given location, from low altitudes up to heights above the F_2-layer maximum. Satellites, on the other hand, provide information on the nature of the ionosphere in different areas over Earth's surface. Thus, the two systems have separate spheres of application, each providing data to supplement that from the other. One advantage of the sounding rocket over the ionosonde method for obtaining electron density profiles is that, in the former case, the observations can be correlated with the actual heights of the rocket as measured from the ground. As seen in § 8.168, the ionogram gives only equivalent heights which require appropriate correction.

---

* An oscillographic trace showing the frequency as a function of time is shaped like a nose, with the minimum frequency at its tip.

8.182. An obvious means of probing the ionosphere above the altitude of the maximum electron density in the F_2 region is to place an ionosonde on a rocket or satellite. The combination of transmitter and receiver to be used in this manner is called a *topside sounder*. Because the altitude of a sounding rocket varies with time, the topside sounding technique is more appropriate for use on satellites. It is then possible to make a continuous study of the ionosphere from a known high altitude over large areas of Earth. A circular (or near-circular) orbit is desirable, since the altitude would then be the same at all locations.

DISPERSIVE DOPPLER EFFECT

8.183. The majority of ionospheric electron density measurements from space have been made by utilizing what is known as the *dispersive* (or *differential*) *Doppler effect* with continuous wave, high-frequency radio transmission. Suppose radio waves are sent out from a transmitter on a rocket at such a frequency that the refractive index of the medium, as given by equation (8.9), is considerably less than unity but still larger than zero. The transmission will penetrate the ionosphere and reach the ground; but its phase velocity will be increased because of the low value of the refractive index of the ionosphere for the transmitted signal.

8.184. Since the sounding rocket is traveling away from Earth, the radio waves will be subjected to the Doppler effect and the frequency of the signal received on the ground will be less than that at the transmitter. The appropriate form of equation (4.2) for the Doppler shift is now $f_0(v_r/u)$, where f_0 is the frequency of the transmitted signal, v_r is the radial velocity of the rocket, and u is the phase velocity of the radio waves in the medium. Since the phase velocity is increased in the ionosphere, the observed Doppler frequency shift will be less than the normal value, i.e., with no free electrons in the path of the waves. The difference between the normal and the actual shift is the dispersive (or differential) Doppler frequency shift which can be related to the electron density in the vicinity of the sounding rocket.

8.185. In order to determine the normal Doppler shift, another radio-frequency wave is transmitted simultaneously at a much higher frequency which is harmonically related to, i.e., it is a multiple of, the lower frequency. For example, one frequency may be 7.75 megacycles per second and the other six times as large, i.e., 46.5 megacycles per second. At the higher frequency, the refractive index is close to unity and the phase velocity of the radio waves is not appreciably affected by the ionosphere. The observed Doppler shift for this radio-frequency is thus essentially the normal value for a nonionized medium. The differential shift is then obtained in the following manner. The frequency received on the ground from the higher frequency transmission is divided by the appropriate integer, six in the case mentioned above, to bring it close to the lower frequency; if there had been no refraction in the ionosphere the two frequencies would then be identical. The two actual frequencies are compared and the beat, i.e., differential shift, frequency (§ 4.20, footnote) can then be measured. From this result the electron density can be computed.

PHASE VELOCITY COMPARISON

8.186. A less commonly used procedure is a modification of the ionosonde technique, based on a comparison of the phase velocities of radio wave pulses. The transmitter carried aloft by a sounding rocket emits a series of pairs of pulses, one frequency of the pair being much higher than that of the other. The pulse of lower frequency is accelerated in its passage through the ionosphere, but the velocity of the other remains virtually unchanged. The difference in arrival times of the two pulses at a ground station is related to the electron density at the altitude of the rocket.

RADIO-FREQUENCY PROBE

8.187. A third, more recent, method for deriving electron density profiles makes use of a *radio-frequency probe;* the instrumentation is completely contained in the sounding rocket, and the data are telemetered to a ground station for reduction. The technique is very simple, but the presence of the rocket body and the development of a sheath of positive ions around the probe are possible sources of error. The probe consists of two "plates," e.g., two parallel antennas or an insulated part of the rocket itself may constitute one of the plates; these plates, together with the ambient medium as the dielectric material between them, form a capacitor.

8.188. If C is the capacitance* of the probe in the ionosphere, as determined with oscillations of a known radio frequency, and C_0 is the value with a vacuum between the plates, then the *dielectric constant, K,* of the ionospheric medium is given by

$$K = \frac{C}{C_0}.$$

It is well known from electromagnetic theory that the dielectric constant is equal to the square of the refractive index of the medium, i.e., $K = r^2$; hence, using equation (8.9) for r, it follows that

$$\frac{C}{C_0} = 1 - \frac{8.1 \times 10^{-5} n}{f^2}, \tag{8.14}$$

where n is the electron density and f is the frequency in megacycles per second at which the capacitances are determined. Hence, if C and C_0 are measured and f is known, the electron density can be derived from equation (8.14). The value of C_0 is obtained with sufficient accuracy by measuring the capacitance with ordinary, nonionized air between the plates before the sounding rocket is

* The capacitance of a capacitor (or condenser) is equal to the ratio of the charge on either of the plates to the potential difference between them.

launched. The capacitance, C, is then determined at successive altitudes during the ascent of the rocket, using radio oscillations of a convenient known frequency, e.g., 6 to 8 megacycles per second. Various electronic circuits, all relatively simple, have been devised to permit automatic and continuous measurement of the capacitance of the ionosphere as the rocket ascends. In this manner, the electron density profile can be obtained.

POSITIVE ION DENSITY

8.189. Instead of determining electron densities, rocket-borne instruments have been employed to measure the positive ion density. On a macroscopic scale, the ionosphere is undoubtedly neutral electrically; hence, the number of positively charged particles must be identical with the number of those having negative charges. The only positive particles are positive ions, i.e., atoms or molecules that have lost one or more electrons, but the negative particles can be both free electrons and negative ions, i.e., atoms or molecules that have captured an electron. It appears that, in the daytime at least, the upper ionosphere contains comparatively few negative ions, and it is a good approximation to regard the electron density as equal to the density of positive ions.

8.190. To measure the ion density, an electrical potential is applied between the rocket structure (or skin), which serves as a "grounded" electrode, and a collector electrode that is negative with respect to the ground. Positive ions present in the medium between the rocket skin and the collector are attracted to the latter electrode and are discharged. As a result, an ion current flows and its strength can be measured. If the potential of the collector is made increasingly more negative, the ion current first increases and then attains a limiting value. At this stage, all the positive ions present in the ionospheric medium between the electrodes are being collected. The limiting ion current is thus a measure of the ion density. This is the basic principle upon which the *ion-current monitor* (or *probe*) operates. In practice, a grid, with a negative bias, is placed between the rocket skin and the collector, primarily to prevent an electron current from interfering with the measured ion current (Fig. **8.19**). The

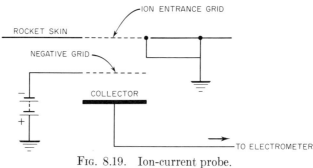

FIG. 8.19.   Ion-current probe.

value of the limiting positive ion current is telemetered to a ground station in the usual manner as the rocket ascends.

INTEGRATED ELECTRON DENSITY

8.191. Both the radio-frequency probe and ion-current monitor can also be employed for determining local electron densities from satellites. The differential Doppler shift technique, however, does not now give the electron density but rather the total number of electrons, i.e., the *electron content* or the *integrated* (or *columnar*) *electron density*, between the satellite and the receiving station on the ground, over the cross-sectional area of the transmitted radio beam. The difference in the information obtainable with the Doppler method from sounding rockets and satellites arises from the difference in their motion with respect to the receiver. The rocket actually measures the integrated electron density at every altitude as it travels upward, but since the altitude is changing, so also is the value of the total electron content. The rate at which this varies with altitude, at any altitude, is the actual (or local) electron density at that altitude.* When measurements are made from a satellite, its altitude when in the vicinity of the ground station is almost constant and so the procedure for deriving the local electron density is not applicable.

8.192. Another method for obtaining the integrated electron density from a satellite makes use of what is called the *Faraday effect*;† this procedure has the advantages of simplicity of equipment and of analysis. The basic principle was discovered as a result of observations on the fading of radar echoes from the Moon, and the data were employed to estimate the total electron content, per unit area, of the ionosphere. Later the technique was adapted for use on satellites to give the integrated (or columnar) electron densities at different heights above the ground.

8.193. When a linearly polarized beam (§ 6.135, footnote) of radio waves traverses an ionized medium in a magnetic field, e.g., the ionosphere in Earth's magnetic field, the plane of polarization is rotated. The extent of this Faraday rotation of the linearly polarized radio waves, as the signal travels from a satellite to a ground station, is related to the electron content of the intervening medium. Radio waves of high frequency, e.g., 40 megacycles (or more) per

---

* If N is the electron content (per unit area) and n is the electron density, then

$$N = \int_0^h n \, dh,$$

where h is the altitude to which N applies. It follows, therefore, that

$$n = \frac{dN}{dh}$$

at any altitude.

† The original Faraday effect, discovered by the famous British scientist Michael Faraday in 1846, is the rotation of the plane of polarization of light by any transparent material in a magnetic field.

launched from California on August 25, 1964. The perigee of its orbit is 540 miles and the apogee 634 miles; the orbital period is 104 minutes and the angle of inclination of the orbital plane to the equator is 80 deg. The sounder is not of the sweep-frequency type, but has six fixed frequencies, from 1.5 to 7.22 megacycles per second. A sounding is made at each frequency every 0.1 second, so that all the observations are made at an essentially fixed location; the cycle of the sweep-frequency sounder on Alouette, on the other hand, requires 18 seconds for a slightly larger frequency range. The Explorer XX satellite also carries an ion probe mass spectrometer which gives ambient ion (and electron) densities and electron temperatures.

8.202. The Beacon Explorer Satellite (Explorer XXII), designed to make a worldwide study of the ionosphere, was launched from California on October 9, 1964 into an orbit of 549 miles perigee and 669 miles apogee; its period was nearly 105 minutes and the angle of inclination about 80 deg. The satellite has an octagonal shape, 12 inches high and 18 inches in diameter, and the total weight is 116 pounds. In orbit, electron density probes protrude from top and bottom, and four panels, 66 inches long by 10 inches wide, covered with solar cells extend from the sides. At the end of each panel is an antenna for radio transmission. Two bar magnets, with dimensions of $5\frac{3}{4}$ by $\frac{7}{8}$ inch, are intended to orient the satellite along Earth's magnetic field lines to provide stable radio signals for the ionospheric experiments, and to keep the laser reflectors, mentioned below, pointing in the required direction.

8.203. The chief objective of the Beacon Explorer Satellites is to detect variations and anomalies in the structure of the ionosphere, and the instruments measure the integrated electron density by the Doppler shift and Faraday effect. The latter technique, in particular, requires very simple ground equipment and so many observers, all over the world, can make measurements daily in real time when the satellite is within radio range. In this manner a comprehensive global representation of the ionosphere can be obtained and its daily changes observed. The electrostatic probe measures electron densities and temperatures in the immediate vicinity of the satellite.

8.204. Explorer XXII has two secondary purposes, in addition to the primary one of studying the ionosphere. The satellite has a corner-reflector system, mentioned in § 4.146, to test the possibility of laser tracking. Furthermore, the Beacon Explorer Satellite transmits radio signals on two frequencies, namely, 162 and 324 megacycles per second, to permit precision tracking by ground stations based on the Doppler effect. This is intended as a contribution to the uses of satellite in geodesy (§ 5.144).

THE MAGNETOSPHERE

EARTH'S MAGNETIC FIELD

8.205. A *magnetic field* is a region in which a magnetic pole, e.g., either end of a compass needle, or a moving electric charge, e.g., a moving electron or proton or a conductor carrying a current, is subjected to the action of a force. Earth is surrounded by such a magnetic field, often called the *geomagnetic field* or the *terrestrial magnetic field*, originating in its interior. As a rough approximation, the geomagnetic field is equivalent to the field that would result if a magnetic dipole, such as a bar magnet, of appropriate strength, were imbedded in Earth's interior. The axis of the hypothetical magnet does not coincide with the geographical axis, so that it does not point in the direction of the geographic north and south poles. Moreover, it is displaced from the center by a distance of somewhat more than 400 kilometers (250 miles); consequently, the geomagnetic field in space is not symmetrical with respect to Earth's surface.

8.206. A *line of force* (or *field line*) in a magnetic field indicates the direction in which the force on a magnetic pole acts at any given point. A compass needle, free to rotate in all directions, would orient itself in the direction of the line of force at its particular location. Another interpretation is that a magnetic pole whose motion was not restricted in any way would always travel in a magnetic field along the line of force passing through the point at which it commenced to move. Some of the lines of force of the geomagnetic field, similar to those of a bar magnet, are indicated in Fig. 8.22. The magnetic

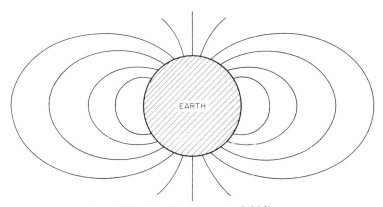

FIG. 8.22.   Earth's magnetic field lines

poles, north and south, are the locations on Earth's surface at which the lines of force are exactly perpendicular, i.e., vertical, to the surface. The geomagnetic axis is a line joining the two magnetic poles. At the magnetic equator, the lines of force are everywhere parallel to Earth's surface, i.e., horizontal.

8.207. For convenience of representation, the magnetic axis in Fig. 8.22 has been drawn vertically, although the north and south magnetic poles are several hundred kilometers from the respective geographic poles. Because of the asymmetry of the geomagnetic field with respect to Earth, the distance is greater in the Southern than in the Northern Hemisphere. Furthermore, the geomagnetic and geographic equators do not coincide. From roughly 170°W eastward to about 30°E the geomagnetic equator is south but at other longitudes it is north of the geographic equator.

8.208. The total geomagnetic intensity, i.e., the total strength of Earth's magnetic field regardless of direction, varies to some extent over the surface. It is strongest, about 0.65 to 0.7 gauss (cf. § 6.105), near the magnetic poles and weakest toward the equatorial region, where its value is 0.30 to 0.35 gauss. However, the variation with latitude is by no means uniform; for example, the exceptionally low value of 0.25 gauss has been recorded in the southeast of Brazil. In addition to the total intensity of the geomagnetic field, it is the practice to record the horizontal and vertical components. The vertical component is a maximum at the poles and zero along the equator; for the horizontal component, the reverse is the case. The horizontal component is relatively large over parts of southeast Asia, but is exceptionally small at the tip of South Africa; the latter effect is called the Capetown anomaly.

8.209. The strength of the magnetic field decreases with increasing distance from Earth. For a small magnetic dipole, the intensity falls off in inverse proportion to the cube of the distance from the center of the dipole. This is approximately true for the geomagnetic field at some distance above the surface. A qualitative indication of the variation of magnetic intensity is provided by the separation of the field lines in Fig. 8.22; the closer the lines, the greater is the geomagnetic field strength. At the surface, the lines of force are closer near the poles than at the equator, and at increasing distances from Earth the lines become farther and farther apart as the magnetic field intensity diminishes.

8.210. From measurements of the strength of the geomagnetic field, going back nearly 400 years, it is clear that the field is by no means a steady one.* The fluctuations are generally divided into two categories, namely, secular and transient (or temporal). The *secular variations* are relatively slow changes taking place gradually over periods of many years, both in the locations of the magnetic poles and in the strength of the field. These variations are irregular, varying in direction and magnitude from year to year, so that it requires many years for the net effect to be significant. Such fluctuations are undoubtedly caused by changes within Earth itself, as will be indicated shortly. The *transient* (or *temporal*) *variations,* which occur rapidly, within periods of days or less, are due to external factors, probably of solar origin. If the transient effects are subtracted, the almost constant residual field is called the *main geomagnetic field.*

8.211. The main field of Earth is commonly regarded as originating in a dynamo action in the interior (§ 8.104). The basic requirement is the existence of a fluid medium that is a good conductor of electricity, and this is satisfied,

---

* The magnetism of rocks indicates that Earth's magnetic field has undergone reversal at intervals of 10 to 50 thousand years.

as is generally agreed, by Earth's interior. Below the 3000-kilometer (1900-mile) thick mantle, there is a shell called the outer core,* of about the same thickness consisting apparently of a liquid nickel-iron alloy at high temperature and pressure. Suppose that a temporary difference develops in the temperature or composition between two regions in Earth's liquid interior; an electric current will then flow through the conducting medium. Because of the large dimensions and high conductivity of the liquid, the current will decay slowly even after its original cause has disappeared. The current will be associated, as always, with a local magnetic field, and motion of the liquid across the field lines will, in turn, produce an electric current as a result of the dynamo effect. Thus, once a current has started, it will continue and perhaps be increased in strength.

8.212. A number of such current regions or eddies may be expected to develop in Earth's interior and each will be associated with a local magnetic field. If no other factors were involved, these fields would probably largely cancel each other; but there is another factor, namely Earth's rotation. The effect of the rotation is to produce a fairly uniform motion of the conducting fluid, with the result that the individual, localized magnetic fields cooperate to produce the overall geomagnetic field. Since the outer liquid core is a shell some 6500 kilometers (4000 miles) in external diameter, and about 650 kilometers (400 miles) internal diameter, it is reasonable to suppose that the fluid motion is not completely stable. Slight deviations, taking place over periods on the order of years, would account for the slow secular changes in the geomagnetic field.

8.213. For many years, it was generally thought that Earth's magnetic field, like its gravitational field, extended more or less indefinitely into space, falling off in strength as the inverse cube of the distance. In developing their theory of magnetic storms, however, S. Chapman and V. C. A. Ferraro (§ 8.226) suggested in 1931 that, at the time of such a storm, a plasma of electrically charged particles from the Sun would surround and enclose the terrestrial magnetic field. The Chapman-Ferraro theory postulated the emission of solar plasma only at times of special activity, but the development of the concept of the solar wind, according to which plasma is being emitted from the Sun at all times, led to the view that the range of the geomagnetic field is always restricted, at least on the daylight side of Earth.

THE MAGNETOSPHERE

8.214. A rough indication of the dimensions of the magnetic field in the direction of the Sun can be obtained by balancing the kinetic energy density, i.e., the kinetic energy per unit volume, of the solar wind, which is equivalent to its pressure, against the kinetic energy density of the terrestrial magnetic field. It is found in this manner that the two opposing kinetic energy densities

* The inner core, at Earth's center, is either solid or a relatively rigid liquid.

(or pressures) become equal at a distance of approximately 64,000 kilometers (40,000 miles) or very roughly 10 Earth radii.* This means that in the Earth-Sun direction, i.e., on the sunlit side of Earth, the geomagnetic field cannot extend beyond about 10 Earth radii. If the lines of force should go farther out, they would be pushed back by the normal solar wind.

8.215. In directions making an appreciable angle with the Earth-Sun line, the motion of the solar wind is not perpendicular to the geomagnetic field lines, and the pressure exerted is less than when the wind encounters Earth's field head-on. Consequently, the geomagnetic field extends farther and farther beyond 10 Earth radii as the angle to the Earth-Sun line increases. On the night side of Earth, i.e., in the opposite direction to that facing the Sun, the solar wind cannot apparently exert any significant pressure on the geomagnetic field; hence, in principle, the field might be expected to extend indefinitely in the direction away from the Sun. Because of the random motion of the particles in the solar wind, however, some pressure is exerted on the geomagnetic field in the direction perpendicular to the wind's motion. Consequently, Earth's magnetic field probably eventually converges on the night side. The region in which the terrestrial magnetic field is thus enclosed by the solar wind is called the *geomagnetic cavity*. Until the latter part of 1964, it was thought that convergence on the antisolar (or night) side of Earth occurred at a moderate distance, e.g., less than about 50 Earth radii. Theoretical calculations and experimental observations made from the IMP-I satellite (§ 8.218) have now indicated that the "tail" of the magnetosphere may extend to a considerable distance, perhaps several astronomical units (§ 6.5). The geomagnetic cavity thus measures some 10 Earth radii in the solar direction and a considerable, but uncertain, distance in the opposite direction. A section through the magnetosphere in the noon-midnight meridian plane is shown in Fig. 8.23.

8.216. The geomagnetic cavity is also referred to as the *magnetosphere*, although this term is more properly applicable to the region in which the geomagnetic forces are dominant in determining the behavior of charged particles in the atmosphere. In this sense, the magnetosphere commences at an altitude of some 600 to 1000 kilometers (400 to 600 miles) above Earth's surface and extends outward into the remainder of the geomagnetic cavity. Because of this minor difference, no serious misunderstanding arises from the alternative use of magnetosphere for the geomagnetic cavity, and vice versa. The outer boundary of the cavity is referred to as the *magnetopause*, by analogy with tropopause, stratopause, etc.

8.217. Since the normal solar wind travels toward Earth with the high velocity of 350 to 700 kilometers (210 to 420 miles) per second, it is to be expected that the region where the wind encounters the geomagnetic cavity, i.e., just be-

---

* When distances are given in Earth radii (6371 kilometers) it is generally understood that they are measured from Earth's center.

yond the magnetopause, should be highly disturbed. In this region, therefore, the magnetic field should show irregular variations. Moreover, theoretical studies have indicated that, because of the high velocity of the solar wind, a collision-free magnetohydrodynamic (or hydromagnetic) shock wave (§ 6.132)

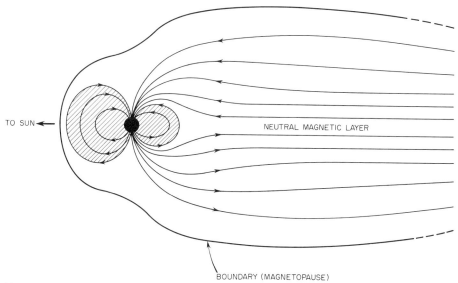

TO SUN ←

NEUTRAL MAGNETIC LAYER

BOUNDARY (MAGNETOPAUSE)

FIG. 8.23. Earth's magnetosphere in the noon-midnight meridian plane; the cross-hatched area is the region of trapped corpuscular radiation described in § 8.267 *et seq.* (after N. F. Ness)

might form as the solar wind approaches the boundary of the terrestrial magnetic field. Several Explorer satellites, e.g., X, XII, and XIV, and a number of space probes, e.g., Pioneer I and Pioneer V and the Russian Luniks I and II, have carried instruments for measuring magnetic field intensities and directions at considerable distances from Earth. Although the results were not always in agreement, possibly because of differences in the conditions, they did tend to show that there was a region, at a distance of roughly 10 Earth radii in the direction of the Sun, in which the magnetic field changed erratically both in magnitude and direction.

8.218. During late 1963 and early 1964, a comprehensive study of the geomagnetic boundary region was made by means of the satellite Explorer XVIII, also known as the Interplanetary Monitoring Platform-I (or IMP-I). This was launched from Florida on November 27, 1963 into a highly eccentric (0.937) orbit, inclined 33.3 deg to the equator, with an initial perigee of 192 kilometers (120 miles), apogee 197,600 kilometers (124,000 miles), and a period of 93.5

hours. For the measurement of intensity and direction of the magnetic fields in space, IMP-I carried a rubidium vapor magnetometer and two fluxgate magnetometers. The rubidium vapor magnetometer determines the Zeeman splitting of the spectral lines of rubidium (§ 6.105), which is directly related to the total magnetic field strength. The purpose of the fluxgate magnetometers, on the other hand, is to derive the direction of the field by observing the relative strengths in two different directions. In the fluxgate magnetometer, a core element, consisting of a rod of easily magnetized material, is surrounded by a coil of wire (solenoid) carrying an alternating current of high frequency, e.g., 10 kilocycles per second. An external magnetic field will then cause a distortion of the high-frequency voltage which is proportional to the strength of the magnetic field in a direction parallel to the core element of the magnetometer.

8.219. The results obtained from IMP-I show that, out to some 10 Earth radii in the direction of the Sun, i.e., within the geomagnetic cavity, the magnetic field is relatively stable, both in magnitude and direction. Then follows a region, about 3 Earth radii in thickness along the Earth-Sun line, in which the magnetic field is disturbed; the magnitude may change by as much as 50 percent of its original value and its direction may occasionally be reversed. Beyond the disturbed region, commencing at roughly 13 Earth radii, the magnetic field has generally an almost constant value of 4 to 7 gammas,* although occasional direction changes are observed with increasing distance from Earth. This relatively stable field, which is inclined to the plane of the ecliptic (§ 7.22), represents the interplanetary magnetic field originating (mainly) in the Sun.

8.220. The interpretation of the foregoing results is that between the two essentially stable magnetic fields, in the geomagnetic cavity and in interplanetary space, there is a highly disturbed transition region where the solar wind interacts with the terrestrial magnetic field. This region is bounded on one side by the magnetopause, which separates the transition region from the magnetosphere, and on the other side by a collisionless hydromagnetic shock front, between the transition region and interplanetary space. The general situation in the ecliptic plane is indicated in Fig. 8.24.

8.220a. Because of the highly eccentric orbit of IMP-I, it spent a considerable time within the tail of the magnetosphere. During this period, it was observed that the magnetic field strength repeatedly decreased to a small (or zero) value and abruptly changed direction as the satellite passed through a layer approximately 600 kilometers (370 miles) thick lying in or near the ecliptic plane. On the north side of this layer the lines of force of the magnetic field are directed toward the Sun, whereas on the south side they point in the antisolar direction. These observations are regarded as indicating the presence of a magnetically neutral sheet (or layer) in the tail of the magnetosphere, as shown in Fig. 8.23 (N. F. Ness, 1964). This layer may possibly play an important role in permit-

---

* The gamma is a unit of magnetic field equal to 10^{-5} gauss; it is used in connection with weak magnetic fields or to express small changes in fields of moderate strength.

ting electrically charged particles from the Sun to enter the terrestrial magnetic field.

Geomagnetic Field Variations

8.221. Of the variations in the terrestrial magnetic field mentioned in § 8.210, the small and erratic secular changes are apparently caused by motions within Earth's interior; consequently, they lie outside the scope of this book. In any

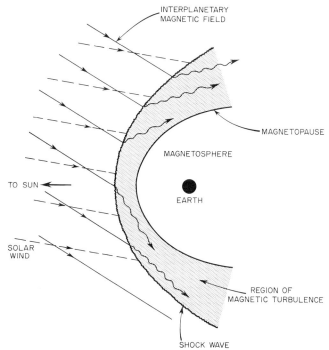

Fɪɢ. 8.24. Formation of hydromagnetic shock wave by the solar wind and disturbed region beyond Earth's magnetopause (after N. F. Ness, C. S. Scearce, and J. B. Seek)

case, little is known about these minor fluctuations. The temporal (or transient) variations, on the other hand, are of considerable interest and are related to several solar and terrestrial phenomena. Two major categories of temporal changes in the geomagnetic field are recognized; the first includes relatively small and regular daily variations, and in the second are disturbances of a more violent nature known as magnetic storms.

8.222. The worldwide transient geomagnetic activity is expressed by two different indexes, K_p and A_p. Magnetometers at a number of stations indicate a local 3-hourly (or K) index, ranging from 0 to 9. It is a measure of the variations in the field strength over a 3-hour period; thus $K = 0$ indicates a quiescent condition and $K = 9$ implies a very intense disturbance. The K indexes from different places are then combined to give the planetary (or worldwide) index, K_p (or Kp). The other representation of geomagnetic activity, by the index A_p, is based on half the maximum fluctuation in field strength expressed in gammas. The 3-hourly values from individual stations are first combined to give the planetary index a_p, and these are averaged over a 24-hour period to obtain the A_p index.

8.223. The daily *quiet magnetic variations* generally average about 0.1 percent of the quiet day value of the magnetic field strength. The latter is approximately 0.5 gauss, on the average, and so the deviations are in the vicinity of 5×10^{-4} gauss or roughly 50 gammas or so. Systematic observations of these changes in the geomagnetic field have shown that they can be definitely correlated with the Sun and the Moon. Atmospheric solar and lunar tides produce motions in the ionosphere, and the resulting dynamo currents are accompanied by magnetic fields, as described in § 8.114. These small magnetic fields are superimposed on the main geomagnetic field and represent the fairly regular daily fluctuations in the measured field strength at Earth's surface.

Sudden Commencement Magnetic Storms

8.224. Of the transient magnetic disturbances, the most striking are magnetic storms of the *sudden commencement* type. Within several hours to a day or so, the average time being 21 to 22 hours, after some, but not all, solar flares, there is frequently a sudden increase of about 20 to 30 gammas in the horizontal component of the geomagnetic field (Fig. 8.25). This is observed almost simultaneously all over the globe. The increase, which occurs within a few minutes, is called the *sudden commencement phase* of the magnetic storm; the field strength

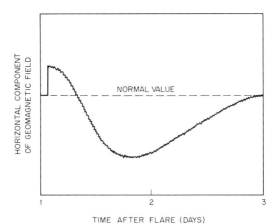

Fig. 8.25. Variation with time of horizontal component of Earth's magnetic field in a sudden commencement storm.

then starts to drop during the *initial phase* and from 2 to 8 hours may elapse before the prestorm value is reached. The decrease continues during the *main phase*, lasting from 12 to 24 hours, in which the horizontal component falls to about 50 to 100 gammas below normal. During this period there may be large positive and negative fluctuations of short duration. Finally, a day or more after the sudden commencement, there is the *recovery phase*, in which the geomagnetic field strength returns in a somewhat irregular manner to the quiescent value. Provided no other disturbance occurs in the meantime, the recovery phase requires one or two days.

8.225. There is now little doubt that a sudden commencement geomagnetic storm owes its origin to a cloud (or burst) of plasma, consisting essentially of protons and electrons of a few kilo-electron volts energy, emitted from the vicinity of a solar flare and moving at a velocity of 1000 to 2000 kilometers (600 to 1200 miles) per second. A fuller discussion of the manner in which this plasma travels from the Sun to Earth will be given in § 8.235, but for the present it is sufficient to state that when it encounters the geomagnetic cavity, about a day after leaving the Sun, it produces a sudden commencement storm all over the world. Because both the particle density and kinetic energy of the flare plasma are greater than in the solar wind, the kinetic energy density (or pressure) will also be larger. The lines of force near the boundary of the magnetosphere are thus compressed from all directions. This compression moves rapidly, perhaps by the action of hydromagnetic shock waves, toward Earth and produces the observed sudden commencement increase in the geomagnetic field, especially in the horizontal component. As the compression relaxes, the field recovers its original value, thus marking the end of the initial phase of the storm.

8.226. An explanation of the main phase was proposed by Adolph Schmidt in Germany in 1916 and developed by Sydney Chapman and V. C. A. Ferraro in England in a series of publications dating from 1931. In order to account for the decrease in the magnetic field strength as determined at Earth's surface, it was postulated that a current of perhaps a million amperes was flowing in a ring encircling Earth at a distance of between 5 and 10 Earth radii. Such a *ring current* implies that charged particles, either protons or electrons (or both moving in opposite directions), are traveling in a closed path and, consequently, produce a magnetic field. The ring current may exist at all times, but it would have to be enhanced by an increase in the density and perhaps energy of the charged particles at the time of a magnetic storm. These particles would presumably originate in the solar plasma and be introduced in some manner into the geomagnetic cavity. Once within the cavity they would be forced to circulate about Earth by the normal geomagnetic field, as described in § 8.289. The slow decay of the ring current would lead to the gradual increase in the terrestrial field strength during the recovery phase.

8.227. Evidence has been sought from magnetometers and charged-particle detectors carried on various spacecraft for the existence of the ring current within the magnetosphere. Unfortunately, the results are not always consistent. Perhaps the best evidence for the formation of a ring current was obtained by A. H. Davis and J. M. Williamson in 1962. They observed that, at the time of a geomagnetic storm, the intensity of protons in the energy range from 0.1 to 4.5 million electron volts at a distance of about 3 to 4.5 Earth radii increased by a factor of three. These protons would drift westward under the influence of Earth's magnetic field, and thereby produce a ring current.

8.228. Since not all major solar flares are accompanied by geomagnetic storms, it would be advantageous to be able to predict in advance whether a particular solar activity will cause a storm or not. This is so, for example, because geomagnetic storms of the sudden commencement type are generally accompanied by interference with long-distance radio communication. Moreover, the increase in the corpuscular radiation intensity might represent a hazard to man in space. The appearance of Type II and Type IV radio bursts from the Sun (§ 6.178 *et seq.*) is commonly associated with a geomagnetic storm of the sudden commencement type, but the correlation is not exact. In any event, the radio signal would give only 24 hours notice, at best, since this is the approximate time elapsing between the detection of the radio emission and the onset of the storm.

8.229. An attempt has been made to relate the development of storm-associated solar flares to the magnetic character of sunspots, since a clear relationship of this kind could provide a longer warning period. Here again, some probabilities have been established but not complete agreement. Sunspot groups that are most likely to be followed by moderate or severe geomagnetic storms within about three days are those with complex magnetic polarities (§ 6.140). It has also been observed that sunspot groups associated with geomagnetic storms occur much more frequently in the northern than in the southern hemisphere of the Sun. This effect has been traced over more than 30 years and does not appear to be related to the 11-year and 22-year cycles (§ 6.113).

Weaker Magnetic Disturbances

8.230. As is to be anticipated, sudden commencement storms are more frequent when the Sun is active than during the quieter periods; thus, there is an approximate 11-year variation corresponding to the regular sunspot cycle. Another kind of geomagnetic storm, considerably weaker than the sudden commencement type and of shorter duration, exhibits a different periodic behavior. Regardless of the degree of solar activity, there is a tendency for individual storms to recur at fairly regular intervals of about 27 days. Since this is very close to the rotational period of the Sun, it is conjectured that they are caused by an active solar region that persists for several rotations.

8.231. It is strange, however, that there is no obvious activity on the Sun's surface that can be associated with these minor recurrent geomagnetic storms.

The disturbances, like the sudden commencement storms, are undoubtedly caused by rapidly moving plasma from the Sun, and the areas from which the plasma is emitted have been called *magnetically active regions* or, more commonly, *M regions* by Julius Bartels, the German authority on geomagnetism. Attempts have been made to identify the M regions with characteristic features of the Sun but they have not been very successful. There appears to be no obvious type of activity that persists through several solar rotations with which the recurrent storms can be correlated. It has been suggested that coronal streamers (§ 6.155) are rays of particles emanating from the M regions, but this still does not identify these regions. Incidentally, the various radiation emissions from the M regions may be responsible for the periodic changes in the density of the upper atmosphere mentioned in § 8.53.

8.232. The geomagnetic storms that recur at 27-day intervals are probably associated with solar plasma emission of a less energetic character than that responsible for sudden commencement disturbances. While on its way from Earth to Venus, an instrument on the spacecraft Mariner II was used to determine velocities of the interplanetary plasma. During the latter part of 1962, when the Sun was not particularly active, the data were found to fall into a number of overlapping groups with reference to time. In each group the velocity varied in an approximately regular manner, from a minimum of about 350 kilometers (220 miles) per second to a maximum of roughly 700 kilometers (440 miles) per second, with a cycle of something like 27 days. Furthermore, these cycles corresponded very closely to variations in the planetary magnetic activity index (§ 8.222). It appears, therefore, that the geomagnetic storms which recur every 27 days are caused by plasma emitted with a velocity about twice that of the normal solar wind. Some correlation was also found between the increase in plasma velocity and the strength of the local interplanetary magnetic field at the same time, but further clarification of this matter is required. It is of interest that the plasma observed by Mariner II exhibited so many ups and downs in velocity from day to day that there was actually no normal or steady solar wind.

8.233. A geomagnetic fluctuation of a relatively minor character, lasting for about 30 minutes or so, is the phenomenon known as *magnetic crochet* (French, *crochet*, "hook"), which occurs simultaneously with a sudden ionospheric disturbance (§ 8.119). A curve showing the variation of the horizontal component of the geomagnetic field as a function of time, as drawn by a recording magnetometer, indicates a fairly sharp drop followed by a somewhat slower return to normal; the hook-like shape of the curve has led to the use of the name crochet to describe the effect. A magnetic crochet occurs almost simultaneously with the observation of an associated solar flare; hence, the crochet disturbance, like the SID, is caused by electromagnetic rather than corpuscular radiation from the Sun. A plausible explanation of the effect is that photoionization by radiations of short wavelength, i.e., X-rays and far ultraviolet, results in an increase in the electrical conductivity of the ionosphere. Dynamo currents are then produced which cause the observed changes in the magnetic field at Earth's surface.

8.234. Among other types of minor variations in the geomagnetic field that have been reported, mention may be made of the *micropulsations* of a few gammas in magnitude. They recur at fairly regular short intervals, ranging from a fraction of a second to a minute or so; that is to say, the frequencies vary from several cycles down to less than one cycle per second. The suggestion has been made that hydromagnetic waves of the corresponding frequencies in the upper atmosphere are responsible for the micropulsations.

Sun-Earth Relationships

8.235. An attempt will be made in this section to describe, in simplified form, the concept that is now emerging with regard to the interactions of solar particles and magnetic fields with Earth and its environment. These interactions lead to the various ionospheric and geomagnetic disturbances already described, as well as to other phenomena to be considered later.

8.236. Because of the solar wind of plasma, mainly proton and electrons, that is expelled continuously, although with varying intensity, from the Sun, the

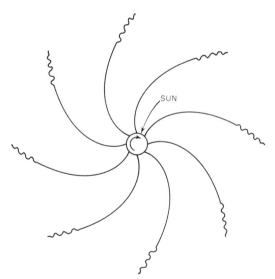

Fig. 8.26.   Magnetic field lines of the Sun in its equatorial plane.

lines of force of the solar magnetic field are extended outward, i.e., in a radial manner. At least one end of each field line remains attached to the Sun itself, but since the Sun rotates, the effect will be to curve each line of force into an Archimedian spiral. An idealized representation of the magnetic field in the cquatorial plane of the Sun is depicted in Fig. 8.26;* this general form has been confirmed by measurements made by IMP-I (§ 8.218). At considerable distances from the Sun, probably several astronomical units, the lines of force may be expected to become somewhat distorted and irregular because of the decrease in energy density of the solar plasma.

8.237. When there is an appropriate disturbance on the Sun, e.g., as manifested by a particular kind of solar flare, a quantity (or cloud) of plasma, consisting of particles of moderately high energy—probably a few kilo-electron volts—is expelled from a local region on the solar surface. Since the energy of the particles is greater than that in the normal solar wind, their emission will be accompanied by a modification in the Sun's magnetic field; two somewhat different models have been developed to describe the nature of the change. According to the views of Thomas Gold (1958) and others in the United States, the kinetic energy of the flare plasma cloud is so great that as it leaves the Sun it carries with it the solar magnetic field in its immediate area. Because of the high electrical conductivity of the plasma, the magnetic field remains within the plasma cloud and moves with it. There is consequently formed a protuberance or "tongue" of plasma, within an imbedded magnetic field, extending out from the Sun (Fig. 8.27).

8.238. Furthermore, the electrically charged particles in the plasma, unless they have very high energies, cannot readily cross the field lines. They are thus compelled to move back and forth along them, following a spiral path, as will be described in § 8.278. In other words, the plasma particles are trapped in what is referred to as a *magnetic bottle*. Escape from the bottle is possible only as a result of collisions among the plasma particles (or

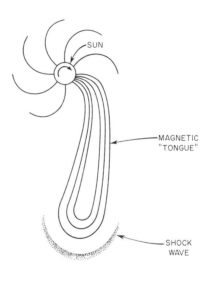

FIG. 8.27. Ejection of plasma and magnetic field tongue from solar flare

with particles in the atmosphere) or if the magnetic field is distorted. In any event, it occurs slowly because of the moderate and low energies of the trapped particles.

* The curvature of the field lines has been colloquially misnamed the "garden hose" effect, because of the similarity of the pattern in Fig. 8.26 to the water streams ejected from a rotating lawn-sprinkler; the water is expelled from the jets in a radial manner but rotation of the sprinkler head causes the streams to become curved. A more appropriate description would have been the "garden sprinkler" effect or, perhaps, the "pinwheel" effect.

8.239. Since the plasma tongue moves away from the Sun at high velocity, from 1000 to 2000 kilometers (600 to 1200 miles) per second, it is preceded by a collision-free hydromagnetic shock wave. For the trapped solar plasma in the vicinity of Earth, the solar magnetic field strength, as indicated by Pioneer V and Mariner II measurements, may be about 40 gammas, i.e., 4×10^{-4} gauss, and the proton density is roughly 10 to 20 particles per cubic centimeter; according to equation (6.13), the velocity of a hydromagnetic wave in these circumstances should be about 280 kilometers (175 miles) per second. Since the actual velocity is several times greater, a hydromagnetic shock front will develop somewhat ahead of the tongue, as indicated in Fig. 8.27. In such a shock wave, the energy density (or pressure) at the front is greater than it would normally be in the plasma.

8.240. The thickness of the shock may be several hundred or even thousands of kilometers and so when it encounters the geomagnetic cavity, about a day or so after leaving the Sun, the cavity is compressed. The compression is carried down toward Earth, possibly by the action of local hydromagnetic waves, and the result is a sudden commencement geomagnetic storm. A short time later, the bulk of the plasma tongue arrives and some of the protons and electrons are trapped by Earth's magnetic field. They thus become available, either directly or indirectly, to produce the ring current or other phenomenon that is responsible for the main phase of the storm.

8.241. The escape of the trapped protons at moderate and high latitudes in the atmosphere is responsible for the additional ionization that causes auroral ionospheric storms. The gradual release of the protons from the magnetic bottle, as it passes over Earth during the course of a day or two, can account for the duration of both geomagnetic and ionospheric storms. Intense luminous auroral effects are observed at the same time, but it appears that these are caused by electrons (§ 8.347).

8.242. Not all solar flares are accompanied by geomagnetic and ionospheric disturbances. One possible reason is that the density and energy of the solar particles may not be sufficient to permit the plasma tongue to reach the vicinity of Earth. The cloud may detach itself from the Sun, as all plasma tongues must do eventually, before reaching Earth and break up into disorganized regions that will become dissipated in interplanetary space. There will then be essentially no effects in the vicinity of Earth. Another possibility is that the plasma tongue emerging from an active solar region is oriented in such a manner that it does not encounter Earth. In view of the bending of the Sun's magnetic field lines as a result of rotation, it is to be expected, in agreement with observations, that the greatest terrestrial disturbances occur when the source is on the western side of the Sun (cf. Fig. 8.27). If the activity is on the eastern half of the solar disc, it has to be very intense to produce effects in the vicinity of Earth. Furthermore, in these cases there is a longer time delay between the appearance of the flare and the onset of geomagnetic and ionospheric storms.

8.243. The other model of the interaction of solar plasma with Earth is that proposed by E. N. Parker (1960) in the United States. Objection is taken to the plasma tongue description on the following grounds: the hydromagnetic shock should be so far ahead of the bulk of the plasma that the latter would not reach Earth until some six hours after the shock front. The phenomena, however, exhibit no such delay. Whether this contention is correct or not does not appear to have been established. But assuming that the argument is valid, it is suggested that the plasma emitted from the Sun at the time of a flare travels along the curved lines of force established by the solar wind. This plasma scoops up the interplanetary (solar wind) plasma ahead of it to form a hydromagnetic shock as indicated by the sharp local flattening of the field lines (Fig. **8.28**).

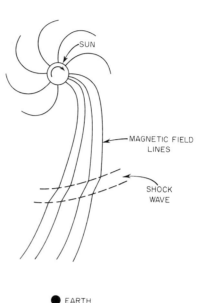

8.244. The closer spacing between the lines implies that the magnetic field is stronger in this region. Thus, plasma is trapped behind the shock front, since it cannot cross the field lines. When the shock reaches Earth, it compresses the magnetosphere and is followed immediately by plasma. The geomagnetic and ionospheric effects already described will then ensue. There is probably no fundamental difference between the plasma tongue and hydromagnetic shock models, the distinction being largely a matter of detailed interpretation.

Fɪɢ. 8.28. Formation of hydromagnetic shock in magnetic field from solar flare

Cᴏsᴍɪᴄ Rᴀʏs: Gᴀʟᴀᴄᴛɪᴄ ᴀɴᴅ Sᴏʟᴀʀ

8.245. It has been known since the beginning of the present century that highly penetrating, ionizing radiations can be detected in the vicinity of Earth at all times, but the source of these radiations was uncertain for several years. Between 1911 and 1914, however, detection instruments carried by balloons up to heights of 9000 meters (30,000) feet indicated that the radiation intensity increased with altitude. These observations established that the radiations, subsequently called *cosmic rays,* were of extraterrestrial origin. Cosmic rays are not rays in the strict sense of the term; they consist initially of (primary) positively charged particles which interact with nuclei in the atmosphere to produce a highly complex (secondary) mixture of corpuscular and electromagnetic radiations. The study of cosmic rays has led to a number of notable discoveries, especially in nuclear physics, but the discussion here will be restricted mainly to their interaction with Earth's atmosphere and the terrestrial and solar magnetic fields.

8.246. Until 1942, it was thought that the primary cosmic-ray particles all came from outside the solar system, but on February 28 of that year an increase in the intensity was observed soon after the appearance of a solar flare. Since that date, it has been established that many, but not all, large flares that are accompanied by Type IV radio bursts are also associated with an increase in cosmic rays. In some situations it is convenient to distinguish between *galactic cosmic rays*, which originate outside the solar system but probably within the local galaxy (Milky Way), and *solar cosmic rays*, which come from the Sun. In both cases, the primary particles are mainly hydrogen nuclei (protons) of high energy, with a small proportion of helium nuclei (alpha particles) and considerably lesser amounts of some heavier nuclei. For the present purpose, however, it is adequate to consider only the protons.

8.247. Cosmic-ray protons of a given energy are indistinguishable in their behavior, regardless of their origin. Nevertheless, galactic and solar cosmic rays differ in an important respect: both the average and maximum energies of galactic protons are much larger than the energies of solar protons. The energies of the primary protons in cosmic rays cover a considerable range (or spectrum) and, in general, the intensity increases with decreasing energy. But the presence of protons with the extraordinarily high energy of a billion billion (10^{18}) electron volts has been inferred in galactic cosmic rays, and the average energy per proton is estimated to be about 10 billion (10^{10}) electron volts. In solar cosmic rays, however, the proton energies range from about 10 million (10^7) to a few billion (10^9) electron volts, with an average around 100 million (10^8) electron volts. These energies are very high by common standards, but they are low in comparison with those of protons of galactic origin.

8.248. When cosmic-ray protons enter the atmosphere, the air density at an altitude of 16 to 32 kilometers (10 to 20 miles) is large enough for an appreciable number of collisions to occur between them and the atomic nuclei, mostly nitrogen and oxygen, of the air. The capture by a nucleus of a galactic proton of sufficiently high energy causes a complete disruption of the nucleus; as a result, protons and neutrons of fairly high energy and *mesons*, i.e., particles of mass intermediate between electrons and protons, are emitted. The protons and neutrons can, in turn, cause disintegration of additional nuclei, producing more protons and neutrons; this chain of reactions continues until the energies are too small to permit further nuclear reactions to occur. The mesons do not generally interact with nuclei but undergo spontaneous decay, in a millionth of a second or less, to produce gamma rays (§ 6.49) of high energy and fast electrons, both positive and negative. It is this complex system of secondary protons, neutrons, mesons, gamma rays, and electrons that is detected as "cosmic rays" in the vicinity of Earth. With solar protons, the energies are generally not large enough to permit the formation of mesons, but interaction with atmospheric nuclei still leads to a mixture of protons, neutrons, and some gamma rays.

8.249. It is evident, therefore, that the true nature of the primary cosmic rays can be studied only at high altitudes. Hence, radiation detection devices, usually Geiger counters, ion chambers, and nuclear emulsions (§ 8.293), have been carried aloft for this purpose by balloons, and also by sounding rockets, including rockoons (§ 1.101), and by satellites and space probes. In spite of their limitations, balloons are still used, especially for investigating cosmic rays from the Sun. They can be launched at short notice, when situations of interest are indicated by intense solar flares or by the onset of polar cap absorption (§ 8.121), and they can remain aloft for many hours.

8.250. The fact that galactic protons generate mesons and their decay products in the atmosphere, whereas solar protons usually do not, provides the basis of a method for distinguishing between the two types of cosmic rays. A simple ground-based procedure is available, in addition, for determining variations in the intensity of solar cosmic rays. It utilizes a *neutron monitor* (or *neutron pile*), consisting of a number of neutron detectors surrounded by wood and paraffin, in a lead box which is, in turn, enclosed in more wood and paraffin. The lead serves two purposes: it screens the detector from interfering radiations and also produces neutrons when struck by cosmic-ray protons. The detectors are more sensitive to slow (low-energy) neutrons than they are to fast ones, and the wood and paraffin, by utilizing the hydrogen they contain, slow down both fast neutrons originating in the lead or other neutrons formed by proton interactions in the atmosphere.

8.251. A neutron monitor of this type responds most readily, either directly or indirectly, to protons of a few billion electron volts energy, such as are present in solar cosmic rays. It will also, of course, detect galactic protons of the same energy. When the Sun is quiet, however, the contribution of solar protons is negligible and the base readings of the monitor indicate the almost constant intensity of galactic cosmic rays. At the time of a solar disturbance, the readings will increase by amounts related to the solar (high-energy) proton intensity; in this manner, variations in the solar cosmic rays can be determined. There may be some change simultaneously in the galactic cosmic rays and this can be identified by a meson detector which does not respond to solar protons.

Solar Cosmic Rays

8.252. Only a small proportion of solar flares are associated with the appearance of high-energy protons in the vicinity of Earth. These flares are generally of Class 3 or 3^+ in importance (§ 6.141) and are accompanied by Type II and Type IV radio bursts; they most frequently appear on the western part of the Sun's face (cf. § 8.242). The flares of interest are almost invariably in the northern solar hemisphere, but the reason for this is not known. At the times when the Sun is active, several large flares may occur in the same region within the course of a few days. As a result, the cosmic-ray phenomena are complex and difficult to analyze. There are apparently some regular types of behavior, and of these two general situations have been identified.

8.253. In the first category, some hours after the appearance of an appropriate solar flare, protons having a range of energies, from a billion electron volts or so down to about 10 million electron volts, can be detected near Earth. They arrive from all directions, i.e., they have an almost isotropic distribution, and persist for some time, growing slowly weaker in intensity and in energy. Provided a second flare does not occur in the meantime, the normal cosmic-ray flux will be restored within one or two days.

8.254. The second type of solar cosmic-ray behavior is characterized by the arrival on Earth of solar protons with relativistic energies, i.e., about a billion electron volts or more,* within 10 or 15 minutes after optical observation of the flare. These particles must consequently have traveled from the Sun to Earth with a velocity approaching that of light. Their distribution in space is highly anisotropic; that is to say, they nearly all come from roughly the same direction. The proton intensity rises rapidly to a maximum in a few minutes and then falls off gradually; the particles arriving later generally have lower energies (and velocities). This initial group of solar protons is followed by another, from one to several hours later, which closely resembles that causing the first type of solar cosmic-ray behavior. The spatial distribution of these protons is essentially isotropic, coming almost equally from all directions; they have somewhat lower energies than the protons which arrived earlier, and they continue for a day or two with steadily decreasing intensity and energy.

8.255. The solar cosmic-ray phenomena described above can be readily explained in terms of the plasma tongue model developed in § 8.235 *et seq.* Apparently under certain circumstances, which also generally lead to Type II and Type IV radio bursts, protons of high energy from several million to a few billion electron volts are emitted at the same time as, or soon after, the plasma cloud. These protons are presumably accelerated by the strong magnetic fields associated with some flares, but it is not known where or when this acceleration takes place.

8.256. Suppose that the situation is such that high-energy protons are produced simultaneously with the plasma emission. There will be a tendency for these protons to be trapped in the magnetic bottle; unless they have very high energies, the solar protons cannot readily escape from inside. The protons then spiral back and forth along the magnetic field lines many times as they are carried along in the plasma tongue. Consequently, when they reach the vicinity of Earth the individual protons are moving in all directions and have an essentially isotropic distribution. In Earth's atmosphere, some of the high-energy protons escape from confinement and are observed as solar cosmic

---

* According to the statement in § 6.181, footnote, a relativistic proton has an energy in excess of 939 million electron volts.

rays a day or so after the occurrence of the solar flare. The first type of behavior described in § 8.253 can consequently be explained in this manner. Incidentally, since the protons cannot readily cross the geomagnetic field lines,
they will tend to follow the field lines and enter the atmosphere in the polar
regions, thus producing the ionization responsible for the PCA effect (§ 8.121).

8.257. If a second solar disturbance, accompanied by high-energy protons,
follows within a day or so of an earlier one that may or may not have protons
associated with it, the situation that develops is the second type, as referred
to in § 8.254. If the plasma tongue from the first disturbance has reached Earth
by the time the protons from the second one are emitted from the Sun, these
protons can travel (spiral) along the existing magnetic field lines and reach
Earth in a very short time. They have velocities approaching that of light
and so can enter the atmosphere and be detected as solar cosmic rays in 20
minutes to an hour or so after leaving the Sun. Since the protons will have
come more or less directly from the Sun, their distribution should be anisotropic,
as actually observed. Some time after the arrival of what may be called the
prompt protons, others which have traveled back and forth along the field
lines in the plasma tongue will reach Earth and be observed as solar cosmic
rays of somewhat lower energy having an isotropic distribution.

8.258. There is evidence that some high-energy protons are either not trapped
or that they can escape from the magnetic bottle before it reaches Earth. A
situation of this kind developed during the period of November 11 and 12,
1960. A flare of moderate size occurred at 0305 hours on November 11, but no
significant number of high-energy protons was produced. The plasma cloud
traveled at the relatively slow rate of 800 kilometers (500 miles) per second,
but before it reached Earth, some 40 hours later, there was a second, much
more intense (Class 3+) flare, on November 12 at 1325 hours.

8.259. Within 15 minutes of observing the latter, solar cosmic ray protons
were detected on Earth. These protons traveled from the Sun to Earth in about
23 minutes, although the magnetic field lines in the solar plasma were not extended as far as Earth. It would appear, therefore, that the protons from the
second flare had escaped from the magnetic bottle formed by the first flare
(or were not trapped) and traveled directly to Earth. The plasma tongue en-
veloped Earth some six hours after the second flare, as indicated by the accompanying geomagnetic storm. At the same time, a neutron monitor recorded
the arrival of a second group of high-energy protons which had presumably
been trapped.

GALACTIC COSMIC RAYS AND THE GEOMAGNETIC FIELD

8.260. Since the primary cosmic rays are positively charged particles,* they
are affected by the magnetic fields of both Earth and the Sun. Two geomag-

* There is a small proportion of (negative) electrons in primary cosmic rays, but their
effect is not significant.

netic effects are of interest. Protons traveling in a direction at right angles to
or, in general, making a large angle with, the lines of Earth's magnetic field
tend to be deflected, whereas those moving along (or close to) the direction
of the field lines will not be affected (Fig. 8.29). If the galactic cosmic-ray

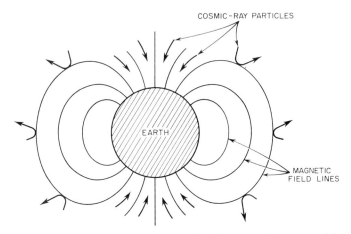

FIG. 8.29. Effect of Earth's magnetic field on cosmic-ray particles

particles come from all directions, as they apparently do, only those of very
high energy will be able to cross the field lines near the geomagnetic equator,
but closer to the magnetic poles a larger number will be able to follow the
field lines down to Earth. There is consequently a *latitude effect* in galactic
cosmic-ray intensity. Near the geomagnetic equator the intensity is a minimum,
but it increases fairly rapidly with geomagnetic latitude up to about 60°; at
higher latitudes the further increase is relatively small, for reasons that are
not altogether clear.

8.261. A second geomagnetic effect is the *east-west asymmetry;* more primary galactic cosmic-ray protons appear to be coming toward Earth from
the west than from the east. This observation, when first made in 1935, established that the particles were positively charged. According to an elementary
principle of electromagnetism, the geomagnetic field should produce an eastward deflection of particles with a positive electrical charge. Consequently,
to an observer on Earth, a larger number of protons would appear to be traveling toward the east than to the west; that is to say, more protons would be
coming from the west, as indeed they do.

8.262. Because of the importance of magnetic fields in determining the path
of a cosmic-ray particle, it has become the practice to describe such particles
in terms of the *magnetic rigidity,* rather than of their energy. The magnetic
rigidity is proportional to the product of magnetic field strength and the

radius of curvature of the path into which the charged particle is deflected by that field. Hence, in a given magnetic field, a particle of high magnetic rigidity will suffer less deflection than one of low rigidity. If a particle of rest mass m_0 and carrying a charge of Z units has an energy of E electron volts, the magnetic rigidity, M.R., in volts is given by

$$\text{M.R.} = \frac{\sqrt{E^2 + (m_0 c^2)^2}}{Z},$$

where c is the velocity of light.* In order to be consistent, the term $m_0 c^2$ must be expressed in electron volts; it is 939 million electron volts for a proton, for which $Z = 1$, and 3.725 billion electron volts for an alpha particle (helium nucleus), with $Z = 2$. Thus, a proton with an energy of 2 billion electron volts would have a magnetic rigidity of 2.2 billion volts; in general, for protons of energies of 2 billion electron volts or more, the energy in electron volts is not greatly different from the rigidity in volts. For a helium nucleus, however, this simple relationship does not apply.

Galactic Cosmic Rays and the Sun

8.263. The Sun causes variations in the intensity of galactic cosmic rays as observed in the general vicinity of Earth. The modifications, which are undoubtedly related to the solar magnetic field, may be either of regular occurrence, when they are small in magnitude, or irregular and large. The behavior is reminiscent of disturbances in the geomagnetic field and, in fact, both kinds of phenomena apparently have the same basic cause. The periods of the regular, but minor, variations are one day, 27 days, and approximately 11 years. The first is clearly related to rotation of Earth relative to the Sun and the second to rotation of the Sun, which brings active regions to face Earth every 27 days. The 11-year cycle is of particular interest since it shows clearly that the galactic cosmic-ray intensity is inversely related to the sunspot number. In other words, the galactic cosmic rays are most intense when the Sun is least active, and vice versa.

8.264. An extreme illustration of this inverse relationship was the discovery in 1937 by Scott E. Forbush in the United States that a marked decrease in intensity of galactic cosmic rays occurs soon after some solar flares. This is the large change of irregular occurrence mentioned above. For over 20 years it was not certain whether the *Forbush effect*, as it is designated, was due to disturbed (flare) conditions on the Sun extending toward Earth or whether the fluctuations in the geomagnetic field associated with the flare were responsible. A solution to the dilemma was provided by data obtained from the

---

* Some scientists express the magnetic rigidity in units of billion electron volts divided by the velocity of light, i.e., BeV/c; this is actually the momentum of the particle which, in these units, is numerically equal to Z times the rigidity in billion volts.

Pioneer V space probe. On March 30, 1960, when the probe was about 5 million kilometers (3 2 million miles) from Earth, there was a solar flare of Class 2^+. Some 20 hours later, several events were recorded almost simultaneously by the Pioneer V instruments: a plasma cloud, evidently coming from the Sun, passed by moving at a rate of almost 2000 kilometers (1200 miles) per second, the magnetic field strength increased to roughly ten to 20 times its normal average value in interplanetary space, and there was a marked Forbush decrease. A short time later, a somewhat smaller Forbush decrease was observed on Earth, accompanied by a sudden commencement geomagnetic storm. These observations appear to establish a direct relationship between the activity of the Sun, leading to an increase in the interplanetary magnetic field, and the decrease in the intensity of galactic cosmic rays.

8.265. In view of what has already been stated, it is evident that certain solar flares should be accompanied by a decrease in the galactic cosmic rays but an increase in those of solar origin. This correspondence was clearly demonstrated during the period of very intense activity on the Sun in the first part of November 1960, to which reference was made in § 8.258. On November 12, soon after the occurrence of the Class 3^+ flare, neutron monitors on Earth indicated a large increase in the intensity of solar protons with relativistic energies; at the same time, meson detectors, sensitive only to galactic cosmic rays, recorded a definite Forbush decrease.

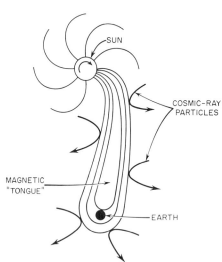

FIG. 8.30. Explanation of Forbush decrease of galactic cosmic-ray intensity

8.266. The solar plasma tongue concept described earlier provides a ready explanation of the Forbush decrease in the intensity of galactic cosmic rays at the time of certain solar flares. The magnetic field associated with the plasma tongue tends to deflect charged particles and only those having a moderately high energy and magnetic rigidity can penetrate the field lines (Fig. 8.30). Consequently, Earth is protected to some extent from the galactic particles by the plasma tongue; only the particles of higher energies can get through and so there is a decrease in the total intensity. The observations made on March 30, 1960 by the instruments on Pioneer V, namely, envelopment by a plasma cloud about 20 hours after a Class 2^+ flare, an increase in the magnetic field strength, and a Forbush decrease, are entirely compatible with the plasma tongue model.

EARTH'S RADIATION BELT

DISCOVERY OF THE VAN ALLEN RADIATION BELT

8.267. The discovery of what is now called the *Van Allen belt* of electrically charged particles surrounding Earth in 1958 is one of the most interesting results of recent space studies. That such a belt (or belts) exist within the magnetosphere came as a surprise to the scientific community, although their presence was, in a sense, anticipated. It has long been known that a magnetic field can confine electrically charged particles, and as far back as 1904 Carl Störmer in Norway had suggested that the geomagnetic field could act in this manner. Subsequently, others, including Hannes Alfvén (§ 6.132), whose theoretical studies have contributed greatly to the understanding of the behavior of plasmas in magnetic fields, considered the trapping of charged particles by the terrestrial magnetic field. In an experimental simulation of the phenomenon, Willard H. Bennett allowed a stream of electrons to impinge on a sphere with a magnetic field resembling that of Earth. Some of the patterns obtained bore a striking resemblance to that currently accepted for Earth's radiation belt.

8.268. As recently as 1957, S. F. Singer (§ 1.108) had proposed to account for ring currents, which may be responsible for the main phase of sudden commencement geomagnetic storms, by postulating the existence of a belt of trapped protons and electrons of relatively low energy surrounding Earth. In the same year, in a U.S. Atomic Energy Commission document of restricted circulation, Nicholas Christofilos had discussed the trapping by the geomagnetic field of charged particles resulting from the interaction of cosmic rays with the atmosphere. In this document, a test was proposed involving the introduction of electrons at high altitudes by the explosion of a fission bomb.* On the whole, therefore, by the year 1958, the existence of a belt (or belts) of corpuscular radiation, i.e., of protons and electrons, should not have been unexpected; what could not have been anticipated, however, was the permanence of the belts and the remarkably high energies of many of the trapped particles.

8.269. In continuation of their studies of cosmic rays, James A. Van Allen (§ 1.100) and his associates in the United States had prepared suitable instrumentation toward the end of 1957 for inclusion in the early Vanguard satellites, but these failed to go into orbit. Consequently, when plans were made to launch Explorer I (§ 1.114), a simple package of instruments was assembled hurriedly to be carried aloft by this satellite; the instruments included a Geiger counter for cosmic rays and a radio-telemetry system for direct, i.e., real time, transmission of data to Earth.

---

* The test was carried out successfully as Project Argus (§ 8.326) by exploding three bombs at an altitude of about 300 miles over the south Atlantic Ocean in August and September 1958, but by that time the discovery of the Van Allen belt had been announced.

8.270. Explorer I was launched successfully into an elliptical orbit (perigee 217 miles, apogee 1155 miles) at the end of January 1958, but the data received during the next few weeks were somewhat disconcerting. The number of cosmic-ray particles at first increased with altitude in a normal manner, as expected, but at a distance of over 800 kilometers (500 miles) from Earth, especially in the vicinity of the equator, the particle count appeared to drop sharply, sometimes falling almost to zero. It was highly improbable that there were no cosmic rays at these altitudes; hence, it was considered possible that the Geiger counter was not functioning properly.

8.271. Since the Explorer I instruments transmitted data in real time, the signals could be picked up only intermittently when the satellite was in range of a ground station. It was thus impossible to monitor the cosmic-ray intensities in a continuous manner. Consequently, detection equipment, similar to that used on Vanguard, was designed to permit continuous storage of information on tape and transmission to the ground upon command. This was included in Explorer III placed in orbit on March 26, 1958 (perigee 117 miles, apogee 1741 miles). The results were consistently in agreement over many orbits with those obtained from Explorer I. At altitudes of up to 500 kilometers (300 miles), the cosmic-ray particle count was normal; at 800 to 950 kilometers (500 to 600 miles), it increased rapidly up to many times the expected value, and then dropped to zero.

8.272. The explanation for the zero readings from the Geiger counters, proposed by Carl E. MacIlwain, is as follows. The entry of a charged particle or a high-energy (short wavelength) photon of electromagnetic radiation causes ionization of the gas in the Geiger counter; as a result, an electrical discharge can pass between the electrodes in the counter tube. By counting the rate at which these discharges take place, the rate of entry of charged particles or photons can be determined. It is a peculiar feature of the Geiger counter, however, that if discharges occur too rapidly to be differentiated, the device becomes saturated and ceases to count at all. Consequently, the zero readings received from the instruments carried to high altitudes by Explorer I and Explorer III could well have been due to extremely large counting rates. This interpretation proved to be correct.

8.273. Based on these conclusions, Van Allen reported on May 1, 1958 a new major phenomenon in geophysics, namely, the existence of a permanent, toroidal, i.e., doughnut-shaped, belt (or belts) of high-energy radiation, probably consisting of protons and electrons, surrounding Earth at an altitude above 650 to 800 kilometers (400 to 500 miles). An important point is that these high-energy particles are found at low and moderate, but not at high, latitudes. The presence of such particles in regions near the poles where auroras are commonly observed would not have been surprising, but the belt does not extend above geomagnetic latitudes of about 75°N or S.

8.274. The Geiger counters on the Explorer satellites could not distinguish between corpuscular and electromagnetic radiations. But the latter were ruled out as components of the belt because there was no known way in which they could be confined; charged particles, on the other hand, can be retained by a magnetic field, in this case that of Earth. In order to verify the conclusions reached from the early observations, particularly that the zero readings of the Geiger counters were indeed caused by an unexpectedly high intensity of charged particles, further experiments were included on Explorer IV which was placed in orbit (perigee 157 miles, apogee 1388 miles) on July 26, 1958. The instrument package included two Geiger counters, one of which was capable of giving high readings without becoming saturated, and two scintillation detectors. In one of the latter, the scintillator material was a plastic that responded only to electrons and protons of high energy, over 650 kilo-electron volts for electrons and above 10 million electron volts for protons. The other scintillator was a crystal of cesium iodide that was intended to measure the total energy of the incident particles rather than to count them individually.

8.275. The data from Explorer IV confirmed that the number of energetic particles did, in fact, increase steadily up to the maximum altitude of the satellite, i.e., 2235 kilometers (1388 miles), at latitudes between 50°N and 50°S. Moreover, it seemed certain that the belt of corpuscular radiations extended to greater altitudes, and this was proved to be so by instruments carried on Pioneer I, launched on October 11, 1958. The readings were not completely satisfactory, but they were clear enough to indicate that the radiation belt extended to tens of thousands of kilometers from Earth, with a maximum intensity at a distance of roughly 16,000 kilometers (10,000 miles).

8.276. Up to this point there was a question as to whether there was one radiation zone around Earth or whether there were two such zones. An answer was provided by the space probe Pioneer III, sent aloft on December 6, 1958. Although the apogee of its highly elliptical orbit did not reach the vicinity of the Moon, as had been intended, it transmitted excellent data, both on its outward and return journeys, at altitudes up to nearly 100,000 kilometers (62,000 miles) through the region of trapped corpuscular radiation. The results showed clearly that there were two distinct regions of high-energy particles (Fig. 8.31). In the inner zone, the peak intensity was attained at a distance of about 5000 kilometers (3000 miles) from Earth's surface, and in the outer zone at roughly 16,000 kilometers (10,000 miles); the latter maximum was the one detected by Pioneer I. Beyond 16,000 kilometers, the radiation intensity was found to fall off steadily and to be undetectable farther out than some 65,000 kilometers (40,000 miles). On the sunlit side of Earth, this approaches the limit of the geomagnetic cavity (§ 8.215).

8.277. Several Russian satellites, e.g., Sputnik II and Sputnik III, and space probes, e.g., Lunik I (Mechta) and Lunik II, launched during 1958 and 1959, and subsequently others, have carried Geiger counters for the study of cosmic radiations. The results apparently differ in some minor respects from those

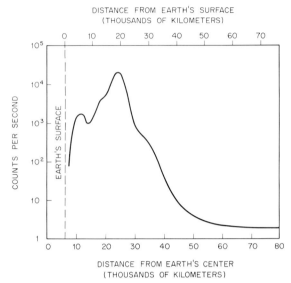

FIG. 8.31. Response of radiation counter on the spacecraft Pioneer III on December 6, 1958 (after J. A. Van Allen and L. Frank)

described above, but they provided definite confirmation of the broad concept of the existence of two regions of energetic charged particles extending outward from an altitude of approximately 800 kilometers (500 miles) to considerable distance in space. Although there are two zones of high-energy particles, it will be seen later that they may be regarded as components of a single radiation belt. Some of the characteristic properties and behavior of this radiation belt and speculations concerning its origin will be given later; the next section, however, will be devoted to a discussion of the factors which make it possible for the geomagnetic field to trap electrically charged particles, i.e., corpuscular radiation.

TRAPPING IN MAGNETIC FIELDS

8.278. Any charged particle in a magnetic field is subjected to a force acting at right angles both to the direction of the field and to that of particle motion (cf. § 3.197). As a result, a charged particle moving in a *uniform* magnetic field generally follows a helical (or spiral)* path of constant radius about a line of force, as indicated in Fig. 8.32. The only exceptions to this generalization arise when the charged particle happens to be moving exactly perpendicular to or parallel to the lines of the uniform magnetic field. In the former case, the spiral is flattened into a circle and in the latter case it is extended into a straight line.

---

* A helix is a three-dimensional curve whereas a spiral is generally, although not necessarily, two-dimensional, i.e., it lies in a plane. In the present connection, both terms are used indiscriminately, although helix is more precise.

These situations are unusual, however, because collisions with other particles would change the direction of motion.

8.279. In a magnetic field of uniform strength, the lines of force are parallel, but if the field is nonuniform, i.e., its strength changes from one point to another, the field lines are no longer parallel. Suppose, for example, that the field strength increases from left to right; the lines of force will converge, as in Fig. 8.33. The path of a charged particle in such a field is then a spiral of decreasing radius with tighter turns; moreover, the turns of the helix be-

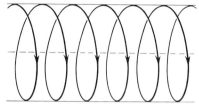

Fig. 8.32. Motion of electrically charged particle in a uniform magnetic field

come closer and closer to being perpendicular to the field lines. In other words, the *pitch angle*, i.e., the angle a turn of the helix makes with the field direction

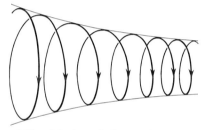

Fig. 8.33. Motion of electrically charged particle in a nonuniform magnetic field

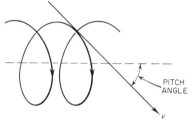

PITCH ANGLE

Fig. 8.34. Pitch angle of moving charged particle in a magnetic field

(Fig. 8.34) approaches **90** deg. The magnetic field then causes the direction of motion of the particle to be reversed, so that it now commences to spiral back in the opposite direction (Fig. 8.35).

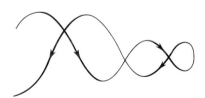

Fig. 8.35. Reversal of motion (reflection) of charged particle by a magnetic field

8.280. The reversal in motion of charged particles in a magnetic field of increasing strength is described as *reflection* in a *magnetic mirror*, and the point where reversal occurs is called a *mirror point*. If the magnetic field is stronger at both ends than in the middle, there will be two *conjugate* mirror points, one at each end. A charged particle can then be reflected at each mirror point and as a result it will, in principle, spiral back and forth continuously from one conjugate point to the other. In other words, the charged particle is trapped or confined by the magnetic field. Actually, as will be seen shortly, for trapping to result, certain conditions must be met, but it will be assumed for the present that this is the case.

8.281. Since Earth's magnetic field is stronger near the surface than it is at a distance, the lines of force are close together near Earth in one Hemisphere, then become farther apart as they move outward, and finally are close again in the other Hemisphere. There are thus mirror points at both ends, i.e., in each Hemisphere, and charged particles entering the geomagnetic field can be trapped. They will spiral back and forth, around the lines of force, from one Hemisphere to the other (Fig. 8.36). In general, this is how the Van Allen

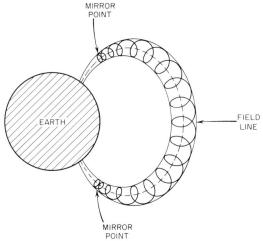

FIG. 8.36.   Spiral motion and mirror points of charged particle in Earth's magnetic field

radiation belt is formed. Because the charged particles are usually unable to move across but only along the geomagnetic field lines, the belt is effectively attached to and rotates with Earth.

CONDITIONS FOR REFLECTION

8.282. For reflection to be possible, the particle, while in the weaker region of the magnetic field, must have a significant component of velocity (or kinetic energy) in the direction perpendicular to the field lines. The actual velocity (vector), v, can be regarded as having two components at right angles to each other; one, $v_\perp$, is the component perpendicular to the field lines and the other, $v_\parallel$, is parallel to these lines (Fig. 8.37). Then, if $v_\perp$ is the perpendicular component in the region between the mirrors where the magnetic field is fairly uniform, at a strength B, the *minimum condition* for reflection is

$$\frac{v_\perp}{v} = \sqrt{\frac{B}{B_m}}, \qquad (8.15)$$

where B_m is the field strength at the mirror point. Since Earth's magnetic field is relatively uniform (and weakest) in the equatorial plane, the quantities $v_\perp$, v, and B in equation (8.15) refer to the values for a particle on a particular line of force in this plane.

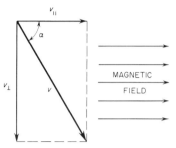

8.283. If the velocity component, $v_\perp$, perpendicular to the field lines is relatively small with respect to v, i.e. the pitch angle α is not large (cf. Fig. 8.34), then $v_\perp/v$ is also small; equation (8.15) shows that B_m must then be large for reflection to occur. In the case of Earth's magnetic field, the required value of B_m may exist only below the surface, and then trapping for

Fig. 8.37.   Components of velocity vector of charged particle in a magnetic field

the particular $v_\perp/v$ will not be possible. Consequently, if trapping is to take place, $v_\perp/v$ must be such that equation (8.15) can be satisfied with a magnetic field strength that exists above Earth's surface—actually as will be explained shortly, at an altitude of over about 650 to 800 kilometers (400 to 500 miles). It should be noted that the actual value of the particle velocity (or kinetic energy) is not important; it is the ratio $v_\perp/v$ that determines whether reflection is possible or not.

8.284. Another way of expressing the reflection condition is based on the fact that $v^\perp/v$ is the sine of the pitch angle, i.e., $\sin \alpha$, as is apparent from Fig. 8.37; hence, the condition expressed by equation (8.15) may be written as

$$\sin \alpha = \sqrt{\frac{B}{B_m}}.$$

The pitch angle of significance is the value the particle has in the equatorial plane. The smaller this pitch angle, the larger the value of B_m at which reflection will occur. In other words, the smaller the equatorial pitch angle (or $v/v_\perp$), the nearer to Earth's surface will be the mirror point, assuming reflection is possible.

8.285. If the charged particle descends to a level below 650 kilometers (400 miles) or so from Earth before being reflected, the chances that reflection will take place are greatly decreased. At these relatively low altitudes, the density of the atmosphere is such that the charged particle will probably collide with an atom or molecule. Electrostatic (coulomb) interaction between the charged particles and either positively charged nuclei or negative electrons present in the atoms (or molecules) causes the particles to be scattered, i.e., the direction of motion is altered. As a result of this scattering, the values of $v_\perp/v$ (or $\sin \alpha$) for some particles will be changed in such a manner as to make trapping impossible. Thus, the Van Allen belt of electrically charged particles surrounding Earth does not reach below about 650 kilometers. Most particles descending to lower levels before being reflected, because of the small values of $v_\perp/v$ (or of their pitch angles) in the equatorial plane, are not trapped. At higher altitudes, scattering collisions are so rare that they have an insignificant influence on the loss of particles from the magnetic mirror system.

8.286. Because of the asymmetries in the geomagnetic field, the altitude of the mirror points varies in different parts of the world. A charged particle with a certain value of $v_\perp/v$ (or pitch angle), moving along a given line of force, will always be reflected at the same value B_m of the magnetic field, as required by equation (8.15). Since the dependence of the geomagnetic field strength on altitude is not everywhere the same, reflection will take place at different altitudes. As a consequence of this situation, the lower boundary of the Van Allen belt varies correspondingly. It is especially low over the south Atlantic Ocean, for example, because of the magnetic field anomaly in this region.

8.287. Trapping of charged particles can be affected by the nature of the magnetic field. The condition of equation (8.15) is strictly applicable to an undistorted dipole field and the geomagnetic field has this character, approximately at least, in much of the magnetosphere. Toward the boundary of the geomagnetic cavity, where the field lines are distorted by the solar wind (cf. Fig. 8.23), trapping of charged particles cannot be realized. This sets a rough upper altitude limit to the Van Allen belt. An increase in the energy density (or pressure) of solar plasma associated with activity in the Sun may cause compression and distortion of the normally undisturbed outer regions of the geomagnetic field. Many particles previously trapped in this region will then escape when they reach their former mirror points.

8.288. As a consequence of the outer boundary limits, determined by the geomagnetic cavity, the Van Allen radiation belt lies between approximately 75°N and 75°S latitude on the sunlit side of Earth and between 70°N and 70°S latitude on the dark side. At higher latitudes, charged particles cannot be trapped but will tend to follow the field lines into the atmosphere in the polar regions.

DRIFT OF TRAPPED PARTICLES

8.289. In addition to the back and forth spiral motion of charged particles between the conjugate mirror points in Northern and Southern Hemispheres, there is another type of movement caused by the decreasing strength of Earth's magnetic field with increasing altitude, i.e., in the radial direction. The effect of this radial gradient in the geomagnetic field is to introduce a force on a charged particle in a direction perpendicular to the field lines. The result is that the particles are caused to drift around the globe, the positively charged particles (protons) from east to west, and those with negative charges (electrons) from west to east. It is the combination of this drift, the lower and upper altitude limits, and the latitude limits that is responsible for the doughnut-like (or toroidal) shape of the trapped particle region. The toroid is, of course, not symmetrical because of the asymmetry of the magnetic field within the geomagnetic cavity (Fig. 8.38).

8.290. The drift of the electrically charged particles in opposite directions is equivalent to a ring current. But the normal current in the Van Allen belt is not large and does not have any great effect on the geomagnetic field. When

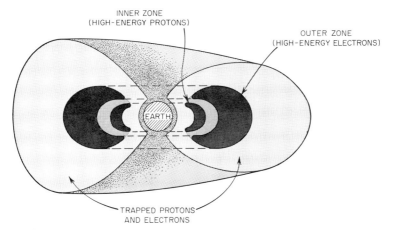

INNER ZONE
(HIGH-ENERGY PROTONS)

OUTER ZONE
(HIGH-ENERGY ELECTRONS)

EARTH

TRAPPED PROTONS
AND ELECTRONS

Fig. 8.38. Section through a toroidal region of trapped electrically charged particles in Earth's magnetosphere

the plasma accompanying a solar flare reaches the vicinity of Earth, there could be an increase in the number of charged particles. If so, it can be seen from the foregoing discussion that, if they were trapped, they would automatically produce a ring current such as has been postulated to account for the main phase of a sudden commencement type of geomagnetic storm.

Characteristics of the Radiation Zones

8.291. It has become apparent, as a result of continued studies, that there is actually only one radiation belt surrounding Earth, in which both positive and negative particles are trapped by the geomagnetic field. But when the energy distribution of the charged particles is considered, it is clear that there are two (and possibly more) distinct zones. These two regions are called the *inner* and *outer zones*, respectively, of Earth's (Van Allen) radiation belt. By early 1959, the data from Pioneer III had established that there were two regions of energetic particles, but the instruments could not distinguish between protons of moderate energy and electrons of higher energy. Soon afterward it was determined with the aid of suitable detectors, described below, that the inner zone contained energetic protons. But two years were to elapse before the high-energy particles in the outer zone were shown to be electrons.

8.292. Between the two zones is a region where the intensity of energetic charged particles is considerably lower than within the zones; this has been called the *slot*. It should be understood that in the slot there are fewer protons and electrons of high energy per unit volume than in the inner and outer belts, respectively; but the total number of protons or electrons of all energies, mostly of low energy, per unit volume will not be greatly different in the several regions. Attention so far has been focused on the trapped high-energy particles, largely because their existence presents a scientific problem of considerable interest. They are also more important than charged particles of low energy as far as radiation hazards to human beings in space (§ 13.102) and damage to solar cells (§ 3.255) are concerned. It is from the energetic particles that means for protection must be sought.

8.293. From preliminary rough observations made with Explorer IV instruments, it appeared probable that the energetic, highly penetrating radiation of the inner zone was made up of protons with energies on the order of 100 million electron volts. This was confirmed by S. C. Freden and R. S. White in the United States early in 1959 by means of *nuclear emulsions* flown in sounding rockets with recoverable nose cones. A nuclear emulsion is a type of photographic film which, after development, shows tracks produced by electrically charged particles; from the character and length of the tracks the particles can be identified and their energy evaluated. The results showed that the inner Van Allen zone contained energetic protons, many with energies in the range from 20 to 40 million electron volts; some even had energies as high as 600 to 800 million electron volts. Subsequent experiments have indicated a very wide range of energies, from 0.1 (and less) up to 800 million electron volts; the number of protons having a particular energy decreases as the energy increases.

8.294. After it was found that the high-energy particles in the inner zone of the Van Allen belt are protons, it was assumed that those in the outer zone are electrons. Data from the lunar probe Pioneer IV, launched March 3, 1959, were susceptible of two different interpretations: there was either a very large number of electrons of moderate energy, e.g., less than 0.1 million electron volt, in the outer zone, or a smaller number with considerably higher energies. It was not until toward the end of 1961 that the more refined instruments carried by the satellite Explorer XII, launched on August 15, 1961 (perigee 180 miles, apogee 47,800 miles), showed that the energetic radiation of the outer Van Allen zone consisted of electrons with energies in excess of 1 or 2 million electron volts.* There are, in addition, large numbers of electrons of low energy and an approximately equal intensity of low-energy protons.

8.295. In a series of reports, starting in 1960, K. I. Gringauz and his associates in the U.S.S.R. have argued in favor of a third radiation zone of elec-

---

* Because of its smaller mass, an electron has a much higher velocity than a proton of equal (kinetic) energy. It is not possible to state a definite relationship for the high energies under consideration, because relativity effects change the masses.

trons located at about 10 Earth radii. Other observers, e.g., J. W. Freeman, J. A. Van Allen, and L. J. Cahill (1963), have confirmed from measurements with Explorer XII that there is sometimes an increase in the density of electrons of moderate energy (about 10 kilo-electron volts), but it occurs in the disturbed region beyond the magnetopause (§ 8.219).* The electrons are not trapped by the geomagnetic field and should therefore not be regarded as part of Earth's radiation belt. This point of view will be adopted here. In addition to the two normal radiation zones, which will be considered first, artificial zones, some transient and one of longer duration, have been produced by the explosion of nuclear devices. These will be discussed separately because they must be regarded as being temporary in nature.

GYROMAGNETIC RADIUS

8.296. One reason why protons of high energy are not found in the outer radiation zone is that the loops of the spiral path they follow along the magnetic field lines are large enough to bring them into the lower regions of the atmosphere. As a result, they become scattered and can escape from Earth's magnetic trap. The radius, r, of the helical path of a particle of mass m, carrying an electric charge e, moving in a magnetic field of strength B, and having a velocity component $v_\perp$ perpendicular to the field lines is

$$r = \frac{mv_\perp c}{eB},\tag{8.16}$$

where c is the velocity of light in a vacuum. This is the *gyromagnetic radius* of the particle often, although incorrectly, called the Larmor radius. It is the radius of gyration of the charged particle about a magnetic field line. In comparing protons and electrons, it is apparent that, other things being equal, the gyromagnetic radius of a proton will be about 1840 times that of an electron, since this is the ratio of their masses. Furthermore, in general, an increase in the total velocity (or energy) will be accompanied by an increase in the component $v_\perp$ for the trapped particles. Hence, an increase in energy will also cause an increase in radius of the helical path.

8.297. It follows, therefore, that a proton of high energy may follow a spiral path of such large radius as to bring it below the 650-kilometer (400-mile) altitude level in the course of its gyrations. Such a proton will tend to escape from the geomagnetic trap. It can be seen from equation (8.16) that the radius is decreased when the field strength, B, is increased. Hence, energetic protons can remain trapped only in parts of the Van Allen belt near to Earth because the geomagnetic field is then relatively strong. At greater distances, only protons of low energy, with relatively small gyromagnetic radii, can be prevented

---

* Some of the observations from Lunik II were apparently made in the magnetically neutral layer in the geomagnetic tail (§ 8.220a), where energetic electrons are expected (N. F. Ness, 1964).

from escaping in the manner described. This restriction does not apply to electrons because the energies are rarely, if ever, large enough for the gyromagnetic radii to be more than a few kilometers; for protons these radii may well be several hundred (or even thousand) kilometers.

PROTON FLUX CONTOURS

8.298. The Van Allen radiation belt undoubtedly contains electrons and protons of energies covering a wide range, from a fraction of an electron volt to several million electron volts. Furthermore, the spatial distribution is not only different for the two types of charged particles, but it also depends on the particular energy (or energy range) under consideration. Even with the limited data that have been obtained so far, a representation of the structure of the radiation belt is a complicated matter. Additional problems arise from the variability of the composition and dimensions with time, and from the differences on the day and night sides of Earth caused by the distortion of the geomagnetic cavity.

8.299. A general picture of the structure of the Van Allen belt may be obtained by considering separately the distributions of protons and of electrons in a few limited energy ranges, as in the contour diagrams in Fig. 8.39 A and B. The contours are lines of constant proton *flux*,* expressed as the number of protons passing through an area of 1 square centimeter per second. The flux is numerically equal to the product of the particle density, i.e., number of protons per cubic centimeter, and their velocity (for the given energy), in centimeters per second.

8.300. Figure 8.39 A shows the constant flux contours in the inner radiation zone for protons of energies in excess of 30 million electron volts. The distances are in units of Earth radii, as measured from the center of Earth; the altitude is thus 1 Earth radius less at each point on the axis. The contours in Fig. 8.39 B are for protons of lower energy, in the range from 0.1 to 5 million electron volts; they extend to about 10 Earth radii and so include both inner and outer radiation zones. The data in Fig. 8.39 are not to be regarded as precise because the energy and space distributions of the protons are somewhat variable. The idealized contours are intended only to provide a general idea of the distribution of protons in two limited energy ranges that are trapped in the magnetosphere.

8.301. The inner zone is remarkably constant in the number of energetic particles and in the distribution of energy among them. Small changes have been observed but they occur gradually over a period of time. There is some correlation with solar activity, but the effects may arise from atmospheric density variations rather than from any significant change in the number of energetic protons. As far as is known, the inner radiation zone is symmetrical

---

* Radiation instruments generally measure the rate at which particles enter and this is related to the particle flux, as defined here.

about Earth's axis, i.e., it is much the same on the day and night sides. This is presumably due to the fact that the zone is so close to Earth that it is essentially unaffected by the asymmetry of the magnetic cavity.

8.302. Upon referring to Fig. 8.39 A, it is evident that the maximum flux of high-energy protons is attained at about 1.5 Earth radii, i.e., at a distance of

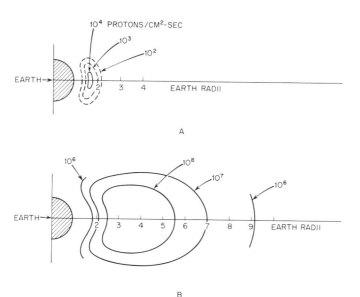

FIG. 8.39. Idealized proton flux contours: (A) protons with energies greater than 30 million electron volts (a secondary maximum at 2.2 Earth radii is not shown); (B) protons with energies between 0.1 and 5 million electron volts (after J. A. Van Allen)

roughly 3200 kilometers (2000 miles) from the surface. A slightly lower peak has been reported at 2.2 Earth radii, but this is difficult to show on the small scale of Fig. 8.39 A. The region of maximum flux at 1.5 Earth radii is often referred to as the *heart* of the inner radiation zone. It is important to realize in connection with the contours that, although the proton fluxes appear to be high, the actual number of protons with very high energies is quite small. A proton kinetic energy of 30 million electron volts corresponds to a particle velocity of 7.6×10^9 centimeters per second.* The maximum indicated flux in Fig. 8.39 A of 10^4 protons per square centimeter per second thus represents a density of $10^4/(7.6 \times 10^9)$, i.e., $1/(7.6 \times 10^5)$ protons per cubic centimeter, i.e., an average of only one energetic proton in about 7.6×10^5, i.e., nearly a million, cubic

---

* The kinetic energy in ergs is $\frac{1}{2}mv^2$, where m is the proton mass in grams, i.e., 1.67×10^{-24}, and v is the velocity in centimeters per second; since 1 million electron volts is 1.60×10^{-6} erg, it is readily found that v is 7.6×10^9 centimeters per second. This calculation is valid for nonrelativistic protons, i.e., with energies appreciably less than 939 million electron volts (§ 8.254, footnote).

centimeters. Away from the heart of the inner belt the density of these high-energy protons is even less.

8.303. The number of highly energetic protons is thus seen to be small and, moreover, they constitute a small proportion of the total number of protons present in the inner zone of the radiation belt. A re-examination by D. N. Anderson, W. H. Bennett, and L. C. Hale in 1964 of data obtained earlier by the latter from a sounding rocket indicates that the total ion (proton) density in the atmosphere increases steadily from an altitude of 4200 kilometers (2600 miles) up to 5400 kilometers (3400 miles), the maximum height attained. The observed increase, from 1.4×10^3 to 4×10^3 protons (of all energies) per cubic centimeter, is almost certainly due to trapping by the geomagnetic field. If the kinetic temperature of the particles is assumed to be 2000°K, the average energy would be about 0.3 electron volt. Hence, the radiation belt must contain protons (and presumably electrons) of low (and moderate) energy in very much greater numbers than the particles of high energy.

ELECTRON FLUX CONTOURS

8.304. The idealized electron flux contours are shown in Fig. 8.40 A and B. In Fig. 8.40 A, the contours are for electrons with energies in excess of 1.6 million

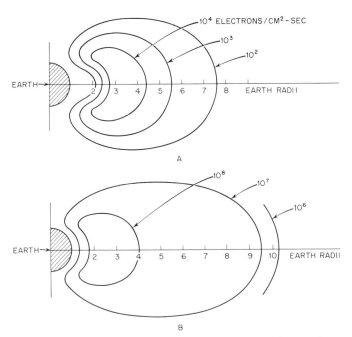

FIG. 8.40. Idealized electron flux contours: (A) electrons with energies greater than 1.6 million electron volts; (B) electrons with energies greater than 40 kilo-electron volts to scale (after J. A. Van Allen)

electron volts; this diagram consequently represents the distribution of these particles in the outer zone of the Van Allen belt. The electron velocities are close to the velocity of light, i.e., 3×10^{10} centimeters per second.* The structure and dimensions of this belt are subject to marked fluctuations, especially at times of exceptional solar activity (§ 8.315). The data in Fig. 8.40 A are roughly applicable to the daylight side of Earth under normal relatively quiet solar conditions. On the night side, the contours of the lower fluxes are squeezed together to some extent, so that the 10^7 electrons per square centimeter per second contour intersects the horizontal axis at about 7 Earth radii. At greater distances, the flux decreases rapidly, falling to 10^4 and less within a very short range.

8.305. It is seen from Fig. 8.40 A that, under normal conditions, the heart of the outer radiation zone is at about 3.5 Earth radii, i.e., some 16,000 kilometers (10,000 miles) from the surface. The so-called slot between inner and outer zones, where the flux of highly energetic charged particles is less than it is at both smaller and larger distances from Earth, is just beyond 2 Earth radii, i.e., at an altitude of about 12,700 kilometers (8000 miles).

8.306. Figure 8.40 B shows the flux contours of electrons of somewhat lower energy, in excess of 40 kilo-electron volts, i.e., 0.040 million electron volts,† extending throughout the radiation zones. Since the fluxes of high-energy electrons, as given in Fig. 8.40 A, are quite small in comparison with the values at the same locations in Fig. 8.40 B, the latter may be taken as indicating effectively the constant flux contours for electrons with energies between 40 kilo-electron volts and 1.6 million electron volts (and probably less).

8.307. An examination of Figs. 8.39 B and 8.40 B shows that they are not very greatly different. This means that protons and electrons of moderate energies, and probably also of low energies, are spread in a more-or-less similar manner throughout both zones. This is the justification for the statement made in § 8.291 that there is really only one belt around Earth in which charged particles are trapped by the geomagnetic field. Protons and electrons of high energy, however, are found in different zones of the radiation belt.

ORIGIN OF THE INNER RADIATION ZONE

8.308. The flux of high-energy protons in the inner zone is relatively steady, whereas the energetic electron flux has been known to change as much as a thousandfold soon after the occurrence of a solar flare. It is reasonably certain, therefore, that the energetic particles in the two zones come from different sources. The view suggested by N. Christofilos (§ 8.268) and developed by S. N.

---

* These electrons are relativistic (energy in excess of 0.51 million electron volt) and so their kinetic energy cannot be represented by $\frac{1}{2}mv^2$, where m is the conventional (or rest) mass of the electron.

† Electrons of this energy are nonrelativistic and their velocity can be calculated in the conventional manner by taking the electron mass to be 9.1×10^{-28} gram. The velocity of a 40-kilo-electron volt electron is thus found to be nearly 1.2×10^{10} centimeters per second.

Vernov in Russia, and by S. F. Singer and others in the United States, is that the protons in the inner zone originate mainly in galactic cosmic rays. Because their energies are so high, many cosmic-ray protons (and other nuclei) can cross the lines of the geomagnetic field and reach down into the tangible atmosphere. Here they interact with atomic nuclei to produce neutrons and other particles, as described in § 8.248. The neutrons have a wide range of kinetic energies as a consequence of the distribution of energies among the cosmic-ray protons.

8.309. A neutron is stable while it is a constituent of an atomic nucleus, but is unstable when in the free state; it then breaks up (or decays) into a proton and an electron. The half-life, i.e., the time required for half the neutrons present at any instant to decay in this manner (cf. § 3.242), is about 15 minutes. Since the mass of a proton is very close to that of a neutron, whereas the mass of an electron is very much less, essentially all of the original kinetic energy of the neutron is transferred to the proton into which it decays. Consequently, the protons have roughly the same energy distribution (spectrum) as did the original neutrons. The electrons, however, acquire a very small proportion of the neutron's kinetic energy, and the maximum energy they can attain is a little more than 0.78 million electron volts, i.e., the energy always released when a neutron decays. Thus, the interaction of cosmic rays with the atmosphere can result in the formation of protons with energies up to many million electron volts, but the accompanying electrons will have energies ranging from essentially zero to about 0.8 million electron volt.

8.310. Before they undergo decay, the neutrons are free to travel in all directions; since they have no electric charge, they can cross the geomagnetic field lines without hindrance. The neutrons moving upward, away from Earth, are called *albedo* (or *reflected*) *neutrons* (cf. § 5.18a). Many of these will decay at altitudes above 650 kilometers (400 miles) or so, and then the protons and electrons formed will be trapped by the terrestrial magnetic field. It is in this manner that the inner radiation zone could be formed and replenished. Galactic cosmic rays are thought to be responsible for the protons in the inner part of the belt, out to 1.6 Earth radii; at greater distances, solar cosmic rays apparently make a significant contribution.

8.311. According to the neutron-albedo theory, the rate of injection of energetic protons by this mechanism is only about one particle per cubic centimeter in a million years. This may seem very small, but it will be recalled that the density of highly energetic protons in the inner zone is also extremely small. There are reasons for believing that, on the average, a proton remains trapped for several hundred years. Thus, a very slow injection rate would be sufficient to maintain the inner radiation zone.

8.312. The neutron-albedo theory appears to account reasonably well for the energy spectrum of the high-energy protons and also, to some extent, for the variation of the flux with altitude. It does not explain, however, some of the minor features of the inner radiation zone, including the secondary maximum in the flux of high-energy protons at 1.22 Earth radii. Moreover, the neutron-albedo theory fails completely when applied to the electrons, in either the inner or outer zone. For these and other reasons, some scientists have felt the theory is inadequate and propose to reject it. Be that as it may, it must be admitted that the neutron-albedo theory is the only reasonable working hypothesis proposed so far to explain quantitatively any of the features of the inner Van Allen zone. Additional mechanisms must presumably be involved to account for the low-energy protons and the electron distribution.

Origin of the Outer Radiation Zone

8.313. The origin of the high-energy electrons in the outer radiation zone is even less well understood. Because there is some correspondence between solar activity and the flux of energetic electrons, it is probable that the energy of the electrons originates in the Sun. The presence of electrons (and protons) is not surprising, since they are continually being brought in by the solar wind and solar plasma, but it is difficult to understand why the electrons have such high energies. Suppose that the outer Van Allen zone were in temperature equilibrium; an average kinetic energy of 1 million electron volts would correspond to the impossibly high temperature of about 10 billion (10^{10}) degrees. Such electrons could not possibly have come *directly* from the Sun or from any other known source.

8.314. The proton-electron plasma accompanying many solar flares travels with a velocity of about 1600 kilometers (1000 miles) per second, on the average; the kinetic energy of an electron with this velocity would be only 7 electron volts.* This is insignificant in comparison with the electron energies in the outer radiation zone. The relatively low energy of the electrons in the plasma from the Sun has been confirmed by observations from the space probe Pioneer V. It encountered a cloud of solar (flare) plasma about 8 million kilometers (5 million miles) from Earth, but the Geiger counter, which was sensitive only to electrons with energies in excess of 20 kilo-electron volts, showed no significant increase in counting rate. Evidently, the electrons in the solar plasma have low energies.

8.315. Before attempting an explanation of the origin of the highly energetic electrons in the outer radiation zone, it is of interest to consider the behavior of this zone at the time of a solar flare associated with a geomagnetic storm. As a general rule, but not necessarily always, within a short time after instruments on Earth's surface indicate the onset of a storm, the flux of highly energetic electrons may decrease, sometimes by a factor of four or so; the decrease is most marked at the heart of the outer zone, and there may be an accompanying increase at closer distances, indicating that some kind of rearrangement is

---

* The energy of the accompanying protons would be 1840 times greater, i.e., about 13 kilo-electron volts, because of their larger mass.

taking place. The overall high-energy flux then increases to a maximum that may be ten to a thousand times as great as the prestorm value. Subsequently, there is a gradual decrease, over the course of several days, to something like the initial value of the energetic electron flux.

8.316. Observations such as these appear to establish a relationship between the solar plasma and the structure of the outer Van Allen zone. Under normal, quiescent conditions, it may be the solar wind that supplies the electrons and possibly also the protons for the outer zone. But how these charged particles of low energy are able to cross the magnetic field lines and enter the magnetosphere, and how they are subsequently accelerated are matters for speculation.

8.317. Although the manner in which electrons enter the outer trapped radiation zone is uncertain, there is some evidence that entry may occur through the tail of the geomagnetic field (§ 8.215). Observations, made by J. H. Wolfe and R. W. Silva (1964) with instruments on the IMP-I and IMP-II satellites, of the plasma in the turbulent boundary zone lying beyond the magnetopause indicated that the particle energy in the tail region is not very different from that on the sunward side of Earth. Since the magnetic field is much weaker in the former region, it would be easier for charged particles to enter the magnetosphere through its tail. Furthermore, theoretical considerations lead to the view that the magnetically neutral sheet, which apparently exists on the dark side of the geomagnetic cavity (§ 8.220a), should be the repository of charged particles of high energy. This plasma may be the source of the energetic electrons trapped in the radiation belt. Some low-energy electrons are always present in the magnetosphere as a result of the ionization of hydrogen atoms by solar radiation; the problem of crossing the magnetic field lines does not then arise. Such electrons (and others of low energy) might be accelerated, and their energy increased, by distortion of the outer regions of Earth's magnetic field by the solar wind. Another possibility is that oscillations of the geomagnetic field, possibly induced by hydromagnetic waves in the solar wind, accelerate the electrons as a result of the *betatron effect.**

8.318. It was explained in § 8.240 that the cloud (or tongue) of plasma associated with certain solar flares may cause severe distortion of the lines of force of the outer geomagnetic field. As a result, high-energy electrons already trapped could either have their energies reduced or they could escape into the atmosphere by a decrease in the altitude of their mirror points, or both of these and other changes could occur. In any case, the effect would be to decrease the flux of energetic electrons in the outer radiation zone, as has been observed. Subsequently, as the magnetic field recovered, electrons, either those of low energy already present or others trapped from the solar plasma, would be accelerated, thereby producing the observed increase in the high-energy flux. In due course, electrons in excess of the normal value would be lost, by escape

---

* The action is similar to that in the laboratory device called a betatron in which electrons are accelerated to high velocities by means of an oscillating magnetic field.

or by redistribution of their energy. The general behavior of the outer radiation zone at the time of a geomagnetic storm might be accounted for in this
manner.

8.319. Auroral displays, for which electrons of about 10 kilo-electron volts
energy are believed to be responsible (§ 8.349), frequently accompany magnetic
storms. It was consequently postulated at one time that the auroral electrons
were those which had been "dumped" from the outer zone into the atmosphere
soon after the onset of the storm. Later, however, it was realized that the
total energy of the electrons lost from the radiation belt was quite insufficient
to excite the aurora. Furthermore, sounding rocket studies of the electrons in
the auroral regions showed that the energy spectrum was completely different
from that in the outer radiation zone.

8.320. An alternative view is that the outer Van Allen zone is not the
source of the auroral electrons, but merely an incidental region in which a
relatively small proportion of accelerated electrons are trapped at the time
of a solar disturbance. The majority of the electrons from the Sun are not
trapped but escape into the auroral regions. It is suggested that the high-
velocity plasma from the Sun distorts the geomagnetic field with the result
that, in some manner not yet understood, the low-energy electrons already
present in the magnetosphere and those coming in from the Sun are accelerated
to some extent. The spiral trajectories of most of these electrons apparently
have very low pitch angles, so that they are precipitated into the atmosphere
at high (auroral) latitudes.* Electron energies of about 10 kilo-electron volts
are sufficient to cause the formation of auroras and the large X-ray bursts that
are often observed at the same time.

8.321. A small proportion of the electrons will inevitably have an appreciable
velocity component perpendicular to the field lines, i.e., large pitch angles; these
are consequently trapped by the geomagnetic field and remain in the outer
radiation zone. As they spiral back and forth along the field lines from one
mirror point to the other, the electrons are presumably accelerated further by
disturbances in the magnetic field until they attain energies of about a million
electron volts.

8.322. Direct observations of energetic electrons leaving the radiation belt
during periods when the Sun is quiet have shown that, over a wide range of
latitudes and at distances from 2 to 10 Earth radii, the rate of escape is much
greater in the daytime than at night. This result suggests that the normal solar
wind distorts the magnetic cavity sufficiently to permit some of the trapped
electrons to leak out of the trapping region. The escape that sometimes
accompanies a geomagnetic storm may thus be regarded as one of the conse-

---

* In order to avoid the word "dumping" which is associated with the now discarded
theory, it has been proposed that "precipitation" be used to indicate the complex process
occurring in the geomagnetic field. The end result is that electrons of moderately high
energy enter the atmosphere and produce various effects, including auroras.

quences of the extensive disturbance of Earth's magnetic field. Within a short time, however, the loss is more than made good by the process outlined above.

8.323. It will be apparent from the foregoing discussion that, although a general picture of Earth's radiation belt is emerging, there is a great deal about its origin and behavior, including numerous phenomena not mentioned here, that cannot yet be explained. Clearly, much further study is required and new experimental techniques must be developed to provide data that have not been available hitherto. The results in this significant area of space science will eventually provide a clearer understanding of many geomagnetic and atmospheric phenomena.

Artificial Radiation Zones

8.324. Several artificial zones of trapped radiation, of various lifetimes, have been produced by deliberately introducing electrons into Earth's magnetic field. When nuclear fission occurs (§ 3.165), essentially all of the fission product nuclei formed are radioactive, emitting beta particles, i.e., electrons, with an average energy of roughly a million electron volts. The rate of particle emission is very great immediately after fission, but it falls off gradually with time. Consequently, by exploding a nuclear fission bomb at a high altitude, it is possible to inject large numbers of high-energy electrons into the geomagnetic field. Furthermore, the decay of neutrons released in the explosion of a thermonuclear (fusion) weapon also results in the liberation of electrons. Observation of these artificially injected electrons should make it possible to obtain information concerning the trapping characteristics of Earth's magnetic field.

8.325. On August 1 and August 12, 1958, nuclear bombs, each with a total energy yield in the range of a megaton, i.e., a million pounds of TNT equivalent, were exploded at altitudes of approximately 80 kilometers (50 miles) and 44 kilometers (27 miles), respectively, over Johnston Island in the Pacific Ocean at 16°N latitude. Within a second or less of the detonation, in each case, a brilliant aurora was observed to form in the vicinity of the weapon residues. About a minute later, an aurora was seen at Apia, in the Samoan Islands, more than 3200 kilometers (2000 miles) away at 14°S latitude. These auroras were undoubtedly excited by the trapped electrons as they spiraled along the geomagnetic field lines between the conjugate mirror points, i.e., in the Northern and Southern Hemispheres. Although the weapon residues rose after the explosion, the mirror points of many electrons were fairly low in the atmosphere with the result that they suffered scattering collisions that permitted them to leak out of the geomagnetic field trap. After a few days, most of the electrons in the artificial radiation belt created by the nuclear explosion had escaped and had been absorbed in the atmosphere.

8.326. A few weeks later, on August 27, August 30, and September 6, 1958, three small fission bombs, with energy yields between 1 and 2 kilotons, i.e., 1000 to 2000 tons TNT equivalent, were set off about 500 kilometers (300 miles) above the south Atlantic Ocean in connection with the secret Project Argus. The electrons traveled back and forth, between the conjugate mirror points in the Northern and Southern Hemispheres, and at the same time drifted from west to east around the globe. Consequently, each of the three shots produced a well-defined radiation belt about 100 kilometers (60 miles) deep at from roughly 1.7 to 2.2 Earth radii. Measurements with Geiger counters on the Explorer IV satellite showed that energetic electrons were trapped in the artificial belts for several weeks, but they gradually escaped.

8.327. A different situation developed after the Starfish event of July 9, 1962 in which a 1.4-megaton nuclear device was detonated at a height of 400 kilometers (250 miles) over Johnston Island. Brilliant auroras were observed both near the burst point and some 4800 kilometers (3000 miles) away in the Southern Hemisphere near New Zealand. The Starfish explosion produced a belt of intense radiation, which severely damaged solar cells of the p-on-n type (§ 3.255) carried by the Transit IVB, TRAAC, and Ariel satellites. In addition, it caused considerable disturbance of the geomagnetic field and increased the ionization in the ionosphere to such an extent that radio communication was disrupted over a large area. These two effects disappeared after a few days, but the radiation belt, although decreasing in intensity, is likely to remain for several years.

8.328. The residues from the Starfish explosion rose with great rapidity into the extremely tenuous atmosphere; hence, most of the electrons were released at much greater heights than the injection altitude of 400 kilometers. These electrons rapidly formed a radiation belt around Earth within the lower levels of the natural inner radiation zone. The high-energy proton flux in this zone was disturbed to some extent but the distribution returned to normal within a few months. The situation with regard to the electrons, however, was quite different. Three satellites capable of measuring radiation fluxes, namely, Injun I, Ariel, and TRAAC, were in orbit at the time of the Starfish explosion and another, Telstar I, was launched the following day. Ariel and TRAAC provided a limited amount of data before their solar cells were too severely damaged, but Injun I and Telstar I continued to operate for some time.

8.329. All the instruments indicated a very marked increase in the flux of energetic electrons, commencing at an altitude of some 650 kilometers (400 miles) and extending to approximately 4 Earth radii. Considering electrons with energies in excess of 0.25 million electron volt, the flux rose rapidly with increasing distance from Earth and attained a maximum at an altitude of about 1300 kilometers (800 miles); it then decreased fairly slowly out to roughly 1.7 Earth radii (altitude 4500 kilometers or 2800 miles), and then more slowly into the outer part of the Van Allen belt. The initial flux of additional electrons at the maximum was estimated to be as high as 10^9 electrons per square centimeter per second.

8.330. Since it was first formed, the Starfish radiation zone has decayed in a peculiar manner which throws some light on the lifetime of electrons in the normal radiation zones. At the lowest levels, which reach into the atmosphere, the loss of electrons has occurred fairly rapidly, but at higher altitudes, particularly between 1.2 and 1.7 Earth radii, i.e., in the inner zone, the decay has been relatively slow. Estimates indicate that the added electrons in this region will be detectable for perhaps as long as ten years or more. Beyond 1.7 Earth radii, the decay rate was much more rapid; at approximately 2.5 Earth radii, for example, the high-energy electrons had practically disappeared within two months after the explosion. It is considered that the loss of electrons from the artificial belt up to 1.7 Earth radii is mainly the result of atmospheric scattering; since this is not very effective at altitudes above 650 kilometers, the radiation decays slowly. Beyond 1.7 Earth radii, i.e., in the outer radiation zone, the dominant factor is thought to be fluctuations in the geomagnetic field, possibly as a result of solar disturbances; but this is pure conjecture as direct evidence is lacking.

8.331. An interesting feature of the artificial Starfish belt is the associated synchrotron electromagnetic radiation (§ 6.181). Electrons with relativistic energies, i.e., greater than about 0.5 million electron volts, when spiraling about the lines of force of Earth's magnetic field should produce synchrotron radiation in the radio-frequency range. Such radiation should therefore be emitted by the electrons in the outer zone of the Van Allen belt. Efforts to detect it by means of instruments on the ground have not given positive results because the expected intensity of the synchrotron radiation is not greatly in excess of the general background of radio noise.

8.332. Following the Starfish explosion, the large flux of energetic electrons in a region where the geomagnetic field strength is greater than in the outer radiation zone caused a marked increase in the synchrotron radiation. This was observed unequivocally in the frequency region around 50 megacycles per second and provided confirmation of the theoretical arguments that such radiation should be emitted by relativistic electrons in a magnetic field. The synchrotron radiation from the Starfish electron belt has decreased slowly in the course of time, in accordance with the slow decay of the energetic electron flux at distances between 1.2 and 1.7 Earth radii.

8.333. Three nuclear bombs were exploded at great heights by the U.S.S.R. on October 22, October 28, and November 1, 1962. Artificial radiation belts were produced at altitudes higher than the Starfish belt, namely, about 2 Earth radii, i.e., in the slot between the inner and outer Van Allen zones. As seen above, decay of the high-energy electron flux in this region takes place fairly rapidly; hence, the belts disappeared within a few weeks. The rapid decay may have been partly due to disturbances in the geomagnetic fields but an important consideration might be the high latitude at which the Russian bombs were exploded. In view of the form of the geomagnetic field, charged particles injected at latitudes above 70° or 75°N would tend to escape readily (cf. § 8.288).

THE AURORA

8.334. The most striking visible phenomenon of the night sky is the luminosity called the *aurora;** it is most frequently observed in a roughly circular band between about 65° and 70° magnetic latitude, known as the *auroral zone,* in the Northern Hemisphere. There is a similar zone in the Southern Hemisphere which is less well defined because of scarcity of data; it appears, however, to be a few degrees closer to the south magnetic pole. Auroras occur less frequently at higher latitudes and at lower latitudes down to about 45°. Only at times of intense auroral activity can auroras be seen below this geomagnetic latitude. The top of a distant aurora can, however, sometimes be detected in middle latitudes as a glow just above the horizon.

8.335. Many different auroral types have been described and classified according to their appearance (Fig. 8.41). Broadly, two general categories may be recognized, namely, auroras with rays and those without rays; in each category there are various shapes, e.g., arcs, bands, draperies, etc. The patterns are sometimes steady and at other times in continuous motion. Frequently, there is a change from one shape to another, either gradually or suddenly, often with a quiet period in between. The most common auroral colors are green, greenish yellow, or greenish blue. When the activity is strong, the auroras are often reddish, and color changes from green to red have been reported. On rare occasions auroras are orange, blue, or violet.

8.336. From photographs of auroras obtained simultaneously from two stations, from 35 to 350 kilometers (22 to 220 miles) or so apart, it is possible to compute the altitude. The presence of a known star in the background helps to identify the respective directions in which the photographs are taken. For the great majority of auroras, the lower border (or base) is at an altitude of 100 to 115 kilometers (60 to 70 miles); auroras with bases below 80 kilometers (50 miles) or above 160 kilometers (100 miles) are uncommon. The upper level is variable, but a height of 320 kilometers (200 miles) appears to be a reasonable average. Sunlit auroras, to which reference will be made shortly, can be seen at greater heights. Long horizontal arcs generally extend, often for hundreds of kilometers, along parallels of magnetic latitude; that is to say, the geomagnetic field strength is the same over the whole of their length. From below, these arcs are seen to be quite narrow, e.g., about 800 meters (0.5 mile) or less,

---

* The name *aurora borealis* or northern dawn (from *Aurora,* the Roman goddess of dawn, and *Boreas,* the Greek god of the north wind) was proposed by the French philosopher Pierre Gassendi about 1620. At the latitude of northern France, the most common appearance of the aurora is as a faint dawnlike glow above the northern horizon. The corresponding phenomenon in the Southern Hemisphere was later called *aurora australis,* from the Latin, *auster,* "south wind" or "south."

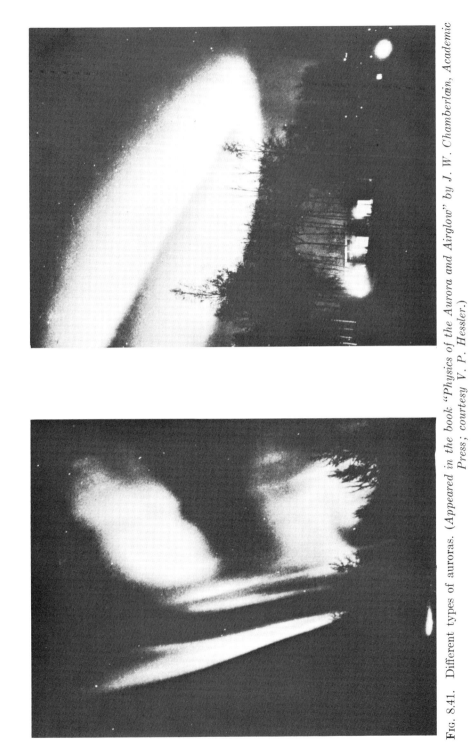

Fig. 8.41. Different types of auroras. (*Appeared in the book "Physics of the Aurora and Airglow" by J. W. Chamberlain, Academic Press; courtesy V. P. Hessler.*)

566

and sometimes several form parallel bands. Rays are generally directed along Earth's magnetic field lines. The location of the auroral zone and the relation of auroral structure to the geomagnetic field suggest that electrically charged particles play an important role in the development of the luminosity. This has been confirmed in various ways.

8.337. A high electron density in the aurora is demonstrated, for example, by the ability to reflect radar waves, just as do meteor trails (§ 7.93) and the ionosphere. Thus, the radar echo technique has proved a useful means for studying auroras, especially in the daytime. The results show that they occur predominantly at night, although echoes have been obtained before sunset during periods of marked auroral activity.

8.338. There is a definite correlation between the frequency and intensity of auroras and solar activity, thus providing further evidence for the influence of charged particles. Auroras are more common in years near sunspot maximum than at sunspot minimum. In addition to this 11-year cycle, there is the same 27-day cycle, attributed to the solar M regions, as has been found for geomagnetic storms, solar wind velocity, etc. In view of these facts, it is not surprising that auroras are especially intense, and are observed at low latitudes, at times when solar flares produce terrestrial disturbances. It should be mentioned, however, that at certain times of the year, particularly near the equinoxes in March and September, there is a display somewhere in the auroral zone almost every night, except when the sunspot number is small.

8.339. If observations are made soon after sunset, when the lower atmosphere is in shadow but the upper levels are still in sunlight, auroras can be seen at these higher altitudes extending up to 500 or 750 kilometers (300 or 450 miles) and occasionally above 1000 kilometers (600 miles). These are called *sunlit auroras.* Later at night, they cease to be visible and only the normal auroras can be seen at lower altitudes. During the transition period, the sunlit auroras are often observed to extend downward into the shadow region. There is then a break or, at least, a marked decrease in brightness between the dark and sunlit portions of the aurora.

Auroral Spectra

8.340. Auroral spectra have been studied extensively; they consist of a large number of lines, including the line spectra of atomic oxygen and nitrogen and, to a smaller extent, hydrogen, and the band spectra of neutral and ionized nitrogen molecules. Since the auroral luminosity usually begins above an altitude of 100 kilometers (60 miles), where oxygen molecules are not common, the spectra of molecular oxygen are either absent or weak.

8.341. An important aspect of most auroral spectra is the green line of atomic oxygen at 5577 Å, called the auroral *green line,* which also occurs in nightglow spectra (§ 8.86). It is responsible for the green color frequently seen in auroras. For many years the identity of this line was in doubt, and it was not until

1928 that it was observed in laboratory spectra of atomic oxygen. The auroral green line is a forbidden line, although in a somewhat different respect than the forbidden lines in the solar corona (§ 6.156). The upper (excited) energy level of the oxygen atom involved in the transition leading to emission of the green line (cf. Fig. 8.10) is a *metastable state;* that is to say, if undisturbed, it can exist for a moderately long time—an average of almost a second *—before its excess energy is radiated as the 5577 Å line.

8.342. Under laboratory conditions, the excited atom will usually strike the walls of the containing vessel or collide with other atoms or molecules frequently during its lifetime; as a result, its excess energy will be dissipated as heat. The green spectral line will then not be produced. At auroral (and nightglow) altitudes, however, the atmospheric density is so low and collisions so rare that the excited oxygen atom can retain its energy for at least a second. The radiation transition to the lower (intermediate) energy state can then take place with the emission of the energy difference as the 5577 Å green line. This line has now been obtained in the laboratory by taking precautions to prevent the excited state of atomic oxygen from losing its energy during its normal lifetime.

8.343. The red auroral luminosity is due partly to the three closely spaced (triplet) lines of atomic oxygen at 6300, 6364, and 6391 Å that are characteristic of the high-level nightglow. Like the auroral green line, the triplet is forbidden because the upper energy state has a long average lifetime, namely, 110 seconds. For the reason given in § 8.91, the red line spectrum of atomic oxygen extends to higher altitudes than does the green line. The forbidden triplet has been produced in the laboratory, so that it is now known definitely to belong to the spectrum of atomic oxygen.

8.344. An important contribution to the red color of auroras, particularly at the lower altitudes, is made by the (first positive) band spectrum of molecular nitrogen; these bands also extend into the infrared. Other auroral spectra of nitrogen molecules include the forbidden Vegard-Kaplan bands in the visible (green and blue) region and a (second positive) band system in the ultraviolet. The spectrum of molecular nitrogen ions, N_2^+, is also present; the first negative band system is strong in the blue, violet, and ultraviolet, and the Meinel negative system appears in the infrared. The latter band spectrum was first detected in auroral spectra and subsequently obtained in the laboratory. Incidentally, the first negative system of N_2^+ ions is especially strong in the sunlit auroras and accounts for their gray-violet and blue colors.

8.345. Forbidden lines of atomic nitrogen have been detected in the spectra of high-altitude aurora; these include a violet line (3466 Å) and a doublet (5198 and 5201 Å) in the blue region. They arise from metastable states of long life and so can be produced only at great heights where the atmospheric

---

* As a general rule, the lifetime of an excited state is on the order of a hundred-millionth part (10^{-8}) of a second.

density is extremely low. Moreover, it is only at these high altitudes that significant concentrations of nitrogen atoms exist.

8.346. The Balmer lines of atomic hydrogen (§ 6.81) in auroral spectra are of special interest; they are exceptionally broad and are shifted considerably in the direction of shorter wavelengths. These phenomena are due to the Doppler effect arising from motion of the hydrogen atoms toward Earth at high velocity, up to 3200 kilometers (2000 miles) per second. The direction of motion was found to be along the geomagnetic field lines and so the source of the hydrogen atoms producing the spectra appears to be protons and electrons entering the atmosphere from outside. The atoms, being neutral, would travel in all directions, and not preferably along the lines of force as electrically charged particles do.

ORIGIN OF AURORAS

8.347. Charged particles evidently enter the atmosphere during periods of auroral activity. The measured velocity of the hydrogen atoms does not, however, provide any specific information concerning the velocity (or energy) of the protons from which they originate. In order to produce a line spectrum, the proton must first capture and combine with an electron to form a neutral (excited) hydrogen atom, and this cannot take place until the proton has slowed down to the observed velocity of the atom, i.e., about 3200 kilometers per second. The only conclusion that can be drawn, therefore, is that the protons entering the atmosphere must have had at least this velocity, i.e., an energy of at least 5 kilo-electron volts. Direct observations made with sounding rockets show that protons with a few hundred kilo-electron volts energies are actually present in auroral regions.

8.348. In reviewing the facts presented above, it is apparent that electrically charged particles, either protons or electrons (or both), are responsible for the formation of auroras. Such particles of moderately high energy can cause excitation of oxygen and nitrogen atoms and nitrogen molecules, and also ionization of the latter with subsequent excitation of the molecular nitrogen ions, thereby accounting for the observed spectra. In the sunlit spectra an additional process occurs, namely, excitation of the N_2^+ ions by sunlight, and the subsequent emission of the lines of the first negative band system as a result of fluorescence scattering (§ 8.95, footnote).

8.349. To obtain further information on the origin of auroras, sounding rockets have been flown into auroras and auroral regions; the results of these flights are of considerable significance. In the first place, bursts of X-rays, with photon energies (cf. § 6.76) of about 10 kilo-electron volts, often accompany auroral displays. The most reasonable explanation of these radiations is that they are bremsstrahlung (§ 6.51) produced by electrons in the same energy range. Radiation detectors on sounding rockets have indicated the presence of both energetic protons and electrons; but whereas there is a good correlation between the electron flux and the auroral intensity, this is not the case for the protons. In agreement with the X-ray observations, electrons with energies of about 10 kilo-electron volts are most prominent in auroras, and fluxes of over 10^{11} electrons per square centimeter per second of this energy have been recorded. It is concluded, therefore, that auroras are produced largely by the interaction of these electrons with the atoms and molecules in the atmosphere. Most of the interaction takes place at altitudes between 100 and 320 kilometers (60 and 200 miles) where the majority of auroral displays occur.

8.350. At times of solar activity there is an increase in the amount of the proton-electron plasma reaching Earth from the Sun; on these occasions the auroral activity increases. It is certain, however, that the charged particles do not enter the atmosphere directly. In the first place, the electrons do not have sufficient energy; furthermore, if they came in directly they would enter the atmosphere preferably along the field lines leading to the magnetic pole, whereas auroras are most frequent at about 20° latitude from the poles. The conclusion to be drawn, as described in § 8.320 *et seq.*, is that the low-energy plasma enters the outer part of Earth's radiation belt, where the charged particles are temporarily trapped and are accelerated in some manner. They then escape into the atmosphere at the higher latitudes and the electrons with energy in the vicinity of about 10 kilo-electron volts excite the aurora. The rate at which the more energetic electrons leave the belt during quiescent periods is greater in the daytime (§ 8.322), but it would appear that the auroral electrons escape more readily at night.

8.351. Two other observations favor the view that the electrons are held, for a short period at least, in the outer region of the radiation belt. First, electrons will escape mainly at the latitudes of the so-called "horns" of the belt, i.e., where the flux contour lines approach Earth most closely (cf. Fig. 8.40). The reason is that the geomagnetic field lines along which the most of the electrons spiral enter the atmosphere in these regions. The prevalence of auroras around the geomagnetic latitudes of 70°N and 70°S and the tendency for some auroras to follow the lines of geomagnetic latitude can thus be accounted for. At times of strong solar activity, the electrons enter the atmosphere at lower latitudes and auroras are visible down to about 45° geomagnetic latitude. Second, it has been found that auroras occur simultaneously in Northern and Southern Hemispheres. While temporarily trapped by the geomagnetic field, the electrons will travel back and forth, from north to south, along the field lines; hence, it is probable that some will escape and produce auroras in each Hemisphere.

SATELLITES FOR GEOPHYSICAL AND INTERPLANETARY STUDIES

THE OBSERVATORY SPACECRAFT

8.352. In the earlier Explorer satellites and the Pioneer space probes, from which were obtained many of the data given in earlier sections of this chapter, it was necessary to achieve a high degree of integration among the experiments and also between the experimental equipment and the subsystems of the space-craft itself, e.g., for attitude and thermal control, communication and data handling, etc. This situation was determined chiefly by the desire to make full use of the somewhat limited capability of the launch vehicles. Each spacecraft was thus designed and constructed for a single mission, and considerable mechanical, electrical, and thermal redesign was necessary to mount a different set of experiments.

8.353. The space observatory concept has been developed in order to over-come this drawback and to provide greater flexibility by making the experi-mental and spacecraft subsystems essentially independent. The availability of more powerful launch vehicles, such as the Atlas-Agena combination (§ 3.149), has made this possible. Satellites and probes of the individual type will still be useful for specialized experiments; but the observatories will permit changes to be made from one set of experiments to another for successive missions with-out the necessity for a complete redesign of the spacecraft.

8.354. An important objective of the Orbiting Geophysical Observatories (OGO) is to make a wide variety of measurements to provide a better under-standing of Earth's atmosphere, ionosphere, and magnetosphere, and of Earth-Sun relationships. While in orbit, parts of the spacecraft can be oriented to-ward or away from Earth and the Sun, as well as forward and aft in the orbital plane of the satellite.

Basic Structure of the OGO

8.355. The basic structure of the OGO is a rectangular box, measuring 6 feet by 3 feet by 3 feet; the size is limited by weight restrictions and the need to fit within the nose fairing of the Agena upper stage rocket. One of the 3-foot by 6-foot faces is always oriented toward Earth; on the inside of this and the parallel face are mounted the experiments carried in the interior. The instru-mentation for most of these experiments is contained in 8-inch cube boxes, but a bigger space is available in the interior of the structure for exceptionally large equipment. Although the first OGO's will carry about 20 experiments, it will be possible to increase the number up to 50 in due course.

8.356. The solar cell arrays are mounted on two panels attached to a shaft that passes through the faces at right angles to those described above. Since the solar arrays are always maintained perpendicular to the incident sunlight, the faces through which the shaft passes are never exposed to the Sun; they can thus be used to radiate heat from the experimental equipment in the interior. Two Solar Oriented Experimental Packages (SOEP), attached to the solar-cell panels, are for instruments that must be oriented toward the Sun, whereas the Orbital Plane Experimental Packages (OPEP), on a shaft at right angles to the one carrying the panels, are for experiments that face parallel to the plane of the satellite orbit.

8.357. Two booms, each 22 feet in length, which extend in orbit, are provided for experiments that are especially sensitive to the proximity of the main body of the spacecraft. The four shorter booms, 4 feet long, are for experiments that are not sensitive to location or for those requiring limited angles of observation. The radio beacon (tracking) and telemetry antennas are also mounted on booms to maintain proper antenna patterns and to remove them from the field of view of the body-mounted experiments. Gas-jet nozzles for attitude control are attached to booms to provide leverage and thus minimize the mass of gas required.

8.358. With booms and panels extended (Fig. 8.42), the overall measurements of the OGO are 59 feet by 50 feet. Its total weight is over 1000 pounds, of which about 170 pounds consists of instruments for experiments. The vehicle

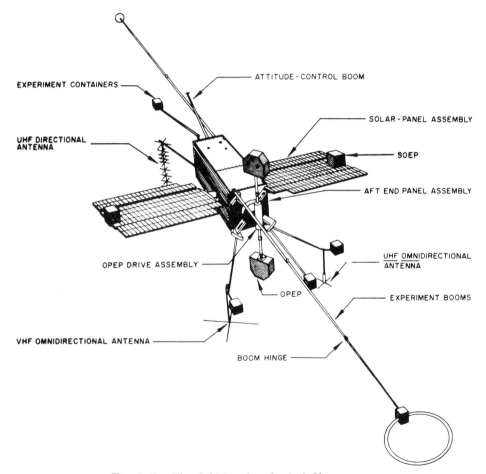

Fig. 8.42.   The Orbiting Geophysical Observatory

is designed to permit an increase in weight to 1500 pounds, with most of the increase to be available for experiments. A possibility being considered is the capability of carrying a subsatellite, weighing 300 pounds, which will separate from the OGO in orbit; the subsatellite will either permit a completely separate environment that may be needed for some measurements or make possible experiments requiring a large distance between component parts.

8.359. Two types of orbit are planned for the OGO's. One is highly eccentric, to permit the spacecraft to reach out to more than 20 Earth radii; the angle of inclination of the orbital plane is to be about 30 deg. A spacecraft launched on such an eccentric orbit is sometimes referred to as an EGO (Eccentric Geophysical Observatory). The second type of orbit has a much smaller eccentricity, a smaller apogee distance, but a larger inclination, namely about 80 deg, of the orbital plane; the vehicle is then called a POGO (Polar Orbiting Geophysical Observatory). A satellite in one of these orbits will stay within the ionosphere, but below the Van Allen radiation belt; by virtue of its near-polar orbit, it will cover the whole of Earth at least once every day (cf. § 5.34).

8.360. Among the experiments to be carried on the OGO's in eccentric orbits are measurements of the following quantities: solar plasma flux, energy, and direction; galactic and solar cosmic-ray flux and energy; geomagnetically trapped proton and electron fluxes and energies; charged particle densities and composition; atmospheric composition; magnetic field strength and direction; and Lyman-α and radio-noise bursts from the Sun. One of the main objectives of the OGO's in near-polar orbits is to map the geomagnetic field at relatively low altitude in all latitudes and longitudes, thus providing a link between surface and space observations for the World Magnetic Survey. Other quantities to be measured include ionosphere and atmospheric composition; ionization and cosmic rays over polar regions; proton and electron fluxes in auroral zones; energy spectrum and composition of galactic and solar cosmic rays; spectrum of the airglow; and galactic and terrestrial radio emissions.

Orbiting Geophysical Observatory-I

8.361. The first Orbiting Geophysical Observatory (OGO-I) was launched from Florida on September 4, 1964 by means of an Atlas-Agena rocket, first into a low-altitude orbit, and then by restarting the Agena upper stage into a highly eccentric orbit. The perigee was 175 miles and the apogee 92,200 miles, i.e., about 23 Earth radii; the orbital period is almost 64 hours, and the angle of inclination 31 deg. One of the experimental booms did not extend properly in space, and as a result the Earth sensor was obscured. The satellite was then spin-stabilized, but this partially impaired some of the experiments.

Interplanetary Explorer Satellites

8.362. The primary mission of the series of Interplanetary Explorer Satellites, formerly called the Interplanetary Monitoring Platforms (IMP), is to

measure magnetic fields, cosmic rays, and solar wind in the space lying outside Earth's magnetosphere. Some of the instruments carried are rubidium-
vapor and fluxgate magnetometers to measure the strength and direction of the
interplanetary magnetic field; Geiger counters and ionization chambers to
study the energetic charged particles; and electrostatic and other analyzers
to determine the characteristics of the solar wind. In order to avoid interference of the weak magnetic field of the satellite itself, the magnetometers
are mounted on booms which extend to a distance of 6 feet for the rubidium-
vapor device and 7 feet for the fluxgate instruments (Fig. 8.43). Although the

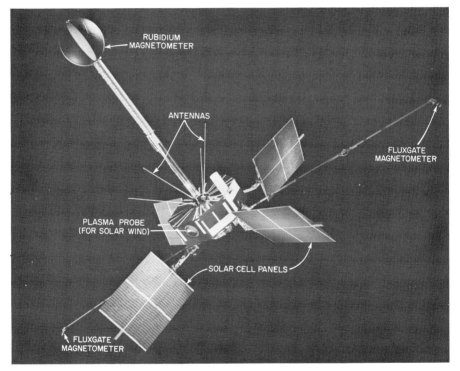

FIG. 8.43. Interplanetary Explorer Satellite (or Interplanetary Monitoring Platform,
IMP-I)

main objectives of the Interplanetary Explorer Satellites will be the same, the
experiments will probably vary from one flight to another. The first member
of the series, which discovered the shock wave beyond the magnetosphere, was
referred to in § 8.218.

APPENDIX

GRAVITATIONAL POTENTIAL

8.363. The gravitational potential of Earth at a point exterior to its surface can be expressed as the sum of a series of spherical harmonics. But if, as a first approximation, the variation of the potential with longitude is neglected, and an appropriate north-south center point (or equatorial plane) is chosen, the expression for the geopotential, U, reduces to the form

$$U = -\frac{GM}{R_0}\left[\frac{R_0}{R} - \sum_{n=2}^{\infty} J_n \left(\frac{R_0}{R}\right)^{n+1} P_n(\sin\theta)\right],$$

where G is the universal constant of gravitation, M is the mass of Earth, R_0 is Earth's equatorial radius, R is the distance from Earth's center at which U is the potential, the J_n's are constants, P_n represents the Legendre polynomial of order n, and θ is the latitude of the point under consideration. The J_n's, starting with J_2, are the quantities, commonly referred to as the zonal harmonics, which are determined from a study of satellite orbits. It is seen that if all the J_n's are zero, the potential reduces to $-GM/R$; this is the value for a sphere and is equivalent to $-K/R$ in § 2.103.

THE BAROMETRIC EQUATION

8.364. Consider a vertical column of gas of unit cross section in which the particles (molecules, atoms, and ions) have come to equilibrium with gravity. Let p be the pressure at an altitude h and $p - dp$ at the altitude $h + dh$; it will be noted that the pressure decreases with increasing altitude. Since equilibrium exists, the difference in pressure dp between the two layers dh apart, acting upward, is balanced by the gravitational force, acting downward, of the particles contained between the two layers. If ρ is the density of the gas, the downward pressure (force per unit area) is $\rho g dh$, where g is the acceleration due to gravity; both ρ and g refer to the altitude h (or $h + dh$). It follows, therefore, that

$$dp = -\rho g dh.$$

If n is the number of particles per unit volume and m is the average mass of the particles, then ρ is equal to mn, and hence,

$$dp = -mng dh.$$

Furthermore, by the kinetic theory of gases, $p = nkT$, where k is the Boltzmann constant, i.e., the gas constant per particle, and T is the absolute temperature; consequently, if T is constant,

$$dp = kTdn = -mngdh$$

or

$$\frac{dn}{n} = -\frac{mg}{kT}\,dh.$$

For two altitudes, h_1 and h_2, that are not too far apart, both T and g are essentially constant, so that the foregoing expression may be integrated; thus,

$$\int_{n_1}^{n_2} \frac{dn}{n} = -\frac{mg}{kT} \int_{h_1}^{h_2} dh$$

and hence

$$\ln \frac{n_1}{n_2} = -\frac{mg}{kT}\,(h_1 - h_2),$$

where n_1 and n_2 are the particles densities at the two altitudes. This is the barometric (or hypsometric) equation given in § 8.45.

The Geopotential Altitude

8.365. The work done in raising a unit mass vertically through a distance dh against gravity at a point where the gravitational acceleration is g is given by gdh; this represents the potential energy of the unit mass. The potential of the unit mass at a height h above sea level, where the geopotential is arbitrarily taken as zero, is then obtained by integrating gdh from zero to h; thus,

$$\phi = \int_0^h gdh.$$

The geopotential altitude, h', is defined so that the potential ϕ is equal to $h'g_0$, where g_0 is the gravitational acceleration at sea level; hence,

$$h' = \frac{1}{g_0} \int_0^h gdh.$$

Since g varies inversely as the square of the distance from Earth's center, it follows that

$$g = g_0 \left(\frac{R_0}{R_0 + h}\right)^2$$

and upon making this substitution, the expression for h' becomes

$$h' = R_0{}^2 \int_0^h \frac{dh}{(R_0 + h)^2}$$

$$= \frac{R_0 h}{R_0 + h},$$

as in § 8.45.

The Adiabatic Lapse Rate

8.366. According to § 8.26, the lapse rate may be represented by $-dT/dh$, and this may be readily evaluated by writing

$$-\frac{dT}{dh} = -\frac{dp}{dh} \cdot \frac{dT}{dp}.$$

From the first equation in § 8.364,

$$-\frac{dp}{dh} = \rho g.$$

For an ideal gas, the entropy change, dS, per unit mass for a given process can be written as

$$dS = c_p \frac{dT}{T} - r \frac{dp}{p},$$

where c_p is the specific heat (per unit mass) of the working substance and r is the gas constant per unit mass. For an adiabatic change, $dS = 0$, and so it follows that

$$\frac{dT}{dp} = \frac{rT}{pc_p}$$

Furthermore, for an ideal gas, $\rho = p/rT$, and hence it is readily found that, for adiabatic expansion (or contraction) in the atmosphere, the lapse rate is given by

$$-\frac{dT}{dh} = \frac{g}{c_p}.$$

The adiabatic lapse rate is generally expressed in °K (or °C) per kilometer, and the simplest way to evaluate it in these units is to derive it first as °C per meter, i.e., in MKS units, and then multiply by 1000. Thus, g is 9.82 meters per second per second and c_p for air is 1.02×10^3 joules per kilogram per °C; hence, it follows that the adiabatic lapse rate is 9.6°C per kilometer.

Chapter 9

THE MOON

INTRODUCTION

9.1. The prospect of investigations by means of instrumented spacecraft and at a later date by manned expeditions has made the study of the Moon one of the most important current aspects of space science. Telescopic observations extending over a period of more than three hundred years have revealed the general characteristics of the lunar surface and in recent years photometric, radar, and other techniques have provided information on some details. But, as will be seen in the course of this chapter, there are few aspects of the Moon's origin, history, and structure concerning which there is general agreement among scientists. Moreover, there is little hope that the controversial issues can be resolved without direct access to the Moon. The photographs taken from the Ranger spacecraft in 1964 and 1965 have clarified some points, but there are still many questions that remain unanswered. When more is known, however, of the chemical and mineral composition, physical characteristics, and distribution of the lunar material, both on and below the surface, the situation may well undergo a spectacular change.

9.2. Among the bodies of significant size in the solar system, the Moon is probably one of the few that have preserved many of the basic features of their past history. The factors which produce changes on Earth's surface, namely, erosion by the atmosphere (wind) and by flowing water, are virtually or completely absent from the Moon. The appearance of the lunar landscape, with the numerous craters in many areas, indicates that there has been little large-scale distortion of the surface as a result of tectonic (deformation) activity such as has led to the formation of mountains on Earth.

9.3. The Moon's surface has undoubtedly disintegrated to some extent under the continuous impact of small meteorites and perhaps as a result of the action of cosmic (including solar) radiations. The effect of such bombardment would be expected to be greater than on Earth because the virtual absence of an atmosphere on the Moon would mean that the meteoroids are not slowed down and the radiations are absorbed to a minor extent only. On the whole, however, the changes, other than those produced by large meteorites, are relatively minor. Consequently, many of the existing broad features of the Moon are probably more than four billion (4×10^9) years old. It is commonly believed, therefore, that a detailed study of the lunar surface will not only provide information concerning the history of the Moon itself, but will also supply important clues relating to the origin of the solar system.

THE SUN-EARTH-MOON SYSTEM

MOTION OF THE EARTH-MOON SYSTEM

9.4. The Moon is a natural satellite of Earth, so that, in the simplest terms, the Moon may be regarded as revolving about Earth, under the influence of the terrestrial gravitational field, while Earth revolves around the Sun. But the actual motions of both the Moon and Earth are much more complicated. The Sun, Earth, and Moon constitute a three-body system in which each member attracts—and is attracted by—the other two. The mathematical equations representing the motions in such a system are so complex that they are considered to be insoluble (cf. § 7.55). Approximations must consequently be used in order to describe the motions of Earth and the Moon, and these approximations are later refined by applying successive corrections. The situation is favored by the fact that the gravitational influence of the Sun on the Moon (or the Earth-Moon system) is significantly less than that of Earth. This is indicated by a comparison of the lengths of the orbital periods, i.e., a year and a month respectively. As a first step, therefore, it is permissible to treat Earth and the Moon as constituting a separate system.

9.5. It was realized by Isaac Newton when he developed the theory of gravitation (§ 2.13) that, under the influence of their mutual attraction, two bodies would revolve, with the same period, about their *common center of mass* or *barycenter* (Greek, *baros*, "mass"). Let M_A and M_B in Fig. 9.1 be the masses of two such bodies, with M_A being greater than M_B. The point A is the center of mass of M_A and B is the center of mass of M_B (§ 2.46, footnote); the barycenter of the two-body system is then at the point C, where

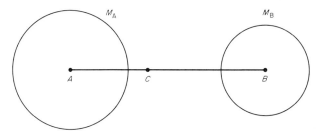

FIG. 9.1.   Two-body system and barycenter

$$M_A \times AC = M_B \times BC. \tag{9.1}$$

Thus, the barycenter is closer to the center of mass of the heavier of the two
bodies. In the case of the Earth-Moon system, for example, the barycenter
actually lies within the interior of Earth (§ 9.7, footnote) because the mass of
the latter is more than 80 times that of the Moon. For an artificial satellite of
Earth, the ratio of the masses is so large that the barycenter may be regarded
as being located at Earth's center of mass.

9.6. The revolution of the two bodies about their barycenter is represented
in Fig. 9.2; the body A is at A_1 when B is at B_1, A is at A_2 when B is at B_2,

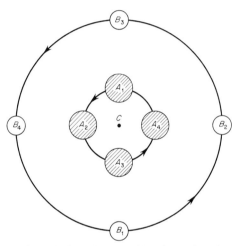

FIG. 9.2.   Revolution of two bodies about their barycenter

and so on. The behavior is essentially the same as if the two bodies were attached to each other by a rod which rotates about an axis through the barycenter of the system at C. It is seen from the figure that each body revolves
in the same direction, with an orbit of the same shape. The radii of the orbits
are inversely proportional to the masses, in accordance with equation (9.1);
in other words, the larger the mass of the body, the smaller is its orbit. For
simplicity, the orbits in Fig. 9.2 are assumed to be circular, but the general
conclusions are applicable to elliptical orbits, as is the case in the Earth-Moon
system.

9.7. In considering the motion of the Earth-Moon system about the Sun, it
is a good approximation, in view of the large mass and the great distance of the
latter body, to suppose that it is the Earth-Moon barycenter that revolves
about the Sun in accordance with Kepler's laws (§ 2.48).* Thus, strictly speak-

* The Earth-Moon barycenter actually revolves about the Sun-Earth-Moon barycenter.
The latter is, however, only some 300 miles from the center of the Sun.

ing, it is the barycenter, and not Earth itself, that moves in an elliptical orbit around the Sun. Actually, both Earth and the Moon follow separate paths that are now on one side and now on the other side of the Keplerian orbit. The situation is depicted, in somewhat exaggerated form, in Fig. 9.3. The full line is the

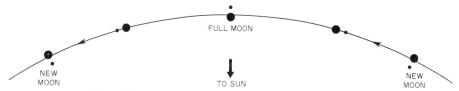

Fig. 9.3.   Motion of Earth-Moon system in orbit about the Sun

elliptical orbit of the Earth-Moon barycenter about the Sun; the larger dot represents Earth and the smaller dot is the Moon. The figure shows the motion of the two bodies over a period of one month, during which time Earth and the Moon make a complete revolution about their common center of mass. The distance from the Earth-Moon barycenter to Earth's center is 4670 kilometers, i.e., 2900 miles (§ 9.52),* whereas the distance to the center of the Moon is nearly 380,000 kilometers (236,000 miles). The wobble of the Moon's path about the Sun is thus considerably larger than that of Earth. In fact, for most purposes, the deviation of 4670 kilometers from the Keplerian orbit may be neglected in comparison with the Earth-Sun distance of nearly 149.6 million kilometers (93 million miles).

Sidereal and Synodic Months

9.8. If a distant fixed star is taken as the reference point, the average period of revolution of the Moon about Earth—and of Earth about the Moon—is 27 days 7 hours and 43 minutes, i.e., 27.322 days; this is the *sidereal month* (§ 2.62). Because of the perturbing effects of the Sun on the Moon's orbital motion, the length of the sidereal month varies from one revolution to another, and extreme values are several hours greater or less than the mean value given above. The *synodic month* is the time between two successive conjunctions (or alignments) of the Moon with the Sun, as observed from Earth. As will be seen shortly, this is also the time between successive new (or full) moons, and is consequently called the *lunar month*. From the arguments in § 7.16, it can be readily shown that, since both Earth and the Moon revolve in direct, i.e., counterclockwise, orbits and the orbital period of Earth about the Sun is greater than the period of the Moon about Earth, that

* The average radius of Earth is 6371 kilometers or 3959 miles; hence, the Earth-Moon barycenter lies within Earth's interior.

$$P = \frac{SE}{S + E}$$

or

$$\frac{1}{S} = \frac{1}{P} - \frac{1}{E},$$

where P is the average sidereal month, S is the average synodic (or lunar) month, and E is the sidereal period of revolution of Earth about the Sun, i.e., 365.256 days. The observed average lunar month of 29 days 12 hours 44 minutes, i.e., 29.531 days, is in agreement with these expressions. Just as the sidereal period of the Moon varies from month to month, so also does the length of the lunar month, the total range being about 13 hours.

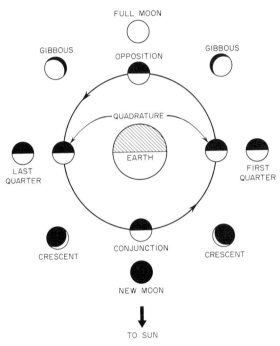

FIG. 9.4.   Configurations (or aspects) and phases of the Moon

PHASES OF THE MOON

9.9. The characteristic positions (or configurations) of the Moon relative to Earth are shown in Fig. 9.4, together with the phases as seen from Earth. As is the case with the planets, the Moon emits essentially no visible radiation and its luminosity is due entirely to reflected sunlight.* This is indicated in the

* A relatively minor but interesting exception is provided by the red glows that have been reported as being occasionally seen on the lunar surface (§ 9.136 *et seq.*), but even some of these may be excited by solar radiations.

figure by leaving white that half of the Moon which faces the Sun, whereas the other half is black. It is only at full moon, therefore, that a terrestrial observer can see the whole illuminated lunar disc. At other times of the month, as the position of the Moon relative to Earth changes, only parts of the illuminated surface are visible. At new moon, the dark side of the Moon is directed toward Earth so that it cannot be seen at all.

9.10. The line which separates the bright and dark areas of the Moon is known as the *terminator*. To an observer located at the terminator, the Sun would appear on the lunar horizon. Between new moon and full moon, i.e., when the Moon is waxing, the Sun would be seen rising, whereas during the period the Moon is waning, i.e., from full moon to new moon, the Sun would be setting. In any event, as seen from the visible portion of the lunar disc close to the terminator, the Sun is always near to the horizon and casts long shadows of elevated regions. It is for this reason that the terminator appears to be slightly uneven, instead of a sharp line.

9.11. The light of the Moon is mostly sunlight that has been reflected directly from the lunar surface. A small portion, however, is sunlight that has been reflected first by Earth on to the Moon and then back from the Moon to Earth. When the Moon is in a crescent phase, the dark portion can sometimes be seen to emit a faint, somewhat bluish light; this is sunlight that has been reflected from Earth. The reflected earthlight is commonly referred to as the *earthshine* or *ashen light* of the Moon. The faintness and color are attributed to absorption and modification of the original sunlight resulting from its passage three times through the terrestrial atmosphere, i.e., from the Sun to Earth, from Earth to the Moon, and back from the Moon to Earth.

THE LUNAR ORBIT

9.12. Observations of the lunar orbit show that it is slightly elliptical, with an average eccentricity (§ 2.44) of 0.0549; perturbations by the Sun, however, result in positive and negative deviations of up to 0.0119 from the mean value. The eccentricity of the orbit is sufficiently large for changes in the orbital velocity of the Moon to be readily observed. The average orbital velocity is 1.022 kilometers (0.635 mile) per second, with a maximum at perigee, i.e., when closest to Earth, of 1.11 kilometers per second, and a minimum at apogee, when farthest from Earth, of 0.945 kilometer per second.

9.13. The semi-major axis of the lunar orbit is essentially equal to the mean distance between the centers of Earth and the Moon. This quantity is determined most directly by means of the radar echo technique. The time required for a radar pulse to travel to the Moon and be reflected back was first measured in 1946 by members of the U.S. Army Signal Corps and found to be 2.56 seconds. Since then, numerous observations of the delay time have been made and the results lead to a value of 384,400 kilometers (238,860 miles) for the mean distance from Earth to the Moon. The average perigee and apogee distances are approximately 356,000 and 407,000 kilometers, respectively, a difference of 51,000 kilometers or more than 30,000 miles.

9.14. A procedure commonly used before the development of radar techniques was identical with the parallax method described in § 6.10 for determining the distance of the Sun. Observations of the apparent change in position of the Moon against the background of the stars showed that the horizontal lunar parallax ranged from about 53.9 min of arc at apogee to 61.5 min at perigee, with an average of 57.04 min, i.e., 0.9501 deg. Although this is considerably larger than the Sun's parallax, it is nevertheless still a reasonably good approximation to take tan θ as equal to θ, where θ is the parallax in radians (cf. Fig. 6.2). Consequently, the average distance, D, from Earth to the Moon, may be calculated by means of equation (6.1), where R_0 is Earth's mean radius, i.e., 6371 kilometers, and θ is 0.9501 × 0.01745 radian; thus,

$$D = \frac{6371}{0.9501 \times 0.01745}$$

$$= 384,400 \text{ kilometers}$$
$$= 238,800 \text{ miles},$$

in agreement with the value obtained by the radar method.

9.15. An accurate procedure for determining the average distance from Earth to the Moon is based on the use of Kepler's third law, i.e., equation (2.26), with appropriate corrections for various perturbations. This requires, among other things, a knowledge of the lunar orbital period, i.e., the sidereal month, and also the masses of Earth and the Moon. An approximate value for the average distance from the center of the Moon to the Earth-Moon barycenter can be obtained by neglecting the mass of the Moon relative to that of Earth and using equation (2.28), namely,

$$P = 2\pi \sqrt{\frac{a^3}{K}}.$$

Since P is 27.32 days, i.e., 2.36 × 10⁶ seconds, and K is 3.985 × 10⁵ in kilometer-second units, it is found that a is 383,000 kilometers. If to this value there is added 4800 kilometers for the distance between Earth's center and the Earth-Moon barycenter, it follows that the approximate distance between the centers of Earth and the Moon is 388,000 kilometers or 241,000 miles. The error in this result is largely due to the failure to allow for perturbation effects, in particular of the Sun.

9.16. The plane of the Moon's orbit is inclined to the ecliptic plane (§ 7.22) by an angle which varies between 4 deg 59 min and 5 deg 18 min, with an average value of about 5 deg 9 min, i.e., 5.15 deg, of arc. The points at which the lunar orbit crosses the ecliptic, i.e., the apparent path of the Sun in the heavens, are called the nodes (§ 2.86); the *ascending node* is the one where the Moon crosses from south to north of the ecliptic plane and the other is the *descending node* (Fig. 9.5). As a consequence of perturbations caused by the Sun, the nodes regress, i.e., they move around the ecliptic in a retrograde (east-to-west) direction with reference to the background of fixed stars. Because the distance of the Moon from the Sun varies, the rate of regression of the nodes is not constant. However, the time required to make a complete circuit of the ecliptic is 18.60 years.

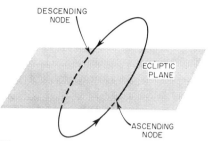

FIG. 9.5.   Ascending and descending nodes of the Moon's orbit

9.17. The Sun also causes a rotation of the line of the lunar apsides (§ 2.88), i.e., the direction of the major axis of the Moon's orbit rotates in the orbital plane (cf. Fig. 2.25). It has a direct, i.e., west-to-east, motion relative to the fixed stars, the rate being such that the perigee of the lunar orbit makes a complete revolution in 8.850 years.

ROTATION OF THE MOON

9.18. Telescopic observations show that the Moon always presents the same face toward Earth. This means that the Moon rotates around its axis in the same time as it makes a sidereal revolution about Earth, or, more correctly, about the Earth-Moon barycenter. The period of rotation of the Moon is thus 27.322 days. That such is the case, will be apparent from Fig. 9.6, in which the

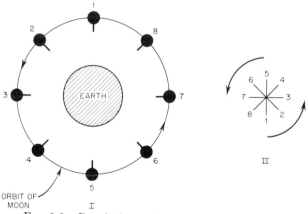

FIG. 9.6.   Revolution and rotation of the Moon

effect of longitudinal libration (§ 9.27) is disregarded. A hypothetical characteristic feature in the center of the lunar disc is represented by a protruding line in Fig. 9.6, I; as the Moon revolves in its orbit, this line always points directly toward Earth. If the positions of the line in the eight phases in Fig. 9.6, I are transferred to Fig. 9.6, II, it is seen that the Moon makes a complete direct (counterclockwise) rotation in the same time as it completes a sidereal revolution about Earth.

9.19. The equality of the period of rotation of the Moon with its sidereal period of revolution is apparently the result of tidal action. It is well known that the gravitational attraction of the Moon (and to a lesser extent of the Sun) is responsible for the formation of tides on Earth, both in the oceans and in the solid crust. The periodic changes in level are most marked in the oceans because of the lower rigidity, but similar changes, although only of a few inches, definitely occur in the crust. If the Moon did not always face the same way toward Earth, periodic tidal effects of even greater magnitude, resulting from the gravitational attraction of Earth, would occur in the Moon in spite of the absence of oceans.

9.20. It appears probable that, in the long distant past, the Moon was rotating about its axis more rapidly than at present. The tidal changes in the Moon could not adjust rapidly as the Moon rotated because of frictional effects in its interior. The decay in adjustment (or phase lag) resulted in the development of a drag force which gradually slowed down the rate of the Moon's rotation. Finally, when the rotational period became equal to the period of revolution about Earth, as it is now, the Moon faced the same way at all times. This condition is sometimes called *trapped* (or *captured*) *rotation*. The gravitational bulge on the Moon is thus stationary relative to Earth; hence, there can be no phase lag and no drag force to cause further slowing down.

9.21. Just as in the past there has been a phase lag in the tides on the Moon, so the frictional (or rigidity) forces in the oceans and in the crust cause a lag in Earth tides produced by the Moon and the Sun. The result is that the rate of rotation of Earth has been, and still is, steadily decreasing. In other words, the length of the sidereal day on Earth is continuously increasing; this has been established, for example, from the recorded times of eclipses in the past. Apart from irregular changes, probably related to motions in Earth's interior, it has been found that the length of the day increases at the rate of 1.8×10^{-5} second per year, i.e., approximately 5×10^{-8} second per day.*

9.22. The daily increase is quite small, but it accumulates over a period of years to produce a considerable error. For example, in timing a past event in terms of the current day, there would be an error of 5×10^{-8} second the first day, plus $2(5 \times 10^{-8})$ second the next day, plus $3(5 \times 10^{-8})$ second the third day, and so on. In the course of 100 years, i.e., 36,500 days, the total accumu-

* Because of the erratic variations in the length of the day, in 1960 the American *Ephemeris and Nautical Almanac* and the British *Astronomical Ephemeris* replaced Universal (Greenwich) time by Ephemeris time. The second is defined in terms of the tropical year (§ 9.37) rather than the terrestrial day.

lated error would amount to 33 seconds.* Such a discrepancy is readily detectable in the timing of total eclipses of a hundred years ago.

9.23. An interesting observation relating to the changing length of the day has been reported by J. W. Wells in 1963. Recent corals are known to form about 360 ridges per year in their skeletal structures, thus suggesting a daily growth cycle. Examination of fossil corals from the Middle Devonian Period, possibly some 400 million years old, indicates that about 400 such ridges were formed per annum. If the growth is indeed diurnal, the length of the day must then have been about 21.6 hours.

9.24. The necessity for the conservation of angular momentum (§ 4.30) means that the slowing down of Earth's rotation must be accompanied by an increase in the rate of revolution of the Moon. Consequently, in accordance with the arguments presented in Chapter 2, the size of the Moon's orbit must increase correspondingly.† This increase must, of course, be accompanied by an increase in the period of revolution, as required by equation (2.28); in other words, the length of the month must increase as the length of the terrestrial day increases. Calculations show, however, that the day increases faster than the month, so that eventually the two should coincide. It is estimated that this should occur when both the month and the day are about 47 times the length of the present day. A stable state should then exist in which the same hemisphere of Earth is always turned toward the Moon.

9.25. In arriving at the foregoing conclusion, the effect of the Sun on the rotation of Earth has not been taken into consideration. Just as tidal effects in the past have slowed down the rotation of the Moon until its period is equal to the period of revolution about Earth, so tides produced in Earth by the Sun decrease the rate of rotation of Earth. Eventually, the terrestrial day will have the same length as the year, as is already the case with the planet Mercury and possibly also with Venus. Although the terrestrial day (and year) will not be the same as the current year, it will undoubtedly be more than 47 days of present length. The increase in length of the day caused by solar tides will tend to slow down the motion of the Moon and, unless other effects intervene, its orbit will become smaller and the month will be shorter. It seems very improbable, therefore, that the Earth-Moon system will ever be stabilized in the manner described in the preceding paragraph.

Librations of the Moon

9.26. In spite of the fact that the Moon always presents the same face to Earth, it is possible to see somewhat more than half of the lunar surface, although not, of course, at the same time. This is the result of both apparent

---

* This result is obtained as the sum of an arithmetic progression of 36,500 terms, in which the first term is zero and the difference between successive terms is 5×10^{-8} second.

† Cf. § 7.106, footnote.

and real rocking motions, relative to Earth, called lunar *librations*.* Four types
of libration have been identified: three are apparent (or optical) motions
whereas the fourth is a real, physical (or dynamical) motion of the Moon. In
addition to increasing the area of the Moon visible from Earth, the lunar
librations have provided information concerning the shape (or figure) of the
Moon (§ 9.59).

9.27. The length of the sidereal period of rotation of the Moon around its
axis is identical with its sidereal orbital period, i.e., the sidereal month. Although the rate of rotation is essentially uniform, the velocity of the Moon in
its elliptical orbit is not. Consequently, the rotation is sometimes ahead and
sometimes behind the orbital motion, as represented in exaggerated form in
Fig. 9.7. The Moon thus appears to rock (librate) back and forth in the east-

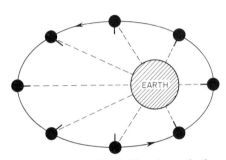

FIG. 9.7. Longitudinal libration of the
Moon

west direction. Because of this *longitudinal libration*, it is possible to see
from Earth an additional 7.7 deg at
both eastern and western limbs of the
Moon.

9.28. Another type of libration,
known as *latitudinal libration*, arises
from the inclination of 6 deg 41 min,
i.e, 6.7 deg, of the Moon's axis of rotation to a line perpendicular to the
lunar orbital plane. The direction of
the axis of rotation remains fixed in
space as the Moon revolves about
Earth, as indicated in Fig. 9.8 which shows the positions of the Moon at two
points in its orbit half a month apart. There is consequently an apparent
rocking motion in the north-south direction. It is thus possible to see from
Earth an additional 6.7 deg at the lunar north pole, when the Moon is in the

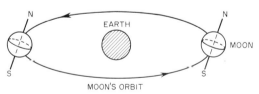

FIG. 9.8. Latitudinal libration of the Moon

left-hand location in Fig. 9.8, and at the south pole, when it is in the right-
hand location two weeks later.

9.29. The *diurnal libration* is a parallax effect due to the rotation of Earth.

* The Latin word *libra* means "balance"; the term liberation is, therefore, used here to
indicate an oscillatory motion similar to that of the swinging arms of a balance. The word
is employed in another sense in § 9.45.

The position of an observer at Earth's equator will change by nearly 13,000 kilometers (8000 miles) during the course of 12 hours, i.e., from point A to point B in Fig. 9.9. The Moon is thus viewed from slightly different angles at the different times. This results in an apparent lunar libration of about 1 deg

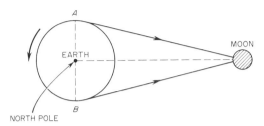

Fig. 9.9.   Diurnal libration of the Moon

at the western edge of the Moon when it rises and at the eastern edge when it sets.

9.30. In addition to the apparent librations described above, there is a true libration called the *physical* (or *dynamical*) *libration*. Because the Moon always faces the same way with respect to Earth, the lunar bulge caused by terrestrial gravitational attraction lies on the equatorial diameter directed toward Earth. As a consequence of the factors responsible for the librations in latitude and longitude, this diameter is sometimes not pointed exactly at Earth's center. At these times, Earth exerts an attraction on the bulge tending to pull the diameter into line with the center of Earth. As a result, the Moon experiences true (or physical) librations in both latitude and longitude. The magnitude of these librations is, however, small in comparison with the corresponding optical (apparent) librations.

9.31. The overall effect of the librations is to make it possible to observe from Earth about 59 percent of the Moon's total surface. No more than 50 percent of the lunar surface can be visible at any one time, i.e., at full moon, but it is not always the same 50 percent that can be seen. Of the total area, 41 percent is always visible at full moon, and there is another 18 percent around the edges of the Moon that can be observed, but not more than half at any one time. Finally, there is 41 percent of the lunar surface, commonly referred to as the "far side" of the Moon, that is never seen from Earth. Crude photographs of the far side were taken by the Russian spacecraft Lunik III in 1959 (§ 9.113).

PRECESSION AND NUTATION OF EARTH

9.32. An effect of the Moon (and the Sun) on the motion of Earth, known as *precession of the equinoxes* or, more commonly, as *precession*, is a consequence of two properties of Earth; first, that its shape is approximately an oblate (or flattened) spheroid rather than a sphere (§ 8.4) and second, that its axis of rotation is always at an angle of 23.5 deg to a line perpendicular to the ecliptic plane. The situation is depicted in Fig. 9.10 in which the dimensions of Earth's so-called equatorial bulge are exaggerated. From the standpoint of attraction by the Moon (and the Sun), Earth may be regarded as consisting of three parts:

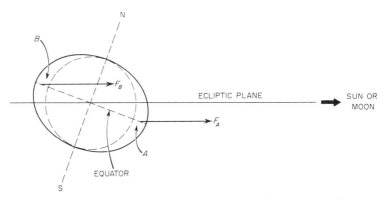

Fɪɢ. 9.10.   Attraction of Moon and Sun on Earth's equatorial bulge

a central sphere, shown dotted in Fig. 9.10, and two hemispherical bulges, A and B. The bulge A is always closer to the Moon (or the Sun) than the other, and so it is attracted more strongly than the bulge B, i.e., the force F_A is greater than F_B.

9.33. The net result is that an attracting body on the ecliptic plane, as is the Sun, or close to it, as is the Moon, produces a turning force (or torque) about Earth's center. This torque tends to bring the rotation axis of Earth into the direction perpendicular to the ecliptic plane. Both the Sun and the Moon have this effect, regardless of their positions relative to Earth. But since the Moon is closer, the magnitude of the torque it produces is actually greater than that of the Sun, in spite of its smaller mass. There is consequently a tendency for the equatorial bulge of Earth to be tilted into the orbital plane of the Moon which is inclined at an angle of 5 deg to the ecliptic plane.

9.34. It should be noted that there are a few occasions when the torque described above does not exist. Twice each month, in the course of its revolution about Earth, the Moon is in the same plane as the terrestrial equator. The attractive forces of the Moon on the two bulges are then also in that plane and there is consequently no torque. Similarly, when Earth's equatorial plane crosses the plane of the ecliptic, as happens twice a year at the equinoxes (§ 9.36), the Sun exerts no torque on Earth.

9.35. As a consequence of its equatorial bulge, the spinning Earth behaves like a gyroscope, i.e., it displays a tendency to resist any force which would produce a change in the direction of the spin axis. The net result is a precession of this axis, as described in § 4.30. Earth's axis thus retains the same orientation, in the respect that it is always inclined at an angle of 23.5 deg to the line perpendicular to the ecliptic plane, but it continuously changes its direction in space. The axis will, in fact, traverse the surface of a cone, as indicated in Fig. 9.11, once in approximately 26,000 years in a direction opposite to

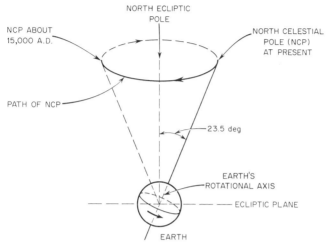

FIG. 9.11.   Lunisolar precessional motion of Earth's axis

Earth's rotation. This is the *lunisolar precession*, i.e., the precession due to the combined action of the Sun and the Moon. There is also a much smaller effect, called the *planetary precession*, caused by the gravitational attraction of other planets on Earth's equatorial bulge.

9.36. The term precession of the equinoxes is based on the definition of the *equinox* (Latin, "equal night") as the point (or date) at which the Sun's apparent path, i.e., the ecliptic, crosses the celestial equator, i.e., the great circle where Earth's equatorial plane intersects the celestial sphere (Fig. 9.12). The crossing occurs twice a year, around March 21 (vernal or spring equinox in the Northern Hemisphere) and September 23 (autumnal equinox), and day and night are then of equal length.* As Earth's axis precesses, the direction of the equatorial plane changes, although the angle it makes with the ecliptic does not. The positions in space at which the Sun's path crosses the celestial equator therefore change correspondingly. The use of the word precession arises from the fact that the equinox precedes the point (and time) at which Earth completes its orbit about the Sun, as indicated by the fixed stars.

9.37. Since the time between two successive equinoxes of the same type is less than Earth's true orbital period, i.e., the sidereal year, it would appear that the calendar date of the equinoxes would come earlier and earlier in suc-

* The reason is that Earth's axis is then perpendicular to the Earth-Sun line.

cessive years. But this is not so. The reason is that, according to the Gregorian calendar, the average length of the year over long periods is 365.2425 days, and this is almost identical with the interval between successive vernal equinoxes, i.e., the tropical year, of 365.2422 days. The sidereal year, which is the true orbital period of Earth about the Sun, is slightly longer at 365.25636 days.

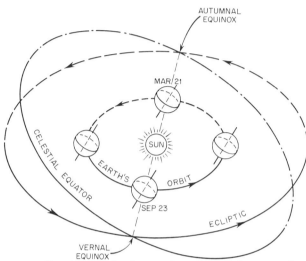

FIG. 9.12.   Apparent directions of the Sun at the vernal and autumnal equinoxes. (The dates show the respective locations of Earth in its orbit)

9.38. It is seen from Fig. 9.11 that, as a result of precession, the north (and south) celestial pole, i.e., the point to which Earth's axis is directed, describes a circle on the celestial sphere. Consequently, Polaris, the most prominent star near to the north celestial pole at present, will not always be the North Star. In about 12,000 years hence, for example, the brilliant star Vega will probably be recognized as the North Star. When the Great Pyramid of Cheops (Khufu) was built in Egypt, approximately 4800 years ago, the North Star was the star now called Alpha Draconis.

9.39. The path of the north (or south) celestial pole on the celestial sphere due to precession is not exactly a circle because a small periodic disturbance is associated with the regression of the nodes of the lunar orbit. Although the Moon's orbital plane is always inclined at an average angle of about 5 deg to the plane of the ecliptic, the regression causes the inclination of the orbital plane to the celestial equator to change from $23.5 - 5 = 18.5$ deg to $23.5 + 5 = 28.5$ deg in the course of 18.6 years. This produces a regular variation in the precessional circle; the effect is called *nutation* (Latin, *nutare*, "to nod") because Earth's rotational axis appears to nod back and forth as it precesses. Consequently, the precessional circle, instead of being uniform, has a wavy form, each wavelength representing a period of 18.6 years.

9.40. An eclipse of the Sun occurs when the Sun casts a shadow of the Moon on to Earth (Fig. 9.13). An essential requirement is that the Sun, Moon, and Earth should be at least approximately in a straight line, with the Moon between the Sun and Earth. This can occur only if two conditions are satisfied:

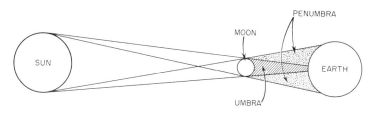

FIG. 9.13.   Eclipse of the Sun

first, that the Moon is new so that it is in conjunction with the Sun (Fig. 9.4), and second, that the Moon is near one of the nodes of its orbit, for only then is it close to the ecliptic plane which contains the Sun and Earth. If the relative positions of the Sun, Moon, and Earth should be such that the Moon's *umbra*, i.e., the part of the shadow in which the Sun's light is completely cut off, falls on Earth, a total eclipse of the Sun will be observed in the umbral area. Within the *penumbra*, i.e., where the Moon does not cut off the light from the Sun completely, the solar eclipse is partial.

9.41. For a total eclipse to be possible, the Moon must be quite close to a node and also near the perigee of its orbit, i.e., relatively close to Earth. If the first condition is satisfied, but not the second, the tip of the umbral shadow cone will fall short of Earth. An observer on Earth within the extension of the umbral cone, called the *annulus cone*, will find that the center of the Sun's disc is obscured by the Moon but not the limb. The result is an *annular eclipse* (Latin, *annulus*, "ring"), in which all that is visible of the Sun is a bright outer ring. Because the apparent size (or angular diameter) of the Sun and the Moon are not very different, as seen from Earth,* the Moon almost completely covers the Sun even when the eclipse is annular.

9.42. When a solar eclipse can be seen as total or annular from some parts of Earth, it will inevitably be partial in other parts that are located in the penumbra. If the Moon should not be close enough to a node, however, both the umbral cone and its extension will miss Earth completely. The eclipse can then be neither total nor annular anywhere on Earth. But in those areas upon which the lunar penumbra falls upon Earth, a partial eclipse of the Sun will be observed. Of course, if the Moon is so far from a node that even the penumbra misses Earth, no solar eclipse (total or partial) will be observed.

---

* The reason is that the ratio of the diameters of the Sun and Moon is approximately equal to the ratio of their respective distances from Earth.

9.43. In an eclipse of the Moon, the Sun casts a shadow of Earth on to the Moon (Fig. 9.14). The requirements are that the Moon be in opposition to the Sun, i.e., a full moon, and that the Moon be near to one of the nodes of its orbit. When the Moon lies within the umbra, the eclipse is total, but as it moves out of

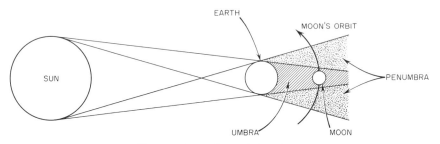

Fɪɢ. 9.14.   Eclipse of the Moon

(or into) the penumbra, so that part is in the umbra and part in the penumbra, the lunar eclipse is partial. Only a portion of the Moon is then in Earth's shadow. If the Moon is so far from a node that it does not enter the umbra, but only the penumbra, the phenomenon is referred to as a *penumbral eclipse* or a *lunar appulse* (Latin, *appulsus*, "approach"). All that is observed in an appulse, and also in the penumbral shadow of a total eclipse, is a gradual change in the general brightness of the Moon, a decrease as it enters and an increase as it leaves the penumbra. Even during totality, the Moon is not completely dark; sunlight refracted, i.e., bent, around Earth by its atmosphere reaches the Moon and gives it a dull coppery hue.

9.44. It will now be evident why the apparent path of the Sun projected on the celestial sphere is called the ecliptic (§ 7.22). The Sun is, of course, always on the ecliptic and a solar eclipse occurs when the Moon is also on (or close to) the ecliptic plane, between the Sun and Earth. Similarly, for an eclipse of the Moon to take place, the Moon must lie in (or near) the plane of the ecliptic, but now Earth is between the Sun and the Moon. Hence, eclipses, both solar and lunar, can occur nowhere but on or near the ecliptic.

Lɪʙʀᴀᴛɪᴏɴ Pᴏɪɴᴛs ᴏғ ᴛʜᴇ Eᴀʀᴛʜ-Mᴏᴏɴ Sʏsᴛᴇᴍ

9.45. A simple form of the three-body system, considered by J. L. Lagrange (§ 7.55), is that of a third body of negligible mass revolving with one member of a much heavier two-body system about its barycenter. In the situation of present interest, the third body is a lunar satellite, which may be regarded as being attached to the Moon, and so revolves with it about the Earth-Moon barycenter. If the perturbing effects of other bodies, e.g., the Sun, are neglected, it is found that there are five locations at which all forces acting on the third body balance out to zero. Because of the balancing of the forces, these locations, indicated in Fig. 9.15 for the Earth-Moon system by L_1, L_2, L_3, L_4, and L_5, are generally called the *libration points* of the system. They are also sometimes referred to as the *Lagrangian points* or *equilibrium points*.*

9.46. Of the five libration points, the three collinear points, L_1, L_2, and L_3 are

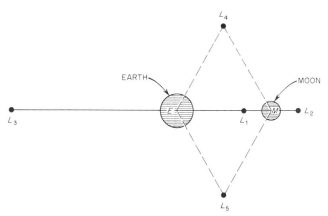

Fɪɢ. 9.15.   Libration points of the Earth-Moon system

in unstable equilibrium; thus, if a body located at one or other of these points suffers a small displacement due to a perturbing force, the body will tend to move still farther from its equilibrium position. On the other hand, L_4 and L_5, whose distances from both Earth and the Moon are equal to the Earth-Moon distance, i.e., EL_4M and EL_5M are equilateral triangles, are points of stable equilibrium.

9.47. In the absence of perturbations, a lunar satellite with zero orbital velocity relative to the Moon placed at either of the triangular libration points L_4 or L_5 will stay there. To an observer on the Moon, the libration point satellite will seem to be stationary, and to an observer on Earth it will appear to move in the same orbit as the Moon, but separated by a distance of **384,400** kilometers (**238,800** miles). Because of the perturbing effect of the Sun (and other bodies), however, the satellite will actually move in a series of orbits about the theoretical equilibrium point.

9.48. A spacecraft located at a triangular libration point might be of special interest. Since it would be located outside Earth's magnetosphere (§ 8.214), it would be particularly useful for making measurements of long duration on the emission of charged particles (solar wind) from the Sun. Interplanetary magnetic fields, interplanetary dust, and space radiation could be studied better from a libration-point spacecraft than from an Earth satellite or space probe.

---

*The Trojan asteroids (§ 7.55) are located at the libration points L_4 and L_5 of the Sun-Jupiter system.

PHYSICAL PROPERTIES OF THE MOON

The Lunar Radius

9.49. The mean radius of the visible disc of the Moon is calculated from the angular radius of the full moon and the known distance from Earth, in the manner described in § 6.21, using an expression analogous to equation (6.4). The angular diameter varies between **29.35** and **33.50** min of arc, with an average of **31.09** min of arc,* i.e., **0.5182** deg; hence, the angular radius is **0.2591** deg or 4.521×10^{-4} radian. If D is taken as **384,400** kilometers, the average distance from Earth to the Moon, it follows from equation (6.4) that the mean radius of the Moon is

$$
\begin{aligned}
R_m &= 384,400 \times 4.521 \times 10^{-4} \text{ kilometers} \\
&= 1738 \text{ kilometers}, \\
&= 1080 \text{ miles}.
\end{aligned}
$$

Since the mean radius of Earth is **6371** kilometers, the lunar radius is somewhat more than one fourth, actually **27.3** percent, of that of Earth. Assuming both the Moon and Earth to be spherical, the Moon's volume is **2.03** percent, i.e., a little over one fiftieth, of the volume of Earth.

The Lunar Mass and Density

9.50. In order to obtain the mass of the Moon, use is made of equation (9.1) which relates the masses of Earth and the Moon to the distances of their respective centers of mass from the barycenter of the Earth-Moon system. In practice, the problem is reduced to the determination of the distance from Earth's center to the Earth-Moon barycenter, since the total distance from Earth to the Moon is known. The required quantity is derived from observations on the parallax of the Sun or, preferably, of a closer planetary body.

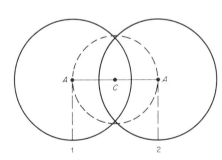

Fig. 9.16. Motion of Earth's center about the barycenter of the Earth-Moon system

9.51. In Fig. 9.16, A is the center of Earth and C is the center of mass (barycenter) of the Earth-Moon system, as in Fig. 9.2. The difference between the two figures is that Fig. 9.16 is drawn closer to scale, showing the barycenter within the interior of Earth. The dotted circle indicates the (approximate) monthly path of Earth's center; the full circles represent Earth in its two positions at an interval of half a month, e.g., at the beginning of the first and last quarters. Since the locations

* This value is not very different from the angular diameter of the Sun, namely, 32.0 min, as stated in § 9.41; hence, even in an annular eclipse of the Sun, only a thin ring is visible.

are shown relative to the barycenter, the orbital motion of the system around the Sun can be disregarded.

9.52. An observer on Earth at the point 1 will be at point 2 half a month later, so that his displacement relative to C is twice the distance AC. This change in position results in an apparent east-west displacement (or parallax) of the Sun or other celestial body. If θ_1 is the observed parallax of the Sun, for example, at the half-month interval due to the revolution of Earth about the Earth-Moon barycenter, and θ_2 is the normal solar parallax, i.e., 8.795 sec of arc, as given in § 6.17, it can be seen from a comparison of Fig. 6.4 with Fig. 9.16 that

$$\frac{\theta_1}{\theta_2} = \frac{2 \times AC}{R_0},$$

where R_0 is Earth's radius. It has been found from extensive astronomical studies that θ_1 is 2×6.444 sec,* and so

$$AC = \frac{2 \times 6.444}{2 \times 8.795} \times 6371 \text{ kilometers}$$

$$= 4670 \text{ kilometers}$$
$$= 2900 \text{ miles.}$$

9.53. The distance AB in Fig. 9.1 is 384,400 kilometers; hence BC is $384{,}400 - 4670 = 379{,}700$ kilometers. Consequently, from equation (9.1),

$$M_e = \frac{379{,}700}{4670} \times M_m$$

$$= 81.30 M_m,$$

where M_e and M_m are the masses of Earth and the Moon, respectively. Since the mass of Earth is 5.975×10^{24} kilograms, the mass of the Moon is $(5.975 \times 10^{24})/81.30 = 7.35 \times 10^{22}$ kilograms, i.e., 7.35×10^{19} metric tons.

9.54. The value of 81.30 for the ratio of the masses of Earth and the Moon has been confirmed by tracking of the spacecraft Mariner II on its way to Venus and of Ranger VII during its journey to the Moon. The trajectory of Mariner II showed a periodic variation due to the rotation of Earth about the Earth-Moon barycenter from which M_e/M_m was calculated. The path of Ranger VII was, of course, influenced by the gravitational fields of Earth and the Moon.

9.55. If Earth were a completely rigid body, it should be possible to calculate the Earth-Moon mass ratio from observations on the precession and nutation of Earth's axis. The value of the ratio obtained in this manner is 81.8, indicating, as expected from the statement in § 8.17, that Earth is not perfectly rigid.

9.56. A reasonable approximation to the density of the Moon may be obtained by assuming it to be a sphere with a radius of 1738 kilometers, i.e.,

---

* The value generally quoted in the literature is $\frac{1}{2}\theta$, i.e., 6.444 sec.

1.738×10^8 centimeters; the volume would then be 2.200×10^{25} cubic centimeters. Since the mass of the Moon is 7.35×10^{22} kilograms, i.e., 7.35×10^{25} grams, it follows that

$$\text{Average Density of the Moon} = \frac{7.35 \times 10^{25}}{2.20 \times 10^{25}}$$

$$= 3.34 \text{ grams per cubic centimeter,}$$

which may be compared with 5.57 grams per cubic centimeter for the mean density of Earth.

Lunar Gravity

9.57. The acceleration due to gravity at the lunar surface can be calculated by means of equation (2.4), i.e.,

$$a = \frac{GM}{R^2}.$$

The value of G is 6.67×10^{11} with length in meters, time in seconds, and mass in kilograms (§ 2.16); the mass, M, of the Moon is 7.35×10^{22} kilograms and its radius, R, is 1.738×10^6 meters. It follows, therefore, that

$$\text{Acceleration} = \frac{(6.67 \times 10^{11})(7.35 \times 10^{22})}{(1.738 \times 10^6)^2}$$

$$= 1.62 \text{ meters per second per second.}$$
$$= 5.32 \text{ feet per second per second.}$$

The gravitational acceleration on the Moon is thus slightly less than one sixth of the value (9.83 meters per second per second) at Earth's surface.

9.58. According to equation (2.9), the circular velocity of a satellite orbiting the Moon is $\sqrt{Ra}$, where a is the acceleration determined above and R is the radius of the orbit. At altitudes not far from the lunar surface, R may be taken as 1.74×10^6 meters; hence, the circular orbital velocity is

$$v_c = \sqrt{(1.74 \times 10^6)(1.62)}$$
$$= 1680 \text{ meters (1.68 kilometers) per second}$$
$$= 1.04 \text{ miles per second.}$$

The escape velocity is $\sqrt{2}$ times the circular velocity (§ 2.69) and so the escape velocity from the lunar surface is 2.38 kilometers (or 1.48 miles) per second. The gravitational fields of the Sun and Earth have an appreciable effect on the lunar escape velocity. Under favorable conditions, at full moon, the escape velocity is decreased to 2.20 kilometers (1.37 miles) per second; on the other hand, at the quarters, it is increased to about 2.44 kilometers (1.52 miles) per second. For convenience, the physical characteristics of the Moon are summarized in Table 9.1.

TABLE 9.1 CHARACTERISTIC PROPERTIES OF THE MOON

Distance from center of Moon to center of Earth (average)	384,400 kilometers
	238,860 miles
Angular diameter (average)	31.09 min
Radius (average)	1738 kilometers
	1080 miles
Mass	7.35×10^{22} kilograms
	7.35×10^{19} metric tons
Density (average)	3.34 grams per cubic centimeter
Gravitational acceleration	1.62 meters per sec per sec
	5.32 feet per sec per sec
Circular velocity	1.68 kilometers per second
	1.04 miles per second
Escape velocity	2.38 kilometers per second
	1.48 miles per second
Barycenter to Earth's center	4670 kilometers
	2900 miles
Sidereal period	27 days 7 hours 43 minutes
Synodic period (lunar month)	29 days 12 hours 44 minutes
Eccentricity of orbit (average)	0.0549
Inclination of orbital plane to ecliptic plane	5 deg 9 min
Inclination of lunar equator to ecliptic plane	1 deg 32 min
Inclination of lunar equator to orbital plane	6 deg 41 min

THE FIGURE OF THE MOON

9.59. Observations of the lunar optical librations in latitude and longitude have been utilized to provide some indication of the shape (or figure) of the Moon. By determining the parallax of a clearly identifiable feature on the surface as a result of libration, it is possible to calculate the difference between the radius or, more correctly, the semi-axis of the Moon in the direction facing Earth and that in other directions. Because the parallax is small, observations of the highest accuracy are necessary to yield reliable results. It is required to observe the apparent shift in position of a clearly defined point on the lunar surface, but the limited resolving power of even the best telescopes makes precise measurement impossible. Consequently, the data presently available vary over a considerable range. Nevertheless, there appear to be good indications that the Moon's semi-axis in the direction pointing toward Earth, i.e., in the direction OA in Fig. 9.17, is about 1 kilometer, i.e., 0.6 mile or 1100 yards, longer than the polar semi-axis, i.e., in the direction OC, at right angles to OA.*

9.60. Another approach to the problem of the shape of the Moon is to calculate the ratio (or difference) of its *moments of inertia* from observations of the physical librations. In order to understand the significance of the moment of inertia, consider any solid body, such as that in Fig. 9.17, with three axes, OA, OB, and OC, perpendicular to each other and intersecting at O, the lunar

---

* Earth's gravitational attraction would result in an increase of only 40 meters (45 yards) in this direction.

center of mass. The body is assumed to be divided into a very large number of small regions (or elements) of volume dV, the density in each volume element being represented by ρ. This density may be constant throughout or it may vary from one region to another. Let x_A be the perpendicular distance of a given

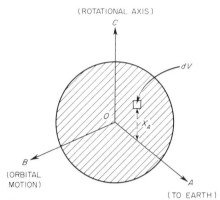

Fig. 9.17.   Rectangular axes of the Moon

volume element from the axis OA; the moment of inertia about this axis is then defined as the sum (or integral) of the quantities $x_A{}^2\rho dV$ for all the elements of volume into which the body has been divided. Similarly, the moments of inertia about the axes OB and OC are the integrals of $x_B{}^2\rho dV$ and $x_C{}^2\rho dV$, respectively, where x_B and x_C are the perpendicular distances from these two axes.

9.61. For a perfectly spherical body, the three axes OA, OB, and OC would be equivalent to each other. Consequently, if the density distribution were the same in all radial directions, i.e., from the center of the sphere outward, the three moments of inertia would be identical. It should be understood that the requirement for the density to be symmetrical about the center does not mean that the density is constant from the center outward. But such variations as do exist must be the same in all radial directions. This condition would be satisfied, for example, if the body consisted of a series of perfectly spherical shells (or layers) with different densities (cf. § 2.16).

9.62. If, as is the case with the Moon, the moments of inertia are not identical, the deviations may be due to either or both of two factors. First, the body may not be a true sphere so that distances along (or perpendicular to) the axes OA, OB, and OC are different; and second, the density distribution is not the same in all radial directions from the center outward. A larger value of the moment of inertia about a particular axis means that either the length of the semi-axis is shorter, making the perpendicular distance x larger, or that the average density is greater in the direction of that axis, or both.

9.63. For the Moon, it has been found that, of the three moments of inertia, the one about the OC is the largest, that about OB the next, and the moment of inertia about OA is the smallest.* If the density distribution is assumed to be the same—or almost the same—in all radial directions, this means that the semi-axis directed toward Earth is the longest, whereas the polar semi-axis, in the direction about which the Moon rotates, is the shortest. The figure of the Moon is thus described as being triaxial, i.e., it has different dimensions along the three perpendicular axes passing through the center of mass, with an appreciable protuberance (or bulge) in the region closest to Earth.

9.64. Even if the density distribution in the interior of the Moon is the same in all directions about the center, there is still a question concerning the manner, if any, in which the density changes from the center outward. For Earth, for example, the central region is considerably more dense than the outer layers; it would be of great interest to know whether or not a similar density variation occurred in the Moon. Some light may be shed on the problem by considering the dimensionless quantity $I/M_mR_m{}^2$, where I is the moment of inertia along any of the three axes, and M_m and R_m are the lunar mass and average radius, respectively. According to theory, if the density is uniform throughout, this quantity should be equal to 0.4; if it is less, then the density is greater in the interior than in the outer region, but if it is larger than 0.4, the reverse is the case.

9.65. The moments of inertia of the Moon are not known to any great degree of accuracy and, in any event, the values about the three axes are not the same. Nevertheless, there is no indication that in any case is $I/M_mR_m{}^2$ less than 0.4. It is probable, therefore, that the density distribution in the interior of the Moon does not vary greatly from the center outward. There certainly appears to be no evidence of a central region of high density, such as is present in Earth's interior. This conclusion, which is in harmony with the much lower average density of the Moon as compared with Earth, is of significance in connection with the Moon's early history (§ 9.190).

9.66. The differences in the three moments of inertia, as well as in the lengths of the semi-axes, indicate that the interior of the Moon has considerable mechanical strength. The rotation of the Moon, although not rapid at present, would produce a flattening, similar to that of Earth. The radius along the rotational axis, i.e., OC in Fig. 9.17, would then be less than in the directions at right angles. But the actual differences are much greater than those calculated on the basis of hydrostatic equilibrium (§ 8.3). It is evident, therefore, that the interior of the Moon has appreciable strength even at considerable depths and is able, like Earth, to withstand stresses. It has been estimated that the stresses in both the Moon and Earth are in the vicinity of 300 pounds per

* The best available values are $I_A = 0.8849(42)$, $I_B = 0.8851(09)$, and $I_C = 0.8854(98)$ in 10^{35} kilogram-(meter)^2 units; the figures in parentheses are uncertain.

square inch. In the Moon, at least, such stresses have probably existed for many millions, perhaps billions, of years.

9.67. There has been some discussion concerning the origin of the protuber-ance (or bulge) on the Moon that is directed toward Earth. It may have been produced by Earth's gravitational pull over a long period of time, it may be the remains of an equatorial bulge formed when the Moon was rotating faster than it is at present, or it could have been formed by the local deposition of material from outside the Moon. The fact that the bulge is now directed toward Earth does not necessarily mean that it was formed in this location. No matter how or where the bulge originated, the gravitational attraction of Earth would eventually lead to its present orientation.

9.68. Another dimensionless quantity involving the moments of inertia, which can be derived from observations on the physical libration, is the ratio $I_B(I_C - I_B)/I_A(I_C - I_A)$, where I_A, I_B, and I_C are the moments of inertia about OA, OB, and OC, respectively. It has been shown theoretically that, if the shape of the Moon became fixed after the period of rotation became equal to the period of revolution about Earth, the ratio given above should be 0.25. The actual value is, however, much larger, about 0.6, at least. Such a result does not necessarily mean that the present figure of the Moon was established while it was rotating freely, since a similar effect could be produced by the local accumulation of material at a later time.

9.69. It is clear that there are many outstanding problems relating to the shape of the Moon and the density distribution in its interior. But there seems to be little hope of solving them with the means available at present. When reliable orbital data can be obtained from artificial satellites revolving about the Moon, it is probable that much light will be shed on the situation (cf. § 8.10 *et seq.*).

SURFACE FEATURES OF THE MOON

MARIA AND UPLANDS

9.70. As a result of the earliest observations of the Moon, made at the be-ginning of the seventeenth century with the newly-invented telescope, two main types of surface structure were identified. First, there are the dark areas, which Galileo Galilei called *maria* (plural of the Latin, *mare*, "sea"); their apparently smooth and level surfaces, as seen at low magnification, made them look like large bodies of water. The maria cover somewhat less than half of the Moon's observable surface. The remainder consists of the *terrae* (plural of the Latin, *terra*, "land"), usually translated as highlands or uplands; in contrast to the maria, these areas are brighter in appearance and are very rough and broken on a large scale. Although there are many other characteristic features of the lunar surface, the division into maria and uplands is a convenient point of departure for further discussion.

9.71. The photograph in Fig. 9.18 is a view of the visible face (or near side) of the Moon, showing the bright (upland) and dark (maria) areas. The picture appears to be one of the full moon, but is actually a composite of two photographs taken at the first and last quarters.* This is a device used to accentuate

Fig. 9.18.   Composite photograph of the lunar surface. (*Courtesy H. C. Urey*)

surface details, especially in the region of the terminator. At full moon, the Sun is shining directly on to the lunar surface from overhead and there are essentially no shadows; although the light and dark areas are then clearly distinguishable, there is little or no indication of depth. At the times of quarter moon, the Sun, as seen from near the terminator, is low on the horizon and

---

* A close examination of Fig. 9.18 shows that, in the right half of the photograph, taken at the first quarter, the shadows are cast by the Sun from the right, but in the left half, taken at the third quarter, the Sun is at the left.

consequently casts long shadows. Differences in elevation can then be clearly seen, as is the case in Fig. 9.18.

9.72. In accordance with an agreement between the National Aeronautics and Space Administration and other U.S. Government agencies, pictures of the Moon are shown, as in Fig. 9.18, as they would be represented by a person actually on the Moon. North is at the top and east and west are at the right and left, respectively. It should be mentioned that in astronomical works, photographs of the Moon are given in the manner in which they appear in a telescope. North is then at the bottom, and according to the convention in the Northern Hemisphere (§ 6.106, footnote) east and west are to the right and left, respectively.

LUNAR CRATERS

9.73. Dominant structural features of the Moon's surface, especially of the upland areas, are the circular (or approximately circular) regions, each of which is surrounded by a wall or rampart. These structures are referred to as *craters*, the word being used in its general sense as a cup-like (or bowl-like) depression (Greek, *krater*, "bowl"). Since craters are very much more common in the uplands than in the maria, it seems probable that the great majority of lunar craters originated prior to the formation of the maria. Whatever may have caused the latter (§ 9.99), it appears that the craters in the areas of the maria were largely destroyed or covered. Some evidence for the latter occurrence is found in the appearance of "ghost" craters in the maria; they are faint circular outlines of craters which apparently existed before the surrounding mare was formed (Fig. 9.19). The fact that some distinct craters are present in the maria indicates that they were produced at a later stage. These *post-mare craters*, as they are called, are much less common than the *pre-mare* craters, as represented by at least nine tenths of those in the uplands.

9.74. It has been estimated that some 300,000 craters are visible in the best telescopes, but the total number of lunar craters is very much greater. The photographs taken by the Ranger VII spacecraft (§ 9.233) revealed numerous craters of all sizes, down to less than 0.5 meter (18 inches) in diameter, which are far beyond the limit of telescopic visibility. The number of craters of a given size increases with decreasing size; hence, the total undoubtedly runs into many millions.

9.75. The largest crater, Clavius, near and slightly west of the Moon's south pole, has a diameter of 227 kilometers (146 miles). There are four other craters with diameters down to 200 kilometers (120 miles) and 32 with diameters between 200 and 100 kilometers (120 and 60 miles). The outlines of such large craters are often polygonal, with rounded corners, rather than circular; it is possible that they may have been distorted after formation. This is not certain, however, since certain crater-like depressions on Earth, caused by volcanic action, have similar shapes (§ 9.87).

9.76. In view of their large diameters and relatively low ramparts (or walls), many craters are more aptly described as *walled plains*. The height of the walls, as determined from the length of the shadows cast when the Sun is in a known position close to the lunar horizon, is rarely more than 5 kilometers

FIG. 9.19.   Portion of a lunar mare near the crater Copernicus showing a ghost (submerged) crater; the light-colored rays from Copernicus can also be seen. (*Mount Wilson and Palomar Observatories*)

(3 miles) above the interior of the crater and generally only a few thousand feet above their surroundings on the outside. Thus, for the larger craters, the heights of the ramparts are only about 2 or 3 percent of the distance across the interior plain. Photographs with long shadows, such as the one in Fig. 9.20, often give a misleading impression of the depths of the craters and their general configuration. This will be strikingly apparent from Fig. 9.21 which is a profile, drawn to scale, of Theophilus, the large crater near the center of Fig. 9.20. With smaller craters, the height of the rim may be as much as 10 percent of the width so that they are more like meteorite craters on Earth. The maximum slope of the interior side of the wall may then be as much as 30 deg, but it is generally less on the outside. As a rough generalization, it may be stated that lunar slopes are, on the average, somewhere about 10 deg.

9.77. In most craters, such as the walled plains, the central region is well below the level of the surroundings. But in many instances, there is a peak or sometimes a group of peaks near the center of the interior, rising to heights of up to 2.5 kilometers, i.e., 1.5 miles (cf. Figs. 9.20 and 9.21). In a few cases,

FIG. 9.20. The crater Theophilus with central peak, near the center of the picture.
(*Yerkes Observatory, University of Chicago*)

the central peaks have small craters in their summits, somewhat similar to terrestrial volcanic craters. A small number of craters in the uplands have raised interiors but no central peaks. The walls of these craters are badly damaged, suggesting that they are probably the oldest lunar formations of this type.

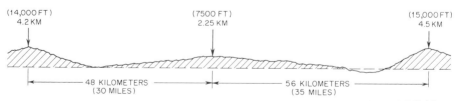

FIG. 9.21. Profile across the crater Theophilus (data from University of Michigan Observatory)

9.78. Where the crater density, i.e., number per given area, is large, as it is in the uplands, there is frequent overlapping of one crater by another. The indications are clear that such craters originated at different times. By examining their rims, it is often possible to determine the order in which they were produced. The one with a complete rim is obviously the more recent of two in an overlapping pair. The larger and older craters, such as Clavius (Fig. **9.22**),

Fɪɢ. 9.22.   The crater Clavius. (*Mount Wilson and Palomar Observatories*)

with raised interiors and broken and distorted ramparts, frequently have several smaller craters within them and in their walls.

9.79. Of special interest are the *ray craters;* only about a dozen or so are well defined, although others may exist. The characteristic feature of these craters is that they are centers of streaks of light-colored material, often extending to distances of several hundred miles, apparently without interruption, across the lunar surface. The rays do not cast shdows and are most clearly seen when the Moon is full, rather than at the quarter phases. Consequently, it is concluded that the rays do not have any significant thickness. The nature and origin of the rays will be described later.

9.80. Several of the more conspicuous ray craters, such as Copernicus, Kepler, and Aristarchus, seen on the left side of Fig. 9.18, occur in maria and are undoubtedly of post-mare origin. The same is probably true for the upland ray craters, e.g., Tycho, near the south pole. The rays from these craters cross adjacent maria without a break, and so they must have been formed after the maria. Since the ray craters cut into other features, but are not themselves cut into, they are believed to be among the most recent lunar craters of appreciable size.

9.81. Although several different types of craters have been recognized, only one further category need be mentioned here. In most instances, craters appear to have a more or less random distribution. But frequently a number of small craters appear close together in the form of a chain; occasionally such a chain occurs in a cleft in the lunar surface. It is probable that each system of chain craters was formed in a single event, possibly connected with the development of a cleft in some circumstances.

MARIA AND OTHER LUNAR FEATURES

9.82. Two classes of maria have been described on the basis of their general appearance; they are the *circular maria,* e.g., Mare Imbrium, Mare Crisium, and Mare Serenitatus, and the *irregular maria,* e.g., Mare Tranquillitatis, Mare Fecunditatis, Mare Nubium, and Oceanus Procellarium. The former apparently contain no ghost craters, whereas the latter do. All the maria have true post-mare craters of various sizes, as well as the ray craters mentioned earlier, but the density is quite small compared with that in the uplands. In general, the level of a mare is below that of its surroundings.

9.83. On a macroscopic scale, maria seem to be fairly smooth between craters, but they actually possess many features that become visible under appropriate conditions of illumination and magnification. The photograph of the western portion of Mare Imbrium in Fig. 9.23, for example, shows a number of ridges; these are most clearly seen at the right, near the terminator. Their magnitude will be appreciated better when it is realized that the smallest object that could appear in this photograph must have dimensions of at least half a mile.

9.84. In addition to ridges and wrinkles in the surface of the maria, there are often clefts or cracks, up to 5 kilometers (3 miles) in width and sometimes a few hundred kilometers long, called *rilles* or *rills* (German, *rille,* "furrow" or "groove"). Low domes, resembling volcanic formations on Earth, are quite common in some maria (cf. § 9.250).

9.85. Another feature of the lunar landscape is a small number of what appear to be mountain ranges, in which the highest peaks attain altitudes of roughly 3 to 6 kilometers (2 to 4 miles). It may be significant that these ranges gen-

FIG 9.23.   The Mare Imbrium. (*Mount Wilson and Palomar Observatories*)

erally occur around the circular maria; for example, the Carpathians, the
Appenines, the Caucasus, the Alps, and the Harbinger mountains follow the
outline of the Mare Imbrium. It should be mentioned, however, that the highest
lunar mountains appear in the Doerfel Range, located in the uplands near the
lunar south pole. It is not impossible, of course, that this range was formed in
a different manner from the mountain chains that border the maria.

ORIGIN OF THE LUNAR CRATERS

9.86. Until toward the end of the nineteenth century, it was generally considered that lunar craters originated from volcanic action. An alternative theory
of crater formation, which is now widely accepted, has been developed, as will
be seen shortly; nevertheless, the volcanic theory still has some support. It is
true that many craters on the Moon differ in appearance from those of volcanic
origin known on Earth, but it is agreed that the great majority of lunar craters

were produced some billions of years ago, whereas the existing terrestrial craters are all relatively recent. It is not improbable that, during the intervening period, in which Earth has cooled, volcanic action and crater formation will have undergone some change. Craters on Earth of the same age as those on the Moon would have disappeared long ago as a result of erosion by air and water, as well as of more deep-seated changes. Lunar craters, on the other hand, have retained their original form with little modification, apart from the rounding of edges.

9.87. Craters on the Moon have been compared in particular with two types of presently existing terrestrial craters, namely, calderas and maars. *Calderas* are large, shallow depressions formed by the collapse of the central region of a volcano due to the rapid expulsion (or subterranean withdrawal) of molten magma, i.e., lava. It is of interest that a number of lunar craters have features in common with some terrestrial calderas, e.g., a polygonal shape, a central raised region, and a small crater in the top of a cone.

9.88. The name *maar* or *maar-type volcano* has been given to certain terrestrial craters that are similar to the water-filled, circular depressions, locally called maars, in the Eifel plateau near the Rhine in West Germany. The maars are of volcanic origin and are up to 5 kilometers (3 miles) across and 180 meters (600 feet) in depth. They have funnel-shaped vents which are often filled with tuff and rocky debris, and they almost invariably occur in chains or rows. In their size, form, and alignment, the lunar chain craters resemble maars. But, as already mentioned, the lunar chains often occur in rilles, of which there is no known equivalent on Earth.

9.89. As the result of a detailed study published in 1893, Grove Karl Gilbert, senior geologist of the U.S. Geological Survey, concluded that the differences between terrestrial and lunar craters were so marked, especially in size, that most of the craters on the Moon could not be of volcanic origin. It has been pointed out since that the lower lunar gravity would permit explosive boiling to occur at much greater depths than on Earth, thus making it possible for large craters to form. Although the theory of the volcanic origin of the majority of lunar craters is not widely held at present, there is a growing opinion that the Moon has nevertheless experienced significant volcanic activity, as will be apparent in due course.

9.90. An alternative theory, developed—but not originated—by G. K. Gilbert, is that lunar craters were produced mainly by the impact of large meteoritic bodies.* About 30 years were to elapse before the impact theory received significant support, but at the present time most authorities accept this point of view. It is admitted that some craters on the Moon, such as the walled plains, are similar to calderas and that the chain craters resemble maars. These may possibly have arisen from internal volcanic action, but it is generally con-

---

* An earlier proponent of this theory in 1873 was the well-known English astronomer and science writer, Richard A. Proctor; it is reported, however, that he later abandoned it.

sidered that the great majority of lunar craters were formed by impact. The discovery, mentioned in § 7.120, that the relatively shallow Ries Kessel in Bavaria, which is some 50 kilometers (30 miles) across, is probably an impact crater has strengthened the view that the majority of craters on the Moon originated in the same general manner.

9.91. Meteorites striking the Moon's surface would undoubtedly have come from various directions and not necessarily from vertically above the surface. Hence, one of the problems of the impact theory is to explain why lunar craters are nearly all circular. A body approaching from space will strike the Moon's surface with a high velocity. As a result of its large kinetic energy, such a body will penetrate the outer layers of the surface before coming to rest. Most of the energy of motion is consequently converted into ground shock, and ultimately into heat, below the surface. It has been shown by E. M. Shoemaker (§ 7.119) that the ground shock would cause material to be thrown out in a symmetrical manner. The size of the crater would be much larger than that of the impacting body and it would be circular in shape, regardless of the direction from which the meteorite body came. An alternative suggestion is that the high temperatures generated by the impact caused vaporization of the surface material; expansion of the vapor then resulted in an explosion which produced a large symmetrical crater. The central peaks found in several large craters could be caused by rebound after relief of the compression of the surface material due to the impact.

9.92. Among the evidence for the impact theory is the existence of the light-colored rays emanating from some post-mare craters. These rays are believed to be formed by material of various sizes, i.e., ejecta, thrown out in all directions by the meteorite impact. The crater Copernicus, for example, is surrounded by many hundreds of small craters, visible in the telescope; the form of these craters, namely, elongated shape, shallow depth, and rounded rims, suggests that they resulted from secondary material thrown out from Copernicus (E. M. Shoemaker, 1961). Furthemore, photographs obtained from the Ranger VII spacecraft revealed that the rays of the crater Tycho are marked by a very large number of small craters, far too small to be visible from Earth by telescope (Fig. 9.24). These are undoubtedly secondary (and perhaps tertiary) craters produced by the ejecta from Tycho when it was formed. The areas of light coloration probably indicate the presence of pulverized material thrown out by the impacts.

9.93. It should be noted that some craters, which are similar to the ray craters in other respects, and are probably of post-mare origin, do not have rays. In the volcanic theory of crater formation, the rays are attributed to material exuding from fissures in the Moon's surface. Such fissures could be produced by the great internal disturbance that resulted in formation of the crater, but not all volcanic action would necessarily be accompanied by fissures

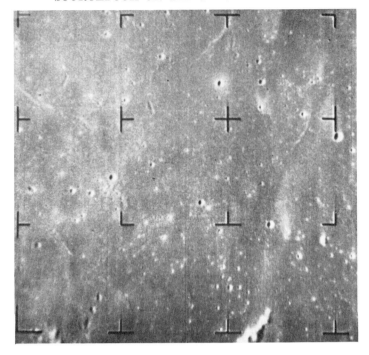

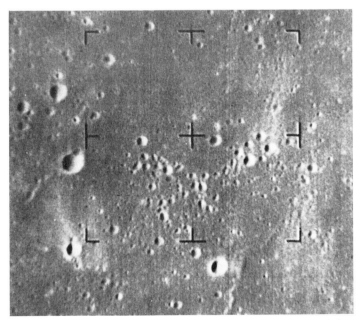

FIG. 9.24.   Ranger VII photographs of the lunar surface. Upper: 288 kilometers (179 miles) from the surface (scale: 1 cm = 10 km; 1 inch = 15.8 miles); lower: top right corner of above, 85 kilometers (53 miles) from the surface (scale: 1 cm = 2.9 km; 1 inch = 4.6 miles)

and, hence, by rays. The argument against this viewpoint is that the rays are associated with rock debris lying on the surface in their vicinity; the general appearance as well as the existence of large numbers of what are evidently secondary craters of all sizes are also indicative of an external rather than an internal source.

9.94. A comparison of the dimensions and topography of the smaller lunar craters with the corresponding characteristics of terrestrial meteorite craters, e.g., Meteor Crater in Arizona, has revealed a number of similarities that suggest the craters on the Moon were indeed produced by impact. There are also some resemblances between lunar craters and craters resulting from the underground explosion of nuclear bombs. It is not certain that the mechanism of crater formation due to high-velocity impact is necessarily the same as for the detonation of an explosive material, although ground shock formation is to be expected in each case.

9.95. An attempt has been made to determine the rate of formation of post-mare craters from records of terrestrial impacts. E. M. Shoemaker and his collaborators estimated in 1961 that, over the past 500 million years, roughly 50 to 150 impact craters of 3 kilometers (1.9 miles) or more in diameter were formed per million square kilometers (386,000 square miles) of Earth's surface. If this rate of impact is assumed to have been the same on the Moon and have remained constant over a long period of time, it is found that all the craters larger than 3 kilometers in diameter on the lunar maria would have been produced during the past 4.5 billion (4.5×10^9) years. In other words, according to this estimate, the maria are about the same age as Earth (§ 7.204). There is other support for this conclusion, but it will be seen shortly that it is not universally accepted.

9.96. Since the age of the solar system is probably not very much more than 4.5 billion years, the pre-mare craters, which have a density about ten times that of the post-mare craters, must have been formed in a moderately short period of time. Hence, if the age of the maria is indeed 4.5 billion years, the pre-mare craters must have been produced at a relatively fast rate. There is some evidence, derived from a study of the characteristics of adjoining maria by H. C. Urey (1952), that the period of very rapid production of craters, prior to the formation of the maria, may have lasted some 100,000 years. This is a very short interval on the time scale of the history of the Moon and of the solar system in general.

9.97. Urey has speculated that this relatively short period of rapid cratering may have corresponded with the final stage of the accumulation (or accretion) of nebular dust and gas that led to the formation of Earth and the other planets (§ 7.192). At this time, many solid objects of various sizes, ranging from small to quite large, were presumably orbiting in the vicinity of Earth. The introduction of such a massive body as the Moon in a similar orbit would then perturb the orbits of the smaller objects and they would impact upon the

Moon. Many lunar craters would thus be formed during a short period of time. Other objects would have collided with Earth and some would have escaped entirely from the Earth-Moon system.

9.98. Many scientists find it difficult to accept the view that the pre-mare craters were produced in such a short time interval as 100,000 years. Calculations made by T. J. Kreiter (1960) in the United States and by others suggest that the maria may have been formed no more than a few hundred million years ago. In this event, the rate of formation would have been approximately the same for both pre-mare and post-mare craters. It would not be surprising, however, if impact craters were produced at a somewhat greater rate in the very early stages of the Moon's history because the amount of debris in interplanetary space probably decreased with time.

Origin of the Maria

9.99. The dark color and fairly smooth surfaces of the maria have led many scientists to voice the opinion that the maria consisted originally of liquid lava which solidified in a moderately short time, perhaps about 100,000 years. According to the volcanic theory of crater formation, the maria were formed simply by the flooding of low-lying areas by lava produced in the Moon's interior. The alternative theory is that some maria resulted from impacts by large bodies from outside just as did the majority of the lunar craters. The impact maria are those which are circular in outline, contain no ghost craters, and are almost completely surrounded by mountain ranges. The formation of such maria by impact would account for their shape, and the mountains would represent material ejected or pushed out by the impinging body. The complete destruction of pre-existing features in the impact area would explain the absence of ghost craters.

9.100. Maria which are irregular in outline, contain ghost craters, and are not associated with mountain ranges are considered to belong in another category. It is suggested that they were produced by the flooding of low-lying areas by lava without any significant topographic changes. Hence, outlines of the rims of pre-existing craters would still be visible in many instances.

9.101. Perhaps the most characteristic of the circular maria is the Mare Imbrium, which is more than 800 kilometers (500 miles) in diameter. A detailed description of this mare and of its surroundings was included by G. K. Gilbert in the classical report he published in 1893 (§ 9.89). He drew attention to what he called the *Imbrian sculpture*, consisting of a series of ridges and troughs (or furrows) extending for several hundred miles beyond the boundaries of the mare. Gilbert suggested that the large basin and the associated sculpture could have been produced as the result of a glancing collision, i.e., at a small angle with the horizontal, of a large body moving with a relatively low velocity. More recently this point of view has been developed by R. B. Baldwin, G. P. Kuiper, H. C. Urey, and others. Although Gilbert thought the troughs were furrows formed by low-angle ejecta from the main impact, many geologists are now of the opinion that they are normal faults in the lunar surface. Whether or not they are the consequences of the disturbance resulting from an impact cannot be determined.

9.102. It has been argued that impact upon the Moon by a solid body of sufficient size and mass to produce a mare some hundreds of miles across should have been accompanied by obvious effects at great distances. But there is not always clear evidence of such effects. For this and other reasons, Zdeněk Kopal, an authority on the Moon, suggested in 1960 that collisions with large comets should not be overlooked as a possible cause of the formation of maria; small comets might even have produced some craters with low ramparts, such as Ptolemy, Plato, and Archimedes, whose floors are very similar in appearance to the surrounding maria. As seen in § 7.79, the head of a comet is believed to consist largely of a mixture of "ices" with an inclusion of mineral material; upon striking the surface of the Moon, the ices would vaporize rapidly and the high-pressure gases formed would produce an effect equivalent to an explosion. A comet's head probably contains a conglomerate of small bodies and has little tensile strength in comparison with a meteoritic mass. The effect of the impact of a comet with the lunar surface might, therefore, well be restricted to the immediate vicinity.

9.103. The possibility that tektites originate on the Moon (§ 7.148), specifically as ejecta from impacts on the maria, has led Paul D. Lowman (1963) in the United States to propose a novel theory concerning the origin of lunar maria. He suggests that they are similar to terrestrial lopoliths. These are large saucer-shaped depressions, with areas of the same order as the maria, formed by intrusion of siliceous magmas from below and subsequent subsidence. The existence of lopoliths on the Moon would imply that the temperature in the interior had been sufficiently high to cause silicates to melt; the resulting magmas would then escape toward the surface through fissures and cracks in the lunar crust, as in the formation of terrestrial lopoliths.

Contents of the Maria

9.104. It will be seen shortly that not all students of the Moon accept the view that the maria contain solidified lava, but those who do are divided in their views concerning the origin of the lava. Some scientists (G. K. Gilbert, H. C. Urey) are of the opinion that the very high temperatures generated by impact caused considerable melting of the rocks, thus forming the lava. Others contend, however, that impact would result in crushing and powdering rather than extensive melting. Consequently, they consider that the lava was produced by high temperatures in the interior of the Moon, just as it is in Earth.

9.105. Assuming an internal origin for the lava, if indeed there is lava in the maria, it could have already existed below the surface and merely been released by the impact that produced the mare (G. P. Kuiper). Alternatively, lava formation might have occurred in the lunar interior subsequent to the impact, the lava then flowed out to fill the depressions formed by impact or in other ways (R. B. Baldwin). An argument in favor of this latter view is that maria generally contain more craters in their rims than in the interior; this may be seen, for example, in Fig. 9.23. Furthermore, maria rim craters often exhibit apparent subsidence on the side of the mare, suggesting that they have been undermined by the lava. It seems unlikely that these situations would exist if the lava were formed at the time of impact.

9.106. Another approach to the nature of the maria has arisen from the tentative suggestion made in 1961 by E. M. Shoemaker and R. J. Hackman that their flatness and relative smoothness could be produced by ignimbrite, i.e., compressed and welded volcanic ash (tuff). This point of view was developed by John A. O'Keefe and Winifred S. Cameron in 1962. They showed that the maria could contain ash flows of volcanic origin, such as are now known to have been fairly common on Earth (cf. § 9.250). Ash flows consist of very fine volcanic dust particles which are cushioned by a gas layer so that they can flow like a fluid of low viscosity.* Thus, ash flows can travel with high speed and cover large areas. In due course, the compressed ash (or tuff) welds under its own weight to form a relatively smooth, hard mass resembling obsidian. The tendency for ash flows to reproduce the underlying topography could account for the existence of ghost craters in maria. According to O'Keefe and Cameron, the maria were formed by subsidence caused by masses of dense rock covered by welded tuff.

9.107. Much of the discussion concerning the source of the contents of the maria centers about the past history and nature of the lunar interior. The subject is considered further later in this chapter, but it is doubtful if the situation will be fully resolved until more information is available from direct observations made on or near to the Moon itself.

LUNAR DUST

9.108. There is evidence, as will be seen shortly, that the whole of the surface of the Moon is covered with a layer of fine particles or dust, probably in a somewhat coherent form. Until 1955, the common view was that the dust layer was not very thick, but in that year T. Gold (§ 8.237) suggested that the lunar surface may have a considerable thickness of dust and that the maria are filled with dust to a depth of about a kilometer (1100 yards) or more.† The relatively smooth surface is then due to dust, rather than to solidified lava or other material. The dark color of the maria, as compared with the light coloration of the rays, which may be due to rock dust, is attributed to the con-

---

* The fluidization of finely divided solids, in fluidized-bed systems, by means of a stream of gas has many applications in chemical engineering.

† The possibility that the maria and some craters might contain an appreciable depth of dust was considered by T. J. J. See in the United States in 1910.

tinuous exposure to cosmic (and solar) radiation of the moving particles as they traveled from the uplands, where they were produced, to the maria, where they finally settled.

9.109. Gold has pointed out that the rims of older craters, as indicated by the overlap criterion (§ 9.78), are much lower and more rounded than are the rims of more recent craters of the same size. Furthermore, the interiors of the older craters are fairly flat, as has been already mentioned. It is concluded, therefore, that some kind of erosion has occurred during the past few billion years; this erosion is attributed to the action of small meteorites and to solar radiations, leading to the formation of fine particles. The continual denudation of the uplands in this manner is said to account for their lighter color.

9.110. The simultaneous liberation of gas, probably oxygen by photochemical decomposition of minerals, would prevent the "healing," i.e., re-attachment of the eroded particles, that might normally be expected to occur in the almost complete vacuum on the surface of the Moon. The migration of dust particles from the uplands to the maria was originally attributed to the presence of an electrical charge on the particles which would permit them to float over the charged lunar surface, but more recently (1964) Gold has indicated that impact by many small meteorites would cause the dust to spread over large areas. Ultimately, the particles may be expected to settle and accumulate in the low-level regions, including the maria and some craters.

9.111. The problem of whether the maria contain a considerable depth of dust or not is more than of mere academic interest. It has an important bearing on plans for landing vehicles, especially manned vehicles, on the Moon, because the maria appear to be the most promising areas for such landings. If the surface is covered with a deep layer of relatively loose dust, heavy vehicles might well become submerged.

9.112. The general feeling is, however, that if the maria were filled with eroded dust (or with ash flows) the material would have become compacted into a rigid solid, like ash flows on Earth. This would result partly from its own weight and partly from sputtering caused by charged particles in the solar wind. Laboratory experiments by G. K. Wehner in the United States in 1963 showed that when a finely divided powder is bombarded by ions, a solid crust develops. Since crust formation would be occurring continuously in the sunlit areas, there should be little loose powder (cf. § 9.160).

THE FAR SIDE OF THE MOON

9.113. The far side of the Moon, representing 41 percent of its area not visible from Earth, has long been tantalizing to astronomers. Apart from mere curiosity concerning its appearance, it was possible that the far side might reveal information of scientific interest. The first observations of regions of the Moon that could not be seen from Earth were made from the Russian spacecraft Lunik III launched on October 6, 1959. The following day, it passed within about 40,000 miles of the Moon and its cameras made a series of exposures on the far side. These were developed on the spacecraft and the pictures were later transmitted to Earth by means of a television system. The actual photographs were about an inch in diameter and the definition, as received, was not too good. But by superimposing a number of exposures, a reasonably good representation was obtained of some 70 percent of the far side of the Moon; one of these photographs is shown in Fig. 9.25.*

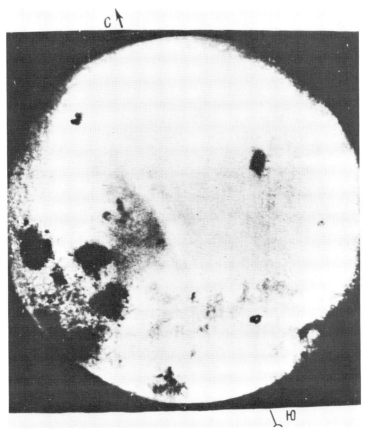

FIG. 9.25.   Photograph of the far side of the Moon taken from Lunik III. Most of the mare at the lower left can be seen from Earth as a result of the lunar librations. (*U.S.S.R. Academy photograph*)

9.114. About 30 percent of the picture, near the left limb shown in the photograph, represents an area that can be seen from Earth. In the lower left quadrant are a number of maria which are normally visible, either entirely or

* In Fig. 9.25, as in other lunar photographs in this chapter, the north pole of the Moon is at the top.

partially. Although there are differences of opinion among Russian and American experts concerning the exact significance of some features of the photograph, there is agreement on one point: the far side of the Moon consists mainly of uplands with very few maria. In fact, only one small mare, called Mare Moscovium, in the top right quadrant of Fig. 9.25, has been definitely identified. It will be recalled, for comparison, that nearly half of the visible surface of the Moon is covered with maria.

9.115. The striking difference between the near and far sides suggests that most of the maria were formed, by the impact of bodies orbiting between Earth and the Moon, at a time after the rotation of the Moon had been synchronized with its revolution about Earth. Since the age of the maria is thought by many to be about 4 billion years, it would appear that the synchronization occurred early in the history of the Earth-Moon system. This conclusion is admittedly speculative, since there may well be other explanations of the undoubted difference in character between the two sides of the Moon.

LUNAR RADIATIONS

Reflection and Emission of Radiation

9.116. A study of the electromagnetic radiations reflected or emitted by the Moon, covering a range of wavelengths in the visible, infrared, microwave, and radio-frequency regions, has provided much information concerning the nature of the lunar surface. An unequivocal interpretation of the data is not always possible, but the results are nevertheless of considerable interest.

9.117. The most obvious radiation from the Moon is, of course, ordinary moonlight; this is reflected radiation from the Sun in the visible part of the spectrum. In addition, the Moon has been used as a reflector for radio (or radar) waves transmitted from Earth. Regardless of whether the incident radiation arises from natural or artificial sources, i.e., sunlight or radar, respectively, the radiation reflected is modified in some manner by the lunar surface. It is from the observed changes that certain conclusions can be drawn concerning the character of the Moon's exterior.

9.118. Apart from its behavior as a reflector, the Moon acts as an emitter of electromagnetic radiations. The most important of these are the thermal radiations emitted by virtue of the temperature at or close to the lunar surface. By treating the Moon as a black body, i.e., as a perfect radiator (§ 6.61), measurements of the intensity of the emitted radiation at different wavelengths can be related to the temperatures on or below the surface in various circumstances. The information so obtained can be used to shed further light on the nature of the lunar surface.

9.119. In a sense, investigations of the reflected and emitted lunar radiations are complementary to the telescopic observations of the Moon and also to the pictures taken from the Rangers. Because of the limitations resulting from atmospheric turbulence, the best (long-focus) telescopes now available, designed especially for photographing the Moon and the planets, cannot give a resolution of the lunar surface better than about 300 meters or a fifth of a mile. In other words, any object on the Moon less than 300 meters (1000 feet) or so across cannot be photographed from Earth even with the very best instruments. It is claimed that visual observation can provide a resolution about one third that of a photograph, because the eye adapts itself to the slight flickering of the telescopic image caused by Earth's atmosphere. Such observations, however, are inevitably subjective in character and, as has often proved to be the case, susceptible to erroneous interpretation. It is true that the Ranger photographs may have resolutions down to less than a meter, but this is still insufficient to indicate surface roughness on a small scale. Special interest attaches, therefore, to the fact that reflected radiations are affected by variations of quite small magnitude in the lunar surface.

Photometric Studies of Moonlight

9.120. The photometric study of moonlight involves measurement of the intensity of the visible light reflected by the Moon. An immediate and obvious conclusion from such studies is that the albedo (§ 5.18a), i.e., the fraction of incident light that is reflected, of the maria is very much less than that of the crater-covered uplands. Because the reflectivity varies somewhat with the phase of the Moon, it is not possible to give a precise value of the albedo, even for a specific region. It can be stated, however, that on the average, the maria have an albedo of about 0.05; hence, about 5 percent of the visible sunlight falling on these areas is reflected. This value is exceptionally low, to judge from laboratory observations made with terrestrial rocks, but it is claimed that it can be matched by porous volcanic lava.

9.121. The relative brightness of the upland areas shows that their albedo is somewhat higher than that of the maria. The values are mostly in the range of approximately 0.10 to 0.15, although higher albedos have been reported for especially bright regions. These data are about the same as for granites and similar rocks found on Earth.* Caution should be used in drawing conclusions from laboratory measurements in which small samples are used, because in determining the lunar albedo light is received from very large areas.

9.122. Photometric measurements made across the whole lunar surface at full moon have revealed the somewhat surprising fact that, after allowing for local variations for maria and uplands, the limb of the Moon is as bright as the central part of the disc. Since the surface is curved, it is to be expected that, near the limb, sunlight will be reflected into space, away from Earth, as indicated in Fig. 9.26. The luminosity of a smooth (specular) reflecting sphere should thus

---

* The albedo of Earth as a whole is about 0.4, but the reflection of sunlight by clouds and by the oceans makes such a large contribution that comparison with the Moon has little significance.

be considerably less at the limb than at the center. The only reasonable explanation of the almost uniform brightness* across the lunar disc at full moon is
that the surface is quite rough. A rough surface would tend to scatter sunlight
in all directions, so that, apart from local variations, approximately the same
proportion would reach Earth from all portions of the visible lunar surface.

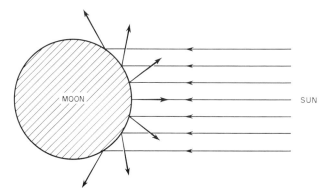

FIG. 9.26.   Reflection of sunlight from specular spherical surface

9.123. Observations have been made of the variations in brightness of the
Moon over a *lunation*, i.e., from one new moon to the next. The results are
generally represented by a curve, called the *photometric function*, in which the
total brightness, based on an arbitrary value of 100 for the full moon, is plotted
against the phase angle (§ 7.32). The phase angle is here the angle between the
line joining the centers of the Sun and the Moon and that joining the centers of
the Moon and Earth; it increases from −180 deg for the new moon, through 0
deg at full moon, to +180 deg at the next new moon. The observed photometric
function of the Moon is shown by the full curve in Fig. 9.27.

9.124. As is to be expected, the brightness of the lunar surface is a maximum
at full moon and falls off on either side as less of the sunlit face of the Moon is
observed during a lunation. The sharpness of the decrease is, however, greater
than expected, as indicated by the dotted (calculated) curve in Fig. 9.27 based
on Lambert's law, which is applicable to a smooth, matt (diffusive) spherical
reflector.† The form of the lunar photometric function, like the uniform brightness of the full moon, can also be explained by roughness of the surface. At full
moon, the Sun is at the zenith, i.e., directly overhead, and shadows are virtually
absent. But any departure, even the slightest, from full moon will cause uneven
features of the surface to cast shadows. Such shadows will have the effect of

* The *brightness* is the quantity measured by a photometer, e.g., a photographic light
meter (cf. § 12.67 *et seq.*).

† Lambert's law, which is obeyed moderately well by a number of terrestrial rocks, states
that the intensity of the reflected light is proportional to the cosine of the angle of incidence but is independent of the angle of reflection.

decreasing the apparent brightness much more sharply than would be expected from the decrease in the visible sunlit area of the Moon.

9.125. Several Russian astronomers, e.g., V. V. Sharonoff (1954), N. N. Sytinskaya (1959), have expressed the view that the photometric behavior of

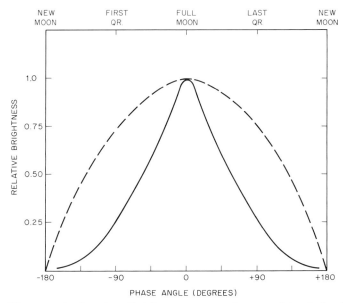

Fɪɢ. 9.27. Photometric function (brightness versus phase angle) of the Moon; full curve observed (after H. N. Russell), broken curve calculated from Lambert's law.

most of the lunar surface, including uplands and maria, is equivalent to that of a scattering material completely covered with small hemispherical (or almost hemispherical) pits. In fact, the surface of the Moon has been described as consisting of a highly porous, sponge-like clinker or slag, which has been referred to as "rock froth."

9.126. A comprehensive study of the photometric properties of a variety of materials, reported by B. W. Hapke and H. Van Horn in the United States in 1963, has led to a somewhat different conclusion. It was found that the only type of surface that can scatter light in the way the Moon does must have not only an extremely porous and open structure, but the cavities must also be interconnected. The material described as rock froth does not satisfy the latter requirement. The significance of the foregoing conclusions in the interpretation of the structure of the lunar surface is considered in § 9.160.

Polarization of Moonlight

9.127. A highly important property of moonlight is its partial polarization (§ 6.135, footnote). The electromagnetic vibrations in the light from the Sun

are distributed fairly equally in planes in all directions, but after being reflected (and scattered) by the Moon, the intensities in different planes are no
longer equal; thus, the light is partially plane-polarized. The proportion of
light that is polarized is defined by

$$P = \frac{I_1 - I_2}{I_1 + I_2},$$

where I_1 is the intensity of moonlight in the direction of the Sun-Earth-Moon
plane and I_2 is the intensity at right angles.

9.128. The first systematic measurements of the polarization of moonlight
were made by the French astrophysicist Bernard Lyot in 1924. The curves in
Fig. 9.28 show the value of P, as defined above, as a function of the phase angle.

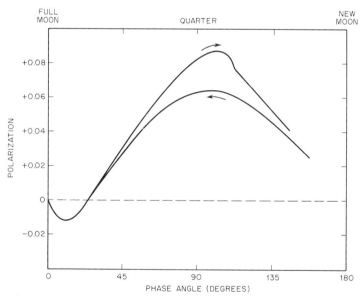

FIG. 9.28.   Polarization of lunar surface as a function of phase angle (after B. Lyot)

The lower curve is for the waxing Moon, i.e., from new to full moon, and the
upper one for the waning Moon, from full to new. The larger value of the
polarization in the waning Moon, around the time of the last quarter, as compared with the waxing Moon near the first quarter, is attributed to the larger
area occupied by maria in the former case. In general, there appears to be an
inverse relationship between albedo and polarization, i.e., lower albedo is associated with a higher degree of polarization. It is of interest that, at small
phase angles, i.e., near full moon, the polarization, P, becomes negative; this
means that the electromagnetic vibrations in the moonlight are then mainly in

the Sun-Earth-Moon plane.* The reason for this phenomenon is not altogether clear, but it has been ascribed to multiple refraction (or bending) of the light at the lunar surface.

9.129. Since scattered light is invariably polarized, it may be inferred that sunlight is partially scattered at the Moon's surface. Moreover, the variation of the polarization with the phase angle, i.e., the angle at which sunlight is incident upon the surface, indicates that the surface is rough. Studies of various materials by Lyot showed that the polarization curves in Fig. 9.28 could be closely duplicated by means of a powder consisting of a mixture of volcanic ashes. Subsequent tests, made in France by Lyot's colleague, Audouin Dollfus, have confirmed that opaque powders have polarization properties similar to those of the lunar surface.

9.130. It may be concluded from the polarization data that the surface of the Moon, including both maria and uplands, is covered with a powdery material or dust, although probably not in a loose form. This conclusion does not eliminate the possibility that the surface has irregularities, perhaps hemi-spheroidal cavities, as has been suggested. It means, however, that the irregularities are covered with fine particles. The powder must even adhere to the few relatively steep slopes that are known to exist on the Moon. Thus, at a phase angle of 28.5 deg, near the zero of polarization in Fig. 9.28, no difference was found in the polarization of moonlight received from sloping regions and from adjacent flat areas. At the polarization maximum, when the phase angle was 94 deg, the polarization of light from the slopes was the same as for surrounding regions of the same brightness. These results could not have been obtained if the slopes were merely bare rock.

REFLECTION OF RADIO (RADAR) WAVES

9.131. Photometric studies of moonlight indicate that the lunar surface is rough but the measurements can place no upper limit to the degree of roughness. Observation on the reflection of radio-frequency waves can, however, do so. If a radar pulse is reflected from an ideal, smooth and flat surface, the echo received will have precisely the same form as the initial pulse. But if the reflecting surface is spherical or spheroidal, as is the Moon, the return signal will be spread out in time because the distance from Earth to the limb is greater than to the center of the disc. The first portion of the echo signal will thus come from the center and later parts from regions at increasing distances out to the limb. From an examination of the manner in which the return signal changes with time, it is possible to draw certain conclusions concerning the reflecting surface.

9.132. Detailed observations of radio and radar echo power as a function of time have been made by G. H. Pettingill (1960), by R. L. Leadabrand, *et al.*

---

* The vibrations are always perpendicular (transverse) to the direction of propagation of electromagnetic waves.

(1960), and by J. V. Evans (1962) in the United States and V. A. Hughes (1961) in England, following earlier studies along the same lines by others, e.g., J. H. Trexler of the U.S. Naval Research Laboratory. The manner in which the reflected power decreases with time shows that about 50 percent comes from a region at the center of the lunar disc with a radius of about 160 kilometers (100 miles), i.e., about one tenth of the radius of the Moon. This part of the radar reflection is relatively sharp and does not exhibit appreciable scattering for wavelengths in the decimeter and meter range, indicating that the lunar surface is relatively smooth on a scale of 10 centimeters (4 inches) or more. Observations by V. L. Lynn, *et al.*, in 1963 showed that scattering of 8.6-millimeter waves is quite different from that at longer wavelengths. It may be concluded, therefore, that there are irregularities which cover most of the Moon's surface, but they are of small dimensions, probably between 1 and 10 centimeters.

9.133. The change in the radar echo power with delay time is compatible with a smooth but undulating surface, with an average slope of about 10 deg over distances on the order of a meter, i.e., a few feet. It is of interest that this slope is approximately the same as that estimated from shadow measurements of the larger features of the lunar surface (§ 9.76). A further conclusion drawn from the scattering of the radar echo delay measurements is that, although the surface of the Moon is moderately smooth and undulating, some 8 percent, on the average, exhibits a degree of roughness equivalent to irregularities, such as boulders or rubble, 2 feet across. Since the scattering results vary with the wavelength of the incident radar waves, it follows that the irregularities have a range of dimensions.

9.134. From absolute measurements of the total power in the echo signal, it is possible to make an estimate of the dielectric constant (§ 8.188) of the material constituting the surface of the Moon. The value found in this manner is about 2.8, which is similar to the dielectric constant of dry, sandy soil on Earth. It may be significant in this connection that radar echo signals from the Moon are similar in many respects to those obtained from aircraft flying over dry, sandy terrain. The dielectric constants of common terrestrial rocks are about 5, but the lunar surface would be expected to have a much lower value if, as seems probable, it is covered with a powdery material of some kind.

9.135. Another radar technique for investigating the surface of the Moon is based on the Doppler frequency broadening of the echo signal received from a rotating body (cf. § 6.109). The power of the returned signal determined at each frequency or, in practice, in a narrow range of frequencies, can be related to the scattering properties of the reflecting surface. Since signals from different parts of a spherical surface are received at different times, as mentioned above, a complete scan of the surface is possible, in principle, from a study of the radar echo. Preliminary observations of this kind have been made by G. H. Pettingill (1960), utilizing the Moon's libration to provide the Doppler shift. The results show that the radar scattering varies markedly over the lunar surface, but the data are not yet precise enough to permit a detailed interpretation. A considerable advance may be expected, however, from a program which will take advantage of the high resolving power of the radio telescope at the Arecibo Ionospheric Observatory (§ 8.174).

LUNAR LUMINESCENCE

9.136. In describing the radiations from the Moon, reference must be made to two different types of luminescence. In 1783, and again in 1787, the famous astronomer William Herschel (§ 6.45) claimed to have seen, on the dark side of the terminator, reddish spots "resembling burning charcoal" which he attributed to volcanic action. Subsequently, others have reported similar signs of lunar activity from time to time, but until recently most, if not all, were regarded as being illusions. On October 26, 1956, Dinsmore Alter, at the Mount Wilson Observatory, noted that in photographs taken with a blue filter, a rille in the crater Alphonsus was almost invisible for a time, whereas a rille in the nearby Arzachel was seen clearly. With a red filter, however, the rilles were visible in both craters. Alter suggested as a possible, but not the only, explanation the presence of a layer of gas in the Alphonsus crater.

9.137. Largely as a result of Alter's observation, the Russian astronomer Nikolai A. Kozyrev started a systematic spectroscopic study of the interior of Alphonsus, and on November 3, 1958 he obtained a spectrum of what appeared to be fluorescent gases coming from the crater's central peak. The lines in the spectrum were identified with the familiar Swan bands of the diatomic carbon molecule, C_2, in the visible spectrum. Kozyrev suggested that a gaseous carbon compound was emitted from the Moon and it was dissociated under the influence of solar radiation, yielding C_2 radicals among other products. Further signs of activity, which Kozyrev thought were of volcanic origin, were observed in Alphonsus on October 23, 1959 and in Aristarchus in November-December 1961.

9.138. There has been some controversy concerning the interpretation of Kozyrev's spectrum, but even if it is substantiated, it does not follow that the carbonaceous gas was an indication of volcanic action. One possibility is that the gas had been trapped below the surface for a long time and released as the result of the occurrence of a crack in the lunar surface. It has been suggested by H. C. Urey that moisture below the surface of the Moon might react with carbides to produce acetylene. Decomposition by solar radiation, e.g., ultraviolet light or protons, would then result in the formation of C_2 molecules.

9.139. On October 29, 1963, two competent observers, James A. Greenacre and Edward Barr, at the Lowell Observatory, Arizona, reported as having seen three red glows, one on the rim of the crater Aristarchus and two in Schröter's Valley, a conspicuous rille in the vicinity. The phenomenon lasted for about 20 minutes. Again, on November 27, 1963, a glowing red area, about 20 kilometers (12 miles) in length and some 2.4 kilometers (1.5 miles) wide, lasting for nearly an hour and a half, was observed in the rim of Aristarchus from both the Lowell and Perkins Observatories. In each case, the red glows were seen roughly two days after sunlight reached Aristarchus. It is of interest that, toward the end of 1963, Winifred S. Cameron (§ 9.106) had put forward the theory that certain sinuous rilles, such as Schröter's Valley, were of volcanic origin and suggested that spectroscopic observation of the region might be rewarding. There is now little doubt that the red glows, including those reported by Herschel, are genuine lunar phenomena, and there is a tendency to ascribe them to volcanic action.*

9.140. Another phenomenon has been described by Z. Kopal and T. W. Rackham in England, based on studies made at the Pic-du-Midi Observatory, France, on the night of November 1-2, 1963. Spectrograms taken from the neighborhood of the crater Kepler exhibited considerable enhancement at the red end. The area involved was more than 60,000 square kilometers (23,000 square miles), which is much larger than the 50 square kilometers (18 square miles) or so of the red glow on the rim of Aristarchus, referred to above. Moreover, the intensity of the reddening in Kepler was such that it could not have been detected visually without special filters. It would appear, therefore, that there are two different types of luminescence.

9.141. Kopal and Rackham attributed the effect they observed to the action of protons from a solar flare on the material of the lunar surface for the following reasons. First, the luminescence appeared a few hours after a solar flare and seemed to be correlated with it, and second, exactly the same luminescence had previously been obtained in the laboratory by exposing an enstatite (high magnesium/calcium ratio) achondrite (§ 7.125) to protons of 120 kilo-electron volts energy, i.e., about 5000 kilometers per second velocity, such as might be emitted by a solar flare. A possible conclusion is that the crater Kepler was formed by the impact of a stony (achondrite) meteorite, the remains of which are still present in the crater. Incidentally, the idea that lunar minerals become luminescent under the influence of solar radiations is not new. It was proposed by F. Link in France in 1946 to account for certain effects observed during a solar eclipse, and received strong support from N. A. Kozyrev (1956) and others. The studies of Kopal and Rackham, however, represent the first direct correlation between the lunar luminescence and enhanced activity on the Sun, as well as the identification of the former with an effect found in the laboratory.

LUNAR THERMAL RADIATIONS

9.142. A rough indication of the maximum lunar surface temperature may be obtained by considering the Moon to behave like an ideal, black-body

---

* A simple instrument, called a Moon Blink, is being developed to facilitate detection of red colorations on the Moon. Red and blue filters are rotated past the image in a telescope and when a red spot develops, it appears to blink. With this device, L. Johnson, an amateur astronomer, detected a reddish glow, visible for about 45 minutes, in the crater Alphonsus on October 27, 1964.

radiator to which the Stefan-Boltzmann equation (6.5) is applicable. Such a body would be in radiative equilibrium with its surroundings; that is to say, it would emit electromagnetic radiation energy at the same rate as it received such energy from outside, although in a different wavelength range. Essentially all the radiation energy received by the Moon comes from the Sun and, as seen in § 6.31, this amounts to 2.0 calories per square centimeter per minute at Earth's distance. The distance from the Sun to the Moon is, on the average, the same as that to Earth, and so it may be accepted that each square centimeter of the lunar surface receives 2.0 calories per minute of radiation energy. Equation (6.5) gives the rate of radiation emission, E, by a black body in terms of calories per second; the equivalent form per minute is then

$$E = 8.34 \times 10^{-11} T^4 \text{ calories per minute per square centimeter,}$$

where T is the absolute (Kelvin) temperature.

9.143. If this rate of radiation emission is set equal to the rate at which the Moon receives energy from the Sun, i.e., 2.0 calories per minute per square centimeter, it follows that, since the Moon's albedo is small and can be neglected, the corresponding lunar temperature would be given by

$$T = \left(\frac{2.0}{8.3 \times 10^{-11}} \right)^{0.25}$$
$$\approx 400°K.$$

This should represent the maximum temperature of the Moon at a *subsolar point*,* e.g., the center of the full moon, for then the solar radiation would be coming in perpendicular to the surface. At other points, the solar radiation strikes the surface at an angle, and the temperature would be lower. It will be seen shortly that the calculated lunar temperature of 400°K, i.e., about 127°C or 260°F, is in surprisingly good agreement with the temperature at the subsolar point at full moon.†

9.144. Another approach to the problem of determining the lunar temperature is a modification of the foregoing procedure. Instead of assuming that the rate of emission of thermal radiation from the Moon is equal to the rate at which it is received from the Sun, the emission rate is actually measured. Since the Moon is a relatively cold body, essentially all the radiation it emits is in the infrared region of the spectrum, with a small proportion at the longer (microwave and radio-frequency) wavelengths. From equation (6.7), the wavelength where the rate of energy emission from a black body is a maximum can be calculated. It is found that, at a temperature of 400°K, this wavelength

---

* The subsolar point on the Moon is the point where the line joining the centers of the Sun and the Moon intersects the lunar surface.

† It will be apparent, of course, that the calculation given above, with allowance for the albedo, should also give the maximum temperature on Earth, if it behaved like a black body. The presence of the atmosphere, however, makes Earth a far from ideal absorber and emitter of radiation (§ 8.82).

would be 7×10^4 angstroms, i.e., 7 microns, which is in the infrared region. Measurements of the infrared (or heat) radiation from the Moon should thus be adequate for estimating its temperature by means of the Stefan-Boltzmann equation.

9.145. The first experimental observations of the lunar thermal radiation were made by the Irish astronomer William Parsons, Earl of Rosse, in 1869, and some years later, in 1884, by Samuel P. Langley, the American physicist, astronomer, and pioneer in aeronautics.* For his measurements the Earl of Rosse used a thermocouple and this type of instrument was employed by subsequent workers prior to 1952. More recently, however, sensitive bolometer devices (§ 6.28) have been used to make observations on limited areas of the lunar surface. In this manner, the temperature distribution over the disc can be ascertained.

9.146. The first reliable determinations of the lunar temperature were made by E. Pettit and S. B. Nicholson in the United States in 1930; they reported the maximum temperature at the subsolar point on the full moon to be 407°K (134°C, 273°F), decreasing to 358°K (85°C, 185°F) at quarter phase. The reason for this difference is that the subsolar point is closer to the limb of the Moon in the latter case. As is to be expected, the temperature decreases from the center of the lunar disc toward the limb at full moon, and also toward the terminator at other times. The minimum lunar temperature, as observed by Pettit and Nicholson at new moon, was 120°K (−153°C, −243°F). At the present time, the maximum lunar temperature is taken to be about 390°K (117°C, 243°F) and the best value of the minimum appears to be 104°K (−169°C, −272°F). The temperature variation on the Moon's surface is thus about 290°C or 520°F.†

9.147. Because the surface of the Moon is not at all uniform, there are undoubtedly many local temperature variations even within a relatively small area. It is possible, however, to make some general correlations of the average or apparent temperatures with different lunar conditions. The changes in such temperatures near the center of the Moon's disc throughout a lunation are shown in Fig. 9.29. The small circles represent the observed values and the full curve is derived from a theoretical treatment described below. It is seen that, after the first quarter, the temperature increases very rapidly as more and more of the visible disc is exposed to the Sun. Then, after full moon, the temperature drops sharply toward the minimum value at new moon.

9.148. The change at the center of the Moon of over 250°C (450°F) in the surface temperature between new moon, i.e., lunar midnight, and full moon, i.e., lunar midday, is very much larger than the equivalent change on Earth.

* Langley Field, Virginia, and the Langley Research Center of the National Aeronautics and Space Administration are named for S. P. Langley.

† Since the Moon does not radiate as a black body and absorption of the lunar radiation by Earth's atmosphere is uncertain, the temperature values must be regarded as approximate.

Closer to the limb, the temperature difference between lunar day and night is not so large because the temperature is less than at the center of the disc even at full moon. Nevertheless, even at the limb, the temperature variation is at least 100°C (180°F). There are two main reasons for this important differ-

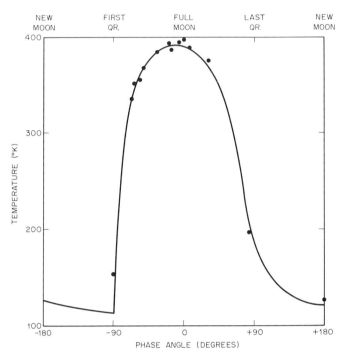

Fig. 9.29. Variation of surface temperature at center of Moon's disc during a luna-tion; points observed by W. M. Sinton and by R. W. Shorthill, full curve calculated by W. M. Sinton

ence in behavior between the Moon and Earth. First, Earth's atmosphere de-creases the heat loss by radiation at night, and second, the oceans on Earth serve as a heat reservoir which prevents rapid variations in temperature. The absence of an atmosphere and of bodies of water on the Moon inevitably results, therefore, in large temperature changes as the Sun rises and sets during the course of a month over the visible lunar surface.

9.149. The situation on the Moon is aggravated by the low specific heat, density, and thermal conductivity of the surface material. As a consequence of the low specific heat and low density, areas exposed to the Sun soon become very hot. But when the Sun goes down, as the Moon wanes, these areas radiate the heat away into space and the temperature drops. Because of the low thermal conductivity of the lunar surface material, heat is not transferred from warmer regions, still exposed to the Sun, to the colder shaded areas. Thus, very rapid temperature changes, either increase or decrease, occur in response to the rising or setting of the Sun, respectively.

9.150. A quantitative approach to the interpretation of the changes in temperature near the center of the disc during a lunation is based on a theoretical treatment in which the surface of the Moon is regarded as a homogeneous, semi-infinite solid material. It is this treatment which yields the full curve in Fig. **9.29.** The conduction of heat away from any given point and the heat loss by radiation are balanced against the heat energy received from the Sun. Allowance is made for the partial exposure at different times of the month and for the albedo of the surface. The details of the curve depend on the assumed midnight (new moon) temperatures and on a parameter generally referred to as the *thermal inertia*. The latter is equal to $1/\sqrt{k\rho c}$, where k is the heat (thermal) conductivity of the material, ρ is its density, and c is its specific heat. The larger the so-called thermal inertia, the more rapidly does the lunar surface material undergo changes in temperature resulting from variations in the amount of exposure to the Sun during the course of a month.*

9.151. The value of the thermal inertia that gives the curve in Fig. 9.29, which is seen to provide a good representation of the experimental temperatures during a complete lunation, is about 450, with k, ρ, and c expressed in the centimeter-gram-second system of units. The result is based on a lunar midnight temperature of 120°K, but this quantity is very difficult to determine accurately and is possibly 16° too high; the effect of the lower midnight temperature will be considered shortly. Of terrestrial materials, solid basalt and granite have thermal inertias of about 20, and dry soil and sand from 50 to 100. The highest thermal inertia values of natural substances on Earth are those of pumice and gravel, namely, 100 to 250, but even these are lower than is required to account for the rate of temperature variations on the Moon. The difference is undoubtedly due, in part at least, to the absence of an atmosphere on the Moon, so that the surface particles are essentially in a vacuum. Laboratory experiments have shown that under these conditions there is a marked decrease in the thermal conductivity of powdery materials. A thermal inertia of about 500 to 1000 has been found to be fairly typical of powdered or porous rock (or mineral) in a vacuum.

9.152. Striking evidence of the poor thermal conductivity of the lunar surface has been obtained from the rapid response in temperature during the course of an eclipse. In a lunation, the temperature variation, as recorded in Fig. 9.29, takes place over a period of several days, but in an eclipse the changes occur in the course of an hour or two. Temperature measurements during a lunar eclipse were first made on June 14, 1927 by Pettit and Nicholson, who observed the temperature variation at a location close to the Moon's southern

---

* The designation "thermal inertia" is not altogether satisfactory, because a large value of $1/\sqrt{k\rho c}$ means that there will be a rapid temperature response. Some writers use the reciprocal, but it has the drawback of being a small fractional quantity in the common units.

limb. The curve in Fig. 9.30 is drawn through the temperature data points obtained by Pettit from an area near the center of the Moon during the lunar eclipse of October 27, 1939. The rapidity with which the temperature changes, as the Moon moves into the penumbra and then into the umbra of Earth's

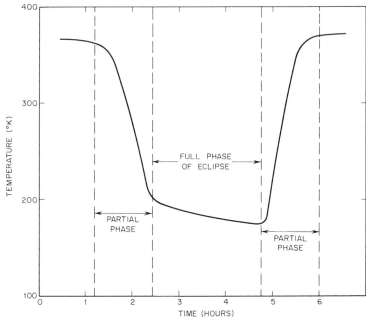

Fig. 9.30. Variation of Moon's temperature during a lunar eclipse (after E. Pettit and S. P. Nicholson)

shadow and out again, is very striking. Thus, in the course of little over an hour the temperature near the center of the lunar disc dropped from about 105°C (221°F) to −73°C (−99°F) during the initial penumbral (partial) phase of the eclipse. There was an even more rapid increase in temperature as the Moon passed from totality into partial shadow and finally into complete sunlight.

9.153. Analysis of the data in Fig. 9.30 by the procedure described in § 9.150 indicates that they can be accounted for by attributing a value of about 1000 to the thermal inertia of the lunar surface material. This is roughly twice that given above, as derived from the temperature change during a lunation. As already stated, the value of 450 was based on an assumed temperature of 120°K for the Moon at lunar midnight, i.e., at new moon. But if this is taken as 104°K, as is indicated by more recent measurements, the corresponding thermal inertia would be increased to about 1000. The thermal inertia values required to correlate the temperature variations during both a lunation and a lunar eclipse can thus be brought into agreement.

9.154. The general conclusion to be drawn from the temperature measurements is that the lunar surface, including uplands and maria, is covered with a finely divided powdered, although probably adherent, material. In the almost complete vacuum conditions that exist on the Moon, the density, thermal conductivity, and possibly also the specific heat of such a material would be so low that a thermal inertia on the order of 1000 is not surprising. The results appear to rule out completely the possibility that any large part of the Moon is covered by bare rock. The question of what underlies the powder is, however, still unsettled.

9.155. During the course of the lunar eclipse of March 13, 1960, Richard W. Shorthill and his collaborators in the United States noticed that, although the temperature fell over most of the surface, the floors of the ray craters Tycho, Aristarchus, and Copernicus were considerably warmer than their environs. This observation was confirmed in the eclipse of September 5, 1960 by Shorthill and by William M. Sinton. At totality, for example, the temperature within Tycho was 40° to 60°C (72° to 108°F) higher than that of the surrounding lunar surface. Smaller thermal anomalies, both positive and negative, were also observed in several craters during the lunar eclipse of December 29, 1963. Infrared scanning of the Moon in the eclipse of December 18, 1964 revealed the presence of hundreds of regions which were significantly hotter than their surroundings. Such conditions are thus believed to be common in lunar craters.

9.156. A related phenomenon was recorded by B. C. Murray and R. L. Wildey (1963) in the course of scans of the Moon made under normal conditions in the infrared wavelength range of 8 to 14 microns. So-called "hot spots," with temperatures several degrees warmer than the adjacent regions, were found in two areas associated with the rayed craters Tycho and Copernicus and two less prominent areas on the borders of a mare; it is possible that the latter may have been related to small rayed craters but this is not certain. It is evident that the material in the hot spots is a better conductor of heat than is most of the surface of the Moon. One suggested explanation is that the interiors of the rayed craters, which are of relatively recent origin, consist of rock covered with a thin layer of dust. Presumably there has not been sufficient time for the processes responsible for dust formation to produce thick layers.

RADIO-FREQUENCY EMISSION FROM THE MOON

9.157. Instead of determining the temperature by applying the Stefan-Boltzmann equation to the total rate of radiation emission per unit area of the lunar surface, an alternative method is to observe the thermal radiation emission at a particular (long) wavelength. Assuming black-body behavior, the corresponding brightness temperature is calculated (§§ 6.65, 6.220). For this purpose, radiations in the microwave and radio-frequency regions are particularly useful because they can be measured with a fair degree of accuracy even though they are of low intensity. The earliest observations of thermal radio waves (microwaves) emitted from the Moon, at a wavelength of 1.25 centimeters (24,000 megacycles per second frequency), were made in the United States in 1946 by R. H. Dicke and R. Beringer. Shortly thereafter, in 1949, J. H. Piddington and H. C. Minnett in Australia carried out an extensive series of measurements at the same wavelength. Since that time, numerous observations of the lunar thermal radiation have been made during lunations and eclipses over a range of wavelengths from 1.5 millimeters to 75 centimeters.* At longer wavelenths, the thermal radiation from the Moon is too weak to measure with reasonable accuracy.

9.158. An important observation made by Piddington and Minnett was that the brightness temperature during a lunation, as derived from the radio-frequency emission, varied between 200° and 300°K near the Moon's disc, as compared with a range of about 100° to 390°K derived from infrared data. Furthermore, it was noted that the temperature changes indicated by thermal radio-wave measurements lagged more than three days behind the infrared values. In other words, the maximum and minimum radio-frequency emissions are not attained at full moon and new moon, respectively, but some three days later in each case. With increasing radio-frequency wavelength, the temperature range was found to become smaller and the lag longer. At wavelengths in excess of about 10 centimeters, the average brightness temperature over the whole disc appears to remain constant regardless of the phase of the Moon. In harmony with this result is the observation that the temperature indicated by the longer wavelength radiations does not vary significantly during the course of an eclipse.

9.159. The explanation of the temperature behavior just described is that the infrared radiation comes almost entirely from layers near the surface of the Moon whereas the radio-frequency waves originate at various depths, down to a few feet below the surface. Although the actual surface temperature varies markedly with the phase of the Moon, i.e., with the time of the lunar day, the temperature becomes constant at depths below about 1 meter (3 feet). This constant value is approximately 230°K, i.e., about −40°C (−40°F). It may appear somewhat surprising that, at a yard or so below the surface of the Moon, the temperature can be more than 100°C greater at new moon or less at full moon than the temperature on the surface.

The Lunar Surface

9.160. By combining the results of telescopic, photometric, radar, and thermal radiation observations of the Moon with those of laboratory experiments on

---

* The techniques used by W. H. Sinton (1955) at 1.5-millimeter wavelengths were similar to those employed for infrared radiation rather than for radio waves.

the behavior of fine powders in an ultra-high vacuum, a conceptual picture is being developed of the upper layers, at least, of the lunar surface. It is now generally agreed that there is a layer of dust, but it is probably not in a loose form such as might be expected on Earth. It has been found that, in a very high vacuum such as exists on the Moon, small particles tend to adhere to each other to form a complex fibrous, fern-like, or dendritic (tree-like) structure— also described as resembling cobwebs or cotton candy—of appreciable strength. Such structures, to which the name of "fairy castles" has been given by B. W. Hapke (§ 9.126), satisfy the requirements needed to account for the light-scattering properties of the lunar surface, mentioned earlier. Furthermore, they have the low density and poor thermal conductivity and heat capacity indicated by the large value of the thermal inertia. A fairy-castle structure made by Hapke and Van Horn, by sifting in vacuum finely divided silver chloride which had been darkened by exposure to ultraviolet light, duplicated almost exactly the photometric behavior of the surface of the Moon.

9.161. In the uplands, as well as in the maria, the ground may be partly strewn with rubble and boulders of various sizes, as implied by the radar echo measurements. Hence, the depth of the dust structure will not be of uniform thickness but will vary from one location to another. On this matter, there is probably general agreement. An important point at issue, however, concerns the nature of the underlying medium, especially in the maria. Some authorities favor the view that there is a considerable depth of dust structure which may have become compacted into a solid mass, whereas others are of the opinion that the base material is rubble, although less coarse than in the upland, or lava. It may be of interest that there were apparently no boulders as large as 0.5 meter or so (18 inches) in that part of the mare (§ 9.248) in which the Ranger VII spacecraft landed. A few rock-like masses were observed, however, by Ranger VIII in Mare Tranquillitatis, especially near the rim of a small crater.

9.162. If it is assumed that all lunar dust is of meteoritic origin, the total amount that has accumulated over 4.5 billion years, the approximate age of the Moon, can be estimated from the known rate at which meteoroid and micrometeoroid particles enter Earth's atmosphere. On this basis, it appears that even if all the lunar dust were collected in the maria, the total thickness would not be more than a few feet. The theory mentioned in § 9.108, however, postulates that much of the dust on the Moon has been formed in other ways, and if this is the case the depth estimate based on the rate of meteoroid particle fall may have little significance. In any event, there is evidence from laboratory experiments that some of the ejecta produced by impact of these particles will probably leave the lunar surface; the rate of particle arrival may thus have no obvious relationship to the thickness of the dust layer. A resolution of the problem concerning the depth of the dust structure in the maria must await the time when direct observation is possible.

COMPOSITION AND HISTORY OF THE MOON

THE LUNAR ATMOSPHERE

9.163. One of the few matters concerning the Moon upon which there appears to be general agreement is that it has essentially no atmosphere. The evidence in favor of this view is based on both theoretical considerations and observations of various kinds. The theoretical aspects of the problem will be examined first.

9.164. In principle, if the velocity of a gas molecule (or atom) exceeds that required to escape from the gravitational field of a body, e.g., a planet or the Moon, then it should be able to leave the environment of that body. If the gas pressure is moderately high, as it is in the vicinity of Earth, the molecules collide among themselves with great frequency; the probability that a molecule will escape is thereby reduced, even if it has sufficient velocity. At low pressures, however, when the mean free path is long, as it is in Earth's exosphere (§ 8.34), the lighter molecules with high velocities can escape. The gas pressure on the Moon is so small that its exosphere begins essentially at the lunar surface; the escape velocity thus becomes the sole criterion of whether a molecule will remain in the atmosphere or not.

9.165. As a general rule, the molecules of a gas do not all have the same velocity. Even if they did, collisions would bring about exchange of kinetic energy among the molecules, leading to a particular distribution of velocities covering a wide range, in principle from zero to infinity.* The majority of the molecules have velocities close to the average value, as determined by the temperature and molecular weight, but there are always some with much higher and others with much lower velocities. Consequently, although the average velocity may be considerably less than the escape velocity, a small, but calculable, proportion of the molecules will have velocities equal to or greater than the value required for escape. The latter will then escape from the environment of the parent body, i.e., a planet or the Moon. As they do so, however, collisions among the remaining molecules will result in other molecules acquiring sufficiently high velocities to permit them to escape, and so on. Hence, in theory, any gas will escape in the course of time, assuming that it is not being replaced. The greater the difference between the average molecular velocity and the escape velocity, the longer the time required. Pressure also plays a role, because at low pressures, when collisions are infrequent, the redistribution of velocities will be a slow process.

9.166. It was shown by J. H. Jeans (§ 7.194) that, if the average velocity of the molecules of a gas is equal to or greater than one fifth of the escape velocity, the gas will escape almost completely from the gravitational attraction of a given body in the course of about a billion years. Since the age of

---

* This is known as the *Maxwell distribution,* as developed mathematically by J. C. Maxwell (§ 6.47) in 1860.

the Moon is a few billion years, this is a convenient criterion for determining whether the Moon could retain an atmosphere, assuming one was present at the time of its formation. The assumption is also made, tentatively, that there is no replacement of the gas molecules as they escape.

9.167. Calculations based on the kinetic theory of gases show that the average (or mean) velocity of the gas molecules, v_m, is given by the expression

$$v_m = 0.158 \sqrt{\frac{T}{M}} \text{ kilometers per second} \qquad (9.2)$$

$$= 0.098 \sqrt{\frac{T}{M}} \text{ miles per second,}$$

where $T°$K is the absolute temperature of the gas and M is its molecular weight.[*] Hence, if the escape velocity is represented by v_e kilometers per second, the requirement that gas molecules will have escaped almost entirely from the given gravitational field over a period exceeding a few billion years is that

$$0.158 \sqrt{\frac{T}{M}} > 0.2 v_e.$$

9.168. The temperature at the lunar surface varies over a wide range, as already seen, but the maximum temperature, i.e., about $390°$K, should be used to determine if the escape of gas molecules from the Moon's environment is possible. If this value is inserted for T into the expression given above and the escape velocity is taken as **2.38** kilometers (**1.48** miles) per second, as derived in § 9.58, the condition for a gas to have escaped from the Moon is found to be that the molecular weight should be less than **43**. This result does not mean, of course, that gases with molecular weights less than **43** will have escaped whereas those with larger molecular weights will be retained. Actually, a considerable proportion of the latter will also have left the Moon in the course of a few billion years, but the probability of escape decreases as the molecular weight increases.

9.169. It may be concluded that the common gases of Earth's atmosphere, namely, nitrogen ($M = 28$) and oxygen ($M = 32$), can be present in no more than traces in the lunar atmosphere. The same will be true for the less common lighter gases, hydrogen ($M = 2$), helium ($M = 4$), and water vapor ($M = 18$), although there may be detectable quantities of heavier gases.

9.170. It is of interest to mention that, in 1949, G. P. Kuiper (§ 9.101) considered the possibility that appreciable amounts of sulfur dioxide (SO_2), molecular weight 64, might be found in the lunar atmosphere, especially as this gas is known to be produced by volcanic action on Earth. Spectroscopic studies

---

[*] The velocity defined by equation (9.2) is not strictly the mean velocity but the square root of the mean of the squared velocities of the molecules, commonly referred to as the *root mean square velocity*. This quantity, which is actually required for the present purpose, is 8.5 percent larger than the true mean (or average) velocity.

of the Moon, however, showed no trace of the spectral lines of sulfur dioxide; hence, it appears that the quantities of this gas near the lunar surface must be very small. In any event, if sulfur dioxide were liberated, it would probably react chemically with lunar rocks and so be absorbed. Another possibility is that the chemically inactive gases krypton ($M = 84$) and xenon ($M = 131$) may exist in the atmosphere of the Moon. These gases, which are found in small proportions in Earth's atmosphere, might well have been present when the Moon was formed and, in addition, xenon-139, may have been produced over a period of years by the decay of iodine-139, with a half-life of some 17 million years (§ 7.205). Moreover, isotopes of krypton and xenon will have been liberated by the spontaneous fission of uranium-238, a probable constituent of lunar rocks.

9.171. The formation of krypton and xenon by the fission of uranium may be regarded as somewhat speculative, but there is little doubt that argon ($M = 40$) is being continuously released on the Moon by radioactive decay of potassium-40. To judge from the composition of the Sun, as indicated by its Fraunhofer spectrum (§ 6.70), of Earth, and of stony meteorites, it seems certain that the Moon contains something like 0.1 percent by weight, i.e., 7.35×10^{18} kilograms, of potassium, of which 0.012 percent, i.e., 8.82×10^4 kilograms, is the radioactive isotope, potassium-40. The half-life of the latter is 1.3 billion years and its decay leads to the continuous liberation of argon-40. Most of this gas is formed in the interior of the Moon and how much will penetrate to the surface is uncertain; nevertheless, it is to be expected that significant quantities of argon-40 will be released to the lunar atmosphere. A gas molecule of such high molecular weight will escape at a relatively slow rate from the Moon's gravitational attraction, and so an appreciable atmosphere of argon gas might be anticipated.* Helium is probably also being continuously released from the lunar surface by the radioactive decay of uranium, thorium, radium, etc. But this gas has such a low molecular weight that it could escape very readily.

9.172. The observational evidence, to be considered below, indicates that the density of gas molecules near the lunar surface is extremely small, much smaller than would be estimated from the rate of formation of argon-40, not to mention the possibility of helium, krypton, and xenon produced by fission and radioactive decay of uranium. Because the Moon probably has a weak magnetic field (§ 9.213), the normal solar wind, with protons traveling at a velocity of about 350 to 700 kilometers (210 to 420 miles) per second (§ 6.171), will reach down very close to the lunar surface. It was pointed out by J. R. Herring and A. L. Licht in the United States in 1959 that, as a result of impacts with these fast-moving protons, molecules of helium, argon, krypton, and xenon will acquire sufficiently high velocities to permit them to escape. A very low density

* Argon-40 constitutes almost 1 molecular (and volume) percent of Earth's atmosphere at sea level.

of these and other gas molecules in the lunar atmosphere would therefore not be surprising.

9.173. A simple indication of the absence of any appreciable atmosphere on the Moon is the general sharpness of shadows cast by the Sun, except on rough ground or when light is reflected from adjacent surfaces. Gas molecules, if present, would cause scattering of sunlight and the shadows would probably be blurred at the edges, especially near the limb in the crescent phase, because of the greater depth of atmosphere that would have to be penetrated there. This is apparently not the case. Evidence of an analogous type is provided by the instantaneous occultation of stars, i.e., cutting off of their light, by intervention of the Moon in its passage across the sky. If the Moon had an appreciable atmosphere, twinkling and an apparent change in position would be observed, due to scattering and refraction, respectively, of the starlight as it passed through the lunar atmosphere on its way to Earth. The fact that no such effects are observed and the light from the star is cut off suddenly shows that nothing occurs until the solid body of the Moon intervenes. Similarly, during a solar eclipse, the outline of the lunar limb remains quite sharp as the Moon appears to pass across the face of the Sun.

9.174. A more precise method for determining whether there is an appreciable lunar atmosphere or not is to observe if there is a phenomenon equivalent to twilight when the Moon is in either of its crescent phases. The effect, which is well known for the planet Venus, appears as a luminous extension of the cusps. A careful study of the crescent moon was made by B. Lyot and A. Dollfus (§ 9.129) in 1949, using a coronagraph (§ 6.42) to obscure the light from the Moon and thus render the "twilight," if any, easier to detect. They failed, however, to observe any luminosity extending beyond the cusps. Further, these astronomers concluded that the density of the lunar atmosphere must be less than a one hundred-millionth part (10^{-8}) of the density of the atmosphere at Earth's surface.

9.175. Another sensitive test for the presence of a lunar atmosphere was reported by A. Dollfus in 1952. Light scattered by a hypothetical lunar atmosphere at an angle of 90 deg, i.e., in the direction of Earth at the first and last quarters, should be completely polarized. But no such effect was observed, indicating that the lunar atmospheric density was less than a one-billionth part (10^{-9}) of the normal density of the terrestrial atmosphere.

9.176. A different type of technique for studying a possible atmosphere, or rather an ionosphere (§ 8.104), on the Moon was tested by B. Elsmore and his co-workers in England in 1955 and subsequently. It was seen in § 8.156 that the electrons in an ionized medium can cause refraction of radio waves, the extent of the refraction being dependent on the electron density. By observing the bending of radio waves from the Crab nebula as they passed close by the Moon, the electron density in the lunar ionosphere was estimated to be 10^3 to 10^4 electrons per cubic centimeter. This value is regarded as being consistent with a total particle density of less than 10^{-13} of the density at Earth's surface. Such a low value, equivalent to that more than 800 kilometers (500 miles) above Earth, is about the same as the density in the very best vacuum attainable in the laboratory.*

THE LUNAR INTERIOR

9.177. All that is known concerning the composition and structure of the interior of the Moon is based on speculation. As determined in § 9.56, the average density is 3.34 grams per cubic centimeter, but much of the lunar interior is under high pressure and may well be at a considerably higher temperature than near the surface. H. C. Urey has estimated that, if it were at ordinary temperature and pressure, the average density of the lunar material would probably be about 3.4 grams per cubic centimeter. This is somewhat greater than the average density of rocks near Earth's surface but less than that of chondritic (stony) meteorites. In general, these meteorites contain more iron than do rocks of terrestrial origin, and Urey has suggested that the composition of the Moon may be similar to that of chondritic meteorites, i.e., mainly calcium and magnesium silicates, but with less iron, e.g., about 10 percent, compared with something like 20 percent or more for most chondrites.

9.178. The smaller iron content of the Moon is of special interest, as it would tend to make the composition of this body much more like that of the Sun than of Earth. There are other ways, however, of accounting for the average lunar density without postulating a low proportion of iron. For example, the iron may be present mainly as oxide, rather than in such more dense forms as the element (metal) or the sulfide. Other possibilities that could account for the density of the Moon being lower than that of chondrites are the presence of more carbon or of water in a combined form. But all this can be no more than conjecture, and the composition of the Moon will not be known until direct observations are made by instruments or by man.

9.179. A knowledge of the condition of the lunar interior is important as it may throw some light on the origin of the liquid lava that is considered by many scientists to have filled the maria. In order to determine whether the Moon is now or ever has been liquid, calculations on the thermal history of the Moon have been made by H. C. Urey (1952 *et seq.*), G. J. F. MacDonald (1959 *et seq.*), and Z. Kopal (1962) in the United States, and by B. J. Levin (1960 *et seq.*) in Russia. As a starting point for these calculations, an assumption must be made concerning the temperature of the Moon at the time it was formed, at least 4.5 billion years ago. In this connection, two general possibilities have been considered, although various modifications are conceivable.

9.180. One extreme view is that the Moon was originally cold and remained

---

* By assuming that the lower gravitational acceleration on the Moon, as compared with that on Earth, is compensated by the higher molecular weight of the gas molecules, the atmospheric pressure near the lunar surface would appear to be less than 10^{-13} terrestrial atmosphere.

at a fairly low temperature for some time, although its interior has become gradually warmer as a result of contraction under the influence of lunar gravity. It is postulated, however, that the Moon was not large enough for any considerable heating to have arisen from this source. The cold condition would preclude the formation of lava and would account for the rigidity of the Moon in the early stages of its history, as indicated by its shape and by the mountains surrounding the circular maria.

9.181. At the other extreme is the possibility that the Moon was sufficiently hot some 4.5 (or more) billion years ago for lava to have been present in the interior. Since gravitational heating could not have been large, it is necessary to postulate, in this case, the presence of significant quantities of radioisotopes, e.g., aluminum-26, of relatively short half-life. The fairly rapid decay of these isotopes over the course of a few million years could supply the necessary heat to produce extensive melting of the lunar interior. There would then be an abundant source of lava. But it has been argued that since the interior of the Moon would have been liquid at the time the mountain ranges were formed, they would have subsided to the general lunar level.

9.182. It is probable that neither of the foregoing situations represents the true state of affairs. Regardless of whether the Moon was initially cold or hot, the decay of radioactive species of long half-life, namely, uranium, thorium, and particularly potassum-40, would be accompanied by the continuous liberation of heat during the period that has elapsed since the Moon was formed. Even if the Moon were initially cold, heating by radioactive decay could well have raised the temperature to a point at which magma formation would have been possible.

9.183. On the other hand, if the Moon had originally been molten, loss of heat by radiation from the outer layers could have resulted in the development of a solid crust of sufficient thickness to support the mountains. A factor which may have prevented the interior temperature from becoming too high is the differentiation (or separation) of materials from the magma. The radioactive materials would then tend to concentrate near the outside rather than in the interior. Most of the heat liberated by radioactive decay would thus be lost by radiation from the lunar surface. The fact that the radioactive element content of Earth's crust is considerably greater than that of chondritic meteorites indicates that a differentiation of this kind may have occurred.

9.184. Calculations have been made of the expected temperature changes in the lunar interior, as mentioned earlier. These are based on two postulates: first, that heat is generated by radioactive decay and that the proportions of radioactive isotopes in the Moon are the same as in chondritic meteorites, and second, that heat is transferred from the interior to the surface by thermal conduction. The results indicate that, if the Moon were originally cold, the temperature of the lunar interior would have increased steadily over the past 4.5 billion years or so. The temperature of the outer layers, down to a depth of about 240 kilometers (150 miles) would have passed through a maximum and would now be cooling, because of the loss of heat by radiation.

9.185. The important conclusion is, however, that a substantial part of the lunar interior could have been so hot that material having the composition of chondrites could have melted at a depth of about 400 or 500 kilometers (roughly 250 to 300 miles). This is deeper than on Earth, where volcanic lava is believed to exist below about 100 kilometers (60 miles). Nevertheless, release of magma could occur locally on the Moon, as it does on Earth, through fractures in the crust extending to considerable depths (P. D. Lowman, 1963). Furthermore, decrease of pressure in the lunar interior, which accompanies the formation of such fractures, would lower the melting point of silicates and thus facilitate the formation of liquid magmas.

9.186. It has sometimes been argued that a body like the Moon, which has sufficient strength to preserve its departure from hydrostatic equilibrium, could not have an exterior sufficiently hot to produce lava. But J. A. O'Keefe has pointed out that Earth has a nonequilibrium figure and has about the same internal strength as the Moon yet it contains lava at relatively shallow depths. The general conclusion to be drawn from the foregoing discussion is that the condition of the lunar interior is still a controversial issue, although it is not improbable that there is (or has been) molten magma at a depth of a few hundred kilometers. Some evidence pointing in this direction has been obtained from Ranger VII pictures of the Moon (§ 9.249).

TEKTITES AND THE MOON

9.187. The revival in recent years of the theory of the lunar origin of tektites (§ 7.148) has led to speculations concerning the implications for the problem of lunar structure. The density of the great majority of tektites is about 2.4 grams per cubic centimeter, but if the material were crystalline, rather than in the glassy (vitreous) state, the density would probably be about 2.8 grams per cubic centimeter. The mean density of the Moon adjusted to normal temperature and pressure is approximately 3.4 (§ 9.177), whereas the densities of the crust and mantle of Earth are 2.8 and 3.3 grams per cubic centimeter, respectively. If tektites came from the Moon, these data imply, according to J. A. O'Keefe (1963), that the Moon, like Earth, has a thin outer crust that is less dense than the interior. It follows, therefore, that the lunar interior must have been at a high temperature, since the only way in which a low-density crust could have formed on the Moon appears to be by separation (or differentiation) from a fluid magma. The rubidium-strontium isotope dating indicates that tektite material was separated from a primary magma a few hundred million years ago (§ 7.146). If magma had existed in the Moon at that time, then it would probably still be present in the interior.

9.188. Another argument in favor of melting and differentiation in the Moon is given by D. R. Chapman and H. K. Larson (1963). The average chemical composition of Earth's crust is very similar to that of tektites, but differs in several respects from the composition of the Sun and the stars.* In both Earth's crust and tektites, the abundances of potassium, uranium, and thorium are relatively high, whereas those of chromium, nickel, and cobalt are low; this is characteristic of matter that has become differentiated through the molten (magma) state. If tektites originated on the Moon, it would appear that the average abundances of the elements in the lunar crust are approximately the same as in Earth's crust. Consequently, as undoubtedly occurred on Earth, it must be concluded that there has been heating, presumably by radioactive decay, leading to melting and differentiation on the Moon.

9.189. The most likely source of tektites, if they come from the Moon, is the maria. Since tektites have a relatively high silica content, the maria must then be composed of siliceous (acidic) minerals. These are probably igneous in nature, i.e., they result from the action of heat, because they would have been formed by differentiation from a magma, as described above. O'Keefe and Cameron have stated that it is only as ash flows that acid igneous eruptions can form level surfaces, and this led them to propose the theory given in § 9.106. It has been pointed out by J. D. Lowman (1963) that, if the maria are silicic, at least on their surfaces, then the uplands must be largely like chondrites in chemical composition. This is a reversal of the views commonly held that the maria consists of basaltic lava, which is relatively basic, whereas the uplands are silicic (acidic).

Origin of the Moon

9.190. Theories of the origin of the Moon fall into three general categories: first, that the Moon was originally part of Earth and escaped in some manner; second, that the Moon and Earth were formed simultaneously as a sort of double-planet system; and third, that the Moon and Earth were formed quite independently as members of the solar system and that the Moon was captured by Earth and became its satellite. The arguments for and against these three points of view will be discussed briefly. But the situation can be well summed up in the following words of H. C. Urey: "All explanations for the origin of the Moon are improbable."

9.191. In 1880, the English mathematician and astronomer George H. Darwin, son of Charles Darwin, developed a theory of which the calculations made by E. A. Roche, described below, were a special case. Darwin suggested that, as a result of resonance (§ 7.54) between the natural period of oscillation of Earth and the period of the tides raised in Earth by the Sun, the amplitude of the tides increased to such an extent that part of the mass separated from Earth and became the Moon. In support of this theory is the fact that the average density of the Moon is approximately the same as Earth's mantle,

---

* The average composition of stony meteorites, however, resembles that of the Sun and stars, except for the volatile elements and lithium (cf. § 7.123).

although it is appreciably lower than the overall density of the terrestrial planets This argument would imply that, when the Moon separated, differentiation had already occurred in Earth's interior, with the formation of a metal core of high density and outer (silicate) layers of considerably lower density. Another favorable point is that the known rate at which the Moon is receding from Earth is compatible with a small separation 4.5 billion years ago.

9.192. Mathematical calculations made in the United States by F. R. Moulton in 1909, and later by H. Jeffreys (1930) and R. A. Lyttleton (1963) in England indicated, however, that the tidal origin of the Moon proposed by Darwin was physically impossible. If the Moon was not too far from Earth when it separated, it would probably return under the influence of Earth's attraction; on the other hand, if it was greater than a certain distance away, it would escape entirely.

9.193. Another argument has been based on the theorem propounded by the French astronomer Edouard A. Roche in 1849. He showed that if a satellite approached closer than a certain distance to its primary, the tidal force exerted by the latter would exceed the gravitational cohesion with the result that the satellite would disintegrate. If the satellite and primary have the same density, this distance, called *Roche's limit,* is 2.44 times the radius of the primary. Because Earth and the Moon do not have the same density, the Roche limit is about 2.9 Earth radii, and it is concluded that the Moon could not have been closer than this distance to Earth.

9.194. Darwin's tidal theory of the origin of the Moon was generally discarded after the 1930's, but in recent years the possibility that the Moon was formed by separation from Earth has been revived. One reason is that the alternative theories are not very convincing, and another is that the arguments against the separation theory are not decisive. For example, the difficulty of the Moon breaking up while within the Roche limit has been countered by the claim that, when the satellite is relatively heavy in comparison with the primary, mutual gravitational attraction will tend to stabilize the satellite against disintegration.

9.195. If the Moon and Earth were originally one body from which the Moon separated, then the difference in densities shows that separation must have occurred during or after the formation of Earth's metallic core, which has a density much greater than the average value. The possibility that the Moon separated from Earth at the time the core was formed was mentioned by T. S. Lovering in 1960, and calculations by D. U. Wise (1963) and J. A. O'Keefe (1964) show that the formation of the core would increase the rotational instability of Earth so that part of the mantle could separate and form the Moon.

9.196. The next theory to be considered is that Earth and the Moon developed simultaneously, as primary and satellite, respectively, by the accumulation of material that originally formed the solar nebula. There are two problems, in particular, associated with this point of view. In the first place, it is necessary to account for the difference in density between the two bodies. A possibility is that the less dense silicate material accumulated first and the heavier metal particles came later. If, at this stage, Earth was, for some reason, more massive than the Moon, it might tend to attract the more dense materials at a greater rate.

9.197. The second problem is to explain how the Moon remained a satellite while it and Earth developed. The fact that it did, would mean that both bodies had grown in such a manner that the centrifugal effect, corresponding to the varying velocity of the Moon in its orbit, always balanced the changing gravitational attraction of Earth. This would appear to be a relatively improbable situation. The chances are that the orbit of the Moon would either have decreased gradually, so that the Moon would fall to Earth, or it would have increased, with the result that the Moon would have escaped.

9.198. Finally, there is the possibility that Earth and the Moon were formed quite independently and at a distance, as separate members of the solar system. Some time later, as a result of special circumstance, not clearly understood, the Moon was captured and became a satellite of Earth. This theory is in harmony with the difference in density of the Moon and Earth, and would support the indications that the composition of the Moon is somewhat similar to that of the nongaseous (mineral) elements in the Sun. The Moon would then probably be older than Earth. It is difficult to understand, however, why the density of the Moon should be so different from that of the terrestrial planets unless it was formed elsewhere in the solar system. In this event, its capture by Earth would certainly require very special circumstances.

9.199. A modification of the capture theory, proposed by H. Alfvén (§ 6.132) in 1963, is that the Moon at one time approached closer to Earth than the Roche limit. As a result the Moon, which was considerably larger than it is now, was torn apart, and a portion fell on Earth and eventually formed its continents. This novel point of view would account, among other things, for the similarity in densities between the Moon and Earth's mantle. Evidently, the density argument can be used both ways! The average density of the continents, including the crust, is significantly less, however, than the average density of the Moon.

9.200. Regardless of the views held as to the origin of the Moon, it is widely agreed that, at one time, the Moon was much closer to Earth than it is now. This does not exclude the possibility that the Moon was considerably farther away when (and if) it was captured by Earth. For example, R. A. Lyttleton (1962) has shown that accretion of meteoritic (or similar) material by Earth and the Moon would cause the orbit of the Moon to contract. This contraction could have continued until the tidal effects described in § 9.20 *et seq.* caused the lunar orbit to increase, as it is doing now.

LUNAR STUDIES FROM SPACECRAFT

Introduction

9.201. The study of the Moon by means of unmanned spacecraft has two somewhat overlapping objectives, namely, to obtain scientific information about the Moon and to determine the best conditions for landing men on its surface. Lunar probes which merely fly past the Moon, even at a moderately close distance, have limited application and have not been used to any extent. The possible observations and measurements to be described below refer particularly to those that can be made from spacecraft which take pictures while crash landing on the Moon, or make a soft landing with instruments, or go into lunar orbit.

9.202. A description will first be given of the observations and what can be learned from them, and subsequently reference will be made to specific types of space vehicles. All the instruments and devices mentioned have been designed in compact forms suitable for being carried on spacecraft. They can be operated by radio command and the information they acquire can be transmitted to Earth by telemetry.

Visual Observations

9.203. By means of television cameras on the spacecraft, pictures can be taken of the lunar surface with a high degree of resolution. Until quite recently, it was not possible to do more than conjecture as to what the surface is really like. The first step in advancing knowledge of the Moon has thus been to make a photographic study of its appearance. With a crash lander, i.e., a spacecraft which approaches the Moon at high velocity and crashes on it, a series of television pictures have been taken at short intervals as the vehicle nears the lunar surface. Thus, smaller and smaller areas are photographed with increasing detail. The final pictures obtained in this manner may have a resolution of about 1 meter (3 feet) or less (see § 9.247).

9.204. With a crash lander, the television cameras are destroyed upon impact. For more detailed visual studies of the lunar surface, soft landers must be used. It is proposed in this manner to land a system of television cameras and mirrors capable of viewing through an angle of 360 deg from close in to the spacecraft out to the horizon. It is hoped that, as a consequence, a resolution down to a fraction of an inch can be attained.

9.205. The disadvantage of cameras that are landed on the Moon is that they can view only the area in their immediate neighborhood. The surface of the Moon is far from uniform and a comprehensive picture would require that cameras be located at many different points. Although this procedure would be very desirable, it is unfortunately not practical. The landers will therefore be supplemented by spacecraft which orbit the Moon at a moderate altitude, e.g., about 40 kilometers (25 miles). As the Moon rotates, it should be possible to obtain pictures of most of the surface.

SURFACE COMPOSITION

9.206. A relatively simple measurement related to the composition of the lunar surface can be made by means of a gamma-ray spectrometer. The more common radioactive species, uranium, thorium, and potassium-40, emit gamma rays of characteristic energies. A suitable spectrometer can sort out these gamma rays and measure their intensities. In this way it is possible to determine the relative abundances of the various radioactive isotopes, and to compare them with those in meteorites and in terrestrial minerals. The data should help in solving some of the problems concerned with the thermal history of the Moon. Other activities, such as those produced by the action of cosmic rays, may also be detected by the gamma-ray spectrometer.

9.207. From the scientific standpoint, the composition and nature of the lunar minerals are of considerable interest. When men are landed on the Moon, they will be able to bring back samples for complete analysis. In the meantime there are various ways in which limited analyses can be made automatically from unmanned lunar soft-landers.

9.208. The first analytical technique to be tested is called the *alpha-scattering experiment*. A collimated (parallel) beam of alpha particles (helium nuclei) from a radioactive curium-242 source is allowed to fall on a small part of the lunar surface. The alpha particles scattered through a large angle (about 160 deg) fall on a detector which gives the number (or intensity) of the scattered particles as a function of their energy. For each element heavier than aluminum (atomic weight 27), the cut-off energy, beyond which no scattering occurs, is typical of the element. Hence, the scattering energy spectrum can provide a method for determining the elements present in the lunar surface. In addition to the alpha particles that are scattered, some are captured by certain nuclei, and protons (hydrogen nuclei) of characteristic energy are emitted. These are observed by separate proton detectors and provide information concerning the lighter elements in the target. It is claimed that the alpha-scattering instrument is capable of detecting all elements, except hydrogen, helium, and lithium, present in amounts larger than 1 atom percent in the sample under examination.

9.209. Of greater scientific interest than the nature of the elements in the lunar surface is the characterization of the rocks. Tests made on Earth indicate that the alpha-scattering measurements can distinguish between materials arising from meteoritic accretion, from differentiation, and from the solidification of lava (basalt). Such a distinction would provide some clarification of the theories of lunar surface formation.

9.210. Another proposed analytical procedure is based on the fact that every element has an X-ray fluorescence spectrum that is characteristic and specific for that element. If fast electrons strike a material, fluorescence X-rays are produced and by means of an X-ray spectrograph, the elements present can be identified. It is not improbable that, in the essential absence of a lunar atmosphere, electrons from the Sun are sufficient to excite X-rays from materials on the surface of the Moon. Thus, an X-ray spectrograph alone might be sufficient to provide a method of analysis.

9.211. A novel technique for performing analyses on the surface of the Moon utilizes fast neutrons, produced in a compact device, to interact with the lunar material. As a result, certain elements become radioactive and emit gamma rays of known energies. With a gamma-ray spectrometer, these radiations can be measured, thus permitting identification of the elements and determination of their relative amounts. The drawback to this procedure is that it provides no information concerning elements which do not become radioactive when bombarded with fast neutrons.

9.212. A somewhat indirect approach to the determination of the chemical composition of lunar minerals is by means of an X-ray diffractometer, which determines the characteristic X-ray diffraction patterns of crystalline materials. Comparison with the known patterns of terrestrial minerals may thus permit identification of those on the Moon.

9.213. If the Moon has been struck by many meteoritic bodies, as seems probable, their iron (or iron-nickel) content would be significant. An instrument has been developed for detecting the presence of small particles of these metals by measurements of magnetic susceptibility on the lunar surface. Iron and iron-nickel alloys are materials that readily become magnetized when placed in a magnetic field; in other words, they have a high magnetic susceptibility, whereas most minerals do not.

9.214. It would be of considerable interest to know if there are on the Moon any organic compounds, particularly amino-acids, of the type which may have been the precursors of living organisms on Earth (cf. § 10.164). A complete answer to the question of whether such substances are present or not must await the return of samples taken from well below the lunar surface. Until this can be achieved, it is proposed to obtain some provisional information by a gas chromatograph and a mass spectrometer. The gas chromatograph is an instrument which can separate and identify specific gases, and one has been designed that can detect 28 different gaseous substances, including a variety of organic compounds. The mass spectrometer should provide information concerning the composition of lunar minerals, on the abundances of various isotopes which can be utilized in age determinations (§ 7.201), and possibly on organic materials. Both the chromatograph and the mass spectrometer require that the material to be analyzed should be in the form of a gas or vapor, and it is proposed to vaporize the lunar surface material by sputtering, i.e., by bombarding it with high-velocity charged particles, probably protons.

MECHANICAL PROPERTIES OF THE SURFACE

9.215. From the standpoint of landing a manned space vehicle weighing almost 14 tons on the Moon (§ 13.39), the mechanical properties of the surface are of the utmost importance. In view of the controversy over the structure of the lunar surface, as described earlier in this chapter, various measurements will be made of its strength and related properties.

9.216. The *soil mechanics experiment* is designed to determine the nature and mechanical character of the lunar surface. From the results it should be possible to classify the surface material as granular, porous, or solid. Moreover, a rough estimate may be made of the modulus of elasticity and the yield strength. The instrument consists of a mechanical arm, called a surface sampler, which can be extended about 5 feet, with a scoop at its end. The scoop can be loaded with different forces and allowed to drop onto or travel across the lunar surface. Recording instruments measure deceleration, impact velocity, depth of penetration, horizontal forces, etc., and from these data, telemetered to Earth, the mechanical properties of the surface of the Moon can be evaluated.

9.217. Further information will be available from the *touchdown dynamics experiment;* this will give a history of the linear and angular motion of a (Surveyor) spacecraft with three landing legs (§ 9.239) as it makes contact with the Moon. A number of sensors, e.g., accelerometers, strain gages, crushable blocks, etc., are attached to the frame of the spacecraft to provide the required data. The motion of the center of gravity of the spacecraft as it lands and the extent of penetration, if any, of the landing legs will indicate the bearing strength and shear strength (coefficient of friction) of the surface material. It should also be possible to determine surface contours on the scale of the spacing of the landing legs, i.e., about 10 feet.

MICROMETEORITES AND IMPACT EJECTA

9.218. Measurements will be made of the flux, momentum, and gross trajectory of particles at the lunar surface in the vicinity of the spacecraft. Two different types of sensors are proposed for this purpose. First, an impact plate of about 1000 square centimeters in area is attached to a microphone; the strength of the signal produced when the plate is struck by a particle is a measure of the momentum of the micrometeorite particle striking the plate.[*] The second type of detector is a capacitor formed by placing a thin film of dielectric, backed by a layer of conducting material, on each side of the impact plate. Penetration of the capacitor by a particle produces a signal related to

---

[*] It will be noted that the term micrometeorite is used here rather than micrometeoroid, as in Chapter 7. The reason is that the measurements are made at the surface of the Moon and the particles would strike the surface if not deflected by instruments.

the energy of the particle. From the momentum and energy as determined from the two instruments, the mass and speed of the micrometeorite can be calculated. The system is sensitive to masses down to 10^{-13} gram and speeds of 1 kilometer (0.6 mile) per second.

9.219. It is hoped that the data will permit a distinction to be made between primary micrometeorite particles that strike the lunar surface and ejecta thrown out by the impact. The results should provide some insight into the nature of the surface and evolutionary processes on the Moon. Furthermore, a partial estimate can be made of the micrometeorite hazard to be taken into account in both manned and unmanned lunar exploration.

THERMAL PROPERTIES OF THE SURFACE

9.220. Much of the speculation concerning the nature of the lunar surface and the past history of the Moon is related to the thermal properties of the surface layers. Observations will, therefore, be made by means of soft landers of the actual temperatures, to be compared with those inferred from various radiation measurements. Determinations of temperature will be made at various depths so that the temperature gradient and the thermal conductivity of the surface material can be evaluated. The data will be useful in checking the theories that have been developed in relation to such parameters as the thermal inertia, for example.

SEISMIC ACTIVITY

9.221. As a result of the temperature changes which are probably occurring in the interior of the Moon, it is expected that internal stresses develop which lead to seismic (or "moonquake") activity. A seismograph on the lunar surface might provide information on such matters as the presence or absence of a crust, of lava layers, or of thick deposits of dust. Preliminary data could also be obtained on the mechanical properties of the materials below the surface of the Moon and on the nature, i.e., solid or liquid, of the lunar core. It is from the study of seismic waves that much has been learned about Earth's interior. Similar data would undoubtedly help to solve some of the problems relating to the thermal history of the Moon and would provide information concerning the processes operating in the lunar interior. Moreover, it is expected that impacts on the Moon of moderately large meteorites can be detected and counted by means of a seismograph.

9.222. Seismographs (or seismometers) used to study disturbances in Earth are sensitive in three directions at right angles, namely, one vertical and two horizontal. Such three-axis instruments are, however, of delicate construction and would require very careful landing on the lunar surface. For the first experiments, therefore, a rugged single-axis (vertical) seismometer has been devised. It is mounted in a protective structure of balsa wood, so that it can survive a rough landing at a velocity of several hundred feet per second. The information obtained from this instrument will be largely qualitative, that is, it will indicate whether there are seismic disturbances on the Moon or not. If such disturbances are detected and further study appears to be warranted, a soft-lander spacecraft (or man) will be used at a later date to place a three-axis seismometer on the lunar surface.

LUNAR MAGNETIC FIELD

9.223. It is considered that the terrestrial magnetic field results from the combination of circumstances that Earth rotates and has a liquid core that is a good electrical conductor (§ 8.211). Unless a magnetic field can arise in other ways (§ 9.225), it is expected that the lunar field would be much weaker than that of Earth. In any event, measurements of the Moon's magnetic field are desirable, since the field strength is undoubtedly related to the structure of the lunar interior. Furthermore, the behavior of cosmic and solar radiations in the vicinity of the Moon would be markedly affected, as it is near Earth, by the character of the magnetic field, if any. There has been considerable experience in the measurement of magnetic fields by means of magnetometers carried by spacecraft, and observations near to or on the Moon should present no difficulties.

9.224. Studies made with a magnetometer carried by the Russian lunar probe Lunik II,* launched on September 12, 1959, indicated that the magnetic field strength was less than 0.001 gauss (100 gammas) at a height of 50 kilometers (30 miles) above the surface of the Moon. Although the lunar magnetic field is probably weak, the Russian measurements do not indicate the actual value. The reason is that they were made on the sunlit side of the Moon where the solar wind would cause considerable compression of the lunar magnetosphere (§ 8.214). Consequently, a magnetic field might not be detectable at a height of 50 kilometers, whether it existed or not.

9.225. An interesting and possibly significant phenomenon was observed on December 14, 1963 when the magnetometer on the spacecraft Explorer XVIII or IMP-I (§ 8.218) indicated an unusual fluctuation in the interplanetary magnetic field. It attained a maximum value of 14.6 gammas for a period of 4 hours, compared with the normal average of 4 to 7 gammas. At the time, the spacecraft was in a line with the Moon and the Sun, and a possible explanation of the abnormal behavior is that the magnetic field of the Moon was interacting with the solar wind and hence affecting the interplanetary magnetic field strength. If this is the case, the Moon must have a field of appreciable strength. Such a field cannot have the same origin as the terrestrial magnetic field, as seen above, and so it may be due either to a permanent state of magnetization of ancient origin or to the capture of magnetized solar plasma arising from

---

* Lunik II struck the Moon on September 13, 1959, some 35 hours after launch; it was the first man-made object to make a lunar impact. An impact on the far side of the Moon was made by the U.S. spacecraft Ranger IV on April 26, 1962.

the finite electrical conductivity of the Moon. Magnetic field measurements from spacecraft orbiting the Moon will probably be necessary to clarify the situation.

CORPUSCULAR AND ELECTROMAGNETIC RADIATIONS

9.226. Because of the absence of an atmosphere and the weak magnetic field, the lunar surface is almost completely exposed to the corpuscular (protons and electrons) and electromagnetic radiations from the Sun and from space, i.e., cosmic rays. The exact nature of these radiations must be defined for the protection of man and to insure the operation of instruments on the surface of the Moon. As seen in § 3.255, solar cells and other solid-state (semiconductor) devices are adversely affected by some space radiations.

9.227. Instruments for the detection and measurement of various types of radiation and of different energies are well known. These can be landed on the Moon and also carried in orbiting vehicles. In the latter case, information will be obtained on the possible existence of a radiation belt similar to that surrounding Earth. The belt around the Moon, if it exists at all, will probably be much less marked because of the considerably weaker magnetic field.

LUNAR MASS DISTRIBUTION

9.228. It was indicated in § 9.69 that the exact nature of the mass distribution in the Moon will not be known until it is possible to make accurate observations on the orbital characteristics of lunar satellites. Such measurements are not only desirable, but they are necessary for computing the paths of manned vehicles to be used in landing on the Moon. The required data will be obtained from orbiting lunar satellites (§ 9.256). Ultimately, direct measurements of the lunar gravitational field may be made with gravimeters on the surface.

THE LUNAR ATMOSPHERE AND IONOSPHERE

9.229. There is no doubt that the density of the lunar atmosphere is extremely low. Nevertheless, the pressure is believed to be measurable by means of the very sensitive ionization gages that have been developed for high-vacuum experiments. In addition, there is a possibility that the constituents of the atmosphere might be identified with a mass spectrometer.

9.230. Ground-based studies of cosmic radio sources have indicated that the Moon might have an ionosphere (§ 9.176). This could be investigated by observing the variations in the signals received from such sources by instruments located on the lunar surface.

THE U.S. LUNAR PROGRAM

9.231. The program of unmanned lunar studies in the United States involves a considerable amount of supporting laboratory research and development, in addition to spacecraft experiments. The brief review presented here, however, is concerned only with the general nature of the space vehicles and their prime functions.

9.232. The Ranger program has undergone a number of changes since its inception. Originally, it was planned that the spacecraft would fly by the Moon and make a number of scientific observations, e.g., magnetic field, cosmic rays, micrometeoroids, etc., in its vicinity. Later Rangers were to drop packages of instruments onto the lunar surface. Subsequently it was decided that the Block III spacecraft, i.e., Rangers VI through IX, were to make crash landings on the Moon and to be utilized for photographic missions only.

9.233. Rangers I and II were launched in 1961 to test the spacecraft and launch vehicles and were not directed at the Moon, but Rangers III, IV, and V were intended to land instrument capsules on the lunar surface. Of these, Rangers III and V, launched January 26, 1962 and October 18, 1962, respectively, passed by the Moon completely. Ranger IV, launched April 23, 1962, impacted on the far side of the Moon, but the instrumentation did not function and so no data were obtained.

9.234. The first of the spacecraft designed to take photographs of the surface of the Moon, Ranger VI, was launched on January 30, 1964, and it landed within 20 miles of the intended impact point. Unfortunately, the television cameras failed to operate apparently because of an electrical fault that developed when the spacecraft was being launched. Ranger VII, however, launched on July 28, 1964, was a spectacular success; it transmitted excellent photographs of the lunar surface, some of which have been presented earlier in this chapter. Similar successes were achieved by Ranger VIII and Ranger IX (§ 9.243 *et seq.*). The maximum resolution obtained was about a thousand times better than from Earth-based telescopes especially designed to take photographs of the Moon.

9.235. Ranger IX is to be followed by the Surveyor program, commencing toward the end of 1965 or the beginning of 1966. The Surveyor spacecraft is designed to make a soft landing on the lunar surface. The only instruments on the first four members of the series will be television cameras. Some of the cameras will be capable of observing the photometric and polarimetric properties of the surface material. The later Surveyor spacecraft will carry, in addition, instruments for the chemical analysis of lunar rocks and for studying the mechanical properties of the surface.

9.236. It was intended at one time to modify the Surveyor spacecraft into a form that would go into orbit around the Moon instead of landing on the surface. The Surveyor Orbiter, as it was called, has now been discarded in favor of the simpler Lunar Orbiter. The new program will be operated concurrently with the Surveyor program and the orbiting spacecraft will be used largely to obtain photographs of fairly large areas. Regions that may appear to be of special interest, e.g., for manned lunar landings, can then be studied in greater detail by a Surveyor vehicle.

THE RANGER SPACECRAFT

9.237. The general appearance of Rangers VI through IX is shown in Fig. 9.31. The objective of these spacecraft is to obtain television pictures of the Moon's surface, at heights ranging from over 1600 kilometers (1000 miles) to

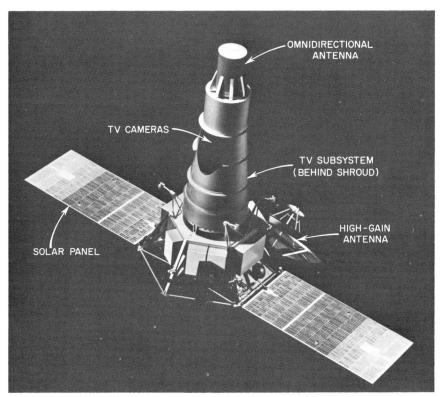

FIG. 9.31.   The Ranger (Block III) spacecraft

about 500 meters (1600 feet). The pictures are transmitted to Earth immediately after being taken by the cameras and the spacecraft makes a crash landing on the surface at a speed of some 2.4 kilometers (1.4 miles) per second and is thus destroyed. The earlier Ranger spacecraft were sterilized by heating in order to prevent possible contamination of the Moon by living organisms. It is suspected that the high temperatures may have caused deterioration of some electronic components and this was largely responsible for the failures experienced. To eliminate this possibility, the Block III Ranger spacecraft were not completely sterilized, especially since the chances that any form of life can survive on the Moon are vanishingly small.

9.238. In Fig. 9.31 the two large panels, covered with nearly 10,000 solar cells to provide electricity for operating the subsystems, are shown spread out, as they are in space. But for launching, the panels are folded up and covered by a protective nose-cone shroud. About an hour after launch, the shroud drops away and the solar-cell panels are extended. The spacecraft is then 15 feet across and just over 10 feet high. The total weight is about 806 pounds of which the television subsystem, including cameras, electronics, batteries, and transmitter, represents 382 pounds.

9.239. The basic structure (or bus) of the spacecraft is a hexagonal frame-work of aluminum and magnesium, with a cone-shaped superstructure. The axis of this superstructure is the roll axis of the spacecraft. Attached to the hexagon are cases containing silver-zinc storage batteries which are charged by the solar cells and various subsystems for communications, command, atti-tude control, telemetry data encoding, etc. One of these subsystems is the Central Computer and Sequencer which receives commands from Earth and stores them until the proper time for their execution.

9.240. The television subsystem is in the conical housing, with the six cameras facing outward and downward through the aperture seen in Fig. 9.31. The spacecraft has two antennas, one low-gain and the other high-gain. The omni-directional (low-gain) antenna, located at the top of the conical structure, is utilized to receive radio commands from the ground, but it does not transmit except during the launch period and when the midcourse correction is being made to the trajectory. At all other times, transmission of telemetry and of tele-vision pictures is from the dish-shaped (high-gain) antenna which is directed toward Earth. This antenna is hinged to the bottom of the hexagonal frame-work and is moveable. The 50-pound thrust monopropellant (hydrazine) rocket motor for the midcourse guidance correction is set inside the frame-work, with the nozzle facing downward.

9.241. The Ranger television system includes six cameras; two are wide-angle or F (full-scan) cameras and the other four are narrow-angle or P (partial-scan) cameras. The exposure times are 1/200th and 1/500th of a second, respectively. The cameras are mounted on the spacecraft bus so that they are pointed at an angle of 38 deg to the roll axis. By the use of lenses with different focal lengths and different apertures, a certain proportion of the pictures taken should be satisfactory over a wide range of lighting conditions on the Moon. Behind every camera is a vidicon tube with a photoconduc-tive face plate that retains an impression long enough to permit scanning by an electron beam. Each of the F cameras is exposed once every 5.12 seconds and the P cameras once every 0.8 second; between exposures, the vidicon face-plates are scanned, erased, and prepared to record another picture. The scanning outputs are amplified, combined in one of two video combiners, and sequencers (cf. § 4.159), one for the F cameras and one for the P cameras, and then converted into frequency-modulated signals. These are transmitted to Earth by two 60-watt transmitters, one for each set of cameras, at different frequencies close to 960 megacycles per second. The signals are received by two 85-foot paraboloid antennas at the Goldstone Tracking Station, California, of the Deep Space Network, and are recorded both on magnetic tape and on film.

RANGER LAUNCH PERIOD AND TRAJECTORY

9.242. The launch periods of the Ranger spacecraft on a lunar mission are dependent upon a number of factors, some of which are shown in Fig. 9.32. Furthermore, the time of approach to the Moon must be such that the spacecraft is in line-of-sight with the Goldstone Tracking Station where the receiving equipment is located. There is a permissible launch period of about six days

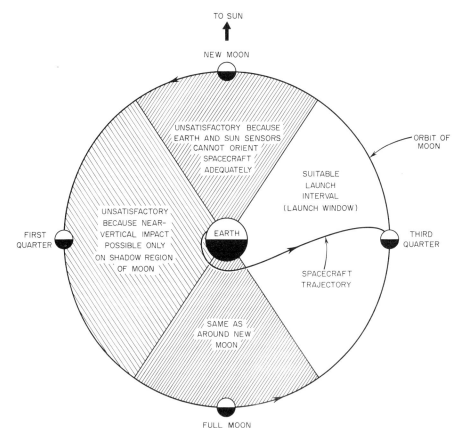

FIG. 9.32. Suitable launch period (or launch window) for taking photographs of the Moon

each month, with a *launch window*, i.e., the useful time interval on any given day, which decreases from about $2\frac{1}{2}$ hours to $1\frac{1}{2}$ hours during the course of the period. In calculating the trajectory from Earth to the Moon, allowance must be made for rotation of Earth and the motion of the Moon in its orbit. Account must also be taken of the necessity for avoiding inhabited areas and shipping lanes in the early stages of the launch phase. The spacecraft is first placed into a temporary, parking orbit, and when the proper location, which varies with the day of the month and the time of day, is reached, the vehicle is injected into a lunar trajectory. For the midcourse guidance correction to be within the capability of the motor on the spacecraft, injection from the parking orbit into the lunar trajectory must take place somewhere in a circular region about 16 kilometers (10 miles) in diameter; furthermore, the velocity must be within 0.0072 kilometer per second (16 miles per hour) of the desired value of about 10.95 kilometers per second (24,500 miles per hour) with reference to Earth. The required injection velocity, like the injection point, depends on the date and time of injection. Great accuracy is therefore required in establishing the location of the injection point and the velocity of the spacecraft at the time.

Ranger Missions

9.243. Ranger VII was launched on July 28, 1964 from the Kennedy Space Center, Florida, by means of an Atlas booster with an Agena upper stage. The Atlas having been jettisoned soon after burnout, the Agena-Ranger combination was placed in a parking orbit at an altitude of about 115 miles. After coasting in this temporary orbit for some 20 minutes, to reach the appropriate injection point, the Agena rocket was restarted and the velocity of the system increased to 10.949 kilometers per second (24,490 miles per hour), as required for the lunar trajectory at that time. About 3 minutes after completing its second burn, the Agena was detached, leaving Ranger VII to continue to the Moon.

9.244. Approximately 20 minutes later, the solar-cell panels were opened out and the attitude control system was activated. First, sensors directed the spacecraft to point its roll axis to the Sun, so that the solar cells were exposed to full sunlight, and later, by the use of other sensors, the high-gain antenna was oriented toward Earth. Telemetry transmission of engineering data from the spacecraft, which had hitherto been from the omnidirectional antenna, was now switched to the high-gain directional antenna.

9.245. Changes in attitude, as described above and during the midcourse maneuver, as well as maintenance of proper attitude during flight, were carried out by means of 12 jets of cold nitrogen gas. Five pounds of this gas were stored at a pressure of 3500 pounds per square inch in two lightweight titanium reservoirs.

9.246. By tracking Ranger VII during the first 15 hours or so of its flight, it was determined that the spacecraft was slightly off its intended trajectory. The required midcourse correction was calculated and a command, for later execution, was sent from Earth and stored in the Central Computer and Sequencer. Soon thereafter, an order was given for transmission from the spacecraft to switch to the omnidirectional antenna, and for the high-gain dish antenna to swing away, out of the path of the midcourse-maneuver rocket exhaust. At the appropriate time, roughly 17 hours after launch, when Ranger VII was almost 100,000 miles from Earth, the spacecraft began to execute the stored instructions. First, pitch and roll turns were made to bring the rocket motor (and spacecraft) into the required direction; then, the motor was fired for 50 seconds to change the velocity vector by 57 miles per hour. Subsequently, the spacecraft was reoriented to the Sun, the high-gain antenna was restored to its Earth-directed position, and transmission returned to it. Ranger VII was now on a course which was to bring it within 10 to 14 kilometers (6 to 8 miles) of the calculated impact point near the northwest edge of Mare Nubium. The distance of the flight from Earth was 392,130 kilometers (243,660 miles) and the elapsed time from launch was 68 hours 35 minutes.

9.247. It would have been possible to command Ranger VII to perform a terminal maneuver as it approached the lunar surface in order to point the cameras in the proper direction. Observations showed, however, that this was unnecessary and that the spacecraft was already oriented in a satisfactory manner; pictures were actually taken in a direction about 12 deg from the lunar vertical. After being warmed up, upon a command received from Earth, the cameras began taking and transmitting pictures when Ranger VII was about 1600 kilometers (1000 miles) from the lunar surface. The F (wide-angle) camera operated for 17 minutes 13 seconds, taking some 320 pictures, and the P (narrow-angle) cameras took almost 4000 pictures in 13 minutes 40 seconds before impact. Altogether, 4316 pictures were received, the last one, which is shown in Fig. 9.33, was taken at an altitude of about 480 meters (1600 feet) at 0.18 second before Ranger VII struck the lunar surface; the spacecraft crashed before transmission was complete. The area shown in the photograph is roughly 30 by 50 meters (100 by 165 feet) and the resolution is estimated to be less than 0.5 meter (roughly 18 inches).

9.248. Some of the conclusions drawn from the Ranger VII pictures have been described earlier in the chapter. For purposes of review, it may be mentioned here that the most significant discoveries were the following: (a) the occurrence of lunar craters of all sizes, from very large down to a foot or less in diameter, (b) the presence of numerous secondary (and perhaps tertiary) craters within the rays (of Tycho) presumably formed by impact ejecta from the central crater, and (c) the apparent absence of large boulders and of cracks or fissures in the vicinity of the impact point in a small mare between Oceanus Procellarum and Mare Nubium.* The pictures, however, do not indi-

* At the International Astronomical Union meeting in 1964, it was agreed to name this area Mare Cognitum.

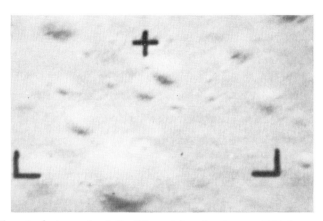

FIG. 9.33.   Closest photograph of the Moon taken by Ranger VII from a distance of 480 meters (1600 feet). The dimensions of the area shown are approximately 30 meters by 50 meters (120 feet by 165 feet); the smallest observable details are roughly 0.5 meter (18 inches) across

cate definitely whether or not there are significant dust layers on the surface.

9.248a. Ranger VIII, launched on February 17, 1965, approached the Moon at a smaller inclination to the surface than did Ranger VII. It was thus able to take some 7000 pictures during a period of about 23 minutes, covering a much larger area. The spacecraft landed in the southwest corner of Mare Tranquillitatis which appears from Earth to be much darker than, and is roughly 1600 kilometers (1000 miles) distant from, the mare into which Ranger VII crashed. Nevertheless, the close-up pictures of the surface obtained in the two mare are remarkably similar (cf. Fig. 9.33). The only obvious difference, as mentioned in § 9.161, is the presence of a few rocks in Mare Tranquillitatis.*

9.249. Attention has been called by J. A. O'Keefe (1964) to a possibly significant feature of the Ranger VII photographs, such as the one in Fig. 9.34 which was taken at a distance of about 320 kilometers (200 miles) and shows an area of roughly 147 by 147 kilometers (91 miles). At the top and bottom of the figure are seen a number of sharp ridges (or *arêtes*), as indicated by the shadows being at the right, all running in the same direction from NE by N to SW by S. There are also several less conspicuous wrinkle ridges, which have been known for some time, that are roughly parallel to the arêtes. Wrinkle ridges are commonly accepted as having an internal (volcanic) origin and their general alignment with the arêtes has led O'Keefe to suggest that the latter were produced by lava flows. The steep sides of the arêtes indicate that the lava was of a viscous type, i.e., with a high silica content.

_____

* The Ranger program was completed with Ranger IX, launched on March 21, 1965, which returned nearly 6000 pictures of the Moon before crashing in the crater Alphonsus. Chains of small craters lying along deep cracks (rilles) within Alphonsus are highly suggestive of volcanic activity (cf. § 9.136 *et seq.*).

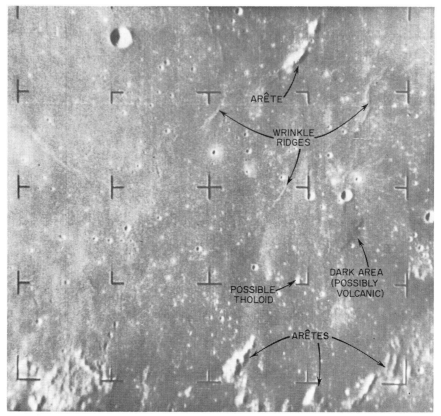

FIG. 9.34.   Ranger VII photograph, taken at a distance of 325 kilometers (202 miles) from the lunar surface, showing possible indications of volcanic activity

9.250. About the middle of the right of Fig. 9.34 is seen a dark marking on the same line as the arête at the bottom center; Ranger VII photographs taken nearer the lunar surface show that it is either a low ridge or a series of mounds. Presumably, this feature is also of internal origin. It is of special interest to note, therefore, that the black marking appears to cut across the lighter ray material, implying that volcanic action has occurred in the Moon subsequent to the formation of the rays, possibly within the past few hundred million years. About half way between the black marking and the arête at the bottom center of the picture, but slightly to the north, there is a conspicuous mound. This is very similar in appearance to a terrestrial *tholoid* (Greek, *tholos*, "dome") formed by the gradual extrusion of viscous lava. It is perhaps significant, in connection with the arguments in § 9.106, that ash flows on Earth are commonly associated with tholoids and related extrusions, e.g., the lunar arêtes.

9.251. The purpose of the Surveyor program, with a first flight late in 1965 or early in 1966, is to take photographs and make scientific measurements on the surface of the Moon. The spacecraft, which is designed to make a soft landing, is shown in Fig. 9.35. The total weight after injection into lunar

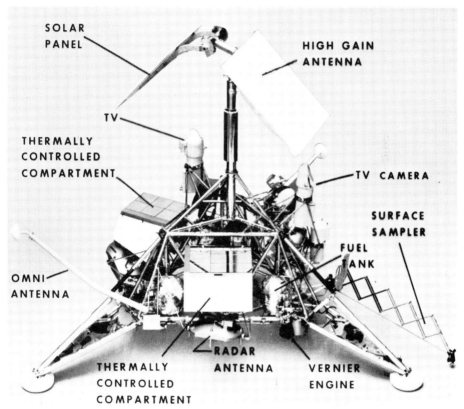

FIG. 9.35.   The Surveyor spacecraft for lunar landing

trajectory is about 2150 pounds; of this, nearly 1400 pounds is propellant for midcourse and terminal guidance, and for decelerating the spacecraft to a low velocity for landing. Surveyor will be launched and injected by the Atlas-Centaur rocket vehicle (§ 3.152). In space, the three landing legs and two omnidirectional antenna booms will be extended, and a radio signal is transmitted to permit tracking from Earth. The reference points for the midcourse guidance maneuver are the Sun and Canopus (§ 4.63), rather than the Sun and Earth as for Ranger.

9.252. In addition to the usual midcourse correction, a series of maneuvers are performed near the Moon to insure a soft landing. For this purpose, a large solid-fuel retro-motor and three smaller vernier rocket engines with hypergolic liquid propellants are employed. The initial commands for the terminal operations come from Earth, but when Surveyor is at a distance of roughly 13 kilometers (8 miles) from the lunar surface and the main retro-rocket has burnt out, radar reflections from the Moon are used to control the vernier engines. At an altitude of some 4 meters (13 feet), when the spacecraft is dropping at a rate of less than 5 meters (16 feet) per second, the vernier rockets are turned off. The spacecraft then falls the remaining distance to the surface, the touchdown being cushioned by three pads, one at the end of each landing leg, and by crushable blocks under the frame of the vehicle.

9.253. Once Surveyor is settled on the Moon, a command is received through the omnidirectional antennas for the solar-cell panel to face the Sun and for the high-gain antenna to be directed toward Earth. When communication is established through this antenna, the experiments on the spacecraft can be started.

9.254. Television cameras are the only experimental equipment carried by the first four Surveyors. A single camera provides pictures of the spacecraft landing area on the Moon during the approach phase, taken from altitudes of 1600 to 80 kilometers (1000 to 50 miles). One frame can be taken every 3.6 seconds, and at least 50 percent of the lunar area in each picture, other than the first, appears in the preceding picture.

9.255. The survey television camera to be used after landing has a lens of variable focal length, so that it can operate in various modes, ranging from narrow-angle to wide-angle. An automatic iris adjusts the lens aperture to the existing lighting conditions. Provision is also made for the insertion of colored and polarized filters upon command. With the aid of a mirror, that can be rotated and tilted, the camera is capable of viewing all directions (360 deg) around the vertical and 20 deg above and 45 deg below the horizontal plane of the spacecraft.

9.256. One obvious piece of information that can be obtained from the spacecraft camera pictures is whether or not appreciable quantities of dust are stirred up by Surveyor upon landing on the Moon's surface. If dust collects on the lens, filter, or solar cells, the optical transmission system will be seriously affected. If transmission is reasonably good, however, the survey camera can provide qualitative data about small-scale roughness, slopes, and dust layers with an optimum resolution of 1 millimeter close to the spacecraft. It should be possible to discriminate between different types of surface by their light-scattering properties, and perhaps to correlate them with disruption of the surface by the landing legs or with geological features. Photometric, polarimetric, and colorimetric data will supply information concerning the roughness of the lunar surface on both small and large scales.

9.257. The fifth, sixth, and seventh Surveyors are expected to carry one television approach camera and two survey cameras; the latter will permit a limited amount of stereoscopic viewing of the surface. In addition, there will be instruments for alpha-scattering, soil mechanics, touchdown dynamics, and micrometeorite experiments, and a single-axis seismometer. The various devices and the data they can provide have already been described. The objectives of subsequent Surveyor missions will be largely determined by the results of the earlier flights. The ultimate purpose of the experiments is to provide information that can be utilized in the Apollo program for landing men on the Moon (see Chapter 13).

THE LUNAR ORBITER

9.258. The main mission of the Lunar Orbiters, which are expected to make a first flight in 1966, is to take photographs over the whole illuminated surface of the Moon. The objective is to facilitate the choice of a site for the Apollo landing. The Lunar Orbiter is expected to weigh about 820 pounds and will be launched and injected by an Atlas-Agena D rocket (§ 3.149). A 100-pound thrust engine with hypergolic liquid propellants will be used to place the spacecraft in orbit around the Moon. Cameras on the Lunar Orbiters will take pictures at both low and high resolutions from altitudes of not less than 35 kilometers (22 miles). By combining the wide-range pictures, it should be possible to obtain stereoscopic coverage with a resolution of about 8 meters (25 feet). The narrow-range cameras should give resolutions down to about 1 meter (3.3 feet).

9.259. Since the orbiting spacecraft will not always be within line-of-sight of a receiving station, the pictures will be taken on film, developed, and stored. Upon command, the film will be scanned and the signals transmitted to Earth for reconstruction into photographs of the lunar surface.

9.260. Although photography of the Moon is the primary objective of the Lunar Orbiter program, secondary objectives are to obtain information on the lunar gravitational field, on the micrometeoroid flux, and on possible high-energy particle radiation. Measurements may also be made of the Moon's magnetic field, radar reflection from the surface, and on the distribution of infrared radiation emission.

CONCLUSION

9.261. It is certain that much valuable information will be obtained from the Ranger, Surveyor, and Lunar Orbiter spacecraft. It is equally certain, however, that instruments alone cannot perform all the functions that will be necessary to secure a reasonably complete understanding of the structure, history, and origin of the Moon. In order to increase the area that can be studied from a single spacecraft, the use of remotely-controlled mobile vehicles, which can travel across the surface has been proposed. But, in the last resort, it will be a human scientist, making observations directly on the lunar surface, who will supply answers to the many remaining questions.

Chapter 10

THE TERRESTRIAL PLANETS:
MERCURY, VENUS, AND MARS

INTRODUCTION

10.1. In Chapter **7**, the planets were considered as members of the solar system; in the present chapter and the next, some of their individual characteristics will be described. Mercury, Venus, and Mars, together with Earth, constitute a group known as the *terrestrial planets*, in which the members have dimensions and masses that are somewhat similar. In spite of the resemblance in these respects, there are some important differences in their physical properties, as will be seen in the course of this chapter. Nevertheless, as a group, the terrestrial planets are so different from the other (Jovian) planets, with the exception of Pluto, that they should be discussed together.

THE PLANET MERCURY

THE ORBIT OF MERCURY

10.2. Mercury is the planet closest to the Sun and, apart from Pluto, its orbit is more elliptical (eccentricity = 0.206) and its orbital plane more highly inclined to the ecliptic (7.004 deg) than any other planet of the solar system. The distance of Mercury from Earth has been determined by the parallax method (§ 6.10) and also by the radio echo technique (§ 4.14). From the results, the distance of Mercury from the Sun has been calculated. At perihelion, i.e., when Mercury is closest to the Sun, the separation is about **46.2** million kilometers (**28.7** million miles), and at aphelion, i.e., when farthest apart, it is **70.2** million kilometers (**43.6** million miles). The average Mercury-Sun distance, which is essentially the length of the semi-major axis of the orbit of the planet, is **58.3** million kilometers (**36.2** million miles). Since the average distance of Earth from the Sun is **149.6** million kilometers, the minimum possible distance between Earth and Mercury is roughly $149.6 - 70.2 = 79.4$ million kilometers and the maximum distance is $149.6 + 70.2 = 219.8$ million kilometers, i.e., **49.4** and **136.7** million miles, respectively. These particular separations arise when

664

inferior and superior conjunction (§ 7.14), respectively, occur at (or near) the aphelion of Mercury.

10.3. The true (or sidereal) orbital period of revolution of Mercury about the Sun is **88.0** days and the apparent (or synodic) period, as seen from Earth, i.e., from one inferior (or superior) conjunction to the next, is **116** days. As a result of the eccentricity of its orbit, the orbital velocity of Mercury varies from about 35 to 58 kilometers per second, with an average value of approximately 48 kilometers (30 miles) per second.

10.4. Because of the perturbations caused by other planets, the orbit of Mercury exhibits the phenomenon of rotation of the line of the apsides (§ 2.88). The position of the perihelion advances at the rate of **9 min 34 sec** of arc per century, whereas the calculated rate is **8 min 51 sec** per century. The small, but definite, difference of **43 sec**, which has been known for about a hundred years, has been accounted for by means of the theory of relativity. This matter will be considered more fully in Chapter 12.

Physical Characteristics of Mercury

10.5. Neither the radius nor the mass of Mercury has yet been determined with any degree of precision. As is usual for the planets, as well as for the Moon, the radius of Mercury is derived from measurement of the angular diameter when at a known distance from Earth (§ 6.21). Because of the relatively small size of the planet, the maximum angular diameter of Mercury is only about **12.5** sec of arc, when it is closest to Earth. Consequently, if the angular radius is taken to be **6.25** sec when the Earth-Mercury distance is **79.4** million kilometers, the actual radius of Mercury is found from equation (6.4) to be roughly **2400** kilometers, i.e., **1500** miles. The mean radius recommended by A. Dollfus (1963) is **2420** kilometers, and this value will be adopted here. It will be noted that the radius of the planet Mercury is only about 50 percent greater than, i.e., one and one-half times, that of the Moon.

10.6. The mass of Mercury is known with even less accuracy than is the radius. Results have been obtained from observations of the perturbations by Mercury of the orbits of other planets, e.g., Venus, and of asteroids, e.g., Eros. The mass indicated in this manner is 3.2×10^{23} kilograms (3.2×10^{20} metric tons) with a possible error of several percent. From this mass and the radius of **2420** kilometers, the mean density of Mercury is found to be **5.4** grams per cubic centimeter. Published values of the density cover a wide range, but the one derived here appears to be an acceptable average based on the best available data for the mass and radius of the planet.

10.7. From the known mass, i.e., 3.2×10^{23} kilograms, and radius, i.e., 2.4×10^{6} meters, the acceleration due to gravity at the surface of Mercury can be obtained from equation (2.4). With mass expressed in kilograms and length in meters, the value of the gravitational constant G is 6.67×10^{-11}; hence,

$$a = \frac{(6.67 \times 10^{-11})(3.2 \times 10^{23})}{(2.4 \times 10^6)^2}$$

$$= 3.6 \text{ meters per second per second}$$
$$= 12 \text{ feet per second per second,}$$

compared with **9.83** meters (**32.2** feet) per second per second on Earth. In view of the uncertainty in the mass of Mercury, in particular, there is no justification for expressing the results to more than two significant figures.

10.8. The circular velocity of a satellite orbiting about Mercury, at a height not far above the surface, can now be derived from equation (**2.9**). Thus, with linear dimensions in meters and time in seconds,

$$v_c = \sqrt{(2.4 \times 10^6)(3.6)}$$
$$= 3.0 \times 10^3 \text{ meters per second.}$$

The circular velocity is thus 3.0 kilometers (1.8 miles) per second. The escape velocity, which is $\sqrt{2}$ times the circular velocity, is consequently 4.2 kilometers (**2.5** miles) per second.

10.9. For convenience, some of the orbital and physical characteristics of the planet Mercury are summarized in Table 10.1.

TABLE 10.1   ORBITAL AND PHYSICAL CHARACTERISTICS OF MERCURY

Distance, Mercury to Sun (max)	70.2×10^6 kilometers	43.6×10^6 miles
Distance, Mercury to Sun (min)	46.2×10^6 "	28.7×10^6 "
Distance, Mercury to Sun (average)	58.3×10^6 "	36.2×10^6 "
Distance, Mercury to Earth (max)	220×10^6 "	137×10^6 "
Distance, Mercury to Earth (min)	79×10^6 "	49×10^6 "
Angular diameter, from Earth (max)	12.5 sec	
Angular diameter, from Earth (min)	4.7 sec	
Eccentricity of orbit	0.206	
Inclination of orbit to ecliptic	7.004 deg	
Inclination of equator to orbital plane	about 7 deg	
Orbital period (sidereal)	88 days	
Orbital period (synodic from Earth)	116 days	
Average orbital velocity	48 kilometers (30 miles) per second	
Radius (average)	2420 kilometers (1510 miles)	
Mass	3.2×10^{23} kilograms	
Average density	5.4 grams per cubic centimeter	
Gravitational acceleration	3.6 meters (12 feet) per sec per sec	
Escape velocity	4.2 kilometers (2.5 miles) per second	
Rotation period	88 days	

TELESCOPIC OBSERVATIONS OF MERCURY

10.10. Since Mercury is close to the Sun, the angular distance between these two bodies in the sky is always small. The maximum elongation (§ 7.30) is **28** deg when it coincides with the aphelion of Mercury, and **18** deg when it occurs at perihelion. Because of its proximity to the Sun, the observation of Mercury, either with the unaided eye or by means of a telescope, presents problems. When the sky is dark, i.e., just before sunrise or after sunset, the planet is close to the horizon and the depth of atmosphere through which the light has to pass results in poor seeing conditions. On the other hand, during the daytime, when Mercury can be well above the horizon, the glare of the Sun is a disturbing factor. Nevertheless, telescopic studies of the planet are generally made in daylight.

10.11. As is to be expected of an interior planet, Mercury exhibits phases during its orbital motion around the Sun (§ 7.31). The full phase occurs at superior conjunction, the quarter phases near the two (east and west) maximum elongations, and the new phase at inferior conjunction. These conditions render it difficult to make observations of Mercury. At the full phase, for example, when the whole disc is exposed, the planet is farthest from Earth and is also close to the Sun. Representations of Mercury are thus constructed from studies made during the partial phases, close to the maximum elongations.

10.12. Since the resolving power of the eye is better than that of a photographic plate, the best records of the appearance of Mercury are in the form of drawings, such as that shown in Fig. 10.1. It is seen that the planet exhibits light and dark markings, similar to those observed on the surface of the Moon by the unaided eye. There are several other respects in which Mercury resembles the Moon, as will be apparent shortly.

10.13. A study of the markings on the surface of Mercury indicates that the period of direct (counterclockwise) rotation of the planet about its axis is the same as the period of revolution around the Sun, i.e., 88 days. The result has been confirmed in recent years by observations on radar echoes. Thus Mercury exhibits the phenomenon of captured (or trapped) rotation, as the Moon does with respect to Earth, and always presents the same face toward the Sun. The other side, unlike the Moon's far side, is always in darkness. The captured rotation of Mercury is undoubtedly the consequence of factors similar to those responsible for the equal periods of rotation and revolution of the Moon, namely, retardation of the rotation of Mercury by tides produced in it by the Sun (§ 9.20). It is probable that the planet has a bulge (or protrusion) directed toward the Sun, although nothing is known of its dimensions.

10.14. As a result of the marked eccentricity of Mercury's orbit, there is considerable libration in longitude (§ 9.27) relative to the Sun; it amounts to 23.7 deg on each side (east and west) of the planet. The equatorial plane of Mercury is inclined at an angle of approximately 7 deg to its orbital plane, and so there is also a small latitudinal (north and south) libration. As a result of these librations, only about 37 percent of the surface of Mercury is in perpetual darkness. Another 37 percent is always in sunlight and the remaining 26 percent, mainly at the eastern and western limbs, is alternately light and dark.

10.15. The average visual albedo of Mercury is 0.07 and is thus the same as the mean value for the Moon. Furthermore, the variation of the brightness and the polarization with the solar phase angle, i.e., the Sun-Mercury-Earth angle, is similar to that exhibited by the Moon (§§ 9.123, 9.127). Another resemblance between the two bodies is that the polarization is greater for the dark (low-

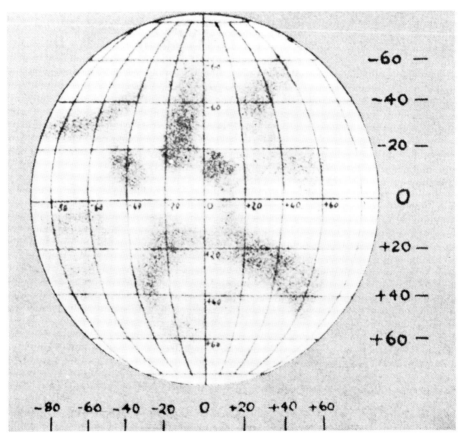

Fɪɢ. 10.1. Composite drawing prepared from ten photographs of Mercury taken in 1942 and 1944. (*Courtesy A. Dollfus*)

albedo) regions of Mercury than it is for the lighter (high-albedo) areas. These striking similarities suggest that the surface of the planet has the same small-scale roughness as the Moon. From the scattering of radar echoes by Mercury it appears that there are irregularities over most of the surface with dimensions of about a foot or so. No shadows are observed near the terminator of the planet, indicating that the elevations cannot be much, if at all, higher than those on the Moon.

The Atmosphere of Mercury

10.16. The absence of any significant diffusion or refraction of light and the sharply defined appearance of Mercury when it makes a transit across the face of the Sun suggest that the planet has little or no atmosphere. The polarization of light from Mercury has been interpreted as implying the presence of an atmosphere of very low density. In 1950, for example, A. Dollfus found that, with increasing phase angle, the polarization increases more rapidly at the cusps than at the center of the planet's surface. The additional polarization at the cusps was attributed to a low-density atmosphere, and assuming the composition to be the same as that of air, Dollfus estimated that the pressure would be not more than 3 millibars, i.e., roughly 3×10^{-3} of the normal, sea-level atmospheric pressure.*

10.17. Mercury is usually difficult to observe because of the glare of the Sun, as already stated, but the time of a total solar eclipse provides an unusual opportunity to study the planet. Measurements made during the eclipse of 1961 failed to reveal the presence of any detectable atmosphere on Mercury. But in the spectrum of the planet obtained during the total solar eclipse of 1963, N. A. Kozyrev (§ 9.137) claimed to have detected the presence of hydrogen lines. He concluded, therefore, that Mercury has an atmosphere and that it contains hydrogen.

10.18. The escape velocity from Mercury, i.e., 4.2 kilometers per second, is somewhat larger than from the lunar surface, but the temperatures are also somewhat higher in the former case, so that the atmospheres might be expected to have similar compositions. It would appear, therefore, from the arguments in § 9.163 *et seq.*, that only heavy gases can be present in the atmosphere of Mercury. From the standpoint of molecular weight, the only reasonable possibilities would seem to be argon (from the radioactive decay of potassium-40), krypton and xenon (from spontaneous fission in uranium), and possibly sulfur dioxide and carbon dioxide. Kozyrev has argued, however, in view of his spectroscopic observations, that, because of the proximity of Mercury to the Sun, the hydrogen lost by escape from the gravitational field is being continuously replaced by gas captured from the solar wind. Hydrogen gas, in spite of its lightness, might thus be present in the atmosphere of Mercury. This conclusion, somewhat surprising at first sight, awaits confirmation.

Temperatures on Mercury

10.19. From the accepted value of the solar constant (§ 6.31) and the known average distance from the Sun to Mercury, as compared with that to Earth,

---

* A bar is a unit of pressure equal to 10^6 dynes per square centimeter, and 1 millibar is one thousandth of a bar. The normal atmospheric pressure (760 millimeters of mercury) is equivalant to 1.013 bars or 1013 millibars.

it can be readily calculated that solar energy falls on the surface of Mercury at the average rate of 13.2 calories per square centimeter per minute. By assuming the planet to radiate as a black body and allowing for the albedo, J. C. G. Walker (1961) calculated that the maximum temperature on the sunlit side of Mercury should range from 695°K at perihelion to 565°K at aphelion. At the mean distance from the Sun, the calculated temperature is close to 621°K, i.e., 348°C or 658°F. Actual measurements of infrared radiation emission by E. Pettit and S. B. Nicholson (§ 9.146) in 1936 indicated an average temperature of roughly 610°K (337°C, 638°F) at the subsolar point (§ 9.143, footnote). On the other hand, the brightness temperature (§ 6.65), as derived from the microwave radiation intensity measurement in the wavelength region of 3.5 centimeters, made in 1961 by W. E. Howard and his associates in the United States, suggest a temperature of $1050 \pm 350°K$ on the sunlit side of Mercury. There are reasons for believing, however, that various corrections might reduce the microwave value to about 600° or 700°K for the surface temperature, in fair agreement with the result obtained from infrared measurements.

10.20. Until recently, measurements of the brightness temperature of the unilluminated side of Mercury were in doubt, and so attempts were made to determine it by theoretical means. By taking into consideration the heat generated in the interior of the planet by radioactive decay and the heat conducted through the planet's mantle from the sunlit side, it was calculated that the temperature at Mercury's antisolar point, i.e., the point farthest from the Sun, was approximately 30°K ($-243°C$, $-444°F$). This extremely low temperature did not seem to be unreasonable, because the apparent absence of a significant atmosphere would mean that heat could be transferred from the relatively hot sunlit side to the dark side only through the body of the planet and this is a poor conductor.

10.21. In 1964, however, observations made with the 250-foot dish antenna in New South Wales, Australia, indicated a brightness temperature at radio-frequency wavelengths of about 290°K (17°C, 62°F) for the unilluminated side of Mercury. The only reasonable explanation of this result, if it is correct, is that the planet has sufficient atmosphere to transfer heat from the light to the dark side. The unexpectedly high temperature of the latter side and Kozyrev's contention that hydrogen in Mercury's atmosphere is being continuously replaced by the solar wind open upon some interesting new problems.

THE INTERIOR OF MERCURY

10.22. The nature of the interior of Mercury can be inferred from the average density, which is only slightly less than that of Earth. In fact, some authorities claim that Mercury actually has the higher density of the two planets. In any event, the values are sufficiently alike to suggest that their internal structures are similar. In general, it is assumed, therefore, that Mercury has a heavy-metal core of high density, e.g., iron-nickel with perhaps small amounts of carbon and silicon, and less dense outer layers. In view of the very slow rate of rotation of the planet, it is unlikely that it will have a significant magnetic field.

Studies of Mercury from Space

10.23. Although no definite plans have been formulated in the United States for a space probe to study Mercury, the matter has received unofficial consideration. The distance of the planet from Earth, the large inclination of its orbital plane to the ecliptic, and the high temperatures in its vicinity, due to the proximity of the Sun, introduce problems that will delay for several years the investigation of Mercury by means of spacecraft. It is of interest, nevertheless, to consider what data could be obtained from a space vehicle. A fly-by mission could take photographs of the planet's surface and could obtain information about its temperature. Something could also be learned about its atmosphere, ionosphere, and magnetic field, if they should exist. The sunlit area is probably too hot for instruments to operate. If the temperature on the dark side of Mercury is that given in § 10.21, it would be ideal for the landing of various scientific instruments.

THE PLANET VENUS

The Orbit of Venus

10.24. The planet Venus is the second closest to the Sun. Its orbit is more nearly circular than that of any other planet, its eccentricity being only 0.00679. The inclination of the orbital plane to the plane of the ecliptic is 3.39 deg. The average distance of Venus from the Sun, as determined by the radar echo technique, is 108.2 million kilometers (67.2 million miles). The actual separation ranges from 107.4 million kilometers (66.7 million miles) at perihelion to 109.0 million kilometers (67.7 million miles) at aphelion. The distance of Venus from Earth varies between a minimum of about 42 million kilometers (26 million miles) at closest approach (inferior conjunction) to 260 million kilometers (160 million miles) at superior conjunction, when the separation is a maximum. As a consequence of the considerable ratio of these distances, more than six to one, the diameter of Venus appears much larger in the crescent phase, when the planet is near to inferior conjunction, than it does as it approaches the full phase, close to superior conjunction (Fig. 10.2). Thus, the angular diameter of Venus has a maximum value of about 65 min of arc and a minimum of some 10 min.

10.25. The sidereal period of revolution of Venus around the Sun is 224.7 days and the synodic period as apparent from Earth is 583.9 days. Because of the small eccentricity of the orbit, the velocity of revolution of the planet about the Sun is almost constant at 35.05 kilometers (21.78 miles) per second.

F<small>IG</small>. 10.2.   Photographs of Venus in various phases. (*Lowell Observatory*)

P<small>HYSICAL</small> C<small>HARACTERISTICS</small> <small>OF</small> V<small>ENUS</small>

10.26. The mass of Venus has been calculated from the perturbations it produces in the orbits of Mercury, Earth, and particularly of Eros. A much more accurate value, however, was obtained in 1963 from observations on the trajectory of the Mariner spacecraft (§ 10.82) as it approached the planet. The result is 4.875×10^{24} kilograms, i.e., 4.875×10^{21} metric tons.

10.27. Venus is surrounded by a layer of clouds, as will be seen below, and so it does not have a sharp outline; consequently, the angular diameter cannot be determined very precisely. The best value of the mean radius, which must be regarded as approximate only, is 6100 kilometers or 3800 miles. From this radius and the mass given above, the mean density of the planet is found to be 5.1 grams per cubic centimeter.

10.28. The mass and radius can be utilized to derive the acceleration due to gravity at the surface of Venus; the value is 8.7 meters (28.6 feet) per second per second. The circular velocity of a body orbiting near the planet is 7.3 kilometers (4.5 miles) per second and the escape velocity is 10 kilometers (6.2 miles) per second. The results are given to two significant figures only because it is felt that greater precision is not yet possible.

10.29. The pertinent data relating to the distances, orbital period, mass, radius, etc., for the planet Venus are collected in Table 10.2. As far as these characteristic properties are concerned, Venus is similar to Earth (cf. Table 7.3) ; hence, Venus has sometimes been described as the twin of Earth. Although

TABLE 10.2   ORBITAL AND PHYSICAL CHARACTERISTICS OF VENUS

Distance, Venus to Sun (max)	107.4×10^6 kilometers	67.7×10^6 miles
Distance, Venus to Sun (min)	109.0×10^6 "	66.7×10^6 "
Distance, Venus to Sun (average)	108.2×10^6 "	67.2×10^6 "
Distance, Venus to Earth (max)	257×10^6 "	160×10^6 "
Distance, Venus to Earth (min)	42×10^6 "	26×10^6 "
Angular diameter, from Earth (max)	65 min	
Angular diameter, from Earth (min)	10 min	
Eccentricity of orbit	0.00679	
Inclination of orbit to ecliptic	3.39 deg	
Inclination of equator to orbital plane	Approx. 6 deg	
Orbital period (sidereal)	224.7 days	
Orbital period (synodic from Earth)	583.9 days	
Average orbital velocity	35.05 kilometers (21.78 miles) per second	
Radius (average)	6100 kilometers (3800 miles)	
Mass	4.875×10^{24} kilograms	
Average density	5.1 grams per cubic centimeter	
Gravitational acceleration	8.7 meters (28.6 feet) per sec per sec	
Escape velocity	10 kilometers (6.2 miles) per second	
Rotation period	247 ± 5 days (retrograde)	

the interiors of the two planets probably resemble one another, the atmospheres are very different as will soon be apparent.

TELESCOPIC OBSERVATION OF VENUS

10.30. Because the fraction of the area of Venus that is visible increases whereas the angular diameter decreases as the planet moves from inferior to superior conjunction, the actual area that is visible at first increases and then decreases. The reverse behavior occurs as Venus passes from superior to inferior conjunction. As a result, the planet appears to be brightest between the crescent and quarter phases, about 36 days after and before the time of inferior conjunction. The elongation is then about 39 deg, compared with the maximum of 45 deg at the quarter phases.

10.31. The exceptional brightness of Venus is due partly to its size and proximity to the Sun and to Earth, but also to its high albedo. The actual value varies with the wavelength of the reflected radiation, but it is between 0.7 and 0.8 for visible light. The variation of the planet's brightness with the solar phase angle, after allowing for the changing distances from the Sun to Venus and from Venus to Earth, is quite different from that observed for the Moon, Mercury, or Mars. It is very similar to that expected for a smooth sphere reflecting light in the diffuse manner that is characteristic of clouds. Furthermore, the albedo of Venus is much the same as that of terrestrial clouds. Thus, the brightness and high albedo are attributed to the presence of a layer of clouds that surround the planet.

10.32. As seen through a telescope, Venus has a largely featureless appearance; what is observed at visible wavelengths is not the actual surface of the planet but the tops of the clouds. The Venusian* clouds differ from terrestrial clouds in the respect that they cover the planet completely (or almost completely) at all times. Faint markings which change from day to day, however, indicate that a certain amount of movement is taking place. Some astronomers have claimed that surface features of the planet are occasionally visible through breaks in the clouds, but this is not certain.

THE ATMOSPHERE AND CLOUDS OF VENUS

10.33. The formation of clouds suggests that Venus has an appreciable atmosphere and various observations provide support for this view. For example, the marked extension of the cusps observed in the narrow crescent phases, close to inferior conjunction, and the blurred appearance of the terminator result from the scattering of light by atmospheric particles. Furthermore, when a transit of Venus occurs, a bright rim is seen around the body of the planet just before and just after it crosses the Sun's limb. This is caused by the diffraction of sunlight in the upper, low-density region of the Venusian atmosphere above the clouds.

10.34. Perhaps the most convincing evidence for an atmosphere is found in the occulation of a bright star by Venus. Such an event occurred on July 7, 1959 when Venus occulted Regulus, a star of the first magnitude (§ 12.67), in the constellation Leo. The world-wide observations were reviewed by G. de Vaucouleurs and D. H. Menzel who found that the brightness of the star was reduced to half as the light passed through the Venusian atmosphere at an altitude of some 56 kilometers (35 miles) above the top of the cloud layer. Since the decrease in brightness commenced at a greater distance from the planet, it is evident that an appreciable atmosphere must extend to a considerable height above the surface of Venus.

10.35. It was shown by B. Lyot (§ 9.128) in 1929 that the polarization of light reflected from Venus as a function of phase angle can be duplicated reasonably well by droplets of water with a diameter of 2.5 microns, i.e., 2.5×10^{-4} centimeter or one ten-thousandth part (10^{-4}) of an inch. It must not be concluded, however, that the Venusian clouds consist of droplets of water because the cloud temperatures are probably too low for liquid water to exist. Actually, any small particles, liquid or solid, having roughly the same refractive index would be expected to behave in a similar manner. Two suggested components of the Venusian clouds, corresponding to two different models of the atmosphere to be described shortly, are ice and magnesium (and calcium)

---

* There is no general agreement concerning the adjective to be used when referring to the attributes of the planet Venus. The most obvious one is, of course, Venusian, as employed here, with Venerian (Latin, *Venerius*, "of Venus"), as a possible alternative. Some writers, however, prefer the adjective Cytherean, derived from the alternative name Cytherea for the Greek goddess Aphrodite who was later identified with the Roman Venus. The Ionian island of Kythera (Cythera in Latin) was one of the important centers of the cult of Aphrodite.

carbonate. Other possibilities which have been considered are a solid polymer of carbon suboxide, i.e., $(C_3O_2)_n$, and droplets of hydrocarbon oils. It would thus appear that the nature of the particles in the clouds of Venus is at present uncertain. If J. S. Strong's claim (1964) to have obtained spectroscopic evidence, from a telescope carried to high altitude by a balloon, of significant amounts of water in the form of small ice crystals above the clouds is confirmed, the situation would be changed.

10.36. As for the gaseous atmosphere which lies below and above the clouds, only the presence of one constituent, namely carbon dioxide, has been definitely established. Some of the absorption bands of carbon dioxide gas in the near (photographic) infrared were detected in the spectrum of Venus by W. S. Adams and T. Dunham in the United States in 1932. Subsequently, additional bands have been reported by other observers. It is of interest that the isotope ratios carbon-12 to carbon-13 and oxygen-16 to oxygen-18 in the carbon dioxide on Venus, as determined from the spectral intensities, are essentially the same as in terrestrial carbon and oxygen, respectively. The agreement suggests that there was a common origin of these elements on the two planets.

10.37. The observed infrared spectrum of carbon dioxide probably results mainly from absorption of radiation by molecules of the gas above the clouds. But in view of the relatively high molecular weight of carbon dioxide, i.e., 44.0, it is undoubtedly also present below the clouds. It should be noted in this connection that the escape velocity and atmospheric temperature in the vicinity of Venus are such that only the lightest gases, e.g., hydrogen, helium, and perhaps atomic oxygen, would have left its gravitational environment.

10.38. Carbon monoxide and oxygen, formed by photochemical decomposition of carbon dioxide by ultraviolet radiation from the Sun, undoubtedly exist in the Venusian atmosphere. But spectroscopic measurements indicate that the amounts must be very small. Other gases which might be present are nitrogen, argon, and water vapor. There has been some indication of the emission lines of molecular nitrogen ions, N_2^+, in the spectrum of Venus, although this has not been confirmed. Nevertheless, it is felt that nitrogen is a major component of the atmosphere, just as on Earth. There is little doubt that some argon-40, the product of the radioactive decay of potassium-40, is also present. Spectroscopic studies have shown that the following gases are either completely absent from the Venusian atmosphere or are present in the merest traces: hydrogen (H_2), nitrous oxide (N_2O), methane (CH_4), ethylene (C_2H_4), ethane (C_2H_6), ammonia (NH_3), and formaldehyde (CH_2O).

10.39. The general consensus at present is that the gaseous atmosphere of Venus contains some 90 molecular (or volume) percent of nitrogen, a few (5 to 10) percent of carbon dioxide, roughly the same quantity of argon as in the terrestrial atmosphere, i.e., about 1 percent, and perhaps a little oxygen. There is probably also a very small amount of water vapor; the proportion is in doubt but it appears to be considerably less than on Earth. It should be pointed out, however, that the minute water vapor content of the Venusian atmosphere does not by itself rule out the possibility that the clouds consist of small ice crystals. The temperatures of the clouds are so low that the pressure of water vapor in equilibrium with ice would be extremely small.

THE ROTATION OF VENUS

10.40. Because of the inability to distinguish surface features on Venus, the rate of its rotation has been a long-standing problem which may have a somewhat surprising solution. Estimates of the period of rotation, i.e., the length of the Venusian day, based on visual, spectroscopic, and photographic observations, and sometimes on pure guesswork, have ranged from 20 hours to 225 terrestrial days, the period of revolution of the planet around the Sun. There is no detectable Doppler shift in the spectral lines (§ 6.109) and so it is argued that Venus must be rotating very slowly, if at all. The apparent absence of any flattening in the shape of the planet might imply that the rotation has been slow for a long time, but it could also mean that the interior is not at all rigid. Because of the cloud cover, conventional methods are useless for determining the rate of rotation of Venus with any degree of precision. The only possibility lies in the application of radar techniques, since radio-frequency waves are able to penetrate the clouds and are reflected from the actual surface of the planet. But even with these methods, the interpretation of the results is evidently not unequivocal. Thus, in 1961, V. Kotelnikov and I. Sklovsky in the U.S.S.R. concluded from their radar measurements that the rotational period of Venus is 11 days, but more recent work in the United States has indicated a very much slower rate of rotation.

10.41. Around the time of the inferior conjunction of Venus in 1962, R. M. Goldstein and R. L. Carpenter made extensive studies of radar reflections from Venus. One experiment involved observation of the Doppler broadening (or spread) in the frequency of a continuous wave radar echo resulting from the relative velocities of different parts of the rotating planet. The reflected radio-frequency wave is affected by the rotation in exactly the same manner as a spectral line originating in the planet, but the broadening is more readily detected than it is for radiations of shorter wavelength, i.e., in the visible spectrum. The returning signals from Venus exhibited a characteristic feature which might have been a reflection from a particular topographical detail in the planet's surface. Observations of this feature indicated that Venus was rotating in a *retrograde* direction, i.e., clockwise as seen from the north celestial pole, in a period of 230 days, with a probable error of plus or minus 40 to 50 days.

10.42. A second series of measurements were made by the "range-gate" method in which the receiver on Earth accepts radar echoes from a specific distance only. In effect, a series of settings of the "gate" permits signals to be received in turn from a circular spot and a number of concentric rings, resembling a rifle target, on the planet's surface. From observations on the Doppler broadening of radar pulses reflected from different areas over an interval of several days, it was concluded that the rotational period of Venus is about 250 days; again, the indications were that the rotation occurs in a retrograde direction.

10.43. The estimates quoted above for the period of rotation were based on the assumption that the rotational axis is perpendicular to the orbital plane of Venus, i.e., the equator lies in the orbital plane. The only information available at the time was derived from what appeared to be a roughly banded structure that could be seen in photographs of the planet taken in violet and ultraviolet light. It was conjectured that these bands represented cloud layers formed approximately parallel to the equator as a result of the planet's rotation. On the basis of this somewhat uncertain interpretation, different astronomers concluded that the equator of Venus makes an angle of either 14 or 32 deg with its orbital plane. During 1964, observations reported from the Arecibo Observatory (§ 8.174) and the Jet Propulsion Laboratory (§ 1.84, footnote) showed that the angle between the equatorial and orbital planes is about 6 deg. Furthermore, the retrograde direction of rotation of the planet has been confirmed and the rotational period determined to be 247 ± 5 days.

10.44. The possibility that Venus rotates in a retrograde direction had been considered as long ago as 1903 by V. M. Slipher and by others in later years. But the combination of retrograde motion with essentially trapped (or captured) rotation, since the apparent rotational period is not greatly different from the period of revolution of Venus about the Sun, is unique and unexpected. If it is correct, then Venus does not always present the same face to the Sun, as Mercury does or as the Moon does to Earth. The nature of the motion, assuming that the periods of rotation and revolution are exactly the same, will be apparent from Fig. 10.3. In this figure, a hypothetical surface feature on the planet, indicated by a short line, is used as a reference point, just as it

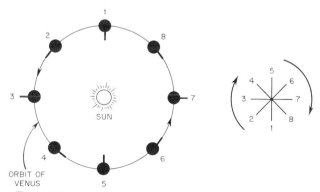

Fɪɢ. 10.3.   Revolution and retrograde rotation of Venus

was in Fig. 9.6 for the motion of the Moon around Earth. It is seen that all areas of the planet are directed toward the Sun twice during each Venusian year (or day). In other words, as viewed from Venus, the Sun rises (in the west) and sets (in the east) twice every 225 terrestrial days. Thus, all parts of the planet are exposed to the Sun at one time or another. Since the rotational period is evidently not exactly 225 Earth days, the situation described above is modified to some extent, but the general character remains.

TEMPERATURES ON VENUS

10.45. Observations of the temperature of Venus have produced results that are of considerable interest even if their significance is not completely understood. Determinations of the infrared radiation emission in the range of 8 to 13 microns, reported in 1955 by E. Pettit and S. B. Nicholson, gave an equivalent black body temperature of 230°K, i.e., −43°C or −46°F. This value has been confirmed by means of bolometric measurements, in about the same wavelength range, made by W. M. Sinton and J. S. Strong in 1960 and by the brightness temperature at 3.75 microns measured by W. M. Sinton in 1962. It is also in agreement with the temperature (230°K) calculated from the radiation balance, using a procedure similar to that in § 9.143, after allowing for the high albedo. The average temperature given by infrared observations is the same for both illuminated and dark areas of Venus, as determined during partial, e.g., quarter, phases.

10.46. Brightness temperatures of Venus were derived from the thermal microwave emission, at wavelengths from about 3 to 10 centimeters, by C. H. Mayer, by L. E. Alsop, and by F. D. Drake, and their respective collaborators, in the United States in 1956 and subsequent years. The values obtained were approximately the same in all cases, namely about 600°K, that is, 370°C (670°F) higher than the infrared temperatures. Furthermore, there was apparently some variation in temperature with the phase angle, whereas the infrared measurements indicated no significant difference. The results obtained at wavelengths of 3.15 centimeters (C. H. Mayer, *et al.*) and 10.0 centimeters (F. D. Drake) are summarized in Fig. 10.4. The brightness temperature is seen to be in the vicinity of roughly 650° to 700°K (380° to 430°C; 720° to 810°F) on the sunlit side of Venus, at superior conjunction, and about 550° to 600°K (280° to 330°C; 540° to 630°F) on the dark side, at inferior conjunction. There is thus a temperature difference of at least 100°C (180°F) between the illuminated and unilluminated areas of the planet.

10.47. The brightness temperatures derived from measurements at wavelengths of 3 and 10 centimeters are seen to be in general agreement. But at wavelengths of 0.4 and 0.8 centimeter, the results are quite different. Thus, J. E. Gibson and R. J. McEwan (1959) in the United States and A. D. Kuznin and A. E. Salomonovich (1960) in Russia found temperatures some 200°C

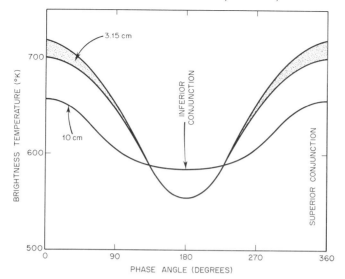

Fig. 10.4.   Brightness temperature of Venus versus phase angle for 3.15-cm and 10-cm radio waves (data from C. H. Mayer, *et al.*, and F. D. Drake)

(360°F) lower than those given above for the longer wavelengths. Some reference is made below to possible explanations for this difference.

Structure of the Venusian Atmosphere

10.48. Three different models have been proposed for the atmosphere of Venus based on the observed temperature variations; they are called the greenhouse aeolosphere, and ionosphere models, respectively.* In the *greenhouse model* (C. Sagan, 1960) the microwave brightness temperature in the vicinity of 650°K on the sunlit side of the planet is regarded as the surface temperature, whereas the infrared temperature of 230°K is attributed to the tops of the clouds. The higher temperature at the surface is then accounted for by the greenhouse effect (cf. § 8.82). The planet absorbs solar radiation which penetrates the clouds and the atmosphere and as a result the temperature of the surface is increased. The heated surface emits infrared radiation, but this is largely trapped by absorption in carbon dioxide, water vapor, hydrocarbon, or other molecules in the atmosphere. The surface thus absorbs heat but loses relatively little by radiation; the cloud tops, on the other hand, radiate heat into space and are consequently much colder than the surface.

10.49. A rough estimate of the cloud height in the greenhouse model may be

---

* Some scientists have suggested that the microwave radiation from Venus is nonthermal in nature and has no relation to the existing temperatures. This interpretation does not seem very probable, although it is not impossible.

made in the following manner. The maximum (or theoretical) rate at which the temperature of a stable atmosphere decreases with increasing height above the surface, i.e., the adiabatic lapse rate (§ 8.26, footnote), is equal to g/c_p, where c_p is the specific heat of the atmospheric gases, determined at constant pressure, and g is the acceleration due to gravity. Since the composition of the Venusian atmosphere is not known, it is not possible to make more than an approximate estimate of the specific heat. Fortunately, however, the results are not very sensitive to variations in composition of a gas mixture consisting mainly of nitrogen and carbon dioxide. If the proportion is assumed to be that given in § 10.39, the adiabatic lapse rate of the Venusian atmosphere near the planet's surface is calculated to be about 8°K per kilometer. According to the arguments presented earlier, the difference in temperature between the surface and the cloud tops is roughly $650 - 230 = 420$°K. Hence, if the lapse rate is assumed to be constant, the height of the clouds is about 53 kilometers (35 miles). An alternative estimate by L. D. Kaplan (1962), taking other factors into consideration, leads to a value of almost 95 kilometers (Fig. 10.5).

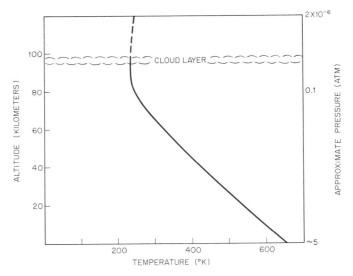

FIG. 10.5. Temperature and pressure in the Venusian atmosphere according to the greenhouse (and aeolosphere) model

10.50. One of the consequences of the greenhouse model is that the surface temperature should be somewhat lower in the dark areas of the planet than in the sunlit regions, since the former are not exposed directly to solar radiation. This is in agreement with observation (see Fig. 10.4), provided that the microwave brightness values are the surface temperatures, as postulated. It should be noted, however, that the temperature variation of about 100°C (180°F) is less than would be expected, by comparison with the temperatures of the sunlit and dark sides of the Moon (§ 9.146) and of Mercury (§ 10.20).

10.51. The difference in behavior is accounted for by the presence of a substantial gaseous atmosphere around Venus. The gas is able to transfer heat from the hotter to the colder side of the planet by the process of convection. This particular type of convection is thought to be a consequence of the slow rotation of Venus. On Earth, which rotates much more rapidly, convection occurs between the equator and the two poles, i.e., in a latitudinal direction. But for a slowly rotating body, it is expected that convection would take place in the longitudinal (or east-west) direction, i.e., from the sunlit side to the dark side. This is apparently the situation on Venus according to the greenhouse model. The cloud tops are at the same temperature on both sides of the planet since it is presumably not affected by the surface temperatures or by the atmospheric motions.

10.52. Both water vapor and carbon dioxide molecules have significant absorption bands in the infrared region of the spectrum, but nitrogen does not. At one time, it was considered that there was sufficient water vapor in the Venusian atmosphere to permit a large proportion of the infrared radiation from the surface to be absorbed, but this now seems doubtful. Consequently, the main criticism of the greenhouse model is that carbon dioxide alone would not provide the infrared absorption required to maintain the high surface temperatures unless its pressure were very high. It is probable that the atmospheric pressure at the surface is actually quite high, several times the normal terrestrial atmospheric pressure. This is indicated by the broadening of the lines in the absorption band spectrum of the carbon dioxide (§ 10.62) and in other ways. Furthermore, there is a possibility that the cloud particles can absorb some of the infrared radiation from the surface. The lack of water vapor in the Venusian atmosphere is thus not necessarily a fatal objection to the greenhouse model.

10.53. In the original presentation of the model, it was postulated that the visible clouds that surround Venus consist of minute ice crystals, but this is not essential to the theory.* If the water vapor content of the atmosphere should be found to be too small to be in equilibrium with ice even at a temperature as low as 230°K, then alternatives must be considered. Among these may be polymerized carbon suboxide (§ 10.35), hydrocarbon droplets, and particles of magnesium (and calcium) carbonate. The latter material is, in fact, a requirement of the model to be described next.

10.54. The *aeolosphere model* (E. J. Öpik, 1961), from *Aeolus*, the Greek god of the winds, resembles the greenhouse model in the respect that it ascribes

---

* According to J. S. Strong (§ 10.35) the presence of ice crystals would make the greenhouse model inapplicable. It is suggested that the crystals reflect most of the solar radiation and the surface temperature of Venus is therefore much cooler than the 650°K postulated in § 10.45. The microwave emission is regarded as being nonthermal in origin (§ 10.60).

the high (microwave brightness) temperature to the surface of the planet and the lower (infrared) temperature to the cloud tops. The heating of the surface, however, is considered to result from the friction of dust particles carried by strong winds that keep the dust in motion. In view of the large differences in both temperature and pressure that exist in the Venusian atmosphere, such strong winds would be expected. In an atmosphere that is stirred in this manner, the temperature and pressure variations with altitude would probably be much the same as in the greenhouse model.

10.55. According to the aeolosphere model, the atmosphere of Venus acts as a gigantic heat engine that converts energy from solar radiation into surface heat by friction. But it is not easy to understand how such an engine would operate. Moreover, if the surface of the planet is not heated by direct sunlight, there is no simple explanation of the significant difference in temperature between the illuminated and dark areas. In any case, assuming that there were a plausible explanation, it is probably that indirect heating, i.e., by friction, would be associated with a significant time lag as the phase angle changed. No such lag has been observed (cf. Fig. 10.4).

10.56. The theory postulates that the dust is a mixture of magnesium and calcium carbonates produced by interaction of the atmospheric carbon dioxide with magnesium and calcium silicates. These substances are undoubtedly present on the surface of Venus, just as they are in stony meteorites and in Earth's crust. The chemical reaction, in the case of the more abundant magnesium silicate, is

$$MgSiO_3 + CO_2 = MgCO_3 + SiO_2,$$

and calcium silicate, $CaSiO_3$, reacts in an analogous manner.

10.57. In 1952, H. C. Urey postulated that these reactions between carbon dioxide and magnesium and calcium silicates, occurring in the presence of liquid water, were the main source of carbonates on Earth. If the temperatures of Venus are as high as 650° to 700°K, as implied by the greenhouse and aeolosphere models, there is certainly no liquid water on the planet at the present time. If there never was any appreciable amount of liquid water, there could not have been anything like as much interaction of silicates with carbon dioxide on Venus as there was on Earth. It has been suggested, in fact, that the high proportion of carbon dioxide in the Venusian atmosphere, as compared with the terrestrial atmosphere, is an indication that such was the case. Nevertheless, it is possible that, at high temperatures, the slow reaction of carbon dioxide and silicates, even in the absence of liquid water, could have produced substantial quantities of carbonates over a period of billions of years. Hence, it is by no means impossible that carbonate dust clouds exist on (or above) the surface of Venus.

10.58. The third structure proposed for the Venusian atmosphere is the *ionosphere model* (D. E. Jones, 1961). It is suggested that a highly ionized (ionosphere) region of considerable depth exists at the top of the atmosphere (cf. § 8.104 *et seq.*). Such an ionosphere would be opaque to, i.e., it will absorb, radio-frequency waves in the centimeter range, but would be relatively transparent to shorter waves in the millimeter wavelength region. The brightness temperatures of about 300° to 400°K, indicated by the 8-millimeter wavelength emission (§ 10.47), is then ascribed to the surface of the planet. In the greenhouse and aeolosphere models, on the other hand, it is considered that this radiation from the surface is absorbed in the lower layers of the Venusian atmosphere and the observed emission originates from intermediate levels where the temperatures are lower than at the surface.

10.59. If the surface temperature is as low as 350°K, i.e., 77°C or 170°F, as indicated by the ionosphere model, then there is a possibility that there may be liquid water, at least in some of the colder areas of the planet. The pressure of water vapor in the atmosphere would then be relatively high and visible clouds would form at a low level, as they do on Earth. The observed infrared temperature of 230°K would then be the temperature of these clouds. Thus, the temperature of the Venusian atmosphere would decrease from about 350°K at the surface to 230°K at the top of the cloud layer, at a height of a few kilometers (Fig. 10.6).

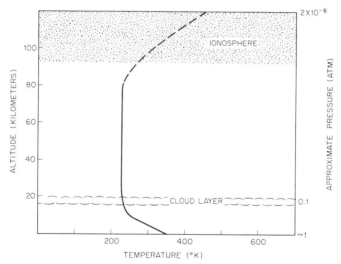

Fig. 10.6. Temperature and pressure in the Venusian atmosphere according to the ionosphere model

10.60. Finally, according to the ionosphere model, the centimeter microwave radiation originates from the ionosphere as a result of free-free transitions, i.e., bremsstrahlung radiation emitted by free electrons when they interact with other electrically charged particles (§ 6.51). It is not certain that the brightness temperatures derived from the centimeter-length radio waves have any thermal significance. But, in any event, these temperatures would apply to the ionospheric region. Since the electron density in the ionosphere of Venus would be determined by the solar radiation, as it is in Earth's ionosphere, a difference in (apparent or real) temperature would be expected between the sunlit and unilluminated areas of the planet, in agreement with observation.

10.61. A serious difficulty of the ionosphere model is the very high electron density that would be required to provide the necessary opacity for microwaves of centimeter length. If the thickness of the Venusian ionosphere is assumed to be about the same as Earth's, i.e., 100 to 200 miles, the electron density would have to be between 10^9 and 10^{10} electrons per cubic centimeter, compared with a maximum of about 10^6 electrons per cubic centimeter in the terrestrial ionosphere. There is little doubt that Venus has an ionosphere, but it is unlikely that the charged particle density can exceed 10^8 electrons per cubic centimeter.

10.62. Experiments carried on the Mariner II space probe appear to have ruled out the ionosphere model of the Venusian atmosphere (§ 10.65), but an additional point is worthy of mention. The spectrum of carbon dioxide gas in the near infrared region consists of what are called vibration-rotation bands. The lines in each band result from various quantum changes (§ 6.79) in the energy of rotation of the molecules, superimposed upon a particular change in the energy of vibration. Both temperature and pressure can affect the form of the band spectrum, although the wavelength (or frequencies) of the individual lines remain unchanged. A rise in temperature increases the proportion of molecules having larger amounts of rotational energy and thus alters the relative intensities of the rotational line. Hence, from a comparison of the intensities of the components of the spectral band, the temperature of the gas producing that particular spectrum can be calculated. Furthermore, the effect of increasing pressure is to broaden the rotational lines, as a result of molecular interactions (cf. § 6.87). Consequently, observation of the line contours makes it possible to estimate the pressure of the gas. An examination of the vibration-rotation spectrum thus permits an evaluation of the temperature and pressure in the Venusian atmosphere.

10.63. The spectra of Venus, obtained by Adams and Dunham (§ 10.36), were studied in 1962 by H. Spinrad in the United States along the lines indicated above. It was found that, although the temperatures and pressures varied over a considerable range for different spectral plates, e.g., about 220° to 440°K in temperature and 1.5 to about 5 (Earth) atmospheres in pressure, a definite correlation was found between temperature and pressure. An increase (or decrease) in one was associated, in general, with an increase (or decrease) in the other.

10.64. A reasonable explanation of the results is that the various plates, obtained on separate occasions, represent the spectra of carbon dioxide from different levels in the Venusian atmosphere. The atmospheric temperature is then higher where the pressure is higher, i.e., near the surface of the planet, and lower at the higher altitudes where the pressure is less. The highest temperature derived from the carbon dioxide spectrum was 440°K and the pressure was then about 5 atmospheres. Such a pressure could exist only near the surface of the planet and it is there that the atmospheric temperature is evidently highest. The general conclusions are thus not in agreement with the requirements of the ionosphere model but are compatible with the other models.

RESULTS OF MARINER II EXPERIMENTS

10.65. The Mariner II spacecraft, launched in August 1962, will be described in a later section, but it is convenient to review here the results which have a bearing on the structure of the atmosphere of Venus. A distinction between the greenhouse and aeolosphere models, on the one hand, which postulate that the centimeter wavelength radiation comes from the surface, and the ionosphere model, on the other hand, according to which this radiation originates at a high altitude in the ionosphere, could be made by observing the variation in the radiation intensity across the disc of the planet. If the centimeter-length microwave emission is mainly from the surface, the phenomenon of "limb darkening" should be observed, i.e., the intensity should be less at the limbs than near the center of the disc. The reason, as indicated in Fig. 10.7, I, is that the radiation from the limbs would pass through a greater thickness of colder atmosphere and so more absorption would occur. On the other hand, if the centimeter radiation came from the ionosphere, there should be limb brightening, as a result of the increased depth of the ionospheric layer at the limbs (Fig. 10.7, II).

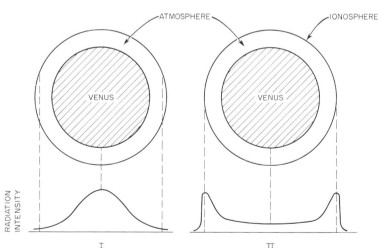

FIG. 10.7.   Theoretical radiation intensities from Venus: (I) greenhouse and aeolosphere models; (II) ionosphere model

10.66. Because of the relatively poor angular resolution of even the best microwave antenna on the ground, it has not been possible to determine with instruments on Earth the manner in which the centimeter-wave intensity varies across the Venusian disk. But a directional microwave radiometer carried by a spacecraft approaching within a short distance of the planet can make such a scan of the surface. This was achieved by Mariner II when within a distance of about 34,800 kilometers (21,600 miles) from the surface of Venus. Measurements of the intensity of 1.9-centimeter microwave radiation, by the technique outlined in § 10.89, indicated definitely that there is limb darkening at this wavelength, contrary to expectation from the ionospheric model. The brightness temperature obtained near the terminator was 570° ± 85°K, with temperatures of 400° ± 60°K and 460° ± 69°K near the bright and dark limbs, respectively.

10.67. In order to throw some light on the disputed question of the water-vapor content of the atmosphere of Venus, microwave intensity measurements were made at a wavelength of 1.35 centimeters, where water vapor has an absorption band, for comparison with the results at 1.9 centimeters. The small difference in the intensities at the two wavelengths indicates the presence of a very little water vapor in the Venusian atmosphere, possibly about a thousandth part of that in Earth's atmosphere.

10.68. In addition to the microwave radiometers, Mariner II carried two infrared radiometers to measure radiation intensities at wavelengths in the ranges of 8.1 to 8.7 and 10.2 to 10.5 microns, respectively. Carbon dioxide absorbs strongly in the latter region but not in the former; hence, the atmosphere of Venus should be transparent to 8.1- to 8.7-micron radiation but partially opaque in the range of 10.2 to 10.5 microns. Consequently, if there were a significant break in the cloud cover over the planet, so that radiation would be received from lower levels, at or near the surface, a higher intensity should be observed at the shorter infrared wavelengths where there is no absorption by carbon dioxide. The measurements showed no significant difference in intensity in the two wavelength regions, thus implying a continuous cloud layer with no detectable breaks, at least over the areas scanned. Moreover, if the infrared radiation comes from the tops of the clouds, as now appears probable, the absence of any appreciable difference in the intensities implies that there was very little carbon dioxide above the clouds at the time the readings were taken. The temperature calculated from the infrared intensities was 240°K, in agreement with that estimated from Earth-based measurements.

10.69. The Mariner II infrared radiometers indicated an anomalous temperature, about 10°C (18°F) below the surroundings at a location on the southern part of the terminator. Such an anomaly could arise from the presence of a very high mountain which would force the clouds upward and thus lower their temperature. This interpretation of the results must not be regarded as definite, however, as other explanations are possible. It is of interest that the existence of colder areas at the tops of the Venusian clouds had been suggested pre-viously by infrared measurements in the wavelength range of 8 to 13 microns made from Earth.

Interior and Surface of Venus

10.70. In view of the similarity in the dimensions and average density of Venus and Earth, it is probable that the internal structures of the two planets are similar. Thus, it would appear that Venus has a fairly large dense central core, consisting of iron and nickel and possibly some carbon and silicon, in the liquid (or partly liquid) state. Surrounding the core there is presumably a mixture of silicates of lower density, apparently resembling Earth's mantle and crust.

10.71. Although the central core of Venus is, at least partially, liquid, the planet has only a very weak magnetic field. Readings of the magnetometer on the Mariner II probe (§ 10.92) indicated that the magnetic field strength at some 35,000 kilometers from Venus was not significantly different from that in interplanetary space. At most, the field strength at the given distance could not have been more than a hundredth part of the Earth's magnetic field at the same distance from the surface. Moreover, there was no evidence of any in-crease in the flux of charged particles that might be trapped in a radiation belt similar to that in the terrestrial magnetosphere (§ 8.267). It is true that the magnetometer observations were made on the sunlit side of the planet where the solar wind would cause the Venusian magnetic field to be com-pressed, and thus decrease its strength at a distance of 35,000 kilometers. Nevertheless, there is no doubt that the magnetic field of Venus is very much weaker than Earth's field. Since the interiors of the two planets are probably similar, the marked difference in the magnetic fields must be attributed to the very slow rate of rotation of Venus, in accordance with the theory mentioned in § 8.211.

10.72. If the temperature at the surface of Venus is indeed as high as implied by the microwave radiation measurements, i.e., about 400°C or 720°F, and if such temperatures have existed for a long time, the outer silicate layers of the planet must be considerably hotter than the equivalent terrestrial layers. By assuming that the heating in these layers results essentially from the decay of radioactive isotopes present in the same concentrations as in chondritic meteorites (§ 7.122), G. J. F. MacDonald (1962) calculated that temperatures at a depth of about 120 miles in Venus are about 200°C (360°F) higher than at the same depth in Earth. It is to be expected, therefore, that molten silicate magma (or lava) will exist at relatively short distances below the Venusian surface. Volcanic activity would then have been relatively common in the past and may still be at present; this would presumably have had an important effect on the topography of the planet. Incidentally, the large proportion of liquid in the core of Venus, and the consequent damping due to tidal friction, could account for the trapped rotation of the planet in spite of its relatively large distance from the Sun. The low rigidity associated with such a core is also in agreement with the absence of any appreciable flattening of the planet, even if the rate of rotation were at one time greater than it is now (cf. § 10.40).

10.73. A related problem of interest concerns the nature of the surface of Venus. The large proportion of carbon dioxide in the atmosphere, as compared with that on Earth, has been attributed to the deficiency of water. An alternative possibility, mentioned by F. L. Whipple and D. H. Menzel in 1955, is that the surface of Venus is completely covered by liquid water; the carbon dioxide would not then have access to the silicate minerals with which it would normally interact. For liquid water at a temperature of 300°C (570°F), the pressure of water vapor near the surface would be over 100 atmospheres, and this does not seem to be compatible with the very small concentration of water vapor at higher altitudes. Furthermore, at 400°C (750°F), which is above the critical temperature, liquid water cannot exist at all. The mean dielectric constant of the Venusian surface material, as derived from radar measurements (§ 9.134), is found to be definitely less than 7 and may possibly be as small as 2 or 3, compared with the known value of about 70 for water.

10.74. It has been suggested by the British astronomer Fred Hoyle (1955) that the surface of Venus may consist of liquid hydrocarbons, somewhat like petroleum oil. This apparently surprising concept cannot be easily eliminated, improbable as it may appear at first thought. For example, the dielectric constant of hydrocarbons is about 2, which is not greatly different from the experimental value for the Venusian surface. In addition, the possible existence of hydrocarbons can be correlated with the high carbon dioxide content of the atmosphere. H. C. Urey (1952) has argued that much of the oxygen in the cosmos was originally in the form of water (H_2O). The presence of carbon dioxide indicates, therefore, that at one time there were substantial amounts of water on the planet. These would be necessary to supply the oxygen required to convert carbonaceous materials, possibly hydrocarbons, into carbon dioxide. Since there is little water at present, there may be considerable quantities of unoxidized hydrocarbons still remaining.

10.75. Regardless of whether there are large quantities of hydrocarbons on Venus or not, it is probable that loss of water from this planet occurred more rapidly than from Earth. This is indicated, for example, by the absence of oxygen from the Venusian atmosphere. The greater rate of loss from Venus can be accounted for by its proximity to the Sun. The higher temperature would cause increased vaporization and the greater intensity of ultraviolet radiation would result in more photochemical decomposition of the water.

10.76. A more conventional view is that the surface of Venus is solid, like that of Earth, consisting mainly of silicates and carbonates of magnesium and calcium. Such a surface is, of course, essential to the aeolosphere model of the atmosphere, since a liquid layer could not produce dust. The dielectric constant of very dry terrestrial soils ranges from about 2 to 4 (cf. § 9.134), in harmony with the value for the Venusian surface derived from radar measurements. Because of the high temperatures on Venus, hydrated minerals, such as exist on Earth, are probably absent.

10.77. Observations of radar echoes from Venus have been interpreted as implying a fairly even but somewhat rocky surface. The general nature of the spread of the time delay is similar to that of the Moon, but Venus is apparently a better radar reflector. On a scale of a few inches, the roughness of Venusian surface is perhaps about the same as on the Moon, but the characteristic very small irregularities of the lunar surface are probably not present on Venus. Erosion caused by strong winds on the planet have undoubtedly affected the details of the surface structure.

Studies of Venus from Space

10.78. Although the Mariner II project was a remarkable success, as indicated by the results already mentioned and others to be described below, the properties of Venus studied were relatively limited. There still remain many problems concerning this cloud-covered planet that can be solved only by means of observations made from space. It had been intended to launch another Venus probe at the next favorable opportunity, which was about March 1964, but in order to permit adequate time for a complete analysis of the large amount of data from Mariner II, it was decided to postpone the next approach to the planet until the end of 1965. By that time, the availability of launch vehicles with larger thrust should make it possible to carry more experiments than did Mariner II.

10.79. Among the subjects that may be studied in a fly-by mission is the variation of the centimeter-length microwave transmission on the illuminated and dark sides of the planet in order to distinguish between the greenhouse and aeolosphere models of the Venusian atmosphere. In addition, it may be possible to determine the composition of the atmosphere, the nature of the clouds, and the electron density of the ionosphere.

10.80. Proposals are being considered to follow the Mariner by the Voyager spacecraft which will take advantage of the powerful Saturn I-B rocket (§ 3.153). It is expected that this launch vehicle will be capable of sending to Venus a spacecraft weighing some 6000 to 7000 pounds. The most useful mission for the Voyager class of spacecraft appears to be a combined orbiter-lander system, i.e., to orbit around Venus and land instrument capsules on its surface. Many detailed studies can then be made of the planet's surface, and the distribution of composition, pressure, and temperature in the atmosphere can be investigated.

10.81. The "bistatic" (or two-station) radar technique may prove a relatively simple means for studying the ionosphere and surface of Venus and also the rotation of the planet. The great drawback of the conventional radar procedure is that the echo signal received on the ground is extremely weak. It is, therefore, difficult to extract reliable data from it, especially in view of the inevitable background of noise. In the bistatic radar method, the transmitted signal is sent out from a station on Earth, but the echo is received by simple, lightweight equipment carried on a spacecraft close to the reflecting surface, e.g., Venus. The echo signal is then amplified and transmitted to Earth. The signal received on the ground is thus much stronger, and can provide more useful information, than an echo obtained directly from Venus or other planet.

THE MARINER II VENUS PROBE

INTRODUCTION

10.82. The flight of the Mariner II space probe past Venus did not yield scientific results that could be described as being either spectacular or revolutionary. Nevertheless, it was an historic event of the greatest significance to space science. In the first place, the data obtained provided answers to questions that could not possibly have been resolved in any other manner. Furthermore, the demonstrated ability to take instruments to within some 35,000 kilometers (21,000 miles) of Venus, to make measurements, and to transmit the results to Earth, about 56.5 million kilometers (35 million miles) away at the time, represent outstanding achievements in technology. It is of interest, therefore, to describe here some of the main features of the Mariner II spacecraft and of its mission to Venus.*

THE MARINER II SPACECRAFT

10.83. The main framework of the Mariner II spacecraft consisted of a hexagonal base surmounted by a tubular superstructure (Fig. 10.8). The base contained all the equipment necessary for guidance, attitude control, midcourse maneuver, and communication to and from Earth, whereas the apparatus for the experiments to be performed in space was attached to the superstructure. With the high-gain, directional transmitting antenna and the solar-cell panels folded to provide a more compact structure for launching, Mariner II was 5 feet across at its base and almost 10 feet high. In space, after the nose-cone shroud used to protect the spacecraft against heating by atmospheric drag had dropped away, the antenna and panels were extended. The height was then nearly 12 feet and the wingspread was 16.5 feet. The total weight was 447 pounds, of which the scientific experiments represented only 41 pounds. That so much could be achieved with so little weight is a tribute to the designers and fabricators of the instruments.

10.84. The 50-pound thrust rocket motor for the midcourse-guidance correction was located in the center of the hexagonal base. It used anhydrous

---

* Mariner I was launched on July 22, 1962, but it had to be destroyed after almost 5 minutes of flight because of a guidance error.

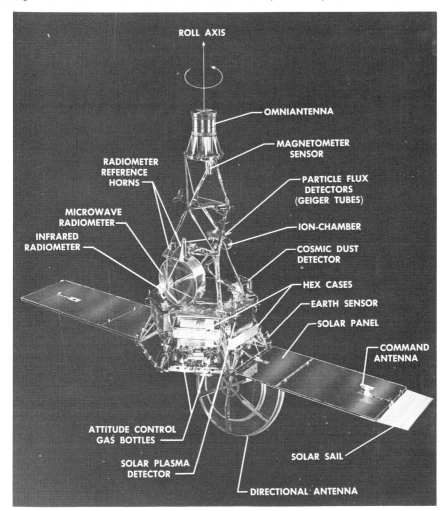

FIG. 10.8.   The Mariner II Venus spacecraft. (*Jet Propulsion Laboratory, California Institute of Technology*)

hydrazine, pressurized with nitrogen gas, as the monopropellant (§ 3.24). Around the motor were located six cases containing electronic, electromechanical, and related equipment. Two sections of the hexagon were occupied by the radio receiver and transmitter and the control system for the experiments, and two others by the electrical power system, including a silver-zinc storage battery which was charged by some 10,000 solar cells on the panels.* A fifth segment contained equipment required for converting information from the

* To provide space for the required number of solar cells, the length of one of the panels was increased over the original design. A blank extension, designated the "solar sail," was added to the other panel to balance the effect of solar radiation pressure on the two panels.

spacecraft into the digital form suitable for telemetering to Earth. The final section held the Central Computer and Sequencer, which stored instructions in its memory unit, performed computations, and provided the basic timing control for the subsystems that operated in a sequence program. The gyroscopes for control of orientation (or attitude) of the spacecraft were also housed in this segment.

10.85. Mariner II had a total of four radio antennas for its communication system. Two of these, one on each side of the solar-cell panels, were for receiving radio commands from ground stations for the midcourse maneuver and for other operations. These antennas were small because command signals could be sent from Earth at relatively high power and directed at the spacecraft; high-gain antennas were, therefore, not essential. The other two antennas were utilized to transmit scientific and operational data from the spacecraft to Earth. The dish-shaped, high-gain antenna, having a diameter of 4 feet, was hinged to the bottom of the hexagonal base of the spacecraft. During most of the flight, this antenna was directed toward Earth by means of an Earth-sensor, thus facilitating detection of the weak signal from the transmitter which had a power of only 3 watts. Because it was necessary to protect the sensor in the early stages of the trajectory and to move the high-gain antenna away from the rocket nozzle for the midcourse maneuver, this antenna was not effective during these periods. The omnidirectional antenna at the top of the superstructure was then employed to send information to Earth. The signals received at the ground stations at these times were much weaker than when the high-gain antenna was in operation. The antennas of the three Deep Space Network (DSN) stations, described in § 4.136, were used to transmit commands to and receive signals from Mariner II.

10.86. In addition to the Earth-sensor to control the antenna, a Sun-sensor was mounted on the base of the spacecraft. Its purpose was to insure that the solar-cell panels were directed toward the Sun at all times, except during the midcourse maneuver when a different orientation was necessary. The power for operating the spacecraft subsystems was then provided by the storage batteries. Nitrogen gas jets were used to maintain the required attitude of Mariner II in space. The gas was contained in two lightweight titanium reservoirs, each containing initially 4.3 pounds of nitrogen at a pressure of 3500 pounds per square inch. Ten small nozzles connected to the reservoirs and controlled by the gyroscopes and the Earth- and Sun-sensors, produced the gas jets for making any adjustments in orientation that were required.

10.87. A difficult problem in the design of the Mariner II spacecraft was in connection with the temperature control system. Since some pieces of equipment were continuously exposed to radiation from the Sun, it was feared that they might become overheated and cease to function properly. That this fear was justified was demonstrated by the fact that some minor failures did occur, but fortunately they did not interfere with the operation of the spacecraft and the experiments. A degree of thermal control was achieved by utilizing various surface coatings, e.g., paint patterns, thin gold plating, and polished aluminum, to provide variations in the reflection and absorption of sunlight at different locations. The hexagonal base of the spacecraft was protected both above and below by fixed thermal shields. In addition, an adjustable louver-type shield was provided for the sensitive computer and sequencing equipment; the eight sections of this shield were opened or closed automatically, as was necessary, in response to signals from temperature indicators.

THE MARINER II EXPERIMENTS

10.88. The experiments carried on Mariner II fell into six groups, namely, microwave radiometers, infrared radiometers, magnetometer, cosmic dust detectors, charged-particle detectors, and solar plasma spectrometer. The results of the microwave and infrared radiometer experiment and some of the magnetometer measurements have been referred to earlier in this chapter. Other data obtained from Mariner II were given in Chapter 8 and more will be reviewed below.

10.89. In the *microwave radiometer* experiment, the microwave energy, collected by a 19-inch diameter parabolic receiving antenna attached to the tubular framework of the spacecraft (Fig. 10.8), was focused into a receiving horn. In order to scan the surface of Venus, the antenna was driven by an electric motor in an up-and-down (north-south) direction; the sideways or lateral (east-west) movement was provided by the motion of the spacecraft across the face of the planet. When the radiometer indicated that the scan had reached the limb and was exposed to empty space, the direction of the motor drive was reversed. The surface of Venus was scanned in this manner (see Fig. 10.12).

10.90. By means of a device called a *diplexer*, microwave radiations at the two wavelengths of 1.35 and 1.9 centimeters could be received without interfering with one another. The signals from Venus were compared with those from two reference horns, matched to the two wavelengths and pointing into space. A microwave receiver located behind the antenna measured the difference between the signal from the planet and from space, on each wavelength, and telemetered the result to Earth.

10.91. The *infrared radiometer* was firmly attached to the microwave antenna, so that infrared and microwave scans were made simultaneously of the same areas. The infrared radiometer contained two sensors, one of which was directed at the surface of Venus and the other was aimed at an angle to provide a reference reading from space. The infrared radiation received was passed through filters to separate the two wavelength regions, i.e., 8.1 to 8.7 microns and 10.2 to 10.5 microns, and the respective intensities were determined by means of sensitive bolometers. A rapidly rotating disc with two apertures provided alternate readings, about 20 times per second, from Venus and from empty space. The differences were measured, encoded, and transmitted to Earth in the usual manner.

10.92. The fluxgate *magnetometer* on Mariner II contained three magnetic core sensors to permit the determination of field strengths in three directions perpendicular to each other (§ 8.218). The instrument was located just below the omnidirectional antenna to remove it as far as possible from spacecraft components that might have magnetic fields associated with them. The sensitivity of the magnetometer was about 0.5 gamma, i.e., 5×10^{-6} gauss. Measurements of the ambient magnetic field were made every 20 seconds during the flight of Mariner II from Earth to Venus and beyond. Some of the results obtained in interplanetary space were given in Chapter 8.

10.93. One of the *charged-particle detectors* was an ionization chamber instrument for counting particles of high energy, e.g., protons with energies in excess of 10 million electron volts and alpha particles (helium nuclei) of at least 40 million electron volts (§ 8.245). In addition, there were three Geiger tubes for detecting particles of both low and high energies. With these instruments observations were made of the intensity and distribution of corpuscular radiations in space and near Venus. There was no significant increase in intensity near the planet, thus indicating the absence of a radiation belt; this result is in agreement with the very weak Venusian magnetic field. Measurements were also made to determine the possible hazard from radiation that an astronaut might be exposed to during a long flight through space.

10.94. A *crystal microphone* with a sounding plate served as a detector of cosmic (or interplanetary) dust particles (§ 7.163). It had a sensitive area of 55 square centimeters and was capable of recording impacts with particles of mass as low as 1.3×10^{-9} gram. The microphone was able to detect micrometeoroids of both low and high momentum and could provide a rough indication of their direction of travel. Only two impacts were experienced in the course of the flight of Mariner II. It is of interest, however, to mention that on September 8, 1963 the spacecraft lost its attitude control for about 3 minutes. A possible cause may have been collision with a fairly large object in space.

10.95. The purpose of the *solar plasma spectrometer* was to study the nature of the solar plasma (or solar wind) in interplanetary space. The instrument consisted essentially of a pair of parallel curved deflection plates across which an electrical voltage was applied. A charged particle, e.g., a proton (hydrogen nucleus) or an alpha particle (helium nucleus), entering the space between the plates was forced to travel in a curved path as a result of the action of the electric field. By adjusting the voltage, only protons (or alpha particles) of a certain known energy were able to pass through the plates and impinge on the collector at the end. In this manner, the number of protons of a given energy could be counted. The voltage across the plates was varied in ten steps, at intervals of 18 seconds, so that it was possible to count protons with energies ranging from 240 to 8400 electron volts. The results of the solar plasma experiment were reviewed in § 6.171 and § 8.232.

THE MARINER II TRAJECTORY

10.96. The choice of a trajectory for a Venus probe to be launched from Earth involves a number of considerations. In theory, the energy expenditure for an interplanetary transfer is a minimum for a Hohmann path (§ 2.72); that is, the spacecraft leaves Earth in a direction tangential to the terrestrial orbit and meets the planet, e.g., Venus, at a tangent to the orbit of the planet. This trajectory is strictly applicable to the situation in which both planets have circular orbits and these orbits both lie in the same (ecliptic) plane. In practice, of course, neither of these conditions can be satisfied for any two planets; hence, the actual trajectory must deviate somewhat from the ideal Hohmann orbit.

10.97. There are also certain requirements for an interplanetary probe which complicate the choice of its trajectory. For example, the elongation angle of the planet (§ 7.29) at the time of encounter with the spacecraft must be fairly large, otherwise radio noise from the Sun will interfere with the telemetry from the vehicle. The distance between Earth and the planet at encounter must be within the range of satisfactory radio reception; and the approach velocity of the spacecraft near the planet must be slow enough to permit adequate time for scientific observations to be made.

10.98. By taking into account the foregoing considerations, the available rocket thrust (or energy), and the total mass of the system to be launched, a number of possible trajectories can be derived for taking a space probe from Earth to the vicinity of a given planet, e.g., Venus. Largely because of energy limitations and the desire to maximize the payload, these trajectories require that the spacecraft be launched between certain dates; this launch interval occurs once during each synodic period, i.e., once in every 584 days or roughly 19 months for Venus. Based on the use of the Atlas-Agena rocket combination (§ 3.149) as the launch vehicle, a suitable launch interval for Venus occurred in 1962 lasting from about July 20th to September 12th; it was during this period that Mariner II was launched. Subsequent launch intervals for Venusian missions are about 19 months apart, i.e., around March 1964, October 1965, June 1967, and January 1969. The availability of a more powerful launch system than the Atlas-Agena could extend the interval from six weeks to about 3 months, but it will probably be utilized preferably to increase the payload.

10.99. For a spacecraft to follow a trajectory that will lead to an encounter with Venus, it must escape from control by Earth's gravitational field and become a satellite of the Sun. The first requirement is, therefore, that the geocentric injection velocity, i.e., with respect to Earth, must exceed the terrestrial escape velocity at the injection altitude, i.e., approximately 11.2 kilometers (7 miles) per second near the surface (§ 2.69). Furthermore, since the orbit of Venus is closer to the Sun than is Earth's orbit, the spacecraft must be drawn in toward the Sun. This is achieved by launching it in a direction opposite to that in which Earth is traveling in its orbit. The heliocentric velocity of the spacecraft, i.e., with reference to the Sun, is then less than that of Earth and the craft follows an elliptical orbit about the Sun with its apocenter (aphelion) close to the point of injection.*

10.100. In order to take advantage of Earth's rotation and for safety reasons, rocket vehicles from the Kennedy Space Flight Center, Florida, are launched in an easterly—actually south-easterly—direction. If the escape trajectory is to be in a direction opposite to Earth's orbital motion, the launching must take place when the launch point is facing that direction of motion, i.e., between local midnight and midday. On any particular date, there is an optimum launch window (§ 9.32) of about 2 hours for a given location, because of the inclination of the terrestrial equator to the plane of the ecliptic. If liftoff is not possible within this time, the launching must be postponed until the next day because of rocket power limitations.

10.101. The situation in the case of a Venus probe is illustrated in Fig. 10.9.

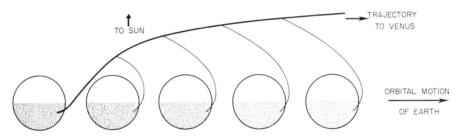

FIG. 10.9.   Launch trajectory of a Venus probe

The thin line indicates the hyperbolic escape path of the probe with respect to Earth and the heavy line is the actual trajectory relative to the Sun. This trajectory is the result of combining the escape path with Earth's orbital motion. It is seen that, after launching, the spacecraft lags behind Earth in its orbit and is being drawn into a trajectory closer to the Sun. In due course, as the spacecraft moves away from aphelion, where its heliocentric velocity is a minimum, this velocity increases as a result of the attraction by the solar gravitational field. Consequently, the probe catches up and overtakes Earth, as will be seen below.

10.102. The spacecraft Mariner II was lifted off at 1:53 A.M. (E.S.T.) on August 27, 1962 by means of an Atlas-Agena rocket combination. About 5 minutes after liftoff, the Agena and its payload, now traveling in an almost horizontal direction, separated from the Atlas vehicle and the Agena

* The situation for launching a space probe to a planet farther than Earth from the Sun, e.g., Mars, is described in § 10.194.

engine was ignited. After firing for almost $2\frac{1}{2}$ minutes, which increased the velocity sufficiently to launch the rocket and its attached spacecraft into a parking orbit at an altitude of about 116 miles, the engine was cut off. A coasting period of some 16 minutes then brought the vehicle to a point over the middle South Atlantic, the best position for injection into the required trajectory at the particular time. The Agena was then restarted and after burning for a little over $1\frac{1}{2}$ minutes, the desired escape velocity of 11.38 kilometers (7.07 miles) per second was attained. A few minutes later, the spacecraft was separated from the Agena B rocket by means of an explosive charge. Expulsion of residual gases then caused the rocket to turn aside and Mariner II was on its way alone to Venus just more than half an hour after liftoff.

10.103. In Fig. 10.10 is shown a representation of the relative positions of Earth, Venus, and the spacecraft on the launch date and at various subsequent times. Although it was initially behind, Venus gradually overtook Earth, because of the shorter Venusian orbital period (225 days). On December 14, 1962, on the 109th day of the flight, when Mariner II encountered Venus, the planet was somewhat ahead of Earth. As stated earlier, the heliocentric (orbital) velocity of the spacecraft was initially less than that of Earth, but it gradually increased; by October 30, 1962 it had caught up again and moved ahead toward its encounter with Venus. Subsequently, Mariner II went into an elliptical orbit about the Sun and it is now an artificial planet with an orbital (sidereal) period of 346 days.

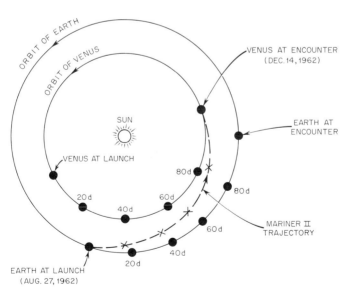

FIG. 10.10. Relative positions of Earth, Venus, and the Mariner II spacecraft from launch to encounter

THE MIDCOURSE MANEUVER

10.104. As the result of small but virtually unavoidable errors in injection, the original trajectory would have caused Mariner II to miss Venus by about 370,000 kilometers (230,000 miles). This was greatly in excess of the useful distance of 13,000 to 65,000 kilometers (8000 to 40,000 miles) for which the experiments were designed. In anticipation of such an eventuality, the spacecraft had been provided with a rocket to permit a midcourse correction to be made. On September 4, 1962, when Mariner II was nearly 2.4 million kilometers (1.5 million miles) from Earth, the spacecraft, which was then appropriately oriented toward Earth and the Sun, was commanded to disregard the sensors so as to permit it to rotate freely about its axes. The high-gain directional antenna was also moved out of the way of the rocket motor nozzle. The command was then given to make the required roll and pitch turns to bring the rocket motor in the correct direction for firing (Fig. 10.11).

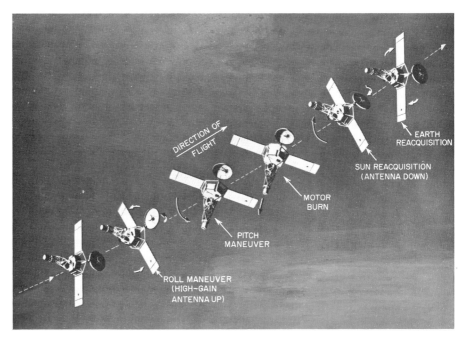

FIG. 10.11. Midcourse maneuver of Mariner II on way to Venus

10.105. At the proper time, the motor was ignited and it burned for nearly 28 seconds, thereby increasing the heliocentric velocity of Mariner II by 76 kilometers (47 miles) per hour. The high-gain antenna was then returned to its normal position and the Sun and Earth sensor system was reactivated, so that the spacecraft resumed its required orientation. It had been hoped that the midcourse maneuver would bring the probe within 16,000 kilometers (10,000 miles) of Venus, but the actual distance of closest approach was about 34,750 kilometers (21,600 miles), well within the useful range. The delicacy of the operation will be realized, however, when it is stated that the discrepancy was the result of an error of about 3.2 kilometers (2 miles) per hour in the heliocentric velocity of the spacecraft; after the correction, this velocity was 60,164 (instead of 60,162) miles per hour. The error was not in the calculations but was probably due to a very slight time delay in the cutoff of the rocket motor.

10.106. One of the objectives of the midcourse maneuver was to make sure that when the encounter of Mariner II with Venus occurred, the planet would be above the horizon at the Goldstone, California, station of the DSN from which the necessary commands for the experiments could most conveniently be transmitted. Early in the morning of December 14, 1962, the signal was sent from Goldstone, about 56 million kilometers (35 million miles) away, for the equipment driving the radiometer antenna on the spacecraft to be switched on. Then, at about 8 A.M. (E.S.T.), when Mariner II, approaching from the dark side of Venus, was between the planet and the Sun, the antenna started a slow scan of the disc to obtain microwave and infrared data. Three "up and down" passes were made, as indicated in Fig. 10.12; five readings were taken on the dark side of the planet, eight on the terminator, and five on the illuminated side. It is from these scans that the results described in § 10.66 were secured.

10.107. On January 2, 1963, when the spacecraft was 86.8 million kilometers (53.9 million miles) away, radio contact with Earth was lost. Fortunately, by that time, Mariner II had served its purpose and completely fulfilled its objectives, in spite of several difficult situations, not described here, that had to be dealt with in the course of the long flight. The midcourse maneuver performed at a dis-

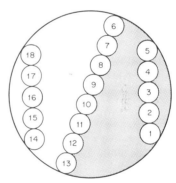

FIG. 10.12.   Scan of the disc of Venus by Mariner II radiometer antenna

tance of 2.4 million kilometers (1.5 million miles), the close approach of the spacecraft to Venus after traveling about 290 million kilometers (180 million miles) through space, the scanning of the disc of the planet, and the receipt of clear telemetry from a 3-watt transmitter at a distance of some 56 million kilometers (35 million miles) together constitute a most remarkable technical accomplishment.*

* It has been estimated that the amount of power received on Earth from the transmitter on Mariner II at the time of its closest approach to Venus was only 10^{-18} watt!

THE PLANET MARS

The Orbit of Mars

10.108. The orbit of Mars, the fourth terrestrial planet, lies beyond that of Earth and it is therefore an exterior planet. The average distance of Mars from the Sun is 227.7 million kilometers (141.6 million miles), but as a result of the relatively large eccentricity of the orbit, namely, 0.0933, the actual distance ranges from 206 million kilometers (128 million miles) at perihelion to about 249 million kilometers (155 million miles) at aphelion. The closest possible approach to Earth is thus about 56 million kilometers (35 million miles); this occurs when Mars is simultaneously in opposition (§ 7.14) and at or near to the perihelion of its orbit. When conjunction coincides with the aphelion of the Martian orbit, the Earth-Mars distance has its maximum value of some 400 million kilometers (249 million miles). The sidereal period of revolution of Mars about the Sun is almost exactly 687 terrestrial days and the synodic period as observed from Earth is 780 days, i.e., nearly 2 years and 2 months by terrestrial time. The mean orbital velocity of the planet is 24.1 kilometers (15.0 miles) per second, and the inclination of the orbital plane to the ecliptic is 1.85 deg.

10.109. Since Mars is an exterior planet, it exhibits only full phases, which are seen at opposition and conjunction, and gibbous phases, near quadrature, as explained in § 7.34. Consequently, the major portion of the disc is visible at all times. Because of the great range of distances separating Mars from Earth, the former planet is most conveniently observed at opposition when it is both closest to Earth and visible at night. Even then, the Earth-Mars distance varies from 56 to 101 million kilometers (35 to 63 million miles). Unfortunately, opposition occurs only once in a synodic period, i.e., in more than 2 years, and the most favorable oppositions, when Earth and Mars are at their closest, are realized only every 15 or 17 years. The next such opposition, in March 1971, may be expected to be a time of great activity in the study of Mars.

10.110. Permanent features of the Martian surface can be readily distinguished in a telescope because the atmosphere of the planet is not very dense and there is no continuous cloud layer as on Venus. Consequently, the time of rotation of Mars about its axis is known with considerable precision. Measurements made over many years indicate that the sidereal period of rotation is 24 hours 37.4 minutes; the mean Martian solar day, i.e., the average time between two consecutive transits of a meridian by the Sun as observed from Mars, is 24 hours 39.5 minutes, or roughly 40 minutes longer than a solar day on Earth. Thus, the lengths of the Martian and terrestrial days are approximately the same. Another similarity between the two planets is the angle of inclination of the equator to the orbital plane; this is not known accurately for Mars, but it is about 25 deg, compared with 23.5 deg for Earth.

10.111. As a result of the inclination of its equator, Mars has seasons similar to those on Earth, although they are longer because of the greater length of the Martian year. Furthermore, as a result of the eccentricity of the orbit of Mars, the seasons, i.e., the times between successive equinoxes and solstices,* are of unequal duration, whereas on Earth they have the same length within a day or two. Thus, in the northern hemisphere of Mars, spring lasts 199 terrestrial days, summer 182 days, autumn 146 days, and winter 160 days. The summer solstice in the southern hemisphere occurs when Mars is close to perihelion; it is therefore nearest to the Sun and is traveling at its fastest orbital velocity. Consequently, spring and summer are shorter and hotter than in the northern hemisphere whereas autumn and winter are correspondingly longer and colder.

Physical Characteristics of Mars

10.112. The radius of Mars is obtained, in the usual manner, by measuring the angular diameter at (or near) the time of opposition. The value is not known with any degree of certainty, however, because the angular diameter varies with the wavelength of the light in which the telescopic image is observed. This effect arises from a peculiarity of the Martian atmosphere to which reference will be made in due course. The mean radius adopted here is 3360 kilometers (2090 miles), which is little more than half Earth's radius. Like Earth, Mars has a slight equatorial bulge; the radius at the equator is some 16 kilometers (10 miles) larger and the polar radius roughly the same amount smaller than the average value. From these data, the flattening (or optical ellipticity) of the planet, as defined in § 8.4, is about 1/100. On the other hand, the value, called the *dynamic ellipticity*, derived from observations on the orbital motions of the two natural satellites of Mars (§ 10.159) is 1/190.† Calculations based on the assumption of hydrostatic equilibrium give a result in general agreement with the observed dynamic ellipticity.

10.113. It should be noted that the optical ellipticity is obtained from actual dimensional (angular diameter) measurements, whereas the dynamic ellipticity, which is smaller, is derived from the gravitational attraction or mass distribution. If the difference between the two values is real, the implication is that there is a considerable quantity of material of lower than average density in the region of the Martian equatorial bulge. The significance of this conclusion is uncertain, and the matter requires further investigation.

10.114. Although the radius of Mars is not known very precisely, the mass has been determined with fair accuracy from observations on the orbital characteristics of its two satellites; it is 6.44×10^{23} kilograms (6.44×10^{20} metric

---

* The spring and autumn equinoxes (§ 9.36) occur where the equatorial plane of a planet intersects its orbital (ecliptic) plane; the summer and winter solstices are at 90 deg from the equinoxes where the equatorial and orbital planes are farthest apart.

† For Earth, the flattening derived from surface measurements is essentially the same as is obtained from the orbital behavior of artificial satellites (cf. Chapter 8).

tons). From this value of the mass and the average radius given above, the average density of Mars is found to be 4.05 grams per cubic centimeter. Densities ranging from 3.92 to 4.25 grams per cubic centimeter are to be found in the literature, because of the uncertainty in the radius of the planet.

10.115. From the mass and radius, the acceleration due to gravity, the circular velocity, and the escape velocity can be calculated in the usual manner. The gravitational acceleration is 3.8 meters (12.5 feet) per second per second; the circular velocity near the surface is 3.6 kilometers (2.2 miles) per second and the escape velocity is consequently 5.0 kilometers (3.1 miles) per second. Because of the low density and small size of Mars, as compared with Venus and Earth, the gravitational acceleration and escape velocity are also much lower. In fact, in these respects Mars does not differ greatly from the planet Mercury, although it is different in other ways, e.g., in its temperature and atmosphere. The characteristic physical properties of Mars are summarized in Table 10.3.

TABLE 10.3   ORBITAL AND PHYSICAL CHARACTERISTICS OF MARS

Distance, Mars to Sun (max)	249×10^6 kilometers	155×10^6 miles
Distance, Mars to Sun (min)	206×10^6 "	128×10^6 "
Distance, Mars to Sun (average)	228×10^6 "	142×10^6 "
Distance, Mars to Earth (max)	400×10^6 "	249×10^6 "
Distance, Mars to Earth (min)	56×10^6 "	35×10^6 "
Angular diameter, from Earth (max)	25 sec	
Angular diameter, from Earth (min)	3.5 sec	
Eccentricity of orbit	0.0933	
Inclination of orbit to ecliptic	1.85 deg	
Inclination of equator to orbital plane	25 deg	
Orbital period (sidereal)	687 days	
Orbital period (synodic from Earth)	780 days	
Average orbital velocity	24.1 kilometers (15.0 miles) per second	
Radius (average)	3360 kilometers (2090 miles)	
Mass	6.44×10^{23} kilograms	
Average density	4.05 grams per cubic centimeter	
Gravitational acceleration	3.8 meters (12.5 feet) per sec per sec	
Escape velocity	5.0 kilometers (3.1 miles) per second	
Rotation period	24 hours 37 minutes 23 seconds	

THE ALBEDO OF MARS

10.116. The albedo of Mars varies with the location on the surface and it also depends on the wavelength of the reflected light. For red light, for example, at a wavelength of 7000 Å (0.7 micron) the average albedo is about 0.3, but it decreases to 0.04 at wavelengths below 4500 Å (0.45 micron), i.e., in the blue and violet regions. The presence of large red-colored areas on the Martian surface accounts for the relatively large albedo in red light and for the general reddish appearance of the planet. The low values in the blue and violet, on the other hand, are the result of the so-called "blue haze" which absorbs very strongly at the shorter visible wavelengths (§ 10.139). In the yellow portion of the spectrum, there are certain (bright) areas on the surface of Mars with an albedo of 0.15 and other (dark) areas where the albedo is 0.05. The average value for the whole planet in visible light is generally quoted as 0.15; this is larger than the albedo of the Moon and Mercury, but considerably less than that of Venus or Earth.

TEMPERATURES ON MARS

10.117. Because Mars is farther from the Sun than is Earth, the solar radiation received per unit area on the former planet is less and, hence, lower temperatures are to be expected. Measurements of infrared emission from Mars were made in 1927 by E. Pettit and S. B. Nicholson and by others in subsequent years. The most recent observations by W. M. Sinton and J. S. Strong (1960) indicated that, in the Martian equatorial region, the average maximum surface temperature, attained shortly after local noon, is 295°K, i.e., 22°C or 70°F; the minimum temperature, before sunrise, is about 203°K, i.e., −70°C or −94°F. The microwave brightness temperature, reported by J. A. Giordmaine, *et al.*, in 1959, is 211 ± 28°K; this is probably a rough average of day and night temperatures at a short distance beneath the surface.

10.118. The diurnal temperature range on Mars is evidently more than 90°C (162°F); this is considerably greater than occurs on Earth even in desert regions. The difference in behavior is attributed to the low density of the Martian atmosphere and to the absence of bodies of water. On Earth, the atmosphere and the oceans reduce the difference between day and night temperatures. It is of interest that the average daytime temperatures on Mars are not very greatly different from those on Earth, but the nights are much colder.

10.119. During the day, the Martian temperatures vary in a manner similar to temperatures on Earth, i.e., a steady increase during the daylight hours before noon and a decrease after midday. As is to be expected, there are also variations with latitude; thus, the temperatures in the polar regions are appreciably lower than at the equator. In the polar winter, the infrared temperature may fall as low as about 170°K, i.e., roughly −100°C or −150°F.

THE SURFACE OF MARS

10.120. Telescopic studies of Mars reveal the presence of three distinct surface types, namely, bright areas, dark areas, and the polar caps, in addition to the so-called canals and oases. The bright areas, with the higher albedo in yellow light, sometimes referred to as *deserts*, are reddish or orange in color and cover almost three fourths of the planet's surface. They are apparently of constant size, but are reported to exhibit temporary color changes becoming whiter from time to time. It is frequently stated that the absence of shadows (cf. § 9.76) indicates there are no elevations exceeding 800 meters (2500 feet) in the reddish areas of Mars. But C. W. Tombaugh (§ 7.11) has pointed out that 5000 meters (16,000 feet) is about the minimum height that could be detected under the very best conditions by the observation of shadows at the terminator. In most circumstances, it is doubtful if elevations under about 8000 meters (25,000 feet) could be recognized; hence, all that can be said at present is that there are no mountains on Mars higher than 8000 meters. This information is not very illuminating because such high mountains are hardly to be expected on a planet with a mass that is little more than one tenth that of Earth.

10.121. Two different suggestions have been made concerning the nature of the red-orange material that covers most of the surface of Mars. According to A. Dollfus (1951), the polarization of sunlight reflected from the planet is the same as that given in the laboratory by the reddish-brown mineral limonite, a hydrous iron (ferric) oxide having the approximate formula $2Fe_2O_3 \cdot 3H_2O$. From an examination of the spectrum of Mars in the wavelength range of 0.4 to 2.5 microns, i.e., from the blue into the near infrared, G. P. Kuiper (1952) concluded, on the other hand, that the deserts may consist of an igneous material similar to felsitic rhyolite, a rock of volcanic origin consisting mainly of silica with small amounts of dark-colored minerals, several of which contain iron. Unlike the familiar emission or absorption spectra of gases, polarization properties of reflection spectra do not provide specific means of identification. There thus appears to be no way of determining the composition of the Martian surface without landing suitable instruments upon it.

10.122. A highly controversial aspect of the Martian surface is related to the so-called canals; most of these cross the desert areas but they can also be seen on other parts of the planet. The argument started in 1877 when the Italian astronomer Giovanni V. Schiaparelli gave the name *canali* (plural of the Italian *canale*, meaning "channel" or "canal"), translated into English as *canals*, to the long and narrow streaks which he claimed to see in the telescopic image of Mars.* Subsequently, other astronomers confirmed the existence of these darker linear markings on the reddish (and other) areas, but there was not always complete agreement concerning their identity.

10.123. The existence of the Martian canals would have remained a matter of mainly scientific interest had it not been for the somewhat startling views published by Percival Lowell (§ 7.10) in 1908. He suggested that the canals had been constructed by intelligent beings on Mars to convey water from melting ice at the poles, across the deserts, for irrigation purposes. Whatever the nature of the canals may be, it is certain that they do not carry liquid water from one place to another. For one thing, it is doubtful if there is enough water on Mars to produce any significant volume of liquid, and for another, it is prob-

---

* It is frequently stated that Schiaparelli was the first to detect the Martian canals. It is true that he studied and recorded them in detail and named them, but linear formations had apparently been noted by earlier observers.

able that, if ice exists at the poles, it is converted into water vapor, rather than liquid, during the Martian spring and summer.

10.124. The identification of the canals, of which over 400 have been reported, has depended almost exclusively on visual observations with the telescope. A few of the largest canals appear on photographs but only as faint linear markings. As already mentioned, the eye is superior to the photographic plate in its ability to resolve the fine structure in a telescopic image. Although there is no unanimous opinion concerning the existence of the canals, most astronomers would probably agree that there are apparently linear (or approximately linear) markings, perhaps 40 to 160 kilometers (25 to 100 miles) or more across and of considerable length. According to A. Dollfus (1948), at times of perfect seeing these linear markings can be resolved into a large number of small and irregular discontinuous areas. Under less favorable viewing conditions, the small regions blend together to give the appearance of a continuous straight line. An explanation is still lacking, however, for the existence of large numbers of this unusual type of surface formation.

10.125. Another aspect of the problem is that many of the canals intersect or meet at large dark areas which have been referred to as *oases*. The diameters of these regions are on the order of 150 kilometers (100 miles), and some 200 of the oases have been identified. If the canals are natural geological features, as seems certain, their existence must be correlated with the oases.

10.126. During the local Martian winter, definite white areas, called *polar caps*, are seen to cover the polar regions (Fig. 10.13). The caps gradually diminish in size during the spring and summer, but start to increase again in the autumn. The southern cap may disappear completely during the warm season, but at the north pole a small cap may remain throughout the summer. The permanence of the northern cap has been attributed to the presence of a plateau with an elevation of about 1000 meters (3000 feet) where the atmospheric temperature is lower than in the surrounding areas. The north polar cap, extending to a latitude of about 70°N at maximum and covering an area of roughly 4 million square kilometers (1.6 million square miles), is smaller than the cap in the southern hemisphere which extends to latitude 60°S.

10.127. At one time it was thought that the polar caps might consist of solid carbon dioxide, but observations on the infrared spectra (G. P. Kuiper, 1948) and polarization (A. Dollfus, 1957) of sunlight reflected from the caps has indicated fairly conclusively that they are composed of small ice crystals, like hoar frost, but not solid ice.* Hoar frost is formed by direct deposition of solid from water vapor upon cooling; there is no production of an intermediate liquid state such as occurs in normal ice formation. The direct change from vapor to solid takes place only below 273°K, i.e., 0°C or 32°F, a temperature which is probably never exceeded in the Martian polar regions.

10.128. In the local autumn and winter, the very small amounts of water

---

* For another possibility, see § 10.145.

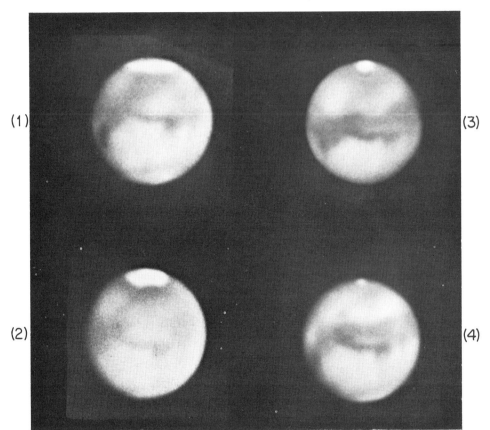

FIG. 10.13. Seasonal changes, in the order (1), (2), (3), (4), on Mars during summer in its southern hemisphere; the south polar cap (top of figure) gradually disappears and dark areas appear nearer to the equator. (*Lowell Observatory*)

vapor, which are known to be present in the atmosphere of Mars, condense to form the polar caps of hoar frost. In the spring and summer, the reverse process occurs. As the atmospheric temperature increases, the ice crystals sublime, i.e., they turn directly into vapor, and so the outer edges, which warm up first, gradually recede to higher latitudes. Around the middle of spring, a narrow black border, turning dark blue in the northern hemisphere, forms around the polar cap; this may possibly be moist ground where the local temperature conditions permit the formation of some liquid water. The black border disappears during the summer as the temperature increases.

10.129. The thickness of the hoar-frost layer constituting the polar caps undoubtedly varies with both location and time. A rough estimate, made by G. de Vaucouleurs (1954), based on the rate at which the caps decrease in area in the spring and the thermal radiation received from the Sun, implies an average thickness equivalent to about 1 centimeter, i.e., less than half an inch, of solid ice. Since the hoar-frost structure of very small ice crystals undoubtedly includes some entrapped atmospheric gases, the actual thickness of the layer is somewhat greater than this calculated value. In any event, the total quantity of water on Mars is believed to be relatively small, and if allowance is made for the amount present in the atmosphere and clouds, it appears highly improbable that there can be any significant amount of liquid water on the surface, even in the summer.

10.130. The dark areas of low albedo, especially in yellow light, on the surface of Mars have been called *maria*, but like the lunar maria they are definitely not bodies of water. The Martian maria cover somewhat more than one fourth of the planet's surface and are located mainly in the southern hemisphere. On the whole, the maria are permanent in form, so that they have been mapped in some detail (Fig. 10.14), but they exhibit regular seasonal alterations in color and size. Occasionally, new dark areas form and may last from a few months to several years; for example, E. C. Slipher reported in 1954 that since 1952 a dark area of nearly 2.5 million square kilometers (600,000 square miles) had developed.

10.131. In the Martian winter, the maria are gray (or blue gray), but in the spring a dark coloration is seen to spread down from the poles. The rate of advance of the wave of darkening is about 40 kilometers (25 miles) per hour. In the northern hemisphere, the dark areas are said to exhibit a range of colors from brown to black in the summer, but in the southern hemisphere they have a greenish hue. Frequently, the dimensions of the dark areas increase as their color changes in the warmer season. It is of interest to note that some canals and oases, as well as isolated regions in the desert, also become significantly darker in the summer.

10.132. Several theories have been proposed to account for the seasonal color changes of the maria and other areas. The development of the dark color is definitely associated with the decrease in size of the polar caps. As seen above, there is a good possibility that these caps consist of water (hoar-frost) crystals. Furthermore, the rate at which the wave of darkening advances is roughly the same as the rate of transfer of water vapor from the receding polar cap in the warming hemisphere to the one forming in the other hemisphere. It is reasonable to postulate, therefore, that there is a close connection between the coloration of the dark regions and the presence (or absence) of water vapor. The possible explanations of Martian color changes reviewed here will therefore be confined to those in which water is assumed to play a major role (see, however, § 10.145).

10.133. One view is that the maria contain a chemical substance which changes color according to the water vapor pressure (or concentration) in the ambient atmosphere. A number of inorganic compounds that behave in this manner are known. No suggestion has been made, however, of a specific mate-

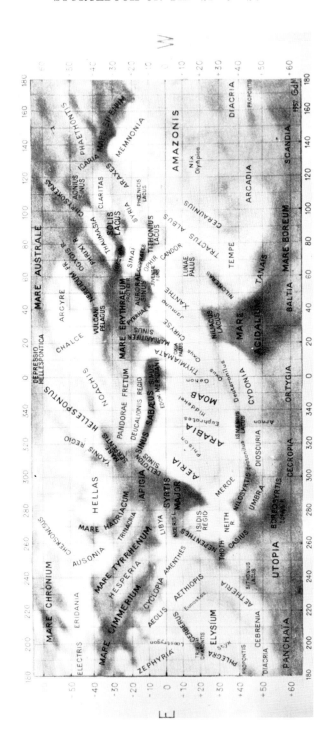

Fig. 10.14. Drawing of Mars in Mercator projection based on numerous visual observations with the telescope. (*International Astronomical Union*)

rial that would become dark brown when exposed to a moderately high concentration of water vapor and would change to gray when the concentration was decreased.

10.134. A much more intriguing theory is that primitive forms of plant life, possibly resembling lichens, mosses, or microscopic algae, exist on the maria. In the winter, the plants are dormant, owing to the low temperature and the lack of moisture. But in the spring, as the temperature increases and the water vapor in the atmosphere increases, they revive and grow. The transition from dormant to active states, and the reverse, would result in color changes. One of the arguments for the vegetation theory is that, when the dark areas become coated with yellowish dust, as a result of one of the not uncommon dust storms (§ 10.136), they often recover their original appearance in a few weeks. Growth of a primitive form of plant life would provide a simple explanation of this phenomenon. The question of the possible presence of living organisms on Mars is discussed more fully later in this chapter.

Martian Clouds and Haze

10.135. Clouds and haze of various types appear frequently in the Martian atmosphere. Sometimes they are quite small in area and are not easily detected, but occasionally large clouds cover much of the planet. The visible clouds are usually either yellow or white, but there are also some indications of blue clouds. In addition, there is the so-called blue haze, which is not visible, but definitely obscures the surface features.

10.136. The general view is that the *yellow clouds* are composed of dust stirred up by windstorms.* When first observed, these clouds cover limited areas and are seen to be in motion, as if driven by the wind. As they move, the clouds grow in extent and may ultimately cover large parts of the planet. During the favorable opposition of 1956, an exceptionally extensive yellow cloud was seen to obscure almost the whole of Mars for a period of several weeks. It would appear not unreasonable to identify the reddish desert areas as the source of the yellow dust, in spite of the difference in color. It is well known, for example, that a red or brown solid appears much lighter in color when in a finely divided state than it is in a coarser form.

10.137. The *white clouds* apparently form in regions or at altitudes where the temperatures are low. Although they may be seen at one time or another over any part of Mars, they are frequently observed near the sunrise and sunset limbs of the planet. The white clouds formed at sunrise may disappear within an hour or two as the atmosphere warms up. Clouds seen near the sunset limb are usually larger and brighter than the sunrise clouds; and they may reappear on several successive days over the same surface regions, especially the desert areas. White clouds commonly occur over the polar caps during the Martian autumn and winter, but they disappear when spring ar-

* For an alternative interpretation, see § 10.145.

rives. There is some evidence, based on studies made by A. Dollfus (1957) of the polarization of light reflected by the clouds, that the white clouds consist of very small crystals of ice, just as do cirrus clouds in the terrestrial atmosphere. It is not impossible, however, that some of the white clouds are made up of particles of solid carbon dioxide; in the gaseous form, this compound is a fairly abundant constituent of the Martian atmosphere (§ 10.151).

10.138. Some astronomers have reported seeing tenuous *blue clouds* under the same conditions that favor the appearance of white clouds. It is not certain whether the blue and white clouds are distinct or whether the former are merely thin layers of small crystals, perhaps of water, similar to those present in the white clouds.

10.139. The phenomenon designated the *blue haze*, also sometimes called the *violet layer*, has been misnamed; it is not a visible haze (or layer) and if it could be seen it would probably not appear blue in color. As already stated, visual images and photographs of Mars in white light, i.e., without colored filters, show distinct markings, unless they are obscured by white or yellow clouds. The details are also apparent in images and photographs in infrared, red, or yellow light. But if a blue, violet, or ultraviolet filter is used, the surface features of the planet generally disappear completely, regardless of whether visible clouds are present or not. In these circumstances about the only parts of Mars that can be seen clearly are the polar caps (Fig. 10.15). Evidently there is some kind of layer surrounding Mars that prevents radiations of shorter wavelength, i.e., blue, violet, and ultraviolet, reflected by the planet from reaching Earth. Consequently, when a photograph is taken with a blue filter, the Martian surface details are no longer seen. It is this layer, which is invisible, that is called the blue haze. If the action of the haze is to absorb blue and violet radiation, it would probably have a reddish or orange color, but it is not certain that this is the case.

10.140. Occasionally, the Martian blue haze dissipates and surface features can be seen in blue or violet light; this effect is known as the *blue clearing*. Sometimes the clearing is local, but quite often it occurs over almost the whole of the planet. In the course of a few days or even hours, the blue haze disappears and the atmosphere transmits light of short wavelength for several subsequent days; then the haze develops again within a short time. The planet-wide clearing seems to occur most commonly near favorable oppositions, but it has also been observed near unfavorable oppositions and at other times. It is not impossible that the apparent correlation between the blue clearing and favorable oppositions is merely the result of the circumstance that Mars is then closest to Earth and intensive observations are made at such times.

10.141. The nature of the Martian blue haze is not yet understood. A widely held theory (E. Schatzman, 1941; G. P. Kuiper, 1952; S. L. Hess, 1958) is that the haze consists of an optically thin layer of very small crystals of ice, about 0.3 micron, i.e., 3×10^{-5} centimeter, in diameter. The conditions in the Martian atmosphere are certainly such that small ice crystals could exist, but so also could solid carbon dioxide which is much more plentiful.

10.142. It is postulated that the extremely small crystals cause forward scattering, i.e., toward the planet, of the shorter wavelengths in sunlight, whereas the longer wavelengths, i.e., yellow, red, etc., are scattered outward, i.e.,

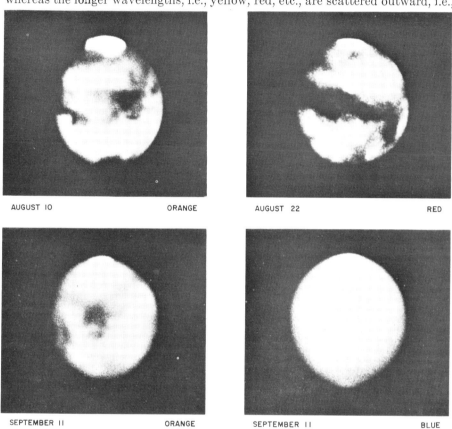

| AUGUST 10 | ORANGE | AUGUST 22 | RED |
| SEPTEMBER 11 | ORANGE | SEPTEMBER 11 | BLUE |

Fig. 10.15.   Photographs of Mars taken in 1956 with filters of different colors. (*Mount Wilson and Palomar Observatories*)

toward Earth. These longer wavelengths are absorbed by a blue filter, and so no details can be seen in a photograph taken in blue light. A serious objection to this theory is that it is incompatible with the low albedo of the surface of Mars for blue and violet radiations. If the particles constituting the blue haze permit forward scattering of blue light, then a large proportion of such light reflected from the surface would reach Earth. The albedo would then be expected to be fairly high, but it is not.

10.143. An alternative point of view is that the blue haze acts by the absorption, rather than forward scattering, of light of short wavelength. This would be the case if the haze consisted of small, dark-colored particles. In the presence of the absorbing particles, the only radiations that can be transmitted to Earth from the Martian surface are those toward the red end of the spectrum. Hence, photographs taken in blue light would show no surface details. One suggestion is that the dark-colored particles consist of black carbon formed by the photochemical decomposition of carbon dioxide in the Martian atmosphere by solar ultraviolet radiation (B. Rosen, 1953; E. J. Öpik, 1960).

10.144. Another theory (H. C. Urey and A. W. Brewer, 1957) is that protons from the solar wind cause ionization of carbon dioxide and nitrogen molecules in the upper atmosphere of Mars. The resulting positive ions, such as CO_2^+, CO^+, and N_2^+, are known to absorb radiations in the blue and violet regions of the spectrum. Although in the original presentation of this theory it was postulated that only protons, and perhaps electrons, caused the ionization, it will be seen shortly that the theory may be extended to include ionization by solar ultraviolet radiation.

10.145. A somewhat novel suggestion to account for the blue haze and other characteristics of Mars was put forward by C. C. Kiess, *et al.*, in the United States in 1960. It is postulated that the action of ultraviolet radiation from sunlight in the high atmosphere of Mars produces nitrogen dioxide (NO_2), two molecules of which can combine, especially at moderately low temperatures, to form nitrogen tetroxide (N_2O_4). Nitrogen dioxide is a brown-colored gas, but the tetroxide is pale yellow and condenses at about $-9°C$ ($16°F$) to a whitish solid. According to Kiess, the polar caps of Mars do not consist of water (hoar frost) but of solid nitrogen tetroxide. Furthermore, the yellow clouds, which are commonly attributed to dust, are said to be nitrogen dioxide with some tetroxide. Of particular present interest is that by absorbing blue and violet light, as it does, nitrogen dioxide would readily account for the Martian blue haze. Although Kiess claimed that the spectrum of Mars showed the presence of nitrogen dioxide lines, this has been disputed by H. Spinrad (1963). A careful search by the latter has failed to reveal any significant indications of this substance; consequently the theory that the Martian atmosphere contains oxides of nitrogen has not received wide support.

10.146. A possible means of deciding between scattering and absorption as the primary function of the blue haze is by determining whether the Martian limb appears lighter or darker in blue light. If the blue haze is largely an absorbing layer, limb darkening is to be expected because of the greater thickness of the atmosphere that has to be penetrated by light reflected from the limb. On the other hand, a forward scattering layer over a dark surface would probably produce a brightening of the Martian limb in blue light. It has been known for some time that photographs of Mars taken with blue filters exhibit definite brightening near the limb. More careful study, however, has shown that the brightening does not extend quite to the limb and is, in fact, followed by a dark border at the limb. Such an effect might be accounted for by a thin scattering layer above one of an absorbing material. Presumably, a single layer of particles could have both scattering and absorbing properties, and produce the observed darkening at the limb with brightening in the adjacent region. If this were so, the solid particles would not have to be as small as suggested above on the basis of pure scattering.

10.147. Explanation of the fairly rapid planet-wide clearing phenomenon is an important aspect of any theory of the blue haze. If small crystals of ice, carbon dioxide, or even nitrogen tetroxide are responsible, then a change in the atmospheric conditions could cause evaporation, i.e., sublimation, to occur and the blue haze would dissipate. Its reappearance could then result from a restoration of the original conditions. It is surprising, however, that the change would take place over the whole of Mars within a period of time that is sometimes as short as a few hours.

10.148. If the blue haze is composed of small particles of carbon or other substance that does not vaporize readily, the clearing is attributed to the settling of the particles under the influence of gravity. But to settle out so completely in a short time would require the suspended particles to increase very considerably in size at a rapid rate. One way in which this could take place was indicated by E. C. Slipher (1962): carbon particles might serve as crystallization centers for atmospheric water vapor (or carbon dioxide). The particles would thus increase in size and mass and settle out when there was a decrease in the ambient temperature. This mechanism would account for the rapidity of the blue clearing, but it is not so apparent how the haze would re-form in a short time.

10.149. A special feature of the theory that ionic species in the Martian atmosphere act as absorbers of radiations of short wavelength is that it claims to account for the supposed greater frequency of blue clearing when Mars is in opposition. At such times, the solar wind must pass Earth on its way to Mars, and it would be deflected by the terrestrial magnetic field. The ionization of the gases in the Martian atmosphere would thus be decreased and, hence, also the absorption of blue light. The clearing effect would then be observed. Although this explanation for the blue clearing appears plausible, C. Sagan (1962) has claimed that it is untenable when examined from a quantitative standpoint.

10.150. The failure to account for what might be, after all, a subjective phenomenon must not be regarded as an argument against the underlying concept that the blue haze consists of absorbing ions. If the supposed correlation between blue clearing and opposition is disregarded, as it is in other theories of the blue haze, then it may be postulated that electromagnetic radiations, i.e., ultraviolet and X-rays, from the Sun, as well as protons in the solar wind, could cause ionization. It is because the former would not be deflected by the terrestrial magnetic field that they were omitted from the original theory. As an alternative to deflection of the protons, it may be suggested that the blue clearing arises from recombination of the positive ions and free electrons.

Both recombination and reionization could take place rapidly, although the conditions which would favor one of these processes over the other at different times are not clear.

THE MARTIAN ATMOSPHERE

10.151. Only two gases, namely carbon dioxide and water vapor, have been definitely identified in the Martian atmosphere, although others are undoubtedly present. Carbon dioxide was first detected by G. P. Kuiper (1948) in the infrared spectrum of the light from Mars. From the broadening of the spectral lines and the accepted value of the total atmospheric pressure at the surface, it was estimated that the carbon dioxide constituted roughly 2 molecular (or volume) percent of the atmosphere. More recent studies of the Martian spectrum, however, indicate that the proportion may be as much as ten times as large, i.e., about 20 percent by volume. In any event, there is little doubt that carbon dioxide is an important constituent of the atmosphere of Mars.

10.152. The presence of water vapor in the atmosphere had been inferred, mainly from the characteristics of the polar caps, but it was not until 1963 that H. Spinrad, G. Münch, and L. D. Kaplan in the United States obtained positive evidence. They observed several spectral (rotational) lines in the near infrared (cf. § 10.62), around the wavelength of 0.82 micron, which are characteristic of water vapor. It is probable that A. Dollfus (1962) had also detected this substance by means of its spectral band in the vicinity of 1.4-microns wavelength. The proportion of water vapor in the Martian atmosphere is undoubtedly a variable quantity, but it is extremely small, very much less than in the terrestrial atmosphere on a clear day in the desert.

10.153. The other components of the atmosphere of Mars are not known, but by comparison with Earth it is assumed that nitrogen is a major constituent. There is also probably a few percent of argon formed by radioactive decay of potassium-40 in the solid material of the planet. The presence of these gases is difficult to confirm because their normal (neutral atom) spectra are in the ultraviolet and can be observed only outside the terrestrial atmosphere. It is not unlikely that the atmosphere of Mars contains small quantities of oxygen and carbon monoxide formed by the photochemical decomposition of carbon dioxide, but neither of these gases has been identified. A search has been made for ozone (O_3), nitrous oxide (N_2O), nitrogen dioxide (NO_2), nitrogen tetroxide (N_2O_4), sulfur dioxide (SO_2), methane (CH_4), ethylene (C_2H_4), ethane (C_2H_6), and ammonia (NH_3), but the quantities, if any, of these gases are below the limits of spectroscopic detection at the present time. Because of their small molecular weights and the relatively low escape velocity from Mars, hydrogen and helium can undoubtedly exist in no more than trace amounts.

10.154. Prior to 1963, the total pressure of the atmosphere at the surface of Mars was thought to be about 80 millibars (cf. § 10.16, footnote). This result was derived from photometric (intensity) and polarization measurements of the light scattered by the atmosphere when free from clouds and blue haze, and the assumption that the scattering was due only to molecules, i.e., Rayleigh scattering. An examination, made in 1963, of the breadth of the rotational lines in the infrared band spectrum of carbon dioxide has led H. Spinrad and his collaborators (§ 10.63) and G. P. Kuiper to conclude that the total atmospheric pressure may be as low as 10 or 20 millibars. The earlier higher value might be accounted for if some of the scattering were caused by small particles in addition to that by molecules. Further investigation will probably be required to establish the Martian atmospheric pressure, but it is definitely low compared with the normal pressure at Earth's surface, i.e., just over 1000 millibars.

10.155. It is generally accepted that the vertical structure of the atmosphere of Mars is similar to Earth's, but there are different opinions concerning the details. The lowest part of the Martian atmosphere presumably consists of a region resembling the terrestrial troposphere in which the temperature decreases with increasing altitude. If the atmosphere of Mars is assumed to consist mainly of molecular nitrogen, carbon dioxide, and argon, the maximum (adiabatic) lapse rate (§ 8.26) is calculated to be 3.7°C (6.7°F) per kilometer. The temperature thus decreases more slowly with altitude than in Earth's troposphere in which the lapse rate is almost twice as great. Corresponding to the less rapid decrease in temperature in the Martian atmosphere, the pressure also falls off more slowly with altitude. Consequently, at a height above about 50 kilometers (30 miles) or so, the atmospheric pressure on Mars may be greater than at the same level in the terrestrial atmosphere.

10.156. As a result of this difference, the thermosphere and ionosphere, which presumably exist in the Martian atmosphere, will occur at higher altitudes than on Earth. Since there is very little oxygen in the atmosphere of Mars, heating of the thermosphere will probable result from the energy liberated in the recombination of carbon monoxide and oxygen atoms; these are the products of the photochemical dissociation of carbon dioxide by solar ultraviolet radiation of short wavelength. There has been some speculation concerning the ions present in the Martian ionosphere, e.g., N_2^+, O_2^+, and O^+ ions. But the basic information upon which the inferences are based is so sparse that the conclusions must be regarded as tentative.

The Interior of Mars

10.157. The observed mean density of Mars is close to 4 grams per cubic centimeter, and after allowing for the compression and heating in the interior, the normal density would not be very different. Since the density of ordinary silicate materials, such as are common in Earth's crust and mantle and probably also on Mars, is about 3 grams per cubic centimeter, it is evident that the proportion of heavy metals, e.g., iron and nickel, in the planet must be relatively small, probably 10 to 15 percent by weight. Consequently, if the condition in the interior of Mars permitted the separation of these metals from the silicates, the central metallic core will occupy only a few percent of the planet's total volume. If the Martian deserts should contain significant amounts of iron oxides, as has been suggested, the volume of the central core would be very small, at best.

10.158. At present, it cannot be clearly established whether Mars has a liquid metal core or not. If it has, then since the planet rotates fairly rapidly, it should certainly have a magnetic field although appreciably weaker than that of Earth. Magnetometer observations in the vicinity of Mars would thus be of considerable scientific interest. Moreover, if the planet has a magnetic field, then it will also possess a radiation belt, similar to the terrestrial Van Allen belt.

SATELLITES OF MARS

10.159. Mars has two natural satellites (or moons), named Phobos and Deimos,* which were discovered by the American astronomer Asaph Hall in 1877. The orbit of Phobos, the inner of the satellites, has an average radius of 9450 kilometers (5850 miles), so that it is roughly 6100 kilometers (3750 miles) from the surface of the parent planet. Its sidereal period of revolution is 7 hours 39 minutes, i.e., less than a third of the Martian period of rotation (or day). The synodic orbital period of the satellite, as seen from Mars, is about 11 hours. The inclination of the orbital plane to the equatorial plane of Mars is only 1.7 deg. Phobos is reputed to be the only natural satellite in the solar system with a period of revolution less than the rotational period of its primary. To an observer on Mars, Phobos rises (in the west) and sets (in the east) twice each day. Between rising and setting, the satellite would be seen to pass through a considerable part of its cycle of phase changes. The size of Phobos is too small to measure directly, i.e., from its angular diameter, but from its observed brightness and an assumed albedo the diameter is estimated to be very roughly 16 kilometers (10 miles). Because of its proximity to the parent planet and the shortness of its orbital period, Phobos frequently passes through the shadow of Mars cast by the Sun and is eclipsed.

10.160. The outer satellite, Deimos, is apparently only about 8 kilometers (5 miles) across. It has an orbital radius of some 23,500 kilometers (14,500 miles) and is thus roughly 20,000 kilometers (12,000 miles) from the surface of Mars. The orbital plane of Phobos makes an angle of about 1 deg with the Martian equatorial plane. The sidereal orbital period of the satellite is 30 hours 18 minutes and the synodic period is about 5½ terrestrial days. From the central planet, Deimos would be seen to rise in the east and travel slowly across the sky

---

* According to Homer's *Iliad*, the war god Ares, the Greek equivalent of the Roman god Mars, was attended by Phobos ("fear") and Deimos ("dread"); they are also sometimes described as the sons of Ares.

and set in the west some $2\frac{1}{2}$ Martian days later. The outer satellite suffers many eclipses although they occur less often than those of Phobos.

10.161. Both Phobos and Deimos make frequent transits across the Sun's disc, but these can hardly be called solar eclipses because the area obscured is so small. The characteristics of the orbits of the satellites have been utilized to calculate the mass and the dynamic ellipticity of Mars (§ 10.112 *et seq.*).

10.162. It has been suggested that the Martian satellites might be useful as space stations for observing the planet or for staging manned landings, if such problems as the radiation hazard and the extremely low gravity could be overcome. The advantage of making observations of Mars from a satellite is that, as the latter orbits about the planet, almost the whole of the surface could be studied from one location. The determination of entry and return trajectories and the choice of a suitable landing area on Mars would be greatly facilitated in this manner.

THE POSSIBILITY OF LIFE ON MARS

10.163. Perhaps the most exciting prospect of current space science is the possibility of discovering the presence of living organisms on Mars. This is the only member of the solar system upon which the conditions, e.g., temperature, presence of water vapor, and carbon dioxide, are such that life, similar to primitive forms on Earth, could possibly exist. It is of interest, therefore, to consider the circumstances under which life may have originated and developed on Earth, and to see to what extent they might be applicable to Mars.

10.164. Among the more plausible hypotheses proposed to account for terrestrial life is one which postulates that, during the early history of Earth, when there was little or no free oxygen and no ozone to absorb the ultraviolet radiations from the Sun, complex organic molecules containing nitrogenous bases were produced in the primitive atmosphere. These compounds accumulated in the ocean and from them, together with phosphorus, there developed in the course of time a molecular system that was capable of replication, i.e., of duplicating or reproducing itself. This complex molecule may have been similar to the substance known as deoxyribonucleic acid (DNA), which is believed to be present in all forms of terrestrial life. Together with the related ribonucleic acid (RNA), the DNA molecule provides the instructions for the formation of various proteins from amino acids in the living organism.* Furthermore, DNA carries the genetic code which causes one generation to resemble the preceding one. Small variations in the replication of the DNA, produced by chance or by the environment, could lead to the gradual evolution of new life forms.

* DNA and RNA do not represent specific compounds, but rather structural types that can exhibit a very large number of variations depending on the order in which the four bases, adenine, cytosine, guanine, and thymine (or uracil in one kind of RNA) are attached to a long molecular chain. In DNA this chain is made up of units of the sugar-like compound deoxyribose attached to a phosphoric acid residue. In RNA, the sugar is ribose which contains an oxygen atom more than deoxyribose.

10.165. In 1952, H. C. Urey presented arguments to show that Earth's primitive atmosphere consisted mainly of hydrogen gas and hydrogen compounds of light elements, namely, methane, ammonia, and water vapor. Consequently, it appeared probable that from these substances were formed the basic units or building blocks of the proteins and other materials essential to life. In recent years, a number of scientists in the United States have accumulated evidence in the laboratory which tends to support this point of view.

10.166. Acting upon Urey's suggestion, S. L. Miller (1953) exposed liquid water together with a mixture of methane and ammonia gases, with or without hydrogen, to the action of either ultraviolet light, such as might have come from solar radiation, or an electrical discharge, to simulate lightning. Analysis of the highly complex products revealed the presence of at least six amino acids and other compounds related to the materials found in living matter. Subsequently, S. W. Fox (1958) found that heating amino acids, especially in the presence of large proportions of aspartic and glutamic acids, both of which had been identified among Miller's products, gave rise to polymers resembling proteins. These polymers could be obtained as small spherical particles which might have formed the basis for primitive living cell forms.

10.167. In addition to the more complex compounds, Miller found that the simple substance hydrogen cyanide (HCN) had been formed in his experiments. It is also obtained when electrons of moderately high energy are passed through a mixture of methane, ammonia, and water vapor. Hydrogen cyanide readily combines with ammonia to yield ammonium cyanide, and upon heating a concentrated aqueous solution of this salt for several days, J. Oró (1960) identified the compound adenine among the products. This essential constituent of the nucleic acids (DNA and RNA) and of other biologically important substances, e.g., adenosine triphosphate (ATP), was also obtained by Ceylon-born C. Ponnamperuma (1963) and his associates in two other ways starting from primitive materials. One method was to irradiate a mixture of methane, ammonia, hydrogen, and water with electrons, such as might be emitted as beta particles by the radioactive potassium-40, a component of many minerals; the other was to expose a dilute aqueous solution of hydrogen cyanide to the action of ultraviolet light. In the latter case, the related compound guanine, another constituent of nucleic acids, was also identified.

10.168. Among the products of the action of particle radiation or of an electrical discharge on a mixture of methane, ammonia, and water is formaldehyde; when exposed to ultraviolet radiation, the sugars ribose and deoxyribose are formed, in addition to other substances. Thus, two of the basic organic components, namely, adenine and ribose, of ATP, which is the principal source of energy transfer in living systems, have been synthesized from primitive materials. By irradiation of a mixture of adenine, ribose, and the diethyl ester of polyphosphoric acid with ultraviolet light, Ponnamperuma and his co-workers were able to obtain ATP itself.

10.169. The work described above and other investigations along similar and related lines have established that several compounds involved in life processes could very well have been formed during the early history of Earth. It is not improbable that, in the course of two billion years, a series of gradual stages led from the relatively simple organic compounds to various complex molecules, such as DNA, and subsequently to a single-celled organism. During the next two billion years or so, this would have evolved, by the processes of mutation and natural selection, into the multifarious life forms that now exist on Earth.

10.170. In its early stages, the conditions on Mars probably resembled those on Earth. Hence, simple amino acids and other organic molecules could have been produced by the action of ultraviolet radiations, electrical discharges, and charged particles on mixtures of hydrogen, methane, ammonia, and water. If the arguments outlined above concerning the origin of life are accepted, then there is a definite possibility that living organisms may have existed at one time on Mars, even if there are none now.

10.171. Although the conditions on Mars and Earth may have originally been similar, the changes which took place in the course of time were very different. One reason for this difference is the much smaller force of gravity on Mars, so that gases which could be retained by Earth escaped from Mars. It is possible that the amount of oxygen in the Martian atmosphere was never as large as on Earth, but, in any event, oxygen atoms produced by the photochemical dissociation of various gas molecules, under the influence of solar radiation, would tend to escape from Mars. As a consequence of the low oxygen content, there would be little ozone formation, and ultraviolet radiation of short wavelength, which cannot penetrate Earth's atmosphere (§ 8.81), would reach the surface of Mars. Photochemical decomposition of water could then occur and the products, oxygen and hydrogen, would escape in the course of time. The energy required to dissociate nitrogen molecules, however, is larger than for oxygen or water vapor; hence, nitrogen would probably remain on Mars as it has done on Earth.

10.172. It is obvious, therefore, that if a simple living organism had been produced on Mars, its subsequent evolution would be very different from that on Earth. But the conditions are not necessarily such as to make life impossible. The terrestrial autotrophic bacteria, for example, do not require organic matter as a major source of food and energy. Suitable inorganic matter is undoubtedly present on Mars and there is an ample supply of carbon dioxide which is required by these bacteria. The small amount of water vapor present in the atmosphere could be sufficient to sustain life forms if they or their environment have mechanisms for capturing the moisture. It is of interest that under simulated Martian conditions in the laboratory, including temperatures varying from $-60°$ to $20°C$ ($-76°$ to $68°F$), a low-pressure atmosphere consisting of about 95 percent nitrogen, 5 percent carbon dioxide, and a trace of water vapor, and relatively intense ultraviolet radiation, certain terrestrial microorganisms were able to survive. Life forms which had evolved on Mars would, of course, be better adapted to their environments.

10.173. It was mentioned earlier that the seasonal changes in the darker areas of Mars could be explained by the growth and decay of some form of vegetation. In favor of this view is the observation by A. Dollfus (1957) that the polarization of the light scattered from the dark areas, as a function of phase angle, varies with the season. The polarization of the lighter (desert) areas, however, shows no such variation. The implication is that the small opaque particles which scatter light from the darker parts of Mars have different dimensions at different times of the year. Changes in a primitive surface vegetation would readily account for such dimensional variations.

10.174. Studies reported by W. M. Sinton in 1959 and 1961 of the infrared spectrum of sunlight reflected from the surface of Mars indicated the presence of features at wavelengths of 3.45, 3.58, and 3.69 microns in the radiations from the dark areas but not from the bright regions. The carbon-hydrogen bond as found in many organic molecules has a characteristic spectral band at 3.45-microns wavelength, and a band at 3.69 microns is typical of acetaldehyde. The reflection spectra may thus be interpreted as suggesting the presence of organic substances on the dark areas of Mars. The results are not conclusive, however, because there are inorganic materials that have spectral features in the wavelength region of about 3.5 microns.

10.175. It is, of course, by no means improbable that organic compounds are present on Mars, since they have been found in the carbonaceous chondrites (§ 7.128). But this does not prove that life exists or ever has existed on the planet. The combination of evidence, indicating the possible presence of organic compounds only in the dark areas where seasonal changes occur in color and particle size, is nevertheless suggestive.

Exobiology on Mars

10.176. One of the consequences of the increased interest in space research is the development of the science of *exobiology;* its purpose is to study by experimental means the possibility of life beyond Earth. The first target of this new science is obviously the planet Mars. Spectroscopic observations in the infrared and ultraviolet regions made from Mars probes and orbiters would probably supply much interesting data concerning the atmosphere of the planet and the characteristics of the dark areas. But more direct information will undoubtedly be necessary and this can be obtained by landing instruments on the Martian surface.

10.177. A number of experimental techniques have been proposed in the United States for detecting the presence of living organisms, and the principle of some of these will be outlined below. As is usual with instruments designed for space, the devices must be compact and light in weight. In addition, they must provide output signals in a form that can be telemetered to Earth. Furthermore, the instruments must be capable of operating in spite of the wide temperature variations that occur between day and night on Mars.

10.178. The device called *Gulliver* (Fig. 10.16), developed by G. V. Levin and N. H. Horwitz, is based on the fact that carbon dioxide is a product of the

FIG. 10.16.   The Gulliver instrument

metabolic activity of most terrestrial organisms. In order to detect carbon dioxide that may be formed in this manner on Mars, it is proposed to use a liquid nutrient (or culture) solution with a sugar or other organic substance in which the radioactive isotope carbon-14 is present. Strings coated with an adhesive material are attached to projectiles which are shot out from small guns to a distance of about 25 feet on the surface of Mars and then reeled back.

10.179. Any material adhering to the string is scraped off into a chamber containing the culture solution. If living organisms which can utilize the sugar in their metabolism are present, they will produce carbon dioxide containing carbon-14. A Geiger counter or similar radiation detector is attached to the culture chamber and will indicate whether radioactive carbon dioxide gas has been formed. Since the Martian microorganisms, if any, may not metabolize sugar, other possible nutrient materials, suitably labeled with carbon-14, will be included in the culture solution.

10.180. A working model of the Gulliver instrument has been tested under a wide variety of terrestrial conditions, ranging from the sand dunes of Death Valley to an elevation of 12,000 feet on White Mountain in California, and from the salt desert of southern California to the woods of Rock Creek Park, Washington, D.C. In all these places, the instrument was able to detect microbial life in the course of a few hours.

10.181. In the *Wolf Trap*, named for its designer Wolf Vishniac (1960), a sample of soil or dust is sucked into a clear solution containing various possible nutrients for primitive life forms. If living organisms are present in the soil, they should grow and increase in number. It is expected that, as a result, the solution will become cloudy and increase in acidity. The turbidity may be detected by means of a photomultiplier tube, which measures the intensity of the light transmitted by the culture solution, and the acidity by the use of a pH meter (Fig. 10.17).

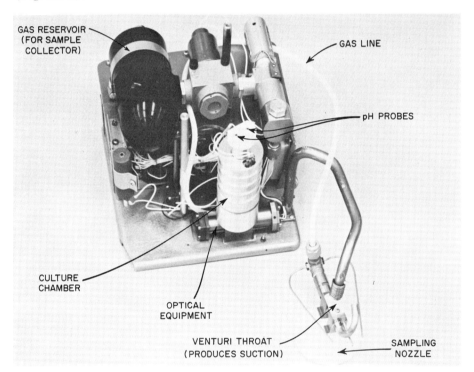

FIG. 10.17.   Model of the Wolf Trap

10.182. Joshua Lederberg and his collaborators have designed an instrument (Fig. 10.18), weighing only 2 pounds, called a *multivator*, an abbreviation for "multiple evaluator." Dust will be sucked into a number of small chambers containing various materials for detecting the enzyme phosphatase and other typical biological molecules or biochemical processes. The presence of such substances or processes will be indicated by the development of fluorescence or color effects at particular wavelengths. These will be observed by means of an arrangement consisting of a light source, suitable filters, and a photomultiplier cell.

10.183. Among the devices which are being studied for use in the search for life on Mars is a combined microscope and television (vidicon) system for ob-

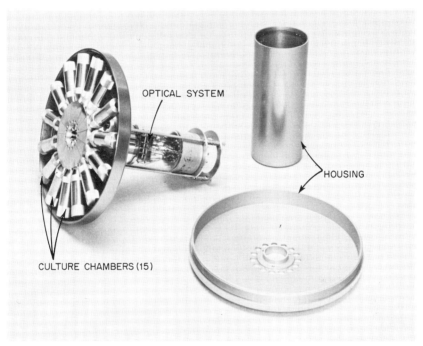

OPTICAL SYSTEM

HOUSING

CULTURE CHAMBERS (15)

Fɪɢ. 10.18.   The Multivator device with housing removed

serving and detecting microorganisms directly. Organic and inorganic (soil) particles will be separated by taking advantage of their density difference and will be examined individually. In addition, there are schemes based on the use of the gas chromatograph and mass spectrometer, and the observation of absorption spectra in the visible and ultraviolet regions to identify organic compounds related to life processes. Another approach is based on the ability of many organic compounds produced in biological systems to rotate (or change) the plane of polarization of light passing through them. The same substances formed by chemical (nonbiological) synthesis are a mixture of equal numbers of molecules which rotate the plane of polarization in opposite directions so that they neutralize each other. By observing the behavior of polarized light, especially near an absorption band in the ultraviolet where the sensitivity is greatest, it may be possible to determine whether material of biological origin is present on the Martian surface.

10.184. If any of the foregoing procedures should yield positive results, scientists will not be satisfied until they can study specimens of Martian life in detail in the laboratory. On the other hand, if the results are all negative, it is certain that no final conclusion concerning the existence of life on Mars will be accepted until a direct examination can be made of the surface material from the dark areas. Consequently, no matter what response is obtained from instruments landed on the planet, the collection and return of samples of Martian soil will be an essential requirement of the science of exobiology.

Decontamination of Spacecraft

10.185. The possibility that living organisms may exist on Mars or that the conditions may be suitable for the support of some forms of terrestrial life raises some important problems in connection with the study of the planet by means of spacecraft. If it is intended that all or part of the space vehicle shall land on Mars or if there is any prospect that it may do so unintentionally, special precautions must be taken to make sure that the spacecraft will not contaminate the planet with organisms of terrestrial origin. It was thought at one time that such organisms might be killed during the spacecraft's long journey through the vacuum of interplanetary space by the action of ultraviolet radiation from the Sun. Laboratory experiments have shown, however, that some forms of life can survive these conditions, and consequently special steps are necessary to prevent contamination of Mars or other planets.

10.186. The ultimate goal in the U.S. space program is to achieve complete sterilization of the spacecraft by production and assembly of components under sterile conditions, followed by heating of the assembled capsule. In order to minimize possible damage to the hardware, the sterilization temperature is kept relatively low, namely, 135°C (275°F), for a period of 24 hours. At the present time, a few spacecraft components cannot withstand this heat treatment without suffering damage and a program is under way to develop hardware that is capable of doing so. In the meantime, the following procedure is being employed for spacecraft intended for planetary landings or which may enter the atmosphere of the planet. Different treatments are adopted for components that can tolerate the sterilization heating conditions and those that can not.

10.187. Materials capable of withstanding the temperature used are first sterilized by heat to insure internal decontamination before being made into particular components. The production is carried out under sterile conditions in what are called "bioclean rooms," as also is the assembly of the hardware. At various stages, the subassemblies are treated with ethylene oxide gas to sterilize the outer surfaces, and the final assembly is given the heat treatment mentioned above.

10.188. The materials not stable to heat are treated with a sterilizing gas, such as ethylene oxide or formaldehyde, or are exposed to suitable radiation. Manufacture of the components is performed in sterile rooms and the parts are assembled in closed glove boxes. The subassemblies are packaged and transferred to a bioclean room where the final assembly with the heat-treated components takes place. The completed spacecraft is then enclosed in a sterilized gas-tight capsule for launching. The capsule is finally opened up when well out in space and there is no danger of contamination by terrestrial organisms.

10.189. For spacecraft that are to land on the Moon, the sterilization procedures are less rigorous since it is generally agreed that the conditions would be too hostile to permit any form of Earth life to propagate. No heat treatment is used, but assembly is carried out in bioclean rooms and ethylene oxide (or other) gas is employed to reduce the number of microorganisms on exposed surfaces. Special handling methods are adopted to minimize contamination prior to launch of the spacecraft.

10.190. Although terrestrial organisms might well survive on Mars, it is doubtful if many would proliferate and compete successfully with established Martian life forms, if any. On the other hand, there is a possibility that Martian organisms introduced on Earth would multiply very rapidly and might perhaps become a serious menace to terrestrial life. This is a matter that will receive serious consideration when the time comes to bring back objects from Mars to Earth. Some thought has even been given to the subject in connection with the return of spacecraft from the Moon.

STUDIES OF MARS FROM SPACE

10.191. There are many reasons why Mars is an object of exceptional interest for investigation by means of spacecraft. A fly-by mission could be used to study the ultraviolet and infrared spectra of the light from the planet and so secure information concerning the composition of its atmosphere and the nature of the material covering the dark areas. Some data may perhaps be obtained that will provide a better understanding of the mysterious blue haze. Scanning the surface with infrared and microwave radiometers, similar to those on Mariner II, would permit the temperature distribution to be determined. The Martian magnetic field and associated radiation belt, if present, could be readily observed by means of a magnetometer and charged particle detectors, respectively. Even from a spacecraft passing at a distance of a few thousand miles of the planet, television cameras could obtain useful photographs that reveal some of the topographic features of Mars. The bistatic radar technique (§ 10.81) might be employed to study the character of the Martian surface and its ionosphere.

10.192. If the fly-by spacecraft comes near enough to Mars to drop a capsule, it may be possible to land some of the instruments described earlier to search for living organisms. This will probably be one of the first experiments to be made on the surface of the planet. Other apparatus will probably include a camera to take close-up pictures of the surface, a seismograph to study the internal structure of the planet, and various devices for making radioactive, chemical, and mineralogical analyses of surface material. In due course, surface samples will be collected and returned to Earth for detailed examination.

10.193. Many, if not all, of the experiments which require the soft landing of instruments on the surface of Mars will not be possible from the Mariner-type (fly-by) spacecraft. These must await the development of orbiter-landers of the Voyager type. An orbiting spacecraft may provide information that will account for the discrepancy between the values of the ellipticity of the planet as derived from optical measurements and from the orbits of its natural satellites. If the atmospheric pressure on Mars is indeed as low as 10 or 20 millibars, as indicated in § 10.154, the aerodynamic drag would be insufficient to provide any significant slowing down of a spacecraft or instrument capsule to be landed on the surface. It will then be necessary to use retro-rockets, such as is the case for soft landings on the Moon.

Mars Trajectory and Launch Periods

10.194. Since the orbit of Mars lies beyond that of Earth in the solar system, the heliocentric velocity of a spacecraft that is to make an encounter with Mars must exceed the orbital velocity of Earth. This is achieved by launching the carrier vehicle in the same direction as Earth is traveling in its orbit; the injection velocity is then added to Earth's orbital velocity. Thus, if the launching is performed from Florida, in a southeasterly direction, the appropriate launch window will be a short period between midday and midnight. The launch point is then on the side of Earth facing away from the direction of its orbital motion (Fig. 10.19).

10.195. The favorable launch intervals for a Mars probe, roughly the synodic period of 780 days (26 months) apart, are, after October-November 1964, December 1966 and February 1969. At the time of launch, Mars is somewhat

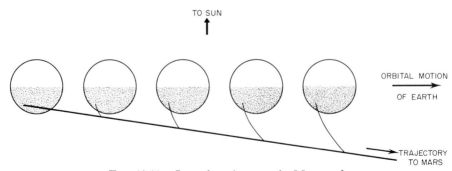

Fig. 10.19.   Launch trajectory of a Mars probe

ahead of Earth in its orbit, but at encounter with the spacecraft Mars is behind Earth. The situation, shown qualitatively in Fig. 10.20, is the reverse of that for the Venus probe trajectory depicted in Fig. 10.9. The duration of the journey of the space probe from Earth to Mars will depend on the launch date, but it ranges from $7\frac{1}{2}$ to $8\frac{1}{2}$ months, and the total distance traveled between launch time and encounter is roughly 560 million kilometers (350 million miles).

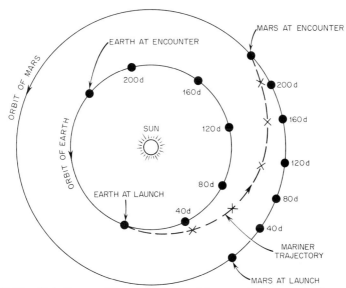

FIG. 10.20.   Relative positions of Earth, Mars, and spacecraft from launch to encounter

THE MARS MARINERS

10.196. The Mariner spacecraft intended for a fly-by mission to Mars is shown in Fig. 10.21. Four large solar-cell panels are attached in a cruciform arrangement to an octagonal framework. Seven of the sections of the latter carry various pieces of equipment and the eighth holds the nozzle of the rocket motor for the midcourse guidance correction. A television camera is mounted on a platform at the bottom of the spacecraft and a mast for the low-gain and high-gain antennas extends from the top. With the panels and mast extended, the dimensions of the Mars Mariner are 22 feet across and $9\frac{1}{2}$ feet high. The total weight is 570 pounds. The vanes, seen in Fig. 10.21 extending from the solar-cell panels, serve as an auxiliary attitude control system by compensating for the effect of radiation pressure on the panels.

10.197. The first Mars Mariners are intended to approach within a distance of about 18,000 kilometers (11,000 miles) from the planet to take pictures across its diameter. Some of the exposures will be made with a green filter and others with a red filter to facilitate the interpretation of the pictures that are obtained of the surface of Mars. Since the spacecraft is some 240 million kilometers (150 million miles) from Earth at the time of encounter with Mars, direct transmission of the pictures, such as was used for the Ranger photographs from the Moon (§ 9.227), is not feasible. A special vidicon tube, capable of retaining an image for 24 seconds, is attached to a telescopic camera. The vidicon screen is scanned after each exposure and the signals are converted to digital form and stored on tape. The data are then read out slowly on the return journey of Mariner toward Earth during the course of about 20 days after encounter. Because of the distance of the spacecraft, a very low data transmission (or bit) rate is mandatory if the results are to be of any value (cf. § 4.174).

10.198. In the hope of learning more about the density (and pressure) of the Martian atmosphere, the trajectory of the Mars Mariner is such as to cause the spacecraft to pass behind the planet as viewed from Earth. The tracking signal from the vehicle will then traverse the atmosphere of Mars and the variations in the received signal strength may provide information about the atmospheric density.

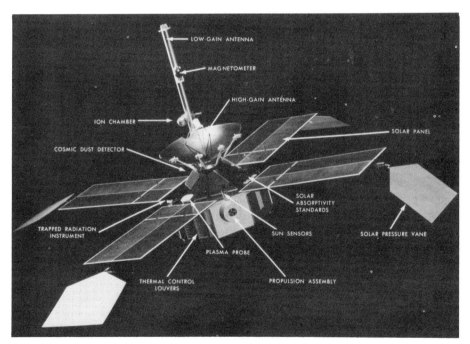

Fig. 10.21. The Mariner IV Mars spacecraft. (The television camera is in the base and does not show in the diagram.)

10.199. Among the novel features of the Mars Mariners are the first use of the star Canopus for attitude reference (§ 4.63) and the employment of a midcourse guidance rocket with restart capability to permit it to be fired twice. Because of the long trajectory to Mars, it may be necessary to make two midcourse corrections. The Mars Mariner must survive at least 9 months in space in order to fulfill its mission—about 8 months or so for the journey and some 3 weeks to return the television pictures. It will be recalled, for comparison, that the effective life of the Mariner II to Venus was a little over 3 months. The data obtained from the early Mariners missions to Mars will largely determine the subsequent program for exploring this interesting planet, possibly by the use of Voyager spacecraft (§ 10.80) which will be able to orbit Mars and land instruments on its surface. The first Voyager, in 1969, is is expected to be an atmospheric probe to investigate the conditions required for landing a spacecraft on the planet. Other missions, which will include a search for possible Martian life, will then follow at about 26-month intervals in 1971, etc.

10.200. Mariner III to Mars was injected into a satisfactory trajectory on November 5, 1964, but the spacecraft's protective shroud failed to jettison and interfered with the deployment of the solar panels. Consequently, the solar cells could not be charged and radio communication ceased due to power failure 9 hours after liftoff. On November 28, 1964, however, a completely successful launch of Mariner IV was achieved. A midcourse correction was made on December 5, 1964 and the resulting trajectory will bring the spacecraft to within 8700 kilometers (5400 miles) of Mars on July 14, 1965, after a journey of 228 days. A second midcourse correction was, therefore, deemed to be unnecessary. The lock of the star sensor on Canopus was lost several times during the early stages of the flight, probably as a result of flashes of sunlight reflected by micrometeoroids in space. After making an appropriate adjustment of sensitivity by radio command on December 17, 1964, the attitude control system, based on Canopus and the Sun, operated successfully.

10.201. The television camera on Mariner IV will take 21 pictures of the Martian surface and the taped data will be transmitted to Earth at the rate of 8 hours per picture. The transmission will be repeated at least twice, if possible, to improve the overall quality of the signals received. In addition to the camera, Mariner IV carried the following instruments: a magnetometer to study the interplanetary and Martian magnetic fields, a cosmic-ray telescope, a micrometeoroid detector, an ionization chamber to measure the charged-particle intensity in interplanetary space, a detector to determine if Mars has a trapped radiation belt similar to that of Earth, and a solar plasma probe.*

* At the time type for this book was being set (February–March 1965), Mariner IV was still on its way to Mars. With some minor exceptions, the instruments were operating properly and returning useful data.

Chapter 11

THE MAJOR PLANETS AND PLUTO

INTRODUCTION

11.1. The *major* (or *Jovian*) *planets*, Jupiter, Saturn, Uranus, and Neptune, differ from the terrestrial planets in the respects that they are, on the one hand, considerably larger and more massive and, on the other hand, much less dense (see Table **7.3**). The difference in density suggests a fundamental difference in composition, and this is certainly true of the atmospheres which are known to contain methane, ammonia, and hydrogen. These gases were probably present at one time in the atmospheres of the terrestrial planets, but they have either escaped or have been oxidized to carbon dioxide, nitrogen, and water, respectively.

THE PLANET JUPITER

ORBITAL AND PHYSICAL CHARACTERISTICS

11.2. Jupiter is the largest and most massive of the planets in the solar system; in fact, the mass of Jupiter is more than twice the sum of the masses of the other planets. The mean distance of Jupiter from the Sun is **778** million kilometers (**484** million miles) but, as a result of the orbital eccentricity of **0.0484**, the actual separation ranges from about **740** million kilometers (**460** million miles) at perihelion to **817** million kilometers (**508** million miles) at aphelion. The minimum possible distance from Earth to Jupiter is **591** million kilometers (**367** million miles) and the maximum is **967** million kilometers (**601** million miles); the corresponding values of the angular diameter of Jupiter as seen from Earth are about 50 and 31 sec of arc, respectively. Hence, from Earth, the planet Jupiter always appears larger than Mars and, in spite of its much greater distance, is sometimes larger than Venus. At its closest approach to Earth, however, the angular diameter of Venus is greater than that of Jupiter.

11.3. The sidereal period of revolution of Jupiter around the Sun, i.e., the Jovian year, is **11.86** terrestrial years and the synodic period as observed from Earth is only **399** terrestrial days. Consequently, oppositions (and conjunctions)

of Jupiter occur at intervals of just over 13 months. The average orbital velocity of the planet is 13.1 kilometers (8.12 miles) per second. The inclination of
Jupiter's orbital plane to the plane of the ecliptic is 1.03 deg.

11.4. The mass of Jupiter is known with fair accuracy from observations on
the orbits of its natural satellites (§ 11.50); it is 1.902×10^{27} kilograms or
1.902×10^{24} metric tons. Because the planet's surface is obscured by cloud
layers of indefinite thickness, measurements of the angular diameter are
subject to some uncertainty; hence, the radius of Jupiter is known approximately only. It will be seen in § 11.43 that the planet rotates very rapidly; as a
result of this and its low density, there is a considerable amount of polar flattening that is readily observed in a telescopic image (cf. Fig. 11.1). The equatorial radius of Jupiter is 71,400 kilometers (44,300 miles) and the polar radius
is 66,500 kilometers (41,500 miles); the optical ellipticity (or oblateness)
derived from these measurements is about 1/15. The dynamic ellipticity obtained from the orbital elements of the Jovian satellites is 1/15.34. In this case,
therefore, the optical and dynamic ellipticities are in general agreement. From
the mass and the average radius, the density of Jupiter is found to be 1.35 grams
per cubic centimeter.

11.5. The theoretical value of the gravitational acceleration at Jupiter's
surface, as determined from equation (2.4), is close to 26 meters (85 feet) per
second per second. As a result of the planet's rotation, however, there is a considerable centrifugal effect at the surface, especially near the equator, which
reduces the effective gravitational acceleration (§ 2.20); thus, at the equator
the acceleration is calculated to be about 24 meters (79 feet) per second per
second. The orbital and physical characteristics of Jupiter are summarized in
Table 11.1.

TABLE 11.1   ORBITAL AND PHYSICAL CHARACTERISTICS OF JUPITER

Distance, Jupiter to Sun (max)	817×10^6 kilometers	508×10^6 miles
Distance, Jupiter to Sun (min)	740×10^6 ``	460×10^6 ``
Distance, Jupiter to Earth (max)	967×10^6 ``	601×10^6 ``
Distance, Jupiter to Earth (min)	591×10^6 ``	367×10^6 ``
Angular diameter, from Earth (max)	50 sec	
Angular diameter, from Earth (min)	31 sec	
Eccentricity of orbit	0.0484	
Inclination of orbit to ecliptic	1.03 deg	
Inclination of equator to orbital plane	3.01 deg	
Orbital period (sidereal)	11.86 years	
Orbital period (synodic from Earth)	399 days	
Average orbital velocity	13.1 kilometers (8.12 miles) per second	
Radius (average)	69,000 kilometers (43,000 miles)	
Mass	1.902×10^{27} kilograms	
Average density	1.35 grams per cubic centimeter	
Gravitational acceleration at poles	26.0 meters (85.2 feet) per sec per sec	
Escape velocity	61 kilometers (38 miles) per second	
Rotation period	9 hours 55 minutes (approximately)	

TELESCOPIC APPEARANCE OF JUPITER

11.6. Jupiter is an exterior planet and consequently exhibits only full and gibbous phases (§ 7.34). Since the distance from the planet to Earth is always large—four to six times the Earth-Sun distance—only a small part of Jupiter's surface is in shadow even in the gibbous phase. The albedo of Jupiter is relatively high, namely, about 0.4, and its angular diameter is moderately large, as seen above; hence, the planet is a conspicuous object in the sky. In the telescope it has a distinctly flattened appearance and shows considerable darkening at the limb (Fig. 11.1).* The limb darkening is a result of the relatively dense at-

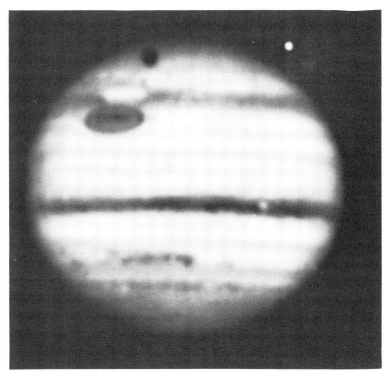

FIG. 11.1.   Jupiter photographed in blue light; the small bright object above the disc at the right is the satellite Europa, whose shadow is seen as a dark spot on the top left of the disc. (*Mount Wilson and Palomar Observatories*)

mosphere that surrounds the planet; light reaching Earth from the limb has to pass through a greater thickness of atmosphere than that from the main part of the disc.

11.7. Jupiter appears to be surrounded by a number of alternate light and

* As is usually the case in astronomical photographs, south is at the top of the picture.

dark bands of clouds running parallel to the equator. The light-colored, yellowish regions are called *zones*, and the dark-colored bands are referred to as *belts*. The latter may be dark gray or brown and occasionally they exhibit blue, dark green, or reddish regions. The main zones and belts have been named according to their location in the planet's northern and southern hemispheres. There is a broad equatorial zone, bounded by north and south tropical belts which are followed by north and south tropical zones, respectively. There are then a temperate belt, a temperate zone, another temperate belt, and finally a polar region in each hemisphere.

11.8. Although the various cloud bands have been identified in the foregoing manner, a close examination shows that they are by no means regular or constant in form. The intensities of the belts and zones change from time to time, but the north tropical belt is usually quite prominent (cf. Fig. 11.1). Irregular darker regions frequently appear in the zones, and light areas are observed in the belts. The temporary and variable nature of these features indicates that large-scale movements are taking place within the cloud system that surrounds the planet.

11.9. Most of the markings on Jupiter's surface change fairly quickly. But there are some of a more permanent nature lasting from periods of months to many years, although with varying intensity. One of the most striking is the Great Red Spot, lying mainly in the south tropical zone, as can be seen in Fig. 11.1. It is an oval area, extending some 45,000 kilometers (30,000 miles) in length and 13,000 kilometers (8000 miles) in width, to which attention was first called in 1831 by S. H. Schwabe (§ 6.111). There are indications, however, from a drawing made by Robert Hooke in England that it existed as far back as 1664, at least. The Red Spot has been observed regularly since the year 1878 when its intense coloration attracted the interest of astronomers. The visibility varies in an irregular manner; at some times the Red Spot is faintly pink but there have been periods of one, two, or three years when it had a conspicuous red color. Even when the Spot itself is barely visible, its location is apparent from the bay-like distortion, commonly referred to as the "hollow," in the south tropical zone extending into the adjacent south tropical belt (cf. Fig. 11.1). Some speculations concerning the nature of the Jovian cloud bands and the Great Red Spot will be reviewed in due course.

COMPOSITION OF JUPITER'S ATMOSPHERE

11.10. It has been known for many years that spectrograms of the light reflected from Jupiter show a number of dark lines. But the identity of the substances responsible for the lines was uncertain until the German-born astronomer Rupert Wildt suggested in 1931 that they were probably the gases ammonia and methane in the Jovian atmosphere. This was confirmed by Theodore Dunham in the United States by comparing a high-dispersion spectrogram of Jupiter with the known spectra of these gases. It was generally realized, however, that there must also be present considerable amounts of hydrogen and probably some helium.

11.11. At the temperatures existing on the planet, the average velocity of hydrogen molecules is about 1.3 kilometers per second and that of helium roughly 0.9 kilometer per second. The escape velocity, however, as given in Table 11.1, is 61 kilometers per second. It is evident, therefore, that very little of the gaseous hydrogen and helium associated with the planet at the time of its formation will have escaped. These gases are abundant in the Sun and were undoubtedly common constituents of the nebula from which the planets evolved. Hence, it appears probable that hydrogen and helium still exist in the atmosphere of Jupiter.

11.12. Evidence for the presence of gases of low molecular weight was reported in 1953 by W. A. Baum and A. D. Code in the United States as a result of studies made of the occulation of the star Sigma Arietis by Jupiter on November 20, 1952. From the rate of decrease in the brightness as the starlight passed through increasing depths of the Jovian atmosphere, it was possible to determine the scale height, as defined by equation (8.2). By taking the average temperature of the gases to be 86°K, the mean molecular weight was calculated to be 3.3. In 1962, E. J. Öpik (§ 10.54) presented arguments in favor of a temperature of 112°K, and from this the average molecular weight of the atmospheric gases was estimated to be 4.3 ± 0.5. The molecular weights of methane and ammonia are 16 and 17, respectively; it is evident, therefore, that there must be large proportions of a gas (or gases) of much lower molecular weight, e.g., hydrogen and helium, with molecular weights of 2 and 4, respectively.

11.13. Direct proof of the presence of molecular hydrogen lines in the spectrum of Jupiter was obtained in 1960 by C. C. Kiess and his collaborators in the United States. From measurements of the intensities of these lines, F. R. Zabriskie was able to make a rough estimate of the amount of hydrogen in the Jovian atmosphere. This value combined with the data obtained by G. P. Kuiper in 1952 from an analysis of the spectral lines of methane and ammonia, led E. J. Öpik (1962) to the somewhat unexpected conclusion that helium is the main constituent—about 97 molecular (or volume) percent—of the atmosphere of Jupiter. The calculated mean value of the molecular weight of the mixture of helium, hydrogen, methane, and ammonia, together with some neon and a small proportion of argon, was found to be 4.0, in fair agreement with the result derived from the occultation observations.

11.14. A further study of the spectrum of Jupiter by H. Spinrad and L. M. Trafton in 1963 has led to the following alternative approximate composition of the atmosphere, expressed in molecular percent: hydrogen 60, helium 36, neon 3, and methane about 1. The average calculated molecular weight is 3.4, compared with the occultation value of 3.3. Although the composition just given is different from that proposed by Öpik, they agree on one point: the atmosphere of Jupiter contains a large proportion of helium gas. The ratio of hydrogen to helium atoms is three to one at most and may be much smaller.

11.15. It will be seen shortly that the general consensus at the present time is that the main body of the planet consists chiefly of hydrogen molecules and helium, in the proportion of 14 atoms of hydrogen to one of helium (§ 11.28). There thus appears to be a marked difference in the ratios of hydrogen to helium in the atmosphere and the (solid) interior that requires explanation. Öpik has suggested that the differentiation resulted from the "snowing out" of hydrogen, i.e., deposition of solid from the gaseous state, at a temperature of about 4°K, in the early stages of the planet's development. At this temperature, hydrogen would solidify whereas helium would remain in the gaseous state. Hence, the body of the planet is chiefly hydrogen whereas the atmosphere contains a larger proportion of helium. According to R. M. Gallet (1962), however, if an appreciable amount of neon is assumed to be present, it is possible to account for the properties of Jupiter's atmosphere with a ratio of hydrogen to helium similar to that in the Sun. No special mechanism would then be required to explain the composition. A solution to this problem concerning the atmosphere will require further information; one approach would be to obtain ultraviolet spectra from beyond the terrestrial atmosphere. Such spectra should make it possible to determine the quantities of helium and neon, in particular.

ATMOSPHERIC TEMPERATURES ON JUPITER

11.16. The temperature of Jupiter, as derived by D. H. Menzel, *et al.*, in 1926 from radiometric determinations in the infrared wavelength range of 8 to 14 microns, is about 130°K, i.e., −143°C or −226°F. This is in general agreement with the maximum temperature of 145°K calculated from the amount of solar radiation absorbed by the planet behaving as a black body (cf. § 9.142). It is probable, however, that the infrared temperature is related only indirectly to the radiation temperature. The reason is that ammonia, an important constituent of the Jovian atmosphere, has a strong absorption band for radiation in the infrared region from 9 to 13 microns. Hence, any radiation emitted by Jupiter in this wavelength range, which corresponds closely to that used in the radiometric temperature determinations, must come from some region near the top of the ammonia atmosphere. Radiation in the given infrared range from lower depths would be absorbed by the ammonia layers above it. The measured temperature of 130°K is thus to be regarded as that at a high altitude in the Jovian atmosphere.

11.17. Ammonia is normally a gas, but it becomes liquid at 240°K (at terrestrial atmospheric pressure) and solidifies at 195°K (−78°C, −108°F) at normal pressures. It is evident, therefore, that most of the ammonia in the upper levels, at least, of Jupiter's atmosphere will be solid at the temperature of 130°K. Consequently, it has been concluded that there is a cloud layer on Jupiter composed of very small crystals of ammonia, just as cirrus clouds on

Earth consist of minute particles of ice. The methane and other constituents of the atmosphere remain in the gaseous form, as they require much lower temperatures for conversion into liquid or solid. According to the spectroscopic measurements, the ratio of gaseous ammonia to methane in the Jovian atmosphere is only about one to 20. But since most of the ammonia is present in the solid state, the intensities of the spectral lines provide no indication of the total quantity of ammonia. There is little doubt, however, that it is much greater than is implied by the proportion in the gas phase.

11.18. A curious observation on Jupiter was reported by B. C. Murray and R. L. Wildey (§ 9.156) in 1963. They found from the infrared radiation emission that the temperature in the shadow cast on the surface by the satellite Ganymede was more than $60°C$ ($108°$) higher than normal. A similar effect was observed in the shadow of the satellite Europa. Two possible explanations have been proposed for this unexpected result: first, that the satellite's shadow disturbs the Jovian atmosphere in some way permitting warmer layers to rise upward, and second, that the cutting off of sunlight by the satellite interferes with a photochemical reaction in Jupiter's high atmosphere, thereby making it more transparent to thermal radiation from below.

11.19. Brightness temperatures as determined from the intensity of the radio-frequency emission from Jupiter in the wavelenth region of about 3 centimeters are definitely higher than the infrared values. Moreover, there are indications that the brightness temperature increases to some extent with the wavelength in the same general frequency range (see Table 11.2). It appears probable, for this and other reasons, e.g., the greenhouse effect of ammonia due to its absorption in the infrared, that the temperature in the atmosphere of Jupiter increases with increasing depth below the ammonia cloud top. It has been suggested, therefore, that below the layer of cirrus-type ammonia clouds, perhaps some 50 kilometers (30 miles) thick, there is a region in which the temperature is such that liquid ammonia and vapor can exist. In this part of the atmosphere, ammonia rainstorms may occur, analogous to the water rainfall on Earth.

11.20. There is no spectral indication of water vapor in the Jovian atmosphere and, in view of the very low temperatures of the upper levels, none is to be expected. Nevertheless, it is quite possible that appreciable quantities of water, either as liquid or ice crystals, do exist on the planet. The hydrides of the three consecutive elements, carbon, nitrogen, and oxygen, are methane (CH_4), ammonia (NH_3), and water (H_2O), respectively; since the first two of these compounds have been detected in the atmosphere of Jupiter, it is not improbable that the third, water, is also present. Water vapor condenses and solidifies at higher temperature than does ammonia; hence, there may be a layer consisting of water (ice) clouds and water vapor, below the region in which ammonia clouds and rain predominate. It should be mentioned that, under all conditions expected in Jupiter's atmosphere, methane, hydrogen, helium, neon, and argon will remain in the gaseous form.

Jupiter's Colored Regions

11.21. Several ideas have been proposed to explain the colored regions, ranging from blue to dark brown, that can be seen in the bands surrounding Jupiter. Two of these theories, which appear to be of major interest, will be discussed here. In 1939, R. Wildt suggested that the colorations are produced by solutions of elemental sodium in solid or liquid ammonia; at low temperatures, such solutions are known to exhibit blue and bronze colors, not unlike those observed on Jupiter. There is certainly ample ammonia on the planet, but the sodium presents a difficulty. In view of the chemical reactivity of this substance in the elemental form, it is doubtful if much could exist in the Jovian atmosphere. It is true that the spectral lines of sodium atoms have been detected in Earth's atmospheric nightglow (§ 8.84), but the quantity of the element is probably small, much of the sodium being present undoubtedly as a compound. Such compounds of sodium in the atmosphere of Jupiter would not yield colored solutions in ammonia. Furthermore, it appears that most of the sodium in the terrestrial atmosphere is derived from the oceans, and it is unlikely that a similar source is available on Jupiter.

11.22. Another viewpoint is that of F. O. Rice (1955) who considered that the colors may be due to the presence of free radicals, such as NH, NH_2, $NHNH_2$, CH_2, CH_3, etc., formed by the action of solar ultraviolet radiations on the ammonia and methane in the Jovian atmosphere. Later, in 1959, H. A. Papazian indicated that charged particles, e.g., electrons, of high energy present in the radiation belt (or belts) surrounding the planet could also contribute to the formation of free radicals. Under normal conditions, free radicals, many of which are colored, are unstable and have very short lifetimes when prepared in the laboratory. But, at low temperatures, such as exist on Jupiter, they are often fairly stable solids. It has been pointed out by H. C. Urey (1959), however, that the free radicals could interact among themselves and with the ammonia and methane molecules to produce somewhat more stable colored compounds of carbon, nitrogen, and hydrogen, such as azomethane (CH_2N_2), diazomethane ($C_2H_6N_2$), tetrazine ($C_2H_2N_4$), and cuprene (C_2H_2)$_n$.

11.23. Until recent years, the only plausible explanation of the Great Red Spot was that it consisted of a large object, presumably solid, floating in a medium of liquid (G. W. Hough, 1905) or highly compressed gas (R. Wildt, 1939) of the same average density. In 1958, the British amateur astronomer R. M. Peek, who has made a detailed study of Jupiter, suggested that the Spot is a floating mass of solid helium. According to these theories, the Red Spot is not attached to its surroundings. Hence its rate of rotation can differ, as indeed it does, from that of the south tropical zone in which it is located. Furthermore, the variations in appearance of the Spot, described earlier, can be explained by the rising and falling of the solid body as a result of small changes in the density of the ambient medium. The main objection to the hypothesis that the Red Spot is a solid is that there is no reasonable material of which it could be composed. In the first place, it is very unlikely that the temperature is low enough for solid helium, hydrogen, or methane to form. Solid ammonia or water is possible, but a large mass would probably sink because of its higher density and not remain suspended in the surrounding medium.

11.24. An interpretation of the Great Red Spot in terms of hydrodynamics, that has considerable merit, was proposed by R. Hide in England in 1961. He showed that if an atmosphere were flowing over a large topographic discontinuity on the solid (rotating) surface of Jupiter, having a height of only a few miles and the lateral dimensions of the Red Spot, an essentially stationary column of gas, called a *Taylor column*,* would be established. This could extend upward from the surface of the discontinuity through the planet's cloud layer. The top of the column, as seen from Earth, is the region occupied by the Red Spot. In order to set up a gas column that will extend through the great depth of the Jovian atmosphere, the surface discontinuity must cover a very large area; there is evidently only one location on Jupiter where such a discontinuity exists.

11.25. According to C. Sagan (1962), the red color of the Spot may be due to the presence of organic molecules formed by the action of electrical discharges or solar radiation on the atmospheric gases (cf. § 10.166). These compounds are presumably carried to great depths and then circulated to the top of the atmosphere by convection in the Taylor column of gas. Variations in the color intensity, from almost invisibility to deep red, may be due to changes in the energy source, of unknown origin, that causes the convective motion in the column.

11.26. The hydrodynamic theory accounts for the apparent permanence of the Great Red Spot and for the fact that it is always seen in essentially the same latitude, within a degree or so. The rotational period of the Spot given in § 11.44 may be taken to be that of a surface discontinuity below the gas column and hence of the solid mantle of Jupiter. The variations that are observed occasionally are then attributed to changes in the rotational rate of the planet itself. As seen in § 9.21, Earth is known to exhibit irregular changes in the rate of rotation, i.e., in the length of the day.

THE INTERIOR OF JUPITER

11.27. For many years, the general opinion, based on the views of R. Wildt (1934), was that the interior of Jupiter consisted of a small central core of high density, made up of compressed silicates and iron, surrounded by a layer of water ice and perhaps solid methane and ammonia, which was enclosed by a mantle of solid hydrogen and helium. With the increased understanding of

---

* Named for the phenomenon described by G. I. Taylor, the British mathematician and authority on hydrodynamics.

the cosmic abundances of the elements and the realization that molecular hydrogen could be compressed to quite high densities, in which it acquires a metal-like structure, theories concerning the Jovian interior have undergone considerable change. The modern views stem largely from the independent work of W. C. DeMarcus in the United States, of W. H. Ramsey in England, and of V. G. Fesenkov and A. G. Massevich in Russia published during 1950.

11.28. The model developed by DeMarcus in 1958 is regarded at present as the most acceptable for the interior of Jupiter. It postulates that the planet consists of **78** percent by weight of hydrogen molecules and the remainder helium, i.e., **14** atoms of hydrogen to one of helium, with the local proportion of the latter decreasing from the center outward. By using the best available equations of state, i.e., pressure-density-temperature relationships, DeMarcus was able to account for the known mass, density, and gravitational field distribution (or shape) of Jupiter within a few percent. The calculations indicate that at a distance of about 0.8 times the planet's radius from the center, the pressure becomes so high, namely about 2×10^{12} dynes per square centimeter, i.e., roughly **2** million times the normal atmospheric pressure or 30 million pounds per square inch, that molecular hydrogen turns into a metallic form, the existence of which had been postulated earlier. Most of the internal volume (and mass) of Jupiter would thus appear to consist of this metallic, presumably solid, hydrogen, containing varying proportions of helium. The calculated pressure at the center of Jupiter is approximately 10^{14} dynes per square centimeter, i.e., **100** million atmospheres or 1.5 billion (1.5×10^9) pounds per square inch, and the density is nearly **31** grams per cubic centimeter.

11.29. It should be made clear that the model just described is used largely as a basis for calculation and is not meant to represent the exact condition of Jupiter's interior. It does, however, provide a picture indicating the general character of the internal structure of the planet in which local variations undoubtedly exist. For example, if the cosmic abundances of the elements are taken into consideration, it seems probable that small proportions of elements other than hydrogen and helium are present in the Jovian interior. The total mass of such elements might be of the same order as the mass of Earth, but this would represent only a very small fraction of Jupiter's mass. It is not known whether these heavier elements would be distributed more or less evenly throughout the planet or whether they might form a small core at its center.

11.30. It will be seen shortly that Jupiter has a strong magnetic field; a question has arisen, therefore, concerning the source of this field. One suggestion is that it is a primordial field which originated in the very early stage of Jupiter's history but has decayed very slowly because of the high electrical conductivity of the metallic molecular hydrogen. The objection to this theory is that the temperature in the interior, estimated to be a few thousand degrees, would be too high to permit the required extremely slow rate of decay of the field. An alternative possibility is the more conventional view that the temperature in the interior of the planet is high enough to permit the formation of a central core of liquid metallic molecular hydrogen,* in spite of the very high pressure. In a rotating planet such a liquid core, being a good conductor of electricity, would provide the necessary dynamo mechanism to produce a magnetic field, just as in Earth (cf. § 8.211).

11.31. Nothing is known about the nature of the surface of Jupiter, but it is probably a strange and complex system. Although much of the interior of the planet may be solid hydrogen (and helium), the pressures in the outer parts are too low and the temperatures probably too high to permit hydrogen to solidify. Hence, there may be some liquid hydrogen (and possibly methane) near the surface of Jupiter. Between this and the atmosphere, it is expected that there will be a transition layer containing solid or liquid ammonia (or both), methane, and possibly ice. The foregoing is admittedly speculation, since the temperature distributions in the atmosphere and interior of the planet are quite unknown.

RADIO EMISSION FROM JUPITER

11.32. Powerful bursts of radio noise from Jupiter were studied by C. A. Shain in Australia during 1950 and 1951, although their origin was not known at the time. It was not until 1955 that the source was identified by B. F. Burke and K. L. Franklin in the United States. This discovery and its subsequent confirmation attracted the attention of radio astronomers to Jupiter with the result that numerous studies have been made of the radio-frequency emissions from this planet. It has now been established that the radiations fall into three distinct categories corresponding to three wavelength (or frequency) regions; these are (a) the centimeter region, (b) the decimeter region, i.e., tens of centimeters, and (c) the decameter range, i.e., tens of meters.

11.33. The radio emission from Jupiter at wavelengths of a few centimeters or less is undoubtedly thermal in origin; brightness temperatures corresponding to the intensities at five wavelengths are given in Table 11.2. The values,

TABLE 11.2   BRIGHTNESS TEMPERATURES FROM RADIO EMISSION

Wavelength (cm)	Temperature (°K)
0.835	144 ± 23
3.03	171 ± 20
3.17	173 ± 20
3.36	189 ± 20
3.75	~ 200

especially in the 3-centimeter region, are somewhat higher than the infrared temperature (§ 11.19), but the differences can be accounted for if, as is not improbable, the radio-frequency emission at 3 centimeters is from regions below the tops of the ammonia clouds in the Jovian atmosphere. The lower tempera-

---

* This peculiar substance is not known on Earth, but theoretical considerations indicate that it might be formed under the conditions existing in the Jovian interior.

ture derived from the 0.85-centimeter radiation has been ascribed to the level of the visible cloud cover.

11.34. The apparent brightness temperature estimated from the emission at a wavelength of 10.3 centimeters is about 650°K; at 21 centimeters it is close to 3000°K and at 31 centimeters roughly 5500°K. It is highly unlikely that these represent actual temperatures. The radiation from Jupiter in the *decimeter wavelength region,* which has been studied in the range from 10 to 68 centimeters, is thus mainly nonthermal in character. Like the thermal radiation at the shorter wavelength, however, it is emitted continuously from the planet although the intensity does exhibit long-term variations.

11.35. The most satisfactory explanation of the decimeter radiation (frequency range roughly 500 to 3000 megacycles per second), proposed by G. B. Field in the United States in 1959, is that it is emitted by electrons of high energy spiraling around the lines of force of the Jovian magnetic field. The electrons responsible for the emission of the decimeter radiation are those trapped in a radiation belt (or belts) similar to the outer Van Allen zone in Earth's magnetic field. As seen in § 8.331, similar (synchrotron) radiation has been detected from electrons in the terrestrial radiation belt.

11.36. The decimeter radiation from Jupiter may be either synchrotron or cyclotron radiation, according as the spiraling electrons are either relativistic or nonrelativistic, i.e., with energies greater or less than 0.5 million electron volts, respectively (§ 6.181, footnote). Basically, the mechanisms of formation of synchrotron and cyclotron radiations are the same; but there are some differences in the radiation characteristics. The effective mass of a relativistic electron increases with its energy whereas for a nonrelativistic electron the mass remains essentially constant regardless of its energy.

11.37. Calculations indicate that, if the Jovian decimeter radiation were cyclotron radiation, the strength of the magnetic field of Jupiter at the poles should be over 1000 gauss, compared with about 0.7 gauss for the terrestrial magnetic field. On the other hand, the observations could be accounted for in terms of synchrotron radiation by means of a field of more reasonable strength, namely, about 5 gauss, but the relativistic electron density would need to be several times greater than in Earth's Van Allen belt. A comparison between the Jovian and terrestrial radiation belts, however, may not be altogether justified. The energy distribution of the relativistic electrons required to account for Jupiter's radio spectrum does not correspond with that known to exist in Earth's radiation belt. Although there does not appear to be any decisive evidence at present, there is a general inclination in favor of the view that the decimeter radiation from Jupiter is synchrotron radiation, i.e., from relativistic electrons with energies in the range of 5 to 10 million electron volts.

11.38. According to theory, both synchrotron and cyclotron radiations should exhibit linear (plane) polarization (cf. § 6.135, footnote). Measurements by V. Radhakrishnan and J. A. Roberts made in the United States in

1960 have shown that the radio-frequency emission from Jupiter at a wavelength of 31 centimeters is polarized in a plane parallel to the Jovian equator. Later observations by others have established that other radiations in the decimeter wavelength region exhibit the same property. The main emission appears to be from the equatorial region at a distance of about three planet radii from Jupiter. These results are to be expected if the decimeter radiation originates from electrons in a radiation belt (or belts) produced by a dipole magnetic field, similar to that of Earth. The direction of the plane of polarization indicates that the magnetic axis is inclined at an angle of about 9 deg to the rotational axis of the planet.

11.39. From an analysis of the 21-centimeter radiation, H. S. Roberts (1962) has concluded that there are two types of decimeter radiation: one is strongly polarized and is related to the activity of the Sun, whereas the other is apparently not polarized and is much less dependent on the solar activity. The spatial extent of the nonpolarized component is quite large, although somewhat less than that of the polarized type. A possible explanation of these observations is that Jupiter has two radiation belts containing high-energy electrons; the polarized radiation is emitted by electrons in the outer of these two belts in which the electron density and energy would be more susceptible to the activity of the Sun. Electrons in the inner belt would then be responsible for the apparently nonpolarized decimeter radiation; there are reasons for expecting that the shapes of the spiral paths of the electrons in this belt would be such as to make the polarization difficult to detect.

11.40. The third type of radio-frequency emission from Jupiter, which was actually the first nonthermal radiation to be discovered, is in the *decameter range*, i.e., at wavelengths in the region of about 10 to 30 meters and frequencies of 30 to 10 megacycles.* The emission is of the noise-storm type; that is to say, it is not continuous but occurs in bursts. These bursts, with a duration of a second or so, are generally emitted in groups lasting for 5 or 10 minutes and continuing intermittently over a period of a few hours. The radiation is circularly polarized and exhibits very complex intensity variations, some of which are probably due to Earth's ionosphere or the interplanetary medium.

11.41. The probability of the occurrence of the decameter radiation from Jupiter is inversely related to the sunspot number (§ 6.111); that is to say, the probability of observing the radiation is high when the sunspot number is low. On the other hand, there are indications that, occasionally but not always, there is a strong emission from Jupiter a few days after a strong solar flare.

---

* Radio waves with wavelengths greater than about 30 meters (frequencies less than about 10 megacycles per second) are unable to penetrate Earth's ionosphere (§ 8.158). To overcome this limitation in the study of radio emissions from Jupiter, the Sun, etc., two Radio Astronomy Explorer satellites are being planned. Each will carry two V-shaped antennas, 750 feet long, mounted opposite one another to form an X. The spacecraft orbit will be roughly circular at an altitude of about 6000 kilometers (3700 miles), i.e., well above the ionosphere.

Another property of the decameter radiation is a definite correlation of the Jovian longitude at which the emission is strongest with the rotation of the planet. This matter will be considered further in the next section.

11.42. There is as yet no satisfactory explanation of Jupiter's decameter radiation. The emission has many of the characteristics associated with lightning on Earth, but the energy from Jupiter is on the order of a billion times greater. There is some evidence that the radiation is of the cyclotron type originating high in the Jovian atmosphere. The connection with the rotation of Jupiter would imply that the emission is stimulated by, although it does not arise from, a fairly permanent, localized distribution of some kind in the planet's interior. This distribution is evidently associated with the magnetic field strength. The relationship between the decameter emission and sunspots has been attributed to the action of Earth's ionosphere; when the Sun is active, the increased ionization in the terrestrial atmosphere prevents the radio waves from Jupiter from reaching Earth. The effect of solar flares, however, is more difficult to understand. Another major problem is to account for the source of the large amounts of energy involved in the radio emission.

THE ROTATION OF JUPITER

11.43. A discussion of the rotation of Jupiter has been deliberately delayed until after the description of the decameter-wavelength radio emission from the planet since this has a distinct bearing on the subject. One way in which the rotation has been studied is by observing some of the semipermanent features of the surface, in the manner that sunspots have been used to study the rotation of the Sun (§ 6.109). The rotational period of Jupiter obtained in this manner varies with latitude, as is to be expected if the markings being observed are part of a nonrigid cloud mass rather than of a solid surface. For reference purposes, two rotational systems have been defined; for System I, extending from 10°N to 10°S of the Jovian equator, the rotational period is taken to be 9 hours 50 minutes 30.003 seconds, and for System II, lying outside this region, the standard rotational period is 9 hours 55 minutes 40.632 seconds. The times given are not intended to represent precise rotational periods, but they are used as reference values for expressing the motion, in degrees of longitude, of spots, etc., lying within the respective systems.

11.44. Individual features on Jupiter frequently have farily constant rotational periods that are different from the period of their apparent environment. The mean period of rotation of the Great Red Spot, for example, has been 9 hours 55 minutes 43 seconds for several years, although there have been minor irregular variations of a second or two from this average. In 1962, however, B. A. Smith and C. W. Tombaugh noted an increase of 2.5 seconds in the rotational period; around November there was a slight decrease in the period leaving a net increase of about 1.4 seconds over the value given above. This matter will be referred to again shortly. The large South Tropical Disturbance, first detected at a latitude close to the Red Spot, but not seen since 1941, had a rotational period some 20 seconds shorter than the Spot. As a result, the Disturbance overtook the Red Spot at intervals of about two years or so. At these times, there was evidence of a marked interaction between the two conspicuous features of the Jovian atmosphere.

11.45. An interesting aspect of the decameter radiation is that its emission, which apparently occurs in sharply focused cones originating from specific locations on (or near) Jupiter, has been definitely correlated with the rotation of the planet. From observations extending back to 1951, before the origin of the radiation was known, until some time in 1960, a well-defined rotational period, called System III, of 9 hours 55 minutes 29.37 seconds was associated with the decameter radio emission. Systematic variations from this period were less than 0.5 second and irregular changes were no more than a second or two. Around 1960, however, A. G. Smith and T. D. Carr began to notice a systematic drift in the longitude of the radio source with respect to System III. The drift rate, which was fairly constant, indicated that the rotational period had increased by about 1.3 seconds over the previous System III value. A similar result was obtained by J. N. Douglas and H. J. Smith and is in agreement with the increase in the rotational rate of the Red Spot.

11.46. It was thought at one time that the System III rotational period of Jupiter was a measure of the rate of rotation of the main (solid) body of the planet. In view of the interpretation of the Great Red Spot given in § 11.24, it would appear that its rotational period is actually that of the solid mantle. Consequently, it has been suggested that the shorter System III period applies to the liquid core in which the magnetic field is generated. In other words, it appears from this point of view that the liquid interior of Jupiter rotates faster than the solid mantle. There is evidently a coupling of some kind, however, between the liquid core and the solid mantle. This is indicated by the almost equal overall changes in the rotational periods of System III and of the Great Red Spot that occurred between 1961 and 1963; they were presumably both due to a disturbance in the interior of the planet.

11.47. In spite of the differences among the various rotating systems and the changes that may occur from time to time, it is clear that the rotational period of Jupiter is close to 9 hours 55 minutes, the shortest period of rotation of any member of the solar system.* The rate of rotation of a point on the Jovian equator is about 12.6 kilometers (7.8 miles) per second, compared with 0.465 kilometer (0.29 mile) per second for Earth. The rapid rotation of Jupiter undoubtedly accounts for the marked band formation of the clouds that surround the planet. The inclination of the axis of rotation to the line perpendicular to the orbital plane, i.e., the inclination of the Jovian equatorial plane to the orbital plane, is only 3.01 deg; this is smaller than for any other planet, apart from Pluto for which the inclination is not known.

* The Martian satellite Phobos (§ 10.159) may be an exception.

11.48. A peculiar phenomenon related to the rotation of Jupiter was first noted by H. Spinrad in 1962. If the slit of a spectrograph is aligned to observe the equator of the planet, the spectral lines are found to be inclined. The reason is that, in Jupiter's rotation, one limb of the planet approaches Earth while the other recedes (cf. § 6.109). The Doppler effect causes the spectral lines from the approaching limb to be shifted to shorter wavelengths, whereas the lines from the receding limb are shifted to longer wavelengths. Consequently, the lines of the spectrum taken across the planet in a direction at right angles to its axis of rotation will be tilted. There are two types of absorption lines in the spectrum of Jupiter: one set represents reflected radiation from the Sun and the other is due to the gases in the Jovian atmosphere. The reflected solar radiation suffers two Doppler shifts, the first resulting from the rotation of Jupiter with reference to the Sun and the second from the rotation with reference to Earth. The Jovian lines, however, undergo only one Doppler shift in frequency. Consequently, the slopes of the lines from the gases in Jupiter's atmosphere should be 50 percent of the slope of the solar lines.

11.49. An examination by Spinrad of spectra taken along the equator of Jupiter showed that the foregoing expectation was not always realized. In 1934, for example, the tilt of the lines of ammonia near 6450 Å wavelength was only 25 percent and in 1961 they were 34 percent, instead of 50 percent of the slope of the solar lines. In 1962, on the other hand, the expected 50 percent tilt was observed for the lines of both ammonia and methane in Jupiter's atmosphere. The Doppler shift of the solar lines was found to correspond to the rotational velocity of the cloud System I. Consequently, Spinrad concluded that at certain times the ammonia (and probably the methane) over Jupiter's equator rotates about 4 to 6 kilometers per second more slowly than the cloud layer.

The Satellites of Jupiter

11.50. Jupiter is known to have 12 natural satellites (or moons) falling into three groups. The five members of the first group have almost circular orbits, i.e., the eccentricities are small (less than 0.0075), and the orbital planes are inclined less than 0.5 deg to the equatorial plane of the parent planet. Such bodies, revolving in a direct (counterclockwise) manner in essentially circular orbits close to the equatorial plane of their primary, are called *regular satellites*. The five regular satellites of Jupiter have orbital radii from 182,000 kilometers (113,000 miles) to 1.88 million kilometers (1.17 million miles) and the sidereal periods range from almost 12 hours to 16 days 16.5 hours.

11.51. The satellite nearest to Jupiter, designated J V because it was the fifth to be discovered, is by far the smallest of the group, its estimated radius being about 120 kilometers (75 miles). But the other four regular satellites have radii that are about the same as or somewhat larger than the radius of the Moon. These four bodies were observed by Galileo in 1609 and 1610, and so they are called the *Galilean Satellites*. In addition to being identified by the symbols, J I, J II, J III, and J IV, in order of their increasing distance from Jupiter, they are named Io, Europa, Ganymede, and Callisto, respectively. Some of the orbital and approximate physical characteristics of the Galilean satellites in order of their increasing distance from the primary body are given in Table 11.3. It should be noted that the values of the mean orbital radius (or semi-major axis) are given in *thousands* of kilometers or miles.

TABLE 11.3   CHARACTERSITIC PROPERTIES OF THE GALILEAN SATELLITES

	J V	J I	J II	J III	J IV
Mean orbital radius (10^3 kilometers)	182	422	671	1070	1880
Mean orbital radius (10^3 miles)	113	262	417	664	1170
Sidereal period (days)	0.498	1.77	3.55	7.16	16.69
Mass (Moon = 1)	—	0.98	0.64	2.1	1.3
Radius (kilometers)	~120	1600	1500	2500	2200
Radius (miles)	~75	1000	950	1500	1350
Average density (gram/cu cm)	—	4.0	3.8	2.4	2.1
Escape velocity (kilometers/sec)	—	2.5	2.1	2.9	2.4

11.52. The masses of the Galilean satellites are seen to be of the same order as the mass of the Moon. The densities decrease steadily from J I through J IV; all are significantly higher than that of the parent planet, and in fact J I and J II have higher densities than the Moon. There is, however, no information available concerning the composition of the satellites. As a result of their low surface temperature of about 150°K, the average velocity of gas molecules will also be low. In view of the relatively high values of the escape velocities (Table 11.3), it is possible that Ganymede (J III), at least, might have an atmosphere, although none has yet been detected. Dark markings similar to lunar maria have been observed on all four Galilean satellites, but it is not known whether they have craters on their surfaces. From observations of the markings, it has been established that these satellites exhibit captured (or trapped) rotation, i.e., the rotational period is the same as the sidereal period of revolution. Since it is so close to the parent planet, it is reasonably certain that the satellite J V behaves in the same manner.

11.53. The visual albedos of the satellites J I and J II are surprisingly high, 0.4 or possibly more, and that of J III is at least 0.2. The ability to perceive definite markings on the surfaces of these satellites shows that they are not surrounded by clouds. Hence, the high albedos are attributed to the presence of light-colored deposits of hoar-frost type crystals of water or ammonia. The albedo of J IV is small, perhaps about the same as that of the Moon.

11.54. Because the orbital planes of the Galilean satellites are so close to the equatorial plane of Jupiter, they are frequently eclipsed by the shadow of the planet caused by the Sun. In addition, they are often seen in transit across the front of the Jovian disc or being occulted when moving behind it. Occasionally one of the inner satellites, J I or J II (Io or Europa), is eclipsed by the shadow of J III (Ganymede), the largest member of the group.

11.55. From observations of the Galilean satellites, the Danish astronomer Olaus Rømer was able in 1676, while working in France, to make the first determination of the velocity of light. By utilizing his measurements of the periods of revolution, Rømer calculated the times at which the satellites should be eclipsed as a result of entering the shadow of the parent planet. He found that the actual eclipses occurred sooner than predicted when Jupiter was near opposition, i.e., closest to Earth, but later when the planet was close to conjunction, i.e., farthest from Earth. Rømer explained the discrepancy in terms of the finite velocity of light, contrary to the view propounded by Galileo that light had an infinite velocity and was detected at the precise instant it left a distant object. If the velocity of light has a finite value, a shorter time would be required for light from Jupiter's satellites to reach Earth when the planet is in opposition than in conjunction. On this basis, Rømer obtained a value for the velocity of light in general agreement with that now accepted. A large part of the error was due to the existing uncertainties in the distances from Earth to Jupiter.

11.56. The second group of Jupiter's satellites contains three members, namely, J VI, J VII, and J X, in order of increasing distance; the Roman numerals represent the order of their discovery. These are definitely *irregular satellites* because they have fairly large eccentricities, from 0.13 to nearly 0.21, and the orbital planes are inclined to the equatorial plane of Jupiter by angles ranging from 24.8 to 29.0 deg. The semi-major axes of the orbits are almost the same for the three satellites, 11.5, 11.7, and 11.9 million kilometers, respectively, i.e., 7.12, 7.29, and 7.45 million miles. The sidereal periods of revolution are thus also approximately equal, 250.6, 259.6, and 263.5 days, respectively. Because of their small size, probably less than 80 kilometers (50 miles) in radius, essentially all that is known about this group of satellites is their orbital characteristics. In view of the striking similarity in these quantities, it appears that the three satellites were produced by the disruption of a single body that was captured by the parent planet.

11.57. Finally, there is a group of four irregular satellites, J XII, J XI, J VIII, and J IX, with orbital elements quite different from those of the second group. There is a general resemblance in the respect that the differences among the individual members are small, again indicating formation from a single capture by Jupiter. The ecentricities, angles of inclination, semi-major axes, and sidereal periods are variable, largely as the result of perturbations caused by the Sun's gravitational field. Average values for the individual eccentricities range from about 0.17 to 0.38, and for the angles of inclination of the orbits from 154 to 164 deg. The semi-major axes are close to 23 million kilometers (14 million miles) and the sidereal periods are from about 630 to 758 days. The most striking fact about this outermost group of satellites is that the members all revolve in a retrograde (clockwise) direction. It has been argued that were it not for the retrograde motion, the highly irregular orbits would have been unstable.

Studies of Jupiter from Space

11.58. It will be some years before a space probe can be sent to Jupiter and still longer before it is possible to launch a spacecraft capable of orbiting this planet. There is little doubt, however, that these feats will be achieved in the future. The earliest studies of Jupiter from space will probably include measurements of its magnetic field, mapping of the spatial and energy distribution of the charged particles trapped in its radiation belts, and spectroscopic observations in the ultraviolet and infrared. The latter should provide more information than is presently available concerning the composition of the Jovian atmosphere.

11.59. Although the problem is by no means simple, procedures will be developed for determining the temperature and pressure distribution in the atmosphere of the planet. To avoid the disturbing effect of the nonthermal decimeter-wavelength radiation, it may be necessary to make observations below the radiation belts in order to measure the thermal emission in this region. It would be very desirable to penetrate below the ammonia clouds with instruments and to land others on the surface of Jupiter. But the difficulties are very great, especially in view of the conditions that may be experienced, including very low temperatures, high pressures, a strong gravitational field, and perhaps rain consisting of liquid ammonia. Instruments that will operate and transmit information in these circumstances will not be easy to design and construct.

11.60. The Galilean satellites of Jupiter are of interest in their own rights and also as bases for the study of the parent planet. Except for their lower average temperatures, the properties of these satellites are not very greatly different from those of the Moon. By utilizing experience gained from landing instruments on the latter body, it will no doubt be possible to place instruments advantageously on Jupiter's satellites.

THE PLANET SATURN

Orbital and Physical Characteristics

11.61. Apart from the unique system of rings that surrounds the body of the planet, Saturn resembles Jupiter in several respects. Saturn is slightly the smaller of the two, but it is considerably less massive as a result of its lower density; nevertheless, Saturn is the second largest planet in mass as well as in size. The density of about 0.72 gram per cubic centimeter is lower than that of any other planet or known satellite in the solar system. Combination of the large radius and small density leads to a gravitational force on the surface that is not very different from that on Earth.

11.62. The orbital and other characteristics of Saturn are summarized in Table 11.4. The value of the gravitational acceleration quoted was calculated

TABLE 11.4   ORBITAL AND PHYSICAL CHARACTERISTICS OF SATURN

Distance, Saturn to Sun (max)	1460×10^6 kilometers	905×10^6 miles
Distance, Saturn to Sun (min)	1420×10^6 "	885×10^6 "
Distance, Saturn to Earth (max)	1600×10^6 "	998×10^6 "
Distance, Saturn to Earth (min)	1280×10^6 "	792×10^6 "
Angular diameter, from Earth (max)	19 sec	
Angular diameter, from Earth (min)	14 sec	
Eccentricity of orbit	0.0557	
Inclination of orbit to ecliptic	2.50 deg	
Inclination of equator to orbital plane	26.74 deg	
Orbital period (sidereal)	29.46 years	
Orbital period (synodic from Earth)	378 days	
Average orbital velocity	9.65 kilometers (6.0 miles) per second	
Radius (average)	57,500 kilometers (35,500 miles)	
Mass	5.69×10^{26} kilograms	
Average density	0.72 gram per cubic centimeter	
Gravitational acceleration at poles	11.5 meters (37.8 feet) per sec per sec	
Escape velocity	37 kilometers (23 miles) per second	
Rotation period	10 hours 30 minutes (approximately)	

from the mass and radius of the planet in the usual manner. As a result of the short rotational period of roughly $10\frac{1}{2}$ hours, the velocity of rotation at the equator is high and this reduces the gravitational acceleration to about **9.7** meters (**32** feet) per second per second, almost the same as at the terrestrial equator. Another consequence of the rapid rotation—and low density—is that Saturn exhibits a greater polar flattening than any other planet. The equatorial radius is about **60,000** kilometers (**37,000** miles) whereas the polar radius is **54,500** kilometers (**34,000** miles); the optical ellipticity (or oblateness) is thus approximately 1/9.

Telescopic Appearance of Saturn

11.63. The general appearance of the body of Saturn is similar to that of Jupiter and its albedo is about the same. It is seen in the telescope as a flattened ball with a number of bands parallel to the equator (Fig. 11.2). The equatorial zone in Saturn is bright, but the other zones and belts are much less distinct than on Jupiter. Photographs in the violet and ultraviolet parts of the spectrum show more details of the band structure than are visible in red light. The intensities of the belts are variable and so also, to some extent, are their locations and dimensions in latitude. From time to time there are signs of unusual activity in the atmosphere (or cloud layer) of the planet, and occasionally bright spots are observed, especially in the equatorial zone. On the whole, however, the activity appears to be much less on Saturn than on Jupiter. Although there are some features of moderate lifetime, there is nothing of a permanent (or semipermanent) nature similar to Jupiter's Great Red Spot.

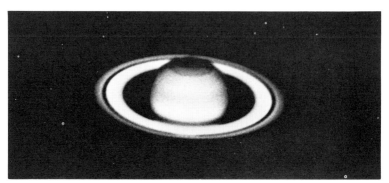

FIG. 11.2. Saturn in 1943 when the rings were at their widest as seen from Earth. (*Lick Observatory*)

11.64. The rotational periods of various regions of the planet, as determined from the few markings that persist for an appreciable time, vary with latitude even more than is the case for Jupiter. In the equatorial region, the rotational period is 10 hours 14 minutes, increasing to 10 hours 38 minutes at intermediate latitudes; the period may be still longer near the poles. The true period of rotation of Saturn is not known and there are no indications at present from radio emissions. The axis of rotation is inclined at the relatively large angle of 26.74 deg to the line perpendicular to the orbital plane. As a result, the appearance of the rings as seen from Earth varies throughout Saturn's orbital period around the Sun; this matter is considered more fully in § 11.71.

CONSTITUTION OF SATURN

11.65. The spectrum of Saturn indicates the presence of both gaseous methane and ammonia, but the proportion of the former is greater and of the latter less than on Jupiter. The smaller amount of ammonia on Saturn is probably the result of the lower atmospheric temperature, leading to a lower pressure of ammonia gas in equilibrium with the solid particles that constitute the cirrus-like clouds. Hydrogen and helium have not been detected spectroscopically, but it is reasonable to believe that they are present in considerable quantities in the Saturnian atmosphere; there may also be small proportions of neon and argon. Determination of the average molecular weight must await the occurrence of a suitable occultation.

11.66. The measured infrared radiometer temperature of Saturn, which is presumably that of the top of the ammonia clouds, is about $125°K$, i.e., $-148°C$ or $-234°F$. The black-body brightness temperature derived from the intensity of the microwave radiation at a wavelength of 3.4 centimeters is $106 \pm 21°K$; this radiation may originate from some depth in the atmosphere. It is of interest in this connection that the maximum temperature calculated from the solar radiation absorbed is $107°K$ and the average is $76°K$, i.e., $-197°C$ or $-323°F$. At such low temperatures methane can solidify, and it is possible that there may be methane clouds of the cirrus type below the ammonia clouds.

11.67. A hydrogen-helium model for the interior of Saturn has been constructed by DeMarcus along the lines described for Jupiter. The lower average density of Saturn, however, requires a smaller proportion of molecular hydrogen, namely 63 weight percent, i.e., 11 hydrogen atoms to one helium atom. As with Jupiter, the model postulates a decrease in the proportion of helium from the center outward. The transition to metallic (solid) molecular hydrogen occurs about half way along the radius, where the necessary pressure given in § 11.28 is attained. At the center, the calculated density is 15.6 grams per cubic centimeter and the pressure, which is less than in Jupiter as a result of the smaller mass, is 55×10^{12} dynes per square centimeter, i.e., roughly 55 million atmospheres or 800 million pounds per square inch. It is very likely that relatively small amounts of heavier elements are present in the interior of Saturn but, as for Jupiter, the quantities and distribution are not known.

11.68. There are indications that Saturn emits synchrotron radiation in the decimeter wavelength region arising from relativistic electrons trapped in a radiation belt (or belts) surrounding the planet. This implies that Saturn, not unexpectedly, has a magnetic field; hence, the rotating planet may have a liquid central core in which the field is generated by a dynamo mechanism. A strange observation is that the plane of polarization of the radiation is perpendicular to Saturn's equator instead of parallel to it, as is the case for Jupiter. The result might be interpreted as meaning, somewhat surprisingly, that the magnetic axis of the planet is at right angles to its axis of rotation. But it appears that there may be another explanation for the observation. For example, the rings of Saturn, lying in the planet's equatorial plane, may provide a means for removing electrons which spend most of their time in the equatorial region of the radiation belt (or belts). Most of the synchrotron radiation received on Earth will then have originated from electrons trapped at higher latitudes, where the direction of the magnetic field lines is almost perpendicular to that in the equatorial regions (cf. Fig. 8.22).

Saturn's Rings

11.69. The circular ring system of Saturn is the outstanding feature of the planet (cf. Fig. 11.2). The presence of appendages to the main planet was recognized by Galileo, but it was the Dutch physicist Christiaan Huygens who identified in 1659 a ring formation surrounding but separate from the body of Saturn. In 1675, the Italian-born astronomer G. D. Cassini, then in France, detected a break which indicated that there were two rings, and in 1850

W. Bond in the United States and W. R. Dawes in England observed a third, dark interior ring. The three rings are designated by the letters A, B, and C, in order of decreasing radius. Ring B is sometimes called the "bright ring" because it is the brightest, often brighter than the equatorial zone of the planet; on the other hand, ring C is often referred to as the "crape (or crepe) ring" on account of its dark appearance.

11.70. The A ring has an outer diameter of about 274,000 kilometers (170,000 miles) and a width of roughly 16,000 kilometers (10,000 miles). It is separated from ring B by a gap of some 4000 kilometers (2500 miles) called the *Cassini division* from the name of its discoverer. The outer diameter of ring B is thus approximately 234,000 kilometers (145,000 miles) and its width is 26,600 kilometers (16,500 miles). After a gap of several hundred kilometers, there is ring C with an outer diameter of roughly 179,000 kilometers (110,000 miles); this ring has a width of about 21,000 kilometers (13,000 miles), so that it extends to within some 13,000 kilometers (8000 miles) of the main body of the planet. In ring A there is an apparent gap, called the *Encke division*, between an outer darker zone and an inner brighter one; it is, however, probably not a real break but merely a region of minimum brightness.

11.71. Because the equatorial plane is inclined at a large angle to its orbital plane, and to the plane of the ecliptic, the planet appears to undergo a north-south rocking motion or latitudinal libration (cf. § 9.28), as seen from Earth. Consequently, at one solstice (§ 10.111, footnote), the northern part of the planet is tilted toward the Sun (and Earth), whereas half a sidereal period later, at the other solstice, the southern portion is directed toward the Sun (and Earth). Since Saturn's rings lie in the equatorial plane, a terrestrial observer will have a maximum view of the northern surface of the rings near the time of one solstice and then, some 15 years later, the southern surface will be seen at maximum. About halfway between the solstices, close to the Saturnian equinox, the rings will be midway between their extreme positions (Fig. 11.3). From Earth, they will then be seen edgeways and will appear, at best, as a thin dark line crossing the planet's disc. From measurements made at such times, it is found that the thickness of the rings is not more than about 16 or 19 kilometers (10 or 12 miles) and may be much less.

11.72. The mass of the rings is not known. But it is possible to assess an upper limit based on the absence of any perturbations in the orbits of Saturn's inner satellites (§ 11.80) that could be ascribed to the rings. This upper limit is somewhat less than the mass of the Moon and thus represents a very small fraction of the mass of the body of the planet.

11.73. The rings of Saturn are made up of enormous numbers of small objects which revolve together around the planet. In 1859, J. C. Maxwell (§ 6.47) showed that, although a solid or liquid ring would be unstable, a ring of small mass—relative to the planet—made up of many independent particles should be stable. It is perhaps significant that the outer radius of the rings is roughly

2.3 times the radius of Saturn and so is less than the Roche limit (§ 9.193) of **2.44** radii within which a satellite of the same density as the primary body would be expected to disintegrate. The orbital radius of the closest known satellite to Saturn is **3.1** times the radius of the planet, and hence is outside the Roche limit.

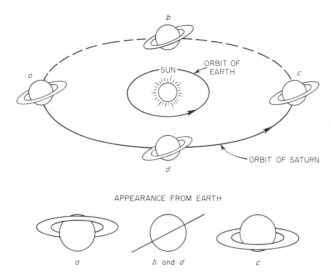

FIG. 11.3.   Orientation and appearance of Saturn during an orbit about the Sun

11.74. There are several observations that confirm the particulate, rather than continuous, nature of the rings. For example, rings A and C exhibit some transparency; thus, the body of the planet can be seen through them, as also can the light from stars. Furthermore, the satellites of Saturn are not completely eclipsed when they pass into the shadow of the rings.

11.75. Additional evidence is provided by the periods of revolution of different parts of the rings as derived from measurements of the Doppler shift of the spectral lines (§ 6.109). If the rings were solid, the period of revolution would be the same at both outer and inner radii. The spectroscopic results, however, show that the inner parts of the rings have shorter periods than do the outer parts, in accordance with expectation for individual bodies (or satellites) revolving about a central mass. Thus, by using the value of K in equation (2.12) that is appropriate to Saturn, the orbital period (or period of revolution) of a satellite at a radius equal to that of the outer edge of ring A is calculated to be about 14 hours, in general agreement with the value derived from the Doppler shift measurements. At the inner edge of ring A, i.e., at the Cassini division, the period of revolution is 11.3 hours.

11.76. Incidentally, the revolution period at the radius of the Cassini division is a simple fraction, namely, $\frac{1}{2}$, $\frac{1}{3}$, and $\frac{1}{4}$, respectively, of the orbital periods of

Saturn's first three satellites. It would appear, therefore, that the gap between rings A and B results from the resonant perturbation caused by these satellites in a manner similar to that in which Jupiter has produced the Kirkwood gaps in the asteroidal system (§ 7.54). The period of revolution at the radius of the space between rings B and C is equal to one third the period of Saturn's first satellite and hence this may also be a resonance gap.

11.77. The only information concerning the composition of the particles in the rings is based on the observation by G. P. Kuiper (1952) that the infrared spectrum is similar to the reflection spectrum of hoar frost. This does not exclude the possibility that similar particles of solid ammonia or of other substances are present.

11.78. There is no explanation for the differences in appearance of the rings; the faint inner ring C is evidently the most tenuous and the outer ring is somewhat more dense although it is by no means uniform in particle density. The number of fragments per unit volume is probably larger in the central bright ring B than in the others.

11.79. Saturn's ring could have been formed in one or other of two different ways. One possibility is that the fragments resulted from the disintegration of a satellite captured close to the planet. Alternatively, the particles may have been part of a larger mass; they may be portions of the nebula, from which the solar system developed, that did not attain a sufficiently high density to permit condensation to occur. Of course, if the particles came within the Roche limit of the main planet, condensation into a single body would be impossible. There is no way at present of distinguishing between the different points of view.

THE SATELLITES OF SATURN

11.80. Of the nine known satellites of Saturn, the first six are regular; the eccentricities are all less than 0.029 and the inclinations of the orbital planes to the planet's equatorial plane are less than 1.5 deg. The semi-major axes of the orbits range from 186,000 kilometers (115,000 miles) to 1.23 million kilometers (760,000 miles) and the sidereal periods from 22.6 hours to 4.5 days. It will be noted that the closest satellite, Mimas, is only some 49,000 kilometers (30,000 miles) beyond the outer edge of the ring system of Saturn.

11.81. The seventh Saturnian satellite, at 1.48 million kilometers (922,000 miles), is almost regular; the angle of inclination of its orbit is very small, although variable, but the eccentricity of 0.104 is moderately large. The two outermost satellites are quite irregular. The orbit of the eighth has the relatively low eccentricity of 0.028, but its orbital inclination is about 14.7 deg; and the ninth satellite revolves in a retrograde direction with an orbital eccentricity of 0.163 and an angle of inclination of 150 deg.

11.82. The average orbital radii (semi-major axes) and sidereal periods and approximate values of the radii, relative to the radius of the Moon (1738 kilometers; 1080 miles), and of the densities of the nine satellites of Saturn are collected in Table 11.5. It will be noted that all the satellites have been given names; the corresponding roman numerals are in order of increasing distance from the parent planet. Satellites I through VI are the regular ones; VII is almost regular, and VIII and IX are irregular. The regular satellites, except

TABLE 11.5   PROPERTIES OF THE SATELLITES OF SATURN

| Satellite | Mean Orbital Radius | | Sidereal Period (days) | Radius (Moon = 1) | Density (grams/cu cm) |
	10³ kilometers	10³ miles			
I. Mimas	185	115	0.94	0.15	0.5
II. Enceladus	240	149	1.37	0.18	0.7
III. Tethys	295	183	1.89	0.35	1.2
IV. Dione	376	234	2.74	0.30	2.8
V. Rhea	527	328	4.52	0.45	2.0
VI. Titan	1220	760	15.95	1.5	2.4
VII. Hyperion	1480	922	21.28	0.12	—
VIII. Iapetus	3560	2210	79.33	0.35	1.3
IX. Phoebe	12,900	8040	550.5	0.09	—

for Titan, have high albedos, possibly because they are covered with small, light-colored crystals of water (hoar frost) or ammonia, or both. In all cases for which observation of the surface features is at all possible, the indications are that the periods of rotation are equal to the respective periods of revolution about Saturn. Satellite VIII (Iapetus) exhibits unusual behavior in the respect that at maximum western elongation, with reference to the parent planet, it appears to be more than five times as bright as at the eastern elongation. Possible explanations of this effect are that the surface characteristics of the eastern and western hemispheres of the satellite are quite different, and hence so also are the albedos, or that the satellite has an ellipsoidal shape, with the result that a larger area is seen at one time than at another.

11.83. The most interesting of Saturn's satellites is Titan (VI); it is almost the same size as Mercury and its radius is half again as large as that of the Moon. All the other satellites are considerably smaller in radius and mass. The escape velocity on Titan is about 2.8 kilometers per second, whereas it does not exceed 0.8 kilometer per second on the others. Hence, Titan should be able to retain an atmosphere at the existing very low temperatures. In 1944, G. P. Kuiper detected lines of methane in the spectrum, thus making Titan the only satellite in the solar system definitely known to have an atmosphere. It is possible that some neon and argon may also be present, but other constituents are doubtful. The temperature is too low to permit any significant amount of ammonia gas or water vapor, and the escape velocity is too small to prevent escape of the very light molecules of hydrogen and helium. The albedo of Titan is much lower than that of the other regular Saturnian satellites and it also differs in having an orange color. The surface of Titan is evidently not covered with hoar frost of water or ammonia as the others appear to be.

STUDIES OF SATURN FROM SPACE

11.84. The remarks made earlier concerning the possible study of Jupiter by means of space probes and orbiters apply equally to Saturn. Both the need for information and the difficulties in obtaining it are just as great, if not greater. The satellite Titan would certainly make a good subject for investigation by means of a fly-by mission or, better, with an instrumented capsule that could be landed on the surface. Although it is **1.23** million kilometers (**760,000** miles) from the body of Saturn and **1.09** million kilometers (**675,000** miles) from the outer ring, Titan might be useful as a base for observing these features of the planet.

THE PLANET URANUS

ORBITAL AND PHYSICAL CHARACTERISTICS

11.85. The next planet in order of increasing distance from the Sun and in size is Uranus. As a result of its low density, however, it is somewhat less massive than Neptune, and so it is the fourth in order of decreasing mass. The main orbital and physical characteristics of Uranus are given in Table 11.6.

TABLE 11.6   ORBITAL AND PHYSICAL CHARACTERISTICS OF URANUS

Distance, Uranus to Sun (max)	3100×10^6 kilometers	1870×10^6 miles
Distance, Uranus to Sun (min)	2760×10^6 "	1710×10^6 "
Distance, Uranus to Earth (max)	3080×10^6 "	1960×10^6 "
Distance, Uranus to Earth (min)	2610×10^6 "	1620×10^6 "
Angular diameter, from Earth (max)	4.0 sec	
Angular diameter, from Earth (min)	3.3 sec	
Eccentricity of orbit	0.0472	
Inclination of orbit to ecliptic	0.77 deg	
Inclination of equator to orbital plane	98 deg	
Orbital period (sidereal)	84.02 years	
Orbital period (synodic from Earth)	370 days	
Average orbital velocity	6.85 kilometers (4.25 miles) per second	
Radius (average)	24,000 kilometers (15,000 miles)	
Mass	8.70×10^{25} kilograms	
Average density	1.56 grams per cubic centimeter	
Gravitational acceleration at poles	9.40 meters (30.8 feet) per sec per sec	
Escape velocity	22 kilometers (13.7 miles) per second	
Rotation period	10 hours 50 minutes (approximately)	

The calculated value of the gravitational acceleration at the surface is **9.40** meters (**30.8** feet) per second per second, but at the equator the effect of the planet's rotation is to reduce this to **8.80** meters (**28.9** feet) per second per second.

11.86. The polar flattening of the planet is clear from its telescopic image and the ellipticity determined from the motion of the nearest satellite is 1/18. The result derived from direct measurement of the equatorial and polar diameters is about 1/12, but since the maximum angular diameter of Uranus as seen from Earth is only 4 sec of arc, it is evident that this value of the ellipticity cannot be very accurate. The equatorial radius is about **1600** kilometers (1000 miles) greater than the polar radius; the average of these two radii is the value given in Table 11.6.

11.87. The rotational period of about **10.8** hours, determined from the Doppler shift of spectral lines, is not greatly different from the periods of Jupiter and Saturn. The direction of the axis of rotation is, however, perhaps the most unusual property of Uranus. This is inclined at an angle of **98** deg to a line perpendicular to the planet's orbital plane, as shown in Fig. 11.4. If the rota-

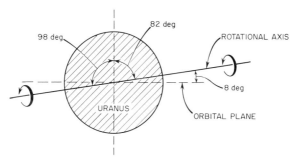

Fig. 11.4.   Retrograde rotation of Uranus

tion is looked at from the end of the axis at the left of the figure, it is counterclockwise, i.e., direct; but from the other end of the axis, at the right, it is clockwise, i.e., retrograde. Since the right end is technically to be regarded as the north pole, as it is north of the orbital plane by some **8** deg, the rotation is retrograde. From this point of view, the rotational axis is inclined **82** deg to the perpendicular to the orbital plane.

Telescopic Appearance of Uranus

11.88. In the telescope, Uranus is seen as a somewhat flattened spherical body with a greenish color; the latter is attributed to the methane in the atmosphere. The albedo is estimated to be about **0.5**, as might be anticipated for a cloud-covered planet. At certain times a whitish equatorial zone and other bands, similar to but fainter than those of Jupiter and Saturn, can be observed. For various reasons, including changes in distances and in the part of the planet directed toward Earth, as explained below, the overall brightness of Uranus fluctuates to some extent.

11.89. Because the rotational axis makes an angle of roughly **90** deg with the orbital plane, and the plane of the ecliptic, the area of Saturn observed from Earth varies throughout the former planet's sidereal period of 84 terrestrial years. Every 42 years, e.g., in 1924, 1966, etc., the full face of the planet can be seen, with the rotational axis directed approximately east and west and the equator roughly north and south. As a result of the rotation of the planet, most of the surface will experience regular night and day every 10.8 hours. One fourth of a sidereal period (21 years) later, i.e., in 1945, 1987, etc., one or other of the poles is directed toward the Sun (and Earth). At these times either the north or the south polar area—alternately every 42 years—is seen from Earth. The greater part of one hemisphere is then exposed continuously to sunlight whereas the other is in darkness; there is then no normal night or day on any significant part of Uranus.

The Structure of Uranus

11.90. Spectroscopic observation shows that the atmosphere of Uranus contains a larger proportion of methane than does Saturn. In addition, some of the bands of molecular hydrogen have been detected. The temperature is so low, the calculated maximum being $70°K$, i.e., $-203°C$ or $-341°F$, that the quantity of ammonia gas in the atmosphere is too small to be detected. Nevertheless, ammonia cirrus clouds or deposits of small crystals of ammonia probably exist in the atmosphere or on the planet's surface, respectively. Other atmospheric constituents may be helium, neon, and argon, but it is not known for certain that these gases are present.

11.91. The smaller size and higher density of Uranus, as compared with Jupiter and Saturn, cannot be correlated with the model of the interior containing only hydrogen and helium. One possibility is that the planet consists mainly of solid molecular hydrogen and ammonia. Calculations indicate that, at a pressure of about 250,000 atmospheres, i.e., approximately 3.5 million pounds per square inch, ammonia and hydrogen would combine to form metallic ammonium, NH_4. The latter would then be the major constituent of the interior of Uranus. It is probable that the planet also contains heavier elements, and it has been suggested by W. S. Porter (1961) that it has a dense core of such elements with a mass about twice that of Earth. In 1962, W. C. DeMarcus and R. T. Reynolds developed a model for the interior of Uranus which does not involve ammonia but only the primitive materials hydrogen, helium, and heavy elements; the latter are assumed to be in the same proportion as in the Sun. It is estimated that the hydrogen content cannot exceed 23 percent by weight.

The Satellites of Uranus

11.92. Uranus is known to have five satellites all of which are remarkably regular; the orbital eccentricities are very small, probably less than 0.005, and the inclinations of the orbital planes to the equatorial plane of the planet are estimated to be less than a minute of arc. The satellite nearest to Uranus, called Miranda and commonly designated by the Roman numeral V, was not discovered until 1948, although the others had then been known for nearly 100 years. The average orbital radii, sidereal periods, and approximate values of the radii of the Uranian satellites are recorded in Table 11.7 in order of in-

TABLE 11.7   PROPERTIES OF THE SATELLITES OF URANUS

Satellite	Mean Orbital Radius		Sidereal Period (days)	Radius	
	10^3 kilometers	10^3 miles		kilometers	miles
V. Miranda	131	81	1.41	~160	~100
I. Ariel	192	119	2.52	~1300	~800
II. Umbriel	268	166	4.14	~650	~400
III. Titania	440	273	8.71	~1300	~800
IV. Oberon	570	364	13.46	~1300	~800

creasing distance from the planet. The radii, which are in kilometers and miles, were estimated from the brightness and an assumed albedo. Since the brightness of such small and distant objects is difficult to measure and the albedos are uncertain, the values may be very much in error. It appears, however, that three of the satellites of Uranus may not be greatly different from the Moon in size.

THE PLANET NEPTUNE

GENERAL CHARACTERISTICS

11.93. In spite of its somewhat smaller radius, Neptune is more massive than Uranus; its density of 2.47 grams per cubic centimeter is the largest for the major planets. Some of the properties of Neptune are collected in Table 11.8.

TABLE 11.8   ORBITAL AND PHYSICAL CHARACTERISTICS OF NEPTUNE

Distance, Neptune to Sun (average)	4510×10^6 kilometers 2800×10^6 miles
Angular diameter, from Earth (average)	2.0 sec
Eccentricity of orbit	0.0086
Inclination of orbit to ecliptic	1.77 deg
Inclination of equator to orbital plane	28.80 deg
Orbital period (sidereal)	164.8 years
Orbital period (synodic from Earth)	367 days
Average orbital velocity	4.5 kilometers (3.4 miles) per second
Radius (average)	22,500 kilometers (14,000 miles)
Mass	1.03×10^{25} kilograms
Average density	2.47 grams per cubic centimeter
Gravitational acceleration at poles	15 meters (49 feet) per sec per sec
Escape velocity	25 kilometers (15.5 miles) per second
Rotation period	16 hours (approximately)

Because of the small eccentricity of the orbit, the minimum and maximum (perihelion and aphelion) distances from the Sun are not very different. The average distance of Neptune from Earth is approximately the same as the distance from the Sun. The angle of inclination of the equatorial plane to the plane of the orbit, i.e., of the rotational axis to the line perpendicular to the equatorial plane, is similar to the value for Earth and for several other planets. The rotational period, as determined spectroscopically from the Doppler shift, is almost 16 hours, but the result is not to be regarded as very accurate. The calculated gravitational acceleration of 15 meters (49 feet) per second per second is decreased by only 0.3 meter (1.0 foot) by the centrifugal effect at the equator. The ellipticity of Neptune has not been determined directly, but it has been estimated to be 1/45.

11.94. Like Uranus, and for the same reason, Neptune has a greenish color. Because of the great distance, the angular diameter of Neptune is only about 2 sec of arc; it is the only major planet that cannot be seen by the unaided eye. The albedo is estimated to be the same as that of the other Jovian planets, namely, about 0.5. Observers have occasionally reported seeing faint irregular markings and a bright equatorial zone on Neptune, but the situation is uncertain.

11.95. The amount of methane detected by its spectrum is the largest for any planet. The presence of hydrogen in the atmosphere of Neptune has also been confirmed spectroscopically. There is undoubtedly some helium and possibly smaller proportions of neon and argon. At the low temperatures existing on the planet, with a maximum value of about $56°K$, i.e., $-217°C$ or $-358°F$, essentially all the ammonia and some of the methane will be in the solid form. The interior of Neptune is expected to be similar to that of Uranus. One suggestion is that Neptune consists of molecular hydrogen and ammonia, much of it in the combined form of solid metallic ammonium, and presumably a fair proportion of heavier elements. These may possibly be concentrated in a central core, as has been postulated for Neptune. Another possibility is that there is no ammonia, but only hydrogen (not more than 14 weight percent), helium, and heavier elements (cf. § 11.91).

THE SATELLITES OF NEPTUNE

11.96. Only two satellites of Neptune are known, both of which are irregular. Although one has an almost exactly circular orbit, the inclination of its plane to the planet's equatorial plane is almost 160 deg (or 20 deg) and, moreover, it revolves in a retrograde direction. This satellite, known as Triton, has an orbital radius of 340,000 kilometers (220,000 miles) and a sidereal period of 5.88 days. It has an estimated radius of some 2100 kilometers (1300 miles), based on the measured brightness and an assumed albedo of 0.2. Triton is therefore larger than the Moon. Its mass has been determined in the same manner as the mass of the Moon is found relative to Earth (§ 9.50), i.e., from the oscillations of the parent planet about the Neptune-Triton barycenter. The mass found in this way is 1.34×10^{23} kilograms, i.e., nearly twice the mass of the Moon. The density, based on the approximate radius given above, is about 3.5 grams per cubic centimeter, slightly higher than the density of the Moon. If the actual albedo is less than 0.2, the estimated radius of Triton would be larger and the density consequently smaller than these values.

11.97. The gravitational force on Triton is large enough and the temperature sufficiently low for it to have retained an atmosphere. But most of the expected gases will be frozen out. A small amount of methane may be present, although its spectrum has not been detected. It is improbable that there will be any hydrogen and helium, as these light molecules will have escaped.

11.98. The second satellite, Nereid, discovered in 1949 has a highly eccentric orbit (eccentricity 0.749) and the angle of inclination to the orbital plane is 27.7 deg. As a consequence of the eccentricity, the distances of Nereid from the parent planet at the periapsis and apoapsis of the orbit are very different, namely, about 1.45 and 9.6 million kilometers (900,000 and 6 million miles), respectively. The sidereal period of revolution about the planet is 359.9 days. An approximate estimate gives the radius of Nereid as roughly 160 kilometers (100 miles).

THE PLANET PLUTO

GENERAL CHARACTERISTICS

11.99. Little is known definitely about Pluto other than the orbital characteristics summarized in Table 11.9. Pluto's perihelion distance is somewhat

TABLE 11.9   ORBITAL CHARACTERISTICS OF PLUTO

Distance, Pluto to Sun (max)	7400×10^6 kilometers	4600×10^6 miles
Distance, Pluto to Sun (min)	4500×10^6	2800×10^6
Eccentricity of orbit	0.249	
Inclination of orbit to ecliptic	17.2 deg	
Orbital period (sidereal)	248.4 years	
Average orbital velocity	4.76 kilometers (2.96 miles) per second	
Rotational period	6.4 days	

less than the aphelion of Neptune; hence, part of the orbit of Pluto lies within that of Neptune, but the two orbits do not intersect because they are inclined at an angle of more than 15 deg. Small but regular fluctuations in the brightness of Pluto have been attributed to the rotation of the planet; the rotational period found in this manner is 6.4 days.

MASS AND DENSITY OF PLUTO

11.100. The measured values of the mass and radius of Pluto provide an interesting paradox. Since the planet does not have a satellite, the only way to determine its mass is from the perturbation it causes in the orbits of Neptune and Uranus. From such data, the mass has been estimated to be somewhat less than that of Earth. In 1956, G. P. Kuiper and M. Humason measured the angular diameter of Pluto, using the world's largest telescope, the 200-inch reflector at the Mount Palomar Observatory, and found it to be 0.23 sec of arc; at the existing distance, this represented a diameter of about 5800 kilometers, i.e., a radius of 2900 kilometers (1800 miles), for the planet. From the mass and radius given above, the density is found to have the unrealistic value of nearly 60 grams per cubic centimeter.

11.101. One way out of the difficulty is the suggestion that Pluto has a very smooth surface, unlike that of any other member of the solar system, and reflects light in a specular manner, i.e., like a polished sphere. In this case, the angular diameter measured would be that of the reflected image of the Sun, which would be smaller than the true angular diameter. The actual diameter of Pluto might thus be appreciably greater than 5800 kilometers, and the density would be considerably less than the value given above. An error of a factor of two in the diameter would decrease the density by a factor of eight. There is, however, no reason to believe that the surface of Pluto is smooth enough to cause specular (mirror-like) reflection of sunlight.

11.102. An alternative possibility is that the mass of the planet calculated from the perturbations of the orbits of Uranus and Neptune is too large; in other words, the perturbations have been overestimated. If the density of Pluto is assumed to be about 3.5 grams per cubic centimeter, which is roughly that of Neptune's satellite Triton, and the diameter is taken as 5800 kilometers, the mass would be about one eighteenth (0.057) of the mass of Earth. A body with such a small mass would not have produced the apparent perturbation of the orbit of Uranus upon which was based the prediction of the existence of Pluto (§ 7.10). If such is the case, the discovery of this planet was a fortunate accident. At the present time there is no simple way of deciding whether the mass based on the orbital perturbations or the radius derived from the observed angular diameter is correct; it is possible, in fact, that both quantities are in error. A suggestion has been made for resolving the situation by means of a space probe with a large telescope oriented to observe the occultation by Pluto of a suitable star. An unequivocal value of the diameter of the planet could, in principle, be obtained in this manner.

The Origin of Pluto

11.103. Another problem concerning Pluto is the nature of its orbit, which is both highly eccentric and inclined to the ecliptic plane. Most astronomers subscribe to the view, first propounded by I. Yamamoto in Japan in 1933, that Pluto was originally a satellite of Neptune that escaped from the parent planet to orbit the Sun. One of the arguments put forward by G. P. Kuiper is based on Pluto's exceptionally long period of rotation of 6.4 days. This is much longer than that of any other planet except Mercury and Venus which owe their slow rates of rotation to proximity to the Sun. As a Neptunian satellite, Pluto would undoubtedly have exhibited captured rotation and then both its rotational period and its sidereal period of revolution would have been 6.4 days. This is a little longer than the present sidereal period of the satellite Triton, and is consequently quite reasonable. When it escaped from Neptune's gravitational field into the field of the Sun, Pluto would have retained the same rate of rotation, but its period of revolution would be determined by its new orbit as a planet in the solar system.

11.104. According to the British astronomer R. A. Lyttleton, the ejection of Pluto from its orbit about Neptune resulted from interaction with the large satellite Triton; it is postulated that, at the same time, Triton's orbital motion was reversed from direct to retrograde. Some change of this kind would be necessary to prevent the return of Pluto to its original character as a satellite of Neptune. If such were the case, the present almost exactly circular orbit of Triton would indeed be surprising. G. P. Kuiper and E. Rabe, on the other hand, are both of the opinion that Pluto was released as a result of the normal loss of material from the protoplanet from which Neptune evolved (cf. § 7.195).

Chapter 12

THE UNIVERSE

GENERAL STRUCTURE OF THE UNIVERSE

INTRODUCTION

12.1. In this chapter it is proposed to outline such information about the universe as may throw light on its present structure (cosmology) and on the origin and evolution of its constituent parts (cosmogony).* On the basis of the results of astronomical observations—visual, photographic, and in the radio-frequency range—a number of theories have been proposed to account for the origin, development, and structure of the universe. Until the eighteenth century, cosmological and cosmogonical theories were largely metaphysical or philosophical, but as more observational data have become available, they have followed more physical lines.

12.2. It is characteristic of the physical sciences that theories have almost invariably been modified or discarded in the course of time as new facts have come to light. Furthermore, in many instances there are alternative theories that appear to account equally well for the observations made hitherto. These limitations, which are particularly applicable to the theories of cosmology and cosmogony, should be borne in mind when reading this chapter. The views expressed are to be regarded as being in the nature of an interim report that will probably need to be amended in due course.

12.3. Although theories are subject to modification, observations are not. It is true that, for various reasons, both instrumental and human errors are made in measurements or the results are interpreted incorrectly. Ultimately, such errors are corrected and the basic data remain. The first part of this chapter will, therefore, be concerned mainly with observations about which there is little, if any, doubt. Later, some aspects of cosmological and cosmogonical theories will be considered.

---

* The Greek word *kosmos* means "order" or "harmony." It is also used for "world" in the sense of the physical universe on the presumption that the universe is an orderly and not a chaotic system.

Galaxies

12.4. In examining the numerous objects in the sky with large telescopes, it has become apparent that galaxies represent convenient units for the study of the structure of the universe. A *galaxy* is an aggregate of stars, dust, and gas with a more or less definite structure. Although both smaller and larger galaxies, respectively, may exist, the diameters of the majority of galaxies range from about 7000 to 150,000 light years, i.e., about 2000 to 50,000 parsecs.* About three fourths of the known galaxies have the outlines of flattish, lens-shaped disks, with a maximum thickness at the center of roughly 10 to 15 percent of the diameter. From the calculated masses and brightnesses of the galaxies it is estimated that each contains from something like a billion (10^9) to a hundred billion (10^{11}) or more individual stars.

12.5. Because of the great distances involved, the resolution of the separate stars in even the nearest galaxies was not possible before large telescopes became available. In fact, until the end of the nineteenth century, galaxies were categorized, with other objects having a diffuse luminosity, as *nebulae* (Latin, *nebula;* Greek, *nephele;* German, *nebel,* "cloud" or "mist"). At present the term nebula (or nebulosity) is preferably restricted to bright or dark diffuse masses consisting of gas or gas and dust. Bright nebulae are associated with hot stars to which they owe their luminosity.

12.6. On the very large scale of the universe, it is probable that the galaxies are distributed uniformly in all directions in space, but on a more local scale there is a tendency to form groups or clusters. Some of the groups consist of only two members, many have between ten and a hundred, and at least one, the Coma cluster, contains over 10,000 individual galaxies. If there are any isolated galaxies, not belonging to one cluster or another, their number must be small. It is possible that the groups may form larger associations, but this is not certain. Within each group, the distances between individual galaxies vary, but one or two million light years (0.3 to 0.6 million parsecs) may be taken as a reasonable average. Similarly, the average distance between adjacent groups is very roughly one or two hundred million light years (30 to 60 million parsecs). By utilizing such numbers as these, it has been calculated that there are, in round figures, 100 billion (10^{11}) galaxies or a total of something like 10^{21} stars in the observable universe.†

12.7. In the telescope, the faintly luminous band in the sky called the Milky

---

* Astronomical distances beyond the solar system are so large that even the astronomical unit (§ 6.5) is too small for convenience; hence the units employed are the light year and the parsec. A *light year* is the distance light travels in a year at a velocity of 299,800 kilometers (186,300 miles) per second; thus a light year is 9.461×10^{12} kilometers (5.879×10^{12} miles) or 6.33×10^4 astronomical units. The *parsec,* which is described more fully in § 12.83, is 3.26 light years, i.e., 1.92×10^{13} miles, 3.08×10^{13} kilometers, or 2.06×10^5 astronomical units.

† If every person now living on Earth counted stars at the rate of one per second, day and night, it would require about 10,000 years to count all the stars in the universe.

Way is seen to consist of a very large number of individual stars. It is visible in both Northern and Southern Hemispheres and hence it surrounds Earth and the solar system. The Milky Way is actually what can be seen of the galaxy, called by the same name, of which the Sun is an average member. The mass, size, and brightness of the Sun lie about midway between the extremes observed for other stars in the Milky Way.

12.8. The Milky Way is sometimes referred to as the local galaxy or as the Galaxy, with a capital G, to distinguish it from other galaxies. It was the realization that there might be other aggregates of stars similar to the Milky Way that led to the introduction of the term galaxy, from the Greek word *galaktos* meaning "milk." The closest galaxies to the Milky Way are the two (Large and Small) Magellanic Clouds, as they are called, visible only in the Southern Hemisphere; they are, respectively, about 160,000 and 190,000 light years (50,000 to 60,000 parsecs) distant. The galaxy in the constellation Andromeda, originally referred to as the Nebula of Andromeda, 1.5 million light years (460,000 parsecs) away, is the largest and best known member of the local group. With the exception of these three galaxies, all the stellar bodies that can be observed with the unaided eye are part of the Milky Way system.

CLASSIFICATION OF GALAXIES

12.9. In 1925, the American astronomer Edwin P. Hubble proposed a scheme for classifying galaxies in accordance with their appearance. Although the categories have been modified in minor respects, the general classification is substantially unchanged. Galaxies are divided into three general groups, namely, elliptical (sometimes called ellipsoidal or spheroidal), spiral, and irregular. *Elliptical galaxies* have photographic images that range from circular (E0) to highly flattened (E7) forms. There are two main types of *spiral galaxies,* namely, *normal spirals* and *barred spirals*. The normal spiral galaxies, referred to by the symbol S, consist of a central (nuclear) region to which a number of spiral arms appear to be attached. The barred spirals (or SB galaxies) differ in the respect that the arms seem to start from a luminous bar that

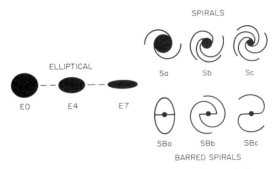

FIG. 12.1.   Types of galaxies; the S0 type is not shown (after E. P. Hubble)

crosses the nucleus. In each of these subgroups there are gradations, indicated by the letters a, b, c, and possibly d, in order of increasing openness of the spiral arms and the density of material in the arms (Fig. 12.1). The Milky Way is probably a galaxy of the Sb type, of which an excellent example is shown in Fig. 12.2. An S0 type (not shown) has also been described, consisting

FIG. 12.2.   The Sb galaxy M 81. (*Mount Wilson and Palomar Observatories*)

of a nucleus and a faint indication of possible arms. The *irregular* (or I) *galaxies* have no particular shape, no central nucleus, and no symmetry.

12.10. Of the galaxies whose forms are known, about 50 percent are normal spirals and 25 percent are barred spirals; about 20 percent of the total are elliptical and the remaining 5 percent are irregular. Many astronomers feel, however, that this does not represent the true distribution of galactic types. There are probably more elliptical and irregular galaxies than indicated, but their shapes are difficult to identify.

12.11. Apart from the differences in their general appearance, the elliptical, spiral, and irregular galaxies differ in other respects. In particular, the quantities of hydrogen gas and dust particles increase in the order given. The irregular galaxies and the arms of spiral galaxies contain, in addition to gas and dust (§ 12.45 *et seq.*), highly luminous blue giant stars which, as will be seen later, are relatively young. There are also many older, red giant and other stars, especially in the nuclei of the spiral galaxies. The almost dust-free elliptical galaxies, however, consist almost entirely of apparently older stars, the brightest being the red giants (or supergiants).

12.12. It was thought at one time that the three categories of galaxies represented an evolving series, from irregular, through spiral, to elliptical. But this view is now being discarded. It is true that the elliptical galaxies contain no young stars, but these galaxies are on the whole more massive than the spiral forms; the irregular galaxies are smallest of all and contain the least mass. The mass differences are such as to make it very improbable that the elliptical forms could have evolved from irregular or spiral galaxies. Evolution in the opposite direction, i.e., from elliptical to irregular, does not seem to be compatible with the essential absence of young stars in elliptical galaxies and their abundance in galaxies of the irregular type. Furthermore, the lack of hydrogen and dust, from which new stars are apparently formed, in the elliptical galaxies makes it unlikely that they can evolve into another class.

12.13. A possibility is that the elliptical galaxies developed from large masses of gas (and perhaps dust) that were rotating relatively slowly and so were able to contract almost completely into stars leaving little residual material. If the gas had been rotating rapidly, however, a large amount of the mass would be thrown off in the early stages and so the quantity remaining would be less than for the elliptical type. The rapid rotation would result in considerable flattening, and the tendency for material to stream off the outer edge would lead to the formation of spiral arms. Some of the primeval gas and dust would remain in these arms and new stars would evolve from this material in the course of time, as indicated by the highly luminous blue stars.

ROTATION OF GALAXIES

12.14. There are several lines of evidence indicating that galaxies are rotating about a central axis. In the first place, most galaxies, especially the spiral forms, have a flattened (lens-like) shape (Fig. 12.3). If the galaxies were formed from a mass of gas and dust, as seems probable, their rotation would cause the flattening, as indicated above. More convincing proof, however, is obtained from the Doppler effect in the spectrum. A spectrograph, fitted to a telescope, is arranged with its slit along the major axis of the galaxy as seen edgeways, as in Fig. 12.3, or almost so. If the galaxy is rotating about a central axis perpendicular to the face of the disc, one edge will be moving toward Earth and the other away from it. The spectral lines will, therefore, be tilted, as explained in connection with the rotation of Jupiter (§ 11.48). From the extent of the tilt, the velocity of rotation of the outer edge of the galaxy can be calculated. The tilt in the spectral lines is not observed, of course, if the slit of the spectrograph is at right angles to the major axis of the galaxy or if the galaxy is viewed face on.

Fig. 12.3.   The spiral galaxies NGC 4565 (above) and NGC 4594 (below), as seen edgeways from Earth. (*Mount Wilson and Palomar Observatories*)

12.15. If the spectra of individual stars or other luminous objects in the galaxy can be studied, as is the case for some members of the local group, e.g., the Andromeda (Sb) galaxy, it is possible to determine how the rotational velocity varies with distance from the center. In this manner it has been found that the central region (or nucleus) of the Andromeda galaxy rotates as if it were a solid body (or a wheel). The nucleus is, of course, not solid but consists of a large number of individual stars. According to the Newtonian theory of gravitation, this type of rotation is to be expected if the stars are distributed in an essentially uniform manner in the nucleus. In the less dense arms of the spiral, the rate of rotation decreases with distance from the center. The period of rotation or, strictly speaking, of revolution then varies in accordance with

Kepler's third law (§ 2.48), i.e., the behavior is like that of a satellite revolving in an orbit around the nucleus.

12.16. An approximate estimate of the total mass of the galaxy may be made in the following manner. At a distance of 10,000 parsecs, i.e., 3.08×10^{17} kilometers, from the center of the Andromeda galaxy, the velocity of rotation is 250 kilometers per second.* This is actually the velocity of revolution of a star in the galaxy at the given distance from the center. If the orbit is assumed to be circular, its circumference is $2\pi(3.08 \times 10^{17})$ kilometers; the period of revolution, P, of the star is then obtained upon dividing the circumference by the velocity, i.e.,

$$P = \frac{2\pi(3.08 \times 10^{17})}{250} \text{ seconds}$$

$$= 2.3 \times 10^8 \text{ years.}$$

Periods of this order of magnitude, i.e., about 100 million years, have been found for other spiral galaxies, including the Milky Way.

12.17. The mass of the star can be neglected in comparison with that of the galactic nucleus. Hence, equation (12.11), which will be derived in § 12.118 on the basis of Kepler's third law, can be written as

$$M = \frac{a^3}{P^2},$$

where M is the mass of the galactic nucleus in terms of the mass of the Sun, a is the orbital radius in astronomical units (§ 6.5), and P is the period in years. The radius is 10,000 parsecs, i.e., 2.06×10^9 astronomical units, and P is 2.3×10^8 years; hence,

$$M = \frac{(2.06 \times 10^9)^3}{(2.3 \times 10^8)^2} = 1.7 \times 10^{11} \text{ solar masses.}$$

Upon making allowance for the mass of the stars in the arms of the galaxy, the total mass of the Andromeda galaxy is estimated to be about 2×10^{11} solar masses. If the average mass of the star is roughly the same as that of the Sun, it is seen that the galaxy contains some 2×10^{11} individual stars.

THE MILKY WAY

12.18. The study of galaxies is hampered by two circumstances. First, exterior galaxies are so far away that structural details are difficult to discern, although the overall character can be determined. On the other hand, an observer on Earth can examine nearby features of the Milky Way in detail, but the more distant aspects of the Galaxy are hidden. However, by combining the large-scale information from exterior galaxies, with the more detailed results

---

* Distances within or across a galaxy are calculated from the measured angular diameter and the distance from Earth by a method similar to that described in § 6.21. The determination of distances from Earth (or the solar system) is considered later in this chapter.

on a smaller scale obtained within the local Galaxy, it has been possible to construct reasonably complete pictures of both the Milky Way and other galaxies. Some indication of how this has been achieved can be obtained from the following discussion of the Galaxy.

12.19. Since the stars of the Milky Way appear to lie on a fairly narrow band, it is evident that the Galaxy has a disc-like form. The greater concentration of stars in the constellation Sagittarius suggests that the galactic nucleus lies in that direction. This is in agreement with the observation that the intensity of nonthermal radio-frequency emission, in the wavelength range from 3 centimeters to 15 meters, is strongest from the same direction.

12.20. Early attempts to determine the location of the Sun* within the Galaxy were based on observations of the distribution in space of stars of similar brightness. But the conclusions drawn were invalid because the absorption of light by interstellar dust (§ 12.46) had been overlooked. The first reliable results were obtained in 1917 by Harlow Shapley in the United States from studies of the globular star clusters. The *globular clusters* are groups of stars, ranging in number from several thousand to a few million with an average around half a million. Over a hundred of these clusters are known in the Milky Way and there are undoubtedly many more. Globular clusters have also been detected in external galaxies. The name arises from the almost symmetrical clustering of the stars in the form of a sphere (Fig. 12.4). The diameters of globular clusters lie mostly between 70 and 600 light years (20 and 190 parsecs), the average being approximately 200 light years (60 parsecs). Although the clusters appear to be a closely packed aggregation, as in Fig. 12.4, the mean distance between the individual stars in a cluster is something like 3 to 4 light years, i.e., roughly 1 parsec.†

12.21. The importance of globular clusters in the present context is that they are found in all parts of the sky, not merely within the disc of the Galaxy. The distribution, as seen from Earth, is not uniform, however, since there appear to be more in the region of the constellation Sagittarius than in the diametrically opposite direction. Determinations of the distances of globular clusters from the Sun and of their distribution in space have established that they surround the Galaxy in a roughly spherical "halo." Until relatively recently, the distance of the center of this halo, which is presumably also the center of the Milky Way, was thought to be located about 26,000 light years from the Sun, but there is evidence that the distance is closer to 33,000 light years, i.e., 10,000 parsecs. The latter value will be used here for the distance between the Sun and the center of the Galaxy.

12.22. The globular clusters apparently extend beyond the galactic disc and

* Although all astronomical observations are made from Earth (or from a spacecraft in the general vicinity of Earth), they may be regarded as being made from the Sun as one of the stars in the Galaxy. The distance from Earth to the Sun is completely negligible in comparison with galactic distances.

† The distance of the nearest group to the Sun is 4.3 light years.

so the diameter of the halo is greater than that of the Galaxy. One way to obtain the galactic diameter is to determine the farthest distance of disc-type stars or of bright nebulae in the direction of the anticenter, i.e., in the opposite direction to the center, of the Milky Way. It may be assumed that such stars are

Fig. 12.4.   Globular cluster, Omega Centauri. (*Harvard College Observatory*)

located at (or near) the outer edge of the disc. The distance found is roughly 14,000 light years (4600 parsecs) from the Sun. Hence, the radius of the Galaxy is about 33,000 + 14,000 = 47,000 light years or approximately 14,500 parsecs. A similar result has been estimated from radio-frequency measurements on the distribution of hydrogen gas in the Galaxy (§ 12.36, *et seq.*).

12.23. The thickness of the galactic disc has been determined from observations on various stellar objects, e.g., bright stars, luminous nebulae, and strong radio sources, about the central plane of the Galaxy. It has been concluded that, at the center, the nucleus is some 10,000 light years (3000 parsecs) thick, but toward the edge, where the Sun is located, the thickness is from 3200 to 4800 light years (1000 to 1500 parsecs).* On the basis of the various distances given, a model of the Galaxy, as seen edgeways, is somewhat like that depicted in Fig. 12.5.

12.24. The next matter to consider is whether the Galaxy has spiral arms or not, i.e., whether it is a spiral or an elliptical galaxy. The highly flattened shape suggests the rapid rotation that is characteristic of spiral galaxies, and this

---

* Most of the stars seen in the sky that appear to be outside the Milky Way are actually within this region of the Galaxy.

expectation has been confirmed in various ways. For example, it is known from a study of external galaxies of the spiral type that the arms invariably contain blue giant stars and luminous nebulae.

It may be assumed, therefore, that if the Milky Way were spiral in form, these objects would be found mainly at specific distances, corresponding to the locations of the individual arms of the spiral. Such has been found to be the case. In view of the distance of the Sun from the galactic center, it is undoubtedly located in one of the arms; this is commonly referred to as the *Orion arm.* Closer to the center is the *Sagittarius arm,* and farther out the *Perseus arm* has been identified. Other arms, both nearer to the nucleus than the Sagittarius arm and more distant than the Perseus arm, have been indicated by radio-astronomical observations of hydrogen distribution in the Galaxy.

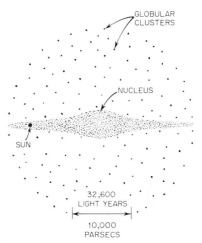

Fig. 12.5. Schematic edgeways view of the Milky Way

12.25. Telescopic studies of external spiral galaxies have shown that the arms, although quite definite, are not sharply defined; this is evident, for example, in the photograph in Fig. 12.2. Furthermore, the arms often have short protruding branches. It is consequently not possible to give precise values for the dimensions of the arms or of their distance apart. Very roughly, it may be stated, however, that the spiral arms in the Milky Way are about 2500 light years (800 parsecs) wide and adjacent arms are separated by something like 6500 light years (2000 parsecs). In the Andromeda galaxy, which is considered to have the same kind of structure (Sb) as the Milky Way but is about 50 percent larger, the arms are from 10,000 to 15,000 light years (3000 to 4500 parsecs) apart.

ROTATION OF THE MILKY WAY

12.26. A study of the rotation* of the Galaxy, originally made by J. H. Oort (§ 7.86) in 1927, has helped to throw light on its structure. Suppose that, as is known to be the case for other spiral galaxies, the stars at different distances from the center of the Milky Way have different rates of rotation. Consider the paths of a number of stars which are (*a*) closer to the galactic center than is the Sun, (*b*) at the same radial distance as the Sun, and (*c*) farther than the Sun

---

* Although the individual stars in the Galaxy revolve about the galactic center in accordance with Kepler's laws, no attempt is made to distinguish between rotation and revolution because the Galaxy as a whole rotates as a result of the revolutions of the stars.

from the center (Fig. 12.6). According to Kepler's third law, the stars that are closer in will have larger rotational velocities than the Sun, whereas those farther out will have smaller velocities. Consequently, to an observer on the Sun (or Earth), the former, in path *a* in Fig. 12.6, will appear to overtake the Sun, whereas the latter, in path *c*, will seem to lag behind. In other words, relative to the Sun, the velocities of the closer-in stars will be directed toward the top of Fig. 12.6, whereas the relative velocities of the stars farther away from

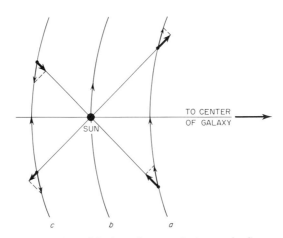

Fɪɢ. 12.6.   Motion of stars relative to the Sun

the galactic center will be directed toward the bottom. Stars with the same rotational velocity as the Sun will appear to be at rest, as far as this type of motion is concerned.

12.27. The relative velocities of the various stars, represented by the thin arrows in the figure, may be split up into two components: one, a relative radial velocity, pointing directly toward (or away from) the Sun, as shown by the thick arrows, and the other, a transverse velocity, at right angles indicated by the broken lines. It is seen that the magnitude and direction of the relative radial velocity of a star depend upon whether it lies on an inner or an outer path and upon its galactic longitude relative to the center of the galaxy, i.e., the angle *l* between the lines joining the Sun to the galactic center and to the given star, respectively (Fig. 12.7). Stars rotating in the same path as the Sun have no relative radial velocity, regardless of their galactic longitude. The relative radial velocity of a star can be determined by the Doppler shift of characteristic lines in its spectrum, and Oort showed that, for stars not too far from the Sun, this velocity, V_r, can be expressed with fair accuracy by

$$V_r = rA \sin 2l, \qquad (12.1)$$

where r is the distance from a given star to the Sun, l is its galactic longitude relative to the center of the Galaxy (Fig. 12.7), and A is a constant, known as *Oort's constant*. The value of this (approximate) constant has been derived from measurements of V_r and l for some stars whose distances from the Sun are known. For conditions under which equation (12.1) is applicable, r may be

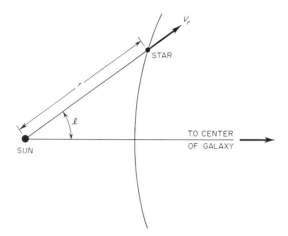

Fig. 12.7.   Galactic longitude of a star and distance from the Sun

taken as the difference between the distances of the Sun and star, respectively, from the center of the Galaxy.

12.28. One of the consequences of equation (12.1) is that, for a given value of the distance r, the plot of the relative radial velocity against the galactic longitude, l, should be a sine curve; two such curves, for different values of r, are shown in Fig. 12.8. Positive values of V_r mean that the relative radial velocity is in the direction away from the Sun, whereas negative values are toward the Sun. If the stars around the Sun were distributed in a purely random manner, then the plot of the measured values of V_r against l should show no regularity. But, if the stars are located at definite radial distances from the galactic center, such as would be the case if they were in different arms of a spiral, the results would fall on or close to specific curves of the form indicated in Fig. 12.8. Observations show that the latter situation is the actual one, thus indicating that the Galaxy has spiral arms.

12.29. If the transverse velocity of a star is determined,* as well as its radial velocity, the actual rotational velocity can be evaluated relative to that of the Sun. From the relative rotational velocities of stars at two different known

---

* Astronomers observe the transverse motion of a star, relative to the solar system (or the Sun), against the background of the celestial sphere; the rate of change with time of the star's angular coordinates is called the (apparent) *proper motion*. If the distance of the star from the Sun is known, the transverse velocity relative to the Sun can be determined from the proper motion.

distances from the Sun, and hence from the galactic center, the rotational velocity of the Sun can be calculated by using Kepler's third law. With this velocity available, the approximate mass of the Galaxy can be estimated in the manner described in § 12.17. The rotational velocity of the Galaxy at the radial

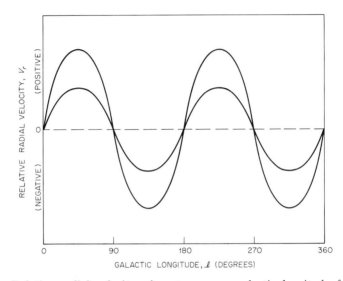

Fɪɢ. 12.8. Relative radial velocity of a star versus galactic longitude for two different distances from the Sun

distance of the Sun found in this manner is approximately 220 kilometers (135 miles) per second, and the galactic mass is some 10^{11} solar masses. At the outer edge of the Galaxy, the velocity of rotation is about 180 kilometers (110 miles) per second.

12.30. The rotation of the Sun about the galactic center could be determined directly if its motion were referred to a stationary (or approximately stationary) frame of reference; two possible frames of reference exist, namely, the globular clusters and external galaxies. The globular clusters are located on a roughly spherical halo surrounding the Milky Way; hence, it seems reasonable to postulate that they do not rotate or, if they do rotate, the rate of rotation is small. If the rate of rotation were significant, the halo would probably be flattened rather than spherical.

12.31. Since the Sun rotates about the center of the Galaxy, it will have a velocity relative to any globular cluster. By determining the Doppler shift in the spectrum, the radial velocity of the Sun relative to a particular globular cluster can be evaluated. If similar measurements are made for several clusters in different directions in the sky, the actual rotational velocity of the Sun and its direction of rotation can be determined. There is some evidence that the halo of globular clusters does rotate slowly and if appropriate allowance is made for this, the rotational velocity of the Sun about the galactic center is found to be in agreement with the value given above. The direction of rotation is approximately at right angles to the line joining the Sun to the center of the Galaxy, implying that the path is almost circular. An indication of how the Milky Way might appear to an observer outside the Galaxy is given in Fig. 12.9. The location of the Sun and the direction of rotation are shown. From the north galactic pole, i.e., from a point on the near side of the Galaxy as represented in Fig. 12.9, the rotation would appear to be clockwise. To an observer on

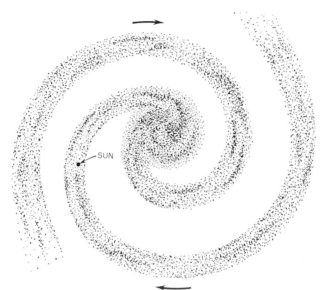

Fig. 12.9.   Schematic view of the Milky Way from the north galactic pole

Earth's Northern Hemisphere looking toward the center of the Milky Way (in Sagittarius), the direction of rotation is to his left.

12.32. The method just described has also been applied by utilizing the Doppler shift of the spectra of a number of galaxies of the local group to determine the radial velocity of the Sun relative to each of these galaxies. The latter may be regarded as being essentially stationary with respect to the Milky Way, and hence the galactic rotational velocity of the Sun can be calculated from the relative radial velocities. The value reported is somewhat higher than that obtained in other ways, but the direction of rotation is the same as indicated from the observations on globular clusters.

PECULIAR VELOCITY

12.33. If all the stars in the same spiral arm of the Galaxy as the Sun, i.e., the stars close to the Sun, were rotating at the same rate in circular paths about the galactic center, the stars in this group would seem to be stationary with respect to each other. It appears, however, that the stars do not move in circles, but rather in ellipses of slightly different eccentricities and inclinations. Consequently, the stars in the vicinity of the Sun are seen to exhibit relative motion. This is true, of course, for all stars. But it is for those within the same arm of the Galaxy as the Sun that the phenomenon is most readily observed, since the stars are visible from Earth. The velocity of any star relative to the average of the surrounding group is called the star's *peculiar velocity*.

12.34. As applied to the Sun, the peculiar velocity becomes manifest by the fact that, on the average, the nearby stars in one direction in the sky, toward a point called the *apex*, have relative radial velocities toward the Sun, whereas in the opposite direction, toward the *antapex*, the relative radial velocities are away from the Sun. Half way between these two directions, the nearby stars exhibit no relative radial motion toward or away from the Sun.

12.35. By observing the Doppler shifts in their spectra, the relative velocities of stars in the vicinity of the Sun have been measured and a statistical study of the results indicates that the Sun has a peculiar velocity of about 20 kilometers (12 miles) per second in the direction of the constellation Hercules. This is where the apex of the Sun's peculiar motion is located. Most stars near the Sun have similar peculiar velocities, with a random distribution. On the other hand, as will be seen later, some stars have much higher peculiar velocities.

DISTRIBUTION OF HYDROGEN IN THE GALAXY

12.36. An outstanding achievement of radio astronomy (§ 12.213 *et seq.*) has been the elucidation of the structure of the Galaxy. It has been known for some time that the spiral arms of galaxies, including the Milky Way, contain hydrogen gas. One indication, for example, is the prominent emission lines of atomic hydrogen in the spectra of bright nebulae, which owe their luminosity to the proximity of bright stars. The short wavelength, i.e., X-ray and ultraviolet, radiation from these stars are able to ionize the hydrogen atoms in their vicinity; that is to say, the atoms are split up into their constituent nuclei (protons) and electrons.

12.37. When proton-electron recombination occurs, as it must from time to time, some of the energy liberated remains as internal (or excitation) energy of the resulting neutral atom. The hydrogen atom in the excited state then emits the excess energy as one or more photons of radiation (§ 6.76). Each such photon carries a quantum of energy corresponding to a specific line in the spectrum of atomic hydrogen. These characteristic lines are observed in the spectra of bright nebulae, and clearly indicate the presence of hydrogen in their vicinity. Localities in which the emission lines of hydrogen are observed are called *H II regions* (cf. § 6.85), because the lines, although emitted by neutral atoms, owe their origin to ionized hydrogen. In addition to the line spectra, the H II regions emit radiations over a range (continuum) of wavelengths. These radiations arise from the capture of electrons by hydrogen ions and by free-free electron transitions, described in § 6.90 *et seq.*

12.38. Luminous nebulae are fairly common but their number is limited; hence, they cannot provide much information concerning the distribution of hydrogen gas in the Galaxy. A way of solving the problem was suggested by H. C. van de Hulst in the Netherlands in 1944. In simple terms, it may be said that the proton and electron have associated magnetic fields resulting from the rotation (or spin) of the electrically charged particles. In the hydrogen atom, the proton and electron magnetic fields can be such that they are in the same direction (parallel) or in opposite directions (antiparallel). In the lowest energy (or ground) state of the hydrogen atom, there is a small energy difference between the parallel and antiparallel configurations, and the transition from the former to the latter will therefore be accompanied by the emission of radiation. The calculations made by van de Hulst showed that the frequency of this radiation should be 1420.4 megacycles per second, corresponding to a wavelength of approximately 21 centimeters, i.e., in the radio-frequency region of the electromagnetic spectrum.

12.39. The somewhat surprising conclusion, regarded by some with scepticism, was therefore that cold neutral hydrogen gas should emit a spectral line at radio wavelengths. This line, now commonly referred to as the *21-centimeter (hydrogen) line,* was first detected by H. J. Ewen and E. M. Purcell in the United States in 1951 and shortly thereafter by J. H. Oort and C. A. Muller in the Netherlands and by W. H. Christiansen and J. V. Hindman in Australia. Since that time, study of the 21-centimeter line has become an important aspect of radio astronomy, especially in the Netherlands and in Australia. The radio-frequency hydrogen line has also been observed in the emissions from other galaxies, especially the Magellanic Clouds.

12.40. Even before the existence of the 21-centimeter radiation had been verified, Oort had pointed out that, if the neutral hydrogen rotated with the Galaxy, such radiation could be utilized in a manner exactly equivalent to that described in § 12.26 *et seq.* to determine the distribution of hydrogen in the Milky Way. The great drawback of the original optical technique is that it is restricted to nearby stars; the presence of obscuring clouds of interstellar dust, especially in and between the arms of the Galaxy, makes it impossible to observe distant objects. The 21-centimeter radiation, however, does not suffer from this handicap, and it has been applied to determine the distribution of neutral hydrogen atoms to the limits of the Galaxy in all directions, except that of the galactic center where strong radiations from the nucleus interfere with the 21-centimeter radiation.

12.41. Locations of neutral atomic hydrogen detected in this manner are called *H I regions.* The ionized H II regions do not emit the 21-centimeter line, but the radiations arising from free-free electron transitions (§ 12.37) cover a range of radio-frequency wavelengths characteristic of the temperature of the gas. Radio astronomy thus provides a means for mapping both H I and H II regions in the Milky Way.

12.42. The method used for studying the distribution of neutral hydrogen (H I) is to point the radio telescope, which is a high-gain antenna, in a given direction (galactic longitude) in the plane of the Galaxy. Measurements are then made of the manner in which the intensity of the approximately 21-centimeter radio wave changes with frequency in the vicinity of 1420 megacycles per second. The same observations are repeated at all possible galactic longitudes. At each longitude, a curve, called a *line profile,* of the form of Fig. 12.10 is obtained, the number, height, and location of the maxima varying with the galactic longitude. From the Doppler shift of each maximum, relative to the normal frequency indicated by the broken vertical line in the figure, the radial velocity of the hydrogen gas relative to the Sun is determined. In fact, the line profiles are commonly plotted directly in terms of intensity (or signal strength) versus the relative radial velocity.

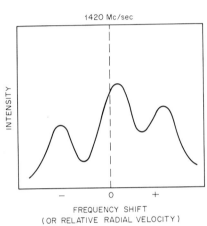

FIG. 12.10.   Profile of the 21-centimeter hydrogen line

12.43. Each maximum in the line profile represents a different radial velocity corresponding to the distance from the Sun of a particular emitting (H I) region; this distance is determined from a form of Oort's equation (12.1). By combining the galactic longitude with the distance, the location of the neutral hydrogen region can be identified. Furthermore, the height of the maximum in the line profile is a measure of the density of neutral hydrogen at that location. In this manner, the distribution of hydrogen in the Galaxy has been determined in considerable detail.

12.44. The highest densities of neutral hydrogen have been found to occur generally along the three spiral arms identified by optical methods (§ 12.24) and on a few other arms and branches. In particular, there is a partial ring close to the nucleus; it is sometimes referred to as an "expanding arm" because it is apparently moving outward. Within this ring, the nucleus, out to a radius of some 5000 light years (1500 parsecs), rotates in the manner of a solid body. In the absence of differential rotation, observations based on the Doppler shift, and the corresponding radial velocity, provide no information concerning the distribution of neutral hydrogen. The galactic rotational velocity of the Sun derived from the 21-centimeter line measurements is in agreement with that given earlier.

Gas and Dust in Galaxies

12.45. In addition to stars of many different types (cf. § 12.59 *et seq.*), galaxies contain substantial amounts of both gas and dust. The gas is largely hydrogen, both ionized and neutral, the presence of which has been demonstrated by spectroscopy (H II regions) and by radio astronomy (H I regions). In a spiral galaxy, most of the hydrogen is found within the arms, with smaller amounts in the spaces between the arms and in the nucleus. The proportion of hydrogen gas varies with the type of galaxy. Elliptical galaxies, which are presumably the oldest, contain very little gas, and in the spiral galaxies hydrogen gas constitutes a few weight percent, e.g., about 2 percent in the Milky Way. The younger galaxies, such as the Magellanic Clouds, may contain 50 (or more) percent by weight of gaseous hydrogen.

12.46. The interstellar medium also contains other elements in addition to hydrogen. This has been established by the discovery of the *interstellar lines,* as they are now called, by Johann Hartmann in Germany in 1904. These absorption lines, observed in the spectra of many stars, do not exhibit the same Doppler effects as do the lines in the true (emission) spectra of the stars themselves. Hartmann suggested that the absorption lines were produced by interstellar clouds and this view received support from V. M. Slipher in the United States in 1909, but it was not until some 15 years later that it became generally accepted.

12.47. The strongest interstellar lines are the H and K lines of ionized calcium (§ 6.122). In addition, lines of neutral calcium, sodium, potassium, and iron, and of ionized titanium have been detected, as well as those of CN, CH, and OH radicals. There are also some lines (or bands) that have not yet been identified. The interstellar lines may vary from one star to another, indicating that the elements and radicals (or molecules) are not always in the same proportions. It is of interest that the presence of OH radicals in space has been confirmed by S. Weinreb, *et al.* (1963) who detected an absorption line at a wavelength of 18 centimeters in the radio-frequency spectrum from the source known as Cassiopeia A.

12.48. The interstellar absorption lines are resonance lines (§ 6.81), resulting from the absorption of energy quanta by the lowest energy (ground) state of the respective atoms or radicals. It is for this reason that the lines of neutral hydrogen and helium are not observed. Although these elements are certainly present in the interstellar gas, the resonance lines are in the ultraviolet region of the spectrum and are absorbed by Earth's atmosphere. They consequently do not appear in the observed stellar spectra. Ionized hydrogen of itself has no line spectrum and so it could not be detected in this manner, in any event.

12.49. The interstellar lines from nearby stars, within the spiral arms of the Milky Way in which the Sun is located, often appear double or as a larger multiple. This effect is attributed to the existence of two or more gas clouds between the Sun (or Earth) and the particular star. The separation of the lines is due to the Doppler shifts caused by differences in the radial motions of the clouds relative to the Sun. When the star under observation lies in one of the other arms of the Galaxy, the wavelengths and multiplicities of the interstellar lines indicate that there are one or more gas clouds in each arm, but essentially none in the space between the arms.

12.50. The presence in galaxies of clouds of very small solid particles (or dust), in addition to the gas clouds, is indicated by the dark nebulae in the Milky Way which often obscure completely the stars lying beyond them. Dark bands and regions of obscuring dust have also been identified in other galaxies, especially when seen edgeways (Fig. 12.3). The existence of a belt in the sky close to the Milky Way in which no external galaxies are observed, called the *zone of avoidance*, is undoubtedly due to dust clouds that cannot be penetrated by the faint light from the distant objects. A dark region of dust clouds, known as the Coalsack, in the Galaxy is seen in Fig. 12.11.

12.51. Some luminous nebulae, the *emission nebulae*, have spectra consisting almost entirely of bright lines; others, however, known as *reflection nebulae,*

FIG. 12.11.   Dark region of dense clouds, known as the Coalsack, in the Milky Way is seen near the center of the picture. (*Harvard College Observatory*)

have dark lines on a continuous (bright) background. In the latter nebulae, the surface of the central star is not hot enough to cause appreciable ionization of the surrounding gas, such as occurs in the emission nebulae. The dark-line spectrum is then produced by the reflection (and scattering) of the starlight by dust particles.

12.52. Apart from the fairly obvious regions of dust in the Galaxy, there are interstellar dust clouds which have been detected in various indirect ways. For example, such clouds reduce the light received from the brighter stars and render the fainter ones invisible. By comparing the numbers of stars of different degrees of brightness (cf. § 12.67) per unit area of the sky at a number of adjacent locations, the presence of dust clouds can be detected.

12.53. The occurrence of interstellar absorption of light by dust particles had been suspected for some time, but the general acceptance of the idea is based on the work in the United States of the Swiss-born astronomer R. J. Trumpler, published in 1930. Besides the globular clusters of stars mentioned earlier, the Galaxy contains star assemblies of another type. These are called *galactic clusters,* because they occur within the galactic disc, and not in the halo as do the globular clusters. They are sometimes known as *open clusters* to indicate that the members form a loosely associated star group.* The number of stars in a galactic cluster is generally only a few hundred, but they are usually of many different types. This latter characteristic of galactic clusters is of special significance, as will be seen in § 12.133 *et seq.,* but for the present another aspect is of interest.

12.54. The galactic clusters fall into a number of classes according to their brightness. All the clusters in a particular class apparently have about the same diameter and the same absolute brightness, i.e., they emit the same total amount of light. The fraction of this light reaching Earth is inversely proportional to the square of the distance of the source; hence, a comparison of the apparent brightness of two galactic clusters of the same type should provide a means of relating their respective distances from Earth. Another way to compare the distances is by measuring the angular diameters (§ 6.21); since the linear diameters are roughly equal, the angular diameter of a galactic cluster should vary inversely as its distance from Earth.

12.55. In his study of galactic clusters, Trumpler found that the distances obtained by the two methods described above were substantially different. From their apparent brightness, the more distant clusters appeared to be farther away than was indicated by their angular diameters. The latter values were undoubtedly the more accurate, and the error in the brightness method was attributed to the absorption (and scattering) of light by interstellar dust. The observed apparent brightness of a distant galactic cluster would thus depend upon the amount of interstellar dust between the cluster and Earth, as well as upon the distance from Earth.

* Open clusters, like the globular clusters, have also been detected in external galaxies

12.56. In addition to absorbing light, the interstellar dust particles cause some scattering. The extent of the scattering, as in the terrestrial atmosphere, is greatest for light toward the blue end of the visible spectrum. Hence, the light from stars is often reddened by interstellar dust, for essentially the same reason, i.e., scattering of the blue component, as the Sun appears red at sunset when its light passes through a considerable distance in the atmosphere. It is of interest that the light from many stars, particularly those exhibiting the reddening effect, is quite strongly polarized (§ 6.135). In order to cause this polarization, the dust particles must be elongated, rather than spherical, and must be aligned predominantly in one direction. It is surmised that the alignment is caused by interstellar galactic magnetic fields, about which more will be said in a later section.

12.57. Estimates based on the absorption and scattering properties of the dust particles indicate that they have dimensions on the order of 10^{-5} to 10^{-4} centimeter, i.e., roughly about one hundred-thousandth part of an inch. Such particles could be seen only with the aid of a microscope. It has been suggested that they are very small crystals of some of the simplest molecules and radicals, e.g., H_2O, NH_3, CH_4, NH, NH_2, CH, etc., such as may occur in the heads of comets (§ 7.79). It must be admitted, however, that little is known definitely about the interstellar dust except that it may contain some ferrous or other material that can be aligned in a magnetic field.

12.58. The average density of dust particles in interstellar space is estimated to be about 10^{-26} gram per cubic centimeter. It should be noted that this is an average based on the assumption that the particles are distributed uniformly throughout the Galaxy. Local densities are undoubtedly considerably higher in some regions. For comparison purposes, it may be mentioned that the average density of neutral hydrogen in interstellar space, as derived from observations on the 21-centimeter line, is roughly 10^{-24} gram per cubic centimeter.* The density of hydrogen atoms is thus approximately 100 times as great as that of dust particles. The quantity of molecular hydrogen is not known, and there are differences of opinion concerning its density in interstellar space. Assuming the proportion of hydrogen molecules to be relatively small, the total mass of hydrogen gas and dust in the Milky Way is probably about 2 percent of the mass of the Galaxy. The amount of gas and dust in the spiral arms, however, is considerably larger, constituting perhaps 50 percent of the mass in some regions.

Stellar Populations

12.59. In 1944, following upon a detailed examination of the characteristics of the stars in the Milky Way and in a number of external galaxies, the

---

* This means that, on the average, a cubic centimeter of space contains approximately a single atom of hydrogen. Under normal atmospheric conditions, the same volume of hydrogen gas would contain almost 6×10^{19} atoms (as half that number of molecules).

German-born astronomer Walter Baade, then in the United States, concluded that most stars could be divided into two categories which he called Population I and Population II. As might have been expected, the division into only two classes represented an oversimplification, and the concept has been extended to five classes. In actual fact, of course, there is a fairly continuous gradation, so that, in principle, stars fall into a large number of categories, as will be evident in due course. Nevertheless, the distinction between the two types as indicated by Baade is useful and interesting.

12.60. Stars of *Population I* are found particularly in the arms of spiral galaxies, e.g., in the vicinity of the Sun, and also in galactic clusters. These regions are characterized by the presence of relatively large amounts of interstellar gas and dust. The brightest Population I stars are the blue giants, such as are fairly common in the Large Magellanic Cloud. The peculiar velocities of the stars of Population I are usually low, about 20 kilometers (12 miles) per second, i.e., roughly the same as the Sun.

12.61. The members of *Population II*, on the other hand, are found in elliptical galaxies, in globular clusters, and in the nuclei of spiral galaxies; these regions are essentially free of gas and dust. The most luminous Population II stars are the red supergiants, but they are much less bright than the brightest (blue giant) stars of Population I. The red supergiants of Population II are, however, considerably brighter than the Population I red giant stars. Population II stars differ from those in Population I by having large peculiar velocities, up to 100 kilometers (60 miles) or more per second.

12.62. The spectra of Population I stars indicate that they contain a larger proportion of elements heavier than helium than do the members of Population II. Thus, such elements may be present to the extent of from 0.1 to 3 atomic percent in stars of Population I, whereas in Population II stars the amount is only 0.01 to 0.03 percent as a general rule. For this reason Population I stars are often described as being "metal rich." The relatively high content of the heavier elements in Population I stars and their association with regions containing gas and dust suggests that these stars were formed relatively recently and some may, in fact, still be in the process of formation (cf. § 12.141). The extreme Population I stars, e.g., the blue giants, are probably not more than 10 million years old, although others, e.g., the Sun, are considerably older. Population II stars are all relatively old and many, such as those in the globular clusters in the Galaxy, have ages of perhaps 10 billion years or more. The large peculiar velocities, which are probably associated with elliptical rather than circular rotational paths, are apparently a consequence of the great age of the Population II stars.

INTERSTELLAR MAGNETIC FIELDS

12.63. Like the Sun, many individual stars have magnetic fields, but there are, in addition, weaker magnetic fields that are associated with the galaxy as a whole. Some evidence for the existence of such galactic magnetic fields was presented earlier in connection with the polarization of starlight. There are a number of other arguments that lead to the same conclusion. For example, the very existence of the arms in a spiral galaxy is attributed to the galactic magnetic field. The direction of rotation of spiral galaxies, and the fact that objects in the outer arms rotate more slowly than in the inner arms suggests that the arms would wind around the nucleus in the course of time. There is no adequate theory of the formation and persistence of the arms of a spiral, but there is fairly general agreement that galactic magnetic fields are involved in some manner.

12.64. In addition to radiations from localized sources within the Galaxy, there is a general emission of nonthermal radio-frequency waves over a range of wavelengths. This emission apparently comes from all directions and is believed to originate in a halo or corona surrounding the Milky Way; similar radiation has been received from other galaxies. The common view is that the radio waves represent synchrotron radiation (§ 6.181) produced by electrons of high energy spiraling about the lines of the galactic magnetic field (or fields). A field strength on the order of only 1 gamma (§ 8.219) appears to be sufficient to account for the observations.

12.65. The origin of the highly energetic particles in galactic cosmic rays (§ 8.246) has been the subject of much speculation, but two theories have received major attention. According to one theory, the particles are emitted from the remains of enormous stellar outbursts, called supernovae (§ 12.165). The Crab nebula is one of the best known examples of such remains. There is little doubt that this nebula is associated with magnetic fields that are capable of accelerating electrically charged particles to very high energy. The other theory postulates a more general, rather than a localized, source for the cosmic-ray particles. It is suggested that these particles are emitted from various stellar sources at low energies. Their energy is then increased as the result of repeated collisions with relatively weak moving galactic magnetic fields.

12.66. For several years radio astronomers have considered the possibility of determining the strength of the galactic magnetic field by measuring the Zeeman splitting (§ 6.105) of the 21-centimeter hydrogen line. This difficult feat was achieved in 1962 at the Jodrell Bank radio observatory in England. The field strength was found to be about 2 gammas, in general agreement with the value estimated from the galactic synchrotron radiation.

THE HERTZSPRUNG-RUSSELL DIAGRAM
AND ITS APPLICATIONS

STELLAR MAGNITUDES

12.67. The most obvious property of a star is its *apparent* (or *observed*) *brightness* or *apparent luminosity,* as indicated by the amount of light received

from it by an observer on Earth.* Astronomers express the apparent brightness by means of a quantity called the *apparent magnitude* or, in brief, the
magnitude, based on a system used by the Greek astronomer Hipparchus and
his disciple Ptolemy (§ 7.5) some two thousand years ago. In the original
scheme, the apparently brightest stars were said to be of the first magnitude,
the next brightest were second magnitude, and so on; the faintest stars observable with the unaided eye were referred to as being of the sixth magnitude. It
should be noted that the higher the magnitude of a star, the smaller is its
brightness. The invention of the telescope, leading to the detection of many
stars that had previously been invisible, and the development of photographic
techniques for comparing apparent brightnesses, thus providing greater refine-
ment than was possible by the subjective method previously used, made it
necessary to modify and extend the scheme for representing stellar brightness.

12.68. The modern system is based on two considerations: first, a characteristic of the human eye which ascribes differences (or intervals) of brightness to
what are actually brightness ratios, and second, the brightness ratio of stars
of the first magnitude to those of the sixth magnitude is approximately 100. The
magnitude scale is defined so that any two stars which differ in magnitude
by 5 units have a brightness ratio of exactly 100. Thus, if the magnitudes of
the two stars are represented by m and m', respectively, and the brightnesses
(or apparent luminosities) by l and l', then

$$m - m' = 5 \quad \text{and} \quad l' = 100\, l.$$

Suppose that a difference of 1 unit in magnitude represents a brightness ratio
of x, then a difference of 5 units represents a ratio of x^5; in other words, in the
case under consideration

$$\frac{l'}{l} = x^5 = 100.$$

It follows, therefore, that

$$x = 100^{0.2} = 2.512.$$

Every decrease of 1 unit in magnitude thus means an increase in apparent
brightness by a factor of 2.512. In general, if two stars have magnitudes m_A
and m_B and the corresponding brightnesses are l_A and l_B, then

$$\frac{l_A}{l_B} = (2.512)^{m_B - m_A}. \tag{12.2}$$

12.69. An alternative representation of the magnitude scale is possible by
noting that

$$2.512 = 100^{0.2} = 10^{0.4}.$$

Consequently, equation (12.2) may be written as

* Writers on astronomy use the term *luminosity* to indicate the actual rate of (luminous)
energy emission of a star; it is often expressed relative to the luminosity of the Sun
(§ 12.126). The quantity that is referred to here as the apparent (or observed) brightness or
apparent luminosity is called the *luminance* by physicists.

$$\frac{l_A}{l_B} = 10^{0.4(m_B - m_A)}. \tag{12.3}$$

Upon taking logarithms of both sides, it follows that

$$\log \frac{l_A}{l_B} = 0.4(m_B - m_A)$$

or

$$m_B - m_A = 2.5 \log \frac{l_A}{l_B}. \tag{12.4}$$

This equation provides the basis for the determination and expression of magnitudes; if the magnitude of any star A is known, the magnitude of any other star B can be obtained by determining the ratio l_A/l_B of the brightnesses of the two stars.

12.70. In order to express magnitudes by means of equation (12.4), it is necessary to establish an arbitrary value for the magnitude of a particular star to serve as a reference point. Originally, Polaris (the polestar) was chosen as the standard and its magnitude set equal to +2.0. The discovery in 1918 that Polaris is a variable star, i.e., its brightness varies periodically although only to a minor extent, made it necessary to introduce other standards, and several stars of constant brightness are now used in this connection.

12.71. Some of the consequences of the magnitude scale described above may be mentioned. For example, magnitudes are not necessarily exact integers, although they were in the ancient system. Furthermore, the scale has been extended both below the first magnitude, so that very bright stars have zero or negative values, and beyond the sixth magnitude for stars that can be seen only by means of telescopes. Thus, the Sun, the most brilliant celestial body, has a magnitude of −26.7, whereas that of the full Moon, the next brightest natural object, is −12.7. At the other extreme, the faintest star that can be seen by the 200-inch telescope at the Mount Palomar Observatory has a magnitude in the vicinity of +23.

12.72. As an illustration of the use of the magnitude scale, the brightness of Sirius, the most luminous star excluding the planets, may be compared with that of Polaris. The magnitude of Sirius is −1.5,* whereas that of Polaris is approximately +2.0; hence, the magnitude of Polaris exceeds that of Sirius by 3.5 units. Consequently, according to equation (12.3), the apparent brightness of Sirius is greater than that of Polaris by a factor of $10^{(0.4)(3.5)}$, i.e., about 25.

THE COLOR INDEX

12.73. The magnitudes given above are visual values; in other words, they are derived from observations of brightness as they would appear to the human eye. Owing to the subjective nature of observations actually made by

_____

* Sirius is actually a double star and this is the magnitude of the bright component (§ 12.120).

the eye, visual brightnesses are now obtained from measurements made with instruments, such as photographic devices and photoelectric cells. The sensitivity of these instruments to different wavelengths, however, is generally not the same as the eye. Consequently, to obtain visual magnitudes, it is necessary to use special photographic plates or photocells with filters, adjusted so that they respond to different wavelengths in a manner similar to the eye.

12.74. The photographic magnitude, as distinct from the visual magnitude, is determined with normal photographic plates which are more sensitive than the eye to light of short wavelength, i.e., in the blue and violet regions of the spectrum, and less sensitive at the longer wavelengths, i.e., in the yellow and red.* The difference between photographic and visual magnitudes is thus not the same for all stars, but varies from one star to another according to its color. Since stars have different surface temperatures, the distribution of radiation energy with wavelength varies accordingly (§ 6.62). The hotter stars radiate more in the short wavelength region, and so the photographic magnitude is less, i.e., the apparent brightness is greater, than the visual value. For cooler stars, on the other hand, the reverse is true; the photographic magnitude is then the greater of the two.

12.75. The difference between photographic magnitude (m_p) and visual magnitude (m_v), i.e., $m_p - m_v$, is called the *color index* of a given star; it provides an indication of the temperature of the star's radiating surface. Since photographic plates vary in their sensitivity, the following standard has been established: for a star belonging to the spectral class A0 as defined in § 12.103, i.e., with a surface temperature of about $11,000°$K,† the apparent brightness as determined with a blue-sensitive photographic plate should be equal to that obtained with one having the same sensitivity as the eye. Hence, the color index is often defined as $m_b - m_v$, where m_b is the magnitude in blue light.

12.76. If the surface temperature of a star is greater than $11,000°$K, the color index is negative, since the star emits more radiation at the blue (short wavelength) end of the spectrum; for a temperature below $11,000°$K, the color index is positive. In general, the smaller the algebraic value of the color index, i.e., including the sign, the hotter is the radiating surface of the star. A very hot star‡ with a surface temperature of $25,000°$K will have a color index of about -0.3, whereas for a relatively cool star, temperature $3500°$K, the color index is approximately $+1.5$.

ABSOLUTE MAGNITUDES

12.77. The apparent magnitude of a star, considered above, is determined by the brightness as it appears to a terrestrial observer, or instrument. It is

* The maximum sensitivity of the eye is to yellow-green at a wavelength of about 5500 Å.
† For conversion to temperatures on the Celsius (centigrade) and Fahrenheit scales, see § 6.192, footnote.
‡ Unless otherwise stated, the adjectives "hot," "hotter," "cool," etc., as applied to a star usually refer to the radiating surface temperature and not to the temperatures in the interior.

therefore, dependent upon the actual (or intrinsic) brightness of the star and its distance from Earth. Many stars are actually more luminous than the Sun, but they appear to be much less so because they are very much farther away. In order to compare actual (or absolute) brightnesses, and the corresponding absolute magnitudes, it is required to determine how the different stars would appear if they were observed from the same distance in all cases. The *absolute magnitude* is consequently defined as the magnitude based on the hypothetical apparent brightness at a distance of 10 parsecs.

12.78. To convert relative into absolute magnitudes, use is made of the fact that the intensity of radiation at any distance from a point source is inversely proportional to the square of that distance. Any star, including the Sun, is sufficiently far away to be treated as a point source, and so the brightness may be taken as varying in proportion to the reciprocal of the distance squared. Let l_{app} be the apparent brightness of a given star as observed from Earth which is d parsecs distant from the star; the brightness l_{abs} at a distance of 10 parsecs would then be given by

$$\frac{l_{app}}{l_{abs}} = \left(\frac{10}{d}\right)^2$$

or

$$\log \frac{l_{app}}{l_{abs}} = 2 \log 10 - 2 \log d$$

$$= 2 - 2 \log d. \tag{12.5}$$

12.79. If m is the apparent magnitude, corresponding to the brightness l_{app}, and $\mathfrak{M}$ is the absolute magnitude, which by definition is the value corresponding to l_{abs}, then by equation (**12.4**)

$$\mathfrak{M} - m = 2.5 \log \frac{l_{app}}{l_{abs}}.$$

Upon comparing the result with equation (**12.5**), it follows that

$$\mathfrak{M} - m = 5 - 5 \log d$$

or

$$\mathfrak{M} = m + 5 - 5 \log d. \tag{12.6}$$

Hence, if the distance of any star from Earth is known, i.e., d parsecs, the absolute magnitude, $\mathfrak{M}$, can be determined from equation (**12.6**) from the apparent magnitude, m. The manner in which stellar distances are obtained will be considered in the next section.

12.80. It should be noted that, in the derivation of equation (**12.5**), no allowance was made for absorption of light from the star by interstellar dust. If there is any reason to believe that dust clouds are present between the star and Earth, the absolute brightness will be greater than the value given by equation (**12.5**). The absolute magnitude from equation (**12.6**) will then be larger than the correct value. It is the practice, therefore, to write equation (12.6) in the form

$$\mathfrak{M} = m + 5 - 5 \log d - A,$$

where A is a term which allows for absorption of the starlight by interstellar dust.

DETERMINATION OF STELLAR DISTANCES

12.81. For the nearer stars, it is possible to determine the distance from Earth (or the Sun) by means of the *trigonometric parallax method*. The adjective trigonometric is not really necessary, but it is used occasionally to distinguish between the method to be considered here and the spectroscopic parallax method given in § 12.107. The principle of the trigonometric parallax method is similar to that described in § 6.10 for obtaining the distances of the planets. The horizontal parallax of a star, as defined in § 6.11, i.e., with a base line equal to Earth's radius, is much too small to be measurable with any accuracy. Consequently, the apparent change in position of the star is determined over a much longer base line, namely, the diameter of Earth's orbit around the Sun, i.e., twice the astronomical unit. The situation is represented in Fig. **12.12**, which

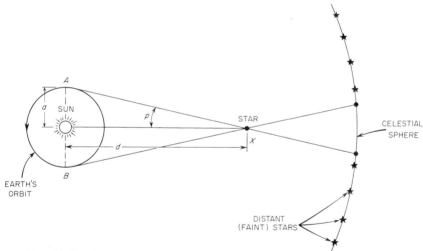

Fig. 12.12.   Determination of distance of a star by the parallax method

is drawn very much out of scale; the distance from Earth to X, the star under observation, is very much greater than indicated.* The *stellar parallax* is defined as the angle p, i.e., half the apparent change in position of the star X

---

* The distance of the closest star, other than the Sun or the planets, to Earth is 270,000 times the radius of Earth's orbit around the Sun.

as observed from Earth when it is at the points A and B. The parallax is determined by observing the locations of the star X against the background of very faint, much more distant, stars at intervals of half of Earth's orbital period, i.e., six months. The parallax is then half the angle representing the apparent change in position of the star. Of course, the background stars themselves move to some extent, but they are so far away that the effect on the measured parallax is small and may be neglected.

12.82. Since the distance from the star to Earth is very much greater than the radius of Earth's orbit, the distances AX and BX are essentially equal to the distance from the Sun to the star; this is represented by d in Fig. 12.12. Furthermore, the parallax angle p is extremely small; hence, in accordance with equation (6.2),

$$d = \frac{a}{p}, \tag{12.7}$$

where a is the radius of Earth's orbit, i.e., the astronomical unit (A.U.), and p is in radians. Thus, the distance d in A.U., i.e., d/a, is equal to $1/p$.

12.83. The astronomical unit is much too small to be convenient for expressing stellar distances; consequently, the *parsec* unit has come into common use for this purpose, as mentioned earlier. The parsec is defined as the distance at which the stellar parallax is 1 sec of arc.* From equation (12.7), it is seen that the distance of a star is inversely proportional to its parallax, and in view of the definition of the parsec, it follows that

$$d \text{ (in parsecs)} = \frac{1}{p \text{ (in seconds)}}.$$

Thus, the distance of a star from the Sun (or Earth) in parsecs is equal to $1/p$, where the stellar parallax p is expressed in seconds of arc. The parsec is a convenient unit because of this simple relationship between parallax and distance.

12.84. Since the distance d in A.U. is equivalent to $1/p$ with p in radians, and in parsecs to $1/p$ with p in seconds of arc, it is evident that 1 parsec is equal to the same number of astronomical units as there are seconds of arc in 1 radian, i.e., 206,300. Hence,

$$
\begin{aligned}
1 \text{ parsec} &= 206{,}300 \text{ A.U.} \\
&= 3.085 \times 10^{13} \text{ kilometers} \\
&= 1.918 \times 10^{13} \text{ miles.}
\end{aligned}
$$

The light year is equivalent to 9.461×10^{12} kilometers, so that

$$1 \text{ parsec} = \frac{3.085 \times 10^{13}}{9.461 \times 10^{12}} = 3.26 \text{ light years.}$$

* The term parsec is a combination of the first three letters of the words "parallax" and "second."

12.85. The simple trigonometrical parallax method for obtaining stellar distances is not applicable to celestial objects that are beyond some 100 parsecs from the Sun. This is the case because with increasing distance the parallax angle becomes so small that the inevitable errors of measurement are comparable with or larger than the required angle. A possible solution to the problem is to increase the length of the base line over which the observations are made; the result would then be to increase the parallax angle for a star at a given distance, thus facilitating its measurement. This is achieved in a procedure which makes use of the average motion of the Sun relative to stars in its vicinity.

12.86. The basic principle of the parallax method for determining distances is that an observer on a body (Earth), which changes its position with time, measures the apparent change in the location on the celestial sphere of an essentially stationary star. Although a single star cannot be regarded as stationary over a long period, a group of stars may be treated as if they were at rest, on the average. With reference to such a group, the Sun has a (peculiar) velocity of 20 kilometers per second. In the course of 10 years, for example, the Sun's position, relative to the star group, changes therefore by 6.3×10^9 kilometers, i.e., about 42 A.U., and this makes a useful base line for determining the parallaxes of distant stars.

12.87. The parallax of a single star measured after a lapse of 10 (or any other convenient number) years is meaningless, because the star is not stationary. But if a group of stars which are fairly close together is considered, the individual motions may be assumed to average out to zero. Hence, the average parallax for the group may be used to obtain an approximate indication of the distance from the Sun. This is the basis of the *statistical* (or *mean*) *parallax method* for deriving the distance of a star group; it can be applied to measure distances up to about 500 parsecs. Of course, the individual stars in the group are quite far apart, but their separation, e.g., a few parsecs, is small in comparison with the average distance of the group from the Sun.

12.88. An entirely different approach to the measurement of stellar distances is based on observations of the pulsating stars called *Cepheid variables* (or *Cepheids*) after the constellation Cepheus in which the first object of this type was discovered. Cepheids occur in the local Galaxy, as well as in external galaxies. The brightness of a Cepheid increases and decreases in a very regular periodic manner, the length of a period (or cycle) ranging from a few hours to many days for different stars. Each Cepheid, however, has a definite and usually constant period.

12.89. In 1912, when studying the Cepheids in the nearby galaxy the Small Magellanic Cloud, the American astronomer Henrietta Leavitt noted that there was a relationship between the mean brightness (or apparent magnitude) of Cepheids and their periods; the brighter the star, i.e., the smaller its apparent magnitude, the longer was its period. A few years later, in 1917, H. Shapley

(§ 12.20) showed that this fact could be used to determine distances, both within and outside the Galaxy, by making the reasonable postulate that the period of a Cepheid, no matter where it is located, is related only to its absolute magnitude. Consequently, if the absolute magnitudes of a number of Cepheids, e.g., in the Milky Way, are determined by measuring their apparent magnitude and distance, a universal relationship can be established between period and absolute magnitude. Hence, by observing the period of any Cepheid, its absolute magnitude is known. Then, from the apparent magnitude, as derived from the apparent brightness, the distance is given immediately by equation (12.6), with allowance for absorption if necessary.

12.90. The relationship between absolute magnitude and period was derived by using the statistical method to determine the distances of Cepheids. A curve was then drawn showing the variation of the period with absolute magnitude, and it was accepted that this curve was applicable to Cepheids of all types. The stars upon which the curve was based were all in the Small Magellanic Cloud, but when Cepheids in other galaxies were studied it was realized, about 1948, that two classes of Cepheids should be distinguished. These are the Type I (or classical) Cepheids, called classical because they resemble Delta Cephei, the first to be observed, and the less common Type II Cepheids which are found in globular clusters and also near the center of the Galaxy. The two types are often referred to as Population I and Population II Cepheids, respectively, because they are found in the same regions as stars of these populations.

12.91. For a given period, the absolute magnitude of a classical (Population I) Cepheid is about 1.5 units less, i.e., they are about four times brighter, than a Population II Cepheid (Fig. 12.13). The two types of Cepheids can be readily distinguished by their spectra. The Population I Cepheids are relatively young stars with high surface temperatures, so that they radiate mostly at shorter wavelengths, e.g., yellow and blue. The members of Population II, on the other hand, have cooler surfaces, and their colors tend toward the red end of the spectrum. It may be remarked, however, that the interiors of the Population II stars are probably much hotter than those of Population I, since they are older stars (cf. § 12.157).

12.92. Variables of a third type, called the *RR Lyrae stars*, because they resemble the RR Lyrae variable,* form a separate category. They are old stars, mostly blue in color, and are members of Population II. But they have short periods and the relationship between period and absolute magnitude is not the same as for the Population II Cepheids. The RR Lyrae stars are sometimes referred to as *cluster variables* because they were discovered in globular clusters. It is true that most of the variables in globular clusters are of this type, but more RR Lyrae stars are now known outside globular clusters than within them.

---

* The systematic method for naming variable stars is to precede the genitive form of the name of the constellation, e.g., Lyrae in constellation Lyra, by a letter, starting with R for the first to be discovered in the given constellation, followed by S, T, etc., to Z, and then by RR, RS, etc.

12.93. The periods of RR Lyrae stars cannot be used to determine their distances because the absolute magnitude is found to be very roughly constant, regardless of the period. If the absolute magnitude is assumed to be constant, however, it is possible to derive the approximate distance of an RR Lyrae star

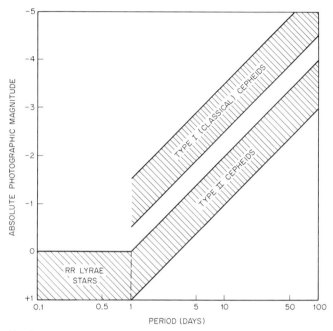

FIG. 12.13. Absolute magnitude versus luminosity period of Cepheids and RR-Lyrae stars

directly from equation **(12.6)**. The absolute magnitude of these variables has been obtained from the known apparent magnitudes and distances of those found in several globular clusters. Thus, with the value of $\mathfrak{M}$ determined, it is necessary only to measure the apparent magnitude, m, of an RR Lyrae star for its distance to be obtainable from equation **(12.6)**. This method has been used to derive the approximate distances of globular clusters in adjacent galaxies.

12.94. Some celestial objects, e.g., the Crab nebula, are expanding and a relatively simple procedure is available for determining their distances. The rate of expansion in the direction toward Earth is first obtained from the Doppler shift in the spectrum. The assumption is then made that the expansion is uniform in all directions, so that the observed rate applies also to the dimension (diameter) perpendicular to the line of sight. The next step is to measure by means of a telescope the rate at which the angular diameter of the object is increasing. If v is the rate of expansion of the diameter, expressed for example in kilometers per year, as derived from the Doppler shift, and ω is the observed rate of increase of the angular diameter in radians per year, it follows from a simple modification of equation (6.4) that the distance D, of the expanding object is given by

$$D = \frac{v}{\omega}.$$

SPECTRAL CLASSIFICATION OF STARS

12.95. A study of the spectra of many stars, both within and outside the Galaxy, has shown that they could be arranged in a definite sequence, generally known as the *Draper* (or *Harvard*) *classification.** Although the transition from one type of spectrum to another is not sharp, it is nevertheless possible to divide the great majority of stellar spectra into seven main groups or classes indicated by the letters O, B, A, F, G, K, M.† Each class can be subdivided, if required, to allow for finer gradations by adding a numeral, from 0 to 9. Thus, B0 represents the first member of class B spectra and the last member is B9, followed by A0 and so on. Typical spectra of stars in various subgroups from class B to class M are shown in Fig. 12.14. A few stars have spectra that fall into the special categories R, N (or R-N), and S which form branches toward the end of the main classification.

TABLE 12.1   CHARACTERISTIC FEATURES OF SPECTRAL CLASSES

Class	Main Spectral Lines
O	Ionized helium, nitrogen, oxygen, and silicon; hydrogen weak.
B	Neutral hydrogen and helium; ionized oxygen and silicon; ionized helium absent.
A	Hydrogen strong; ionized magnesium and silicon; ionized calcium, iron, and titanium begin to appear; helium absent.
F	Ionized calcium (Ca II) strong; some ionized and neutral metal atoms (iron, manganese, chromium, etc.); hydrogen weak.
G	Ionized calcium strong; neutral metal atoms increasing and ionized forms decreasing; molecular bands of CH and CN appear.
K	Neutral metal atoms (including calcium) strong; molecular bands stronger; hydrogen very weak or absent.
M	Neutral metal atoms very strong; TiO bands appear.
R-N	Similar to K and M, but molecular bands of CH, CN, and C_2 strong; TiO absent.
S	Neutral metal atoms strong; oxide (ZrO, LaO, YO) bands strong.

12.96. The most important spectral lines in the various classes are summarized in Table 12.1. An examination of this table shows that, in proceeding through the main classes from O to M (and R-N and S), there is a decrease in

* Named for the American astronomer Henry Draper (1837-1882), who made important contributions to stellar spectroscopy.

† The original intention was to designate the classes by successive letters of the alphabet, but in the course of time some proved to be in the wrong order, whereas others were found to be unnecessary and were eliminated. Furthermore, the need to introduce a class ahead of B (and A) led to the use of the letter O. These facts account for the strange order of the letters representing the spectral classes. The phrase "Oh, Be A Fine Girl, Kiss Me" is the common mnemonic.

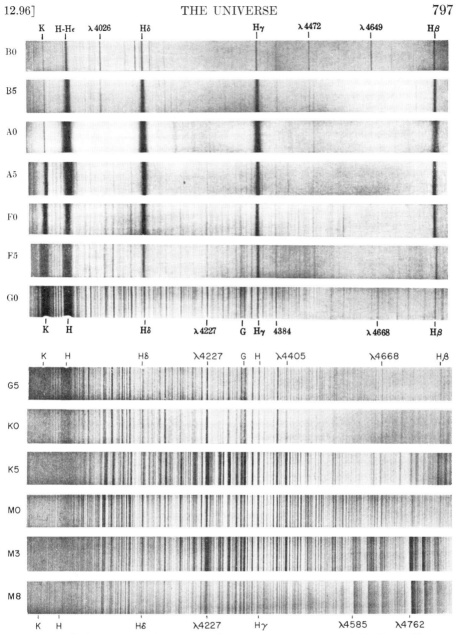

Fig. 12.14. Stellar spectra of classes B through M. (*University of Michigan Observatory*)

the spectral lines of ionized atoms, whereas the neutral atomic and molecular spectra increase in intensity. This indicates immediately that the radiating temperatures are decreasing from one class to the next, a conclusion confirmed in a general way by the color indexes (§ 12.75) and, more precisely, from detailed laboratory studies of the effect of temperature on the spectra of various elements. In order to correlate the spectral classes with the surface (or apparent) temperatures of the stars, these temperatures must be determined.

Stellar Surface Temperatures and Radii

12.97. A number of methods are available for estimating surface temperatures, but they are all based on the assumption that the star behaves as a black body. If the distance of a star is known, its radius can be determined, in principle, by measuring its angular diameter. The angular diameters of even the largest stars are, of course, extremely small; nevertheless, it has been possible to make measurements in some instances with the aid of an instrument called a *beam interferometer* attached to a telescope.* Suppose the radius of the star has been obtained in this manner; the equivalent black-body temperature can then be evaluated with the aid of the Stefan-Boltzmann equation (6.5).

12.98. Let R centimeters be the radius of a spherical star; its surface area is $4\pi R^2$, and the total rate of energy emission is given by equation (6.5) as

$$\text{Rate of energy emission} = (4\pi R^2)(1.38 \times 10^{-12}T^4) \text{ calories per second.}$$

If D centimeters is the distance of the star from Earth, then, at this distance, the energy will be spread over an area of $4\pi D^2$, assuming it to be radiated equally in all directions. The rate at which energy from the star is received, per square centimeter per second, on Earth is thus

$$\text{Rate of energy receipt} = \left(\frac{4\pi R^2}{4\pi D^2}\right)(1.38 \times 10^{-12})T^4$$

$$= 1.38 \times 10^{-12}T^4 \left(\frac{R}{D}\right)^2 \begin{array}{l} \text{calories per square} \\ \text{centimeter per second.} \end{array} \quad (12.8)$$

This quantity can be measured by means of a bolometer (§ 6.28), and if the distance of the star and its radius are known, the temperature can be calculated from equation (12.8). Since the quantity $(R/D)^2$ appears in the equation, it is not necessary to express R and D in centimeters; all that is required is that they should be in the same units of length.

12.99. Another procedure for obtaining the radiating surface temperature of a star is based on Wien's law, as expressed by equation (6.7). It does not require the radius and distance of the star to be known, but only the wavelength at which the rate of radiation emission (or radiant power) is a maximum. The

---

* An interferometer of new design in Australia should be capable of measuring angular diameters of stars down to the 5th magnitude.

temperature is then calculated in the manner described in § 6.67. There are some difficulties, however, associated with this technique: in the first place, it is necessary to make measurements at several individual wavelengths in order to determine the one at which the radiant power is a maximum, and second, for surface temperatures above about 10,000°K, the required wavelength will be in the ultraviolet region where the radiations are almost completely absorbed by the atmosphere.

12.100. A third method for evaluating approximate surface temperature is the simplest and has been used extensively. The basic principle is similar to that employed in the determination of the brightness temperatures of the Moon and the planets (cf. § 6.65). Since the radiation received from a star on a single wavelength is extremely small and susceptible to error, the method is modified by determining the ratio of the radiant power at two different wavelengths. For every temperature, a black body has a characteristic (Planck) distribution curve indicating the manner in which the radiant power varies with the wavelength, as shown in Fig. 6.13. From the measured ratio at two wavelengths, it is not difficult to estimate the corresponding black-body temperature. This method is applicable even when the maximum radiant power is in the ultraviolet part of the spectrum because there is always significant emission at longer wavelengths.

12.101. It is of interest to mention that the surface temperature of a star obtained by either of the last two methods provides an indirect means for determining its radius, by comparison with another star whose radius and temperature have been measured. The other information required is the difference between the absolute bolometric magnitudes,* which can be derived from the apparent brightnesses and distances of the two stars. It can be seen from the arguments in § 12.98 that, assuming ideal black-body behavior, the total rate of energy emission (or radiant power) of a star is proportional to R^2T^4. The actual rate of energy emission of a star is called its luminosity (§ 12.67, footnote), which may be represented by the symbol L. For two stars with radii R_A and R_B, and surface temperatures T_A and T_B, respectively, the ratio of the radiant powers, and hence the ratio of the luminosities, i.e., L_A/L_B, is $R_A^2T_A^4/R_B^2T_B^4$. For a given distance from the two stars, e.g., 10 parsecs, the ratio of the apparent brightnesses is equal to the ratio of the luminosities; it follows, therefore, in view of the definition of absolute magnitude, that equation (12.4) can be written in the form

$$\mathfrak{M}_B - \mathfrak{M}_A = 2.5 \log \frac{L_A}{L_B}. \tag{12.9}$$

Upon introducing the expression for L_A/L_B derived above, it is seen that

* The bolometric magnitude is based on the total energy received from the star at all wavelengths, i.e., ultraviolet and infrared as well as visual. If the temperature of a star is known, the bolometric magnitude can be estimated from the visual value by applying a correction; this ranges from −2.7 at 25,000°K to −0.7 at 4000°K.

$$\mathfrak{M}_B - \mathfrak{M}_A = 2.5 \log \frac{R_A{}^2 T_A{}^4}{R_B{}^2 T_B{}^4}$$

$$= 5.0 \log \frac{R_A T_A{}^2}{R_B T_B{}^2}.$$

Hence, if $\mathfrak{M}_B - \mathfrak{M}_A$, T_A, T_B, and R_A are known, the radius of the star B can be calculated. If L represents the total rate of energy emission, $\mathfrak{M}$ is strictly the bolometric magnitude, but if, as is commonly the case, L is the rate of emission of visible radiation energy, $\mathfrak{M}$ is the absolute visual magnitude.

12.102. Starting with the Sun as star A or with any one of the few large stars whose radii have been measured, it is possible to derive the radii of a series of stars in order of decreasing (or increasing) absolute magnitude. The largest (giant) stars have radii that are several hundred times the solar radius, whereas the smallest (dwarf) stars detected are about the size of Earth.

THE HERTZSPRUNG-RUSSELL DIAGRAM

12.103. The majority of stars near the Sun belong to what is called the "main sequence," which will be discussed more fully in § 12.106; for these stars, the correlation between the spectral class and approximate surface temperature is given in Table 12.2. For stars in external galaxies, and also to some extent

TABLE 12.2 SPECTRAL CLASS AND SURFACE TEMPERATURE OF MAIN-SEQUENCE STARS

Spectral Class	Temperature (°K)	Color Index	Spectral Class	Temperature (°K)	Color Index
O5	50,000	—	F5	6600	+0.44
B0	25,000	−0.32	G0	6000	+0.60
B5	15,600	−0.16	G5	5520	+0.68
A0	11,000	0.00	K0	5120	+0.82
A5	8700	+0.15	K5	4400	+1.18
F0	7600	+0.30	M0	3600	+1.45

within the Milky Way, the radiation received on Earth is too small to be measured, and then the (blue minus visual) color index provides an indication of the temperature. The approximate values of the color index are therefore included in the table. For the hottest (O and B) stars, the color index is negative, and they appear blue or blue-white in color. The F stars are white and the G stars, like the Sun (G2), are yellow; the coolest (K and M) stars have positive color indexes and their colors are orange and red.

12.104. Most stars have surface temperatures between 50,000° and 3000°K, so that they fall within the Draper classification. There are, however, a few with much higher apparent temperatures. In addition, some stars have surface temperatures below 3000°K; these stars are very difficult to observe because

they are faint, i.e., their radiation emission is small and is mainly in the infrared region. There are probably many such cool stars that have not yet been
detected.

12.105. One of the most interesting and useful astronomical generalizations is
the *Hertzsprung-Russell diagram*, which developed largely from the publications of the Danish-born Ejnar Hertzsprung in 1912, then in Holland, and of
Henry N. Russell in the United States in 1914. In the common form of the
H-R diagram, as it is called for brevity, the absolute visual magnitudes of
stars are plotted as a function of the spectral class, as depicted in Fig. 12.15; the

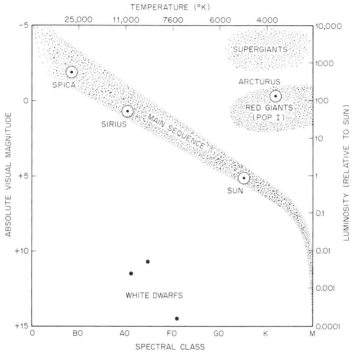

Fig. 12.15. Simplified representation of the Hertzsprung-Russell diagram

corresponding surface temperatures and color indices are also shown. The right-
hand ordinate gives the luminosity of a star relative to that of the Sun, i.e.,
$L/L_\odot$, where $L_\odot$ is the luminosity of the Sun.*

12.106. A large proportion, at least **90** percent, of the known stars fall into a
diagonal band, from top left to bottom right of the figure, called the *main sequence*. As might be expected, the hottest stars, at the left end of the main
sequence, are also the brightest, as indicated by their small, often negative,

---

* According to equation (12.9), the luminosity of a star relative to the Sun is equal to
$10^{0.4(\mathfrak{M}-\mathfrak{M}_\odot)}$, where $\mathfrak{M}$ is the magnitude of the star and $\mathfrak{M}_\odot$ is that of the Sun.

absolute magnitudes. The main-sequence stars show a general decrease in size, and also in temperature, from left to right of the H-R diagram, as may be seen from the following considerations. The absolute brightness of a star is proportional to R^2T^4, where R is its radius and T the surface temperature. If all stars in the main sequence had the same radius, the absolute brightness would vary as T^4. In fact, however, the slope of the main-sequence curve in Fig. 12.15 indicates a variation proportional to a higher power of the temperature, i.e., about $T^{5.5}$. This means that the stellar radii are not constant, but increase with the temperature. Thus, the stars at the upper left of the main sequence are hot, blue giants, whereas those at the extreme lower right are cool red dwarf stars. The Sun, in spectral class G2 and absolute visual magnitude +5, lies somewhere near the middle of the main sequence; it may, therefore, be regarded as an average star in many respects, e.g., in size, surface temperature, absolute brightness, and, as will be seen shortly, in mass.

12.107. The H-R diagram has been utilized to determine the approximate distances from Earth of main-sequence stars when other methods are not applicable. If the spectral class (or color index) has been identified, the absolute magnitude can be estimated from Fig. 12.15. Then, if the apparent magnitude is known, from the observed apparent brightness, the distance can be calculated by means of equation (12.6). Since the distance in parsecs is equal to the reciprocal of the stellar parallax (§ 12.83), the value derived in this manner is often called the *spectroscopic parallax* of the star. It is necessary, of course, to make sure that the star under consideration belongs to the main sequence. Whether this is the case or not can generally be determined from certain characteristics of its spectrum, as will be apparent shortly.

Giant and Dwarf Stars

12.108. Most of the stars that do not belong to the main sequence fall into two general groups, namely, red giants (and supergiants) and white dwarfs. The *red giants* have surface temperatures that range from about 4000° to 6000°K and so are orange or red in color. Because of their large size, they are from a hundred to several thousand times more luminous than main-sequence stars of the same spectral class. It is seen from Fig. 12.15 that the difference in absolute magnitude (or ratio of the brightness) increases with decreasing temperature. Since the absolute brightness (or luminosity) is proportional to R^2T^4, it follows that the brighter stars must have larger radii than those on the main sequence at the same temperature (or spectral class); the former are thus designated giant stars. The star Capella, in the constellation Auriga, for example, has about the same surface temperature as the Sun, but its absolute magnitude is 5.5 units smaller. Hence, the absolute brightness of Capella is roughly 150 times greater than that of the Sun. Since the temperatures are the same, the brightness is proportional to R^2; the radius of Capella is therefore some 12 times the solar radius.

12.109. The *red supergiants* of Population II are even larger than the Population I giant red stars of the same surface temperature. One of the most familiar supergiants is the bright star Betelgeuse in the constellation Orion. It is of special interest as it was the first star to have its radius determined by direct measurement of the angular diameter. The radius of Betelgeuse is over 160 million kilometers (100 million miles); this means that if the center of the star were coincident with the center of the Sun, the exterior would reach beyond Earth.

12.110. Although the spectra of red giants have the same general features as the main-sequence stars, a careful examination has revealed some differences. In the first place, the pressure broadening (§ 6.87) of the lines in the spectra of the giants is less; furthermore, the lines of ionized species are somewhat enhanced as compared with the same spectral class in the main sequence. As seen in Chapter 6, both these effects would be expected if the gas pressures (or densities) in the exterior layers (or atmospheres) of the giants were lower than in the main-sequence stars. As a consequence of the increase in intensity of the ionic lines, the surface temperatures of the red giant stars as indicated by their spectra are somewhat higher than the actual values. Hence, it is generally accepted that the temperatures of the giants are a few hundred degrees below those of main-sequence stars of the same spectral class.

12.111. The *white dwarfs*, which are usually faint blue, white, or yellow in color, are believed to constitute some 3 percent of the total stars in the Galaxy. Their absolute magnitudes are about 10 units larger than stars of the same color (or spectral class) in the main sequence; hence, the radii are smaller by a factor of approximately a hundred. A white dwarf in the same spectral class as the Sun would have a radius similar to Earth. The masses, however, of the white dwarfs are of the same order as the Sun, and so they are extremely dense bodies. More will be said about this matter at a later stage (§ 12.158). Because of their large densities and gravitational forces, the outer layers (or atmospheres) are also very dense and have high gas pressures. This is manifested by the marked pressure broadening of the spectral lines of the white dwarfs.

12.112. It is of interest that the brightest star in the sky, Sirius A, with an apparent magnitude of −1.5, has a white dwarf companion, Sirius B, with an apparent magnitude of about +7.5. The brightness ratio of the two stars is thus approximately 4000. The surface temperatures are not very different and so the radius of Sirius A is about 63 times as great as that of its white dwarf companion.

12.113. A further development in connection with the H-R diagram has resulted from the discovery of a correlation between the absolute magnitude of a star and its mass. Before discussing this aspect of the subject, however, it is necessary to describe how stellar masses are determined. The procedure is similar in its general principle to the method used to obtain the mass of the Sun (§ 6.20).

STELLAR MASSES

12.114. The only direct manner whereby the mass of a star can be evaluated is to observe the orbital period of a companion body and to apply an equation based on Kepler's third law. Fortunately, there are many binary systems, each consisting of a pair of stars revolving about their common barycenter, as do Earth and the Moon (§ 9.5). Binary stars are divided from the observational standpoint into three categories which are not mutually exclusive; they are visual, spectroscopic, and eclipsing binaries.

12.115. In *visual binaries*, both components can be seen in the telescope; in *spectroscopic binaries* the two individual stars may not be visible but their presence can be established by features in the spectrum. If the orbital plane of the two stars is directed in space in such a manner that it is observed edgeways from Earth, then from time to time one will pass in front of and eclipse the other, partially or wholly. In such a system, called an *eclipsing binary*, the brightness of the system varies periodically.* Visual binaries are mostly employed for determining stellar masses and limited data are obtainable from studying spectroscopic binaries. The eclipsing binaries, however, cannot provide any useful information concerning the masses of the components, unless they also happen to be spectroscopic binaries.

12.116. From observation of a visual binary against the star background over a period of years, it is frequently possible to determine the orbit of the brighter component. The two quantities required for computing the mass of the system are the length of the semi-major axis and the orbital period. The former is obtained from a measurement of the average angular separation of the two components of the binary system and its known distance from Earth (cf. § 6.21). If the orbital plane of the binary is not perpendicular to the line of sight, as is usually the case, there is some distortion in the apparent orbit for which a correction is made.

12.117. Consider two binary systems, A and B, with orbital periods P_A and P_B and semi-major axes a_A and a_B, respectively; the semi-major axis is generally taken as the average distance between the two components of the binary (§ 9.6). Let M_1 and M_2 represent the masses of these components in each case.† Then, in accordance with equation (2.26),

$$(M_1 + M_2)_A = \frac{4\pi^2}{G} \cdot \frac{a_A{}^3}{P_A{}^2}$$

and

$$(M_1 + M_2)_B = \frac{4\pi^2}{G} \cdot \frac{a_B{}^3}{P_B{}^2}$$

so that, upon dividing one expression by the other,

---

* Eclipsing binaries are quite different from variable stars; in the latter it is a single star whose brightness exhibits periodic changes.

† It should be noted that the symbol M represents mass and not magnitude.

$$\frac{(M_1 + M_2)_A}{(M_1 + M_2)_B} = \left(\frac{a_A}{a_B}\right)^3 \left(\frac{P_B}{P_A}\right)^2. \tag{12.10}$$

12.118. The foregoing equations are applicable to any two bodies that revolve about each other, and hence system B may be taken to represent the Sun and Earth. In this case $(M_1 + M_2)_B$ is essentially identical with the solar mass, a_B is the astronomical unit, and P_B is one sidereal year. Hence, equation (12.10) may be written in the general form

$$M_1 + M_2 = \frac{a^3}{P^2}, \tag{12.11}$$

where $M_1 + M_2$ is the total mass of the binary in units of the solar mass, a is the semi-major axis in astronomical units, and P is the orbital period in ordinary years. Since a and P have been measured and can easily be expressed in the appropriate units, the mass of the binary can be evaluated in terms of the solar mass. This has been done for a large number of visual binaries.

12.119. Strictly speaking, in order to derive the sum of the masses of the two stars, as just described, it is not necessary that the orbits of both components of the binary be known. An estimate of the semi-major axis can be made by observing only one of the stars relative to the other. If the individual masses are to be determined, however, the orbit of each component must be obtained by observing the positions of both stars relative to the background of fixed stars. Since the two stars revolve about their common barycenter, the position of the latter can be located if both orbits have been established. The ratio of the masses of the two components of the binary can then be obtained by means of equation (9.1); it is equal to the inverse ratio of the respective distances of the apocenters of the two orbits from the barycenter of the system (cf. Figs. 9.1 and 9.2).

12.120. As an illustration of the procedure described above, the Sirius binary will be considered. The orbital period of each component is 50 years, and the mean distance between the two stars is 20.5 A.U.; this may be taken as equal to the semi-major axis. Hence, by equation (12.11),

$$M_1 + M_2 = \frac{(20.5)^3}{(50)^2} = 3.4 \text{ solar masses.}$$

The inverse ratio of the respective distances from the barycenter is approximately 2.4, so that

$$\frac{M_1}{M_2} = 2.4.$$

It is then readily found that M_1, representing the mass of the bright component Sirius A, is about 2.4 solar masses, and M_2, for the faint companion Sirius B, is approximately one solar mass.

12.121. Observations on visual binaries indicate that the masses of main sequence stars range from perhaps 100 times the mass of the Sun down to roughly one hundredth (0.01) of a solar mass. Bodies more massive than about 100 $M_\odot$ are unstable, whereas in those lighter than 0.01 $M_\odot$ the central temperatures do not become high enough for energy release by thermonuclear reactions to be possible. The great majority of known stars have masses from 0.1 to ten times the mass of the Sun.

12.122. If the individual stars in a binary pair cannot be distinguished, either because of the great distance from Earth or because they are close together, the system appears in the telescope as a single star. The existence of a binary may be indicated, however, by the spectrum. Consider, for simplicity, the case in which the plane of the orbits is directed edgeways toward Earth; thus, in Fig. 12.16, the orbits and Earth lie within the plane of the paper. When the

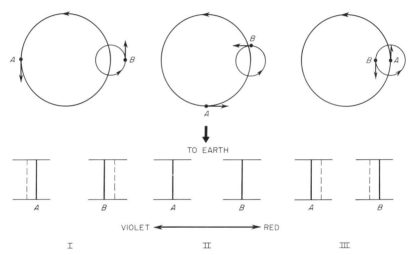

FIG. 12.16.   Doppler shifts in spectra of a binary pair of stars. The full lines represent the normal spectra; the dotted lines indicate the Doppler shifts

stars A and B are in the positions indicated in I, the star A is moving directly toward Earth and B is traveling in the opposite direction. The spectrum of A should thus exhibit a Doppler shift toward the violet (short wavelength) region, whereas that of B is shifted toward the red, as indicated in the figure. In position II, both stars are moving in a direction perpendicular to the line of sight and there is no Doppler shift. Finally, in position III, star A is moving away from Earth and B toward it; the spectral shifts are thus opposite to those in position I.

12.123. From these considerations, it is evident that, if a series of spectra of a binary are taken at several intervals over an orbit, the lines of one component will oscillate in one direction in wavelength whereas those of the second component will change in the opposite direction. From the displacement of each set of lines, it should be possible, in principle, to calculate the orbital period and the average velocities of the two stars; the ratio of these velocities is equal to the reciprocal of the mass ratio.* Consequently, if the mean distance between the two components, i.e., the semi-major axis, were known the individual masses could be calculated. An approximate estimate of this distance can be made by multiplying the sum of the velocities of the two stars by their orbital period to obtain the circumference of the relative orbit. If the latter is assumed to be a circle, the radius is roughly equal to the required semi-major axis.

12.124. The foregoing procedure is based on the supposition that the orbital plane of the binary system is edgeways to the line of sight. When this is actually (or approximately) true, the system is an eclipsing binary and exhibits characteristic variations in brightness. If the orbital plane is inclined to the line of sight, the stars in positions I and III in Fig. 12.16 are not moving directly toward or away from Earth. The observed Doppler shift does not then give the true velocity, but only its radial component, i.e., the component along the line of sight. The ratio of these radial components is still equal to the reciprocal of the mass ratio, but the total mass cannot be obtained unless the inclination of the orbital plane is known. Unfortunately, there is no way of determining this quantity, except in the case of eclipsing binaries when the inclination is small and is not significant, in any event. The best that can be done is to determine $(M_1 + M_2) \sin^3 i$, where i is the angle between the orbital plane and a plane perpendicular to the line of sight. Since $\sin^3 i$ is less than unity, except for an edgeways plane when i is 90 deg and $\sin^3 i = 1$, the quantity obtained is less than the actual mass of the binary system, but how much less cannot be ascertained.

12.125. There are two situations in which spectroscopic binaries can provide no information related to mass. One is when the angle i is zero, i.e., when the orbital plane is perpendicular to the line of sight, for then $(M_1 + M_2) \sin^3 i$ is zero. Furthermore, the radial velocities of the stars are also zero and there is no Doppler shift of the spectral lines. The other case is when one component of the binary is significantly brighter, e.g., one magnitude or more smaller, than the other. A clear spectrum, which is not overexposed, then shows only the lines of the bright component. The orbital velocity of the latter star can be determined, as well as the orbital period, but nothing more.

MASS-LUMINOSITY RELATIONSHIP

12.126. In 1911, J. Holm in South Africa suggested that a relationship might exist between the absolute magnitudes of stars and their masses, and in 1924, the famous British astronomer Arthur S. Eddington treated the subject in some detail. The general trend of the most recent values of the absolute

* This is most easily seen by considering two circular orbits; since the orbital periods are the same for both components, the velocity is proportional to the orbital radius, and this is inversely proportional to the mass by equation (9.1).

bolometric magnitudes and luminosities (relative to the Sun) for main-sequence stars as a function of mass (relative to the solar mass) is indicated in Fig. 12.17. The points do not actually lie on the line shown, but they fall within a narrow band on either side of this line. The mass-luminosity curve can thus

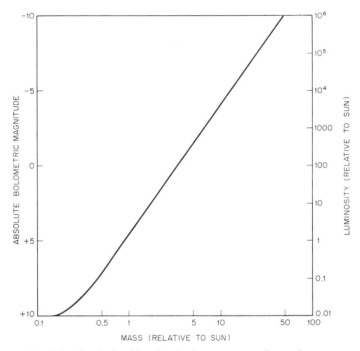

FIG. 12.17.   Magnitude (and luminosity) versus mass for main-sequence stars

be used to estimate the mass of a star from its absolute (bolometric) magnitude or luminosity relative to the Sun.

12.127. It is seen from Fig. **12.17** that the stellar mass increases regularly as the luminosity increases or as the absolute magnitude decreases. It follows, therefore, from the mass-luminosity relation and the H-R diagram (Fig. **12.15**) that the brightest main-sequence stars are the most massive. In other words, in going down the main-sequence curve from left to right, the masses of the stars decrease regularly. As seen in § **12.106**, the radii also decrease in the same direction.

12.128. The slope of the curve in Fig. **12.17** implies that the luminosity of a main-sequence star is proportional to the third or fourth power of the mass. This result has some important consequences. The luminosity, as defined earlier, is a measure of the rate at which a star is radiating energy. If it is assumed that the surface temperature of a star remains constant, as it probably does as long as it stays on the main sequence (§ 12.145), the luminosity must also indicate the rate at which energy is being produced in the star's interior.

12.129. Let M be the mass of a star and L its luminosity, then M/L is a measure of the time required for a certain fraction of the stellar material, which is largely hydrogen, to be consumed in the release of energy (cf. § 6.184 *et seq.*). According to Fig. 12.17, L is roughly proportional to M^3 or M^4; hence, this times varies as $1/M^2$ or $1/M^3$. Thus, the greater the mass of the star, the more rapidly will its energy-producing material be used up. A star that is 10 times as massive as the Sun, for example, will burn itself out in a period from 100 to 1000 times shorter than will the Sun.

MAXIMUM AGE OF STARS

12.130. Calculations show that when about 10 percent of the hydrogen present in a star has been consumed in the liberation of energy, by conversion into helium, it will no longer belong to the main sequence. It was seen in § 6.189 that, during the past 5×10^9 years (or so), the Sun has burnt up about 5 percent of its hydrogen; hence, assuming the rate of energy release to remain constant, the Sun will begin to depart from the main sequence when its age is roughly 10 billion (10^{10}) years.* Consequently, a star with a mass equal to 10 solar masses will reach this stage in 10^7 or 10^8 years. It is apparent, therefore, that the massive main-sequence stars, i.e., the blue giants at the upper left of the H-R diagram, must be young stars compared with the Sun. The older massive stars have long since moved off the main sequence and are now quite different in character. Class B0 stars, for example, that are still on the main sequence, cannot be more than about 10 million years old, but they may be younger. The exact age cannot be determined, but it is reasonably certain that if a star having the mass of a B0 star were more than about 20 million years old, it would certainly not now lie on the main sequence of the H-R diagram.

12.131. If the mass and luminosity (or absolute bolometric magnitude) of a star are known, its approximate maximum age can be determined. Suppose M is the mass of the star relative to that of the Sun and L is the luminosity, i.e., the total rate of energy release, compared with that of the Sun. The time required to utilize a certain proportion of the star's mass in the production of energy, relative to the time for the Sun to use up the same proportion, is then equal to M/L. The total period during which the Sun may be expected to remain on the main sequence is about 10^{10} years; hence, the maximum age of the given star is approximately $(M/L) \times 10^{10}$ years. Thus, if the mass of a star is 10 solar masses and its bolometric luminosity is 2000, its maximum age will be roughly $(10/2000) \times 10^{10}$, i.e., 5×10^7 (or 50 million) years. The maximum ages of main-sequence stars of different masses and the corresponding spectral classes are given in Table 12.3.

---

* By convention, a star is said to be of "zero age" when it reaches the main sequence; its actual age is somewhat greater (cf. § 12.137 *et seq.*).

TABLE 12.3   MAXIMUM AGES OF MAIN–SEQUENCE STARS

Mass (solar masses)	Approximate Maximum Age (years)	Spectral Class
25	2×10^7	B0
4	4×10^8	A0
2	2×10^9	F0
1	10^{10}	G2
0.6	(10^{11})*	K5
0.2	(10^{12})*	M5

* These maxima are probably greatly in excess of the actual ages; there is no evidence of any star with an age exceeding about 1 or 2×10^{10} years.

12.132. The important conclusion to be drawn from the H-R diagram is that the ages of main-sequence stars range from a million years (or so) up to at least 5 billion years, the age of the Sun. It is probable that both younger and older stars exist, but this cannot be determined in the manner under consideration.* Stars less massive than the Sun, lying below it on the main sequence of the H-R diagram, may be younger, older than, or the same age as the Sun, but it is not possible to state which is the case. In any event, it is very clear that the stars (and the Sun) were not all formed at the same time. Some of the more massive blue giant (Population I) stars now on the main sequence, and perhaps some of the less massive stars, reached this stage no more than a few million years ago, although the Sun must have done so almost 5 billion years earlier. Star formation must thus be regarded as a continuing process. The general inference is seen to be the same as that in § 12.62, based on the association of Population I stars with gas and dust.

AGES OF GALACTIC CLUSTERS

12.133. The galactic (or open) clusters provide an interesting application of the use of the H-R diagram to estimate maximum ages of stars. The variation of color index with absolute magnitude (or luminosity) has been determined for the stars in several galactic clusters. The curves obtained by plotting the results on a diagram of the H-R type are shown in Fig. 12.18.† It is apparent that the lower parts of all the curves coincide with one another and with the normal H-R main sequence. The upper parts, for the more massive stars, however, deviate from the main sequence and differ from one cluster to another.

* It is possible that some stars in the Orion nebula became luminous little more than 20,000 years ago.
† Astronomical objects that appear to be nebulous, including galaxies, star clusters, and nebulae, are frequently identified by their M numbers in the list published by Charles Messier in 1784, or by their NGC numbers in the New General Catalogue of Nebulae and Star Clusters issued by J. L. E. Dreyer in 1888. Supplements to the latter are the Index Catalogues of 1895 and 1908; the entries in these are indicated by I.C. numbers.

12.134. The interpretation of the data in Fig. 12.18 is that all the stars in a given galactic cluster were formed, and reached the main sequence, at about the same time.* Since the masses of the stars were presumably not all the same, but covered a range, e.g., from about 100 to 0.01 solar masses, they fell on

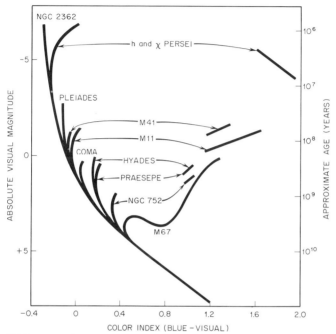

FIG. 12.18.   H-R-type diagram and approximate ages of galactic clusters (after A. R. Sandage)

different parts of the main-sequence curve. The most massive (blue giant) members of a cluster soon consumed the expendable 10 percent of hydrogen and began to move to the right away from the main sequence. In due course, the somewhat less massive stars began to move off, and so on. The color-magnitude curves at different ages would then be similar to the set of curves in Fig. 12.18.

12.135. If a star cluster was formed relatively recently, the majority of the members would still be on the main sequence; only the most massive would have had time to move away. This is evidently the case for the cluster NGC 2362 and for the double cluster (h and χ) in Perseus. At the other extreme, only a small proportion of the stars in the clusters NGC 752 and M 67 are now on the main sequence. These clusters are evidently the oldest of those in Fig. 12.18. All the stars more than about 1.5 times the mass of the Sun are no longer on the main sequence but have become (or are becoming) red giants.

* This is apparently not always the case, but the exceptions do not significantly affect the arguments presented here.

12.136. The right-hand ordinate of Fig. 12.18 indicates approximate ages at which stars of various absolute magnitudes (or masses) would be expected to depart from the main sequence. The values were obtained from calculations made along the lines indicated in § 12.130. The stars in the NGC 2362 cluster are apparently only about a million years old and the age of the Perseus clusters is no more than a few million years. On the other hand, M 67, apparently the oldest open cluster in the Galaxy, is estimated to be some seven billion (7×10^9) years old.

FORMATION AND EVOLUTION OF STARS

From Protostar to Main Sequence

12.137. In the present section, a general theory of the formation and evolution of stars will be examined, mainly in the light of the H-R diagram. It is usually considered that the first stage in the formation of a star is the contraction, under the influence of the force of gravity, of a very large volume of gas, mainly hydrogen, and dust (cf. § 7.192). Turbulence during the contraction phase may cause the large mass to break up into smaller parts thereby leading ultimately to a group or cluster of stars. As a result of the gravitational contraction, the temperature increases and if the path of the *protostar*, as it is then, could be plotted on an extended H-R diagram, it would start well to the right of the main sequence and move to the left, with an upward inclination. In other words, the surface temperature of the protostar would increase considerably, but its absolute brightness would increase less rapidly because of the steady decrease in radius.

12.138. In the early stages, the temperature would be too low for any radiation to be detectable in the visible range, but the protostar would emit in the infrared region of the spectrum. Little effort has yet been made to search for infrared stars (or protostars), but studies in this direction might well form part of a future program in space science. The discovery of such stars would provide partial verification of a purely speculative aspect of the theory of star formation.

12.139. After a certain period, the contracting protostar will become hot enough to be visible as a star, and shortly thereafter it will reach the main sequence of the H-R diagram at a point depending upon its mass. The star will then stay on the main sequence until it has consumed about one tenth of its hydrogen, as explained earlier. It has been calculated that the contraction period, prior to reaching the main sequence, is about one two-hundredth part (0.005) of the time the star remains on the main sequence. Hence, the more massive the protostar, the more rapidly does it contract and become a visible star. Furthermore, a star (or protostar) spends only a small proportion of its lifetime in the contracting phase.

12.140. Evidence that it takes longer for a less massive star to reach the main sequence has been derived from a study of certain galactic clusters which are known to be relatively young, e.g., about a million years, because they contain large numbers of massive and luminous (O-type) stars. In such clusters, the more massive stars belong to the main sequence, as is indicated by their magnitude-color index relationship. The points for the less massive stars, however, lie above and to the right of the main-sequence curve (Fig. 12.19); hence,

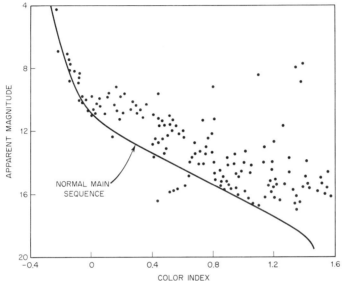

FIG. 12.19. Apparent magnitude and color index of stars in galactic cluster NGC 2264 (after M. F. Walker)

for a given spectral class (or surface temperature) they are brighter, and therefore larger, than the main-sequence stars. If it is assumed that all the stars in the cluster commenced to form at the same time, it appears that the less massive ones have not yet contracted to the stage at which they belong to the main sequence. In a million years, for example, only those stars that are about five times as massive as the Sun will have reached this stage. All others will still be in a state of contraction and will lie above the main-sequence curve on the H-R diagram.

12.141. An interesting group of stellar objects, called the *T Tauri variables*, named after the prototype T Tauri in the constellation Taurus, may represent stars that are still contracting before becoming members of the main sequence. These erratically variable stars, which are always surrounded by dust clouds, are often found in young galactic clusters. The T Tauri stars lie above the main sequence and the fact that they are immersed in dust suggests that they are still in the formation and contraction stage. It is possible that in the T Tauri variables, the development of new stars is actually being observed. The erratic intensity variations are probably the result of instabilities arising during the formation process while the star is still undergoing contraction.

Main-Sequence Behavior

12.142. When the interior of a star becomes hot enough, about 10 million degrees K or more, the conversion of hydrogen into helium by thermonuclear reactions becomes possible, with the accompanying release of energy as heat. The contraction then ceases, and a stationary (or steady) state develops in which the star radiates energy at the same rate as it is produced by the thermonuclear processes. If the rate of energy release should exceed the rate of loss by radiation, the star would expand and the internal temperature would drop, thus decreasing the rate of liberation of energy until a balance was established. On the other hand, if the energy release rate should be less than the rate of loss, the star would contract; its internal temperature would increase and energy would be produced at a greater rate. Thus a steady state would always be restored. The star is then a member of the main sequence. Its absolute brightness, surface temperature, and spectral type, i.e., its location on the H-R diagram, would subsequently remain unchanged until some 10 percent of the hydrogen had been converted into helium.

12.143. The point at which a star reaches the steady state of the main sequence depends upon its mass and composition. The width of the main-sequence band is probably an indication of some variabilities in composition. Further reference to this matter will be made below, but for the present the relatively minor effect of such variations will be neglected; in other words, it will be assumed that all stars have initially the same composition. The more massive a star, the higher will be the interior temperature at which it produces heat at a sufficient rate to counteract the gravitational contraction, so that the radius remains constant.

12.144. For interior temperatures of approximately 15 million degrees K, i.e., the temperature in the interior of the Sun, and below, the main thermonuclear process is the formation of helium from hydrogen by the proton-proton chain (§ 6.191). At higher temperatures, the carbon cycle becomes increasingly important and attains dominance at about 20 million degrees K. The overall rate of the carbon-cycle process increases markedly with temperature, and this probably accounts for the rapid consumption of hydrogen in the more massive (and hotter interior) stars.

Departure from Main Sequence: Globular Clusters

12.145. For some time, depending on its mass as indicated in Table 12.3, the star remains on or very close to the main-sequence curve. When about one tenth of the hydrogen has been used up, the hot core of the star, in which the thermonuclear reactions have been occurring, consists almost entirely of helium.

A change must therefore take place in the energy-producing processes in the interior of the star, which then begins to move off the main sequence. The general behavior of stars with masses somewhat greater than that of the Sun, e.g., 1.1 to 1.4 times the solar mass, is reasonably well understood, at least up to a point. The fate of the more massive stars, however, is somewhat uncertain.

12.146. The magnitude-color index diagrams of several globular clusters, with estimated ages of about 5 to 7 billion years, show certain features in common.* If the magnitude is plotted against the color index for the observable stars of all types in a given cluster, the points are found to fall on or close to a curve of the form in Fig. 12.20. It will be noted that the H-R curve for the

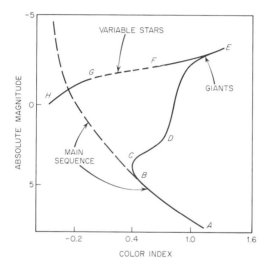

Fig. 12.20.   H-R-type diagram for stars in a globular cluster

old galactic cluster M 67 in Fig. 12.18 is similar, up to a point. The portion AB of the curve represents the main-sequence stars in the globular cluster,† and those in the region DEF are the red giants or supergiants. Between F and G are found variable stars of the RR Lyrae type; since the surface temperatures (and spectral types) of these stars change periodically, they are represented by a broken line. The magnitude-color index characteristics of the stars along GH are somewhat similar to those of the bright upper main-sequence stars, but the former are much less massive and also have a different composition.

12.147. As is the case with galactic clusters, it is reasonable to suppose that the members of a globular cluster were formed—and reached the main se-

---

* According to Fred Hoyle (1962), the oldest known globular cluster is NGC 188 with an estimated age of 15 billion (1.5×10^{10}) years.

† The main-sequence curve AB for globular clusters (Population II stars) differs somewhat from one cluster to another, but it is generally below the normal main-sequence curve of Population I stars in Fig. 12.15.

quence—at about the same time. For the globular clusters, however, the method of estimating the age is not very reliable. The main-sequence stars for several galactic clusters fall close to a single curve, as seen in Fig. 12.18, but it is not certain if this is the case for the globular clusters. If the magnitude-color index curves for several globular clusters are adjusted so as to make the absolute magnitudes of their RR Lyrae variable components (FG in Fig. 12.20) to be the same, as implied in § 12.93, then the main-sequence portions of the curves (AB in Fig. 12.20) do not coincide. On the other hand, if the main-sequence parts are brought into coincidence, the absolute magnitudes of the RR Lyrae stars are different. This behavior, as well as the deviation of the main sequence of globular clusters from that of Population I stars, may be due to differences in composition.

12.148. It is probable that the globular clusters which give magnitude-color index curves of the type of Fig. 12.20 are approximately 5 to 7×10^9 years old. The original masses of the stars still present in these clusters, but which are no longer on the main sequence, were perhaps 1.2 to 1.5 times the mass of the Sun. Those still on the main sequence are the less massive members of the globular clusters.

12.149. In addition to representing the H-R diagram for the stars in a globular cluster, another significance can be attributed to the curves in Fig. 12.20. In a given cluster, the masses of the constituent stars are different. If they were all formed at about the same time, about 5 to 7 billion years ago, the more massive stars will have evolved away from the main sequence, possibly to GH or even into the uncertain region beyond H. The magnitude-color index characteristic of the less massive stars will now be on CDE or EF, whereas the lightest will not yet have left the main sequence, along AB. It would appear, therefore, that although curve $BCDEFGH$ represents the characteristics of stars of different masses at a particular instant, it may be interpreted as showing the general manner in which the color index (or surface temperature) and magnitude of a particular member of the cluster change over the course of time. In other words, the curve, from B to H, may be taken to represent the locus of the life history of a star slightly heavier than the Sun after it leaves the main sequence. The explanation of this behavior, based largely on the views of Fred Hoyle and Martin Schwarzschild (1955) and of others, is outlined below.

EVOLUTION OF RED GIANTS

12.150. A fundamental postulate of the theory of stellar evolution is that there is no mixing of the gases within a star. If mixing did occur, there would be a slow but steady departure from the main-sequence curve toward the left; since this is not the case, at least not to any significant extent, the indication is that there is little or no mixing. Thus, it may be assumed that, after about one tenth of a star's hydrogen has been converted into helium, the latter gas remains in the center (or core) of the star, and is surrounded by a mass consisting mainly of hydrogen.

12.151. In this condition, heat is no longer released in the core, and the gravitational force due to the star's mass compresses the helium. The volume of the core which, like that of the star as a whole, has been virtually constant while the star was on the main sequence, now begins to decrease. But the hydrogen layer immediately around the core is still at a sufficiently high temperature and pressure to undergo conversion into helium. The energy released in this manner and also by the gravitational contraction of the core causes the outer parts of the star to expand. Calculations show that this expansion exceeds the compression of the helium core and the star as a whole increases in size. There is thus an increase in brightness because of the larger radius, with little change in surface temperature at first; the star's position on the H-R diagram is thus slightly above the main sequence, as shown by BC in Fig. 12.20 (see also Fig. 12.18).

12.152. Provided the mass of a star is not more than about 1.4 solar masses, a curious change is taking place in the interior. As the gas becomes more and more highly compressed, the electrons, which are freed from their associated nuclei at the existing temperatures, constitute what is called a *degenerate gas*.* The behavior of such a gas is quite different from a normal gas in many respects, and one of them is that the pressure it exerts is very much greater than would be expected from classical mechanics. As a result of the electron degeneracy, the pressure of the gas in the core of the star increases, and by the time the point C in Fig. 12.20 is reached, it is almost large enough to resist further contraction under the force of gravity. The degenerate core then attains another, although temporary, steady (isothermal) state at a temperature of between 15 and 20 million degrees K.

12.153. The hydrogen in the layer surrounding the core continues to produce energy by being converted into helium, and both the core and the star as a whole now increase in radius. The overall expansion is so rapid that the brightness, which depends on R^2T^4, increases from C to D, although the surface temperature decreases. As the region DE is approached, the star is so large and the surface temperature so low that it now belongs to the red giants of the H-R diagram (Fig. 12.15).

12.154. At some point near D in Fig. 12.20, the temperature of the degenerate core, which has been constant (isothermal) since C, begins to increase again due to gravitational compression. But the surface temperature continues to decrease, first slowly and then more rapidly, as a result of expansion. At E, when the helium core represents about half the total mass of the star, the

---

* The theory of gas degeneracy, which involves quantum statistics, is too complex to be described here. Degeneracy sets in at very high pressures or low temperatures (or both) and occurs more readily the smaller the mass of the particles present, e.g., electrons.

interior temperature approaches 100 million degrees K. The core is then hot
enough for new thermonuclear energy-producing reactions, involving helium,
to occur. The first of these appears to be the formation of carbon-12 nuclei,
in two stages. There is a very weak tendency for two helium-4 nuclei to unite,
i.e.,

$$_2He^4 + {_2}He^4 \rightarrow {_4}Be^8 + energy,$$

leading to a minute concentration of highly unstable beryllium-8.* The latter
is capable, however, of combining with another helium nucleus, i.e.,

$$_4Be^8 + {_2}He^4 \rightarrow {_6}C^{12} + energy,$$

to form the very stable carbon-12. This reaction is then followed by

$$_6C^{12} + {_2}He^4 \rightarrow {_8}O^{16} + energy$$

and

$$_8O^{16} + {_2}He^4 \rightarrow {_{10}}Ne^{20} + energy,$$

both oxygen-16 and neon-20 being stable nuclei.

THE HORIZONTAL BRANCH

12.155. If a stellar core consisted of normal (classical) gas, the release of
energy would cause it to expand; as a result, its temperature would tend to
fall and so also would the rate of the thermonuclear reactions. Thus, the heat
release rate would decline and in a short time a steady state of constant temperature and volume would be established, as is the case for main-sequence
stars. A degenerate (electron) gas, however, does not behave in this manner.
Such a gas is essentially in a state of unstable equilibrium; instead of tending
toward a steady state, it moves in the reverse direction. Thus, the temperature
of the degenerate core continues to increase; consequently, the core expands
rapidly, the pressure decreases, and the degeneracy disappears. The generation
of heat within the helium core permits the degeneracy to be removed, and a
steady state, with a constant temperature, can then be maintained.

12.156. At this stage, the surface temperature of the star, which has been
decreasing, from D to E, starts to increase; its locus EF . . . GH on the H-R
(or the equivalent magnitude-color index) diagram in Fig. 12.20 is called the
horizontal branch. At the same time as the temperature increases, however, the
brightness decreases; this means that the radius of the star is decreasing. Part
of the decrease may be due to loss of matter such as has been observed to occur
from red giants. Because of the large size of the star, the gravitational force
at the surface is low, and hence material streams away from the outer layers.
For some reason that is not altogether clear, an unstable condition develops
in the general region FG where the variable RR Lyrae stars occur. Spectroscopic observations show that both the radii and surface temperatures of
these stars oscillate in a regular manner; hence, the brightness has a definite

* For an explanation of the symbols, see § 6.186.

period from a maximum through a minimum to a maximum again, and so on.

12.157. In the region GH, as noted earlier, the magnitude-color index characteristics are similar to those of the more massive, luminous stars of the main sequence. But there is a great difference between the latter and those which have evolved along $BCDEFGH$. The surface temperatures and radii must be similar for the two types of stars, since these determine their color index (or spectral class) and brightness (or magnitude), but the masses and densities are different. The mass (and density) of the evolved (blue) star, which may be several billion years old, is on the order of one tenth of that of the massive young star on the main sequence. Furthermore, the interior temperature of the old star is probably a few hundred million degrees, compared with about 20 million degrees K of the main-sequence star of the same spectral class and surface temperature. In the latter star, the conversion of hydrogen into helium by way of the carbon cycle is essentially the sole source of energy, but in the evolved star, much of the energy is derived from reactions involving helium.

Novae and White Dwarfs

12.158. The next and apparently final stage in the evolution of the stars under consideration is largely a matter of conjecture. They undoubtedly become white dwarfs, but the nature of the path from H in Fig. 12.20 is uncertain. It seems probable, however, that the variable stars called *novae* (plural of *nova*, Greek "new") represent an intermediate stage. Novae are bluish stars which normally have absolute (visual) magnitudes of about +5, i.e., similar to the Sun. Because of their great distance from Earth, however, the apparent magnitudes may be as large as +10 to +15, and so they are very faint. At certain times, the brightness of a nova increases enormously in a short time, e.g., by a factor of 10,000 or more; its magnitude is then lower by some 10 units. The brightness decreases, at first rapidly and then more slowly, until the original appearance is restored after a period that may range from a few weeks to many months for different novae.

12.159. The initial increase in brightness of a nova is evidently due to the expansion of the outer layers, since the surface temperature, as indicated by the spectrum, is generally unaffected. It appears that part of the star's photosphere (§ 6.37) is detached and expands; the large increase in radiating area, without any significant change in the surface temperature, results in greatly enhanced brightness. The spectra and brightness in the post-nova state are indistinguishable from those of the pre-nova star, and it is estimated that the loss of mass in the nova condition is only about 0.01 percent, i.e., one part in 10,000 of the total. Some novae are known to recur at fairly long intervals and it is probable that the recurrence phenomenon is quite general, although the periods may be too long to have been observed in most cases. On the average, some 20 to 30 novae are detected in the local Galaxy per annum.

12.160. A possible explanation of the behavior of novae, although not the only one, is that, in the course of a star's evolution, the helium and hydrogen are gradually exhausted and the rate of heat generation decreases. As a result, the interior of the star begins to cool and contract. Gas degeneracy then sets in again and extends almost to the exterior of the star. If a disturbance should occur and the temperature near the outside should increase, the instability of the degenerate state will cause the temperature to rise further; hence, the outer hydrogen gas layer expands rapidly and is partially blown off. There is a consequent increase in brightness that is observed as a nova. The loss of energy in the expulsion of the gas causes the temperature of the mass of the star to decrease and the original condition is gradually restored. In due course, another disturbance may result in another outburst, and so on. After a number of such events, the star will have lost all of its hydrogen gas and will be a white dwarf which is completely degenerate, except for a relatively thin outer layer where the pressure is lower.

12.161. The mass of only one white dwarf, namely, Sirius B, is known at all well, but there are indications that the masses are about the same as the mass of the Sun. The radii, on the other hand, as derived from the estimated surface temperature and the absolute brightness (or magnitude), are not very different from Earth's radius. The average density of a white dwarf is thus found to be on the order of several hundred thousand grams per cubic centimeter; thus, a volume of one cubic inch weighs about 30 or 40 tons! Such fantastically high densities are possible only for matter in the degenerate state. The inward pressure due to the enormous gravitational forces in such extremely dense bodies could not be balanced without the contribution of the pressure associated with electron gas degeneracy.

12.162. Except for the nondegenerate outer layer, the temperature in the interior of a white dwarf is probably uniform at a few million degrees. No heat generation by nuclear reaction is then possible and there is no gain of energy due to gravitational compression. Hence, the temperature of the star's interior falls slowly. The surface temperature of some white dwarfs is moderately high, e.g., 10,000 to 15,000°K, but the surface area is so small that the absolute brightness is also small, i.e., the absolute magnitude is large. The rate of energy loss by radiation is then very low so that white dwarfs may be expected to persist for extremely long periods. A few hundred white dwarfs have been identified, but there are probably many more that are still undetected.

EVOLUTION OF MORE MASSIVE STARS: SUPERNOVAE

12.163. It should be emphasized that the foregoing discussion of the evolution of a star, from main sequence to the white-dwarf state, is applicable only to stars of about 1.1 to 1.4 solar masses. Stars of lower mass may possibly behave in a similar manner, but those that are more massive during the main sequence phase apparently will not. One reason is that in such masses the degenerate state does not occur. Because of the large mass, the inward gravitational force cannot be balanced by the pressure of the degenerate electron gas; consequently, the core is compressed and the temperature increases to a point at which degeneracy cannot set in. The history of the massive stars is somewhat uncertain, but it is probable that, after leaving the main sequence, a star of not more than a few solar masses will move somewhat to the right and upward on the H-R diagram when 10 percent of the hydrogen is consumed. This is indicated by the curves for some of the younger galactic clusters in Fig. 12.18. As a result of the gravitational compression of the helium core, the internal temperature increases rapidly to the point at which thermonuclear reactions involving helium can take place. The large rate of heat generation from the hydrogen and helium reactions causes the temperature of the star to increase rapidly and it becomes a red giant or supergiant. The expansion is assumed to be so rapid that very few stars are detected in this stage. Such a situation may account for the gaps between the stars in galactic clusters that have deviated to a small extent only from the main sequence, i.e., at the left of Fig. 12.18, and those which are red giants or supergiants, i.e., at the right of Fig. 12.18. It may perhaps be significant that the Population II Cepheids and other variables occur within this gap, somewhat above and to the right of the RR Lyrae stars.

12.164. The ultimate fate of the more massive stars is not known. It is certain, however, that they cannot become white dwarfs without disposing of part of their mass in some manner. The basis of this statement is that the degeneracy pressure is able to balance the effect of gravitational contraction only if the mass of the core does not exceed 1.44 solar masses.* The requirement is satisfied by the stars considered earlier, especially after the hydrogen in the outer layers has been lost in a number of nova outbursts. If the original mass of the star is not much greater than 1.4 times the Sun's mass, then it could perhaps become a white dwarf after an extended period as a nova. But for still more massive stars, there must be other ways in which supergiants shed much of their mass.

12.165. One possibility is that large stars lose part of their mass by streaming from the surface, such as has been observed for some red giants and other stars. Another is that massive stars ultimately disintegrate as supernovae. A *supernova* is a star that undergoes a fairly rapid increase in brightness by a factor of several hundred millions; this extremely bright phase may last for a year or two and then the activity dies out over a long period of time. At its maximum, the brightness of a supernova may exceed that of all the other stars in the galaxy of which it is a member. Altogether, some 50 supernovae have been recorded, of which only three, in the years 1054, 1572, and 1604, were within

---

* The quantity 1.44 solar masses is often referred to as *Chandrasekhar's limit*, after the astrophysicist S. Chandrasekhar, a native of India, who worked on this problem in the United States.

the Galaxy.* It has been estimated that supernovae occur about once in from 50 to 300 years per galaxy.

12.166. Perhaps the best known supernova is the one which appeared in the Milky Way in 1054, and was reported in Chinese and Japanese records of the time. The Crab nebula in the constellation Taurus is what now remains of the occurrence. Since the distance of this nebula from Earth is about 1050 parsecs (3400 light years) the actual event must have taken place some 4300 years ago. Although more than 900 years have elapsed since the supernova was observed, the nebula is still seen to be expanding at a rate of 1300 kilometers (800 miles) per second. The present diameter of about 2 parsecs implies that this rate of expansion has been almost constant over the intervening period. Estimates of the total mass of the Crab nebula indicate that the original star was several times the solar mass; hence, it could have been a red supergiant or a similar body. The central star of the nebula may now have a mass about the same as the Sun; if this is the case, it may evolve directly into a white dwarf.

12.167. The observed supernovae have been divided into two categories, called Type I and Type II. An important difference between the two classes is that the spectra of Type I supernovae show the presence of heavier elements but little hydrogen, whereas the Type II spectra imply that the gases contain a substantial proportion of hydrogen. It has been suggested by the British astronomer Fred Hoyle that the two types of supernovae arise from stars with different masses in the following manner. If the mass of the original star is less than about six (but more than 1.4) solar masses, it will evolve toward the red supergiant stage, i.e., at some distance to the right and above the main sequence in the H-R diagram, before exploding as a supernova. Such a star will be relatively old and will have consumed much of its hydrogen, and heavier elements will have been produced in thermonuclear reactions involving helium. When it becomes a supernova, it will be of Type I.

12.168. For stars that are more massive still, it is possible for a supernova to occur when little more than a tenth of the hydrogen has been used up, i.e., soon after the star has left the main sequence. The spectrum will then correspond to Type II, with a large proportion of hydrogen, some helium, but relatively small amounts of heavier elements. According to this argument, there should be no red supergiants corresponding to the more massive stars. It is true that they have not been observed in the galactic clusters NGC 2362 and the Pleiades, but they do occur in the Persei clusters which are in between them in Fig. 12.18.

12.169. When a Type I supernova explodes it ejects into space considerable quantities of the heavier elements. This material becomes mixed with the interstellar dust and gas. Hence, when a new (Population I) star is formed, it starts

---

* Radio astronomers claim there is evidence that a supernova occurred about the year 1702, but it was too far away to be conspicuous and hence was overlooked (§ 12.220).

its life with more of the heavier elements than are present in many older (Population II) stars. The general difference in composition between Population I and Population II stars (§ 12.62) can be accounted for in this manner.

ORIGIN OF THE ELEMENTS

THE NEUTRON CAPTURE THEORY

12.170. A problem which may be related to the evolution of stars is that of *nucleosynthesis* or *nucleogenesis*, i.e., the formation of the approximately **280** nuclear species (or nuclides) of the **90** elements from hydrogen to uranium that exist in nature.* Among the several suggestions made to account for the origin of the elements, two are of particular interest: one because it is related to a theory of cosmology that will be described later (§ 12.199), and the other because of its connection with the theory of stellar evolution already considered.

12.171. According to the first point of view, some 10 billion (or so) years ago all the matter in the universe, consisting essentially of neutrons (§ 3.162), was concentrated in a relatively small volume at high temperature and pressure. In the free state, neutrons are normally unstable and break up spontaneously into protons (hydrogen nuclei) and electrons; the half-life for this decay process is about 15 minutes (§ 8.309). At the high temperature and pressure of the primordial gas, however, protons and electrons would recombine to form neutrons. A kind of steady (or equilibrium) state would thus exist in which the gas consisted mainly of neutrons with a relatively small proportion of its decay products.

12.172. The theory then postulates that, in the course of the evolution of the universe, the hot, highly compressed neutron gas began to expand rapidly,† with the result that both the temperature and pressure started to fall. Under these changed conditions, the recombination of protons and electrons would be greatly decreased; hence protons would accumulate in the gas. The situation would then be suitable for protons ($_1H^1$) and neutrons ($_0n^1$) to unite to produce nuclei of the heavier isotope of hydrogen, deuterium ($_1D^2$) i.e.,

$$_1H^1 + {_0n^1} \rightarrow {_1D^2} + \text{energy.}$$

The deuteron would then combine with another neutron to form a nucleus of the third hydrogen isotope tritium ($_1T^3$); the latter is radioactive and decays by the emission of a negative beta particle, i.e., an electron, to yield a helium-3 nucleus, thus,

$$_1D^2 + {_0n^1} \rightarrow {_1T^3} + \text{energy}$$
$$_1T^3 \rightarrow {_{-1}e^0} + {_2He^3}.$$

---

* There should be 92 elements from hydrogen to uranium, but two of these have no stable forms and do not occur on Earth. One of these missing elements has been detected, however, in certain stars (§ 12.189).

† This event is sometimes referred to colloquially as the "big bang."

12.173. It can well be imagined that, in the moderately hot and dense gas, there will be many similar nuclear processes, involving the successive addition of neutrons with intermediate stages of radioactive decay. It is to be expected, therefore, that all conceivable atomic nuclei of reasonable stability might be produced in this manner. Because of the short half-life for neutron decay, almost all the neutrons originally present would have been converted into protons and electrons within a period of an hour or so. Hence, one aspect of the theory under consideration is that most of the nuclides existing at the present time were formed in the first hour after the primordial gas started to expand. There were undoubtedly some changes later, as the original nuclei accumulated into stars, but these, it is contended, would not be very great.

12.174. An argument adduced in favor of the foregoing mechanism of nucleo-synthesis is the general correlation that exists between the relative abundances of various elements in nature and the tendency of the respective nuclei to capture neutrons. The probability that a particular nuclear reaction will occur is expressed by the appropriate cross section (§ 8.38, footnote). Laboratory experiments have shown that, as a general rule, the natural abundance of any element is inversely related to the cross section for the capture of neutrons of high energy, such as might have been present in the hypothetical neutron gas after it started to expand. If the elements were indeed formed by neutron capture, it is to be expected that those with the largest cross sections would be the least abundant because they would have combined with neutrons. Such combination, followed by radioactive (beta) decay, would lead to the formation of a different element. It should be mentioned, however, that although the relationship between abundance and neutron cross section of the elements does provide support for the present theory, it is not crucial, since it does not eliminate other theories. All theories of nucleosynthesis must invoke neutron reactions at some stage, but not necessarily from the very beginning.

12.175. The basic requirement of the neutron-capture mechanism is that there should be no gaps in the buildup of more and more complex nuclei from protons and neutrons. The main objection to the theory is that two such gaps do in fact exist, for nuclei of mass numbers 5 and 8. There is no problem as far as the formation of helium-4 is concerned, but this nucleus is exceptionally stable and will not take up an additional neutron or proton to form a nucleus with a mass of 5 units. Some suggestions have been made for possible means of bridging the gap, e.g., by the combination of helium-4 and tritium nuclei to yield lithium-7, i.e.,

$$_2He^4 + {}_1T^3 \rightarrow {}_3Li^7 + \text{energy}.$$

But it appears that, under the conditions expected to exist, this reaction would be too slow to permit the formation of heavier nuclei within the short time postulated by the theory of nucleogenesis. Furthermore, even if suitable quantities of lithium-7 were produced in some manner, the capture of a neutron followed by radioactive decay would lead to beryllium-8. As seen in § 12.154, this is a highly unstable nucleus and the very small amounts that might survive breakup into helium nuclei could not provide the basis for the rapid generation of the heavier elements.

NUCLEAR SYNTHESIS FROM PROTONS

12.176. The alternative theory of the formation of the elements is much more involved than the one based simply on neutron capture and radioactive decay, but its complexity is its only significant drawback. The important difference between the two theories is, first, that the one described below starts with nuclei of hydrogen, which is the lightest and by far the most abundant element in the universe, and was originally presumably the only one, and second, the process of nuclear synthesis is regarded as a gradual one requiring many millions of years.

12.177. In the course of star formation, gravitational attraction will result in the interior temperature being raised to about 10 million degrees K, as stated earlier. At this point, the proton-proton chain (§ 6.191) will take place at an appreciable rate and, apart from the release of energy which is a secondary consideration for the moment, helium-4 will be formed. In due course, as the hydrogen in the central core of the star is consumed, perhaps after a million years or so for a more massive star and several billion years for a less massive one, gravitational compression will result in an increase of temperature to about 100 million degrees K. Then helium reactions can occur with the formation, first, of carbon-12 (§ 12.154); subsequent additions of helium nuclei in successive steps would lead to oxygen-16 and neon-20, and perhaps magnesium-24, all of which are stable nuclei.

12.178. As the helium is consumed, the theory postulates that compression of the stellar core causes the temperature to increase to several hundred million (or even a billion) degrees when such reactions as

$$_6C^{12} + {}_8O^{16} \rightarrow {}_{12}Mg^{24} + {}_2He^4$$
$$_8O^{16} + {}_8O^{16} \rightarrow {}_{14}Si^{28} + {}_2He^4$$
$$_8O^{16} + {}_{10}Ne^{20} \rightarrow {}_{16}S^{32} + {}_2He^4$$

and so on, can take place. It is possible in this manner to build up nuclei of even mass number and even atomic number as far as iron-56, i.e., $_{26}Fe^{56}$, the most common isotope of the element. The reason why it is not possible to go beyond iron in this manner is that the appropriate processes, in which two nuclei interact, would be accompanied by the absorption of energy. Thus, they could take place only if energy is supplied. All the reactions described above, on the other hand, are accompanied by the release of energy, so that the necessary high temperatures can be maintained in the star. Reactions associated with the absorption of energy, on the other hand, would cause the temperature to drop and soon all thermonuclear reaction would cease.

12.179. For the elements preceding and including iron, therefore, the processes of energy release by nuclear reaction and of nucleosynthesis have been identical. The formation of the elements has been automatically accompanied by the liberation of energy required to maintain the high temperatures. But in the later stages of nuclear buildup the two aspects of stellar evolution must be independent. The synthesis of elements beyond iron can, however, take place if neutrons are available, and so a means must be proposed whereby these particles can be produced.

12.180. Before taking up this aspect of nucleosynthesis, consideration must be given to the formation of the lighter elements which have either an odd mass number, an odd atomic number (cf. § 6.186, footnote), or both. It may be noted, incidentally, that nuclides with both even mass and atomic numbers are, apart from hydrogen, by far the most abundant in nature. These substances include all those which can be derived from helium in the manner already described. The odd nuclei are far less common, but they do exist and the following mechanism can account for their formation as well as for that of neutrons.

12.181. After the production of carbon-12 from helium, interaction of the former nucleus with still remaining protons can lead to stable carbon-13 (via nitrogen-13) and nitrogen-15 (via oxygen-15) by the reactions of the carbon cycle (§ 6.194). Furthermore, at higher temperatures such processes as

$$_6C^{12} + {}_6C^{12} \rightarrow {}_{11}Na^{23} + {}_1H^1$$

and

$$_8O^{16} + {}_8O^{16} \rightarrow {}_{15}P^{31} + {}_1H^1$$

and others lead to nuclei of odd mass number and atomic number.

12.182. Another possibility is the reaction

$$_{10}Ne^{20} + {}_1H^1 \rightarrow {}_{11}Na^{21} + \text{energy,}$$

followed by radioactive decay,

$$_{11}Na^{21} \rightarrow {}_{-1}e^0 + {}_{10}Ne^{21}.$$

By means of these and similar thermonuclear reactions many nuclei of odd mass number can be produced.

12.183. Once carbon-13 and neon-21 are available, the release of neutrons can occur by the interaction with helium nuclei; thus,

$$_6C^{13} + {}_2He^4 \rightarrow {}_8O^{16} + {}_0n^1$$

and, to a smaller extent,

$$_{10}Ne^{21} + {}_2He^4 \rightarrow {}_{12}Mg^{24} + {}_0n^1.$$

The elements already present, as well as those formed in later stages, can therefore capture neutrons, in accordance with the appropriate cross sections, and thus form new elements. In particular, iron-56, after three stages of neutron capture, is converted into radioactive iron-59 which decays into the next element, cobalt-59, i.e.,

$$_{26}\text{Fe}^{59} \rightarrow {}_{-1}e^0 + {}_{27}\text{Co}^{59}.$$

In this manner, as a result of neutron captures and radioactive decays, the elements of higher and higher atomic number and mass number can be built up. Since neutrons can be formed at a fairly early stage in this scheme of nucleogenesis, i.e., after the production of carbon-13, the inverse relationship between neutron capture cross section and natural abundance of the elements mentioned in § 12.174 is not decisive for one theory or the other.

12.184. As suggested above, neutrons are formed in a three-stage process, namely, combination of carbon-12 with a proton to yield nitrogen-13, radioactive decay of nitrogen-13 to carbon-13, and reaction of the latter with a helium nucleus. Consequently, it is to be expected that the neutron density will always be low; as a result, the reactions leading to the formation of the elements beyond iron will inevitably take place slowly. The proportion of such elements in the stars will, therefore, generally be small. It has been suggested that this is the reason why iron is exceptionally abundant in nature; it is formed fairly rapidly in the high-temperature thermonuclear reactions but is removed slowly by the capture of neutrons. Incidentally, neutron capture does not require high temperatures, i.e., it is not a thermonuclear process, and the capture cross sections are in fact generally larger when the temperature is low.

FORMATION OF LITHIUM AND DEUTERIUM

12.185. The main problem associated with nucleosynthesis that starts with the conversion of protons into helium nuclei and then builds up subsequent elements from the latter, is that the elements lithium, beryllium, and boron, which come immediately after helium, are missed completely. A possible route to lithium-7 would be by the reaction between helium-3 and helium-4 nuclei described in § 6.193; the product is beryllium-7 which captures an electron to yield lithium-7. But any lithium-7 formed in this manner would soon be removed by the capture of a proton with the formation of two helium-4 nuclei.

12.186. An entirely different mechanism must therefore be invoked to account for the genesis of lithium, etc. A possible clue is provided by the fact that the spectra of the T Tauri variable stars, which have not yet reached the main sequence (§ 12.141), have stronger lithium lines than do other stars. There may thus be a connection between the behavior of the T Tauri stars and their unusually high lithium content. The suggestion has been made that the increase in brightness is accompanied by the emission of protons of very high energy, e.g., more than a hundred million electron volts (§ 6.75). Such energetic protons are known to be capable of disintegrating heavier nuclei by the process called *spallation*. This nuclear reaction has been studied in the laboratory, and the light elements lithium, beryllium, and boron are commonly found among the products. If these elements were formed in this manner, they should be found mainly in the outer layers of the star or in the surrounding nebular material that may eventually condense into planets. It is of special interest, therefore, to note that Earth and meteorites contain considerably more lithium than does the Sun.

12.187. A related problem is the presence of deuterium, the heavy isotope of hydrogen, on Earth, although it is apparently very rare in the Sun, in the stars, and in interstellar space. A search has been made, for example, for the deuterium line at 91.6-centimeters wavelength, corresponding to the 21-centimeter hydrogen line (§ 12.39), but without success. It is true that a deuterium nucleus is formed in the first stage of the proton-proton chain, but it will either react with another proton to form helium-3, or it will break up into a neutron and proton at the high temperature of the stellar interior. A way in which deuterium could appear on Earth and perhaps other planets, however, is by the spallation process described above. Like lithium, it would be found in the planetary material rather than in the central star.

12.188. There are many aspects of stellar evolution, nucleosynthesis, and the abundance of the elements that have not been touched on in this and the preceding sections. Furthermore, it should be borne in mind that, as has often happened in the past, new discoveries will probably make it necessary to modify the theories and mechanisms that are now commonly accepted. It should be clearly understood, therefore, that the discussion presented can be no more than an attempt to indicate what now appear to be plausible lines of thought. Whether they will remain so in succeeding years, it is of course impossible to predict, but it would not be surprising if they undergo some change.

SPECIAL CASES OF NUCLEAR SYNTHESIS

12.189. In connection with the problem of nuclear synthesis, there are two interesting observations that seem to indicate that some nuclei are still being produced, or at least were when light now reaching Earth left the particular stars. Red giants belonging to the spectral class S differ from the ordinary red giants (classes K and M) in the respect that lines of the oxides of the elements yttrium ($_{39}$Y) and zirconium ($_{40}$Zr), as well as of other heavy elements, are especially prominent in the spectra (Table 12.1). In some of these stars there is clear evidence of the presence of the element technetium ($_{43}$Tc). This is somewhat surprising, at first sight, because technetium does not exist on Earth; all its isotopes are radioactive and none has a half-life longer than 2.6 million years (technetium-97). In view of the probable age of the class S stars, it appears that the technetium was synthesized, presumably by stages of neutron capture and radioactive decay, long after the star was formed. The presence of the nearby elements, yttrium and zirconium, with atomic numbers 39 and 40, compared with 43 for technetium, makes this seem quite probable.

12.190. Another possibly significant observation is that, after the initial outburst, the activity of certain Type I supernovae decays at a rate corresponding to a half-life of 55 days, i.e., the brightness decreases by 50 percent every 55 days. This is precisely the half-life of the unstable element californium-254 (atomic number 98), which breaks up by spontaneous fission. A suggested explanation is that the explosion of the supernova is accompanied by the release of a large number of neutrons. These are captured, one after another, by the nuclei of the heavier elements, and californium is formed, among other unstable (radioactive) species. The californium-254, however, differs from the others in the respect that its decay, by spontaneous fission, is accompanied by the release of a large amount of energy. The fission energy, decreasing with a half-life of 55 days, will then be responsible for much of the energy released after the initial outburst.

COSMOLOGICAL THEORIES

THE EXPANDING UNIVERSE

12.191. An examination of the spectra of a number of distant galaxies, begun by V. M. Slipher in the United States in 1912, showed that the characteristic lines, such as the H and K lines of ionized calcium, all appeared at longer wavelengths than in the spectrum of the Sun and of other stars in the local Galaxy. The change in wavelength toward the red end of the spectrum, which has now been observed for several hundred galaxies, has become known as the *red shift.** The explanation proposed for this phenomenon is that the distant galaxies (or clusters of galaxies) are traveling away from Earth, and the Galaxy as a whole. The red shift then represents the Doppler effect caused by such motion. Various alternative suggestions have been made to account for the red shift, but the great majority of astronomers and astrophysicists at the present time accept the view that it is a Doppler effect arising from recession of distant galaxies (or clusters of galaxies) with respect to the Milky Way.

12.192. If the red shift is indeed a Doppler effect, the velocities of the galaxies can be determined by means of equation (4.17). In 1929, E. P. Hubble (§ 12.9) compared the velocities of recession obtained in this manner with the distances of a number of galaxies and showed, as had previously been suspected by others, that the velocity was approximately proportional to the distance. In other words, the farther the galaxy is away from Earth, the faster it is receding (Fig. 12.21). Although several of Hubble's distances were later found to be incorrect, the general accuracy of the relationship between distance and velocity has been confirmed by subsequent observations on galaxies estimated to be up to approximately 600 million parsecs (2000 million light years) away. These are not the most distant known galaxies, but they are the farthest for which both distance and velocity of recession have been determined. The highest observed

* It should be mentioned that the red shift has not been observed within the Milky Way nor in the cluster of 17 galaxies of which the Milky Way is a member.

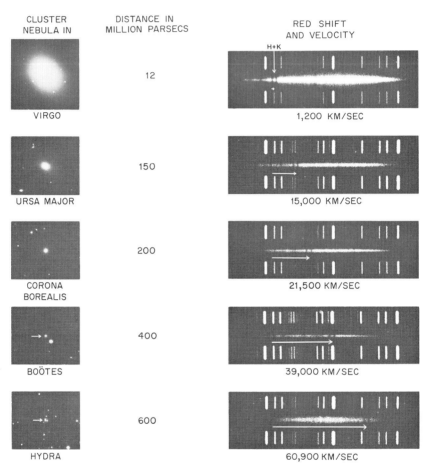

CLUSTER NEBULA IN	DISTANCE IN MILLION PARSECS	RED SHIFT AND VELOCITY
VIRGO	12	1,200 KM/SEC
URSA MAJOR	150	15,000 KM/SEC
CORONA BOREALIS	200	21,500 KM/SEC
BOÖTES	400	39,000 KM/SEC
HYDRA	600	60,900 KM/SEC

FIG. 12.21.   Red shifts, velocities, and approximate distances of five exterior galaxies. (*Mount Wilson and Palomar Observatories*)

velocity of a celestial object, as calculated from the red shift, is 123,000 kilometers (76,000 miles) per second, i.e., 41 percent of the speed of light (§ 12.228). The distance from the Milky Way would then be about 1200 million parsecs (4000 million light years).

12.193. The ratio of the recession velocity of a galaxy, expressed in kilometers per second, to its distance, in parsecs, is called the *Hubble constant*, i.e.,

$$\text{Hubble constant} = \frac{\text{Velocity of recession of galaxy}}{\text{Distance of galaxy}}, \qquad (12.12)$$

and its value is very approximately 100 kilometers per second per million parsecs, although actual reported measurements range from about 50 to 150 kilometers per second per million parsecs. It is not certain that the Hubble constant is an absolute constant (§ 12.208), but the deviations from constancy are probably not large.*

12.194. The range of values for the Hubble constant given above is largely indicative of the uncertainty in determining the distances of remote galaxies. Most galaxies are too far away for the common methods of distance determination, given earlier in this chapter, to be useful; consequently, other more approximate procedures must be employed. One, that is limited to the nearer galaxies in which individual stars can be observed, is based on the measurement of the apparent brightness of the brightest blue giants. The assumption is made that the absolute magnitude of such stars is the same as for similar stars in the Galaxy. Since the distances of the latter may be regarded as known, the distance of the external galaxy can be calculated by equation (12.6).

12.195. For the more remote galaxies, i.e., those which exhibit the red shift, this approach is not possible, since individual stars are not detectable. The method used is based on the observation that the brightest members of the local group of galaxies have an integrated (or total) absolute magnitude of about -19; it is then assumed that the brightest galaxies in a remote group have this same value of the absolute magnitude. Hence, if the apparent integrated magnitude (or brightness) of a remote galaxy is measured, its distance can be readily evaluated. There are two sources of error in this method. First, as a result of the Doppler shift, the light reaching Earth in the visible spectrum actually left the distant galaxy at shorter wavelengths, e.g., in the ultraviolet. The measured brightness may thus not be comparable with that of a nearby galaxy from which the standard value of the integrated absolute magnitude was established. Moreover, the brightness of a distant galaxy is being observed as it was at an earlier time than the nearby galaxy (cf. § 12.206), and there may well be a change over the course of time.

12.196. There are several consequences of the apparent recession of galaxies of which two will be mentioned here. If the Hubble constant does not change significantly with distance, the recession velocity will be equal to 300,000 kilometers per second, i.e., the velocity of light, at a distance of approximately 3 billion (3×10^9) parsecs.† According to Einstein's special theory of relativity, the speed of any body cannot exceed that of light; hence, on the basis of this naïve calculation, 3 billion parsecs (about 10 billion light years) is the maximum possible distance in the universe. In other words, 10 billion light years or so would appear to be the approximate limit of the observable universe. It is

---

* Hubble's original value for the constant was much larger because of the errors in galactic distances mentioned above.

† This distance may be as small as 2 billion or as large as 4.5 billion parsecs, depending on the value used for the Hubble constant.

doubtful, however, if this conclusion has any real physical significance since divergences from the Hubble relationship probably occur (cf. § 12.208) as the speed of a galaxy approaches that of light.

12.197. The phenomenon of galactic recession, as indicated by the red shift, has been observed for galaxies in all directions in space. It appears, therefore, that the galaxies (or clusters of galaxies) are not only receding from Earth (or the Milky Way) but also from each other. Nearly all, if not all, modern theories involve a basic assumption, called the *cosmological principle*, which postulates that, statistically, matter and motion are distributed uniformly throughout the whole of space. Consequently, regardless of the galaxy in which an observer were located, all other (distant) galaxies would seem to be receding from him. This conclusion has led to the concept of the *expanding universe* which states that galaxies are moving away from each other with speeds that are approximately proportional to their distance apart. A simple physical analogy, which must not be taken too literally, is provided by a partially inflated balloon with dots on its surface to represent the locations of galaxies. If the balloon is inflated further so that it expands, each dot recedes from all the others. The same situation would apply to points in the interior of the balloon.

12.198. It was mentioned earlier that some scientists are of the opinion that the red shift is not a Doppler effect and, therefore, that galaxies are not necessarily moving away from each other. These students of cosmology do not accept the theory of the expanding universe. To most cosmologists, however, the concept is basic to any discussion of the origin and structure of the universe. Consequently, it will be adopted in the subsequent treatment.

The Evolutionary Theory of the Universe

12.199. The various theories of cosmology (and cosmogony)* proposed in recent years fall into two general categories, namely, evolutionary and steady state. The *evolutionary theory*, proposed by the Belgian astrophysicist the Abbé G. E. Lemaître in 1931, has been strongly supported by the Russian-born George Gamow in the United States. It postulates that the present universe originated as a very highly condensed mass, and at a particular time this mass became unstable and suddenly started to expand, as stated in § 12.172. In the course of time, estimated to be a few hundred million years, the expanded material aggregated into separate portions which were the *protogalaxies*, i.e., the precursors of galaxies. Contraction within the protogalaxies then led to the formation of galaxies and their constituent stars. The outward motion of the material initiated by the great expansion, the so-called "big bang," is still continuing and is apparent as the expanding universe. The galaxies that had the largest initial velocities are now the most distant from the local Galaxy and from each other.

---

* Because of the difficulty in separating the cosmogonical from the cosmological aspects of the universe, it is a common practice to treat them both under the heading of cosmology.

12.200. If it is assumed that galaxies have been moving at a constant speed since the universe started to expand, then the time that has elapsed is equal to the distance of a galaxy divided by its velocity of recession. Comparison with equation (12.12) shows that the time since the "big bang" is equal to the reciprocal of the Hubble constant. This constant may be taken to be 100 kilometers per second per million parsecs, and since a parsec is about 3×10^{19} kilometers, it follows that

$$\text{Hubble constant} \approx \frac{100 \text{ kilometers per second}}{3 \times 10^{19} \text{ kilometers}}$$

$$= \frac{1}{3 \times 10^{17}} \text{ reciprocal seconds.}$$

The reciprocal of the Hubble constant is thus 3×10^{17} seconds or approximately 10 billion (10^{10}) years. This is then the order of magnitude of the age of the universe on the basis of the evolutionary theory. If the range of reported values of the Hubble constant is taken into account, the age may be from 7 to 20 billion years. It is of interest that independent estimates of the age of the Milky Way give results in the vicinity of 10 to 15 billion years.

12.201. According to the evolutionary theory of the universe, the galaxies are moving farther and farther apart; the question then arises as to whether this will continue indefinitely. The particular solution of Einstein's general theory of relativity proposed by the Russian mathematician A. A. Friedman in 1922 implied that the universe can either expand or contract. It is possible, therefore, that, prior to the present expansion, the universe may have been undergoing contraction. When a sufficiently small volume was reached, the mass would become unstable and start to expand. In the same general sense, the expanding universe could conceivably reach a limiting condition at which it ceased to expand and started to contract once again. Thus, there would be no beginning and no end, but an indefinite series of expansions and contractions, just as much time being required for expansion as for contraction.*

12.202. Another possible evolutionary model derived from the theory of relativity is that there has been a single contraction, starting at some infinite time back, and this was followed, roughly 10 or 15 billion years ago, by the present phase of expansion which will continue indefinitely. This theory appears to be intuitively less satisfying than the concept of alternate expansion and contraction. Calculations based on the observed velocities of recession of the galaxies and their mutual gravitational attraction suggest that the galaxies should ultimately escape from each other completely. This result is stated to be in agreement with the infinitely expanding model of the universe. In reaching this conclusion, however, the assumption was made that most of the mass of the universe is concentrated in the galaxies with little in intergalactic space. If this

---

* During the expansion phase, the entropy of the universe is continually increasing and in the contraction phase it would presumably decrease.

should prove to be incorrect, as is not at all impossible, the argument would be invalid.

The Steady-State Theory of the Universe

12.203. The *steady-state theory* of the universe was proposed by the Austrian-born astrophysicists Hermann Bondi and Thomas Gold (§ 8.237) in England in 1948 and developed along relativistic lines by Fred Hoyle (§ 12.167). In this theory, the cosmological principle is extended by postulating that the statistical (or large-scale) distribution of matter and motion are uniform in time, as well as in space. Since existing galaxies are evidently moving farther and farther apart, if the universe is expanding, the uniform distribution requires that new matter be created to fill the space between the galaxies. The evolutionary theory implies that the average amount of matter per unit volume of space is continually decreasing as a result of expansion. The steady-state theory, on the other hand, postulates that the density of matter in space remains constant in time, in spite of the increase in the volume of the universe. This situation is possible only if new matter is being created at such a rate as to compensate exactly for the increase in the volume occupied. Presumably this creation of matter has been going on indefinitely in the past and will continue indefinitely in the future. A steady-state universe thus needs to have no beginning and no end.

12.204. The continuous creation of matter is, of course, difficult to understand. But since matter exists, it must evidently have been created and the concept of creation should be equally acceptable (or unacceptable) regardless of when it occurs, today or billions of years ago. If matter is being created, it is probably in the form of hydrogen or, perhaps, neutrons* which would decay into hydrogen nuclei (protons) and electrons. Calculations based on the rate of expansion of the universe, i.e., on the Hubble constant, indicate that, in order to maintain a constant overall density of matter in space, it would require the creation of a gram of hydrogen in a volume the size of the Sun in about 250 thousand years. This is far too small to be detected, but within the theoretically "observable" distance of about 3 billion parsecs the total amount of matter produced would be very considerable. It is of interest to mention that the Irish cosmologist W. H. McCrea (1964) has argued that the new matter is not created uniformly throughout space, but mainly in the regions where the density of existing matter is greatest, e.g., in galactic nuclei. Ultimately, perhaps as the result of a galactic explosion, the matter is spread over a large volume of space.

12.205. The steady-state theory requires that new stars and galaxies should be in the process of formation at all times, past, present, and future. Vast masses of hydrogen and interstellar dust gradually break up into protogalaxies and protostars, which then evolve along the lines suggested earlier in this chapter. As

---

* Neutrons represent a higher energy state than hydrogen atoms, and so the formation of the latter might occur more readily.

the universe expands and existing galaxies or clusters of galaxies move farther apart, new ones are gradually formed in the intervening space, so that, on the large scale, the average density of matter remains unchanged. The development of a new galaxy is such an extremely slow process that there would be no possibility of recognizing it directly.

Tests of Cosmological Theories

12.206. Among the tests that have been proposed to distinguish between the evolutionary and steady-state theories of the universe, three will be mentioned here. Since light has a finite velocity, an object in space is not observed, either visually or by its radio emission, as it is now but as it was at the time when the radiation left it; this time depends on the distance of the object from Earth. Consider, for example, two galaxies, one at a distance of a billion light years and the other a million light years away. The observed spectrum of the first galaxy, apart from the red shift, is an indication of its condition a billion years ago, whereas the spectrum of the second represents its state very much more recently.

12.207. According to the evolutionary theory, the two galaxies were formed at about the same time; hence, the spectra depict them as they were at two very different ages. Some difference in the observed spectral characteristics would therefore be expected. On the basis of the steady-state theory, however, new galaxies are being created at all times; hence, galaxies that existed a billion years ago should have the same average age (and overall composition) as those existing a million years ago, or today. On the average, therefore, the spectra should be essentially the same for remote as for less distant galaxies. Sufficient data are not yet available to make possible a reliable test of cosmological theories from the spectra of galaxies.

12.208. Another consequence of the finite speed of light is that the recession velocities of different galaxies as determined at present are actually the velocities at different times. The greater the distance, the earlier the time to which the velocity applies. According to the steady-state theory, the Hubble constant, i.e., the recession velocity divided by the distance, should be independent of time and distance, except for a small decrease at great distances due to the departure of space from Euclidean geometry. The available experimental data, which are by no means accurate, indicate a definite increase in the Hubble constant for very distant galaxies, contrary to the expectation of the steady-state theory. The results are, however, in agreement with one form of the evolutionary theory which requires that the velocities with which galaxies are receding should decrease gradually with time. The Hubble constant for a more remote galaxy, which refers to an earlier time, should thus be larger than for one that is nearer to the local Galaxy.

12.209. A third test of cosmological theories is based on the distribution of galaxies throughout space. According to the steady-state theory, the average density, i.e., the number of galaxies per unit volume, should always be the same. If this average density is N_0, the total number, N, of galaxies lying within a volume of space of radius R is $\frac{4}{3}\pi R^3 N_0$; in other words, the number is proportional to R^3 since the other factors are all constant. Let I be the intensity of radiation received on Earth from a galaxy at a distance R; for visible light this is proportional to the apparent brightness. If all galaxies have the same absolute magnitude on the average, the observed radiation intensity of all the N galaxies within the specified radius R will be equal to or greater than I; it will be equal to I if they are at a distance R and greater than I if they are closer. Hence, the number of galaxies with radiation intensity equal to or greater than I is N, and this is proportional to R^3. For different values of the radius R, the intensity is inversely proportional to the square of the radius, i.e., I is proportional to $1/R^2$.

12.210. The two results derived above can be written as

$$N = \text{constant} \times R^3$$

and

$$I = \text{constant} \times R^{-2},$$

where N is the number of galaxies lying within any specified radius R having radiation intensities equal to or greater than I; the two constants in the foregoing equations are, of course, different. By taking logarithms and eliminating R, it can be readily shown that

$$\log N = -1.5 \log I + \text{constant}.$$

Consequently, the steady-state theory predicts that if the logarithm of the number N of galaxies, with intensities exceeding a certain amount I, is plotted against the logarithm of I, for a series of different values of I, the points should fall on a straight line with a slope of -1.5.

12.211. The test of the steady-state theory just described would not be reliable for the intensity of visual radiation because of the difficulty of measuring the brightness of distant, faint galaxies and the possibility of absorption by dust in space. The radio-frequency emission, however, does not suffer from these drawbacks. If the galactic emitters of radio waves are distributed uniformly throughout space, the arguments given above should be applicable, and the plot of $\log N$ versus $\log I$ should be linear with a slope of -1.5. The observations made so far, however, are not in agreement with this expectation (Fig. **12.22**). They suggest, in fact, that the radio sources are not distributed uniformly, but have a larger space density at great distances than they do nearby. This result is interpreted as favoring the evolutionary theory. The distant galaxies are being observed as they were hundreds of millions of years ago when the universe had not expanded to anything like the present extent. Thus, the more distant galaxies appear to be closer together than the nearer ones which are seen as they were in more recent times.

12.212. The experimental tests made so far seem to favor the evolutionary theory, but it is too soon for any definite conclusion to be drawn. Differences between the two main cosmological theories can be expected to become significant only for the more remote galaxies. But it is in just these circumstances that observational errors may be large (§ 12.195). Furthermore, the distant galaxies recede with velocities approaching that of light and then relativity effects are important. The nature and magnitude of such effects have not been completely established. The problem of distinguishing between evolutionary and steady-state theories is thus an extremely difficult one. In fact, some cosmologists have expressed the pessimistic view that it cannot be solved, at least not with

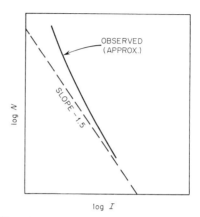

FIG. 12.22. Test of cosmological theories based on distribution of radio sources

presently known techniques, because of a fundamental aspect of nature that makes measurements more uncertain with increasing distance and time.* Nevertheless, the theories of cosmology are of fundamental interest, from both theoretical and experimental points of view, and the last word on the subject is far from having been said.

NONOPTICAL ASTRONOMIES

RADIO ASTRONOMY

12.213. Until instruments or man can be landed on extraterrestrial bodies, all the information concerning celestial objects, whether they be galaxies, stars, or planets, is derived from the radiation they emit or reflect. Prior to the 1930's, the only radiation which had been studied was the narrow band of wavelengths in the visible and near ultraviolet and infrared portions of the spectrum. The conclusions drawn from the observations made in this limited range have been very remarkable but they are inevitably incomplete. The first step in extending the span of wavelengths was taken in 1932 when the American radio engineer Karl G. Jansky described the preliminary results of an investigation into the factors causing disturbances of radio transmissions in the HF band (§ 8.162). In the course of this work, at a wavelength of 14.6 meters, he found that the Milky Way was a strong source of continuous radio emission.

12.214. Jansky's discovery attracted the attention of another radio engineer

---

* This might be somewhat analogous to the well established uncertainty principle on the small scale which states that it is impossible to determine simultaneously both the position and momentum (or any property related to momentum, e.g., energy) of a body.

in the United States, Grote Reber, who constructed the first parabolic antenna, 30 feet in diameter, to receive radio signals from space. In the years from 1940 to 1944, Reber reported on his observations at wavelengths of 1 to 2 meters in a series of papers, which included a radio contour map of the Milky Way. Up to this time, astronomers had shown little interest in radio emissions from the sky, but the discovery in 1942, published in 1945 and 1946, that the Sun is a source of radio waves (§ 6.172) started the rapid growth of the new science of radio astronomy which Jansky and Reber had pioneered.

12.215. Celestial radio emissions can be studied in the wavelength range of about 0.3 centimeter to 20 or 30 meters; this is the so-called radio window of the atmosphere (§ 6.93). Radiations of shorter wavelength are absorbed, whereas those of longer wavelength are reflected by the ionosphere, as seen in Chapter 8. The centimeter (or microwave) region is mainly of interest for the study of thermal emissions (§ 6.172), since the intensity falls off with increasing wavelength. The nonthermal emission, on the other hand, increases with wavelength, so that the meter-length waves are more important. Disturbances in the ionosphere, however, often interfere with reception in this region, causing what is known as "scintillation" of radio-frequency sources (cf. § 8.118).

12.216. Radio astronomy has certain advantages over conventional optical astronomy. For example, the reception of radio waves is not affected by the presence of atmospheric clouds or by dust in interstellar or intergalactic space. Furthermore, radio-telescopes, as the antenna for receiving signals from space are called, have probed the universe to distances greater than is possible with the largest existing optical telescopes. A number of celestial objects were first detected by their radio emissions and then identified in the visible region, but some of the radio sources have not yet been observed by more conventional techniques. Finally, it will be recalled that the 21-centimeter radio-frequency emission line of hydrogen has provided a unique method for investigating the distribution of neutral hydrogen gas within and outside the galaxy.

12.217. Reference has been made in preceding chapters to both thermal and nonthermal radio emissions from the Sun, the Moon, and the planets. The discussion here will be concerned with galactic radio sources, especially those in external galaxies. The application of the 21-centimeter hydrogen line has been referred to earlier, as also has been the use of thermal radio waves from ionized hydrogen to map the H II regions in several luminous nebulae in the Milky Way and elsewhere. Among other radio signals from the Galaxy is a general, nonthermal radio-frequency emission, over a range of wavelengths, that apparently originates in a roughly spherical corona around the Galaxy. There is also an intense source of meter-length radio waves in the plane of the Galaxy, probably in the nucleus, but its nature is still unknown.

12.218. The most important localized (or discrete) sources of nonthermal radio waves in the Milky Way are the remains of supernovae. The nonthermal nature of the emissions has been established by at least two observations: first, the intensity would correspond to impossibly high brightness temperatures, and second, the signal strength increases with wavelength, whereas the thermal radiation intensity decreases. Radio emission from the Crab nebula (§ 12.166) has been studied in detail at wavelengths from about 1 centimeter to 10 meters, and in 1953 the Russian astronomer I. S. Shklovsky suggested that it was synchrotron radiation from high-energy electrons (§ 6.181). Support for this view, which is now generally accepted, is provided by the discovery that the radio waves are polarized, as is to be expected for such radiation.

12.219. The explanation of the nature of the radio emission from the Crab nebula helped to account for a curious anomaly in the optical spectrum of this celestial object. Much of the light from the nebula is continuous radiation over a range of wavelengths, whereas the spectra of other luminous nebulae consist mainly of bright emission lines. It now appears that the visible light from the Crab nebula is also synchrotron radiation of short wavelength. Normally, radiation of this type does not extend into the visible region, but it is evidently possible in the nebula because of the extremely high energies of the electrons present As is to be expected, the visible light from the Crab nebula shows the polarization characteristics of synchrotron radiation.

12.220. The remains of the supernovae of 1572 and 1604 have been identified with discrete radio sources, but these are both very much weaker than the Crab nebula. Another strong radio source is the one called Cassiopeia A; at the time of its discovery, there was no known object in the sky at the same location. Later, however, it was identified by means of the 200-inch telescope as a faint complex filamentous nebula in the Galaxy at a distance of about 3000 parsecs (10,000 light years). It is thought to be the remains of a supernova which was not observed because of its remoteness. From the rate of motion of the filaments, it has been estimated that the supernova explosion occurred about the year 1702.

12.221. Extragalactic discrete radio sources were originally referred to as radio "stars," but in the great majority of cases this description is not strictly correct. Certain red dwarf stars have been identified, however, as true radio stars. These are the *flare* (or *UV Ceti*) *stars* which flare up from time to time in an irregular manner somewhat like the Sun. The existence of these radio stars was finally established in 1963 as the result of a cooperative effort arranged by F. L. Whipple (§ 7.79) in the United States and Bernard Lovell in England. Five Baker-Nunn cameras of the U.S. satellite tracking network (§ 4.133) were used to detect the occurrence of flares while the 250-foot diameter radio telescope at Jodrell Bank, England, was employed to make simultaneous observations of radio waves. Analysis of the data showed a definite correlation between the optical flares and the radio emissions from six flare stars. Although the general behavior is the same as that of the Sun, the disturbances taking place on the UV Ceti stars are evidently much more violent, for otherwise the emissions in the optical and radio-frequency regions of the spectrum would certainly not be observed at such great distances. The nearest flare star is about 8.6 light years, i.e., about half a million times as far as the Sun, from Earth.

12.222. Most of the discrete sources of radio-frequency radiations now known are galaxies, and they are referred to as *radio galaxies*. About a hundred of such galaxies have been identified with objects visible in the telescope and they fall into two broad categories, called normal galaxies and peculiar galaxies. It is not certain that there is a clear line of demarcation between the two types, but for the present this classification is convenient.

12.223. The *normal radio galaxies* are mostly spirals, since they are the most common galaxies that have been observed, but there are also elliptical and irregular galaxies in this category. The essential characteristic of a normal radio galaxy is not its optical appearance, but the fact that its radio emission is regarded as normal. The rate at which energy is radiated as radio-frequency waves is not excessive and is a small, and almost constant, fraction of the energy emitted in the optical region of the spectrum. The radio emission is probably synchrotron radiation, like that in the Galaxy. About 50 such normal radio galaxies have been correlated with visible objects.

12.224. The rate of radio energy emission by a *peculiar radio galaxy* is larger, by a factor of a hundred to a million or so, than the emission from a normal galaxy. Some of the peculiar galaxies seem to be ordinary spiral or elliptical galaxies in the optical telescope. But there are others which appear to be abnormal, although the abnormalities are by no means the same in all cases. The galaxies that are peculiar in both radio and optical respects are of two general types, namely, those which are evidently single galaxies with an abnormality, such as a "jet" extending from the nucleus, e.g., M 87 (Fig. 12.23), and the others which appear to involve two (or perhaps more) interacting or colliding galaxies. The most powerful radio source known, called Cygnus A,

Fig. 12.23.   The peculiar ("jet") galaxy M 87. (*Lick Observatory*)

Fig. 12.24.   Optical counterpart of radio source Cygnus A. (*Mount Wilson and Palomar Observatories*)

is seen in the telescope as two galactic nuclei apparently in contact (Fig. 12.24). It is a curious fact, however, that the radio emissions do not originate in these visible nuclei but in regions some 30,000 parsecs (100,000 light years) on each side of them. A possible explanation is that the two regions were driven apart by some kind of galactic explosion, the origin of which is not known.

12.225. When two galaxies collide, as they must do on rare occasions, there are probably very few, if any, direct collisions between the stars. The individual stars in each galaxy are so far apart that the chances of two coming in contact are very remote. But in the course of a high-speed collision between two galaxies, which may persist for a million years, there will be considerable mutual interaction between their respective magnetic fields, hydrogen gas, and dust clouds. It is this interaction which presumably supplies the large amount of energy that is emitted in the form of radio waves.

12.226. An exceptionally peculiar radio galaxy, known as Centaurus A, coincides with the optical object NGC 5128 (Fig. 12.25). At one time it was thought to consist of a nearly spherical galaxy, of the E0 type, in collision (or contact) with a flattened, presumably spiral, galaxy seen edgeways. Many astrono-

Fɪɢ. 12.25. Optical counterpart of radio source Centaurus A (NGC 5128). (*Mount Wilson and Palomar Observatories*)

mers, however, are now inclined to reject this interpretation. As is the case with Cygnus A, the actual sources of the radio emission are two invisible regions; they lie on each side of, roughly equidistant from, the band which bisects the central body. Again, the general appearance suggests the possibility of a tremendous explosion.

12.227. In addition to the radio galaxies, there are a small number of equally powerful radio sources of a highly unusual character. These objects were thought at one time to be faint stars in the Milky Way, but early in 1963 it was established that they are not stars in the usual sense, neither are they galaxies. For want of a better name, they were called *quasi-stellar radio sources*, later abbreviated to *quasars*. By the end of 1964, over 30 quasars had been identified and several more are suspected.

12.228. The spectra of the quasars show a very large Doppler red shift, implying recession velocities of from 45,000 to 123,000 kilometers per second. On the basis of the value of the Hubble constant given earlier, the distances of the quasars from Earth are thus about 450 to 1200 million parsecs (1450 to 3900 light years). They cannot, therefore, possibly be members of the local Galaxy; they are, in fact, among the most distant known celestial systems. The farthest known object is the quasar 3C 147 * which is estimated to be some 1250 million parsecs (4000 million light years) from the Milky Way. From the known apparent magnitudes and the estimated distances, the visual luminosities of the quasars have been calculated and found to be on the order of a hundred times greater than the larger galaxies. The luminosity of some quasars, at least, is not constant but varies periodically; the shortest period observed is about a year, but others are of several years duration. The angular diameters, which are too small to be measured at all accurately, indicate that the quasars are about a fifth the size of a galaxy, but the rate of variation in luminosity suggests that they may be much smaller, perhaps no more than a few parsecs in diameter. The masses of quasars have been estimated to be on the order of about 10^8 solar masses, and so they are also considerably less massive than the great majority of known galaxies.

12.229. Several different theories have been proposed to account for the properties of quasars but they are speculative and none is completely satisfactory. Quasars are certainly not ordinary stars and apparently not groups of stars like galaxies. If a quasar is a single body, as appears to be the case, then the problem is to account for its existence. According to accepted theory, a mass exceeding about a hundred times that of the Sun is unstable; quasars are evidently not stable, but it is difficult to account for the accumulation of such large masses. Furthermore, the enormous rate of energy emission, which exceeds by a factor of a hundred or so the emission from galaxies about a thousand times more massive, requires explanation. The discovery of quasars in the early 1960's has thus opened up a new and puzzling area in the study of the universe.

X-RAY ASTRONOMY

12.230. In an attempt to observe fluorescence X-radiation† from the Moon (cf. § 9.210), for the purpose of obtaining information about the chemical composition of the lunar surface, a rocket carrying large Geiger counters was lofted to an altitude of about 130 miles. Analysis of the data by R. Giacconi, H. Gursky, F. R. Paolini, and B. B. Rossi in the United States in 1962 indicated that X-rays were being detected, but they did not originate in the Moon. It appeared that there was a considerable background flux of radiation from the night sky with a large superimposed maximum from the direction of the center of the Galaxy. A considerably lower maximum in the X-ray flux came

---

* The symbol 3C stands for Third Cambridge Catalogue of Radio Sources; it records nearly 500 sources of radio-frequency emission, many of which have not yet been identified with objects visible in the telescope.

† The exciting radiation would be electrons or X-rays from the Sun.

from the general direction of the strong radio sources Cygnus A and Cassiopeia A.

12.231. In 1963, S. Bowyer, E. T. Byram, T. A. Chubb, and H. Friedman launched a sounding rocket containing an X-ray detector some ten times more sensitive than that employed in the earlier experiments. As a result, they discovered a very strong X-ray source in the constellation Scorpius and a weaker one apparently in the Crab nebula. The Scorpius source is remarkable in the respect that there is no visual or radio-frequency emission from the same region of the sky, although radiations of both these types come from the Crab nebula. It has been suggested as a possibility that the X-rays are emitted by *neutron stars*. Neutron stars are purely hypothetical, since none has yet been observed, although their existence has been predicted for many years. A neutron star would have an extremely high density and very high internal and surface temperatures. If such an object behaved like a black body, it would emit most of its radiation in the X-ray region, with very little at longer wavelengths, i.e., in the visible, infrared, and radio-frequency portions of the spectrum.

12.232. The concept of a neutron star was first proposed by W. Baade and F. Zwicky in 1934 and it has been the subject of theoretical studies by astrophysicists since that time. A common view held at present is that the very rapid loss of energy from a supernova would lead to gravitational collapse of the residual core. The material might be then compressed to a density a million or more times greater than that of a white dwarf, and the temperature in the interior would rise to a few billion degrees. Under these conditions most of the protons and electrons would combine to form neutrons, and since all atoms are made up of protons, neutrons, and electrons, the result would be the formation of a star consisting mainly of a degenerate neutron gas. Such a neutron star might have a mass about the same as the Sun, but its diameter would be a hundred kilometers or less. At the estimated surface temperature of 10 million degrees K, the radiation emission in the X-ray region would exceed that in the visible by a factor of roughly 10^{10}, i.e., 10 billion.

12.233. The coincidence of a fairly strong discrete X-ray source with the Crab nebula, which is known to be a supernova, indicated that there might be a neutron star at the center. An unusual opportunity to test this possibility presented itself in July 1964 when the Crab nebula was occulted by the Moon. If the X-ray source was indeed a neutron star at the core of the nebula, the intensity of the radiation should have shown little or no decrease until the Moon's edge passed by the center; a sharp cut off should then have occurred. The data obtained by H. Friedman and his associates from a detector sent aloft in a sounding rocket did not fulfill these expectations. The X-ray intensity decreased gradually as the Moon occulted the Crab nebula, and the source of the radiation was identified as an extended region about a light year across. The diameter of the nebula is about 6 light years.

12.234. The neutron star theory of X-ray sources is so attractive that it has not been abandoned, in spite of the evidence that the X-rays from the Crab nebula apparently do not originate from such a star. Efforts will therefore be made to determine if there is a neutron star associated with the X-ray source in Scorpius. It is perhaps significant that in the ancient oriental literature there are records of four celestial events, close to the Scorpius source, which may have been supernovae.

12.235. As mentioned earlier, there are other X-ray sources, one possibly from the galactic center, in addition to the discrete sources just considered. The origin of these galactic and possibly extragalactic radiations is not known, but they presumably arise from interaction of electrons with other charged particles, with photons, or with magnetic fields. In any event, the existence of the radiations indicates some kind of cosmic activity which merits further study. It is possible that the *cosmic X-rays*, as they may be called, can provide information concerning local densities of electrons, temperatures, and magnetic field strength. If fluorescence X-radiation is present, as it may well be, it should provide data concerning the identity and abundance of elements in space. Since X-rays are very penetrating, they may provide a means of studying regions near the center of the Galaxy that are not accessible in other ways. It is too soon to make any predictions, but it is possible that, with the development of better observational techniques, X-ray astronomy may throw new light on the structure of the universe.

GAMMA-RAY ASTRONOMY

12.236. Another method for studying cosmic space, still very much in its infancy, has been called *gamma-ray astronomy*. It was seen in § 6.49 that gamma rays are electromagnetic radiations of very short wavelength, i.e., at the other extreme to radio waves, produced in nuclear reactions or in processes involving the annihilation of matter. As envisaged at present, gamma-ray astronomy is primarily concerned with the existence in space of gamma radiation of high energy.

12.237. High-energy gamma rays are produced, particularly, in two ways. First, when a proton (hydrogen nucleus) of high energy, such as is found in cosmic rays, strikes another proton or, in fact, any other nucleus, a violent disintegrative reaction occurs in which one of the products is a neutral particle, called a neutral pi-meson or *pion* (§ 8.248). The neutral pion has a very short life and soon decays into a pair of gamma rays, each with a minimum energy of 72 million electron volts. The second way in which high-energy gamma rays can be produced also involves a neutral pion, but in this case it is formed when an ordinary proton collides with an antiproton. The latter, of which there are very few in nature, are similar to protons in all respects except that they carry a negative, instead of a positive, charge. When a normal proton and an antiproton meet, they annihilate each other, producing a number of lighter particles, including neutral pions. The decay of the latter leads to the emission of high-energy gamma rays. There are other processes that can lead to such radiations, e.g., the annihilation of a positive and a negative electron, but the two mentioned are of most immediate interest.

12.238. The first "telescope," designed to observe high-energy gamma-ray photons (§ 6.76) in space, was flown on the U.S. satellite Explorer XI in 1961. After carefully screening the data, W. L. Kraushaar and G. W. Clark concluded that the instrument had detected 22 such photons. These photons came from various directions in the sky and there was no statistically significant deviation from a uniform distribution. The general conclusion drawn from the observations is that most of the high-energy, gamma-ray photons did not originate from within the Galaxy but from intergalactic space. Many more investigations with better instruments will be necessary to determine if gamma-ray astronomy can aid in the understanding of the universe.

12.239. One result of the Explorer XI measurement is of some interest. It will be recalled that the steady-state theory of the universe postulates the creation of hydrogen atoms. Some scientists consider that when matter is created it must be accompanied by "antimatter." The antimatter corresponding to the hydrogen atom would consist of an antiproton, i.e., a proton with a negative electrical charge, and an antielectron, i.e., an electron (or positron) with a positive charge. In its wandering through space, the antiproton would eventually encounter a proton, and the two particles would annihilate each other. As seen above, the annihilation would be accompanied by high-energy, gamma-ray photons. The number of such photons encountered by Explorer XI was very much less than would have been expected if the antiprotons were created, with protons, at the rate required by the steady-state theory of the universe. It seems, therefore, that antiprotons are not formed in this manner, regardless of whether protons are created or not.

Neutrino Astronomy

12.240. Of the new methods for exploring the universe, the one which appears to have the greatest potential, although probably the most difficult to implement, is *neutrino astronomy*. The neutrino (diminutive of Italian, *neutro*, "neuter") is a strange fundamental particle of nature; it is electrically neutral and has a negligible mass, but travels with the velocity of light and can carry energy.* There is evidence of the existence of four different kinds of neutrinos, but those of present interest are the two associated with reactions involving electrons. Of this pair, one is a true neutrino whereas the other is the antimatter form, the antineutrino. As far as can be understood in physical terms,

---

* In these respects, the neutrino is similar to the photon, the carrier of electromagnetic radiation (§ 6.76); it differs from the photon in having a half-unit of angular momentum (spin), whereas the photon has a whole unit. There are also other differences which make the neutrino a very elusive particle that is difficult to detect.

the only difference between these particles is that, when traveling in a given direction, one spins in a clockwise manner whereas the other spins counter-clockwise.

12.241. There are several different nuclear or similar processes which are accompanied by the formation of neutrinos or antineutrinos. The best known is the familiar radioactive beta decay; in this reaction, a neutron $(_0n^1)$ in the decaying nucleus breaks up into a proton $(_1H^1)$ which remains in the nucleus, and an electron $(_{-1}e^0)$, i.e., a beta particle, and an antineutrino $(\bar{\nu})$ which are expelled, i.e.,

$$_0n^1 \rightarrow {_1H^1} + {_{-1}e^0} + \bar{\nu}.$$

Antineutrinos produced in this manner have been detected by their interaction with protons, i.e.,

$$_1H^1 + \bar{\nu} \rightarrow {_0n^1} + {_{+1}e^0},$$

where $_{+1}e^0$ is a positive electron or positron. The simultaneous formation of a neutron and a positron is indicative of the capture of an antineutrino by a proton. Neutrinos could presumably be observed by the analogous reaction

$$_0n^1 + \nu \rightarrow {_1H^1} + {_{-1}e^0},$$

in which a proton and an ordinary negative electron are produced. For example, the capture of a neutrino by a neutron in a chlorine-37 nucleus should convert the latter into radioactive argon-37; this can be readily identified by its half-life.

12.242. Unfortunately, neutrinos and antineutrinos are extremely difficult to detect because they have a very great reluctance to interact with any form of matter. It has been calculated that, on the average, an antineutrino would travel a distance of 100 light years, i.e., about 5×10^{12} miles, through water before it would be captured by a proton. Thus, the only hope for detecting neutrinos or antineutrinos is to use very large volumes of material with which the particles would, on rare occasion, interact and sensitive equipment for observing the interaction when it does occur.

12.243. There are two particular directions in which a possible neutrino astronomy might be of special interest. In the first step of the proton-proton chain, which occurs in the Sun and many stars, two protons combine to form a deuterium nucleus plus a positive electron (§ 6.191); theory requires, how-ever, that a neutrino should be formed at the same time, so that the reaction is actually

$$_1H^1 + {_1H^1} \rightarrow {_1D^2} + {_{+1}e^0} + \nu.$$

12.244. The energy liberated is divided in many different ways among the three particles produced, and as a result the neutrino energy must have a spec-trum covering a fairly wide range. The interaction of two protons as indicated above should be accompanied by the less probable process in which a negative electron is taken up, i.e.,

$$_1H^1 + {}_1H^1 + {}_{-1}e^0 \rightarrow {}_1D^2 + \nu,$$

and this would also be accompanied by the liberation of a neutrino. But now the energy is divided between two particles; this means that all the neutrinos have essentially the same energy. The neutrino energy spectrum is now a line spectrum. The width of this line should be a measure of the temperature at which the proton-proton reaction is taking place, whereas its height will be dependent on the density of the protons (hydrogen) in the medium.

12.245. Because of its relative proximity, the Sun offers the best immediate prospect for applying the foregoing theoretical conclusions. If tests prove successful, they could be extended to other stars on the main sequence similar to the Sun in which the proton-proton chain is the chief source of energy. The proton reactions take place in the core, but nearly all the neutrinos produced would escape, since the probability of interacting with the material in the outer layer of the Sun (or star) is small. If a neutrino "telescope," located on Earth, could be designed to determine the spectrum of the neutrinos from the Sun, it should be possible to calculate the temperature and density of its core.

12.246. Another potential application of neutrino astronomy arises from a different type of reaction. At very high temperatures, e.g., a few hundred million degrees, such as are believed to exist in stellar interiors at the red giant and subsequent stages, the radiation photons can produce a pair of electrons, one positive and one negative. Most of the oppositely charged electrons very quickly unite, and annihilate each other, with the regeneration of photons (gamma rays). It has been predicted that in a very small proportion of the positive-negative electron annihilations, the products are a neutrino and an antineutrino; thus,

$$_{+1}e^0 + {}_{-1}e^0 \rightarrow \nu + \bar{\nu}.$$

The probability of this alternative reaction increases with increasing temperature of the stellar interior. Calculations indicate, in fact, that most of the energy leaving the stars with very hot interiors, e.g., the old blue stars (§12.157), is carried by neutrinos (including antineutrinos) rather than by photons.*

12.247. If this is indeed the case, the production of neutrinos might play an important role in the development of supernovae and other unstable conditions in stars. Photons escape from the interior of a star only after they have undergone many interactions, as described in § 6.201. Consequently, the energy remains within the star for a considerable time and serves to maintain the interior temperature without gravitational contraction. Neutrinos, on the other hand, would escape very rapidly, carrying off energy with them. The star would thus contract more rapidly than anticipated from the apparent rate of

---

* As stated in § 6.188, about 2 percent of the Sun's energy is carried off by neutrinos, but these are produced in the reactions between pairs of protons.

energy loss. The surface temperatures indicate the rate at which a star is losing energy as radiation photons, but provide no information about the energy removed by neutrinos. The early stages in the collapse of stars with very hot interiors might thus perhaps be observed with a neutrino telescope.

12.248. In principle, neutrino astronomy could therefore provide information about the stellar interior, whereas optical astronomy, and even radio astronomy, can do no more than study the behavior of the exterior layers. Because of the great difficulty in detecting neutrinos, the design of suitable instruments which could be directed at specific celestial sources presents major problems. Interference by cosmic-ray particles makes it necessary for neutrino detection to be carried out deep underground, where other particles cannot penetrate. In any event, allowance would have to be made for background neutrinos, originating in reactions in which high-energy cosmic rays are involved. In spite of the many difficulties and uncertainties, steps are being taken to study the neutrino emission from the Sun by the interaction with chlorine-37 nuclei, as described in § 12.241.

STUDY OF THE UNIVERSE WITH SPACECRAFT

INTRODUCTION

12.249. Apart from purely mechanical considerations, the astronomical study of the universe has been restricted by a number of circumstances. First, the resolving power of optical telescopes, i.e., the ability to attain good definition, has been limited by poor "seeing" resulting from the motion of air masses within the atmosphere;* second, the night airglow phenomenon (§ 8.84) produces a background of diffuse light against which it is impossible to photograph extremely faint celestial objects; and third, the optical and radio "windows" permit the investigation of only limited ranges of the electromagnetic radiation emitted by stars and nebulae. All these difficulties can be overcome by mounting instruments on a vehicle, preferably a satellite, from which observations can be made above the atmosphere.

12.250. In the United States, preliminary experiments, starting in 1955 and continued in later years, were made with small telescopes and associated spectrophotometers carried by sounding rockets to heights of 100 miles or more. The great disadvantage of this technique is that observation times are very short. Another method for getting astronomical instruments above most of the atmosphere was used in Project Stratoscope I in 1957. A 12-inch telescope, flown to a height of nearly 16 miles in an unmanned balloon, was able to take highly detailed photographs of the Sun (cf. Fig. 6.17). Later, in Project Stratoscope II, in 1963, a 36-inch telescope and an infrared spectrometer were used to study Mars, Jupiter, and a number of stars. In addition, there is the

---

* This movement (or turbulence) of the air is responsible for the familiar twinkling of stars.

U.S. Air Force's Project Stargazer for observing the stars from a manned balloon. A more comprehensive study of the sky, however, requires the use of satellites and such a program is being undertaken in the United States by means of the Orbiting Astronomical Observatories which will be described later in this section (see also § 11.40, footnote).

ULTRAVIOLET AND INFRARED SPECTRA

12.251. The part of the spectrum which is likely to provide most new information, both expected and unexpected, about the universe is the ultraviolet region. The common emission and absorption lines of hydrogen, helium, and other light elements, especially the resonance lines involving the respective ground states (§ 6.81), are in the ultraviolet, as also are many of the lines of heavier elements. Simple molecules also have emission lines in the ultraviolet portions of the spectrum, although these substances can sometimes be detected by absorption bands in the infrared.* Ultraviolet emission spectra should provide more information than is available at present on the composition of stars and nebulae. Furthermore, the few elements and molecular species that have been identified in interstellar dust and gas cannot, by any means, represent all that are present; absorption spectra in the ultraviolet should throw more light on this important aspect of stellar evolution. Finally, although radio astronomy has indicated the presence of neutral and ionized hydrogen atoms, nothing is known about the distribution of hydrogen molecules and of helium, both of which have spectra in the ultraviolet.

12.252. Stars with high surface temperatures, e.g., those in spectral classes O, B, and A, radiate only a small part of their energy in the visible region. Much that is known about such stars has been inferred from extrapolations based on measurements in this region and from calculations. But the conclusions drawn may be incorrect. This is illustrated by the studies made by T. P. Stecher and J. E. Milligan (1962) with a sounding rocket of the class B1 star Epsilon (ϵ) Canis Majoris; at wavelengths longer than 2400 angstroms (Å) there is agreement between observed and calculated energy distributions as a function of wavelength, but at shorter wavelengths in the ultraviolet there is a marked discrepancy (Fig. 12.26). Furthermore, the energy distributions below 2400 Å appear to be different for Epsilon Canis Majoris and for the adjacent star Beta (β) Canis Majoris, although their spectra in the visual region places them both in the same class. On the other hand, the energy distribution of a cooler (class F0) star Alpha (α) Carinae (or Canopus) is in harmony with expectation for all wavelengths observed, namely 1750 Å and above. The discrepancies in the case of the stars with higher surface temperatures is at-

---

* The ultraviolet spectra of molecules arise from electronic energy transitions, whereas the infrared spectra are due to changes in the energy of vibration or rotation or both (§ 10.62).

tributed to absorption of the short-wavelength radiation by abnormal molecular species in the stellar atmospheres.

12.253. Another fact revealed by the preliminary observations with sounding rockets is the existence of ultraviolet nebulosities. Such phenomena have been detected in the wavelength region of 1225 to 1350 Å in the constellation Orion

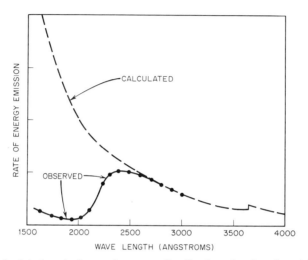

FIG. 12.26.   Calculated and observed energy distributions in the ultraviolet from the star Epsilon Canis Majoris (after T. P. Stecher and J. E. Milligan)

and around the star Alpha (α) Virginis (or Spica), but there are no indications of these nebulosities in visible light. There is apparently no star associated with the ultraviolet nebula in Orion.

12.254. Although the short-wavelength region of the spectrum will probably yield the most interesting results, the long wavelength infrared should not be overlooked. There are undoubtedly many stars with low surface temperatures that have not yet been detected. These stars radiate mainly in the infrared region and their study is essential to understanding the evolution and development of stars.

ORBITING ASTRONOMICAL OBSERVATORIES

12.255. The purpose of the Orbiting Astronomical Observatories is to provide accurately stabilized platforms for making astronomical observations from satellites above Earth's atmosphere. The basic framework has been designed to accommodate optical systems of telescopes up to 48 inches in diameter, 10 feet in height, and weighing 1000 pounds, although it will be some time before use is made of the maximum capabilities of the spacecraft. The Orbiting Astronomical Observatory has been planned, therefore, as a general purpose vehicle that can be readily adapted for use in a variety of astronomical experiments.

12.256. The Observatory has an octagonal body, 80 inches across and 10 feet in length. The observing instruments are housed in a central (optical) tube with a circular cross section 48 inches in diameter (Fig. 12.27); the auxiliary

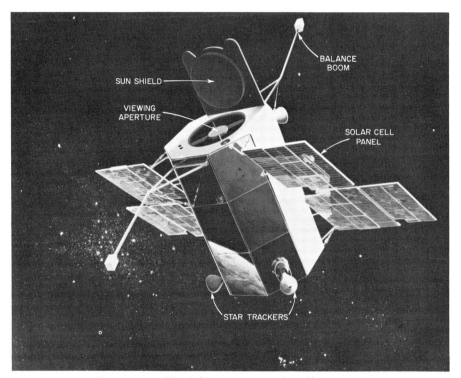

Fig. 12.27.   The Orbiting Astronomical Observatory

electronic equipment is located on shelves in the space around the tube. For launching, the end of the optical tube is covered with a hinged shield for protection, but in orbit the shield opens up to provide a shade that prevents sunlight from reaching the instruments. In the event of a malfunction in the orientation system, the sunshade closes automatically. Electrical power for operation of the spacecraft is provided by arrays of solar cells on paddles which fold up for launching and open up in space. The total weight of the Orbiting Astronomical Observatory with all its equipment is about 3600 pounds. An Atlas-Agena rocket combination should be capable of placing it in an orbit of about 500 miles altitude.

12.257. Pointing of the telescopes at a particular star is achieved by means of six star trackers, although only two are necessary to provide the required information under ideal conditions. Each tracker consists of a 3.5-inch diameter telescope mounted on gimbals with two degrees of freedom; the incoming star image from each telescope is split into two light beams to provide error signals about the two gimbal axes. By means of a servo system, these signals drive torque motors on the gimbal axis and bring the telescope back to the required direction (cf. Chapter 4). After launching, the spacecraft is first stabilized on the Sun and then the desired stellar reference is established upon command from a ground station and maintained by the star trackers. The control system is designed to provide a pointing accuracy of 0.1 sec of arc.

12.258. The Orbiting Astronomical Observatory No. 1 is to carry four independent experiments. One is a photometer-telescope system to measure the energy distribution and emission intensities of stars. In addition, there are three instruments for X-ray and gamma-ray studies. One of these is designed to detect and determine the directions of high-energy gamma-ray sources, in continuation of the work described in § 12.238, whereas another will search for low-energy gamma rays. The third instrument will survey the sky for sources of X-rays, such as those mentioned in § 12.230 *et seq.*

12.259. The photometer-telescope system is for determining the energy distributions of various stars and nebulae in the range from 800 to 3000 Å and for measuring the emission line intensities of diffuse nebulae in the same spectral region. The equipment consists of three optical systems: the first has four 8-inch telescopes with photometers and appropriate filters intended primarily for the study of stars; the second, with a 16-inch telescope and photometric system, is for observing nebulae and other objects covering relatively large areas; and the third is a 7 × 10-inch parabolic objective with a diffraction-grating spectrometer (§ 6.56) for studying line spectra in the ultraviolet.

12.260. The purpose of the Orbiting Astronomical Observatory No. 2 is to make absolute photometric measurements of the emissions of stars and nebulae in the ultraviolet region. It is to be capable of obtaining both steady-state and time-dependent data on stars up to the 11th magnitude. The main instrument is a reflecting telescope with a primary mirror 36 inches in diameter made of beryllium; this unusual metal was chosen because of its stability to temperature changes. A diffraction grating provides a spectrum over the range of 100 to 4500 Å; resolution over a narrow band of wavelengths is obtained by the use of slits. Photocells sensitive to different parts of the ultraviolet spectrum serve as detectors.

12.261. The third Orbiting Astronomical Observatory will carry instruments for determining the composition of interstellar dust and gas by studying the ultraviolet absorption spectra from 800 to 3000 Å. The experiments on the two preceding Observatories, on the other hand, measure emission spectra. The instrument consists of a 32-inch diameter telescope with a fused quartz mirror and a high-dispersion grating spectrometer; the resolution of the latter can be made as small as 0.1 Å. Appropriate photoelectric cells measure the intensities of the weak absorption lines. Since it is desired to determine the composition of the interstellar material as accurately as possible, emphasis is placed on a quantitative study of the intensities of these lines.

12.262. The experiments on the first three Orbiting Astronomical Observatories are explorative in nature. In addition to supplying information of value, they will indicate the directions in which further investigations should be made. In any event, it is certain that the study of celestial objects from above Earth's atmosphere will open up new vistas in astronomy.

Relativity and Gravitation

12.263. One of the areas in which the use of spacecraft may contribute to an understanding of the universe is in experiments designed to test the theory of relativity. In 1915, the German-born mathematical physicist Albert Einstein proposed the *general theory of relativity*, of which his earlier theory of 1905 was a special case. Basically, the general theory of relativity is a theory of gravitation which supersedes the classical Newtonian theory. In the very great majority of cases of interest, the two theories lead to essentially the same results, but there are a few situations in which the classical theory is unable to account for the observations. A particular example is the long-known discrepancy in the rate of advance of the perihelion of the planet Mercury (§ 10.4); the observed rate differs from the value calculated from the Newtonian theory by 43 sec of arc per century. It is true that this amount is very small, but there is no doubt about its reality, and so it needs to be explained.

12.264. In oversimplified terms, the theory of gravitation based on relativity involves two concepts. The first is the principle of equivalence which asserts that the observable effects of inertia, i.e., the property of matter that causes it to resist any change in its motion, and of gravity are indistinguishable. Einstein illustrated this equivalence by considering an elevator falling freely in space, and supposing that a passenger in the elevator releases a mass that he has been holding. Since the elevator and the mass are falling at the same rate, the mass will not drop to the floor but will remain suspended. If the elevator is completely closed and the passenger is unaware of his surroundings, he will be under the impression that there is no gravitational force acting on the mass. Suppose, however, that a constant upward force is applied to the elevator, e.g., by means of a rocket, the mass which has been suspended in mid-air will drop to the elevator floor just as if it had been attracted by gravity. But the effect is actually due to the inertia of the mass and not to gravity.

12.265. The second concept is based on the postulate that all bodies are located in a space-time medium (or continuum); this medium has four dimensions, three of conventional geometrical space and one of time. As a result of its inertia, a body will move on a *geodesic* (or *geodesic line*) which is the shortest distance that can be drawn between two points on a three-dimensional surface in the four-dimensional continuum. The presence of any mass causes a distortion or curvature of space-time and consequently of the geodesics in its vicinity.

12.266. Consider two masses, and suppose for simplicity that one is fixed whereas the other is free to move. The curvature of space-time by the fixed mass causes the other mass to travel along a geodesic which moves it in the direction of the first mass. To an observer it would appear, therefore, as if the fixed mass is attracting the movable one by the force of gravity. What the moving mass does, however, is determined by its inertia and by the curvature of space-time and not because of gravitational attraction exerted by the fixed mass. A physical analogy may be provided by a sheet of rubber stretched across a frame with a mass placed in the center of the sheet. The mass will then distort the sheet, and this may be regarded as representing the curvature of space-time by matter (Fig. 12.28). Another mass placed in the vicinity of the central mass will move toward the latter, not as a result of attraction but rather because of the distortion of the medium in which it is constrained to travel.

Fig. 12.28. Simplified schematic representation of gravity in space-time system

12.267. In the classical, Newtonian theory of gravitation, the mutual attraction of two bodies is the same regardless of whether they are stationary or in motion relative to one another. In relativity theory, however, there is a difference, the magnitude of which increases as the velocity of motion approaches that of light.

TESTS OF RELATIVITY THEORY

12.268. The general theory of relativity shows that, in the motion of a planet about the Sun, there should be a gradual rotation of the line of the apsides (§ 2.88) in addition to that due to classical gravitational considerations. In each revolution of the planet, the line of the apsides should advance by an angle ψ given by

$$\psi = \frac{6\pi v^2}{(1 - e^2)c^2} \text{ radians,} \tag{12.13}$$

where v is the orbital velocity of the satellite, e is the eccentricity of the orbit, and c is the velocity of light.

12.269. When applied to the planet Mercury, equation (12.13) requires that the perihelion of its orbit advance by an angle of 43.03 sec of arc in 100 years. This is in complete agreement with observation. The relativity effect is greater for Mercury than for the other planets because it is closest to the Sun and hence has the highest orbital velocity. Furthermore, the fairly large eccentricity of Mercury's orbit increases the value of the angle ψ to some extent and, more important, it makes the change in position of the perihelion much easier to determine accurately. The perihelion of the planet Venus should advance by about 8.6 sec of arc per century, but the almost circular orbit makes this very difficult to measure.

12.270. Another test of the theory of relativity is based on the deflection of light by the Sun. The special theory (1905) led to the idea of the equivalence of mass and energy (§ 6.187) as expressed by the Einstein equation (6.4), i.e.,

$$E = Mc^2, \tag{12.14}$$

where E is the energy equivalent of the mass M, and c is the velocity of light. Since a photon of radiation carries energy, it must have an equivalent mass, the value of which can be calculated by the Planck quantum-theory equation (6.9), i.e.,

$$E = \frac{hc}{\lambda}.$$

where h is Planck's constant and λ is the wavelength of the radiation. If this value of E is set equal to that giving the mass equivalent, it follows that

$$M = \frac{h}{c\lambda}, \tag{12.15}$$

where M is the effective mass of a photon of radiation of wavelength λ. This mass is extremely small, e.g., about 4×10^{-33} gram* for visible light, but in passing close to the Sun the photon should be deflected as a result of gravitational attraction.

12.271. Calculations based on the Newtonian theory of gravity indicate that the angular deflection of the light from a distant star as observed on Earth should be 0.87 sec of arc. In addition, however, the relativistic effect that is responsible for the advance in the line of the apsides of Mercury and other planets should cause the photon, traveling with the velocity of light, to be deflected by an essentially equal amount. According to the general theory of relativity, therefore, the deflection of the light from a star in passing close to the Sun should be 2×0.87, i.e., 1.74 sec of arc. Observations made during solar eclipses of the apparent change in positions of distant stars, as a result of the deflection of their light by the Sun, have given values in general but not exact agreement with the calculated deflection based on relativity theory.

12.272. The effects considered above have arisen from the differences between the classical and relativistic theories of gravitation. The one to be described next arises from the special theory according to which a photon has a mass, given by equation (12.15). In leaving the Sun or other star, a radiation photon loses energy because it has to do work against the gravitational attraction of the star. The loss of energy means a decrease in the frequency, i.e., an

---

* For comparison, it may be noted that the mass of a single hydrogen atom is about 1.7×10^{-24} gram and that of an electron 9×10^{-28} gram.

increase in the wavelength, of the radiation that leaves the star. This increase, called the *gravitational red shift*, should be applicable to the whole range of the star's spectrum. Upon reaching Earth, the gravitational attraction will increase the energy of the photon and thus decrease the wavelength; the resulting *gravitational violet shift* is, however, negligible in comparison with the red shift because the mass of Earth is small relative to that of a star.

12.273. The magnitude of the gravitational red shift can be readily calculated. By combining equations (2.12) and (2.29), it follows that the velocity an object must acquire to escape from a large and massive body, of radius R and mass M^*, is

$$v_{\text{esc}} = \sqrt{\frac{2GM^*}{R}}$$

where G is the universal gravitational constant. If the escaping object has a mass M, the kinetic energy corresponding to the escape velocity is $\frac{1}{2}Mv_{\text{esc}}^2$, i.e., GM^*M/R. If the object under consideration is a photon, its mass, M, is given by equation (12.15); hence, the loss of energy is represented by

$$\text{Energy loss} = \frac{GM^*M}{R} = \frac{GM^*h}{Rc\lambda}. \tag{12.16}$$

12.274. The energy loss can be related to the change in wavelength by making use of equation (6.9). If E is the energy of the photon and λ the radiation wavelength before escaping from the star, and E' and λ' are the respective values after escaping, then

$$E = \frac{hc}{\lambda} \quad \text{and} \quad E' = \frac{hc}{\lambda'}.$$

The loss of energy, $E - E'$, is therefore

$$\text{Energy loss} = hc\left(\frac{1}{\lambda} - \frac{1}{\lambda'}\right)$$

$$= \frac{hc(\lambda' - \lambda)}{\lambda\lambda'} = \frac{hc\Delta\lambda}{\lambda\lambda'}, \tag{12.17}$$

where $\Delta\lambda$ is the increase in wavelength. If equations (12.16) and (12.17), both of which give the energy loss, are set equal to one another, it is found that

$$\frac{\Delta\lambda}{\lambda} = \frac{GM^*}{Rc^2}, \tag{12.18}$$

where λ has been substituted for λ', to which it is approximately equal, in the denominator on the left side. Equation (12.18) is sometimes expressed in terms of the change in frequency, rather than of the wavelength of the radiation; if Δf is the increase in frequency, then $\Delta f/f$ is equal to $-\Delta\lambda/\lambda$.

12.275. Attempts have been made to measure the gravitational red shifts of the Fraunhofer lines of the Sun's spectrum (§ 6.99). But at a wavelength of

4000 Å, the shift is only 0.01 Å, and hence is difficult to determine accurately. Observations made prior to 1962 indicated that the Sun did produce a red shift, but the results were not reliable. In that year, however, the French astronomers J. E. Blamont and F. Roddier reported on a new and highly accurate technique which indicated that the gravitational red shift of the spectral line from the element strontium in the Sun was in excellent agreement with the value obtained from equation (12.18). Instead of measuring the wavelength of the strontium line in the solar spectrum directly, Blamont and Roddier used the light from the Sun to excite a secondary spectral emission in a beam of strontium atoms in the laboratory. The emitted light was passed through a magnetic field and the intensity determined as a function of the field strength. By comparing the results with the secondary emission produced by a terrestrial strontium source, the shift in wavelength of the strontium line from the Sun could be obtained.

12.276. It can be seen from equation (12.18) that the wavelength increase should be enhanced if M^* is large and R is small; the white dwarf stars have just these properties and they should consequently show a relatively large gravitational red shift. The limited measurements available indicate that equation (12.18) is obeyed, but the results are somewhat uncertain. In the first place, the masses and radii of white dwarfs are known only approximately; more important, however, is that the stars exhibit a Doppler shift due to radial motion. To separate this shift in wavelength from that caused by gravitation requires the radial velocity of the star to be known accurately and this is rarely the case.*

TESTS OF RELATIVITY BY SATELLITES

12.277. At least three methods have been proposed whereby the theory of relativity could be tested by means of artificial satellites. In the first place, the line of the apsides of such a satellite orbiting about Earth should advance at a rate given by equation (12.13), just as is the case for a planet revolving about the Sun. For an Earth satellite, the orbital velocity is considerably less than for Mercury, and so the angle ψ per revolution is smaller. But the shorter orbital period means that the total advance of the pericenter (perigee) in the course of a year can be much greater than for Mercury in a century. An artificial satellite launched into an orbit of moderately high eccentricity and fairly short period can provide a useful means for verifying equation (12.13). Instead of observing the change in the position of the perigee, an alternative would be to determine the precession of a very stable gyroscope on the satellite. The draw-

---

* An apparent gravitational red shift has been detected in studies of the Mössbauer effect, which is a very sensitive technique for determining the change in wavelength (or frequency) of gamma rays emitted from a radioactive crystal. Although there is no doubt about the validity of the results, there is a difference of opinion concerning their interpretation.

back at present is that other perturbing effects are not yet known sufficiently accurately for the necessary allowances to be made.

12.278. A further consequence of the relativity theory of gravitation is that the rotational motion of a central body should produce an additional advance of the pericenter of a satellite's orbit. The predicted effect is too small to be detected either for Mercury or for the Moon, revolving about the Sun and Earth, respectively. It should be significant for satellites of Jupiter and Saturn, because these planets rotate so rapidly, but the motions of the satellites cannot yet be observed with adequate precision. Artificial satellites of Earth, however, may provide a means for determining if the expected effect exists. There are two factors favoring the use of artificial satellites in this connection: one is the faster rate of rotation of Earth as compared with the Sun, and the other is the greater proximity of such a satellite to Earth than is the Moon.

12.279. A third proposed test of the theory of relativity involves the gravitational violet shift. A source of radiation of known wavelength is placed on the satellite and the wavelength of the radiation as received on Earth is measured. Since the mass of the satellite is negligible compared with that of Earth, the shift (decrease) in wavelength would be due to the attraction of the photons by Earth. The resulting violet gravitational shift would be given by equation (12.18) with the sign changed; M^* would be the mass of Earth and R the orbital radius of the satellite. For visible light the shift would be far too small to measure, but for radio waves, with much longer wavelength, it should be possible to determine the expected decrease.

Chapter 13

MAN IN SPACE

PROJECT MERCURY

INTRODUCTION

13.1. Space is a new dimension that must inevitably be explored by man for whatever potential—scientific, military, or political—it may possess as well as to satisfy his natural curiosity. In the United States, definite plans for determining the utility of man in the exploration of space are encompassed by three projects entitled Mercury, Gemini, and Apollo, respectively. Project Mercury, which was completed in May 1963, included two ballistic suborbital flights and four orbital flights, of three, three, six, and 22 orbits, respectively, with one man in each case.* The purpose of Project Mercury was to obtain experience in placing a man in orbit and recovering him safely, and to study his ability to function in the space environment.

13.2. The important conclusion reached from the Project Mercury flights is that man has a definite role in space and that his presence can mean the difference between success and failure of a mission. For example, flight MA-5 with a chimpanzee as a passenger had been planned for three orbits but had to be terminated after two, because of a malfunction of the attitude control system. There is little doubt that, had a human astronaut been present, the mission would have been completed. Similarly, in nearly all the manned flights, the astronauts were able to deal with situations that would have made it necessary to abort the missions in their absence. Thus, by making use of the astronaut's performance capability, the mechanical systems in the space vehicle can be simplified and their reliability thereby increased.

THE MERCURY SPACECRAFT

13.3. The bell-shaped design of the Mercury capsule was developed after extensive wind-tunnel tests showed that this provided the best conditions for

---

* The dates and other information concerning these events are given in Chapter 1. In addition to several checkout flights, the manned flights were preceded by two flights with chimpanzees; one was the suborbital (MR-2) flight on January 31, 1961, and the other (MA-5) was a two-orbit flight on November 29, 1961.

re-entering the atmosphere after completion of an orbital mission. A general view of the spacecraft, including the escape tower, and its main dimensions are shown in Fig. 13.1; this is the form in which it was launched and it then weighed nearly 4300 pounds. In the event of a malfunction occurring before the

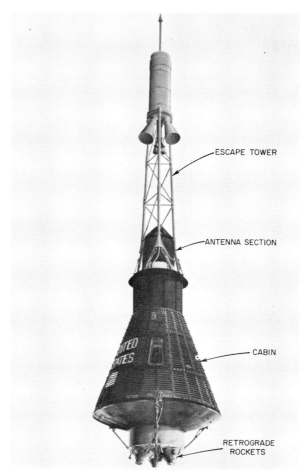

ESCAPE TOWER

ANTENNA SECTION

CABIN

RETROGRADE
ROCKETS

Fig. 13.1.   The Mercury spacecraft with escape tower attached

required orbital velocity was attained, the rockets in the upper part of the escape tower would ignite. The spacecraft would be detached from the launch vehicle, e.g., Atlas rocket, and would follow a ballistic trajectory into the nearby sea. Fortunately, except for tests, the escape tower was never used in the Mercury program. Under normal conditions, such as existed in all the manned flights, the escape tower was jettisoned about 2.5 minutes after liftoff; the weight of the remaining capsule was roughly 3000 pounds.

13.4. The prime consideration in the design of the Mercury spacecraft was to provide complete heat protection for the astronaut during both launch and re-entry phases of a mission. The main structure consisted of a double-shell arrangement with glass fiber insulation in between. The metal titanium was chosen for the interior shell and for the framework of the exterior, because of its light weight and ability to retain its mechanical strength at high temperatures. The double-wall construction provided good heat insulation as well as protection from possible penetration by micrometeoroids (cf. § 7.153 *et seq.*).

13.5. The outer framework of the conical portion of the capsule and of the antenna section (see Fig. 13.1) was covered with a layer of thin shingles made of a metallic alloy capable of withstanding high temperatures; similar, but thicker, shingles of beryllium metal were used on the cylindrical (recovery compartment) section. The shingles were corrugated to increase their surface area and blackened to improve their thermal emissivity, thereby facilitating the loss of heat by radiation. For launching, the narrow end of the spacecraft pointed upward, i.e., in the direction of flight. The conical section was thus subjected to appreciable aerodynamic (drag) heating and the temperature of the metal shingles rose as high as 700°C (1300°F), but the radiation losses and insulation helped to keep the temperature of the interior of the capsule within tolerable limits.

RE-ENTERING THE ATMOSPHERE

13.6. Upon its return to Earth, the spacecraft, with a speed of some 7.5 kilometers (4.8 miles) per second for an orbital flight and almost 11 kilometers (6.8 miles) per second for a lunar mission, must be brought to rest. The most obvious way of doing this would be to apply reverse thrust by means of retrograde (or retro-) rockets. But since the energy required would be equal to that utilized in launching the spacecraft, the use of retro-rockets alone is quite impractical. The Mercury capsules were thus mainly decelerated by utilizing the resistance of the atmosphere.* The large amount of kinetic energy possessed by the spacecraft before re-entry was then converted into heat. The vehicle had, therefore, to be designed to prevent excessive heating of the cabin atmosphere.

13.7. When a body moves through the air at high speed, part of its kinetic energy (or heat load) is spent in producing a high-pressure shock wave and some is dissipated by friction. If the body has a slender, i.e., streamlined, configuration, only a small proportion of the heat load is lost in the shock wave; this was approximately the situation when a Mercury spacecraft was launched. On the other hand, for a body having a blunt (or broad-nosed) shape as it encounters the atmosphere, most of the heat load is transferred to the surrounding air in the form of a bow-shaped shock wave (Fig. 13.2), and there is relatively little frictional heating.

---

* For landing on the Moon, where there is no atmosphere, retro-rockets must be used (§ 13.39); the lower value of gravity, however, makes the problem much less severe than on Earth.

13.8. It is the latter principle which was utilized in the re-entry phases of the Mercury flights. The spacecraft was oriented so that its broad end faced in the direction of motion, as shown in the figure. The design of the space-craft, with a broad nose followed by an afterbody with inward sloping sides, permitted something like 90 to 95 percent of the initial kinetic energy to be spent in forming the shock wave upon re-entry into the atmosphere. The remaining few percent of the heat load appeared as friction heating of the afterbody of the capsule, i.e., the conical, cylindrical, and antenna sections. The maximum temperature attained in these regions was about 540°C (1000°F), which is somewhat lower than that attained during the launch phase of the operation.

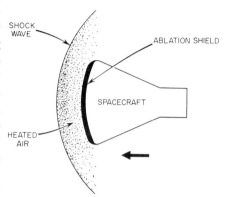

FIG. 13.2.   Formation of shock wave as a spacecraft re-enters the atmosphere with the blunt end forward

13.9. The temperature at the front of the shock wave reached some 5540°C (10,000°F) and a bright, incandescent layer of air surrounded the front of the spacecraft upon re-entry. Excessive heating of the vehicle itself was prevented, however, by means of an ablation shield (cf. § 3.76). This shield, which covered the broad end of the spacecraft, was made of a mixture of a synthetic polymer resin and glass fibers; the main purpose of the latter was to provide mechanical strength and physical integrity to the shield. The resin was heated by the hot air in the shock wave and as a result it melted and charred and also vaporized to some extent. This ablation process prevented the capsule from becoming over-heated. Heat was spent in melting and charring the resin, and the black char served as a good radiator. The gases and vapors produced also helped to carry heat away from the spacecraft; moreover, to some extent they provided a boundary layer that acts like a thermal insulator. The maximum temperature, at the outer surface of the ablation shield, was roughly 1650°C (3000°F), whereas the inner surface, near the spacecraft wall, was no more than 205°C (400°F). The air temperature in the cabin may have been as high as 40°C (105°F) during re-entry, but the cooling system (§ 13.67) prevented the temperature in the astronaut's space suit from rising above 29°C (85°F); this was not too uncomfortable for the short re-entry period.

The Attitude Control System

13.10. Among the many systems included in the Mercury spacecraft, reference will be made here to the one used for attitude control; the environmental control and life support systems will be described in a later section and brief mention will be made of others in connection with the flight program. The purpose of the control system is to provide attitude control (§ 4.80) and stabilization, as may be required in orbit and, in particular, during the re-entry operation. A precisely calculated attitude must be attained for the spacecraft to leave its orbit and re-enter the atmosphere, if landing is to take place within the prescribed recovery area.

13.11. The Mercury capsule had two completely independent control systems; with their aid, the attitude could be adjusted by means of pitch, yaw, and roll rockets (or thrustors) using 90 percent hydrogen peroxide as the monopropellant (fuel). In one system, the astronaut could choose either the automatic stabilization and control system (ASCS) or the fly-by-wire (FBW) system. The ASCS could provide the necessary control of attitude throughout a complete mission, if there were no malfunction, without any action on the part of the astronaut. In the FBW system, however, the astronaut actuated the three-axis hand controller (or control stick) to operate electrical solenoid valves that regulated the propellant supply to the thrustors.

13.12. The second system originally also had two components; one was the manual proportional (MP) system and the other was the rate stabilization control system (RSCS). The latter, which used a combination of manually controlled stick positions and the computing components of the ASCS, was removed from the last Project Mercury flight as it was deemed unnecessary. The MP system differed from the others in not requiring any electrical power; mechanical linkages from the control stick operated the valves for adjusting the hydrogen peroxide propellant. To provide double control in the interest of safety, the ASCS and MP systems could be used simultaneously, as also could the FBW and MP systems. Of the three manual control systems, FBW proved to be the most versatile and more economical in the use of propellant than any other system, manual or automatic.

MERCURY ORBITAL FLIGHT PROGRAM

13.13. The sequence of major events in a Mercury orbital mission were as follows (Fig. 13.3). The Atlas engines were ignited and the rocket vehicle was released from the launch pad when it was certain that the engines were operating properly. Soon after the booster had ceased firing, the escape tower was jettisoned automatically. Following cutoff of the sustainer engine, when the spacecraft was in orbit, three posigrade solid-fuel rockets, located at the blunt end, were fired simultaneously. This gave the spacecraft a small increment in velocity and permitted it to separate from the Atlas vehicle. At this stage, the narrow end of the capsule was pointing in the direction of travel, and it was now turned into the re-entry attitude, i.e., with the blunt end forward and the long axis making an angle of 34 deg with the horizontal, in case a malfunction should require the mission to be terminated.

13.14. Once the space vehicle was safely in orbit, its attitude could be allowed to vary, but it must be established precisely again prior to re-entry into Earth's atmosphere. At the calculated time, three solid-fuel retrograde rockets, also located at the blunt end, were fired at intervals of 5 seconds; a minute later, the

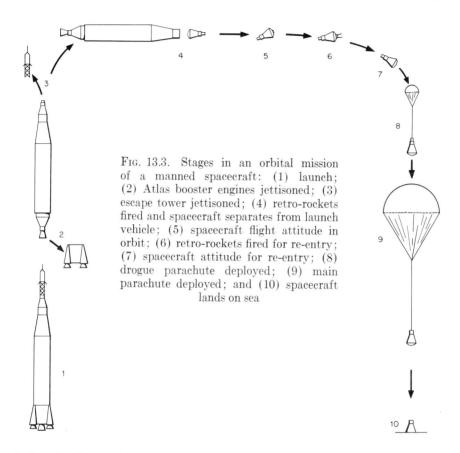

FIG. 13.3. Stages in an orbital mission of a manned spacecraft: (1) launch; (2) Atlas booster engines jettisoned; (3) escape tower jettisoned; (4) retro-rockets fired and spacecraft separates from launch vehicle; (5) spacecraft flight attitude in orbit; (6) retro-rockets fired for re-entry; (7) spacecraft attitude for re-entry; (8) drogue parachute deployed; (9) main parachute deployed; and (10) spacecraft lands on sea

whole retro-fire package was detached from the spacecraft. The retro-rockets decreased the speed of the capsule by only 1 or 2 percent, but this was sufficient to deflect the vehicle from its orbit and cause it to descend in a ballistic trajectory through the atmosphere. In order to provide maximum deceleration, the attitude was maintained so that the blunt-end always faced into the direction of motion. When an altitude of roughly 30,000 feet (more or less) was reached, and the spacecraft was falling almost vertically, a drogue (or drag) parachute, 6 feet in diameter, was released to slow down the rate of fall. The main parachute, 63 feet in diameter, was opened at about 10,000 feet altitude to permit a rate of fall of approximately 30 feet per second when the capsule reached Earth's surface. The parachutes were deployed automatically when a certain value of atmospheric pressure was reached, but they could have been actuated manually.

13.15. To facilitate recovery, the re-entry pattern of the Mercury capsule was such that it alighted on the sea in a predetermined area, and the astronaut was then removed by boat and helicopter.* To minimize the impact on landing, a so-called "landing bag" was used. It was made of rubberized cloth which was folded up and stored during flight at the blunt end between the heat shield and the main body of the spacecraft. Just before landing, a mechanical latch released the heat shield so that it dropped down and the bag (or skirt) extended about 4 feet, filling with air through holes in its sides. The shield remained attached to the lower end of the skirt and the upper end was fastened to the space vehicle. Upon striking the water, air was expelled through the holes in the bag, thus producing a buffering (or shock absorbing) action.

13.16. During the whole flight period, one or other of the 16 stations of the Mercury Worldwide (now the Manned Space Flight) Network tracked the path of the spacecraft by radar (§ 4.140). In addition, two-way voice communication was available between the astronaut and the ground, except for 3 to 5 minutes during the re-entry phase when ionization of the air, caused by the intense heat, produced a plasma sheath that resulted in a radio blackout. Telemetry was also disrupted during this period, but radar tracking was unaffected. Efforts are being made to find a method for eliminating this interference with communication. A promising approach is to inject a stream of water at the center of the forward surface of the spacecraft to decrease the temperature and thus reduce the ionization. Another possibility is to introduce a gas that has a strong affinity for electrons; the free electrons in the plasma sheath would then attach themselves to the gas molecules to form negative ions. It is anticipated that these ions, like positive ions, will not interfere with the transmission of radio waves. Consideration is also being given to the use of a modulated beam of laser light (cf. § 4.144) for communication purposes as an alternative to radio.

Astronaut Training

13.17. An important factor in the success of Project Mercury has been the program for the selection and training of astronauts. In addition to the training given them to improve their reactions to physiological stresses, to which reference will be made later, much emphasis has been placed on obtaining complete familiarity with the spacecraft systems and their operation. Operational training was carried out with the aid of various flight simulators called Procedures Trainers. In these devices, it was possible to simulate the operation of all the Mercury systems and to induce a variety of failures and malfunctions.

---

* It is reported that the earlier Russian cosmonauts descend from their spacecraft by parachute over land. The Voshkod, with its three-man crew (§ 1.118), is said to have made a soft landing on the ground.

The astronauts thus learned how to deal with significant emergencies. The value of this training was amply demonstrated in the actual flights.

13.18. In the Gemini and Apollo missions, which follow Project Mercury, a great deal more responsibility will be placed on the astronaut. This is partly because the operations, which will include rendezvous and docking and possibly activities outside the spacecraft, are more complex and also because advantage will be taken of man's ability to take appropriate actions to simplify many of the systems which were automatic in the Mercury spacecraft. There is little doubt, however, that with proper training, such as that to which the Mercury astronauts were subjected, they will be able to perform all the tasks required of them. A variety of simulators are available for the purpose of providing highly realistic experience of the operations involved in the Gemini and Apollo projects. Preliminary tests have shown that there are no insuperable obstacles to the satisfactory execution of these missions, as far as man is concerned.

PROJECT GEMINI

The Gemini Spacecraft

13.19. Project Gemini has been so named because the spacecraft will carry two men.* The program has two main objectives: one is to study the effects on man of long periods, up to 14 days, of weightlessness and of his psychological and physiological reactions to the various stresses of travel through space (§ 13.79 *et seq.*). The other is to develop the capability of utilizing man to perform rendezvous and docking operations in space. There is also a possibility that Project Gemini will include tests of extravehicular activities, i.e., the ability of the astronauts to leave the spacecraft and perform certain operations outside.

13.20. The shape of the two-man Gemini cabin is similar to the Mercury capsule, but the linear dimensions are about 20 percent greater, resulting in an increase of somewhat more than 50 percent in volume. Instead of an escape tower, the Gemini vehicle has ejection seats with parachutes like those in certain high-speed aircraft. Two large doors located above the seats provide a means of rapid egress in the event of an emergency on the launch pad, in the initial phase of powered flight, or shortly before landing upon re-entering the atmosphere. The structural material of the Gemini spacecraft, like that of Project Mercury, is titanium, with beryllium shingles. The total weight is roughly 7000 pounds.

13.21. In order to provide more space for the astronauts in the cabin, some of the equipment is located in a section attached to the retrograde section, which contains the solid-fuel retro-rockets for re-entry (Fig. 13.4). The combination of retrograde and equipment sections is called the adapter module. In the equipment section are the hydrogen-oxygen fuel cells for providing electric power and drinking water (§ 3.263), the astronaut's main supply of oxygen for

* The Latin verb *gemino* means "to double." The constellation Gemini is depicted as the twins Castor and Pollux side by side.

breathing, and bipropellant hypergolic thrustors for attitude control and for performing maneuvers in space. The propellants are nitrogen tetroxide as oxidizer and a mixture of hydrazines as fuel (§ 3.30). The total weight of rocket and fuel is less than for the monopropellant (hydrogen peroxide) system used

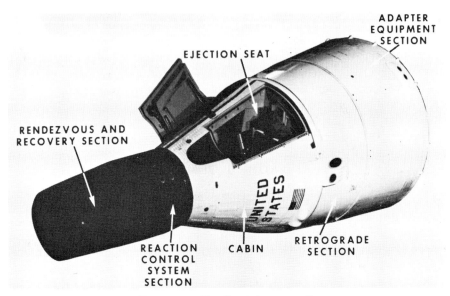

FIG. 13.4.   The Gemini spacecraft

for attitude control in Project Mercury. After the orbital phase of a mission is completed, the equipment section is discarded and when the retro-rockets have been fired, the remainder of the adapter module is jettisoned. Re-entry is then carried out with the broad end of the capsule facing the direction of motion, as in Project Mercury. To supply electric power during this operation, storage batteries will be available in the cabin.

13.22. An important difference between the Gemini and Mercury spacecraft is that, whereas the orbit of the latter could not be changed except for re-entry, this is possible in the Gemini capsule by utilizing the thrustors in the equipment section. Such orbital modification is necessary to permit rendezvous and docking maneuvers.

13.23. Another way in which the spacecraft differ is that the Gemini vehicle has a limited capability for selecting the area in which it will land upon re-entry. Interaction of the Mercury capsule with the atmosphere caused the development of drag forces but no lift (cf. § 4.91); in other words, the lift-to-drag ratio was zero. In the Gemini spacecraft, however, the center of gravity is offset a few inches sideways from the geometrical center, and consequently the vehicle has a significant, although not large, ratio of lift to drag. When re-entering the atmosphere, the ballistic flight path can be changed to some extent by a slight roll produced by means of a small thrustor. As a result, it is possible to change the landing point by several hundred miles along the flight direction and some tens of miles to either side. It was planned at one time to use a paraglider, i.e., a specially shaped parachute with glider capability, deployed at an altitude of between 40,000 and 50,000 feet, to achieve a ground landing on skis. But the paraglider has been eliminated for the present in favor of water landings, like those in Project Mercury.

13.24. Because of its greater thrust and also because it uses hypergolic propellants, so that it can be ready to launch at a predetermined time for rendezvous operations, the Titan II is the primary launch vehicle for Project Gemini (§ 3.150). After checking out procedures with unmanned instrumented "boiler plate" and other models,* manned flights of the Gemini capsule will be made for periods extending up to 14 days. Subsequently, space rendezvous tests will be initiated.

Rendezvous and Docking Operations

13.25. For rendezvous operations, an Agena rocket (§ 3.144) with an engine capable of being stopped and restarted several times, will serve as the target vehicle. It is launched as a satellite into an approximately circular orbit, about 160 miles above Earth, by means of an Atlas rocket. At a precisely calculated time on the following day, when the orbital elements of the Agena satellite have been determined accurately, the manned Gemini spacecraft will be launched by a Titan II rocket vehicle into an elliptical orbit. The apogee of this orbit will be as close as possible to the altitude of the Agena target. Thus, the two orbits should converge close to the apogee of the Gemini orbit.

13.26. It is hoped in this manner to bring the Gemini spacecraft within 20 miles of the target vehicle. But if the separation is greater, the orbit of the Agena target will be changed by restarting its engine upon command from the ground. The orbit of the Gemini capsule can also be changed to some extent, as stated earlier, and the astronauts will be able to make small midcourse corrections as well as terminal guidance and docking maneuvers (Chapter 4). Computers on the space vehicle will provide the information required for these operations by utilizing range and range rate data obtained by radar.

13.27. By adjusting the orbits and taking advantage of the difference in the orbital periods, that of the manned spacecraft being the shorter, the two vehicles will be brought into proximity, with the Gemini capsule somewhat ahead of the target (Fig. 13.5). Then, by appropriate use of the propellant system on the spacecraft, and aided by radar and visual sighting, the astro-

---

* The term "boiler plate" is applied to relatively inexpensive mockups of a spacecraft which have the same configuration, weight, and location of center of gravity as the actual flight vehicle. They were given this name because they are often made of steel plate. Boiler plate models are used extensively for obtaining aerodynamic and thermal data in orbit and to test the performance of various systems, e.g., thrustors, parachutes, etc.

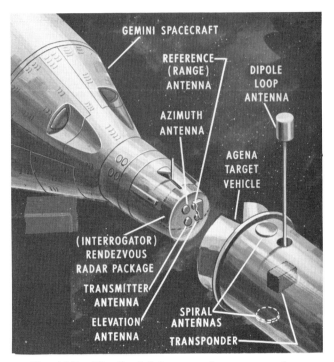

Fig. 13.5. The Gemini-Agena rendezvous operation

nauts will bring together the narrow end of the capsule and the docking collar of the Agena target vehicle. Before returning to Earth, the Gemini capsule will be detached from the target which will remain temporarily in orbit.

PROJECT APOLLO

Direct Approach to the Moon

13.28. The ultimate aim of Project Apollo is to land men on the Moon and return them safely to Earth. There are several possible methods for achieving this objective, but three in particular have been the subject of detailed analysis. The first and simplest in principle is called the *direct approach*. The spacecraft would consist of three separate sections or modules. The uppermost section, known as the *command module*, is the flight control center; it would have a three-man crew and equipment for life support, communications, guidance, and navigation.

13.29. Next would be a *service module*, which is essentially a propulsion stage; it would contain the rocket engine and propellant for takeoff from the Moon and a secondary propulsion system for midcourse corrections and for attitude control during the return to Earth. Some of the spacecraft components that are not needed in the command module, e.g., main electrical power supplies, oxygen for breathing, etc., would be in this module. Finally, the lowest section is the *lunar landing module;* also a propulsion stage, it is intended mainly to decelerate the spacecraft as it approaches the Moon in order to permit a soft landing. This module would contain the thrustors for midcourse guidance and attitude control on the way to the Moon.

13.30. The total estimated mass of the spacecraft upon liftoff for the direct approach to the Moon is estimated to be roughly 150,000 pounds. To launch such a mass, a rocket with a thrust of some 12 million pounds would be required, and this is larger than the thrust of any launch vehicle under development. The spacecraft would be boosted directly into a lunar trajectory. Upon reaching the vicinity of the Moon, after making any midcourse corrections that may be necessary, the main engine in the lunar landing module would be ignited and the vehicle slowed down to bring it into a lunar orbit. When a suitable location is reached, the retrograde thrust of the engine would be used to lower the spacecraft to the surface of the Moon. Two of the astronauts would then leave the vehicle to explore, while the third stays to maintain communication contact with Earth.

13.31. For the return journey, the engine in the service (center) module would be employed; the lunar landing module serving as a launch base would be left behind. Then, as Earth is approached, the service module would be discarded and the command module alone would re-enter the atmosphere. Deceleration would be produced, as in the Mercury and Gemini capsules, by air resistance, with some control provided by the lift capability of the capsule.

EARTH ORBIT RENDEZVOUS

13.32. The main drawback to the direct approach mode of reaching the Moon is the large mass that must be carried, particularly in the lunar landing module, to permit the spacecraft to make a soft landing on the surface of the Moon. A lunar mission by direct approach would therefore have to await the development and testing of a highly advanced launch vehicle. A possible way of avoiding the delay is to use the *earth orbit rendezvous* method for sending a manned expedition to the Moon. This approach could be achieved by means of two Saturn V vehicles, with a thrust of 7.5 million pounds each at liftoff (§ 3.155), instead of a single more powerful rocket that will not be available for several years.

13.33. The spacecraft for the earth orbit rendezvous method is the same as that described above, except that an additional propulsion unit, called the *escape stage,* is attached below the lunar landing module. This combination, carrying the three astronauts but only partially loaded with propellants, is first placed in Earth orbit by means of a Saturn V launch vehicle. The remainder of the propellants required for the mission is contained in an unmanned tanker stage and this is subsequently boosted into orbit with another Saturn V rocket.

A rendezvous and docking maneuver is then performed in Earth orbit, and the propellants are transferred from the tanker to the spacecraft. The procedure would be somewhat similar to refueling an aircraft in flight, except that the speeds are very much greater for the vehicles in orbit.

13.34. When propellant transfer has been achieved and the tanker has been detached, the engine of the escape stage would be ignited to change the Earth orbit into a lunar trajectory. The escape stage is then jettisoned, leaving the spacecraft, consisting of command, service, and lunar landing modules, to proceed to the Moon. Subsequently, the program of operations would be exactly the same as for the direct approach described above.

Lunar Orbit Rendezvous

13.35. The third method for achieving a manned lunar mission, and the one which is actually being adopted for Project Apollo, is the *lunar orbit rendezvous* mode. It differs from the other approaches in the respect that the command and service modules are not landed on the Moon. They remain in lunar orbit, while a relatively light vehicle, known as the *lunar excursion module* (or LEM), and referred to colloquially as the "bug," is detached and lands on the surface with two members of the crew. After exploring the Moon, part of the lunar excursion module will return to lunar orbit and rendezvous with the command and service modules; it is this operation which gives the name lunar orbit rendezvous to the overall procedure. The two astronauts then transfer to the command module

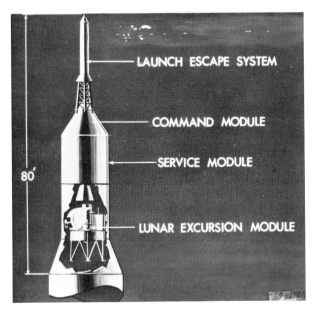

Fig. 13.6.   The Apollo spacecraft

and the lunar excursion module is left in the vicinity of the Moon. The remainder, consisting of command and service modules, will then return to Earth just as in the direct and earth rendezvous approaches.

13.36. The great advantage of the lunar orbit rendezvous method is that the light weight of the lunar excursion module means a decrease in mass by some 60,000 pounds of the propellants required to land it on the Moon and lift it off again. The total mass to be boosted into a lunar trajectory from Earth is thus about 90,000 pounds, and this requires only a single Saturn V launch vehicle. The chief objection raised against the lunar rendezvous mode is that the rendezvous and docking operations are performed in the vicinity of the Moon. In case of difficulty, it would not be possible to obtain help from Earth.

13.37. The Apollo spacecraft, with its launch escape tower, is depicted in Fig. 13.6; the total height is then 80 feet. The main structural material is steel, instead of the titanium used in Projects Mercury and Gemini. The command module has a volume of 300 cubic feet for the three-man crew, whereas the Gemini capsule has 80 cubic feet for its two astronauts. It serves as the control center for all Apollo space operations. The module has a blunt conical body, 13 feet in diameter at the broad end; the total weight is approximately 10,000 pounds (Fig. 13.7). The small nose cone, discarded after the spacecraft has passed through Earth's radiation belt, covers the hollow cylindrical adapter to be used for docking and as a passage for transferring astronauts to and from the lunar excursion module. The command module has an aerodynamic lift-to-drag ratio of about 0.5, which can be utilized, as in the Gemini capsule, to vary within limits the re-entry path in Earth's atmosphere. An ablating heat shield

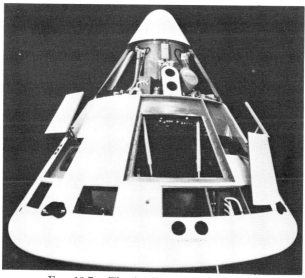

FIG. 13.7.   The Apollo command module

provides protection against the high temperatures encountered during this phase
of the operation. In addition to the navigation and guidance systems, the command module contains all the control systems except for those actually required to land on the Moon and take off again.

13.38. The service module is cylindrical, 20 feet long and 13 feet in diameter;
it weighs 10,000 pounds without propellant and 50,000 when fully loaded. Its
22,000-pound thrust rocket engine, using hypergolic propellants, provides
power for midcourse corrections and for injection into and out of lunar orbit.
The fuel cells that are the main source of electric power and the hydrogen and
oxygen for their operation are in the service module, as well as the oxygen required by the astronauts for breathing. Other systems in this module are the
thrustors for attitude control, radar, and radiators for cooling the spacecraft.

13.39. The lunar excursion module (Fig. 13.8), some 20.5 feet tall and weighing around 27,000 pounds with its propellant load, is located within a cylindrical
adapter extending from the service module (cf. Fig. 13.6). One benefit of using
an entirely independent unit for landing on the Moon is that its design can be
optimized to meet its objectives, i.e., lunar landing, take off, and rendezvous.
Since there is no atmosphere on the Moon and deceleration is achieved by

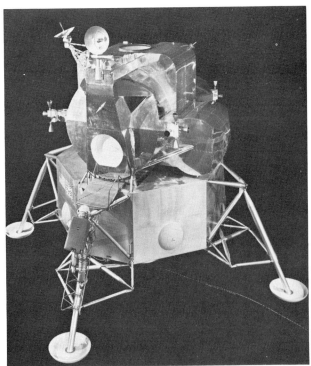

FIG. 13.8.   Lunar excursion module. (*Courtesy Grumman Aircraft Company*)

retrograde thrust, the lunar excursion module does not need to have a blunt shape or a heat shield. Triangular windows with an ample view provide visual reference for the two astronauts during the critical landing and other operations which they will perform standing up, while firmly held in a harness (Fig. 13.9). The upright position will provide much better visibility for the two

Fig. 13.9. Mockup of interior of lunar excursion module showing support harness for the astronaut

crew men when landing than if they were seated. Furthermore, the harness is lighter in weight and occupies less space than a couch. The lunar excursion module has two docking tunnels, one overhead and one in front, to provide greater flexibility. The forward tunnel has the great merit of permitting the astronauts a direct view of the rendezvous operation.

13.40. There are two separate sections in the lunar excursion module, each with its own hypergolic propulsion unit. The lower part consists of the lunar landing gear and descent rocket, whereas the upper portion is the cabin for the astronauts and the engine for use in ascent from the Moon and for rendezvous and docking. When leaving the lunar surface, the lower section will be left behind.

THE LUNAR LANDING PROGRAM

13.41. The actual Apollo mission to the Moon will, of course, not be attempted until all aspects of operation of the three modules have been thoroughly tested in the vicinity of Earth. For its journey to the Moon, the spacecraft will be placed in Earth orbit by means of a Saturn V launch vehicle. A short time after the first stage of the Saturn V is dropped, the escape tower will be jettisoned, and later the second stage will be discarded, leaving the third stage (S-IVB) attached to the spacecraft. When the desired orbit is attained, the S-IVB engine, which is capable of being restarted, is shut off temporarily. The vehicle will then orbit Earth for about 2 hours while the systems are checked. If they are functioning satisfactorily, the S-IVB engine will be ignited to increase the velocity to that required for a lunar trajectory, i.e., about 11 kilometers (6.8 miles) per second.

13.42. As soon as the trajectory has been verified, the cylindrical adapter connecting the command and service modules to the remainder of the vehicle will be released; these two modules will then separate as a unit, leaving the lunar excursion module attached to the S-IVB stage (Fig. 13.10 A). The astronauts in the command module then turn the spacecraft around through an angle of 180 deg and dock it, nose to nose, with the lunar excursion module, utilizing the service module propulsion engine. One purpose of this operation will be evident shortly.* It is performed at this point primarily to permit use of the S-IVB to stabilize the lunar excursion module. When the turn-around is completed, the combination of three units, as shown in Fig. 13.10 B, will separate from the S-IVB engine and proceed to the Moon. Midcourse corrections will be made as required, probably four times during the flight, by means of the service module engine.

13.43. Some 70 hours after launch, the spacecraft will be in the vicinity of the Moon. During the intervening period, the vehicle may change its attitude, but when near the Moon the astronauts will orient it in such a way that the service module engine can be used to decrease the velocity to about 1.6 kilometers (1 mile) per second (§ 9.58). The spacecraft will then go into a circular orbit about the Moon at an altitude of approximately 100 miles (Fig. 13.10 C). If all systems are functioning properly, preparations will now be made for the lunar landing; if not, the lunar excursion module will be detached and the crew will return to Earth.

13.44. For the lunar landing operation, two of the astronauts will transfer from the command module to the lunar excursion module. It was to make this possible that the nose-to-nose attachment was performed earlier. The third member of the crew will stay in the command module which continues in its circular lunar orbit. The excursion module will then be separated from the remainder of the spacecraft and its lower (descent) rocket engine will be fired to change the orbit from circular to elliptical with a pericenter (perilune), i.e., closest approach, 10 miles from the surface. The period of revolution, roughly 2 hours, will be the same as in the original orbit. Consequently, although the two units of the spacecraft will follow different paths, they would come together

* Another is to expose the service module engine.

every 2 hours provided no propulsion is applied to either in the interim period. This would permit the lunar excursion module to rejoin the command module should conditions for landing on the Moon turn out to be unfavorable.

13.45. As the excursion module approaches within 10 miles of the lunar surface, the crew will observe the terrain through telescopes and choose a suitable landing area, based on information obtained from the Ranger, Surveyor,

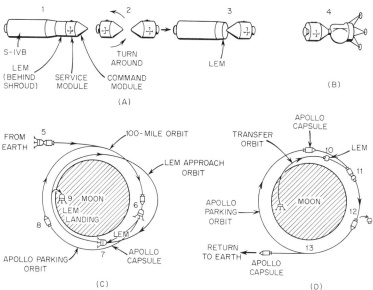

Fig. 13.10. Stages in the lunar orbit rendezvous program: (1) the S-IVB stage with attached command module (CM), service module (SM), and lunar excursion module (LEM) in lunar trajectory; (2) the CM-SM combination is detached and turned around through 180 deg; (3) the CM-SM combination docks nose-to-nose with the LEM; (4) the CM-SM-LEM combination separates from the S-IVB stage and turns around for the journey to the Moon; (5) close to the Moon, the CM-SM-LEM is oriented to permit the SM engine to decrease the spacecraft velocity to correspond to a 100-mile lunar orbit; (6) the LEM separates from the CM-SM and (7) goes into an elliptical approach orbit while (8) the CM-SM remains in a parking orbit, and (9) the LEM lands on the Moon; (10) after exploring the Moon, the upper part of the LEM is launched into a transfer orbit and (11) completes a rendezvous and docking operation with the CM-SM; (12) the LEM is jettisoned, and (13) the CM-SM returns to Earth. Prior to re-entering Earth's atmosphere, the SM is detached and discarded.

and Lunar Orbiter spacecraft (Chapter 9). They will then make another orbit around the Moon and prepare to descend the next time they are near the perilune. The lower rocket engine is fired in a retrograde sense to decrease the velocity and permit the vehicle to drop gently toward the lunar surface. The thrust of the engine can be adjusted so that the module hovers for some 2 minutes roughly 300 feet above the surface. At this altitude the vehicle can travel about 1000 feet horizontally, thereby permitting the astronauts an opportunity to select a landing site. By suitable throttling of the descent engine, the lunar excursion module will drop to the surface at a speed of less than 10 feet per second.

13.46. Upon reaching the lunar surface, the two astronauts, wearing pressure suits with a supply of oxygen and carrying radio communication equipment, will carry out a prescribed program (§ 13.50) and then return to the lunar module. The members of the crew will explore one at a time, so that there is always someone in the module to maintain communications. Liftoff from the Moon will take place when the main spacecraft is in sight; for this purpose, the upper (ascent) rocket engine of the lunar excursion module will be used. The descent engine and landing gear will be left behind to save weight. The ascent trajectory, approximating a Hohmann transfer ellipse (§ 2.72), will be computed to bring the two parts of the spacecraft as close together as possible. At a separation of about 5 miles, the guidance system of the excursion module, under command from radar and optical data, will cause the engine to operate in such a manner as to decrease the distance between the vehicles.

13.47. When the two units are a few hundred feet apart, with the lunar excursion module ahead of the command module (Fig. 13.10 D), the crew of the former will take over control and complete the rendezvous and docking operation. In the event that the occupants of the excursion module are unable to complete the maneuver, it can be performed by the astronaut who has remained in the command module. After the two crew members have returned to this module, the excursion module will be detached and left in lunar orbit. At this stage, the rocket engine in the service module will be ignited to provide the additional velocity required to escape from the environment of the Moon. The spacecraft will then coast toward Earth, with necessary midcourse corrections being made by one of the thrustors in the service module.

13.48. In the vicinity of Earth, the path of the vehicle must be carefully controlled so as to lie within a 40-mile deep *re-entry corridor,* as it is called, in the atmosphere. If the trajectory lies above this corridor, the spacecraft will not slow down sufficiently to permit it to land; instead, it will follow a "skip" path back into space. On the other hand, if the entry occurs below the corridor, the rate of deceleration will be so rapid that it could result in injury to the returning astronauts and might even cause the spacecraft to burn up. Assistance in attaining the correct re-entry path will be provided by precise tracking from the ground. When the final adjustments have been made and its propulsion engine is no longer required, the service module will be jettisoned and the command module will be oriented at the correct angle, with the heat shield at the blunt end facing the direction of travel. The final touchdown, with the aid of parachutes, will probably be on water, since this is considered to be safer than a ground landing.

13.49. Before the discovery of the Van Allen radiation belt (Chapter 8), the favored method for return to Earth from a lunar mission was by means of a series of elliptical orbits of decreasing dimensions (cf. § 2.93), with the perigee coming closer and closer to the surface. It is now realized, however, that the radiation dose received by the astronauts during such a flight, involving several passages within the radiation belt, would be quite intolerable. This otherwise attractive procedure for re-entering the atmosphere has therefore been abandoned.

Lunar Surface Activities

13.50. The two earliest landings on the Moon are each expected to permit a working time of 4 hours on the surface; these are to be followed by missions of 24-hours duration. The activities of the astronauts will fall into two main categories: first, those for the purpose of increasing the probability of success of future lunar expeditions, and second, those which will add to basic scientific knowledge of the Moon. In the former category are studies of the engineering properties of the surface and a detailed assessment of the hazard that may be encountered in its exploration. For example, it is important to know if it will be possible to use any kind of vehicle to travel on the lunar surface. Observations will be made of the texture of the surface material, on both small and large scales, and of its mechanical (bearing) strength and related properties.

13.51. Measurements of a purely scientific nature will probably be largely concerned with geology and geophysics. The astronauts will make geological observations of rock formations and will take photographs of characteristic features that appear to be of special interest. In addition, it is planned to collect some 80 pounds of geological specimens of a variety of types which will be taken back to Earth for microscopic, chemical, and radiochemical examination. Radioactivity measurements will perhaps also be made directly by the astronauts themselves, as far as possible, on and below the surface. Several seismographs will be placed in suitable locations with telemetry equipment to relay information to Earth over an extended period. The great value of man in this respect is his ability to choose a suitable location, with a firm foundation, for these instruments. Devices for counting meteoroids of various sizes can also be placed on the surface and left there.

13.52. When it becomes possible for man to stay for longer periods on the surface, more complex tasks will be undertaken. A hole several feet deep may be drilled to provide subsurface samples and to emplace instruments for temperature determination. Data on heat flow obtained in this manner will help to elucidate the internal structure of the Moon. Additional information in this respect can be obtained from active seismology experiments; these will involve setting a seismometer on a rock and exploding a number of buried charges.

13.53. Geodetic measurements, in which the apparent motion of several stars is followed over the course of a few days, could be used to determine precisely the Moon's axis of rotation and the amplitude of the physical librations (§ 9.30).

The information concerning the lunar moments of inertia derived for these data would be of considerable scientific value for the reasons discussed in Chapter 9. Other studies of interest which could be made by astronauts having a certain degree of mobility are measurements of the Moon's gravitational and magnetic fields.

POST-APOLLO MANNED MISSIONS

13.54. Three manned missions are conceivable to follow Project Apollo; they are (a) an Earth-orbiting space station or laboratory, (b) a permanent base on the Moon, and (c) an expedition to Mars. The manned expedition to Mars would not be possible without much more information concerning the physiological effects on man of long periods in space and the development of methods for life support, as will be seen in the next section. A station capable of orbiting Earth for an extended period would thus appear to be mandatory as a first step; this would provide the experience necessary before undertaking the lengthy journey to Mars and back. Thus, the manned space station project would be related to the Mars mission in the manner that Project Gemini is related to Apollo.

13.55. An orbiting space station is of interest, moreover, for reasons other than those associated with an expedition to Mars. In addition to providing information on the biological response of man to the space environment, the space station can be used to determine man's ability to maintain, adjust, and repair instruments. There is little doubt that many of the failures experienced in the operation of instrumented satellite systems could have been avoided had man been present. The superiority of the human eye over the camera, with which astronomers are familiar and which was demonstrated in Project Mercury, could be of inestimable value in making meteorological and other observations.

13.56. Furthermore, there is a distinct possibility that a space station may have military potential. In this connection, the U.S. Department of Defense has under consideration a Manned Orbital Laboratory (MOL) for launching in 1968, that is, before the actual Apollo mission to the Moon. The MOL is planned as a cylinder, about 25 feet long and 13 feet in diameter, that would be attached to the blunt end (heat shield) of a Gemini-type capsule. The total weight would be about 15,000 pounds and launching into an approximately 200-mile altitude orbit would be achieved by means of a Titan III rocket (§ 3.151). At liftoff, the two-man crew would be in the capsule and when in orbit they would transfer to the laboratory section of the spacecraft through a porthole in the heat shield. The capsule would be used for eating and sleeping, and experiments would be carried out in the laboratory. After 2 to 4 weeks in orbit, the astronauts would return to Earth in the capsule, leaving the remainder of the station in space.

13.57. The MOL would be purely experimental in nature, and is intended to provide basic information by utilizing equipment that is mostly in an advanced stage of development, i.e., the Gemini capsule and the Titan III launch vehicle. The next stage may be an Apollo spacecraft, in which the service and lunar excursion modules are replaced by a laboratory unit; launching of such a station must await the availability of the Saturn V rocket. Subsequent plans call for space stations of more and more advanced types, leading to one with a normal crew of 18 men, requiring continuous support, and a peak crew of 36 who will need support for a few days at a time. The useful life of the station may be from 1 to 5 years, at an orbital altitude of 200 to 300 miles. Such a large vehicle would be launched in sections and then assembled in space by a series of rendezvous operations. The tour of duty of crew members would be only 2 or 3 months at a time, and men and supplies would be carried from Earth by smaller spacecraft serving as ferries.

13.58. Studies are also in progress directed toward the construction and operation of more-or-less permanent bases on the Moon. The bases could serve as centers for lunar exploration and for determining the economic potential, if any, of the Moon's mineral resources. Since there is no lunar atmosphere, the "seeing" with optical telescopes would be greatly superior to that on Earth and radio astronomy would not be restricted to a limited range of wavelengths. Thus, optical and radio telescopes located in a base on the Moon would greatly extend man's knowledge of the universe. Steps would have to be taken, however, to avoid dimensional changes in instruments that would result from the large variations in temperature occurring on the lunar surface (§ 9.147).

LIFE SUPPORT IN SPACE

THE CABIN ATMOSPHERE

13.59. To maintain the atmosphere of a space capsule suitable for breathing, the essential requirements are that oxygen be supplied and that the products of respiration, carbon dioxide and water (vapor), be removed. There are two general means whereby the necessary oxygen may be provided. The obvious way is to duplicate man's normal environment by supplying a mixture of oxygen and nitrogen of the same composition, i.e., 21 volume (or molecular) percent of the former gas and 79 percent of the latter, and at the same total pressure, i.e., 14.7 pounds per square inch, as the normal atmosphere at sea level. It is reported that this is the method used by the Russians in their manned spacecraft.

13.60. The alternative approach, adopted for the United States Projects Mercury and Gemini and provisionally for Project Apollo, is to provide an atmosphere consisting essentially of oxygen alone with no nitrogen. Pure oxygen is toxic if breathed for a length of time which is inversely related to the gas pressure; thus, deleterious effects of hyperoxia, i.e., excess oxygen in the blood, are evident in a few hours at atmospheric pressure and in about 2 days at half this pressure. On the other hand, if the oxygen pressure is less than some 2 pounds per square inch, there is insufficient oxygen in the blood (hypoxia). The partial pressure of oxygen in the normal atmosphere is 3.1 pounds per square inch,* and an atmosphere of pure oxygen at this pressure would probably constitute a suitable breathing atmosphere for at least 2 weeks.

13.61. There is no complete agreement, even in the United States, as to the most desirable conditions for the atmosphere of a manned space vehicle, but the choice of a gas consisting almost entirely of oxygen at a pressure of 5 pounds per square inch was based on the following considerations. In the first place, the use of two gases—oxygen and nitrogen—would increase the complexity of the system to some extent, with the possibility of a decrease in overall reliability. Furthermore, the higher total pressure, 14.7 against 5 pounds per square inch, means a larger leakage rate of gas; although the spacecraft is sealed, there is inevitably some leakage at joints and this increases with the total cabin pressure. Additional oxygen (and nitrogen) would therefore have to be carried to compensate for the gas lost in this manner. Another point is the smaller danger in pure oxygen of decompression sickness (dysbarism), which generally results from the release of nitrogen gas bubbles in the blood, in the event of an emergency situation leading to a loss of atmospheric pressure. An oxygen pressure of less than 5 pounds per square inch would probably have been adequate for respiration purposes, but the somewhat higher pressure provides additional protection; furthermore, the extra gas assists in the removal of heat from the electronic equipment in the spacecraft.

13.62. Because the atmosphere of pure oxygen at a lower total pressure is an unusual environment for man, ground-based tests have been made for periods up to 30 days. Although some minor effects have been noted, nothing detrimental has been observed with most subjects in oxygen gas at a pressure of 5 pounds per square inch for 14 days, the maximum duration of the Gemini and Apollo missions. It is felt, therefore, that for these missions the selected atmosphere of oxygen gas should prove satisfactory. The only significant drawback to the use of such an atmosphere is the increased fire hazard, e.g., from electric sparks or overheated surfaces resulting from electrical short circuits. Since breathing pure oxygen for long periods, even at 5 pounds per square inch, may be detrimental, experiments are being made with other possible atmospheres. One of particular interest is a mixture of equal parts of oxygen and nitrogen at a total pressure of 7 pounds per square inch; the partial pressure of oxygen is thus 3.5 pounds per square inch, i.e., slightly above that in the normal atmosphere. This mixture is being considered as an alternative to pure oxygen in the Apollo spacecraft; if it is used, the capsule will have to be adapted to retain the somewhat higher total gas pressure.

---

* The partial pressure of any gas in a mixture may be regarded as the amount the particular gas contributes to the total pressure; thus, the partial pressure of the 21 molecular percent of oxygen in the normal atmosphere is approximately $(21/100) \times 14.7 = 3.1$ pounds per square inch.

PRESSURE SUITS

13.63. For reasons of safety and in order to gain experience, the astronauts in Project Mercury wore air-tight pressure suits. The atmosphere within the suit, which the astronaut breathed, was maintained at the required pressure, temperature, and purity by means of the environmental control system described below. If a leak had occurred in the spacecraft, e.g., as the result of penetration by a meteoroid, and the cabin pressure was lost, the space suit would have prevented the wearer from suffering decompression. During most of each Mercury flight, the suit remained closed although the visor could be opened for eating and drinking. This was possible because, in normal operation, the pressure was the same in the suit as in the cabin.

13.64. The pressure (or space) suit worn by the Mercury astronauts was made in two layers, namely, an inner lining of fabric coated with neoprene and an outer layer of heat-reflecting, aluminized nylon. The latter was intended to provide protection in the event of a flash fire in the cabin. Furthermore, since the suit is waterproof, as well as air-tight, it would help the astronaut remain afloat in water and provide insulation against the cold. In Project Mercury, the suits were worn during the whole of a mission and the visor was opened for very limited periods only. The pressure suits for Project Gemini, however, are designed to permit the two astronauts, first one at a time and later both simultaneously, to remove helmet and gloves for greater comfort during a lengthy flight. The construction of the Gemini suits is similar to those worn by the Project Mercury astronauts, except that the inner layer, which holds the breathing gas pressure, is coated with a restraining material to prevent ballooning.

FIG. 13.11. Apollo suit and backpack for use on lunar surface. (*Hamilton-Standard Corporation*)

13.65. The Project Apollo suits differ in several respects from the suits worn in the Mercury and Gemini missions. Among the special features are two pressurized layers, the inner one being automatically inflated if the outer one is punctured, and a thermal layer to provide insulation on the lunar surface. While in the command module, two of the astronauts may be permitted to remove their suits, retaining a constant wear garment of loose-weave nylon. In the command module the suits are not normally pressurized, since the cabin atmosphere will be used for breathing. But in the event of a serious loss of cabin pressure, the suits will pressurize to 3.5 pounds per square inch. In the lunar excursion module, the suits are connected to the vehicle's environmental system, as is the case in the Mercury and Gemini spacecraft. Back packs, containing an oxygen supply, purification, and circulation system and a communications and telemetry unit, will be worn by the astronauts on the lunar surface and possibly during transfer between modules (Fig. 13.11). They can also be used for breathing in an emergency.

THE ENVIRONMENTAL CONTROL SYSTEM

13.66. To maintain the conditions in the pressure suit independent of those in the cabin, the Mercury spacecraft had two separate environmental control systems, one for the suit and the other for the cabin atmosphere; these are shown schematically in Fig. 13.12. The average rate of oxygen consumption

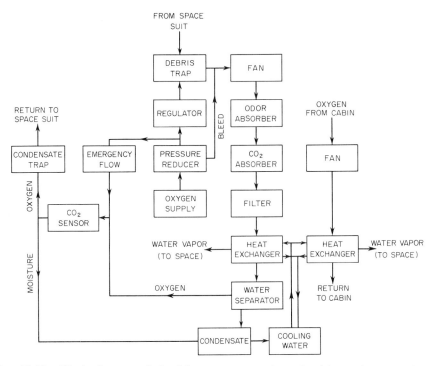

FIG. 13.12.   Block diagram of the Mercury space suit and cabin environmental control system

by a man under normal conditions is almost 2 pounds per day, and an adequate quantity of the gas, with a good margin of safety, was stored in spherical tanks at a pressure of 7500 pounds per square inch. By means of a pressure reducer and regulator, the pressure in the astronaut's suit was maintained at the required 5 pounds per square inch. When the spacecraft re-entered the atmosphere, at the termination of its mission, the oxygen supply was cut off and the pressure in the suit (and in the cabin) was permitted to increase to the ambient atmospheric value.

13.67. Gas was continuously drawn off with a fan from the pressure suit and passed through a debris trap. The gas then went on to an odor absorber of activated charcoal and a canister containing lithium hydroxide which removed the carbon dioxide and some water vapor. The purified gas passed on to a heat exchanger where cooling was achieved by permitting water in a separate circuit to evaporate in the vacuum of space. Evaporation of the cooling water caused the temperature to drop because of the heat absorbed in the process, i.e., the latent heat of vaporization. The temperature of the gas leaving the heat exchanger, and hence the suit temperature, was controlled by adjusting the rate of flow of the cooling water. After passage through a device for separating water droplets that had condensed from the moist gas in the heat exchanger, the purified oxygen was returned to the astronaut's space suit.

13.68. Since the cabin atmosphere was not used for breathing, except for the short times when the visor was opened, its composition remained essentially unchanged. All that was necessary, therefore, was to maintain its temperature and pressure. The temperature was kept constant by passing the oxygen gas through an evaporative heat exchanger similar to the one used for the pressure suit. A relief valve to the outside prevented the cabin pressure from exceeding about 5.5 pounds per square inch, but if it fell below 5.1 pounds per square inch a regulator (not shown in Fig. 13.12) allowed oxygen to enter from the storage tanks. If a fire had occurred or toxic gases had accumulated, the astronaut could have opened a valve and rapidly evacuated the cabin atmosphere to space.

13.69. The environmental control system for the Gemini spacecraft is similar in general principle to that used in Project Mercury, but there are some modifications. Instead of storing oxygen gas at high pressure, the main (primary) supply, located in the equipment section of the spacecraft, is in what has been called the "supercritical" state. The double-walled (insulated) tank is filled with liquid oxygen at atmospheric pressure; by allowing the temperature to increase slightly, so that it exceeds the critical temperature ($-119°C$, $-182°F$), the pressure builds up to about 850 pounds per square inch. Under these conditions, the liquid becomes a low-temperature (cryogenic) gas with a density not greatly different from that of liquid oxygen.

13.70. Thus, the oxygen leaves the tank in the gaseous form, but its relatively high density means a considerable saving in tank size and mass, as compared with the Mercury spacecraft in which the gas was stored at higher temperature and pressure. The temperature of the oxygen gas is so low, however, when it leaves the tank that it must be warmed up before entering the environmental control system. For use in an emergency and during re-entry, when the Gemini adapter module is discarded, oxygen is provided from a secondary supply of high-pressure gas contained in a tank in the cabin.

13.71. Another modification in the Gemini spacecraft is the system for cooling the suit and cabin atmospheres. The quantity of water required for evaporative cooling, such as was used in Project Mercury, would be prohibitive for the eventual two-man, 14-day mission planned for Project Gemini. Consequently, the main cooling system uses a commercial silicon ester coolant which is circulated through the closed-circuit heat exchanger and a radiator. Heat removed by the coolant from the oxygen gas as it passes through the heat exchanger is radiated to space; the coolant at lower temperature then returns to the heat exchanger for further heat removal. On the ground and during the launch and re-entry phases, the space radiator is not expected to be very effective; in any event, the radiator is located in the equipment section which will have been jettisoned prior to re-entry. At these times, therefore, a heat exchanger utilizing evaporative cooling of water, as in the Mercury spacecraft, will be used. It will also serve as a backup in an emergency or should additional cooling be required for any reason during a mission.

13.72. The environmental control system planned for the Apollo command module differs from the Gemini system in a few respects. As mentioned earlier, the astronauts will normally breathe the cabin atmosphere; consequently it will be necessary to purify and remove carbon dioxide and moisture continuously from the oxygen gas in the cabin. The charcoal and lithium hydroxide for removal of odors and carbon dioxide, respectively, will be preceded by a catalytic burner in which various trace contaminants will be oxidized and subsequently adsorbed. Among the many possible trace impurities, mention may be made of methane, carbon monoxide, hydrogen sulfide, ammonia, methyl alcohol, and hydrogen; some of these are produced by the body and others arise from constructional materials. Another difference between Apollo and the preceding manned projects is that the pressure suits will probably be cooled by circulating water rather than oxygen gas. Dehydration of the astronauts, which may have occurred on the Mercury flights (cf. § 13.94), will thus be avoided. The heat will be removed from the water by evaporative cooling.

FOOD, WATER, AND WASTES

13.73. Consumption of food and water was not a serious problem during the Mercury flights because of their short duration. No great difficulty was experienced in swallowing food, in bite-size pieces, and water in spite of the weightless condition in space (§ 13.85). It was found, however, that crumbly food should be avoided. For the longer Gemini and Apollo missions, it is planned to store food in the freeze-dried condition, prepared by simultaneous freezing and dehydration. Such freeze-dried food can be kept for considerable periods without deterioration and can be reconstituted to almost its original appearance and flavor by the addition of water. The food is contained in a plastic bag and water is injected from a special nozzle under pressure; this is necessary because water cannot be poured in the weightless state. The dry mass of the food required for a moderately active man is about 1.4 pounds per day, providing roughly 3000 kilocalories.

13.74. In the Mercury capsules, the drinking water supply was carried in special tanks with reserves available for the astronaut's survival kit. For Projects Gemini and Apollo, however, potable water is produced, as mentioned earlier, by the hydrogen-oxygen fuel cells that provide power for the spacecraft. To facilitate drinking under conditions of weightlessness, the water is supplied directly to each astronaut from a pressurized container. The total water requirement, including that for drinking and for addition to freeze-dried food, averages from 5 to 6 pounds per day per man. Water for toilet purposes would be additional.

13.75. The astronauts' pressure suits have facilities for the elimination of body wastes which are stored for the duration of the mission. The need for defecation is reduced by the utilization of low-residue foods, i.e., foods containing only a small proportion of nondigestible fibrous material. The possibility is being studied of the use of all-liquid diets which are available in a satisfactory form.

LONG-DURATION MISSIONS

13.76. The life support systems described above are adequate for space missions of a month or so, but for appreciably longer periods the weight of oxygen, food, and water that would have to be carried and the disposal of wastes become important considerations. Some of the problems appear to have relatively simple solutions. For example, sodium peroxide (Na_2O_2) and potassium superoxide (KO_2) can serve to absorb water and carbon dioxide and regenerate a large proportion of the oxygen consumed in breathing. Other, more complex, chemical processes could be developed in which the oxygen would be recovered completely from the carbon dioxide and water produced in respiration. It would then be necessary to carry only emergency supplies of oxygen. Furthermore, the recovery of potable water from urine, feces, and other wastes by distillation has been established as a practical procedure. Means for making a space vehicle self-sufficient in oxygen and water, while disposing of waste products, will probably be adopted in the not too distant future.

13.77. A more difficult matter is that of supplying food for a lengthy voyage in space. For example, an expedition to Mars involving at least three men and extending over a minimum period of 14 months would have to carry some 1800 pounds (dry weight) of food. A closed ecological system, which is independent of external supplies, is possible in principle by making use of photosynthesis in green plants such as occurs in nature. In these plants, the green chlorophyll serves as a catalyst, so that, under the influence of sunlight, carbon dioxide and water are converted into carbohydrate and oxygen gas. Under appropriate conditions, a green plant can also produce protein and fat, thus providing the main calorie-supplying components of the diet as well as oxygen for breathing.

13.78. The single-celled green plants called *algae*, of which many types are known, are particularly suitable for this purpose. When exposed to sunlight, algae grow rapidly in an aqueous nutrient medium in the presence of carbon dioxide; this gas and the nutrient materials are waste products of the human body. Apart from their water content, some algae contain about 50 percent of protein and roughly 20 percent each of carbohydrate and fat; the remainder consists of various mineral salts. Unfortunately, the product is not satisfactory as the sole article of diet for man in space. The algae could be used as food for some higher forms of life, e.g., fish or crustaceans, which are more edible; a prolonged diet of this kind, however, would undoubtedly prove to be monotonous. It is generally agreed that an attractive diet will be an important psychological factor in contributing to the success of a long-duration space mission. At the moment, it appears that the only way to obtain such a diet is to carry in dry form much of the food that will be required for the journey.

PHYSIOLOGICAL ASPECTS OF SPACE FLIGHT

ACCELERATION AND DECELERATION

13.79. An astronaut is subjected to the stresses of acceleration during liftoff of the spacecraft from the ground and of deceleration when re-entering the atmosphere. As far as body reactions are concerned, both acceleration and deceleration have the same effect, and so they may be considered together. It will be seen shortly that the essential factor in determining the ability of the body to withstand the stresses of acceleration and deceleration depends upon the direction in which the force is acting. It is this direction, therefore, which is the important consideration.

13.80. The physiological aspects of acceleration have been of interest for many years in connection with aviation medicine, especially in relation to the temporary loss of consciousness, referred to as "blackout," experienced by pilots in rapidly accelerating aircraft. Much of the experimental work in this area in the United States has been carried out with the device called a "human centrifuge." It consists of a 50-foot long beam, pivoted near one end; at the other end of the beam is a gondola in which the human subject is placed. By rotating the beam at high speeds, the man is exposed to a force equivalent to an acceleration which can attain several times that resulting from Earth's gravitational field. In this manner, it has been determined that sustained acceleration can affect the circulation of the blood, the respiratory system, and the ability to see clearly.

13.81. The physiological effects depend markedly, however, on the attitude (or orientation) of the human subject in the gondola. The stresses have been found to be least when the accelerating (or decelerating) force acts from the back to the front of the body; this is referred to as the "eyeballs in" (or EBI) position. In this situation, man can withstand accelerations up to ten times normal gravity, i.e., 10 g, for short times without serious discomfort. A form-fitting (or contour) couch, which keeps the knees bent as in a seated position, has been found to decrease the stresses caused by acceleration or deceleration. Such couches, molded from plastic for each individual, were used in the Project Mercury flights. In some later missions they may be replaced by light-weight couches made from nylon net.

13.82. The design and operation of the Mercury, Gemini, and Apollo cap-sules is such as to permit the optimum orientation of the astronaut during both liftoff and re-entry phases. The stresses during acceleration and decel-eration, respectively, are thereby minimized. In liftoff, the narrow end of the spacecraft is pointed in the direction of travel, and the astronaut, lying supine (Fig. 13.13), is subjected to acceleration which may reach approximately 8 g, with the Atlas launch vehicle, from the back to the front of his body. During re-entry, the broad end of the vehicle is facing toward the ground and the forces acting on the body are also from back to front.

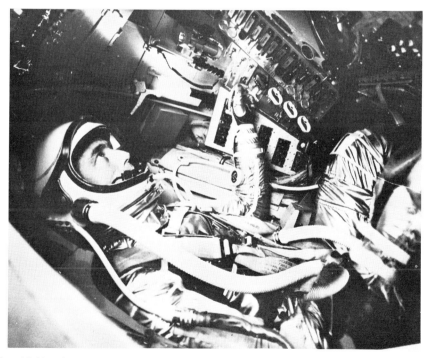

FIG. 13.13.   Astronaut (M. Scott Carpenter) in supine position occupied during launch
and re-entry phases

WEIGHTLESSNESS

13.83. An important physiological aspect of space flight about which relatively little is yet known is concerned with the phenomenon called *weightlessness*. To a human being, the sensation of weight of his body is the reaction to the supporting effect of the ground when standing or of a chair when sitting. Similarly, the sensation of the weight of an object is the effect of the reaction to the hand or other part of the body where the object is located. In a spacecraft in orbit or in a space trajectory, the support and reaction are absent, and this leads to the feeling of weightlessness; that is to say, the subjective sensation of weight is missing. The situation applies to any vehicle in space when it is not acted upon by its own propulsive force or by any resistive forces. Thus, weightlessness commences when the propelling rocket is cut off and it remains until the spacecraft is decelerated by re-entry into Earth's atmosphere or by a retrograde thrust, as in landing on the Moon. Weightlessness is also experienced in a coasting phase between two phases of propulsion.

13.84. The orbit (or trajectory) and speed in space of a body on which no self-propulsive force is operative is determined only by the inertia of the moving body and the action on it of gravitational forces. Hence, every object in the spacecraft, whether it is attached to the vehicle or not, is traveling in the same path and at the same speed as the spacecraft itself, and would continue to do so even if a hole were cut in any of the walls.* This is the basic cause of the sensation of weightlessness. An astronaut will experience no restraint (or support) if he attempts to stand up, sit down, or pick up any loose object. Thus, everything appears to be weightless. In fact, in the space vehicle, "up" and "down" have no meaning.

13.85. Any change in the position of a body with respect to the walls of the spacecraft implies a change in orbit or trajectory, and this can be accomplished only by the expenditure of energy. Hence, there is no tendency for an object to move toward the walls. Loose objects therefore tend to float in the weightless state and liquids will not pour, but break up into droplets.

13.86. In general, it may be stated that weightlessness results when a body moves freely under the combined influence of inertia and gravity only. It is commonly described as the condition of "zero gravity," "zero-g," or "zero-G," but these descriptions are not strictly correct. Certainly, the body behaves as if there were no gravity, but actually the gravitational force is still effective; without it, there would be only inertia and the motion of the body would be quite different. Some writers attribute weightlessness to the exact compensation between gravitational and centrifugal forces; this interpretation is acceptable provided it is realized, as pointed out in § 2.12, that the so-called cen-

---

* This situation would not be applicable to an aircraft as long as it is being propelled by its engines.

trifugal "force" is really another way of describing the inertia of a body moving in a curved path.

13.87. An indication that gravity is involved in the weightless state is shown by the fact that the same effects are observed when an object is in unrestrained free fall, i.e., falling under the influence of gravity with no appreciable resistance from the air. Here again, the only factors operative are inertia and gravity. Free fall is used as a means for studying the behavior of liquids in the weightless condition.

13.88. Prior to the achievement of space flight, a limited amount of experience with the phenomenon of weightlessness had been obtained by means of aircraft flying in what is called a *Keplerian trajectory*.* In this maneuver, the airplane follows a ballistic path in which essentially only gravity and inertia are effective. Periods of weightlessness up to nearly a minute have thus been realized. Such short exposures did not indicate any significant consequences of the weightless state, but no conclusions could be drawn concerning possible effects of long periods in this condition.

13.89. Careful observations have been made of the physiological behavior first of animals and then of man during and after flight in space. The experience so far with both the American and Russian astronauts indicates that weightlessness, at least for periods of a few days, has no significant harmful effects. The fear was expressed at one time that the absence of the sensation of gravity would affect the vestibular system of the inner ear which determines man's ability to orient himself. There appeared to be some support for this view from cosmonaut Titov's (§ 1.118) report of unpleasant sensations, similar to sea or air sickness, after his fifth hour in space. But all other astronauts and cosmonauts have found the weightless condition to be a pleasant experience with no discomfort whatsoever. Among the Americans, there has been no evidence of lack of orientation, except perhaps for the first few minutes. The astronauts may not have been oriented with reference to Earth, but this posed no problem since they remained oriented with respect to the spacecraft.

13.90. It is probable that preflight training is a great help in facilitating adjustment to high acceleration and deceleration as well as to weightlessness. In the United States this training includes flights in airplanes following Keplerian trajectories to familiarize the astronauts with the sensation of weightlessness. In addition, they are trained in the human centrifuge to accustom them to the effects of acceleration and deceleration. To learn to cope with possible disorientation effects that might result from tumbling of the spacecraft in flight, and for other purposes, the Multi-Axis Spin-Test Inertia Facility (MASTIF) trainer was designed by the Lewis Research Center of the

---

* The Keplerian trajectory is often called parabolic, but it is actually part of an ellipse that resembles a parabola.

National Aeronautics and Space Administration. In this device an astronaut can be spun simultaneously about three axes, representing the pitch, yaw, and roll axes of a space vehicle. The U.S. Navy's rotating room at Pensacola, Florida, has also been used for training purposes.

13.91. In the Project Mercury flights, the movement of the astronauts was restricted, since they remained strapped to their couches all the time. The Russians have reported, however, that in their later tests the cosmonauts floated freely for several periods without restraint. The cosmonauts stated that they were able to move about the cabin and to operate instruments and other devices of the spacecraft systems.

13.92. No difficulties have been encountered with the natural functions of the body in the weightless state. Food placed in the mouth is swallowed easily and apparently passes normally through the stomach and intestinal tract. Drinking also presents no problem, provided the liquid is injected into the mouth from a squeeze bottle or from a vessel under pressure. Urination has been normal in timing and volume, and there is no evidence of any problems associated with intestinal absorption. There are no records of defecation; this action was probably unnecessary for the American astronauts, as a result of the low-residue diets and relatively short flight times. But cosmonauts Nikolayev and Bykovsky, who spent about 95 and 119 hours in space, respectively, presumably had the experience. No difficulty has been found in sleeping in the weightless condition.

13.93. Even if there are no specific problems during flight, there is always the possibility of after effects from prolonged periods of weightlessness. It has been thought, for example, that the deceleration stresses experienced upon re-entering Earth's atmosphere may not be tolerated so readily after a long space flight. Nevertheless, both Nikolayev, after about 95 hours of weightlessness, and Popovich, after some 71 hours (§ 1.118), stated that they had no adverse experiences upon re-entry. Whether the same situation would be true for longer flight periods is uncertain.

13.94. Examination of astronauts Schirra, after a 9-hour flight, and Cooper, after 34 hours, showed that there were changes in blood pressure and pulse rate which varied with the position of the body. In addition, Schirra experienced some pooling of the blood in the veins of the legs and feet, which may have been partly due to dehydration, but no such effect was observed after Cooper's longer flight. All changes disappeared, however, after rest in bed. Nevertheless, special attention will be given to the blood circulation system as longer space missions are undertaken. After their extended flights, the Russian cosmonauts, particularly Popovich and Tereshkova (70 hours), exhibited disorders of the central nervous and cardiovascular systems and in the basal metabolic rate. Although recovery occurred in all cases within 15 or 16 days, it is possible that the effects may be proportional to the time spent in space.

13.95. It is well known that immobilization is accompanied by a loss of calcium from the skeleton by way of the urine. There is a possibility that weightlessness may have similar consequences. Thus, increased amounts of calcium were reported in the urine of Nikolayev during his 95-hour flight, although there were no significant changes in the shorter flights of the American astronauts. The loss of calcium and the effects on blood circulation may perhaps be minimized by suitable physical exercises performed by the astronauts in the weightless state.

13.96. One of the unsolved problems of weightlessness is the ability of the astronaut to perform maintenance and repair operations, either manually or with tools. Attempts to turn a nut with a wrench in the weightless condition, for example, may result in the rotation of the man rather than of the tool. Holding on to the spacecraft with one hand permits use of the other to manipulate a tool to some extent, but there is very little stability in this procedure. Various methods are being investigated for enabling man to work in space, e.g., by the design of tools that do not require torque, i.e., a turning force, or by anchoring the man in some way. It is expected that such devices will be tested in the Project Gemini program.

13.97. When manned spacecraft are developed, as they undoubtedly will be, for prolonged occupation as observation and experimental stations, weightlessness may prove to be intolerable to the occupants for physiological or mechanical reasons. One conceivable way in which the situation might be alleviated is by the application of artificial gravity; this could be achieved by causing the space vehicle to rotate about an axis (or hub). The inertia of any object in space during the rotation would cause it to move toward the outer walls; that is to say, the so-called centrifugal effect would produce a sensation similar to gravity. The "down" direction would be toward the circumference of the spacecraft. Since there is essentially no resistance to motion in space, very little energy would be required to sustain the rotation once it had been started.

13.98. A body of mass m moving at a speed v in a circle of radius R is subjected to an inertial effect equivalent to a centrifugal force of mv^2/R (§ 2.23, footnote); hence, the equivalent acceleration is v^2/R. If v is expressed in meters per second and R in meters, the acceleration is $v^2/9.8R$ in terms of normal terrestrial gravity. A more convenient form is obtained by considering a vehicle making n rotations per second; this is equal to $v/2\pi R$, and so the acceleration is $4\pi^2 n^2 R/9.8$ in gravity units. Thus, for a vehicle 10 meters (32.8 feet) in radius, making 3 rotations per minute, i.e., 0.05 per second, the acceleration would be close to 0.1 g. This may be sufficient to provide the sensation of weight.

13.99. A minor drawback to the scheme for producing artificial gravity by rotation is the significant variation over the height of a man, unless the spacecraft has such a large radius that a man's height is negligible in comparison. More serious, however, is the *Coriolis effect,* named for the French scientist G. G. de Coriolis, who described it around the middle of the 19th century. Like the centrifugal force, the Coriolis effect is an apparent force resulting from the inertia of an object located on a rotating body. If the object is moved, the so-called Coriolis force acts in a direction at right angles to the direction of motion. The situation may be illustrated by considering a rotating sphere; an object located at the equator is moving faster, and hence has a larger momentum, than at a higher latitude because it travels a greater distance in the same time, e.g., the period of rotation. If the object is moved from the equator toward either of the poles, it must dispose of the difference in momentum; it does so by exerting an apparent force, the Coriolis effect, in the direction of rotation, and this is perpendicular to the direction in which the object was moved.

13.100. The consequences of the Coriolis effect on different types of motion are depicted in Fig. 13.14, which represents the behavior at the circumference

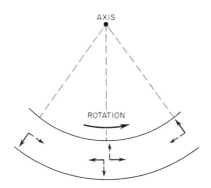

Fig. 13.14. Coriolis effect in rotating spacecraft

of a rotating spacecraft. The dotted arrows indicate four different directions of motion and the corresponding Coriolis forces are shown by the arrows at right angles. For clockwise rotation of the vehicle, the direction of the Coriolis force would be reversed in each case.

13.101. It is apparent from Fig. 13.14 that a man walking in the spacecraft from left to right, i.e., in the same direction as the rotation, will feel heavier than when walking in the opposite direction. In the former case the Coriolis force enhances the artificial gravity whereas in the latter case it opposes it. Furthermore, an object being "raised," i.e., moved toward the axis of rotation, would be forced to the right, whereas one being "lowered," i.e., moved toward the outer circumference, would tend to drift to the left. These effects would be experienced by a man bending down and then standing upright or standing up after sitting down, and they might have unpleasant consequences. One of the purposes of the U.S. Navy's rotating room, mentioned in § 13.90, which can make 10 rotations per minute, is to study the effects of the Coriolis force on man.

IONIZING RADIATIONS IN SPACE

13.102. Among the uncertainties associated with space flight is the possible effect of ionizing radiations on man. Such radiations include electrically charged particles, especially electrons and atomic nuclei, e.g., of hydrogen (protons) and helium (alpha particles), and electromagnetic radiations of short wavelength, i.e., X-rays and gamma rays. The various radiations are grouped together because they have certain features in common.

13.103. The adjective "ionizing" is applied to these radiations because they have the ability to detach electrons from atoms, and hence produce ions, in their passage through matter (§ 3.188). In some media, the electrons are not removed completely but are merely raised to a higher energy state, so that an excited electronic state is produced. Neutrons are commonly included among ionizing radiations although they do not cause ionization (or excitation) directly; they can do so indirectly, however, as a consequence of interaction with hydrogen and nitrogen nuclei in the body. The point of present interest is that all the radiations under consideration are capable of causing similar harmful effects in living organisms. This is a result of ionization and electronic excitation which lead to the decomposition of such vital compounds as enzymes and nucleic acids in the body.

13.104. Injury due to space radiations is similar to that resulting from overexposure to X-rays, to the gamma rays accompanying a nuclear explosion, or to the radiations emitted by radioactive substances such as are present in the fallout from nuclear weapons. The consequences depend to some extent upon whether the radiation dose is "acute," i.e., it is received within a fairly short time, or "chronic," when it is spread over many days or even years. The present discussion will be concerned with exposures lasting no more than a few days. Most injuries are less severe if a given dose is spread over a longer period of time.

13.105. Small doses of ionizing radiation produce no detectable effect, although it is probably not true to say they have no effect at all. Man has evidently become adapted to small amounts of radiation, since he is continuously exposed to cosmic rays (§ 8.245) as well as to gamma rays from radioactive minerals in the soil and in structural materials, such as brick and stone. Furthermore, the body contains significant quantities of the radioactive isotopes carbon-14 and potassium-40 which continuously emit radiations (beta particles) in essentially all soft tissues.

13.106. The degree of injury caused by ionizing radiations depends on a wide variety of circumstances. The quantity of energy absorbed by the body from the radiation is an important factor, but the nature of the radiation, i.e., whether it consists of protons, helium nuclei, neutrons, beta particles (electrons), etc., is often significant. The injury also depends on the extent of the body exposed to the radiation and on the particular organ where the radiation is absorbed. A large dose of radiation on a small area may produce no more than local damage, whereas the same (or a smaller) dose over the whole body could prove fatal. Among the parts of the body that are most sensitive to ionizing radiations are the blood-forming organs, lymphoid tissue, the gastrointestinal tract, the reproductive system, and the eyes. The skin and lungs are of intermediate sensitivity whereas the muscles and fully developed bones are least sensitive.

13.107. When X-rays and gamma rays were by far the most important ionizing radiations to which human beings could be exposed, the dose of radiation exposure was expressed in terms of the unit called a *roentgen*. This may be regarded as the quantity of radiation that produces ions carrying a total of 1 electrostatic unit of electrical charge when it is absorbed in 1 cubic centimeter of dry air at standard temperature and pressure. Laboratory measurements of the amount of energy required to produce ions in air indicated that absorption of a roentgen of X-rays or gamma rays resulted in the deposition of 88 ergs of energy per gram of air. When absorbed in a gram of body tissue, the energy deposited is somewhat larger.

13.108. In order to extend the measurement of dose to other radiations, a unit called the *rad* has been introduced; it is defined as the quantity of any ionizing radiation that leads to the absorption of 100 ergs of energy per gram of irradiated material. In soft body tissue, an exposure of 1 roentgen of X-rays or gamma rays results in the absorption of approximately 100 ergs per gram (1 rad), but in bone the energy absorbed per roentgen exceeds this amount.

13.109. The radiation exposure in rads indicates the quantity of energy deposited in a particular part of the body, but the physiological effect depends to some extent on the nature of the radiation, as already indicated. This dependence is expressed by means of a factor called the *relative biological effectiveness* (or *RBE*) of the radiation, when compared with that of X-rays of moderate energy. If the number of rads absorbed is multiplied by the RBE for the particular radiation, the result is the biological dose expressed in *rems*. It is the radiation dose in rems to which a particular organ is exposed that determines the extent of the resulting injury.

13.110. Unfortunately, the conversion of rads into rems is not a simple matter because the value of the RBE for a given type of radiation varies with the kind and degree of the biological effect, the nature of the exposed organ or tissue, and the rate at which the dose is delivered. In general, however, it appears that X-rays, gamma rays, and beta particles have RBE values close (or equal) to unity, whereas for protons and neutrons of high energy the RBE may be as large as 10 for ocular cataract formation. But as far as overall injury to the body is concerned, it is a fair approximation to assume for simplicity that the RBE values for all ionizing radiations is about unity; the general biological damage is then indicated roughly by the dose in rads.

13.111. The consequences of a particular dose of radiation may vary from one individual to another, and the statements made below refer to what might be expected on the average when a large number of individuals are involved. A radiation dose through the whole body of up to 25 rads will generally produce no observable effects, but an acute dose of 25 to 100 rads, received within a day or so, may be expected to cause slight changes in the blood but no discomfort of any kind. If the whole-body dose is 100 to 200 rads, vomiting will probably occur within 3 hours in many individuals, with a feeling of fatigue and nausea. There are moderate changes in the blood, but there should be complete recovery in all cases in due time. For larger doses, the foregoing symptoms are more severe and occur sooner; there may subsequently be hemorrhage and susceptibility to infection. When the acute whole-body dose of ionizing radiation is as high as 600 rads, a large proportion of the exposed persons will succumb.

13.112. It should be emphasized that the numbers given above refer to acute doses received throughout the whole body. The effects will be less if only part of the body is exposed or if the dose is received over a longer period of time. For example, 100 rads is regarded as an acceptable emergency dose for the whole body, including the blood-forming organs, but for the hands, feet, and ankles, which are much less radiosensitive, the energy dose may be as high as 700 rads without causing serious harm. The eyes, on the other hand, being very sensitive, should not receive emergency exposures in excess of about 25 rads.

13.113. In addition to the immediate (or short-range) effects of ionizing radiations, there are some delayed (or long-range) effects. It appears that radiation doses in amounts not sufficient to have any serious immediate consequences may increase the probability of the development of leukemia and cataracts, if the eyes were exposed, and may decrease the life span by a few years. Mention should also be made of genetic effects of radiation, since these will not become apparent until the next generation at the soonest. Experiments with animals have shown that exposure of the reproductive system to ionizing radiations increases the probability of the occurrence of mutations in their offspring. Some of the mutations are beneficial but most are deleterious. It is presumed that a similar situation exists in man.

13.114. Radiation exposures in space missions can arise from three main sources: first, from the geomagnetically trapped radiations in the Van Allen belt that surrounds Earth; second, from galactic cosmic rays; and third, from solar cosmic rays (Chapter 8). Before discussing the importance of these three sources of ionizing radiations, however, something must be said about shielding. By lining the spacecraft, inside or outside, with a sufficient mass of material, the radiation in the interior of the cabin can be reduced to negligible proportions. In practice, of course, there is a limit to the weight of the space vehicle; hence the shielding is designed to provide the maximum protection compatible with the permissible overall mass.

13.115. In the Apollo spacecraft command module, for example, the metal structure provides considerable shielding; in addition, equipment and water tanks are placed on the walls, as far as possible, thereby further decreasing the radiation dose in the interior (Fig. 13.15). For a given mass, water is particularly effective in slowing down high-energy protons and thus making them less harmful. The pressure suits worn by the astronauts also provide some protection against radiation and the outer parts of the body shield the blood-forming system to an appreciable extent. Thus, the dose received by the radiosensitive parts of the body can be reduced to a small fraction of that at the exterior of the spacecraft.

13.116. The altitudes at which manned orbital flights are carried out are well below the radiation belt; the doses received from the high-energy protons

Fig. 13.15. Interior of Apollo command module with center couch removed. (*Courtesy of North American Aviation's Space and Information Systems Division*)

and electrons in the belt are thus very small.* Furthermore, by trapping electrically charged particles, the Van Allen belt provides considerable protection from cosmic radiations, except in the polar regions. Thus, if polar orbits are avoided, as has always been the case for manned orbital flights, the radiation exposures are not significant. Even in a polar orbit, the galactic cosmic radiation would not be serious, although the solar radiation might be.

13.117. For journeys to the Moon or beyond, the situation is different. The spacecraft must pass through the radiation belt, unless a polar trajectory is used for escape from Earth. Since such a route is rendered impractical by velocity and navigational requirements, passage through the Van Allen belt is unavoidable. But the space vehicle spends only a short time within the regions where the proton and electron fluxes are large enough to be a hazard; hence, the total radiation dose received in this time is quite small. The general consensus is, therefore, that with the proposed shielding, the radiation exposure of

---

* Except for flights soon after the high-altitude nuclear explosion of July 7, 1962, the average radiation dose rate to the Russian cosmonauts was about 10 millirads (0.01 rad) per 24 hours. The American data are in general agreement.

the crew during the passage of the Apollo spacecraft through the Van Allen radiation belt need not be a matter for concern.

13.118. Galactic cosmic rays are not regarded as a serious problem even though shielding against them is difficult. These rays consist mainly of protons and helium nuclei of very high energy; consequently, when they interact with the shielding material the secondary radiation produced may yield a larger dose to the astronaut's body than would the primary radiations themselves. But, in any event, the dose received would not be significant. A special situation might arise, however, from the nuclei of elements heavier than helium that constitute about 2 or 3 percent of the cosmic rays. If such a heavy nucleus enters the body, it would be capable of destroying a large number of cells in a small region. Should this region be in the eye or in a vital part of the brain, the consequences might be serious. Although these possible effects of a single heavy nucleus are somewhat speculative, they must not be overlooked. But the probability that an astronaut will be disabled by the heavy nuclei in galactic cosmic rays is regarded as being extremely small.

13.119. The most important radiation hazard in space flight beyond Earth's magnetosphere is considered to be the solar cosmic radiation, i.e., the stream of high-energy particles, mainly protons, emitted by the Sun at the time of a large solar flare. Such flares occur, on the average, about five or six times a year, but the actual number may vary from two or so to about eight or more. Large flares are not necessarily most frequent during periods of maximum solar activity as indicated by the number of sunspots; however, the most important (Class 3 or 3+) flares apparently do occur around such times. Furthermore, there may then be two or three major flares within the course of a few days, such as was the case in July 1959, November 1960, and July 1961.*

13.120. If flares could be predicted several days in advance, the date of a space expedition might be changed to avoid the hazard due to solar particles. Observations have been made of the Sun with the objective of developing a scheme for predicting solar flares and it is possible that, by the time the first flight to the Moon is undertaken, this aim will have been realized. Methods proposed so far are based on a study of the penumbral areas of sunspots (§ 6.103), of the areas and durations of calcium plage regions (§ 6.139), and of active regions of large area.

13.121. The Apollo spacecraft shielding has been designed so that, should a large solar flare occur during a lunar mission, the radiation dose received by the astronauts within the command module will be tolerable. Calculations have shown that the total maximum skin dose from the succession of solar events of July 1959, probably the largest on record, would have been no more than 160 rads. The shielding effect on the body tissue would have reduced this to 15 rads at the blood-forming organs. As seen earlier, the immediate effects of such a dose of ionizing radiations would probably not be detectable. The present indi-

* The period of sunspot maximum was 1957-1958.

cation is, therefore, that radiation is not more serious than any of the other hazards involved in a manned expedition to the Moon. Nevertheless, studies on the subject of space radiations and their biological effects, and of possible means of improving the shielding, are being continued in order to establish that the lunar mission can be undertaken with the minimum of danger.

13.122. The only serious situation envisaged is one in which a burst of solar cosmic radiation occurs while the astronauts are actually on the Moon. Fortunately, there should be sufficient warning to permit them to return to relative safety. At the time of a single solar event or of the first of a series of events (§ 8.252 *et seq.*), the high-energy protons do not reach the vicinity of Earth (or the Moon) until several hours after the observation of a major flare. If such a flare should be seen from Earth when the Apollo spacecraft is near the Moon, instructions could be sent by radio advising the astronauts either not to leave the command module or to return to it without delay.

13.123. There is thus a considerable probability that the radiation hazard will not prevent a manned flight to the Moon. But for an expedition to Mars, the situation is much more serious. During the journey of more than a year, there would undoubtedly be a few large flares accompanied by high-energy particulate radiation. The shielding required to protect the members of the crew would then have to exceed that provided in the Apollo spacecraft. One possibility, although it appears remote at present, is to surround the vehicle with a magnetic field capable of deflecting the electrically charged particles. But shielding is only one of the many problems that will have to be solved before a manned expedition to Mars can be undertaken.

BIOLOGICAL STUDIES IN SPACE

13.124. Biological studies in space are of two different types: those that are directly concerned with the safety of the astronaut, and those of a purely scientific nature. Some of the experiments in the latter category may, nevertheless, have a bearing on the interaction of man with the space environment.

13.125. Prior to undertaking manned orbital flights, tests were performed in Russia with dogs and in the United States with primates (monkeys and chimpanzees). It was after these preliminary tests revealed no adverse effects on the animals that men were launched into space. In the Project Mercury flights continuous measurements were made of the body temperature, respiration rate, heart action (electrocardiogram or ECG), and blood pressure of the astronauts. The data were transmitted by telemetry to Earth, so that immediate indications were available of any undesirable situation that might make it necessary to terminate the mission.

13.126. For future flights, new instruments are being developed to extend the scope of the physiological measurements; these devices include an electroencephalograph, a galvanic skin response meter, and a vibrocardiograph. With the extension of the flight duration up to 14 days in Projects Gemini and Apollo, and ultimately longer in the orbiting space laboratories, more will be learned about the reactions of the human organism. In particular, it is required to determine the optimum work-rest cycle for man in space; this may not necessarily be the same as on Earth.

13.127. Furthermore, as part of the United States recoverable *Biosatellite program*, to start in 1965 or 1966, it is planned to place small primates in Earth orbit for periods up to 30 days in order to observe the effects of weightlessness on the cardiovascular, central nervous, and vestibular systems of these animals. Studies will also be made of the loss of calcium from the skeleton. Because of their similarity to man, the data obtained from the primates should help to provide a better understanding of how human beings may be expected to respond to long periods in space.

13.128. In the area of more basic biological research, simple organisms and samples of animal tissues have been sent aloft, first in sounding rockets and later in satellites. For example, the Discoverer XVII and XVIII satellites, launched at the end of 1960, each carried a capsule containing living material; the capsules were ejected and recovered after being in orbit for 50 and 70 hours, respectively. These experiments were preliminary and exploratory in nature, and a systematic series of biological studies is projected as a major aspect of the Biosatellite program mentioned above.

13.129. In essence, the purpose of the program is to study the behavior of living organisms under conditions impossible to duplicate on Earth. Various biological materials contained in a capsule will be placed in approximately 200-mile high circular orbits and exposed to weightlessness alone or to a combination of weightlessness and ionizing radiation. After periods of up to 30 days in space, the capsule will be returned to Earth and the exposed samples submitted to examination. Control experiments, under normal terrestrial conditions, will be made for comparison purposes.

13.130. It is well known that plants respond to gravity, exhibiting the phenomenon of *geotropism* (Greek, *ge*, "Earth," and *tropos*, "turning"); thus, roots always tend to grow down while the shoot of a plant grows upward. Hence, experiments on the effects of weightlessness on plant growth would be of considerable interest. Orbital flights provide the opportunity to make such observations. Studies will also be made of the division, growth, and differentiation of living cells under weightless conditions. Furthermore, the consequences of exposure to radiation of living material while weightless might have some bearing on the long-range effects of space flight on man.

13.131. Another biological phenomenon that lends itself to study in a satellite environment is that known as *circadian rhythms* (Greek, *circa*, "about," and *dies*, "day"). Many living creatures display a rhythmic or repetitive behavior at intervals of roughly 22 to 25 hours, i.e., approximately once a day. A striking example of a circadian rhythm is provided by the fiddler crab. These crustaceans come out to feed daily at low tide whatever the actual time may be; on

Cape Cod, for example, it is 50 minutes later each day. In addition, the fiddler crab exhibits a darkening of the skin at sunrise every day. The remarkable fact is that even in the laboratory, away from the shore, the creatures come out to feed at times of low tide and change color at sunrise. If circadian rhythms are related, as appears possible, to the 24-hour period of rotation of Earth, they should be modified in a satellite, since the latter is not affected by Earth's rotation.

13.132. The experiments on the first Biosatellite will include observations of the effect of weightlessness on the following: the leaf-stem angle of pepper plants; the growth of roots and shoots and cell division in wheat seedlings; nuclear division and the evolution of food vacuoles in amoeba; and cell division, growth, and differentiation in fertilized frog and sea urchin eggs. The spacecraft will carry a source of ionizing radiation to permit studies to be made of the combined exposure to weightlessness and known doses of radiation. The materials to be subjected to these tests are as follows: bread mold; the eggs of flour beetles to study wing development; tradescantia plants to determine chromosome behavior; latent viruses to observe their reproduction; and fruit flies to examine whole cell effects during development from the pupal stage and the genetic changes in their offspring. In addition, male wasps exposed to weightlessness and radiation will be mated after recovery to see if weightlessness increases or decreases the genetic effects of radiation.

13.133. Subsequent Biosatellites will probably include experiments on land and marine plants, roaches, rats, hamsters, and human tissue cultures, as well as on primates. As in any new area of scientific research, the results may be surprising, and they will undoubtedly be interesting. And their ultimate consequences for mankind may well be beyond expectation.

MAN IN THE UNIVERSE

TIME DILATION

13.134. In concluding this chapter, brief mention will be made of two special problems related to man in space, in the widest sense of the term. Although these problems are of exceptional interest, it is doubtful if they will be solved for many years, if ever! The first is concerned with what is known as *time dilation* or the *clock paradox*.* The word "paradox" is somewhat misleading in this respect; there is actually no paradox from the purely scientific standpoint, but the conclusions are paradoxical in the sense that they appear to be opposed to conventional concepts.

13.135. One of the results derived from the special theory of relativity (§ 12.270) is that if an instrument which records the passage of time, i.e., a clock in the most general sense, is moving relative to another identical (sta-

---

* For a reason that will become clear in due course, it is also referred to sometimes as the *twin paradox*.

tionary) clock, the moving clock will appear to run at a slower rate than the stationary one. If t_0 is the elapsed time on the stationary clock and t is the corresponding time on a clock moving with a velocity v, then

$$t = t_0\sqrt{1 - (v/c)^2}, \qquad (13.1)$$

where c is the velocity of light. The square root expression on the right-hand side is always less than unity; hence, it follows that t must be less than t_0.

13.136. The slowing down or dilation, i.e., extension, of time does not become significant until the speed of the moving clock approaches that of light. Thus, if the clock moves at the enormous speed of 18,600 miles per second, which is one tenth of the speed of light, the elapsed time is still **99.5** percent of that on the stationary clock. However, when the speed of the moving clock is 0.99 of the speed of light, the time is decreased to about 14 percent, i.e., about one seventh the value on the stationary clock. In other words, one hour on the moving clock would be the same as **7** hours on the stationary one. In the extreme case, if a clock could travel with the speed of light, so that $v/c = 1$, it follows from equation (13.1) that the elapsed time would always be zero. In other words, on a body moving with the speed of light, time would "stand still."

13.137. Consider a purely hypothetical case in which a spaceship travels from Earth to a star a distance of 100 light years away at a constant speed relative to Earth that is 0.99 times the speed of light. It then turns around and returns to Earth at the same speed. The elapsed time for the passengers on the ship would be about $2 \times 14 = 28$ years, but on Earth a little over 200 years would have passed. It appears, therefore, that if one member of a set of identical twins had gone on this space journey while the other remained behind, the traveling twin would have aged by only 28 years upon his return to Earth, whereas his brother would have been long dead! It is this strange situation that has been called the twin paradox. The closer the speed of the space vehicle approaches that of light, the shorter would be the elapsed time for the traveler.

13.138. The case just described is hardly a practical one: in the first place, even if a speed 0.99 times that of light relative to Earth can be attained, the increase would have to be gradual if the passengers were to survive and this would take time; furthermore, the turn-around at such a high speed would require a fantastically large amount of energy. A more reasonable possibility is to suppose that the spaceship is subjected to a continuous acceleration of 1 g, i.e., equal to Earth's gravity (9.82 kilometers per second per second). The passengers would then have the same weight sensations as on Earth.

13.139. In these circumstances, it would require about a year for the speed to attain 0.99 of the speed of light, i.e., $0.99c$; in that time the ship will have traveled a distance of roughly half a light year from Earth. Suppose now that the spacecraft is allowed to coast at constant speed of $0.99c$ while it travels a distance of 99 light years; the elapsed time for the passengers will be **14** percent of 99 years, i.e., slightly less than 14 years. The craft is now continuously decelerated at a constant rate of 1 g, and at the end of another year or so it will have traveled another half a light year, and its speed will be reduced almost to zero. The elapsed time for traveling the distance of 100 light years from Earth is thus about $1 + 14 + 1$ or 16 years. Since the vehicle is now moving at a very low speed, it can be turned around with little expenditure of energy, and the return to Earth made in the same manner as the outward journey. The total elapsed time for a passenger on the spaceship would thus be approximately $2 \times 16 = 32$ years. The elapsed time on Earth, however, would be over 200 years.

13.140. It is natural to wonder if there is not some fallacy in the argument about time dilation. According to most, but not all, authorities on the theory of relativity, there is not. Moreover, there is some experimental evidence that elapsed times are shorter for moving than for stationary objects. For example, it has been found that the rate of decay of the subatomic particles called mu-mesons or muons (cf. § 8.248) apparently decreases as their speed increases, based on measurements with stationary timing devices. Of course, if observations could be made with "clocks" attached to the muons themselves, the rate of decay would be found to be constant, because the clocks would be slowed down correspondingly. In addition, experiments on the Mössbauer effect* have shown that the frequency, i.e., the number of cycles (or waves) per second, of the gamma rays from a particular source is less when the source is moved rapidly on the periphery of a rotating disc than when it is stationary.

13.141. There seems to be little doubt, therefore, concerning the reality of the time dilation phenomenon, and there are prospects that it can be verified by means of highly sensitive nuclear or atomic timing devices carried on a satellite or space probe. But, where human beings are concerned, the chances of being able to confirm or refute the twin paradox are remote. One reason is that, as far as can be seen at present, the only hope of accelerating a space vehicle to a speed approaching that of light is by means of a photon rocket of high specific impulse (§ 3.220). Whether or not such a rocket can be built is uncertain.

INTELLIGENT LIFE IN THE UNIVERSE

13.142. The question of the occurrence of extraterrestrial life in the solar system, discussed in Chapter 10, is of immediate interest because it is likely to be answered within the present century. There is, however, a much broader question about which there has been much speculation and to which an answer is not in sight: do intelligent creatures exist elsewhere in the universe? The following discussion is based largely on the work of the Chinese-American astrophysicist Su-Shu Huang, published in 1959 and subsequent years.

13.143. An advanced form of life, having the capability of man, but not necessarily the same physical structure, can develop only on a planet that has existed for a long period in the vicinity of a star that is neither too hot nor too

* See § 12.276, footnote.

cold. The planet must probably have a surface that is partially solid and partially covered with liquid water. Finally, it would appear that an oxidizing atmosphere is desirable in order to permit the optimum production of energy by metabolic processes.

13.144. Consider, first, the possibility that other stars, besides the Sun, have planets associated with them. Purely on the basis of probability, it is highly unlikely that only one star in the 10^{21} or so present in the universe (§ 12.6) would have a planetary system. But, apart from this general argument, there are some specific lines of evidence. In the first place, the Russian-born astronomer Otto Struve pointed out in the United States in 1950 that main-sequence stars more massive than class F5 (§ 12.103) rotate rapidly; stars that are less massive, on the other hand, rotate relatively slowly. As seen in § 7.189, this fact can be interpreted as indicating that the latter stars have planetary systems which have taken up some of the angular momentum originally possessed by the central body. Another point, which was discussed in § 12.186, is the unusually high lithium content of the T Tauri stars. In a later stage of evolution, these stars will presumably dispose of their excess lithium in the course of formation of planets. A further argument is based on the study of the motions of a few stars, such as 61 Cygni, Lalande 21185, and Barnard's star. The perturbations suggest that they have invisible companions of small mass, similar to the larger planets of the solar system.

13.145. Granting that planets exist, what are the requirements for intelligent life to develop? It has been estimated that some 2 billion (2×10^9) years or more elapsed between the first emergence of terrestrial life and the evolution of man (§ 10.169). The rate at which genetic mutations would occur elsewhere is not necessarily the same as on Earth, but it is probably a requirement for the development of intelligent creatures that the temperature conditions on the planet should not have varied greatly over a period of two or three billion years. This means that the central star (or sun) must be a member of the Hertzsprung-Russell (H-R) main sequence (§ 12.106) of spectral class F4 or beyond, i.e., of about 1.3 solar masses or less. More massive stars would not remain on the main sequence, on which the surface temperature and radius are almost constant, sufficiently long to permit the evolution of advanced life forms (§ 12.131). It is purely coincidental that the rate of rotation indicates that stars below class F5 in the H-R diagram are likely to have planetary systems.

13.146. Hence, 1.3 solar masses may be taken as the upper limit for a star with which intelligent life might be associated. There is probably also a lower mass limit. With decreasing mass on the H-R main sequence, both the surface temperature and the radius of the stars decrease; the rate of energy emission as radiation thus falls off rapidly. The space in which a habitable planet is likely to be found consequently becomes less in going down the main sequence. A fair estimate would be to place the lower limit at about spectral class K5, i.e., roughly 0.5 solar mass. Approximately 10 percent of the stars in the Milky Way then fall into the category, from 0.5 to 1.3 solar masses, of present interest. These are stars which may have planets upon which intelligent life could exist or may exist in the future, provided other conditions are suitable.

13.147. One condition is that the planet should have an orbit about the central star that is approximately circular and stable. If the orbit has appreciable eccentricity, the temperature differences between apocenter and pericenter may be so large as to be intolerable. Furthermore, if the orbit is unstable, the climatic conditions may be too variable for the continuous evolution of living organisms. Orbital instability could arise if the central body were a multiple, e.g.., double, star, and about half the stars in the vicinity of the Sun fall into this category. However, if the two members of a binary are quite close together, e.g., within less than 0.05 astronomical units (A.U.), so that they behave effectively as a single star, or are far apart, e.g., more than about 10 A.U., so that they are essentially independent, a planet could have a reasonably stable orbit. These requirements probably decrease to 3 to 5 percent the number of stars in the Milky Way that might conceivably have planets capable of supporting life.

13.148. The number is decreased further by two interrelated conditions. First, it may be postulated that, if an advanced form of life is to evolve, substantial quantities of liquid water should be available. To prevent the vaporization of the water, at the moderate temperature that must exist, an atmosphere of appreciable density (or pressure) is essential. In order to retain such an atmosphere, the planet must have a relatively large gravitational attraction (§ 9.164). It follows, therefore, that gravity is one of the factors that determine whether intelligent life could develop on a planet.

13.149. The mean density of planets that satisfy other conditions for habitability is not expected to vary greatly. Consequently, the gravitational attraction at the surface will depend mainly on the radius. A rough estimate indicates that, for a planet having about the same average density and temperature as Earth, the radius must exceed about 1000 kilometers (620 miles) if it is to have an atmosphere and consequently be habitable. It will be noted that both the planet Mercury and the Moon, neither of which has an appreciable atmosphere, satisfies this dimensional requirement. If Mercury had been farther from the Sun and also able to rotate more rapidly, however, giving the planet a more uniform temperature, it would probably have had a significant atmosphere. The same is true of the Moon if its density had been higher and its rotation unconstrained.

13.150. There are some primitive forms of life on Earth that derive their energy from reducing reactions, but the more advanced organisms all make use of more efficient oxidation processes. It may be supposed, therefore, that an oxidizing atmosphere is a prerequisite for evolution of higher life form. When a planet is first evolved, its outer layers most probably consist mainly of hydrogen gas which constitutes a reducing atmosphere. For this to be converted into an oxidizing condition, it is necessary that most of the hydrogen should be dissipated. If the planet is fairly large and massive, however, the hydrogen will escape very slowly, as is the case with the planet Jupiter. The development of an oxidizing atmosphere requires, therefore, that the planet should not be too large, and **20,000** kilometers (**12,400** miles) is indicated as the approximate maximum radius, assuming an average interior density and a moderate surface temperature.

13.151. Even if all the foregoing conditions should be satisfied, it is not certain that life will develop and evolve. There are probably many subsidiary requirements, e.g., the presence of solid land and appropriate mineral elements on the planet, that are nevertheless essential. It is consequently almost impossible to estimate the number of planets upon which intelligent life may now be present or upon which it has existed in the past or will evolve in the future. But it is reasonably certain that the number is larger than one.

13.152. A highly conservative approach to this problem has been outlined by H. Shapley (§ 12.20), as follows. Suppose, first, that only one star in a thousand has a planetary system; then, of these, let one in a thousand be at a suitable distance to provide the temperature, water, etc., required for the development of living organisms. This reduces the number to one star in a million that satisfies the conditions so far. Furthermore, it may be supposed that the requirement of an atmosphere decreases the probability by another factor of a thousand, to one chance in a billion. Finally, the necessity for the presence of an oxidizing atmosphere may be supposed to result in another thousand-fold reduction. Thus, the overall conclusion is that one star in 10^{12} should have a planet capable of supporting intelligent life.

13.153. If the solar system may be used as a criterion, this probability is too small by a factor of a thousand at the very least. It would be much more reasonable, therefore, to say that one star in 10^9 falls into the category of interest. This means that there are roughly **200** planets in the Milky Way and a total of about 10^{12} planets in the universe upon which sapient creatures could evolve. Even if the more conservative probability of one star in 10^{12} is accepted, there would still be about a billion (10^9) such planets, although only one in the Milky Way.

13.154. In recent years, some scientists have become interested in the possibility of receiving signals sent out by intelligent beings on other planets in the Galaxy. It was suggested by Giuseppe Cocconi and Philip Morrison in the United States in **1959** that the most favorable wavelength for such communication would be at (or close to) the **21**-centimeter line of hydrogen (§ 12.39). The extraterrestrial radio astronomers would know the importance of this line in the study of the universe, and they would properly assume that astronomers elsewhere in the Galaxy might, in any event, be making observations on the

SUBJECT INDEX